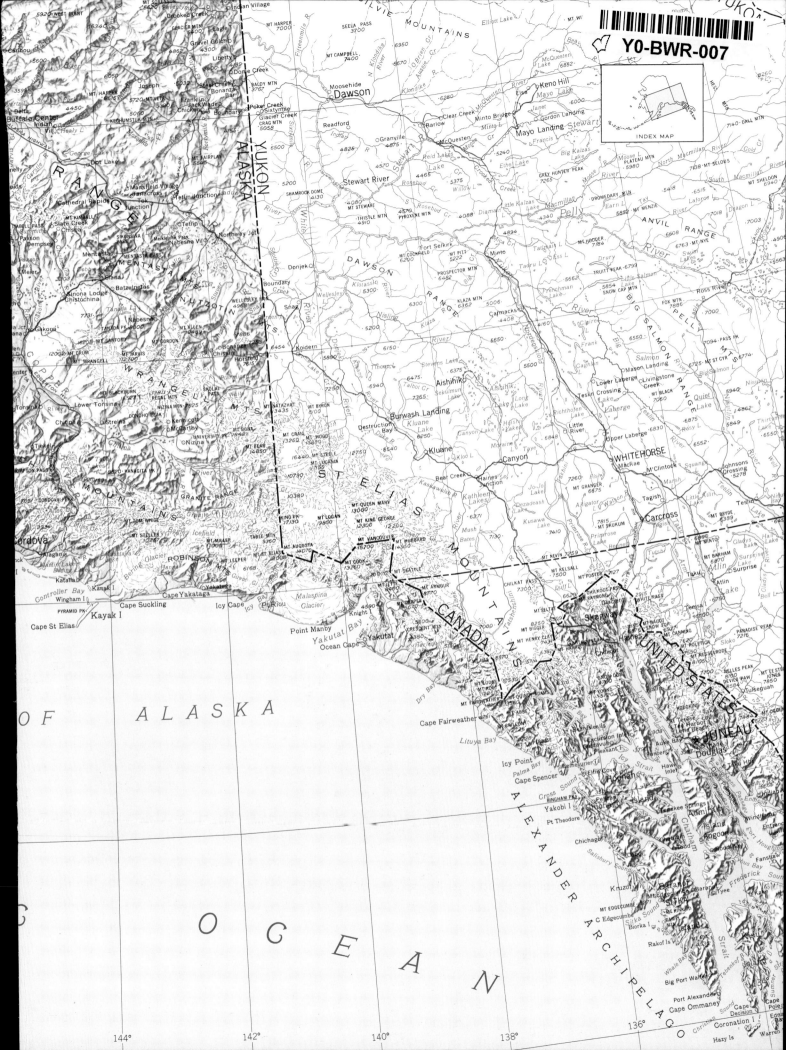

The Great Alaska Earthquake of 1964

COMMITTEE ON THE ALASKA EARTHQUAKE
OF THE
DIVISION OF EARTH SCIENCES
NATIONAL RESEARCH COUNCIL

ll

OCEANOGRAPHY AND COASTAL ENGINEERING

NATIONAL ACADEMY OF SCIENCES
WASHINGTON, D.C.
1972

Geology

Seismology and Geodesy

Hydrology

Biology

Oceanography and Coastal Engineering

Engineering

Human Ecology

Summary and Recommendations

Available from
Printing and Publishing Office
National Academy of Sciences
2101 Constitution Avenue
Washington, D.C. 20418

ISBN 0-309-01605-3

Library of Congress Catalog Card Number 68-60037

Printed in the United States of America

FRONTISPIECE   Downtown Kodiak after the earthquake. The boats were stranded and the buildings damaged by the waves of the major tsunami that swept into the town beginning about an hour after the earthquake and continuing for several hours. U.S. Navy photograph.

COMMITTEE ON THE ALASKA EARTHQUAKE

KONRAD B. KRAUSKOPF, *Chairman*; Stanford University, 1964–
HUGO BENIOFF, California Institute of Technology, 1964
EARL F. COOK, Texas A&M University, 1968–
DOAK C. COX, University of Hawaii, 1964–
ERNEST DOBROVOLNY, U.S. Geological Survey, 1964–
EDWIN B. ECKEL, The Geological Society of America, 1965–
JAMES GILLULY, U.S. Geological Survey, 1964–1965
RICHARD P. GOLDTHWAIT, The Ohio State University, 1964–
J. EUGENE HAAS, University of Colorado, 1968–
GEORGE Y. HARRY, JR., National Oceanic and Atmospheric Administration, 1965–
HAROLD D. HAUF, Consultant, Sun City, Arizona, 1964–
GEORGE W. HOUSNER, California Institute of Technology, 1964–
ROBERT W. KATES, Clark University, 1964–
H. BOLTON SEED, University of California, Berkeley, 1964–
DON TOCHER, National Oceanic and Atmospheric Administration, 1964–

Ex Officio

M. KING HUBBERT, U.S. Geological Survey and Stanford University, 1964–1965
J. HOOVER MACKIN, University of Texas, 1965–1967
JOHN R. BORCHERT, University of Minnesota, 1967–1969
GORDON J. F. MACDONALD, University of California, Santa Barbara, 1969–1970
JOHN C. MAXWELL, University of Texas, 1970–

LIAISON
REPRESENTATIVES

S. THEODORE ALGERMISSEN, National Oceanic and Atmospheric Administration, 1964–
WALTER S. BAER, Office of Science and Technology, 1967–1968
GEORGE E. BECRAFT, U.S. Geological Survey, 1970–
WILLIAM E. BENSON, National Science Foundation, 1964–
RUDOLPH A. BLACK, Advanced Research Projects Agency, 1967–
THOMAS R. CASEY, Office of Emergency Preparedness, 1970–
JOHN M. DeNOYER, Department of Defense, 1966–1967
ROBERT A. FROSCH, Department of Defense, 1964–1966
GEORGE O. GATES, U.S. Geological Survey, 1964–1970
GEORGE A. KOLSTAD, Atomic Energy Commission, 1968–
JAMES L. LEWIS, Office of Emergency Preparedness, 1968–1970
NED A. OSTENSO, Office of Naval Research, 1970–
DAVID Z. ROBINSON, Office of Science and Technology, 1965–1967
CARL H. SAVIT, Office of Science and Technology, 1970–
JOHN S. STEINHART, Office of Science and Technology, 1968–1969
LEONARD S. WILSON, Army Research Office, 1968–1970
VALENTINE ZADNIK, Army Research Office, 1971–
ARTHUR J. ZEIZEL, Department of Housing and Urban Development, 1970–

PANEL ON
OCEANOGRAPHY

DOAK C. COX, *Chairman*, University of Hawaii 1964–
GENE A. RUSNAK, U.S. Geological Survey 1964–
HARRIS D. STEWART, JR., National Oceanic and Atmospheric Administration 1964–
WILLIAM G. VAN DORN, Scripps Institution of Oceanography 1965–
ROLAND VON HUENE, U.S. Geological Survey 1966–

v

G DALLAS HANNA

1887–1970

With sincere regret, we report the passing on November 20, 1970, of Dr. G Dallas Hanna, Curator of Geology at the California Academy of Sciences. Born on April 24, 1887, Dr. Hanna was a geologist, a paleontologist, a naturalist, and an inventor. He was a member of the Panel on Oceanography during the first year of its existence, until the separate Panel on Biology was established, and is the author of the review of marine biological effects of the earthquake in this volume. Word of his death came while the volume was in preparation; we wish he had lived to see it completed.

KONRAD B. KRAUSKOPF
DOAK C. COX

Foreword

Soon after the Alaska earthquake of March 27, 1964, President Lyndon B. Johnson wrote to Donald F. Hornig, his Special Assistant for Science and Technology:

> It is important we learn as many lessons as possible from the disastrous Alaskan earthquake. A scientific understanding of the events that occurred may make it possible to anticipate future earthquakes, there and elsewhere, so as to cope with them more adequately.
>
> I, therefore, request that your office undertake to assemble a comprehensive scientific and technical account of the Alaskan earthquake and its effects. . . .
>
> In defining the scientific and technical questions involved and the related informational requirements for collection and assessment, I hope that you will be able to enlist the aid of the National Academy of Sciences. . . .

In discussions that followed, the Academy was requested by Dr. Hornig to establish the Committee on the Alaska Earthquake, to be charged with three principal tasks—to evaluate efforts being made to gather scientific and engineering information about the earthquake and its effects, to encourage the filling of gaps in the record, and to compile and publish a comprehensive report on the earthquake.

Under the chairmanship of Konrad B. Krauskopf of Stanford University, a twelve-man committee was formed of specialists from related scientific and technical disciplines. Their first meeting was held on June 15, 1964.

The resulting documents, prepared by the Committee and its seven specialized panels, constitute perhaps the most comprehensive and detailed account of an earthquake yet compiled. The Committee has attempted to compile from the available information and analysis a useful resource for present and future scholars in this field. As a result of the present study, much that is new and useful has been learned about earthquakes as well as about natural disasters in general.

In addition to the membership of the central committee, the work of several hundred scientists and engineers is represented in the Committee's report. Many of these are staff members of government agencies that have gathered facts and data about the earthquake and its effects; others are from universities and nongovernmental scientific organizations with an interest in earthquake-related research. Their help and cooperation in making this report possible is deeply appreciated.

PHILIP HANDLER
President
National Academy of Sciences

Preface

South central Alaska (Figure 1), including Prince William Sound and the Aleutian area, is one of the world's most active seismic regions. On March 27, 1964, at about 5:36 p.m. local time (0336, or 3:36 a.m. GMT, March 28), an earthquake of unusual severity struck the Prince William Sound area. Seismologists record earthquake occurrences in Greenwich mean time (GMT). The U.S. Coast and Geodetic Survey, therefore, uses 03h 36m 14.0 ± 0.2s GMT, March 28, 1964, as the time of the earthquake. The coordinates of the epicenter of the main shock have been calculated as lat. $61.04° ± 0.05°$ N and long. $147.73° ± 0.07°$ W, and the focus was within a few tens of kilometers of the surface. Not only was this earthquake of large magnitude (between 8.3 and 8.6 on the Richter scale, on which the greatest known earthquake is 8.9), but its duration (3 to 4 minutes) and the area of its damage zone (50,000 mi^2) were extraordinary. Probably twice as much energy was released by the Alaska earthquake as by the one that rocked San Francisco in 1906.

The shock was felt over 500,000 mi^2. A tsunami (a train of long waves impulsively generated, in this case by movement of the sea floor) or "tidal wave" swept from the Gulf of Alaska across the length of the Pacific and lapped against Antarctica. Water levels in wells as far away as South Africa jumped abruptly, and shock-induced waves were generated in the Gulf of Mexico. An atmospheric pressure wave caused by the earthquake was recorded at La Jolla, California, more than 2,000 mi away. Seismic surface waves, with periods of many seconds, moved the ground surface of most of the North American continent by as much as 2 in.

The magnitude of the earthquake can be calculated only from teleseismic records, and its duration can be estimated only from eyewitness accounts, because no seismic instruments capable of recording strong ground motion were in Alaska at the time. The range of uncertainty in the magnitude calculations (8.3–8.6) is far greater in terms of energy release than the figures suggest; from the most generally accepted relation of magnitude to energy release, it can be

calculated that magnitude 8.6 represents approximately twice the energy release of magnitude 8.3.

Measured crustal deformation was more extensive than the deformation related to any known previous earthquake. Areas of uplift and subsidence were separated by a line of zero land-level change trending both southwestward and eastward from the vicinity of the epicenter, about 80 mi east-southeast of Anchorage; this line parallels the major tectonic features of the region. Areas north and northwest of the zero line subsided as much as 7.5 ft; areas south and southeast rose, over wide areas, as much as 6 ft. Locally the uplift was much greater: 38 ft on Montague Island and more than 50 ft on the sea floor southwest of the island. The zone of uplift was along the continental margin of the Aleutian Trench. Not only was the earth's crust displaced vertically, but horizontal movements of tens of feet took place, in which the landmass moved southeastward relative to the ocean floor. The area of crustal deformation was more than 100,000 mi^2.

The mechanism of the earthquake remains to some extent uncertain. Fault-plane solutions for the main shock and the principal aftershocks, of which there were 10 of magnitudes greater than 6.0 within 24 hours after the initial shock, are consistent either with thrusting of the continent over the ocean floor along a plane dipping 5°–15° north or northwest, or with downward slip of the continent along a near-vertical plane; in either case the strike of the fault is northeast in the vicinity of Kodiak Island to east in Prince William Sound, parallel to the dominant tectonic trend. Although the fault-plane solutions do not permit an unambiguous decision between the two possible planes, several other lines of evidence strongly favor the low-angle thrust alternative.

The strong ground motion induced many snowslides, rockfalls, and landslides, both subaerial and submarine. The submarine landslides created local sea waves or tsunamis, which, together with the major tsunami generated by the crustal deformation, smashed port and harbor facilities,

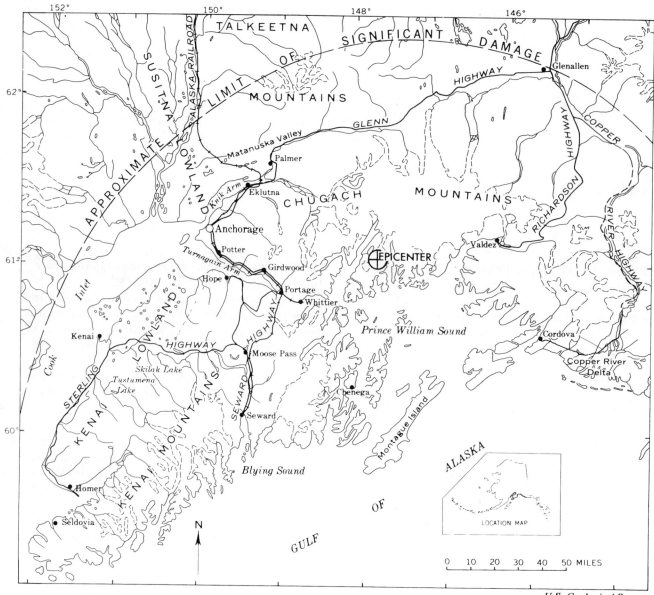

FIGURE 1 Map of south central Alaska.

U.S. Geological Survey

covered sessile organisms and salmon-spawning beds with silt, disturbed and killed salmon fry, leveled forests, and caused saltwater invasion of many coastal freshwater lakes.

The tectonic elevation and depression caused extensive damage to the biota of coastal forests, migratory-bird nesting grounds, salmon-spawning waters and gravels, as well as shellfish habitats, and initiated long-term changes in littoral and stream morphology. Clams, barnacles, algae, and many other marine and littoral organisms perished in areas of uplift. Spawning beds, trees, and other vegetation were destroyed in areas of depression.

Except for the major tsunami, which caused extensive damage in British Columbia and took 16 lives in Oregon

and California, violence to man and his structures was restricted to the area of tectonic land-level change. Tsunamis, major and local, took the most lives. Landslides caused the most damage.

The number of lives lost in Alaska, 115, was very small for an earthquake of this magnitude. Factors that contributed to the light loss of life were the sparse population, the fortuitous timing of the earthquake, a low tide, the absence of fire in residential and business areas, the generally clement weather, and the fact that the earthquake occurred during the off-season for fishing. The earthquake came on the evening of a holiday, when the schools were empty and most offices deserted, but when most people were still wearing their warm clothing. The low tide and the absence of fishermen and cannery workers mitigated the destruction and loss of life from tsunamis.

Public and private property loss was over $300 million. Hundreds of homes were destroyed. A multistory apartment building (fortunately not occupied), a department store, and other buildings in Anchorage collapsed. Oil storage tanks at Valdez, Seward, and Whittier ruptured and burned. Many other structures were destroyed or damaged. Most of downtown Kodiak was inundated by the major tsunami.

Damage to surface transportation facilities was extensive. The Alaska Railroad lost its port facility at Whittier, its docks at Seward, and numerous bridges on the Kenai Peninsula. Many highway bridges, especially on the Seward and Copper River highways, were damaged. Many port and harbor facilities, especially at Seward, Valdez, Kodiak, Whittier, Cordova, and Homer, were destroyed.

The earthquake crippled Alaska's economy because nearly half the people of the state live within the damage area and because the land- and sea-transport facilities on which the economy depends were knocked out.

Relief came quickly. The extensive military establishment proved a great source of strength in implementing emergency measures designed to reduce the loss of life, to ease immediate suffering, and to restore needed services promptly. Financial assistance for relief purposes was provided immediately by the Office of Emergency Planning under provisions of the Federal Disaster Act.

Recovery was rapid. Of major importance in the reconstruction effort was a congressional program to provide additional federal aid not possible under existing authority. This program was recommended by the Federal Reconstruction and Development Planning Commission for Alaska, a unique body appointed by President Lyndon B. Johnson on April 2, 1964. The additional aid included transitional grants to maintain essential public services; an increase in the federal share of highway reconstruction costs; a decrease in the local share of urban renewal projects; debt adjustments on existing federal loans; federal purchase of state bonds; and grants for a state mortgage-forgiveness program. An estimated $330 million of government and private funds financed Alaska's recovery from the earthquake.

The Alaska earthquake is the best documented and most thoroughly studied earthquake in history. Attempts have been made to draw lessons from both the physical event and the human experience. Strong-motion seismographs and accelerographs were installed in Alaska shortly after the earthquake, providing a basis for study of the stronger after-shocks. The tsunami warning system for the North Pacific was greatly improved within a few months, mainly by establishment of three new seismograph stations in south central Alaska as the basic elements in the system. Risk maps for Anchorage, Homer, Seward, and Valdez, based upon exten-

sive geological studies, were prepared by the Scientific and Engineering Task Force of the Reconstruction Commission and were used discriminatingly as a basis for federal aid to reconstruction and as guides to future builders. The entire town of Valdez was relocated. Communities and state and professional organizations in seismic areas outside Alaska reexamined codes and programs related to earthquake hazard in light of the Alaska experience. Finally, the Alaska earthquake turned the nation's attention again, and sharply, to the problems of improving the elements of a national natural-disaster policy: zoning and construction codes; prediction and warning systems; rescue and relief organizations; disaster-data collection and analysis; and disaster insurance and reconstruction aids.

Thus the earthquake had many facets. It was a natural scientific experiment on a grand scale, providing data on a variety of long-standing problems regarding the mechanism and effects of earthquakes. It served as a test of man-made structures under extreme conditions, and as a guide to improvements in the location and design of such structures to make them better able to withstand seismic shocks. It was an object lesson in human response to disaster, pointing the way to increased effectiveness of warning systems, of emergency measures during disasters, and of relief and recovery operations.

The charge to the Committee on the Alaska Earthquake was made to ensure that as much technical and scientific information as possible would be wrung from the earthquake experience and that the results would be assembled into a comprehensive report. At its first meeting the Committee decided that its initial task of evaluating and encouraging efforts to gather scientific and technical information could best be carried out by panels representing the major disciplines involved in the data-gathering: engineering, geography (human ecology), geology, hydrology, oceanography, and seismology. Biology, at first included within oceanography, was later made the basis of a separate panel.

As information for a comprehensive report accumulated, it became clear that the report itself could most appropriately follow the panel structure. Accordingly, this report appears in eight volumes, seven put together by the separate panels and a summary volume prepared by the full Committee.

In the early meetings of the Committee, and especially as it became apparent that many of the physical-science and some of the engineering aspects of the earthquake would be treated comprehensively in government publications and individual studies, there was considerable discussion of the appropriate content of the Committee's final report.

The Committee finally decided that the advantages of having available, under one cover and in one place in a library, a truly comprehensive report on the earthquake would justify the expense of duplicating some material already published. In addition, the Committee agreed, a complete report would provide a better basis for the inclusion of cross-disciplinary papers, for pointing out lessons learned from the Alaska experience, and for making recommendations designed to reduce the loss of life and property in subsequent major earthquakes.

As a model for its work, the Committee could look back to the classic report on the 1906 San Francisco earthquake, published by the Carnegie Institution in 1908. To emulate the comprehensiveness of this magnificent report seemed possible, but not the unity and coherence that it gained from the encyclopedic knowledge of its editor and principal author, A. C. Lawson. The breadth and depth of scientific interest in earthquakes have increased so greatly since 1906 that no one man can hope to master, as Lawson did, a great part of existing technical knowledge on all aspects of earthquakes. A report today must necessarily have many authors and must reflect in its length and diversity the extraordinary development of disciplines and instruments over the past half century.

Despite the Committee's attempt to make the report broadly comprehensive, there are unfortunate and obvious gaps in the record, mainly in those subject-matter fields not included in the work of government agencies. Such gaps are identified in the appropriate volumes of the report.

Apart from these gaps, the report covers a wide variety of subjects in engineering, natural science, and social science. Ranging from seismology to human ecology, it sets forth what is known about the structure of the earth's crust in south central Alaska, especially in relation to possible earthquake mechanisms and to tsunami generation; describes the effects of the earthquake on geologic processes, rocks, and soils; outlines the seismic history of Alaska and gives the seismic parameters of the earthquake; presents the results of energy-release, strain-release, and focal-mechanism studies of the main shock and aftershocks; describes the effects of the earthquake on groundwater and surface-water bodies and on glaciers and snowfields; discusses the generation, propagation, and effects of earthquake-induced tsunamis; describes immediate as well as long-term effects on plants and animals of abrupt land elevation and depression and of slides and tsunamis; sets forth in detail, with analyses, the response of man-made structures to the earthquake; chronicles in narrative form both the physical and human events of the earthquake; describes the impact of the earthquake on individuals, communities, and organizations; and puts forward recommendations that range from geologic mapping for hazard zoning, through methods of assuring site-suited earthquake-resistant construction, to means of improving the human response to disaster.

This volume on Oceanography and Coastal Engineering is one of the eight parts into which the report is divided. Its

papers describe the disturbances caused by the great shock to the bottom and the waters of the ocean as well as their disastrous effects on communities and works of man along the shore. With regard to human life, the earthquake was far more destructive in these indirect effects produced by water movement than in the direct effects of shaking. Among the lessons that the earthquake can teach for the future, none are more important than those concerning prediction and control of the massive surges of water that such events may create.

With its epicenter close to the sea and a crustal movement involving widespread uplift and subsidence of the ocean floor, the earthquake inevitably generated a tsunami that spread far and wide over the Pacific. Destructive as the great waves were to communities along the shores of the deeply embayed Alaskan coastline and to isolated spots as far distant as northern California, it is perhaps cause for wonder that the tsunami was not large enough to wreak havoc even farther afield. The volume of water abruptly displaced was probably as large as that with any recorded earthquake, and yet tsunamis in the past have caused greater and more widespread damage. It is a measure of our ignorance of how tsunamis are generated and propagated that we still cannot predict for a given earthquake how large a wave will be formed and at what points its fury will be concentrated. The careful documentation of the Alaska experience recorded in these pages should provide a basis for better understanding and more accurate prediction in the future.

The earthquake was responsible not only for the major tsunami that traveled across the Pacific basin, but also for violent agitation of the water in many narrow fiords and inlets. The cause of such disturbances was compounded of shaking of the sea bottom, movement of huge underwater slides, and the setting up of harmonic oscillations or seiches. Movements as complex as this will never be predictable in detail, but the vivid records from Alaska will at least give warning of the topographic situation where they may occur and of the immense destruction that they can cause.

Besides the generation of waves, the earthquake affected the ocean by changing its shoreline and bottom configuration in the areas of crustal subsidence and uplift. Geophysical study of the detailed changes in level over large areas has brought to light not only the effects of this one earthquake, but also evidence for similar dislocations of shorelines and sea floor many times in the geologic past.

These and other oceanographic aspects of the earthquake are described and analyzed from both scientific and engineering viewpoints in this volume. Several other volumes of the report contain additional details about specialized subjects related to oceanography. The effect of shoreline changes on living things, mentioned here only briefly, is treated fully in the Biology volume. The mechanism of the major tsunami is discussed in this volume and also in the one on Seismology and Geodesy. The human response to the tsunami warning system, clearly of great interest to social scientists, finds a place in the Human Ecology volume as well as here. The study of processes operating on and near the shoreline belongs properly to both oceanography and geology, and aspects of these processes are touched on in both volumes. Evaluation of engineering damage from the tsunami is largely concentrated in this volume, but engineering analysis of damage to some shoreline structures is also included in the volume on Engineering.

Complete understanding of effects on the ocean produced by a major earthquake is still a distant goal, but the detailed studies of the Alaska event gathered in this volume record a major advance in theoretical knowledge and lead to recommendations for minimizing loss of life and property during future earthquakes that occur close to the ocean shore.

KONRAD B. KRAUSKOPF
Stanford University

Acknowledgments

The Committee on the Alaska Earthquake and the Panels on Oceanography and Engineering are particularly indebted to the National Science Foundation, the former U.S. Coast and Geodetic Survey, the U.S. Geological Survey, the Office of Emergency Preparedness, the Army Research Office, the Atomic Energy Commission, the Advanced Research Projects Agency, the Office of Naval Research, the Office of Civil Defense, and the Department of Transportation for support of the Committee under Contract NSF C-310, Task Order 89; to the Department of Housing and Urban Development for similar support under Contract H-1229; to the Bureau of Land Management, Bureau of Indian Affairs, Bureau of Sport Fisheries and Wildlife, National Park Service, and the U.S. Geological Survey for special support; and to the National Science Foundation for publication support under Contract NSF C-310, Task Order 208; and also for their several projects that culminated in papers appearing in this volume.

The Committee and Panels greatly appreciate the time and effort provided by Professor C. L. Jordan, Florida State University; Dean John A. Knauss, University of Rhode Island; and Dean Robert L. Wiegel, University of California at Berkeley, for their comments and suggestions as reviewers for the Division of Earth Sciences.

They are also grateful to the former U.S. Coast and Geodetic Survey, the American Society of Civil Engineers, the Hawaii Institute of Geophysics and the East-West Center of the University of Hawaii, Science Engineering Associates, the U.S. Army Corps of Engineers' Coastal Engineering Research Center, Tetra Tech, Inc., and The Ohio State University's Disaster Research Center for permission to use, and in some instances to reprint, papers prepared independently of this effort.

The Panels thank the various government and private organizations that made available the time of the authors whose works make up the volume. Special recognition is due the University of Hawaii; the California Institute of Technology; the U.S. Geological Survey; the University of California at Berkeley; the University of California at San Diego, the Scripps Institution of Oceanography; the Lamont-Doherty Geological Observatory; the U.S. Naval Ordnance Test Station, China Lake; the former U.S. Coast and Geodetic Survey; the former Environmental Science Services Administration; and the National Oceanic and Atmospheric Administration; the University of Alaska; the University of Tokyo; Science Engineering Associates; the Geological Society of America; Tetra Tech, Inc.; The Ohio State University, Disaster Research Center; the U.S. Army Corps of Engineers; Ayres, Cohen, and Hayakawa; the University of Michigan; the University of Southern California; and the California Academy of Sciences for making it possible for some of their personnel to serve as Panel members, authors, and reviewers. Similarly, the Panels express their appreciation to Stanford University, the California Institute of Technology, Texas A&M University, the University of Hawaii, the U.S. Geological Survey, The Geological Society of America, The Ohio State University, the University of Colorado, the former U.S. Bureau of Commercial Fisheries, the National Oceanic and Atmospheric Administration, the University of Southern California, Clark University, the University of California, and the former Environmental Science Services Administration for making available their personnel for service on the parent Committee; and also to the Office of Science and Technology, the National Science Foundation, the Army Research Office, the Advanced Research Projects Agency, the former U.S. Coast and Geodetic Survey, the former Environmental Science Services Administration, the National Oceanic and Atmospheric Administration, the U.S. Geological Survey, the Office of Emergency Preparedness, the Atomic Energy Commission, the Office of Naval Research, and the Department of Housing and Urban Development for the time and assistance provided by their liaison representatives to the Committee.

The Panels are grateful to the University of Idaho, the U.S. Geological Survey, and Emory University for making the services of editors and indexers available; to the several organizations and individuals credited for assistance with the illustrations; to the U.S. Army and the U.S. Air Force for transportation to the affected areas; to representatives of The Redevelopment Agency of the City of Crescent City for on-the-scene discussions with Committee and Panel members in California; to the California Institute of Technology for furnishing a meeting place for the Panel on Engineering; and to the California Academy of Sciences, Science Engineering Associates, and the U.S. Geological Survey for furnishing meeting places for the Panel on Oceanography.

Since 1964, reorganizations within federal agencies and departments have involved several of the Committee's supporting agencies. On July 13, 1965, the U.S. Coast and Geodetic Survey and other component agencies were combined to form the Environmental Science Services Administration, under the Department of Commerce. On October 3, 1970, the Environmental Science Services Administration, together with several other organizations, became the National Oceanic and Atmospheric Administration (NOAA), also under the Department of Commerce. Although the Bureau of Commercial Fisheries, the Coast and Geodetic Survey, and the Environmental Science Services Administration no longer exist as organizations, their names are used for historical accuracy, as is that of the Office of Emergency Planning, which was renamed the Office of Emergency Preparedness on October 21, 1968.

Contents

OCEANOGRAPHY

General Introduction—*Doak C. Cox*   3

I. SEISMIC EFFECTS

Introduction—*Doak C. Cox* and *Roland von Huene*   11
Seaquakes—*Roland von Huene*   13
T-Phases—*John Northrop*   19
Seismic Seiches in Bays, Channels, and Estuaries—*Arthur McGarr* and *Robert C. Vorhis*   25

II. TSUNAMIS

Introduction—*Doak C. Cox*   31
The Tsunamis as Recorded at Tide Stations and the Seismic Sea Wave Warning System—*Mark G. Spaeth* and
    Saul C. Berkman   38
Source Mechanism of the Major Tsunami—*William G. Van Dorn*   111
Source of the Major Tsunami—*Eduard Berg, Doak C. Cox, Augustine S. Furumoto, Kinjiro Kajiura,
    Hirosi Kawasumi,* and *Etsuzo Shima*   122
A Model Experiment on the Generation of the Major Tsunami—*William G. Van Dorn*   140
Oceanic Character, Propagation, and Coastal Modification of the Major Tsunami—*William G. Van Dorn*
    and *Doak C. Cox*   147
Runup Heights of the Major Tsunami on North American Coasts—*Basil W. Wilson* and *Alf Tϕrum*   158
The Major Tsunami in the Hawaiian Islands—*Harold G. Loomis*   181
A Numerical Model of the Major Tsunami—*Li-San Hwang* and *David Divoky*   191
Locally Generated Tsunamis and Other Local Waves—*Roland von Huene* and *Doak C. Cox*   211
Human Response to Tsunami Warnings—*Jack M. Weller*   222
Technical Evaluation of the Seismic Sea Wave Warning System—*Doak C. Cox* and *Harris B. Stewart, Jr.* 229

III. MARINE AND SHORELINE GEOLOGICAL EFFECTS

Introduction—*Roland von Huene*   249
Vertical Crustal Movement on the Sea Floor—*Richard J. Malloy* and *George F. Merrill*   252
Offshore Tectonic Features in the Affected Region—*Roland von Huene, George G. Shor, Jr.,* and
    Richard J. Malloy   266
Effects in the Copper River Delta—*Erk Reimnitz*   290

IV. OTHER MARINE ASPECTS

Introduction—*Doak C. Cox*   305
Biological Effects—*G Dallas Hanna*   307
Changes in Tidal Characteristics and Tidal Datum Planes—*Steacy D. Hicks*   310
Nautical Chart Revisions—*Fergus J. Wood* and *Lorne G. Taylor*   315

V. SUMMARY AND CONCLUSIONS

Marine Effects and Hazards of Earthquakes—*Doak C. Cox*   337

COASTAL ENGINEERING

Introduction—*George W. Housner*   353
Review of the Tsunamis—*Doak C. Cox*   354
Effects of the Tsunamis: An Engineering Study—*Basil W. Wilson* and *Alf Tørum*   361

APPENDIXES

Annotated Bibliography   527
Contributors to This Volume   541
English-Metric and Metric-English Conversion Tables   542
Index   545

Oceanography

General Introduction

Most people associate only terrestrial manifestations with earthquakes—the vibration of the ground, possibly the opening of fissures or displacement on faults, the resulting failures of structures, and the associated casualties. The residents of coasts like those of Japan and Chile, however, are of necessity aware of the possible damage from monstrous ocean waves set up by some earthquakes, and the people of Hawaii have learned from bitter experience about the potential of catastrophic waves associated with some earthquakes on the distant rim of the Pacific Ocean.

Although the epicenter of the Alaska earthquake of 1964 was on land, the greater part of the damage it caused in Alaska, exclusive of the city of Anchorage, was related to marine manifestations rather than ground shaking, and 90 percent of the Alaskan casualties were caused by the marine disturbances. The damage included losses of docks, breakwaters, buildings, tanks, and railroad yards because of slumping into the fiords and the crushing or sweeping away of other structures, railroad rolling stock, automobiles, and boats by enormous waves. Most of the casualties were deaths by drowning or those presumed to have been by drowning, after the victims had been dropped into the water by the slumping or swept away by the waves.

The toll of death and destruction by marine effects was not confined to Alaska, however. Damage amounting to more than $20 million and 16 casualties resulted from the passage of the waves down the Pacific Coast from British Columbia to California, although Hawaii, in the middle of the ocean, was spared a major catastrophe. Other waves associated with the earthquake in channels off the Gulf of Mexico were responsible for minor damage to boats and waterfront facilities.

Any major natural catastrophe merits intensive study, but for several reasons the study of the marine aspects of the Alaska earthquake seemed especially pertinent. Because of the deep indentations of the Alaskan coastline with its offshore islands, for example, it appeared that more could be learned about the origin of the destructive waves associated with this earthquake than is usually possible. The extensive slumping clearly needed investigation. Many oceanographers, geologists, and other specialists, acting as individuals, as teams especially organized, or as members of government agencies like the U.S. Coast and Geodetic Survey and U.S. Geological Survey, responded to the challenges, some within days or weeks of the earthquake, others during subsequent months and years. The range in both time and nature of the resulting studies has been beneficial. Some of the evidences of marine effects of the earthquake were evanescent and could be recorded for only a limited time after the shock; others, however, could be investigated only by well-organized and time-consuming surveys. The two major government Surveys undertook, naturally, a considerable share of the work, especially that of a continuing nature. But they could not, alone, have provided from their own staffs the manpower needed for the short-term efforts, and the risk of institutional biases was clearly minimized by the pluralistic nature of the guidance of the overall effort.

THE WORK OF THE PANEL ON OCEANOGRAPHY

At the first meeting of the Committee on the Alaska Earthquake in June 1964, some studies of oceanographic aspects of the earthquake had already been made and others were continuing. It was clear that the investigations completed and in progress and the need for other investigations warranted the establishment of a special oceanography panel of the Committee. It was evident that the tsunamis (the trains of large waves) would be of concern to this panel, as would the submarine slumping and bathymetric changes. Because the significant biological aspects of the earthquake were largely marine, it was considered that these too could be handled by the oceanography panel.

In conjunction with the second meeting of the Committee held in Anchorage in August 1964, an oceanography working group, composed of Eduard Berg (University of Alaska), Doak C. Cox (University of Hawaii), and George Y. Harry, Jr. (Bureau of Commercial Fisheries), compiled lists of topics of interest, with notes on individuals and agencies having or developing pertinent information, and of needs for investigations not yet planned. Because of the importance of biological aspects of the earthquake, the working group recommended the establishment of a separate biology panel, but the Committee decided to proceed, at least for the time being, by including biologists on the oceanography panel.

The Panel on Oceanography was established soon thereafter with the following membership:

Doak C. Cox, *Chairman*, University of Hawaii
G Dallas Hanna, California Academy of Sciences
George Y. Harry, Jr., Bureau of Commercial Fisheries
Gerald W. Prescott, Michigan State University
Gene A. Rusnak, U.S. Geological Survey
Harris B. Stewart, Jr., U.S. Coast and Geodetic Survey

At its first meeting, held in San Francisco in December 1964, much of the Panel's attention was devoted to investigations of the biological effects of the earthquake. At that meeting, plans were laid for a biological expedition to Prince William Sound. The California Academy of Sciences, as requested, agreed to serve as sponsor. Support was successfully sought from the National Science Foundation and the Atomic Energy Commission, and the expedition was carried out in the summer of 1965 under the direction of G Dallas Hanna.

Following the expedition, the biologists of the Panel—Hanna, Harry, and Prescott—met on August 9, 1965, at Auke Bay, Alaska, with others involved in the expedition, to discuss the work completed, the work remaining, and plans for publication of a special biology section in the report of the Committee. Later that month, a full-fledged Panel on Biology was established by the Committee, the biologists of the Panel on Oceanography were transferred to it, and the biological section was planned as a separate volume. The Panel on Oceanography was reconstituted in consideration of its then more restricted interest in physical and geological oceanographic aspects of the earthquake by the addition of a new member, William G. Van Dorn, Scripps Institution of Oceanography.

Recognizing the mutual interests of the Panels on Seismology, Oceanography, and Geography in the problems of tsunamis and tsunami warnings, plans had been laid, at the third meeting of the parent Committee held at Stanford, California, in February 1965, for a special meeting on tsunamis. This meeting, which was held at Stanford on May 28, 1965, involved 19 participants representing the Committee, the three panels concerned, and several governmental and private agencies. The status of investigations on the causative mechanisms and effects of the major tsunami generated in the Gulf of Alaska and of the several local tsunamis generated in fiords and straits was reviewed. Note was made of the importance of local chronologies of seismic, geologic, and oceanographic phenomena in determining cause-and-effect relationships. Various protective measures, such as land zoning, construction codes, and especially the tsunami warning system, were discussed.

The outline of the oceanography portion of the report of the Committee on the Alaska Earthquake was established in approximately its final form at the second meeting of the Panel on Oceanography, held in San Francisco in October 1965. A major need recognized at the meeting was for a comprehensive paper or set of papers on the phenomenology of the major tsunami. The Panel on Engineering, whose technical assistant, Paul Jennings, attended the Panel meeting, was negotiating with Basil Wilson of Science Engineering Associates for a study of the engineering effects of both local and major tsunamis that would necessarily involve some investigation of the nature of the major tsunami. By arrangement with the Panel on Engineering and with the Coastal Engineering Research Center, which supported the work, the study was planned to meet the needs of both Panels. From the resulting major report by Wilson and Tørum has been drawn a paper in the tsunami section of this volume as well as the principal contribution to the Coastal Engineering portion of this volume.

A good many studies resulted, at least in part, from the identification of needs at the October 1965 Panel meeting: a study of the *T*-phases of the earthquake and aftershocks (by John Northrop), a study of the tsunamis locally generated in Alaskan fiords and straits (by Gene Rusnak), a study of the effects of the major tsunami in Hawaii (by H. G. Loomis), a report on the Seismic Sea Wave Warning System and its functioning at the time of the earthquake (by M. G. Spaeth and S. C. Berkman), a critique of the warning system (by D. C. Cox and H. B. Stewart, Jr.), a review of physical oceanographic aspects of the earthquake (by S. D. Hicks), and several interrelated studies of marine tectonic features (by Roland von Huene, G. G. Shor, R. J. Malloy, G. F. Merrill, and others).

At its third meeting in San Marino, California, on June 17, 1966, the Panel added to its membership Roland von Huene, who was already involved in marine geological and geophysical studies related to the earthquake and who agreed to undertake a study of seaquake observations. The Panel was thus brought to its final membership:

Doak C. Cox, *Chairman*, University of Hawaii
Gene A. Rusnak, U.S. Geological Survey
Harris B. Stewart, Jr., Environmental Science Services Administration (later, NOAA)
William G. Van Dorn, Scripps Institution of Oceanography

Roland von Huene, Naval Ordnance Test Station (later with U.S. Geological Survey)

It was clear that the concerns of the Panel on Oceanography overlapped those of other Panels in many aspects. To avoid duplication of major efforts but to ensure a comprehensive coverage of the marine aspects in the oceanography report, the parent Committee decided, generally on the recommendation of the Panel, to include in the Oceanography volume only summaries on (1) the marine seiches from a study more fully reported in the Hydrology volume, (2) marine biological effects from extensive studies reported in the Biology volume, and (3) the human response to the tsunami warnings from the studies more fully reported in the Human Ecology volume. The Committee also decided to yield to the Seismology volume the reporting of the microbarographic waves (which were of interest in connection with tsunami generation) and the marine geophysical aspects, except as those were related to tsunami generation, and to leave to the Human Ecology volume the narrative chronologies that were so important to an understanding of cause-and-effect relationships in the generation of the tsunamis.

The assembly of oceanography reports proceeded in spite of hindrances resulting from changes in the employment of Panel members, particularly the chairman, who had been engaged in tsunami research at the time of the earthquake but who assumed responsibilities for an unrelated research program a year later. During the year 1966–1967, while the chairman was on leave, the Panel met twice with other members serving as temporary chairman: Harris Stewart at San Marino, California, on October 4 and Roland von Huene at Menlo Park, California, on February 2. At the sixth meeting of the Panel, in Menlo Park on November 4, 1967, it appeared that major problems were solved by a decision to combine the tsunami studies to be reported by the Panel on Engineering with those to be reported by the Panel on Oceanography in a single volume to be entitled Oceanography and Coastal Engineering.

The appearance of a solution to the problems was deceptive. Major differences arose among Panel members and outside reviewers concerning the methodology and conclusions of one major tsunami study. These differences were the subject of lengthy discussion at the two meetings of the Panel in 1968—one at Pasadena on May 5 and the other at Menlo Park on September 28. Their resolution involved complete reorganization of the tsunami chapter and more extensive use (than had originally been planned) of papers resulting from studies made or begun before the Committee started its work (those of Van Dorn, Berg and others, and Spaeth and Berkman) and also of papers based on a subsequent hydraulic-model study (by Van Dorn) and on a special review (by Van Dorn and Cox).

Two additional papers concerning marine and shoreline geological effects of the earthquake were added toward the end of the Panel's work—one on the Copper River Delta (Reimnitz) and the other on results of the crustal uplift and depression as they affected navigation and charting requirements (taken from an earlier Coast and Geodetic Survey report by Wood and Taylor). The final paper to be included—a discussion of the application of a numerical-analysis technique to the character and propagation of the major tsunami (Hwang and Divoky)—was solicited for the volume on the basis of a study that came to the Panel's attention only a few months before the manuscript review process was completed.

No attempt has been made in this volume to incorporate all the voluminous data pertaining to the oceanographic aspects of the earthquake or, because of their number and their overlapping coverage, all the descriptive and analytical papers which by now have been written on these aspects. The annotated bibliography that is included should serve as an adequate guide to published sources of additional data and previous reports.

MAJOR CONTRIBUTIONS TO OCEANOGRAPHIC KNOWLEDGE

The oceanographic manifestations of the Alaska earthquake have probably been studied more extensively than those of any other major earthquake, partly because of the improved scientific techniques available for their study and partly because of the physiographic character of the earthquake setting, which promoted early recognition of the gross aspects of the crustal deformation of the shelf, the mass movements, and the resulting sea waves.

Although observations of seaquakes had initially been reported by very few vessels, investigation disclosed that seaquakes were observed by many vessels with both the main earthquake and its aftershocks. The strength distribution of the seaquake phase of the main earthquake suggested a greater seismic intensity off Kodiak Island than in Prince William Sound, probably related to the shelf faulting off Kodiak that was not detected bathymetrically until several years after the earthquake.

Investigations of the T-phases associated with the earthquake and its aftershocks indicated that the hydrophone network, by which they were recorded, had a lower detection threshold than the conventional seismograph network.

Although the epicenter of the earthquake was on land, much of the area of crustal displacement was found to be marine. Perhaps the most significant knowledge derived from the earthquake concerning the displacement was its sheer magnitude. An area of about 180,000 km² of the Continental Shelf in the Gulf of Alaska was uplifted, on the average, about 2 m. Locally, in a faulted zone extending from Montague Island southwest to a point southeast of Kodiak Island, uplifts between faults were in excess of 14 m. Prince William Sound also was uplifted. To the northwest and north of these uplifted areas there was a zone of subsidence primarily involving land areas. Most of the disturbed area was also displaced horizontally southeastward to a maximum of more than 20 m. Rotational slumps and other mass movements in the unconsolidated sediments of deltas were found in many of the fiords that opened onto Prince William Sound and the Gulf of Alaska.

Evidence is well documented for the independent generation of more than 10 tsunamis that had local effects in various fiords and straits. From eyewitness accounts and other information, some of these local tsunamis could be clearly related to the mass movements of sediments; others may have been caused by crustal tilting, by horizontal crustal displacement, or possibly by local faulting.

From several lines of evidence it became clear that the major tsunami that swept out across the Pacific was generated by the general uplift of the Continental Shelf in the Gulf of Alaska. Local faulting and the horizontal crustal displacement may have affected the high-frequency characteristics of the tsunami but could not have contributed significantly to the energy propagating at low frequencies.

It was clear that the major tsunami involved, at least initially, both low-frequency nondispersive components and high-frequency dispersive components. The continuing low-frequency characteristics of the tsunami, in spite of intensive study, remain uncertain. Most tide gages recorded oscillations with periods of about 1.8 hours as a significant or major component of the tsunami. These oscillations have been attributed by different investigators to coherent long-period waves radiating from the source, noncoherent low-frequency energy radiating from the source, and low-frequency conversion of high-frequency energy radiating from the source.

The runup heights of the major tsunami, as those of previous tsunamis studied, varied greatly even in a single coastal region. However, comparisons of the ranges in runup heights with direction and distance from the origin of the tsunami indicated clearly a preferential radiation of energy normal to the long axis of the generating area. This preferential radiation of energy accounts for the difference between the intensity of the effects of this tsunami on the coast from British Columbia to California and the intensity of the effects in Hawaii as compared with the relative intensities for previous tsunamis generated in the Aleutian Islands. The correspondence between the orientation of the long axis of the origin area and the prevailing trend of geologic and tectonic features in the area suggests the possibility of useful estimation of directionality in tsunami warning.

Studies of the major tsunami confirmed the utility of numerical-analysis techniques as supplements to or replacements of graphical techniques for predicting tsunami-arrival times at coastlines distant from the source. In addition, the potentialities of numerical analysis for determining, from the characteristics of the crustal displacement at the source, the character of the tsunami as it crosses the ocean and approaches distant shorelines have now been demonstrated through studies of this tsunami, among others.

Although a warning of the major tsunami had been issued by the Seismic Sea Wave Warning System, the fact that 16 persons lost their lives on the coasts of Oregon and California suggested that the system might be improved. Studies of the performance of the system and the behavior of coastal residents served by it indicated a number of possible improvements. Many of these have subsequently been put into effect: improved seismographic instrumentation and techniques for speedier and more effective analysis of earthquake location and characteristics; additional marigraphic sensors, particularly some on exposed coastlines not so subject to filtering of the waves as are tide gages in the usual protected locations; and improved communications, including telemetry of seismographic and marigraphic data. Perhaps most important, since the primary purpose of the warning system is considered to be minimization of human casualties, is the recognition that the effectiveness of the system is dependent not only on the information transmitted at the time of a probable tsunami, but also on the previous successes and failures of the system as appraised by those it is intended to serve. In this light, major improvements are changes of policy (1) to bring about the appraisal of the hazard of a tsunami, not in general, but with respect to the particular coastal regions to be warned; (2) to endeavor to avoid the issuance of a warning in a particular region unless the risk in that region is significant; and (3) to cancel warnings on a regional basis as soon as the regional risks are abated.

LIMITATIONS TO THE STUDIES OF OCEANOGRAPHIC EFFECTS

It is relatively easy to identify a number of significant limitations to the studies of oceanographic effects of the Alaska earthquake. They may be related to a number of causes: a dearth of information on preearthquake conditions; the low population density and poorly developed transportation and communication systems in the meizoseismal area; an insufficient number of instruments and trained investigators; and lack of financial and organizational support for investigation.

The dearth of preearthquake information was most serious in geological, geophysical, and tectonic studies. Although the number of preearthquake geodetic, topographic, and bathymetric surveys in the meizoseismal area was surprising in view of its low population densities and economic values, the information available from these surveys was inadequate for the needs. In particular, the bathymetric surveys on the Continental Shelf, although of adequate vertical accuracy, lacked horizontal control sufficiently adequate to permit their postearthquake repetition for comparison. Most of the surveys, in addition, had been made so long before the earthquake that it could not be established whether changes had occurred abruptly at the time of the earthquake, gradually over a long time, or by a combination of both.

At the time of the earthquake, the tide gage at Womens Bay, Kodiak, was the only one in operation in the meizoseismic area, and that one was put out of commission by the first wave of the tsunami. The vertical displacements were of such a magnitude that they were indicated better by the shifts in ecological zones relative to sea level than they could have been by tide gages, but the lack of instrumental records of the tsunamis in the region of their generation has seriously hampered the development of understanding of their nature and origin.

The limitations of ordinary tide gages as tsunami recorders have long been recognized. Located, as they generally are, in protected bays behind wide shelves, they produce records subject to active filtering and distortion in the range of periods of interest. There was only one special tsunami recorder in operation, located at Wake Island.

Lacking instrumental records, investigators concerned with the establishment of cause-and-effect relationships among the complex phenomena observed in the fiords and on the open coast of Alaska had to rely on eyewitness accounts and on physical evidences such as scarps and the damage to structures resulting from slumping, bathymetric changes, and debris lines and damage caused by waves. Some of these easily observed evidences—for example, the trim lines left by waves on snow patches—could, however, only be observed during the first few days or weeks after the earthquake. Other evidences—for example, the bathymetric changes and submarine fault scarps—could only be recorded through sophisticated survey techniques that require considerable advance planning. Hence the pattern of staged investigation that developed, in large measure inadvertently, turned out to have considerable advantages. This pattern involved broad surveys by early investigators who could spend little time at any one site, followed successively by more extensive surveys involving more preparation and more time in the field. Adequate mechanisms were lacking, however, at least for some months after the earthquake, for the full utilization of information from the early surveys in the planning of later surveys, except where some single agency was involved in both the early and late activity.

There were particular deficiencies in the recording of eyewitness accounts, which provided generally the only evidence as to time and sequences of events. The inconsistencies among these accounts (even the accounts related to different interviewers by the same witness), which have been preserved only through the accidental redundancy of the pattern of investigation, are valuable reminders of the unreliability of the memory of witnesses as to events involving psychological stress, and of the difficulty of soliciting testimony from a witness without biasing such testimony in the process. In contrast, the consistency among the eyewitness accounts reported by some investigators suggests either that these investigators were unaware of the difficulties of valid interviewing or that they conducted their interviews with a single predetermined hypothesis, or both.

The Chairman of the Panel on Hydrology, whose report was readied for publication only 3 years after the earthquake, has remarked on the difficulties of maintaining the interest of both researchers and research-funding agencies in the initiation or continuance of studies of an "old" earthquake. Now, 8 years after the earthquake, there are still some oceanographic field studies that warrant continuation, for example, studies of continuing postearthquake shoreline changes and perhaps a few additional geophysical and bathymetric surveys for comparison with preearthquake surveys. Generally, however, the period for useful field observations specifically related to the earthquake is long past. The analysis of field data already collected may be expected to continue for a long time, but generally with the stimulus not of the earthquake itself, but of other events—natural events such as future earthquakes or cultural events such as the discovery of new techniques of investigation. At this point it can only be hoped that the basic data collected on the Alaska earthquake, recorded in this volume and in other reports to which reference is made in it, will prove sufficient for the needs of future analyses.

It would be impossible to express adequately the appreciation of the Panel on Oceanography to all who contributed, directly or indirectly, to its work. Acknowledgment of the debt of the Panel is due, however, to each of the authors of papers in this volume for their cooperation in the review process that has been very protracted for most and very difficult for some.

DOAK C. COX
University of Hawaii

I
SEISMIC EFFECTS

Introduction

Oceanographic phenomena associated with earthquakes have various causes. Some are closely related to the seismic vibrations, whereas others are the results of geologic or tectonic accompaniments of the earthquakes. Treated in this chapter are oceanographic manifestations of the Alaska earthquake that are strictly seismic—that is, related closely to the earthquake vibrations. These are vibrations or oscillations of the water that resulted directly from coupling with vibrations or oscillations in the rock—properly considered as seismological consequences of the earthquake, in the sense that the earth includes the hydrosphere as well as the lithosphere.

A seaquake is an earthquake felt at sea. Unlike an earthquake felt on land, it lacks shear vibrations, which cannot be carried by the water, but its compressional vibrations are identical to those in rock. The observation of a seaquake is restricted to the area of high seismic intensity where compressional vibrations of amplitude sufficient to be felt can be transmitted from the crust through the overlying water. Seaquakes have probably been experienced as long as mariners have been sailing in seismically active parts of the world. Their effects on vessels, frequently resembling the effects of running aground, have been responsible for the recording of many of the shoals and reefs shown on older charts with the notation "E.D." (existence doubtful). As discussed by von Huene (this volume), observations of the seaquake associated with the Alaska earthquake were reported in the areas of Prince William Sound and the Continental Shelf in the Gulf of Alaska. The observation farthest from the epicenter was 400 km distant, off Yakataga, but the intensities off Kodiak Island suggested more effective generation in that vicinity. Possibly greater submarine crustal displacements occurred off Kodiak than early earthquake investigations indicated.

The seaquake effects aboard ship were described as being similar to those of going aground, hitting a reef, being hit by another ship, or losing part of the ship's propeller. One boat was shaken enough to cause a strong seiche in its live-bait tank, and at the same site choppy water was reported on the sea surface.

Compressional waves in the ocean were also recorded to distances of many thousand kilometers from the epicenter. The velocity structure of the ocean includes a "sound channel" (sofar channel) lying near the surface in high latitudes and at a depth of about 1,000 m near the equator. In this channel, the energy of sound waves is concentrated by refraction, so that seismic waves may be transmitted over great distances. Seismic waves carried by the sound channel and recorded by hydrophones, or transmitted back into the rock and recorded by seismographs, are called T-phases. As shown by Northrop (this volume), T-phases from the main Alaska earthquake and also from a large number of its aftershocks were recorded at sofar hydrophones off California and several Pacific Islands. Indeed, some aftershocks not reported from seismograph records were identifiable in the hydrophone records.

The main earthquake was of so large a magnitude that its compressional waves were radiated into the ocean from several rock–water boundaries, including an ocean-bottom area some 1,600 km from the epicenter. Aftershock T-phases were, however, derived preferentially from a T-phase "window" so located as to permit the flattening of the wave paths by multiple reflection between the surface and the continental slope.

The once-suggested possible direct use of T-phases as indicators of tsunami generation was long ago disproved. However, Northrop suggests the possible use of certain frequency characteristics of T-phases to discriminate continental-margin earthquakes, possibly tsunamigenic, from deep-ocean earthquakes unlikely to be tsunamigenic.

Most of the gravity waves that visibly affected the sea surface, including those that caused extensive damage in Alaska and as far south as California, were tsunami waves, impulsively generated by tectonic crustal displacements or submarine slides. However, waves were recorded in lakes and rivers across North America and even as far away as Australia (McGarr and Vorhis, 1968, and Hydrology volume). Along the coast of the Gulf of Mexico (Spaeth and Berkman, 1967), which, of course, could not have been reached by a tsunami from Alaska, waves large enough to cause damage were generated 30 to 40 minutes after the occurrence of the earthquake in Alaska. These waves have been shown to be seismic seiches, or standing waves generated by resonant coupling between the seismic surface waves in the crust (Love and Rayleigh waves) and the confined or semiconfined waters of the lakes, rivers, and channels (Donn, 1964; McGarr, 1965, and Hydrology volume). As summarized by McGarr and Vorhis (this volume), the most effective crustal seismic waves were those of about a 15-second period, and the seiche excited might represent either the fundamental or some harmonic of the natural period of oscillation of the water body. McGarr and Vorhis consider that the concentration of seiche activity in both saltwater channels and freshwater lakes and rivers in states adjacent to the Gulf of Mexico was due to the amplification of the seismic surface waves in the thick deposits of sediments of low rigidity bordering the Gulf. Wilson and Tørum (1968) have suggested an additional causative factor in the proximity of this area to a nodal point for the free oscillations of the earth associated with the earthquake. A concentration of seiche activity on the northern part of the Pacific Coast may simply be due to the proximity of this coast to the earthquake epicenter.

The damage resulting from the marine seiches was widespread along the Gulf of Mexico coast from Houston, Texas, to Lake Borgne, Louisiana (Spaeth and Berkman, 1967), but was limited to fairly minor damage to boats and dock facilities.

DOAK C. COX
University of Hawaii

ROLAND VON HUENE
U.S. Geological Survey

REFERENCES

Donn, William L., 1964. Alaskan earthquake of 27 March 1964: Remote seiche stimulation. *Science*, 145 (July 17), 261–262.

McGarr, Arthur, 1965. Excitation of seiches in channels by seismic waves. *Journal of Geophysical Research*, 70 (February 15), 847–854. Also *in* The Great Alaska Earthquake of 1964: Hydrology. NAS Pub. 1603. Washington: National Academy of Sciences, 1968. p. 133–139.

McGarr, Arthur, and Robert C. Vorhis, 1968. Seismic seiches from the March 1964 Alaska earthquake. U.S. Geological Survey Professional Paper 544-E. Washington: Government Printing Office. 43 p. Also *in* The Great Alaska Earthquake of 1964: Hydrology.

NAS Pub. 1603. Washington: National Academy of Sciences, 1968. p. 196–217.

Spaeth, Mark G., and Saul C. Berkman, 1967. The tsunami of March 28, 1964, as recorded at tide stations. Environmental Science Services Administration Technical Report C&GS 33. Washington: Government Printing Office. 86 p. Also *in* The Great Alaska Earthquake of 1964: Oceanography and Coastal Engineering. NAS Pub. 1605. Washington: National Academy of Sciences, 1972.

Wilson, Basil W., and Alf Tørum, 1968. The tsunami of the Alaskan earthquake, 1964: Engineering evaluation. Coastal Engineering Research Center Technical Memorandum No. 25. Washington: U.S. Army Corps of Engineers. 444 p.

ROLAND VON HUENE
U.S. GEOLOGICAL SURVEY

Seaquakes

INTRODUCTION

The 1964 Alaska earthquake and its aftershock sequence were felt on ships at sea. Earthquake effects at sea have been noted, recorded, and recognized as seismic phenomena for about 200 years, but it is not clear whether an earthquake felt at sea, even though its epicenter may be in a continental area, should be termed a "seaquake" or a "terrestrial earthquake felt at sea." In one of the earliest discussions of seaquakes, Rudolph (1887) seems to imply that they are earthquakes that occur under the ocean, but he applies the term to any earthquake felt at sea. Nor do Sverdrup, Johnson, and Fleming (1942) clarify this point in their definition of a seaquake. Gutenberg and Richter (1949) define a seaquake as follows: "The term seaquake is restricted to actual shaking, usually felt on vessels, due to the arrival of elastic (acoustic) waves through water." In this discussion, "seaquake" will be used to mean any shaking or other phenomena related to an earthquake and felt on vessels at sea.

The most complete treatment of seaquakes is by Rudolph (1887, 1895, 1898), who lists most previous accounts and earlier theoretical discussions. Subsequent to his papers, seaquakes are mentioned only briefly in the literature and very little new information has been published. Rudolph and other observers have shown that many "shoals" or "reefs" on earlier charts are actually locations where ships happened to be during a nearby seismic event. Even some so-called banks and reefs have been mapped in places where more recent charts based on systematic surveys show thousands of meters of water.

Sverdrup, Johnson, and Fleming (1942) maintain that seaquakes may be accompanied by large volumes of gas, which, through a doming of the sea surface, may produce large transverse waves. Although rare, such occurrences may have been responsible for the loss of some ships. Another possible cause of violent doming of the sea surface is submarine volcanism, such as that which accompanied the sub-

ABSTRACT: The 1964 Alaska earthquake was felt aboard ships from a position near Yakutat to the waters southeast of Kodiak Island. Sensations aboard ship were similar to those noted in previous seaquake accounts. Off southeastern Kodiak the intensity was greater than in Prince William Sound, just 20 km from the epicenter.

13

marine eruption of Myojin-sho, just south of Japan in 1952. One of these eruptions was observed to produce a 5-m-high rise in the sea surface, with an accompanying tsunami; another produced a 6-m-high tsunami on an island more than 60 km away. It is assumed that one Japanese hydrographic ship was destroyed with the loss of all hands during one of the eruptions of this submarine volcano (Tokyo University, Division of Fisheries [1952]). However, no rise of the sea surface or submarine volcanic event was reported from Alaskan waters during the 1964 earthquake: apparently, all accounts relate a purely seismic event.

SEAQUAKE REPORTS

The following reports are from persons on ships who felt (or did not feel) a seaquake during the 1964 Alaska earthquake. These reports are cited in the following sequence: from southeastern Alaska, around the Gulf of Alaska, to the area of the Alaska Peninsula.

No seaquake was felt aboard ships in southeastern Alaska and off British Columbia. The most distant report of noticeable effects from the Alaska earthquake comes from logs of the ship *Glomar II*, which was off Yakutat (Position 1 on Figure 1). The bridge recorded:

1840 [hours], at latitude 59° 15′ north, longitude 140° 43′ west. Ship experienced submarine earthquake. Vessel vibrated for 30 to 40 seconds; wind west at 5, sea west at 1, swell west at 2 [feet], barometer 29.93 . . . overcast.

The engineer's log of this ship recorded:

1845: ship started shaking—stopped both engines—ship still shaking. 1848: underway—both main engines all OK. Vibration in ship was due to an earthquake in Seward.

The company reports that the 5-minute discrepancy in times between the chief engineer's and the master's log is unexplained (apparently, the clocks on bridge and in the engine room were not compared), but they believe that the chief engineer's log may be more accurate because it is a more detailed description of the occurrence.

The Puget Sound Tug and Barge Company's tugboat *Wando*, towing a barge from Seward to Seattle, reported in her log at 1940 [hours]:

Strong loping effect as if vessel were bumping bottom—or tow line dragging—investigated sounding of 76 fathoms—all in order in engine room and deck.

The ship's position was approximately 29 mi south-southwest of Cape St. Elias (Position 2 on Figure 1). The seas were light, with a southwest chop; a wind south-southwest 5 to 10 knots; sky overcast; barometric pressure 29.92.

Harold Hardin, on the fishing vessel *Roald* at the east side of Wingham Island (Position 3), reported that the initial shock felt hard, "like running into the rocks." He did not pull up his anchor but watched "oil and gas spouts all over the shoreline." About 20 minutes later, "the water went through until the boat was aground." He felt many hard jolts during the night, as though he were hitting rocks, and could hear booming sounds above the engine noises. He felt explosions like depth charges, on the run between Wingham Island and the Hinchinbrook Entrance. The largest one occurred at 0430 (local time), off the lighthouse at Hinchinbrook Entrance, while the engine was shut down to clean the filters.

In Valdez (Position 4), Captain Merrill Stewart, master of the Liberty ship *Chena*, was in the dining room during unloading operations at the freight dock. He and the first mate "felt the tremor, which was followed by some very heavy shocks, and we ran toward the bridge as the ship hopped."

About 1½ mi north of Unakwik Point, about 0.1 mi from the east shore (Position 5), the fishing boat *Quest* was in 50 fathoms of water and under way. On board, Joe Clark reported that the shock felt as if the boat were going aground. He "kicked the clutch out and stopped the motor as I watched the water slosh up on the shore." He heard booming noises a second or so before he felt the hard shock.

Paul Selanoff was in Culross Passage (Position 6) during the initial earthquake. He felt the shock while the boat was under way, thought it was something fouled in the propeller, and stopped the motor.

The *Little Purser* was anchored off Gibbon Anchorage at Green Island (position 7). George Allen, on board, reported that during the seaquake it felt "like the boat was pounding on rocks." He had felt seaquakes before, but this was the strongest he had ever felt; he thought he heard the rumble. After the seaquake, the boat proceeded to Stockdale, at the northern part of Montague Island, for the night and anchored in 15 fathoms of water. Allen heard rumbles intermittently during the night but did not feel any shocks.

At Position 8, Port Ashton in Sawmill Bay, Rex Hancock was aboard his fishing vessel at the time of the seaquake. He reported that he felt a fast jarring motion and that the mountains moved in an east–west direction.

On March 29 at 1209 (local time), 2 days after the main earthquake, the U.S. Coast Guard cutter *Sedge* was 10 mi offshore (Position 9) in 125 m of water when crew members heard a sound like an underwater explosion, similar to that of a depth charge or torpedo. During the next few minutes, they experienced three minor tremors. The engineer reported that it felt exactly like going aground on a reef: when asked to back the engine to full astern, he had inquired of the bridge whether they wanted to go back over the reef again.

At Seward (Position 10), three people aboard a fishing boat in the small-boat harbor reported that the boat began to shudder when the earthquake started. The master of the motor-

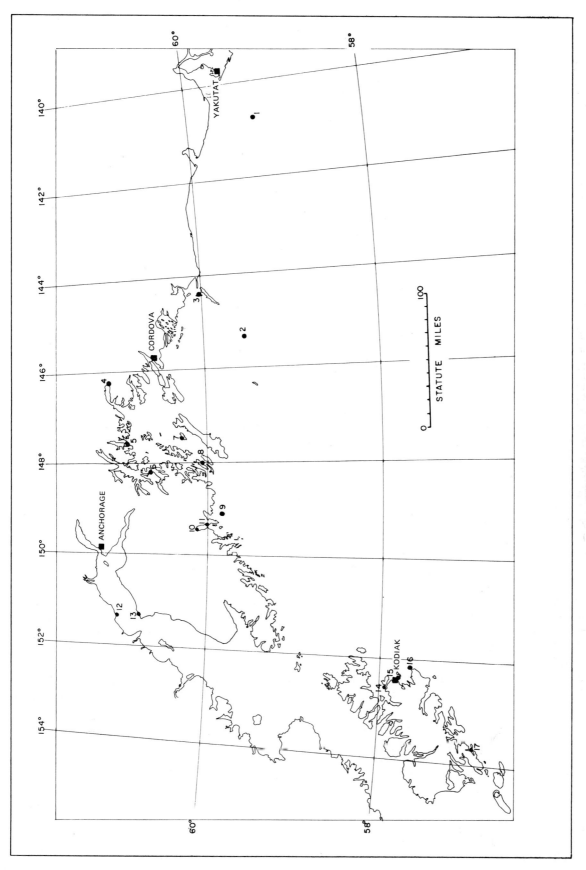

FIGURE 1 Location map.

15

ship *Alaska Standard* reported feeling the seaquake while the ship was tied up along the Seward dock to unload fuel.

In Thumb Cove (Position 11), Bob Hale was waiting aboard a 25-ft boat for his partner ashore. Hale cut the anchor line when he thought it had fouled in the propeller. Whether this action occurred before or during the seaquake is not clear. When the earthquake hit, "the boat started skipping up on the water." Because the boat was vibrating so badly, he thought that the prop had fouled, but he knew that something else was happening when he saw the entire beach disappear.

The *Chilkoot*, a former LCU (Landing Craft Utility), was preparing to unload at Granite Point (Position 12) and was lying to, about 1 mi offshore, prior to beaching. The vessel was hauling supplies for oil-drilling rigs in Cook Inlet. This was right after the ice breakup, and at the time the ice was in pieces about the size of a ship. Harry Olsen, the master of the vessel, first thought that ice was drifting into the boat, for the shocks felt like a collision with blocks of ice. Looking out, he saw that no ice was near the ship. Next he noticed that the trees on the shore were swaying violently, and he knew then that an earthquake was occurring. During the seaquake, the water had a chop of 1 to 1½ ft. He likened the sensation aboard the ship to that of bumping a dock or another ship.

A tanker, the S.S. *Nevada Standard*, was moored at the Kenai pipeline terminal at Nikishki, in Cook Inlet (Position 13). Nothing reported in her log indicates that her crew felt a seaquake.

Harry Knagin was in a fishing boat at Position 14 off Kodiak during the earthquake, in about 70 m of water. He was traveling at about 7 knots at the time, and "it felt like the engine started to vibrate something terrible and we had crab pots on the deck; they were sure jumping. It lasted about 3–4 minutes." It reminded Knagin of a quick jerking motion that he had felt during another seaquake, as though he had run over a "deadhead or something."

Two people at Position 15 reported feeling the seaquake on fishing vessels in Kodiak Harbor. One likened the sensation to that of having his vessel struck by another boat; the other reported that the seaquake shook his boat but was not as hard as the shaking that he had experienced ashore during other earthquakes. Both boats were lying to in the harbor.

At approximately Position 16, the master, Dell Vally, and the engineer, Will Coles, aboard the *Rose Marie*, a power barge converted to a crab boat, reported that the boat vibrated and that it "shimmied and shook—like bumping over waves, only more so—like something bumping the bottom, but I knew we weren't."

Further southwest along Kodiak Island, near the town of Kaguyak, a group of fishing boats were lying to near Jap Bay and Twoheaded Island (Position 17). Fred Ogden and Wayne

Mathewson, aboard the crabber *Fern*, said that the boat jerked and bounced as if striking bottom. During this time, the water became noticeably rougher.

Kaave Aleksa was aboard the king-crab vessel *El Dorado*, which was under way near Position 17 and heading back toward Kodiak. He was at the helm when the earthquake occurred. The sea was very calm, and the surface like glass. Aleksa reported:

I noticed the boat starting to vibrate. I slowed down the engine thinking that something went wrong with it, but the vibration increased rapidly. I started to go down into the engine room but the boat shook so hard by that time I couldn't make my way down. The skipper and owner was in the wheelhouse now, thinking we might have hit a reef, but checking the chart we found we were in deep water. None of us thought of an earthquake. Then, looking out of the pilot-house windows, we observed a column of water rising out of the live hatch (live bait tank) to a height even with the pilot house windows, about 6 feet, and about 1 foot in diameter. All around us the sea was covered with needle sharp cones of water about a foot high.

This phenomenon lasted for more than a minute.

Neil Van Scheele was aboard his crab boat *Shuyak*, anchored inside Jap Bay (Position 17) with several other vessels. He reported that, "It shook hell out of things, and even though it was low tide the water started to run out almost right after the quake."

During the earthquake, the Puget Sound Tug and Barge Company vessel, *Monarch*, was near Unimak Pass at the western end of the Alaska Peninsula. No statement in the log indicates that the crew felt the shaking.

Second- and thirdhand accounts from persons in either small boats or large ships almost invariably reported sensations similar to that of the ship running aground, of something fouling the propeller or screw, or of the engine vibrating very badly. While at sea with the U.S. Coast Guard cutter *Sedge* during the aftershock sequence, I felt sensations similar to those of propeller cavitation, although the ship was running slowly in smooth water and under conditions where cavitation does not usually occur. These sensations may have been related to aftershock activity.

All ships reporting the seaquake were in calm weather and fairly flat seas. Only two accounts mentioned an audible rumble or booming prior to the seaquake, and both of these were from Prince William Sound. In Rudolph's catalog of seaquake reports (1887, 1895), there are many descriptions of a rumble like distant thunder; a large number of the reports are from men who were on the decks of sailing vessels where the background noises were probably much lower than those on motor vessels.

The accounts from the Alaska earthquake report phenomena aboard ship that are similar to those of most other accounts. The most common description is "like going aground," and there is frequent mention of a sensation like that caused by a "vibrating screw or engine." The log of a ship off

Unalaska in 1790 describes a strong vibration, like the keel scraping rough ground; and in 1866, during an earthquake on Kodiak Island, a ship reported terrible vibrations, like those experienced when running across a reef at great speed. Occasionally found in reports from the 1800's is the description "like a depth charge or torpedo," and more than one older account identified a sensation similar to that of a cannon going off directly beneath the ship.

Various descriptions from the Alaska earthquake probably reflect, in part, differences in intensity, but it is very difficult to evaluate those reports in a restricted, quantitative sense. There certainly is a difference in intensity between the intermittent rumble, probably from aftershocks, that was heard by George Allen while his ship was lying to at Stockdale after the main shock and the inability of Kaave Aleksa to make his way to the engine room on the *El Dorado*. The first account indicates a value of I on the somewhat outdated seaquake scale of Rudolph, and the second indicates a value of VII or VIII.

Vertical acceleration of the *El Dorado*, as indicated by the 6-ft-high waterspout from the live-bait tank, accords with reports in Rudolph's catalog, which describes repeated instances in which unrestrained objects and persons were flung into the air, as well as rare instances in which entire ships were reported to have been raised from the water. The needle-sharp cones of water reported by Kaave Aleksa and the chop reported by Harry Olsen are similar to previous descriptions, during a seaquake, of "beams of water" or a sudden boiling appearance of the sea (Rudolph, 1887, 1895; Sievers and others, 1963).

The maximum distance at which a seaquake was felt from the epicentral area during the Alaska earthquake was no greater than some distances reported by Rudolph, although sensitivity to such phenomena was probably greater aboard sailing ships than aboard motorships. Thus, seaquake phenomena reported from the Alaska earthquake are not significantly different from those previously recorded.

SIGNIFICANCE TO THE ALASKA EARTHQUAKE

Aside from providing additional information about seaquakes in general, the seaquake accounts add two points of information about the Alaska earthquake. First, the reports of Harold Hardin on the *Roald* and George Allen on the *Little Purser* indicate many large aftershocks seaward of Hinchinbrook Island during the first 8 to 10 hours after the initial shock. This information complements the preliminary aftershock epicentral data of the U.S. Coast and Geodetic Survey, which show strong aftershock activity in that general area; it also verifies the accounts from men at the Cape Hinchinbrook lighthouse. From these data, it would seem that relatively

less intense aftershock activity occurred in Prince William Sound than seaward of Hinchinbrook Island.

Second, in spite of their crude qualitative character, the seaquake reports suggest a greater initial shock intensity off Kodiak Island than in Prince William Sound. Possibly they suggest a correlation of greater initial shock intensity with proximity to a great and largely submarine fault zone, which is the probable surface expression of a structure active during the 1964 Alaska earthquake (von Huene and others, 1967). The significant difference in earthquake accounts from these two areas is that loose articles were reported to be jumping around only on those boats that were off Kodiak. The difficulty in standing or at least in moving about is not mentioned or implied in the report sent from the mouth of Unakwik Inlet (about 20 km from the instrumentally located epicenter for the main shock) or in the other reports from that vicinity. This omission differentiates the group of Prince William Sound reports from those off Kodiak by one or two divisions on the intensity scale of Rudolph. However, the nonuniformity in reporting and the small number of reports leave a good deal of uncertainty in a correlation between seaquake intensity and the fault zone.

R. L. Wiegel has called attention to the following statement from page 253 of *Earthquake Engineering Research* (Committee on Earthquake Engineering Research, 1969), which provides insight into the control of seaquake intensity:

According to acoustical theory for small displacements normal to the generating plane, the peak sound intensity for pressures less than 1 kilobar is given by the expression $p_{max} = U\rho c$, where U is the velocity of the generator, ρ is the density of the fluid, and c the velocity of plane-wave propagation. Taking, for example, $\rho = 1$ gm/cm^3, c = 1.4 $\times$ 10^5 cm/sec, and U = 100 cm/sec as a reasonable maximum, the peak sound pressure will be 14 atmospheres (200 psi). According to field tests of explosive shock effects on ships, severe hull damage can only be expected at gross shock pressures greater than 2,000 psi, with light damage to machinery and components in the range 1,000 to 2,000 psi.

It appears that the velocity of the generator rather than the magnitude of displacement controls seaquake intensity. Therefore seaquake intensity appears to be an uncertain indicator of the strain released at a particular locality during an earthquake.

REFERENCES

Committee on Earthquake Engineering Research, 1969. Earthquake engineering research. A report to the National Science Foundation prepared by the National Academy of Engineering, Division of Engineering, National Research Council. Springfield, Virginia: Clearinghouse for Federal Scientific and Technical Information. 313 p.

Gutenberg, B., and C. F. Richter, 1949. Seismicity of the earth and associated phenomena. Princeton: Princeton University Press. 273 p.

Rudolph, E., 1887. Über submarine Erdbeben und Eruptionen. [Gerlands] *Beiträge zur Geophysik*, v. 1, p. 133–373.

Rudolph, E., 1895. Über submarine Erdbeben und Vulkane. (Zweiter Beiträge). [Gerlands] *Beiträge zur Geophysik*, v. 2, p. 537–566.

Rudolph, E., 1898. Über submarine Erdbeben und Eruptionen. [Gerlands] *Beiträge zur Geophysik*, v. 3, p. 273–336.

Sievers C., Hellmuth A., Guillermo Villegas and Guillermo Barros, 1963. The seismic sea wave of 22 May 1960 along the Chilean Coast. *Bulletin of the Seismological Society of America*, 53 (December), 1125–1190.

Sverdrup, H. U., Martin W. Johnson, and Richard H. Fleming, 1942. The oceans, their physics, chemistry, and general biology. New York: Prentice-Hall, Inc. p. 543.

Tokyo University, Division of Fisheries [1952]. Report on the submarine eruption of Myojin-sho. Tokyo: Kokusia Bunken Insatsusha. p. 11, 42.

von Huene, Roland, Richard J. Malloy, George G. Shor, Jr., and Pierre St.-Amand, 1967. Geologic structures in the aftershock region of the 1964 Alaskan earthquake. *Journal of Geophysical Research*, 72 (July 15), 3649–3660.

Wiegel, Robert L., 1970. Tsunamis *in* Earthquake engineering. Englewood Cliffs, New Jersey: Prentice-Hall, Inc. 518 p.

JOHN NORTHROP*
SCRIPPS INSTITUTION OF OCEANOGRAPHY

T-Phases

INTRODUCTION

Body waves that are refracted into the water at the ocean bottom are called *T*-waves or *T*-phases. The name was given by Linehan (1940) because the phase or wave was observed as a third arrival following the primary (*P*) and secondary (*S*) waves from Dominican Republic earthquakes recorded at Weston, Massachusetts. The mode of transmission of *T*-waves was not explained until a decade afterward when Tolstoy and Ewing (1950) showed that the velocity of *T* was that of sound in the ocean. If the epicenter is near a submarine slope, the hydroacoustic waves are channeled into continuously refracted waves which travel over very long distances in the ocean (Ewing, Press, and Worzel, 1952; Milne, 1959).

A source area for *T*-phases can be computed from arrival times of *T* recorded at sofar (sound fixing and ranging) depth hydrophones (Johnson, 1966). The most prominent *T*-phases are produced by any earthquake with a hypocenter (or focus) at a depth equal to the distance of that hypocenter from the ocean-bottom slope where the energy from *P*-waves is transformed into *T*-waves (Wadati and Inouye, 1956). This channel of transmission is called the *T*-phase window by Johnson, Northrop, and Eppley (1963). Because the island arc structures of the Pacific are typically associated with intermediate- and deep-focus earthquakes inland from the shallow focus events, the area of strong *T*-phase generation is geographically about 40–300 km wide. It lies inland from the break in slope and parallel to it. Large-magnitude, deep-focus earthquakes occurring farther inland from this zone sometimes excite *T*-phases (Shurbet, 1955), and those occurring seaward of it cause lower-level *T*-phases (Northrop, 1966). In the case of the Alaska earthquake and its aftershocks, most of the epicenters occurred shoreward of the continental rise (Grantz, Plafker, and Kachadoorian, 1964) and caused prominent *T*-phases. Aftershocks that occurred farther offshore caused low-level *T*-phases.

ABSTRACT: *T*-phases from the Alaska earthquake of March 28, 1964 (GMT), were recorded at sofar (sound fixing and ranging) depth hydrophones at Eniwetok, Midway, Wake, and Oahu islands and off the west coast of North America. The main shock caused a *T*-phase arrival at Kaneohe (Oahu) 14.3 minutes earlier (based on velocity of 1.47 km/sec) than the computed time. The earlier arrival may be attributable to a hydroacoustic wave that was refracted into the ocean from body waves at a distance 17° of arc seaward of the epicenter. Additional early arrivals may be identified with hydroacoustic waves radiated from seamounts and insular slopes in the Gulf of Alaska. Arrival of the main *T*-phase overloaded the recorders for 6 minutes, and reverberations obscured *T*-phases from aftershocks for 2½ hours afterward. *T*-phases from later aftershocks were strongest for hypocenters situated beneath the upper portion of the continental slope.

*Now with the Department of the Navy.

19

METHOD

Hydrophones of the Pacific Missile Range Missile Impact Location Stations (MILS) at Oahu, Midway, Wake, and Eniwetok islands were monitored continuously for T-phases. The Helicorder records were mailed to the Tsunami Research Group at the Hawaii Institute of Geophysics where they became available for this study. Standard MILS hydrophones and amplifiers were used, and the signal was passed through a 15-cps low-pass filter prior to recording. This filtering was found to increase the signal-to-noise ratio for T-phases by about 15 db (Johnson, 1963).

Additional records were obtained from Point Sur, California, and mailed to the Marine Physical Laboratory. All hydrophones monitored were situated at the depth of the sound-velocity minimum, or sofar axis. The velocity of sound at sofar depth ranges between 1.45 and 1.49 km/sec, a range that is the speed of travel of T-waves in the Pacific (Ewing, Press, and Worzel, 1952; Byerly and Herrick, 1954; Johnson, 1966). From sofar velocities, the travel time between epicenter and detector was computed. After the resulting travel time was added to epicentral times published on the Preliminary Determination of Epicenters (PDE) cards, T-phase signatures corresponding to U.S. Coast and Geodetic Survey epicenters in Alaska were identified on the records. Events recorded at several stations were further correlated by delay-time positioning (Northrop and Johnson, 1965; Johnson, 1966).

T-PHASES FROM THE MAIN SHOCK

The main shock at 03:36:12 (GMT) on March 28, 1964, produced a T-phase at Kaneohe for which the earliest perceptible arrival (T_1 in Figures 1 and 2) was at 04:10:30. The T-phase signal then increased to a peak at about 04:23:00, which overloaded the recording system for 6 minutes. If 1.47 km/sec is used for the velocity of T, the calculated arrival time was 04:24:50 (T in Figures 1 and 2), which time occurred during the period that the recording system was overloaded. The interpretation made here is that the body waves generated a hydroacoustic wave from the ocean floor 17° seaward from the epicenter near the 5-km bathymetric contour. This arc distance compares favorably with the 17° given for the magnitude-7 Kuril Islands earthquake of January 29, 1963 (Johnson, 1963), and 13° for the 6.5-magnitude Tonga Islands earthquake of December 18, 1963 (Daubin, 1964).

As pointed out by Milne (1959), compressional P-waves in rock are transformed into hydroacoustic sofar waves in the ocean via downslope, bottom-surface reflection paths. This method of transformation of P- to T-waves is achieved most efficiently in areas where the reflecting bottom slope is steep and where the slope intersects the depth of minimum sound velocity in the ocean (Johnson, Northrop, and Eppley, 1963). Therefore, undersea topographic highs as well as islands, atolls, and continental shelves are radiators of T-phases. An inspection of a bathymetric chart of the North Pacific shows that the Emperor Seamount Chain lies 17° of arc from the Kuril Islands along the great-circle route to Hawaii. Therefore, the early T arrival noted on the record for the Kuril Island earthquake of January 29, 1963, may have been radiated from the Emperor Seamount (Johnson, 1963). For the Alaska earthquake, no distant seamount chain lies along the great-circle route between Anchorage and the island stations.

However, the earthquake was of sufficiently large magnitude that a refracted P-wave apparently was generated over the gently sloping ocean floor in much the same way that refracted P-waves are generated in offshore seismic refraction shooting. There is another prominent arrival marked T_2 (Figures 1 and 2) at 04:19:10. The point of T-phase radiation for this arrival lay about 8° from the epicenter along the great-circle path between source and receiver. An inspection of the bathymetry in the area (Menard, 1964) indicates that the Patton Seamount Group lies in this vicinity, and this T_2

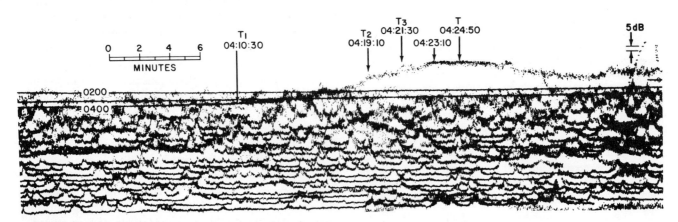

FIGURE 1 Helicorder record made at Kaneohe, Oahu, Hawaii, March 28, 1964. All times are GMT. Record reads from left to right. Events marked T_1, T_2, T_3, and T correspond to notations on Figure 2.

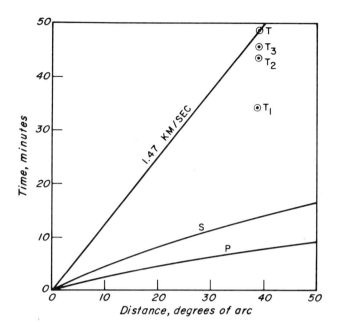

FIGURE 2 *T*-phase arrivals from the Alaska earthquake. Points marked T_1, T_2, T_3, and T are noted on Figure 1.

phase is thought to have been radiated from there.

A third prominent *T*-phase at 04:21:30 (T_3 on Figures 1 and 2) represents the radiation of *T*-waves originating 6° from the epicenter. This *T*-phase may represent radiation from the insular shelf off Kodiak Island.

The beginning of the sofar record of the main *T*-phase arrival at 04:23:10 represents the *T*-phase generated on the Continental Shelf off Alaska. The following 6-minute section of overloaded signal represents the *T*-phase arrival from various points along the Continental Shelf of the North American continent.

DURATION OF THE *T*-PHASE SIGNATURE

Duration of the *T*-phase is largely a function of the area of the ocean floor from which earthquake body-wave energy is radiated into the water as hydroacoustic waves. The Continental Shelf, offshore islands, atolls, seamounts, and even flat areas of the ocean floor act as radiators of the *T*-phase (Johnson, Norris, and Duennebier, 1966). Therefore, the larger the earthquake, the longer the duration of the *T*-phase (for epicenters near the ocean boundary) (Northrop, 1965; Northrop and Johnson, 1965; Daubin, 1964; Brazee, 1965). Because of the characteristically emergent onset and decay of the *T*-phase, the signal-to-noise ratio of the detection system also affects the observed *T*-phase duration. For example, land-based recordings of *T*-phases from conventional seismographic installations on islands, which have high microseism noise at frequencies near 1 cps (Brune and Oliver, 1959; Bradner and Dodds, 1964), generally show *T*-phase signa-

tures that are difficult to distinguish from background noise (Shurbet, 1962). Gupta (1964) has presented a revised formula of Ben-Menahem and Toksöz (1963) for relating the duration of the *T*-phase, recorded on a land-based seismograph on the Island of Hawaii, with the duration of faulting of the Alaska earthquake of July 10, 1958.

The validity of Gupta's formula may be tested by using it to analyze the *T*-phase data for the Alaska earthquake of 1964:

$$\Delta t = (b/V_T) \; [\cos \theta \pm (V_T/V_f)] \, .$$

Here Δt is the duration of faulting, b is the fault length, V_T is the velocity of T, V_f is the velocity of faulting, and θ is the angle between the fault line and the geodesic passing through the initial epicenter and the recording station ($\sim 30°$). If we assume that movement starts at one end of the fault and proceeds toward the station, and if we take 800 km as the value of b (Press and Jackson, 1965) and 3 km/sec for V_f, Δt is 204 seconds. Inspection of Figure 1 shows that during the long *T*-phase signature the period of overload is about twice this value. Therefore, although Gupta's formula may be used to calculate the duration of faulting from land-based seismograph recordings of the *T*-phase, it is not applicable to *T*-phase recordings made on sofar depth-hydrophones.

T-PHASES FROM AFTERSHOCKS

In addition to a large *T*-phase from the main shock, smaller *T*-phases from the numerous aftershocks were observed. The later *T*-phases caused the shorter signals, of 1- to 2-minute duration, which appear on Figure 1 after the main *T*-phase. Many of these do not correspond to epicenters published on the PDE cards, because the hydrophone network is more sensitive to small coastal earthquakes than is the existing seismograph network (Johnson and Northrop, 1966). Thus, *T*-phase signatures appear on the hydrophone recordings in greater number than the number of published epicenters. Northrop (1965) studied the later *T*-phase signatures up to the end of March, correlated 80 signatures with epicenters listed on the PDE cards, and published a report. Figures 3 and 4, taken from that report, show that the strongest *T*-phase signals received came from hypocenters below the upper part of the continental slope. Earthquake epicenters outside this *T*-phase window produced low-level or, in some cases, undetected *T*-phases.

T-PHASES AS A TSUNAMI WARNING

Several years ago, Ewing, Tolstoy, and Press (1950) proposed that earthquake *T*-phases be used to predict tsunamis. It soon became apparent, however, that there were many more *T*-

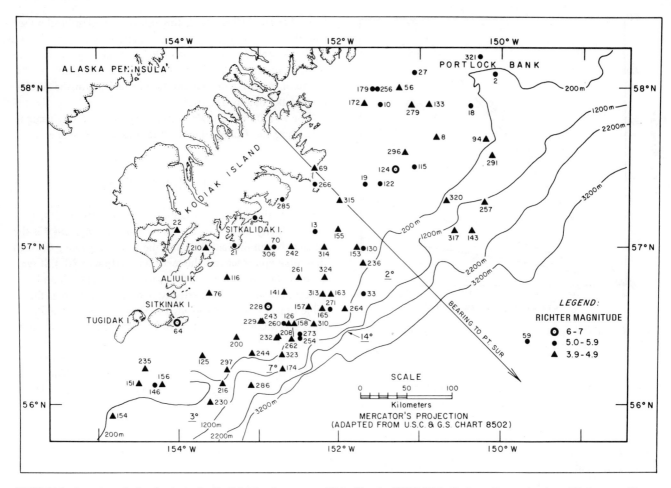

FIGURE 3   Location of aftershocks in the Kodiak Island area, as published by the USC&GS Preliminary Determination of Epicenters. The earthquake numbers, which correspond to the numbered hypocenters of Figure 4, are in order of increasing time after the main shock.

phases than there were tsunamis and, accordingly, that the rate of false alarms from such a warning system would be too great for it to be effective.

There have been large coastal earthquakes for which the *P*-wave data immediately available are inadequate to determine an epicenter, to judge the magnitude of the earthquake, and to decide whether or not to issue a tsunami warning. An auxiliary method of determining the tsunami source area is to log the arrival time of *T* at various hydrophone stations and forward the data to the forecasting center at Honolulu. The source area can then be determined accurately from charts of delay time between hydrophone locations. This process would give a long lead-time on the actual arrival of the tsunami because the velocity of *T* is about six times that of a tsunami over the open ocean. Therefore, the use of *T*-phase arrival times, as well as amplitude (Eaton, Richter, and Ault, 1961), can be valuable adjuncts to the Tsunami Warning System based on *P*-wave amplitudes and arrival times.

For earthquakes that occur offshore in the deep ocean, a high-frequency (30–40 cps) peak has been observed to precede the usual low-frequency (5–10 cps) *T*-phase (Johnson,

Norris, and Duennebier, 1966). The first peak has been found to correlate with a hydroacoustic wave generated directly above the epicenter, and the second peak to be radiated from the continental slope. Therefore, the time difference between the arrival of the two peaks gives a measure of the distance offshore of the epicenter. Because deep-ocean earthquakes are not known to generate large tsunamis, the analysis of the frequency content of the multiple-peaked *T*-phases may be a valuable aid to the tsunami forecaster.

CONCLUSIONS

The Alaska earthquake of March 28, 1964, caused a large *T*-phase that lasted for about 3 hours from its emergent beginning to gradual decay. The peak pressure of the main arrival overloaded the recording system for 6 minutes, a period longer in itself than the time calculated for the duration of faulting. The *T*-phase radiator must be considered an areal, rather than point, source. The earliest forerunner of the main *T*-phase arrival is interpreted as a *T*-phase generated by trans-

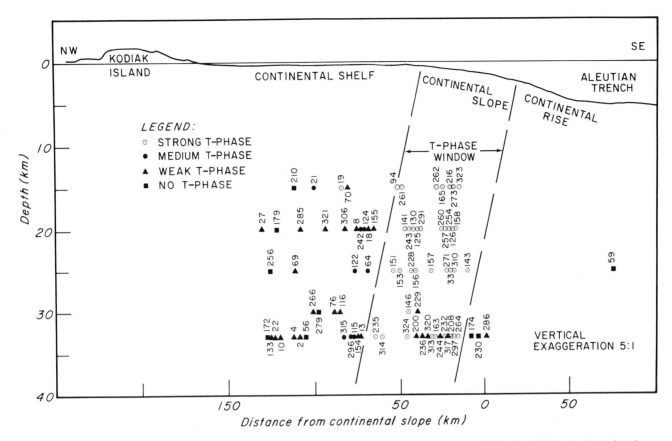

FIGURE 4 Vertical section of Kodiak hypocenters drawn in a plane parallel to the average bearing to Point Sur, California. Note that the strongest *T*-phase signals received came from hypocenters below the upper part of the continental slope.

fer of *P*- to *T*-phase energy on the ocean floor at a distance of 17° from the epicenter. The *T*-phases from aftershocks did not exhibit this forerunner, although many of the aftershocks studied produced strong *T*-phases. The strongest *T*-phases of the aftershock sequence were produced by earthquakes with hypocenters at depth equal to the distance of the epicenter inland from the continental slope. The hydrophone network has a lower detection threshold than the existing seismograph network, and more *T*-phases are noted than epicenters are published on the cards of the Preliminary Determination of Epicenters. Therefore, the presence of a *T*-phase on the records does not in itself appear useful as a tsunami warning, although once a large coastal earthquake has occurred, an inspection of the arrival time and duration of *T* can be used to pinpoint the source area and give an independent estimate of the magnitude of the earthquake. The frequency content of a multiple-peaked *T*-phase can give an indication of the distance offshore of the earthquake epicenter.

ACKNOWLEDGMENTS

The publication of this paper was suggested by Doak C. Cox. The work was supported by the Office of Naval Research under contract Nonr-2216 (05) with the University of California. Records were provided by the Pacific Missile Range and the U.S. Navy through the co-operation of R. H. Johnson and Dr. Marston C. Sargent.

REFERENCES

Ben-Menahem, A., and M. N. Toksöz, 1963. Source-mechanism from spectra of long-period seismic surface waves. Pt. 3. The Alaska earthquake of July 10, 1958. *Bulletin of the Seismological Society of America*, 53 (October), 905–919.

Bradner, H., and J. G. Dodds, 1964. Comparative seismic noise on the ocean bottom and on land. *Journal of Geophysical Research*, 69 (October), 4339–4348.

Brazee, R. J., 1965. A study of T phases in the Aleutian earthquake series of March and April 1957. *Earthquake Notes*, 36 (March–June), 9–14.

Brune, J. N., and J. Oliver, 1959. The seismic noise of the earth's surface. *Bulletin of the Seismological Society of America*, 44 (October), 349–353.

Byerly, P., and C. Herrick, 1954. T phases from Hawaiian earthquake. *Bulletin of the Seismological Society of America*, 44 (April), 113–121.

Daubin, S. C., 1964. *T*-phase detection at a fixed acoustical station and correlation with source events (unpublished manuscript). General Motors Defense Research Laboratories, SBL–64–06296.

Eaton, Jerry P., D. H. Richter, and W. U. Ault, 1961. The tsunami of

May 23, 1960, on the Island of Hawaii. *Bulletin of the Seismological Society of America*, 51 (April), 135–157.

Ewing, M., F. Press, and J. L. Worzel, 1952. Further study of the T phase. *Bulletin of the Seismological Society of America*, 42 (January), 37–51.

Ewing, M., I. Tolstoy, and F. Press, 1950. Proposed use of the T phase as a tsunami warning system. *Bulletin of the Seismological Society of America*, 40 (January), 53–58.

Grantz, Arthur, George Plafker, and Reuben Kachadoorian, 1964. Alaska's Good Friday earthquake, March 27, 1964—A preliminary geologic evaluation. U.S. Geological Survey Circular 491. Washington: U.S. Geological Survey. 35 p.

Gupta, I. N., 1964. Discussion of source-mechanism from spectra of long-period seismic surface waves. *Bulletin of the Seismological Society of America*, 54 (December), 2085–2086.

Johnson, R. H., 1963. Spectrum and dispersion of Pacific T phases. Technical Summary Report 4, June. Honolulu: University of Hawaii, Institute of Geophysics.

Johnson, R. H., 1966. Routine location of *T*-phase sources in the Pacific. *Bulletin of the Seismological Society of America*, 56 (February), 109–118.

Johnson, R. H., and J. Northrop, 1966. A comparison of earthquake magnitude with *T*-phase strength. *Bulletin of the Seismological Society of America*, 56 (February), 119–124.

Johnson, R. H., J. Northrop, and R. Eppley, 1963. Sources of Pacific T phases. *Journal of Geophysical Research*, 68 (July), 4251–4260.

Johnson, R. H., R. A. Norris, and F. K. Duennebier, 1966. T phases with high frequency peaks. Proceedings, 11th Pacific Science Congress, Vol. III (Geophysics), 39.

Linehan, D., 1940. Earthquakes in the West Indian region. *Transactions, American Geophysical Union*, 19 (Section II), 229–232.

Menard, Henry William, 1964. Marine geology of the Pacific. New York: McGraw-Hill Book Co. 271 p.

Milne, A. R., 1959. Comparison of spectra of an earthquake T phase with similar signals from nuclear explosions. *Bulletin of the Seismological Society of America*, 49 (October), 317–330.

Northrop, John, 1965. *T* phases from 80 Alaskan earthquakes, March 28–31, 1964. *Bulletin of the Seismological Society of America*, 55 (February), 59–63.

Northrop, John, 1966. Earthquake generated underwater sound in the Pacific (Abstract). *Transactions, American Geophysical Union*, 47 (March), 170.

Northrop, John, and R. H. Johnson, 1965. Seismic waves recorded in the North Pacific from FLIP. *Journal of Geophysical Research*, 70 (January 15), 311–318.

Press, Frank, and David Jackson, 1965. Alaskan earthquake, 27 March 1964: vertical extent of faulting and elastic strain energy release. *Science*, 147 (February 19), 867–868. Also *in* The Great Alaska Earthquake of 1964: Seismology and Geodesy. NAS Pub. 1602. Washington: National Academy of Sciences, 1972.

Tolstoy, I., and M. Ewing, 1950. The T phase of shallow focus earthquake. *Bulletin of the Seismological Society of America*, 40 (January), 25–52.

Shurbet, D. H., 1955. Bermuda T phases with large continental paths. *Bulletin of the Seismological Society of America*, 45 (January), 23–36.

Shurbet, D. H., 1962. Note on use of sofar geophone to determine seismicity of regional oceanic areas. *Bulletin of the Seismological Society of America*, 52 (July), 689–691.

Wadati, K., and W. Inouye, 1956. On the T phase of seismic waves observed in Japan. Proceedings, 8th Pacific Science Congress, Vol. II-A (Geology and Geophysics), 783–792.

ARTHUR McGARR*
LAMONT-DOHERTY GEOLOGICAL OBSERVATORY

ROBERT C. VORHIS
U.S. GEOLOGICAL SURVEY

Seismic Seiches in Bays, Channels, and Estuaries

INTRODUCTION

The great Alaska earthquake produced seismic waves so large that they set bodies of water into oscillation throughout much of North America. Seismic surface waves, of both Love and Rayleigh types, were primarily responsible for the oscillations, or seiches, because these generally cause the largest amplitude of ground motion of all seismic waves at great distances from an epicenter. As the seismic surface waves passed beneath water-filled basins, their horizontal components generated the seiches. The surface waves most effective in the production of seiches had periods of the order of 15 seconds (or wavelengths of about 50 km). This report describes the distribution of seismic seiches in coastal regions and attempts to explain some features of the distribution.

SEISMIC SEICHES RECORDED AT TIDE GAGES

The seismic seiches of primary concern in this paper were recorded by tide gages in the coastal regions of North America (Table 1). The tide-gage records show the arrival of the seismic surface waves by one or more abrupt increases in amplitude followed by a decay in amplitude. At Port Mansfield, Texas, the record (Figure 1) showed two stages of amplitude increase followed by more than 1 hour of slowly decaying oscillation. The variations in times shown in Table 1 for the seiches reflect inaccuracies in timing of the tide gages rather than different times of occurrence; they are listed simply to show that a given seiche occurred at the approximate time of arrival of seismic surface waves from the Alaska shock.

The seiches at tide gages differed from most of the other seiches studied in that they were generally of higher amplitude and longer duration, probably because they occurred in bodies of water with better resonance characteristics than the streams and small rivers on which most of the other seiches were recorded.

ABSTRACT: The horizontal components of Love and Rayleigh waves from the Alaska earthquake generated seismic seiches recorded on at least 25 tide gages. These were chiefly on the Gulf coast and the northern Pacific coast. The seismic waves most effective in generating seiches had periods of the order of 15 seconds and wavelengths of about 50 km.

*Now at University of Witwatersrand, Johannesburg, South Africa.

25

TABLE 1   Seismic Seiches from the Alaska Earthquake of March 1964, as Recorded at Tide Stations

Tide Station	North Latitude	West Longitude	Approximate Time (GMT)	Seiche Double Amplitude (ft)	Duration of Seiche (min)
Unalaska, Alaska[a]	53°53′	166°32′	03:30	0.96	
Homer, Alaska[b]	59°36′	151°25′	03:45	6.00	
Yakutat, Alaska	59°33′	139°44′	03:40	0.48	14
Juneau, Alaska	58°18′	134°25′	03:40	0.64	8
Sitka, Alaska	57°03′	135°20′	03:38	1.00	3½
Prince Rupert, B.C.[c]	54°19′	130°20′	03:45	0.25	
Bella Bella, B.C.	52°10′	128°08′	03:45	0.35	
Tasu, B.C.	52°45′	132°01′	03:45	1.10	
Victoria, B.C.	48°25′	123°24′	03:45	0.15	
Point Atkinson, B.C.	49°20′	123°15′	04:00	0.40	
Vancouver, B.C.	49°17′	123°07′	03:45	0.40	
Ballenas Island, B.C.	49°20′	124°09′	–	0.40	
Port Moody, B.C.	49°17′	122°52′	–	0.35	
Cambridge Bay, Northwest Territories	69°07′	105°04′	–	0.30	
Friday Harbor, Washington	48°33′	123°00′	03:44	0.20	60
Seattle, Washington	47°36′	122°20′	03:45	0.40	48
Astoria, Oregon	56°13′	123°46′	03:45	Trace	
Port Isabel, Texas	26°04′	97°13′	04:04	0.72	120 to 180
Port Mansfield, Texas	26°33′	97°26′	03:52½	0.22	33 (followed by ten pulses in next 1½ hr)
Rockport, Texas	28°01′	97°03′	04:02	0.84	18 (major motion). Minor motion not distinct on chart.
Freeport, Texas	28°57′	95°19′	03:55	0.66	27
Bayou Rigaud, Louisiana	29°16′	89°58′	04:00	0.27	11 (major motion). Seiche seemingly lasted about 2 hr.
Pensacola, Florida	34°24′	87°13′	04:00	0.49	33
Key West, Florida	24°33′	81°48′	04:05	0.08	16
San Juan, Puerto Rico	18°27′	66°05′	04:15	0.06	12

[a] Seiche consisted of one oscillation or only a few oscillations.
[b] Very unusual record possibly due to land subsidence.
[c] Data for this station and the eight following stations are from a report by Wigen and White (1964).

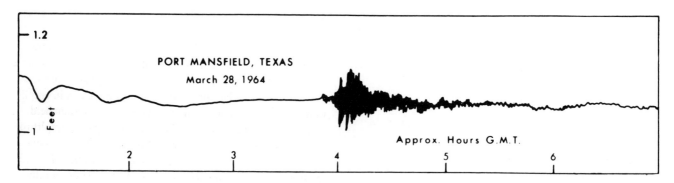

FIGURE 1   Tide-gage record of Alaska earthquake seiche.

With two exceptions, all the seiches listed in Table 1 occurred along the northwest coast of North America or along the Gulf coast; these exceptions were at Cambridge Bay in northern Canada and at San Juan, Puerto Rico. No seiches were recorded by tide gages along the Atlantic coast or along the Pacific coast south of Astoria, Oregon.

To explain any of the features of the distribution of seiches listed in Table 1, it is necessary to know what factors determine whether or not a seiche occurs at a given recording site. The results of a study by McGarr (1965) on the interaction of seismic surface waves with a channel filled with water indicate that the amplitude of a seiche at a given site depends on (1) the horizontal acceleration of the channel caused by seismic surface waves and (2) the size and shape of the channel or basin. The second factor determines the ability of an individual body of water to respond to seismic surface waves and is not likely to vary in any systematic manner with geographic location. On the other hand, McGarr and Vorhis (1968) showed that the horizontal acceleration associated with the seismic surface waves from the Alaska shock does appear to have varied markedly within North America; according to their study of seiches recorded by surface-water gages at the time of the Alaska shock, the amplitude of horizontal acceleration was especially large along the Gulf coast.

In Figure 2, the squares indicate locations of seiches listed in Table 1, and the circles represent seiches recorded by surface-water gages and discussed by McGarr and Vorhis (1968). As shown in this figure, most seiches recorded by surface-water gages and by tide gages in the United States occurred in states adjacent to the Gulf coast; hence, the reasoning used by McGarr and Vorhis (1968) to explain features of the distribution of seiches recorded by surface-water gages probably applies also to those recorded by tide gages. It appears that geological features have an important influence on the horizontal acceleration of seismic surface waves. The

thick deposits of sediments of low rigidity along the Gulf coast, for example, are capable of amplifying the horizontal acceleration of surface waves to a considerable extent; this accounts for the concentration of seiches that occurred along the Gulf coast. Conversely, the northeast coast of North America is devoid of thick deposits of sediments of low rigidity, and tide gages in this region recorded no seiches whatsoever.

It is difficult to explain why so many seiches were recorded by tide gages along the northwest coast of North America (Table 1). The large number of seiches in this region may simply be due to the proximity of these tide gages to the epicenter. Another possibility is that the Cascades acted as a wave guide, causing the relatively low phase velocities to concentrate and channel the surface waves. This channeling could have produced relatively high horizontal acceleration, thereby causing the high density of seiches along the northern Pacific coast.

The Appalachian basin seems somehow to have attenuated surface waves because, with the exception of three small seiches recorded by surface-water gages in Maryland, no seiches were recorded to the southeast of this feature (Figure 2). This basin probably was responsible for the absence

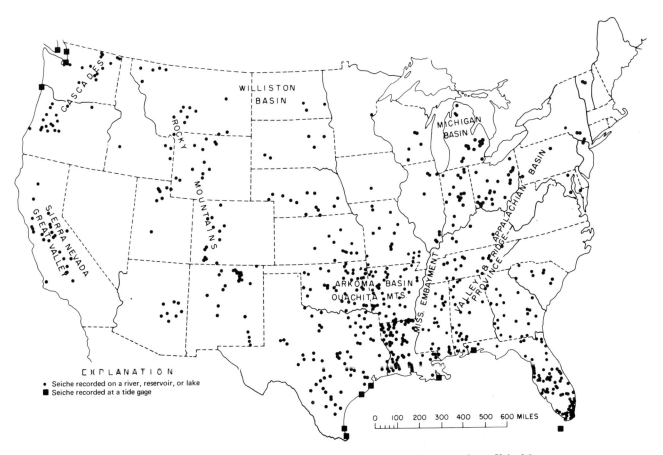

FIGURE 2   Seismic seiches from the Alaska earthquake, as recorded in conterminous United States.

of any seiches recorded by tide gages between North Carolina and New York.

There are several areas where the distribution of seiches recorded by tide gages does not correspond to that for surface-water gages. Seiches were not recorded by tide gages on either the east or west coasts of peninsular Florida, the coast of Georgia, or the coast of South Carolina, even though numerous seiches were recorded by surface-water gages in these areas. It is also strange that no seiches were recorded along the coast of California. The recording of a seiche by a tide gage in San Juan, Puerto Rico, was surprising, in view of the fact that no seiche was recorded by surface-water gages in the Caribbean. The most likely explanation for the lack of correlation is that there are many fewer tide gages than surface-water gages and that the tide gages operating in these areas happened to be situated on bodies of water that did not resonate with the periodic surface-wave oscillations. Unlike the dense network of surface-water gages in the United States, the network of tide gages is not so concentrated that the properties of individual recording sites are averaged out in any given geographical area.

ACKNOWLEDGMENT

Data for tide stations in the United States were supplied by M. G. Spaeth, geophysicist with the U.S. Coast and Geodetic Survey, Environmental Science Services Administration.

REFERENCES

McGarr, Arthur, 1965. Excitation of seiches in channels by seismic waves. *Journal of Geophysical Research*, 70 (February 15), 847–854. Also *in* The Great Alaska Earthquake of 1964: Hydrology. NAS Pub. 1603. Washington: National Academy of Sciences, 1968. p. 133–139.

McGarr, Arthur, and Robert C. Vorhis, 1968. Seismic seiches from the March 1964 Alaska earthquake. U.S. Geological Survey Professional Paper 544-E. Washington: Government Printing Office. 43 p. Also *in* The Great Alaska Earthquake of 1964: Hydrology. NAS Pub. 1603. Washington: National Academy of Sciences, 1968. p. 196–236.

Wigen, S. O., and W. R. H. White, 1964. Tsunami of March 27–29, 1964, west coast of Canada. Canada Department of Mines and Technical Surveys Duplicate Report. Victoria: Canada Department of Mines and Technical Surveys, August. 12 p.

II
TSUNAMIS

Introduction

INTRODUCTION

Within a few minutes after the great Alaska earthquake, even while the ground was still shaking at some points, catastrophic waves began to sweep onto the shores of many of the fiords opening off Prince William Sound and the Gulf of Alaska. At Valdez and Seward the docks collapsed and ships moored at them were plunged about like toys; smaller boats were swamped, overturned, rammed into each other, or tossed on shore. Buildings onshore were smashed or floated off; oil tanks were stove in and caught fire; the railroad tracks at Seward were torn up and the rolling stock was strewn about. At Whittier, the loss of docks, buildings, and oil tanks was repeated; the native village of Chenega was essentially wiped out; and lesser damages occurred at a number of smaller communities.

Other Alaskan communities on the coast of the Gulf of Alaska and in the Kodiak Island group were subjected to the attack of waves arriving later, at some places several hours after the earthquake. At Kodiak the pattern of destruction of small boats, waterside facilities, and buildings was repeated. Most of the village of Old Harbor, all of the village of Kaguyak, and several canneries were destroyed. The waves at most places, particularly those on the coast of the Gulf of Alaska, kept washing in for hours; although their own height decreased, the heights on land to which they swept in many places increased until 10 p.m. or midnight as the tide rose. Within a few hours, the waves had been responsible for a death toll of 103 and damages totaling about $80 million in Alaska.

The damage and loss of life were not restricted to Alaska. At the head of Port Alberni, British Columbia, a series of waves, the first of which arrived 4½ hours after the earthquake, caused damage amounting to about $10 million. On the Oregon coast, the waves did nearly a million dollars' worth of damage. And at Crescent City, California, where the waves arrived about 4 hours after the earthquake, damage exceeded $7 million.

A warning was issued by the Seismic Sea Wave Warning System when confirmation that waves had been generated as an accompaniment of the earthquake reached the Honolulu Observatory of the U.S. Coast and Geodetic Survey just over 3 hours after the earthquake (Spaeth and Berkman, 1967, and this volume). Even though the warning had been issued, four children in a family camped on an Oregon beach were caught by the waves and drowned, and 12 persons lost their lives on the California coast, 10 of them at Crescent City.

The catastrophic effects of the waves were clear even from the earliest radio reports on the consequences of the earthquake. These first reports were, however, incomplete and somewhat confused. Wave effects on the coast of the Gulf of Mexico were discussed, along with effects on the California coast, the Gulf of Alaska coast, and the Alaska fiords. No damage was reported from Hawaii, but it was not clear whether this was the result of lack of damage or lack of reports.

From later reports it was evident that, if the waves occurring shortly after the earthquake in channels on the Gulf of Mexico had any connection with the earthquake, they must have been seiches, that is, resonant oscillations in the channels generated in response to the long-period earthquake waves in the crust (McGarr and Vorhis, this volume). Ocean waves could not have moved from the center of disturbance to the Gulf of Mexico in time to account for the observations even if there had been a direct channelway through the Isthmus of Panama.

INVESTIGATIONS IN ALASKA

It seemed clear from the outset that the waves that spread from the Gulf of Alaska out across the Pacific, causing the catastrophes at Port Alberni and Crescent City, were tsunamis, that is, they had been impulsively generated either by tectonic displacement of the crust associated with the earthquake or by an enormous mass movement such as a submarine landslide triggered by the earthquake.

The association of tsunamis with earthquakes was, of course, nothing new. Such an association had been recognized for centuries on Pacific coasts like those of Japan, Peru, and Chile, as well as Mediterranean, Caribbean, and other earthquake-prone coasts. Iida, Cox, and Pararas-Carayannis (1967, and Seismology and Geodesy volume) have catalogued over 300 earthquakes associated with waves in the Pacific and connecting seas, more than 150 of them since 1900. Still, a major tsunami occurs so infrequently that intensive study of the causes, characteristics, and effects of each is thoroughly warranted. There were, besides, some features of the Alaska tsunami that especially seemed to justify investigation. The deeply indented nature of the Alaskan coast and the inland location of the epicenter suggested that more evidence as to the details of generation might be found for this tsunami than for tsunamis associated with offshore earthquakes. Further, the fact that Crescent City had suffered a major catastrophe, whereas such normally vulnerable places as Hilo, Hawaii, had escaped serious effects, suggested a significantly different pattern of energy propagation from that in other tsunamis at least during the previous century. Hence studies of the character of the waves and their mode of generation from evidences in the meizoseismic area of the earthquake seemed especially worthwhile.

Almost no records of scientific quality were kept of the waves and their relation to the earthquake in the meizoseismal region, the region of highest-intensity seismic effects. Notable exceptions were a log maintained at the Fleet Weather Central, Kodiak Naval Air Station, near Kodiak, by Lt. Barney and Chief Morrow (Berg and others, 1971a; Wilson and Tørum, this volume, Appendix A), and a similar log of observations at Cape Yakataga by C. W. Bilderback (Berg and others, 1971b; Wilson and Tørum, this volume). The U.S. Coast and Geodetic Survey recording tide gage at Womens Bay, Kodiak, was dismantled by the first wave, and the nearest operating gage was at Yakutat (Spaeth and Berkman, this volume). Hence the waves were evidenced mainly by physical indications, such as damage and debris lines, and by eyewitness reports. The detail and reliability of both sorts of evidence deteriorate with time; although a few surveys by competent observers were initiated locally, notably one at Valdez by Migliaccio (1964), it was fortunate that more comprehensive studies with external support were begun early.

The first general study of the wave effects in the generating area was carried out by Van Dorn (1965) of the Scripps Institution of Oceanography and by Brown (1964) of the U.S. Army Corps of Engineers, who visited the meizoseismal area within a week after the earthquake. In the third and fourth weeks after the earthquake, the area was covered in greater detail by a team drawn from the University of Alaska, the University of Tokyo, and the University of Hawaii: Berg, Cox, Furumoto, Kajiura, Kawasumi, and Shima (Berg, 1964; Berg and others, 1965, 1971a, b; Furumoto, 1964; Kawasumi, 1964). Still later field studies, generally in greater detail, have since been made in critical areas by members of the U.S. Geological Survey, notably Coulter and Migliaccio (1966, and Geology volume) at Valdez; Kachadoorian (1965, and Geology volume) at Whittier; Kachadoorian and Plafker (1967) and Plafker and Kachadoorian (1966, and Geology volume) at Kodiak; Lemke (1967, and Geology volume) at Seward; Gene Rusnak (personal communication) in Resurrection Bay and Prince William Sound; and Plafker and others (1969, and Geology volume) at a number of other places.

The result is a composite documentation that, considering the low population density of the Alaskan coast, is remarkably thorough. Because it includes data collected at different times by different people engaged in surveys of different intensities, this documentation probably is a more trustworthy record than one that could have been produced by a single, greatly centralized effort.

NOMENCLATURE

The nomenclature of the large waves associated with earthquakes is confused—partly, no doubt, because they are unknown or at least extremely rare in the homelands of the common scientific languages. They are lumped with other tide or tidelike waves in English as tidal waves, in French as *raz de marée* (etymologically equivalent to tide race but now used in a more restrictive sense for a bore), and in German as *Flutwellen* (flood swells). The Spanish term *maremoto* is etymologically equivalent to seaquake (see von Huene, this volume).

In Japan, such waves have been called *tsunami* (etymologically, harbor wave) or less commonly *kaisho* (etymologically, sea roar). In original common usage, *tsunami* referred to long waves of abnormal runup associated either with earthquakes (*zishin tsunami*) or with typhoons (*kaze tsunami*). In Japanese technical usage, the term has generally come to be limited to waves associated with earthquakes or other impulsive generating mechanisms, unless otherwise qualified.

Restricted to waves of seismic or similar origin, the term *tsunami* has long been in international technical usage, having been introduced into French literature at least as early as 1905 by Montessus de Ballore and into English literature as early as 1907 by Hobbs. An alternative term, *seismic sea wave*, is longer and offers no more advantages in precision since by its etymology it should include seaquakes (von Huene, this volume) and *T*-phases (Northrop, this volume), both of which are compressional waves in the sea, as well as seiches (McGarr and Vorhis, this volume) and long gravity waves in the sea, lakes, and channels, set up by resonance with crustal seismic waves. Again, from its etymology it should not include waves associated with explosions unless they were accompanied by earthquakes, and it should include waves generated by landslides or icefalls only if these mass movements are triggered by earthquakes.

Cox (1963) has defined *tsunami* for technical usage as "a train of progressive long waves generated in the ocean or a small connected body of water by an impulsive disturbance." Defined in this way, it includes waves generated by abrupt bottom displacements, submarine or shoreline landslides, and volcanic or nuclear explosions. It does not include storm surges, astronomic tidal waves, or seiches. Van Dorn (1966) provides the following definition: "the gravity wave system formed in the sea following any large-scale short-duration disturbance of the free surface." By these definitions all the marine waves associated with the Alaska earthquake, except the seiches, were members of tsunamis.

LOCAL TSUNAMIS

From the field studies in Alaska, it soon became clear that there had been not just the one tsunami that swept across the Pacific from the Gulf of Alaska, but several additional tsunamis, independently generated in fiords and straits, many of which were locally quite disastrous. At many places in these enclosed bodies of water, the times elapsing between the earthquake and the arrival of large waves were too short to have permitted the waves to have traveled from the Continental Shelf. In most of the fiords and straits where local tsunamis occurred, there are evidences of at least one possible generation mechanism. The most obvious and perhaps the commonest mechanism was landsliding or slumping of delta sediments at the head or on the sides of a fiord, especially the rotational slumping of a delta. Other possible mechanisms that have been suggested are: (1) horizontal displacements of fiord walls and slopes; (2) tilt of a fiord or strait resulting from differential vertical crustal displacement (Berg and others, 1971a); and (3) block faulting in the floor of a fiord (Gene Rusnak, personal communication). In addition to the local tsunamis that were generated by one of the above mechanisms, seiches were probably generated in many fiords by the resonant coupling of the water to the crustal oscillations of the earthquake.

In Aialik Bay, according to Gene Rusnak (personal communication), there was wave runup as great as 100 ft, so distributed as to indicate wave action transverse to the fiord generated presumably by submarine slides, rather than by the major tsunami entering from the Gulf.

At Seward, near the head of Resurrection Bay a waterfront slump developed during the earthquake, a tanker was tossed about, and the dock to which it was moored collapsed. The resulting wave and subsequent waves caused damage amounting to about $15 million and 11 casualties (Brown, 1964; Grantz and others, 1964; Van Dorn, 1965; Lemke,

1967; Wilson and Tørum, 1968; Berg and others, 1971a; Spaeth and Berkman, 1967). According to Gene Rusnak (personal communication), block faulting of the fiord bottom may have contributed to the generation of the waves.

At least one source and probably several sources of waves were located in Knight Island Passage and connecting fiords and passages. One wave, arriving a few minutes after the earthquake, swept away all the houses of the village of Chenega to a height of 55 ft and caused the deaths of 23. Two other deaths were attributed to waves in this area, one in Sawmill Bay near Port Ashton and one at Point Nowell (Spaeth and Berkman, 1967). The high wave at Chenega has been attributed by Berg and others (1971a, b) to the northerly tilt of the crust, especially in the vicinity of Montague Island, and by Plafker and others (1969) to the southward horizontal crustal displacement. Submarine slides at the north end of Latouche Island (U.S. Coast and Geodetic Survey, 1964) may have been responsible for generating some of the waves in the vicinity.

Three persons were missing and presumed drowned by high waves at Port Nellie Juan. Damage to vegetation elsewhere in that fiord and the connecting Kings Bay suggests at least two separate wave sources. The waves resulted at least in part from submarine landslides (Plafker and others, 1969).

Submarine landslides were also the source of waves in Passage Canal (Kachadoorian, 1965) that had a maximum runup of 104 ft and that were responsible for some $10 million damage and the deaths of 12 at Whittier (Cox, Table 1, *in* Weller, this volume).

The town of Valdez, at the head of Port Valdez, experienced a catastrophe very similar to that at Seward (Berg and others, 1971a; Coulter and Migliaccio, 1966). A dock collapsed and a ship moored there was tossed about. Total damages amounted to over $12 million (Wilson and Tørum, 1968), and 31 persons lost their lives (Spaeth and Berkman, 1967). Waves originating from submarine slides in the western part of Port Valdez caused a runup of 170 ft in the vicinity.

Observations of high waves at Perry Island and at Tatitlek suggest additional sources of waves in the northern part of Prince William Sound near those places (Berg and others, 1971b; Plafker and others, 1969).

Local tsunamis killed a total of 82 in Alaska; 71 of these were in Prince William Sound, and the other 11 at Seward (Cox *in* Weller, this volume).

THE MAJOR TSUNAMI

From a number of lines of evidence, it is clear that the major tsunami that swept out across the Pacific from the epicentral area of the earthquake was generated by the uplift of a large area of the Continental Shelf in the Gulf of Alaska extending from the Copper River Delta at the northeast to a point off the Trinity Islands on the southwest, a length of 750 km, and from the Kenai Peninsula and Kodiak Island on the northwest nearly to the edge of the shelf on the southeast, with an average width of about 150 km. Studies of the arrival time of the tsunami wave front at various distant tide gages (Pararas-Carayannis, 1967) have indicated that the waves spread from this area. From the displacements of shorelines of the continent, its peninsulas, and islands, the average uplift of the whole area could be estimated, and from this the potential energy capable of being radiated from the shelf in the form of a tsunami (Van Dorn, 1965, and this volume; Pararas-Carayannis, 1967; Berg and others, 1971b, and this volume). The estimates by Berg and others, based on later data, are 1.8 m average uplift and 2.2×10^{22} ergs potential energy.

Locally, southwest of Montague Island, there were distinct horsts whose maximum uplift exceeded 17 m (Malloy, 1964; Malloy and Merrill, 1969, and this volume). These local uplifts, as well as the horizontal displacement of submarine slopes, very likely contributed to high-frequency components of the tsunami as proposed by Wilson and Tørum (1968) but probably not significantly to its total energy (Berg and others, 1971b, and this volume).

Most of Prince William Sound also was uplifted, and Cook Inlet and Shelikof Strait were depressed during the earthquake, but these bodies of water are effectively cut off from the ocean by Hinchinbrook and Montague islands, Kenai Peninsula, and Afognak Island and hence contributed little to the major tsunami generation.

Except for the record from Wake Island (Van Dorn, 1965, 1970, and this volume), records of the tsunami were those from tide gages known to be subject to distortions due to nearshore filtering and resonance. In spite of the differences among them, the tide-gage records at most stations showed a long-period component of some consistency, peaked most commonly at about 1.7 or 1.8 hours. The results of both a hydraulic model of the source by Van Dorn (1970, and this volume) and a numerical model of the source by Hwang and Divoky (this volume), checked in each case against pertinent marigraphic records, suggest that there were at least two initial crests separated by a time interval of 1½ to 2 hours. There has been considerable disagreement, however, concerning the continuing radiation of long-period waves with significant amplitudes from the source. Wilson and Tørum (1968) consider that the long-period oscillations shown on the marigrams are the result of a train of coherent, nondispersive waves of about 1.8-hour period emanating from the source. However, Loomis (this volume) found no significant coherence at such long periods among spectra of the tsunami at Hawaiian and other mid-Pacific stations, and Van Dorn and Cox (this volume) point out the considerable variation in period from station to station without systematic geographic distribution. The latter authors consider that the long-period oscillations are the result of either (1) selective amplification, from a broad spectrum of low frequencies radiating from the source, or (2) some coastal process of energy conversion to low frequencies from high frequencies radiating from the source, the similarities among the low frequencies favored being due to similarities of coastal configuration and bathymetry in the recording areas. On the one hand, they cite evidences that tsunamis characteristically have continuing broad low-frequency spectra, with peaks related to the dimensions, orientation, and distance of the tsunami sources and to earthquake magnitude. On the other hand, they indicate that theoretically, even if the source area of a tsunami were capable of sustained low-frequency oscillation, most of the energy should be radiated with the first wave, leaving little energy to be associated with continuing long-period oscillations.

From the area of generation, the tsunami propagated outward across the Pacific at the long-wave velocity well known to depend on depth. Average speeds, tabulated by Spaeth and Berkman (1967), ranged from 159 knots for propagation to Yakutat, Alaska, over a path much of which was on the Continental Shelf, to 473 knots to Nawiliwili, Kauai, Hawaii, over a path mainly at oceanic depths.

The greatest runup height measured for the major tsunami was west of Narrow Cape, Kodiak Island, 60 ft above mean lower low water (Berg and others, 1971b, and this volume). The tide stage of this maximum runup is unknown. It is apparent, however, from this and other large runups that the maximum must have been near an upper bound of tsunami runup maxima in relation to earthquake magnitude defined empirically by Wilson and Tørum (this volume).

As with previous tsunamis for which runup measurements are available, the runup heights of the major Alaska tsunami varied greatly even within short shoreline distances (Van Dorn and Cox, this volume). Nevertheless, it is clear that the wave energy of the tsunami was preferentially radiated in a direction normal to the long axis of the area of uplift on the Continental Shelf (Wilson and Tørum, this volume; Van Dorn and Cox, this volume). The directional pattern of energy radiation accounts for the contrast in the relative intensities of effects on the California coast and in Hawaii between the Gulf of Alaska tsunami and earlier tsunamis originating in the Aleutian Islands and elsewhere. The parallelism between the major axis of the source area and the trend of the features encourages the supposition that, from the trends of the major tectonic features in the epicentral region of an earthquake, the probable direction of preferential energy radiation of an accompanying tsunami may be determined, and hence, taking refraction into account, probable relative intensities of damage may be estimated in a general way for distant coastlines.

The records of the 1964 tsunami have been used (1) by Braddock (1969, 1970) to check a numerical-analysis method for determining tsunami travel times and (2) by Hwang and Divoky (this volume) to check a method for determining—from the location, nature, and dimensions of the source—not only travel times but also the general oceanic character of the waves. From their results, expressible both as maps and as synthetic marigrams, both the directionality of the waves and their temporal characters may be determined.

The major tsunami caused about $31 million damage to fishing boats, docks, and other waterfront property at the town of Kodiak; $11 million damage at Kodiak Naval Station; and $3 million damage to other communities on Kodiak and Afognak islands, including the total destruction of Afognak and Kaguyak villages and near-total destruction of Old Harbor. Elsewhere in Alaska there were damages of more than $2 million. Major tsunamis claimed the lives of 21 people in Alaska, of which 19 were in the Kodiak Islands area (Cox *in* Weller, this volume). In British Columbia there was damage in excess of $10 million, in Oregon damage approaching $1 million and including four deaths (Wilson and Tørum, 1968). The waves were recorded as far away as the Palmer Peninsula, Antarctica, where they had a height of 1 m (Spaeth and Berkman, 1967).

Tsunami warnings that were spread through more or less unofficial channels contributed to the saving of lives in some Alaskan communities where the high waves arrived in the first few hours following the earthquake. In some other Alaskan communities, lives were saved simply through the recognition of a tsunami hazard accompanying a large earthquake (Weller, this volume). The response to the official warning issued 3 hours after the earthquake through the Seismic Sea Wave Warning System by the Honolulu Observatory varied considerably from place to place (Anderson, Human Ecology volume; Weller, this volume). In Hilo, Hawaii, where catastrophic tsunamis have occurred frequently but where the Alaska tsunami caused little damage, there was orderly and complete evacuation. In Crescent City, California, there was some confusion, and areas once evacuated were reoccupied before the highest wave hit, resulting in the deaths there (Yutzy, 1964).

Many improvements have been made in the warning system since the Alaska earthquake, probably the most important being the initiation of a policy of regional evaluation of the risks from a particular tsunami (Cox and Stewart, this volume). A special Alaska Regional Tsunami Warning System has been established with extensive telemetering facilities. However, as pointed out by Cox and Stewart, the low-recurrence frequency of damaging tsunamis at most populated places in Alaska will make successful operation of this system very difficult.

PAPERS IN THIS SECTION

One of the papers in this section, that by Van Dorn, which couples some of the results of the first general survey of the tsunamis in the generating area with an analysis of a record of

a special midocean gage, was first presented at a coastal engineering conference in 1964. Another, that by Berg and others, is part of a larger report, of which portions were presented at conferences and elsewhere starting in 1964; however, the entire report was not published until 1971 although the manuscript was made accessible to several other investigators in the interim. The paper by Spaeth and Berkman, which describes the tsunami from tide-gage records and also describes the tsunami warning system and its operations on the occasion of the Alaska earthquake, was published in an early edition in 1964 and has gone through several revisions prior to its publication here.

The paper by Wilson and Tørum is an extract from a major report by those authors based on a study initiated by the Panel on Engineering of the Committee on the Alaska Earthquake. The second paper by Van Dorn, on the results of a model study of the generation of the major tsunami, was first presented at a tsunami conference in 1969. The paper by Hwang and Divoky resulted from a study (made independently for the Atomic Energy Commission) that came to the attention of the Panel on Oceanography as it was nearing the completion of its work. The remaining papers—those by Van Dorn and Cox, Loomis, Weller, Cox and Stewart, and von Huene and Cox—were prepared especially for this volume.

Missing from this section is a thorough report on the tsunamis locally generated in Alaska fiords and straits, which could not be completed in time because of the illness of its author, Gene Rusnak.

DOAK C. COX
University of Hawaii

REFERENCES

Anderson, William A., 1970. Tsunami warning in Crescent City, California, and Hilo, Hawaii *in* The Great Alaska Earthquake of 1964: Human Ecology. NAS Pub. 1607. Washington: National Academy of Sciences. p. 116–124.

Berg, Eduard, 1964. The Alaskan earthquake of March 1964. University of Alaska Geophysical Institute Annual Report 1963–64. College: University of Alaska, Geophysical Institute. p. 69–82.

Berg, Eduard, Doak C. Cox, Augustine S. Furumoto, Kinjiro Kajiura, Hirosi Kawasumi, and Etsuzo Shima, 1965. The tsunami of 27 March 1964 in Alaska (Abstract) *in* Science in Alaska, 1964: Proceedings Fifteenth Alaskan Science Conference, College, Alaska, August 31 to September 4, 1964. College: Alaska Division American Association for the Advancement of Science, March 15. p. 91.

Berg, Eduard, Doak C. Cox, Augustine S. Furumoto, Kinjiro Kajiura, Hirosi Kawasumi, and Etsuzo Shima, 1971a. Field survey of the tsunamis of 28 March 1964 in Alaska, and conclusions as to the origin of the major tsunami. Report HIG-70-2. Honolulu: University of Hawaii, Institute of Geophysics. 57 p.

Berg, Eduard, Doak C. Cox, Augustine S. Furumoto, Kinjiro Kajiura,

Hirosi Kawasumi, and Etsuzo Shima, 1971b. The source of the major tsunami *in* Field survey of the tsunamis of 28 March 1964 in Alaska, and conclusions as to the origin of the major tsunami. Report HIG-70-2. Honolulu: University of Hawaii, Institute of Geophysics. p. 38–49. Also *in* The Great Alaska Earthquake of 1964: Oceanography and Coastal Engineering. NAS Pub. 1605. Washington: National Academy of Sciences, 1972.

Braddock, R. D., 1969. On tsunami propagation. *Journal of Geophysical Research*, 74 (April 15), 1952–1957.

Braddock, R. D., 1970. Tsunami propagation over large distances *in* Tsunamis in the Pacific Ocean. Proceedings of the International Symposium on Tsunamis and Tsunami Research, Honolulu, Hawaii, October 7–10, 1969. W. M. Adams, editor. Honolulu: East-West Center Press. p. 285–303.

Brown, Delmer L., 1964. Tsunamic activity accompanying the Alaskan earthquake of 27 March 1964. Technical Report, U.S. Army Engineer District, Alaska. Anchorage: U.S. Army Corps of Engineers, April 23. 31 p.

Coulter, Henry W., and Ralph R. Migliaccio, 1966. Effects of the earthquake of March 27, 1964, at Valdez, Alaska. U.S. Geological Survey Professional Paper 542-C. Washington: Government Printing Office. 36 p. Also *in* The Great Alaska Earthquake of 1964: Geology. NAS Pub. 1601. Washington: National Academy of Sciences, 1971. p. 359–394.

Cox, Doak C., 1963. Status of tsunami knowledge. Proceedings of the Tenth Pacific Science Congress, Honolulu, Hawaii, August–September 1961. Doak C. Cox, editor. IUGG Monograph 24. Paris: International Union of Geodesy and Geophysics. p. 1–6.

Cox, Doak C., and Harris B. Stewart, Jr., 1972. Technical evaluation of the Seismic Sea Wave Warning System *in* The Great Alaska Earthquake of 1964: Oceanography and Coastal Engineering. NAS Pub. 1605. Washington: National Academy of Sciences.

Furumoto, Augustine S., 1964. Field survey of the earthquake and tsunami of March 27, 1964, in Alaska. Hawaiian Academy of Sciences Proceedings, 39th year. Honolulu: Hawaiian Academy of Sciences, p. 23.

Grantz, Arthur, George Plafker, and Reuben Kachadoorian, 1964. Alaska's Good Friday earthquake, March 27, 1964: a preliminary geologic evaluation. U.S. Geological Survey Circular 491. Washington: U.S. Geological Survey. 35 p.

Hobbs, W. H., 1907. Origin of ocean basins in the light of the new seismology. *Geological Society of America Bulletin*, 18, 233–250.

Hwang, Li-San, and David Divoky, 1972. A numerical model of the major tsunami *in* The Great Alaska Earthquake of 1964: Oceanography and Coastal Engineering. NAS Pub. 1605. Washington: National Academy of Sciences.

Iida, Kumizi, Doak C. Cox, and George Pararas-Carayannis, 1967. Preliminary catalog of tsunamis occurring in the Pacific Ocean. Data Report No. 5, HIG-67-10. Honolulu: University of Hawaii, Institute of Geophysics, August. 270 p.

Kachadoorian, Reuben, 1965. Effects of the earthquake of March 27, 1964, at Whittier, Alaska. U.S. Geological Survey Professional Paper 542-B. Washington: Government Printing Office. 21 p. Also *in* The Great Alaska Earthquake of 1964: Geology. NAS Pub. 1601. Washington: National Academy of Sciences, 1971. p. 439–459.

Kachadoorian, Reuben, and George Plafker, 1967. Effects of the earthquake of March 27, 1964, on the communities of Kodiak and nearby islands. U.S. Geological Survey Professional Paper 542-F. Washington: Government Printing Office. 41 p. Abstract *in* The Great Alaska Earthquake of 1964: Geology. NAS Pub. 1601. Washington: National Academy of Sciences, 1971. p. 539–540.

Kawasumi, Hirosi, 1964. Outline of the Alaskan earthquake by Japanese-American investigating committee. Architectural Institute of Japan, Vol. 79 (944). p. 511–512.

Lemke, Richard W., 1967. Effects of the earthquake of March 27, 1964, at Seward, Alaska. U.S. Geological Survey Professional Paper 542-E. Washington: Government Printing Office. 43 p. Also *in* The Great Alaska Earthquake of 1964: Geology. NAS Pub. 1601. Washington: National Academy of Sciences, 1971. p. 395–437.

Loomis, Harold G., 1972. The tsunami in the Hawaiian Islands *in* The Great Alaska Earthquake of 1964: Oceanography and Coastal Engineering. NAS Pub. 1605. Washington: National Academy of Sciences.

McGarr, Arthur, and Robert C. Vorhis, 1972. Seismic seiches in bays, channels, and estuaries *in* The Great Alaska Earthquake of 1964: Oceanography and Coastal Engineering. NAS Pub. 1605. Washington: National Academy of Sciences.

Malloy, Richard J., 1964. Crustal uplift southwest of Montague Island, Alaska. *Science*, 146 (November 20), 1048–1049.

Malloy, Richard J., and George F. Merrill, 1969. Vertical crustal movement of the sea floor associated with the Prince William Sound, Alaska, earthquake *in* Volume II-B,C: The Prince William Sound, Alaska, earthquake of 1964 and aftershocks. Environmental Science Services Administration, U.S. Coast and Geodetic Survey. Washington: Government Printing Office. p. 327–338. Also *in* The Great Alaska Earthquake of 1964: Oceanography and Coastal Engineering. NAS Pub. 1605. Washington: National Academy of Sciences, 1972.

Migliaccio, Ralph R., 1964. Earthquake of March 27, 1964. Report of District Geologist, Valdez, to Chief Geologist, College, April 10. Valdez: Office of the District Geologist. 6 p.

Montessus de Ballore, F. de, 1905. La Géographie Séismique. Paris: Libraire Armand Colin. 475 p.

Northrop, John, 1972. *T*-phases *in* The Great Alaska Earthquake of 1964: Oceanography and Coastal Engineering. NAS Pub. 1605. Washington: National Academy of Sciences.

Pararas-Carayannis, George, 1967. A study of the source mechanism of the Alaska earthquake and tsunami of March 27, 1964: Part I, Water waves. *Pacific Science*, 21 (July), 301–310. Also *in* The Great Alaska Earthquake of 1964: Seismology and Geodesy. NAS Pub. 1602. Washington: National Academy of Sciences, 1972.

Plafker, George, and Reuben Kachadoorian, 1966. Geologic effects of the March 1964 earthquake and associated seismic sea waves on Kodiak and nearby islands, Alaska. U.S. Geological Survey Professional Paper 543-D. Washington: Government Printing Office. 46 p. Also *in* The Great Alaska Earthquake of 1964: Geology. NAS Pub. 1601. Washington: National Academy of Sciences, 1971. p. 177–226.

Plafker, George, Reuben Kachadoorian, Edwin B. Eckel, and Lawrence R. Mayo, 1969. Effects of the earthquake of March 27, 1964, on various communities. U.S. Geological Survey Professional Paper 542-G. Washington: Government Printing Office. 50 p. Also *in* The Great Alaska Earthquake of 1964: Geology. NAS Pub. 1601. Washington: National Academy of Sciences, 1971. p. 489–538.

Spaeth, Mark G., and Saul C. Berkman, 1967. The tsunami of March 28, 1964, as recorded at tide stations. Environmental Science Services Administration Technical Report C&GS 33. Washington: Government Printing Office. 86 p. Also *in* The Great Alaska Earthquake of 1964: Oceanography and Coastal Engineering. NAS Pub. 1605. Washington: National Academy of Sciences, 1972.

U.S. Coast and Geodetic Survey, 1964. Preliminary report—Prince William Sound, Alaskan earthquakes March–April 1964 (second printing). Seismology Division Report. Washington: U.S. Coast and Geodetic Survey. 101 p.

Van Dorn, William G., 1965. Source mechanism of the tsunami of

March 28, 1964, in Alaska. Proceedings of the Ninth Conference (1964) on Coastal Engineering (Chapter 10). New York: American Society of Civil Engineers. p. 166–190. Also *in* The Great Alaska Earthquake of 1964: Oceanography and Coastal Engineering. NAS Pub. 1605. Washington: National Academy of Sciences, 1972.

Van Dorn, William G., 1966. Tsunami *in* The Encyclopedia of Oceanography. R. W. Fairbridge, editor. New York: Van Nostrand-Reinhold. p. 941–943.

Van Dorn, William G., 1970. A model experiment on the generation of the tsunami of March 28, 1964 in Alaska *in* Tsunamis in the Pacific Ocean. Proceedings of the International Symposium on Tsunamis and Tsunami Research, Honolulu, Hawaii, October 7–10, 1969. W. M. Adams, editor. Honolulu: East-West Center Press. p. 33–45. Also *in* The Great Alaska Earthquake of 1964: Oceanography and Coastal Engineering. NAS Pub. 1605. Washington: National Academy of Sciences, 1972.

Van Dorn, William G., and Doak C. Cox, 1972. Oceanic character, propagation, and coastal modification of the major tsunami *in* The Great Alaska Earthquake of 1964: Oceanography and Coastal Engineering. NAS Pub. 1605. Washington: National Academy of Sciences.

von Huene, Roland, 1972. Seaquakes *in* The Great Alaska Earthquake of 1964: Oceanography and Coastal Engineering. NAS Pub. 1605. Washington: National Academy of Sciences.

Weller, Jack M., 1972. Human response to tsunami warnings *in* The Great Alaska Earthquake of 1964: Oceanography and Coastal Engineering. NAS Pub. 1605. Washington: National Academy of Sciences.

Wilson, Basil W., and Alf Tørum, 1968. The tsunami of the Alaskan earthquake, 1964: Engineering evaluation. Coastal Engineering Research Center Technical Memorandum No. 25. Washington: U.S. Army Corps of Engineers, May. 444 p.

Wilson, Basil W., and Alf Tørum, 1972. Runup heights of the major tsunami on North American coasts *in* The Great Alaska Earthquake of 1964: Oceanography and Coastal Engineering. NAS Pub. 1605. Washington: National Academy of Sciences.

Yutzy, Daniel, 1964. Aesop, 1964: Contingencies affecting the issuing of public disaster warnings at Crescent City, California. Disaster Research Center Research Note 4. Columbus: The Ohio State University, Disaster Research Center. 8 p.

MARK G. SPAETH
SAUL C. BERKMAN
U.S. COAST AND GEODETIC SURVEY

Reprinted with minor changes from
U.S. Coast and Geodetic Survey, Technical Report C&GS 33,
"The tsunami of March 28, 1964, as recorded at tide stations"

The Tsunamis as Recorded at Tide Stations and the Seismic Sea Wave Warning System

INTRODUCTION

The Prince William Sound earthquake of 03:36:14.0 GMT, March 28, 1964, was one of the largest shocks ever recorded on the North American continent. The epicenter was located at 61.04°N, 147.73°W, between Crescent Glacier and Unakwik Inlet. The magnitude, as determined by the U.S. Coast and Geodetic Survey, was 8.3 ± 0.33. This earthquake, in addition to generating a major tsunami of record size along much of the Pacific coast of North America, caused several local tsunamis which were responsible for locally heavy damage (Table 1) in various arms and inlets of Prince William Sound. It also generated seiches in rivers, harbors, channels, lakes, and swimming pools as distant as the U.S. Gulf Coast states.

The major tsunami connected with the Prince William Sound earthquake was generated by broad crustal warping along a northeast-southwest trending hinge line (Van Dorn, 1965, and this volume). This hinge line (1) runs roughly parallel to the southeast coast of Kodiak Island, (2) passes across Narrow Cape and seaward of Cape Chiniak, (3) turns toward the north and passes across the eastern portion of the Kenai Peninsula and the western portion of Prince William Sound, (4) swings east in the vicinity of the epicenter, and (5) passes just south of Valdez, terminating near the Copper River. South and east of this hinge zone, an area stretching from Kodiak Island to Kayak Island was uplifted as much as 50 ft, according to U.S. Coast and Geodetic Survey (1965) bathymetric surveys. The seaward limits of the uplifted zone have not been definitely established, but the zone includes most of Prince William Sound and the Continental Shelf from Kayak Island to Sitkinak Island. The zone of uplift probably includes portions of the continental slope and may extend seaward as far as the Aleutian trench; it is roughly equivalent to the zone of aftershocks, as shown on Figure 1. North and west of the hinge line, an area that includes most of Kodiak Island, Shelikof Strait, Cook Inlet, the Kenai Peninsula, and the Chugach Mountains subsided by amounts up to more than 7 ft.

ABSTRACT: The tsunami generated by the Prince William Sound earthquake of March 28, 1964 (GMT) was the largest since the 1960 Chilean tsunami. This report contains 105 reproductions of tide curves showing the tsunami. A brief history of the Seismic Sea Wave Warning System (Tsunami Warning System since March 15, 1967) and a report of its operation during the tsunami warning action are included. Fatalities totaled 119, and over $104 million in damage resulted. These are tabulated, together with detailed data on wave heights and arrival times at various stations throughout the Pacific.

TABLE 1   Casualties and Major Damage due to the Tsunami of March 28, 1964[a]

Location	Casualties	Damage ($)
Alaska		
Cape St. Elias	1	–
Chenega	23	100,000
Cordova	–	1,775,000[b]
Kaguyak	3	50,000
Kalsin Bay	6	–
Kodiak (City)	9	31,279,000[c]
(including		(23,714,000 private;
Spruce Cape)		7,565,000 public)
Kodiak Naval Station	–	10,300,000[c]
Old Harbor	1	150,000
Ouzinkie	–	500,000[d]
Port Ashton	1	–
Port Nellie Juan	3	–
Point Nowell	1	–
Seldovia	–	500,000[b]
Seward	11	14,614,000[b]
Valdez	31	12,568,000[b]
(including		(8,453,000 private;
Anderson Bay)		4,115,000 public);
		15,000,000[c]
Whitshed	1	–
Whittier	12	10,000,000[c]
British Columbia, Canada		
Alberni–Port Alberni	–	10,000,000[e]
Hot Springs Cove	–	100,000
Zeballos	–	150,000
Oregon		
Cannon Beach	–	230,000[f]
Florence	–	50,000[f]
Newport	4	–
Seaside	–	276,000[f]
Waldport–Alsea	–	160,000[f]
California		
Crescent City	10	7,414,000[g]
Klamath	1	–
Bolinas Bay	1	–
Long Beach Harbor	–	100,000[g]
Los Angeles	–	175,000 to 275,000[g]
Marin County	–	1,000,000[g]
Noya Harbor	–	250,000 to 1,000,000[g]
Hawaii		
Hilo	–	15,000[h]
Maui	–	52,590[h]

[a] Casualty figures have been revised slightly from those in the earlier edition of this paper in accord with the findings by D. C. Cox (Table 1, in Weller, this volume). Additional damage figures are given by Wilson and Tørum (Coastal Engineering section, this volume).
[b] *Anchorage Daily News*, April 18, 1964.
[c] Tudor, 1964.
[d] *Daily Alaska Empire*, March 31, 1964.
[e] British Columbia Civil Defense (1964) estimated damages of $5 million, excluding damage to heavy industry and private autos.
[f] Sandstrom (unpublished letter).
[g] California Disaster Office (unpublished letter).
[h] Stevenson (unpublished letter).

The generating area of the major tsunami is roughly equivalent to the area of uplift (Figure 2). This illustration is simplified and shows only the source of the first motion registered by tide gages outside this area. Within the generating area, the motion of the water was extremely complex and was further compounded by waves generated by local slides and, particularly within Prince William Sound, by complex local diffraction, refraction, and reflection patterns. If the assumption is made that all elevation changes that occurred during the earthquake happened instantaneously, the initial impulse given to the ocean is somewhat as shown in cross sections A-A′ and A′-A″ on Figure 2.

LOCAL WAVES

In many of the harbors and bays along the south and east coast of the Kenai Peninsula and the northern shore of Prince William Sound, subaqueous landslides occurred and generated highly destructive local waves. The principal destructive local waves occurred at Seward, Valdez, and Whittier. In this section, no attempt has been made to separate the damage caused by the earthquake from the damage caused by the landslides, the tsunamis, or both.

SEWARD

At Seward, a stretch of the waterfront about 3,500 ft long and as much as 300 ft wide, including all waterfront facilities from the Standard Oil Company dock north to the San Juan dock, slid into Resurrection Bay shortly after the earthquake started and while the shaking was still intense. These facilities included the Standard Oil docks and warehouses, the Army docks and warehouses, the city dock, the small-boat harbor, the San Juan dock, the cement plant, and the marine ways.

The slide drew water out from the shoreline and created one or two boil-like disturbances at distances estimated from several hundred feet to perhaps one-half mile from the shore; from these disturbances, waves spread in all directions. Oil from waterfront fuel-storage tanks which had been ruptured by the earthquake immediately ignited, and the waves spread fire along the waterfront.

The ground which slid into Resurrection Bay was watersoaked alluvium. According to charts of the Seward harbor, the preearthquake offshore slope was between 30° and 35°. The instability of this slope under the earthquake-induced vibration was vividly demonstrated. The slide and the tsunami wiped out almost the entire economic foundation of Seward and caused 11 deaths (see footnote *a*, Table 1).

The wave generated by the slide caused considerable damage to the railroad yards and reached a maximum height of about 30 ft at Lowell Point (Grantz, Plafker, and

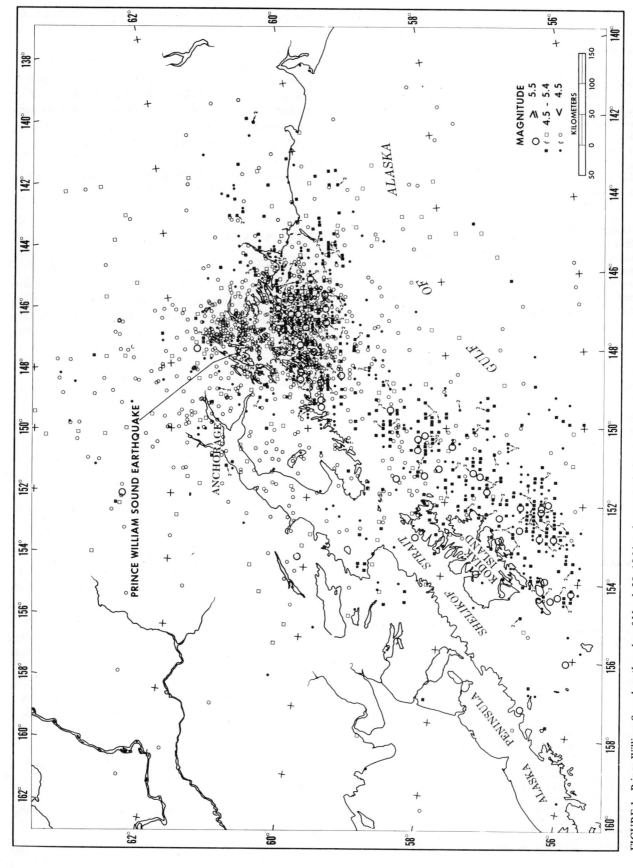

FIGURE 1 Prince William Sound earthquake of March 28, 1964, epicenter and aftershock locations through December 31, 1965. The symbols ○, ■, and ● indicate aftershocks located by using teleseismic data. The symbols □ and ○ indicate aftershocks located by using data from the net of temporary seismograph stations installed after the March 28 earthquake.

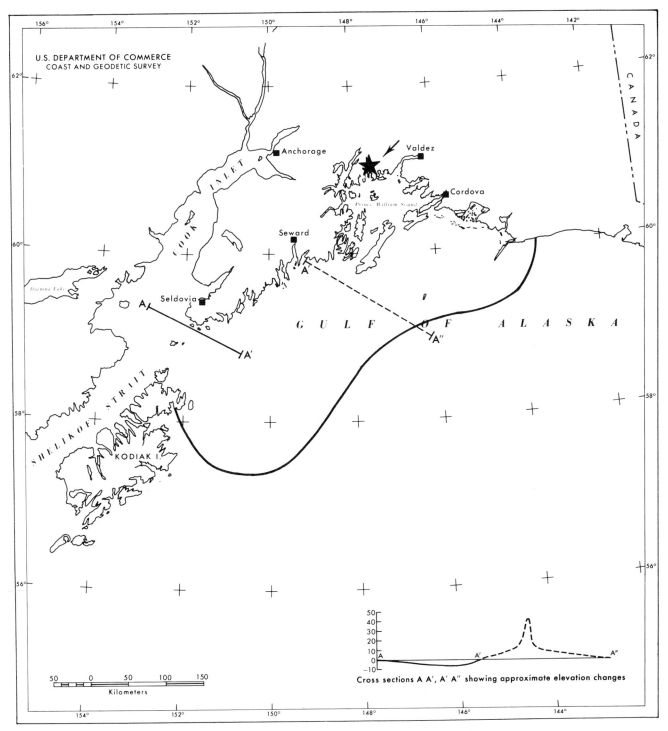

FIGURE 2 Generation area of Prince William Sound tsunami.

Kachadoorian, 1964). Approximately one-half hour later, a wave—probably the first of the major tsunami series—struck Seward, destroying The Alaska Railroad docks, washing out railroad and highway bridges, and piling railroad rolling stock into giant windrows of wreckage. It spread flaming petroleum over the waterfront, igniting the rolling stock, the electrical generation plant, and some residences. This wave also swept many dwellings from the vicinity of the small-boat harbor and washed boats into the lagoon north of Seward and onto the tidal flats at the head of Resurrection Bay.

VALDEZ

Local waves were generated by slides in two separate areas of Port Valdez—one at the town of Valdez and the other near the mouth of Shoup Bay. The wave—generated near Shoup Bay by large submarine slides of portions of the terminal moraine that occupies the mouth of the bay—deposited driftwood at an elevation of 170 ft above lower low water near the site of the Cliff Mine and splashed silt and sand as much as 220 ft above lower low water at the same place (Plafker and Mayo, 1965). Waves from this source washed the Middle Rock Light in Valdez Narrows off the 35-ft reinforced concrete pedestal on which it was mounted.

The town of Valdez was situated on the edge of an outwash delta consisting of unconsolidated silty sand and gravel. This delta lies at the head of the deep, steep-sided fiord of Port Valdez. Before the earthquake, the offshore slope of the delta face was approximately 15°. During the earthquake, the shaking caused failure of the unstable, water-saturated material, and a slice, approximately 4,000 ft long and 600 ft wide, slid into the sea and carried the dock area and portions of the town with it. The slide generated a wave which slammed into the waterfront within 2 to 3 minutes of the onset of the earthquake. In a report to the owners, the captain of the SS *Chena*, which was unloading cargo at the Valdez dock at the time of the earthquake, stated that his ship was raised about 30 ft and heeled over 50° to 70° by the initial wave. This wave demolished what was left of the waterfront facilities, caused the loss of the fishing fleet, and penetrated about two blocks into the town. Thirty-one people lost their lives in the slide and the subsequent waves (Table 1).

WHITTIER

Slides of unconsolidated water-soaked alluvium around the head of Passage Canal generated waves that destroyed much of the Whittier waterfront before the earthquake ended.

According to witnesses, three waves struck Whittier, with the second one causing most of the damage. One of the waves, probably the same one that caused the major damage in Whittier, reached a height of 104 ft above lower low water (Plafker and Mayo, 1965). The waves destroyed two sawmills; the Union Oil Company tank farm, wharf, and buildings; The Alaska Railroad depot; numerous frame dwellings; and the railroad ramp handling towers at the Army pier. They also caused great damage to the small-boat harbor. As at Seward and Valdez, fire broke out at the tank farm and contributed to the destruction. Twelve people were killed at Whittier by the tsunami (see footnote *a*, Table 1). After the locally generated waves dissipated, the tsunami did not reach above the extreme high-water line.

MISCELLANEOUS

Major waves were noted at other localities within Prince William Sound, minutes after the earthquake. Although the wave action at some of these places may have been generated locally, it is probable that most of the disturbances noted were caused by the tectonic warping and were part of the major tsunami. Due to the many islands, inlets, and passages in western Prince William Sound, the waves built to great heights and caused considerable damage in many places. At Chenega, where 23 people were killed, 19 of 20 houses were washed away and the water reached a school which was located 90 ft above sea level. At Port Nellie Juan, the dock was destroyed and three lives were lost. In this general area, maximum heights reached by the tsunami ranged from 50 to 70 ft, although the maximum at Port Nellie Juan was much lower. At Point Nowell, a wave which reached about 40 ft above sea level washed away two cabins and killed their owner. Port Ashton sustained little damage, although one person was drowned.

In many Prince William Sound localities, the water reached the highest level close to the time of high tide which occurred between 1000 and 1100 GMT. At Cordova, the tsunami caused extensive damage to the docks and floated away some houses near the waterfront. Here, the maximum height reached by the tsunami was about 5 ft above the highest high-tide line. At Whitshed, near Cordova, 10 cabins were washed away; one person, who had returned to his cabin when he thought that the danger had ended, was drowned.

THE SEISMIC SEA WAVE WARNING SYSTEM

HISTORY AND DESCRIPTION

After the devastating Aleutian tsunami of April 1, 1946, military and civilian sources criticized the U.S. Coast and Geodetic Survey for the lack of warning in the Hawaiian Islands. The critics correctly pointed out that seismic waves from this earthquake were recorded at Honolulu and other observatories within minutes after the occurrence of the earthquake; consequently, the tsunami could have been predicted. The error in this criticism lay in the fact that seismograph records were changed only once each day and, until the film records were developed, no knowledge of an earthquake occurrence was normally available. In addition, the great majority of underwater earthquakes does not cause tsunamis, and no arrangements were in effect to verify the existence of a tsunami through actual observation.

Another necessity for efficient operation of a warning system was the development of a method to determine quickly and accurately the amount of time between the occurrence of a tsunami-producing earthquake and the arrival of the waves in the Hawaiian Islands. This problem was solved in early 1947 by the preparation of a tsunami travel-time chart for Honolulu. This chart consists of a series of more or less concentric lines overprinted on a chart of the Pacific Ocean; the lines represent distances from Honolulu for each half hour and hour of the wave's travel time. Travel time to Honolulu is obtained by plotting the epicenter of an earthquake on the chart and noting its position with respect to the time lines. With the time of the disturbance given, the arrival time of the first sea wave at the Honolulu tide station becomes immediately available. The need for travel-time charts based on other tide stations became evident early in the operation of the Seismic Sea Wave Warning System (SSWWS). This need was based on two factors: (1) the necessity of estimating when the existence or absence of a wave could be observed at a particular tide station, and (2) the necessity of providing accurate estimates of tsunami arrival times to additional countries and areas. Charts for all tide stations in the SSWWS were completed by 1950. Travel-time charts are prepared on a continuing basis for new tide stations that join the Warning System from time to time. Because the manual preparation of travel-time charts is a tedious, time-consuming task, a computer program is being developed to compute the charts.

Personnel in the U.S. Coast and Geodetic Survey, especially Comdr. E. B. Roberts, believed that the technical problems preventing the establishment of a workable tsunami warning system could be overcome. Although the Coast Survey had no obligation under law to provide tsunami warnings, it saw the need for such warnings and had the scientific know-how and part of the organization necessary for such an undertaking. Furthermore, responsible officials in the Coast Survey considered themselves morally obligated to create and organize such a system. Consequently, under the direction of Comdr. E. B. Roberts, Comdr. C. K. Green, and Mr. W. B. Zerbe, work was initiated on the technical problems involved.

Because some tide stations in the SSWWS had relatively poor communications and because tide gages were normally checked only once a day, Comdr. Green designed a tsunami detector which would be actuated so as to ring an alarm by the wave motion of a tsunami. The alarm, located where it would always be noticed by personnel at a tide station, ensures an early warning that a tsunami has been generated, whether or not a request for tidal data has been received at the tide station. Since the detector is normally actuated by the first part of the wave motion before the arrival of the destructive part, it can be used to sound an alarm locally for the post or community in which it is located. The first detector was installed at Honolulu for testing and adjustment in the fall of 1947. Subsequent detectors were installed at Hilo, Hawaii; Midway Island; and in the Aleutian Islands.

The acquisition of suitable seismographs and visible recording equipment was another problem which had to be solved.

Photographic techniques were generally used by seismologists for recording earthquakes because they were simple, practical, and precise. Visible recording apparatus in existence in 1946 was generally unsatisfactory and of poor accuracy due to electronic problems. Various instrumental systems were tried, the most promising being that designed by Fred Keller, a New Kensington, Pennsylvania, scientist. In 1947 and 1948, equipment following his design was built and installed at Tucson, Arizona; College, Alaska; and Honolulu, Hawaii. These installations were modified during the summer of 1950 by the addition of a highly stable, cathode-coupled, split-beam amplifier developed by R. M. Wilson and L. R. Burgess of the U.S. Coast and Geodetic Survey. This type of amplifier employs a galvanometer to react directly from a seismometer. A light beam reflected from a mirror on the galvanometer moves accordingly and falls more or less intensely on a photocell. The output of the photocell actuates a pen recorder, and the record is continuously available for inspection. When a strong earthquake is recorded by these instruments, an alarm (audible, visible, or both), located where it is always noticeable, is tripped—thus ensuring the prompt observation of all major earthquakes.

The collaboration of the Armed Forces and the Civil Aeronautics Administration (now the Federal Aviation Agency) was sought to establish a rapid, high-priority communications system. The first meeting relative to the formation of the communication network was held in the Navy Department on July 20, 1948, with representatives from the Office of the Chief of Naval Operations and the U.S. Coast and Geodetic Survey. Since it was obvious that it would be necessary to secure the cooperation of the Army, the Air Force, and the Civil Aeronautics Administration (CAA) to implement a warning system, a second meeting was held on August 12, 1948, to discuss a proposed communication plan for the warning system. Attending this meeting were Maj. J. P. Moran and Capt. R. B. Moody, U.S. Air Force; Lt. K. B. Best, U.S. Army; Capt. D. M. Agnew and Capt. H. T. Orville, U.S. Navy; Mr. G. C. Pearson, Civil Aeronautics Administration; and Mr. W. B. Zerbe and Comdr. E. B. Roberts, U.S. Coast and Geodetic Survey. As the various armed services and the CAA were well aware of the need for a seismic sea wave warning system in the Pacific, the tentative plan was approved. Thus, the operation of the U.S. Coast and Geodetic Survey's Seismic Sea Wave Warning System in the Pacific began (Tsunami Warning System since March 15, 1967).

Initially, the Warning System consisted of the U.S. Coast and Geodetic Survey seismological observatories at College and Sitka, Alaska; Tucson, Arizona; and Honolulu, Hawaii; and the following tide stations: Attu, Adak, Dutch Harbor, and Sitka, Alaska; Palmyra Island; Midway Island; Johnston Atoll; and Hilo and Honolulu, Hawaii. However, the Warning System began to expand almost immediately. By November 15, 1949, when the first edition of the *Communication Plan*

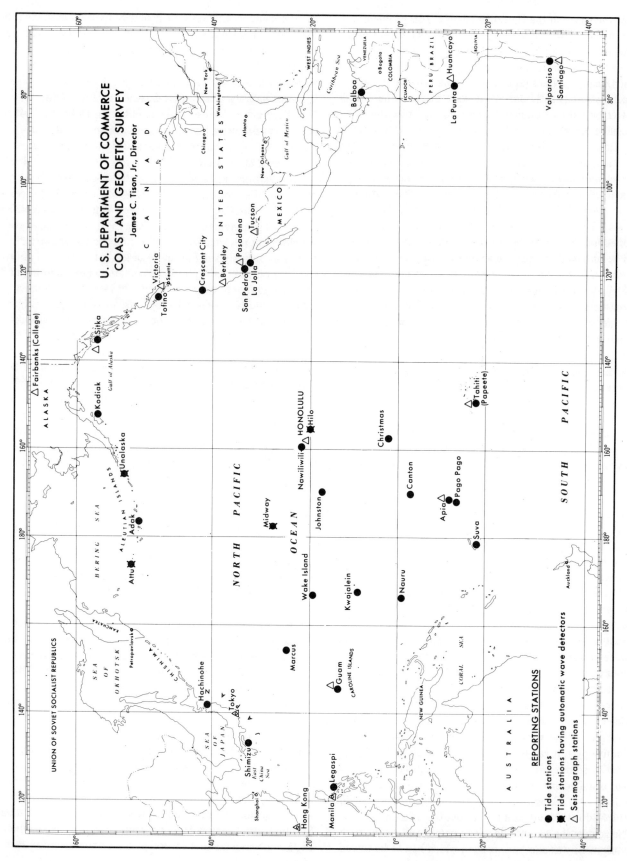

FIGURE 3 Seismic Sea Wave Warning System, showing locations of reporting stations.

44

for the Seismic Sea Wave Warning System was issued by the U.S. Coast and Geodetic Survey, seismological observatories at Berkeley and Pasadena, California, and Tokyo, Japan, and tide stations at Kodiak, Alaska; San Pedro and La Jolla, California; Balboa, Canal Zone; Canton Island; Apra Harbor, Guam; Koror Island; Kwajalein Atoll; Wake Island; and Pago Pago Harbor, American Samoa, had been added. Some seismological and tide stations have joined the SSWWS and others have left it over the years. At the time of the Prince William Sound earthquake, 15 seismological stations and 30 tide stations were participating. The list of actual participants was as follows (see Figure 3 for location):

Seismological Stations

Honolulu, Hawaii (Operational Center of the SSWWS)
Apia, Western Samoa
Berkeley, California
College, Alaska
Guam, Mariana Islands
Hong Kong
Lima, Peru
Manila, Republic of the Philippines
Papeete, Tahiti
Pasadena, California
Santiago, Chile
Sitka, Alaska
Tokyo, Japan
Tucson, Arizona
Victoria, B. C., Canada

Tide Stations

Adak, Alaska
Apia, Western Samoa
Attu, Alaska
Balboa, Canal Zone
Canton Island
Christmas Island
Crescent City, California
Guam, Mariana Islands
Hachinohe, Japan
Hilo, Hawaii
Johnston Atoll
Kodiak, Alaska
Kwajalein Atoll, Marshall Islands
La Jolla, California
La Punta, Callao, Peru
Legaspi, Republic of the Philippines
Marcus Island
Midway Island
Nauru Atoll
Nawiliwili, Hawaii
Pago Pago Harbor, American Samoa
Papeete, Tahiti

San Pedro, California
Shimizu (Tosa), Japan
Sitka, Alaska
Suva, Fiji
Tofino, B. C., Canada
Unalaska, Alaska
Valparaiso, Chile
Wake Island

Originally, the SSWWS was to supply tsunami warning information to the civil authorities of the Hawaiian Islands and to the various military headquarters in the Hawaiian Islands for dissemination to military bases throughout the Pacific and to the U.S. Trust Territory of the Pacific Islands. Beginning on October 14, 1953, the warning information furnished to the civilian authorities of the Hawaiian Islands also was given to the Civil Defense Agencies of California, Oregon, and Washington. In June 1957, the Honolulu Observatory (HO) began supplying estimated arrival times for seismic sea waves on the coasts of these three states. The great destruction caused by the May 1960 Chilean tsunami caused a large number of countries and territories to join the Warning System in order to be warned of future tsunamis. Beginning in November 1960, warnings were supplied to Canada, Alaska, and Tahiti. Additional warning information was supplied to Japan, beginning in February and March 1961. Taiwan started receiving warnings in November 1961, and the Republic of the Philippines and the Fiji Islands in December 1961. During 1962, the HO began supplying warnings to Chile (March), Hong Kong (June), and New Zealand (July). Western Samoa began receiving warnings in January 1963, and American Samoa in November 1963.

The first test of the SSWWS came in connection with the Tonga Islands earthquake of September 8, 1948. Seismograph reports were obtained, and the epicenter of the earthquake was located. A travel time of 6 hours and 35 minutes for the wave from the epicenter to Honolulu was predicted from the travel-time chart, and military and civilian agencies were alerted to stand by for a possible tsunami warning. As wave reports came in, it became evident that the wave would be small, and the alert was cancelled. Later, as predicted, the Honolulu tide-gage record showed that a 6-in. seismic sea wave had arrived.

Several small tsunamis were registered in various parts of the Pacific during the years 1949, 1950, and 1951, but no warnings were issued to the public as a result of the action by the Seismic Sea Wave Warning System. The extreme irregularity of earthquake occurrence was demonstrated in the years 1950 and 1951. In 1950, the Honolulu Observatory requested tide reports in connection with 26 earthquakes, but in 1951, there were only three such occasions.

Regular monthly tests to keep operating personnel familiar with the communication methods and requirements were be-

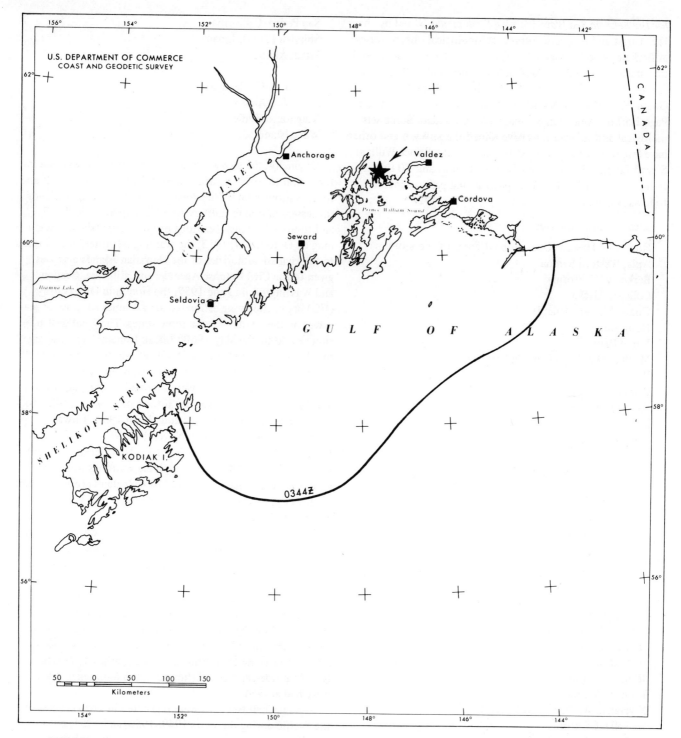

FIGURE 4   Approximate tsunami wave front at 0344Z when the seismograph alarm was tripped at the Honolulu Observatory.

gun early in 1949. These communication tests have been instrumental (1) in eliminating flaws which showed up in the SSWWS from time to time, and (2) in determining the most rapid and reliable communication routes.

The first major tsunami in the Pacific after the formation of the Warning System occurred in connection with the November 4, 1952, Kamchatka earthquake. Advance warnings provided to communities in the path of this tsunami resulted in a reduction of damage and no casualties. The March 9, 1957, Aleutian tsunami, the second major Pacific tsunami following the formation of the SSWWS, caused $3 million damage in the Hawaiian Islands, but once again, due to timely warning, there was no loss of life. The May 1960 Chilean tsunami pointed out a weakness in the Warning System. Although tsunami warnings were broadcast to the residents of the Hawaiian Islands well in advance of the arrival of the wave, 61 people were killed in Hilo, Hawaii, because they failed to heed the warnings.

The 1960 Chilean tsunami stimulated a sizable increase in basic research on tsunamis and also caused a number of countries to request tsunami warnings from the HO. These requests necessitated the addition of tide and seismic stations to secure the coverage necessary to provide timely warnings.

OPERATIONS DURING THE TSUNAMI

Eight minutes after the beginning of the Prince William Sound earthquake, the seismic waves that it generated reached Hawaii and triggered the alarm attached to the seismograph at the U.S. Coast and Geodetic Survey's Honolulu Observatory. The normal working day at the Observatory had ended, and the personnel had returned to their quarters on the Observatory grounds for supper. The food was destined to go uneaten, however, since earthquakes and tsunamis do not respect normal working hours. With the sounding of the alarm, the SSWWS once again began its assigned task of locating major Pacific earthquakes and detecting tsunamis as soon as possible after their generation.

Although the staff at the Honolulu Observatory was not aware of it, the earthquake had destroyed the control tower at Anchorage International Airport, thus destroying a vital communication link through which flowed seismic reports from College and Sitka Observatories and tidal data from Kodiak, Sitka, and Unalaska. Kodiak and Sitka were able to utilize alternate routings, but the receipt of data from both locations was greatly delayed. Locally generated waves had already struck Seward, Valdez, and Whittier, and the wave front of the tsunami was approximately as shown in Figure 4.

Action began immediately at the Honolulu Observatory, after the sounding of the alarm at 0344 (all times are GMT unless otherwise noted). The photographic records were changed, the U.S. Coast and Geodetic Survey Honolulu District Officer and Hawaiian Civil Defense authorities were notified of the earthquake, and requests for seismic readings were sent to the various seismic observatories participating in the SSWWS. At 0419, the first seismic report came in, giving the P reading from the Manila Observatory. By 0452, enough information had been received to permit the HO to locate the earthquake epicenter at latitude 61°N, longitude 147½°W, near Seward, Alaska. An advisory message was prepared and sent to all dissemination agencies in the Warning System at 0502. A second advisory was issued at 0530 by the HO, giving estimated arrival times of the tsunami at the various places in the Pacific for which predictions are made.

After the issuance of the initial advisory, the Honolulu Observatory attempted to obtain tide reports from stations near the epicenter. Requests for data were sent to Unalaska, Kodiak, Adak, Attu, and Sitka, Alaska; Tofino, British Columbia; and Crescent City, California. Unofficial reports that a tsunami was approaching Kodiak had been received. At 0509 and 0510, two messages were received from the Kodiak tide observer, stating that an earthquake had been felt and that the tide gage had been damaged. At 0540, Commander in Chief, Pacific (CINCPAC) reported that Kodiak was evacuated. At 0555, the Kodiak tide observer reported: "EXPERIENCE SEISMIC SEA WAVE AT 280435Z WATER LEVEL 10-12 FEET ABOVE MSL, WILL ADVISE." Since the expected tide stage at that time was not known by the personnel at the HO, they had no information on which to base an estimate of the tsunami amplitude. Consequently, a decision was made to wait for amplification before a warning was issued. A further message arrived from Kodiak at 0611, and, although most of the text had been lost in transmission, enough was received to cause the HO to begin preparing a tsunami warning message for all dissemination agencies in the SSWWS. The complete text of the 0611 message from Kodiak was received by the HO at 0630. It stated that the water rose to 15 to 20 ft above mean sea level in 10 minutes and then fell 15 to 18 ft below mean sea level in 22 minutes.

The Honolulu Observatory issued its tsunami warning bulletin at 0637, after two false starts occasioned by an incoming message and a garble in transmission.

Shortly after 0700, reports began arriving from other tide stations in the Warning System and from various coastal points giving information on wave action and heights. Requests for information were received and answered. At 1100, the Honolulu Observatory issued another bulletin to the dissemination agencies, listing a representative spread of maximum wave heights reported to the HO. The official HO log for the March 28, 1964, earthquake appears on the next six pages.

The accompanying log does not include numerous calls for information from military officials, wire services, and the local press. All were advised of actions taken by the Honolulu Observatory.

Figures 4, 5, and 6 are included to show the approximate location of the initial tsunami wave front when the seismograph alarm was triggered at the HO, when the epicenter was determined, and when the tsunami warning was issued. The arrival time of the tsunami at selected stations is also shown on Figure 6.

EFFECTS OF THE MAJOR TSUNAMI

ALASKA

Outside of the Prince William Sound area and Seward, the only Alaskan area to suffer heavy tsunami damage was the Kodiak Island group. At the Cape St. Elias Lighthouse, a member of the U.S. Coast Guard was drowned by the initial wave, and the other three men stationed there barely escaped.

Seismic Sea Wave Warning Log

HONOLULU OBSERVATORY

G.M.T.	TO	FROM	EVENT OR REMARKS
0344			ALARM SOUNDED. NOTED LARGE EARTHQUAKE. SCALED P PHASE 034354. NO OTHER PHASES READABLE FROM VISIBLE RECORD.
0358			CHANGING PHOTO RECORDS.
0400	HDO	HO	ADVISED DISTRICT OFFICER OF EARTHQUAKE.
0401	MACDONALD	HO	ADVISED DR. GORDON MACDONALD, ACTING TSUNAMI ADVISOR, OF EARTHQUAKE.
0405	BUTCHART	HO	ADVISED COL. BUTCHART, VICE DIRECTOR C.D., OF EARTHQUAKE.
0407	HO	CINCPAC	CALLED FOR INFORMATION.
0413	COLLEGE, SITKA, PASADENA, TUCSON, BERKELEY	HO	REQUESTED IMMEDIATE READINGS EARTHQUAKE OF 0336Z.
0416	JMA TOKYO	HO	REQUESTED IMMEDIATE READINGS EARTHQUAKE OF 0336Z.
0418	GUAM OBS.	HO	REQUESTED IMMEDIATE READINGS EARTHQUAKE OF 0336Z.
0419	HO	MANILA	P 034813.
0423	HO	HONG KONG	P 034334 S 4755.
0425	HO	KUNIA	CALLED FOR INFORMATION.
0430	HO	PTO	TIDES OFFICER CALLED FOR INFORMATION.
0431	HO	GUAM	EP 034706.
0432	HO	FLEET WEA CENTRAL	REPORTED EARTHQUAKE TREMORS IN KODIAK FROM 0332Z TO 0340Z. KODIAK TIDE GAGE DAMAGED.
0433	HO	JMA	MATSUSHIRO P 034516. SAPPORO P 034428 S 5120. SENDAI P 034459. REQUEST YOUR READINGS.
0436	HO	FAA	REPORTED COMMUNICATION CABLES TO ALASKA BROKEN.
0438	HO	BERKELEY	P 034205.
0448	HO	TUCSON	IP 034328 ES 4932.
0449	JMA	HO	HON IP 034554.1. PRELIMINARY MAGNITUDE APPROX 8.
0452			DETERMINED EPICENTER AT 61 N, 147½ W, H = 033610. NEAR SEWARD, ALASKA, MAGNITUDE 8.
0454	HO	FAA	REPORTED INTERNATIONAL TOWER AT ANCHORAGE DEMOLISHED.
0459	HO	PASADENA	IP 034350Z.
0501	HO	COMBARPAC	TIDAL WAVE REPORTED HEADING FOR KODIAK.
0502	NAVCOMMSTA HONO AND FAA HONO FOR AIG 158	HO	ISSUED BULLETIN NO. 1 AS FOLLOWS: *THIS IS A TIDAL WAVE (SEISMIC SEA WAVE) ADVISORY. A SEVERE EARTHQUAKE HAS OCCURRED AT LAT 61 N LONG 147.5 W VICINITY OF SEWARD, ALASKA AT 0336Z 28 MARCH. IT IS NOT KNOWN REPEAT NOT KNOWN AT THIS TIME THAT A SEA WAVE HAS BEEN GENERATED. YOU WILL BE KEPT INFORMED AS FURTHER INFORMATION BECOMES AVAILABLE. IF A WAVE HAS BEEN GENERATED ITS ETA FOR THE HAWAIIAN ISLANDS (HONOLULU) IS 0900Z 28 MARCH.*
0508	CINCPAC	HO	ISSUED BULLETIN NO. 1.
0509	HONO POLICE	HO	ISSUED BULLETIN NO. 1.
0509	HO	KODIAK T.O.	TIDE GAGE DAMAGED BY FIRST TREMOR 280332Z. NO TRACE DUE DAMAGE. REPAIRS WILL BE COMPLETED 280800Z.

Seismic Sea Wave Warning Log—Continued

HONOLULU OBSERVATORY

G.M.T.	TO	FROM	EVENT OR REMARKS
0510	HO	KODIAK T.O.	MODERATE EARTHQUAKE NEAR KODIAK 280332Z TO 280340Z. WILL ADVISE STAFF READINGS. TREMORS CONTINUING.
0511	W.B. DUTY FORECASTER	HO	ISSUED BULLETIN NO. 1.
0512	MACDONALD	HO	ISSUED BULLETIN NO. 1.
0515	KUNIA	HO	ISSUED BULLETIN NO. 1.
0517	HDO	HO	ISSUED BULLETIN NO. 1.
0530	NAVCOMMSTA HONO AND FAA HONO FOR AIG 158	HO	ISSUED BULLETIN NO. 2 AS FOLLOWS: *THIS IS A TIDAL WAVE (SEISMIC SEA WAVE) INFORMATION BULLETIN. DAMAGE TO COMMUNICATIONS TO ALASKA MAKES IT IMPOSSIBLE TO CONTACT TIDE OBSERVERS. IF A WAVE HAS BEEN GENERATED THE ETA'S ARE: ATTU 0745Z, ADAK 0700Z, DUTCH HARBOR 0630Z, KODIAK 0530Z, SAMOA 1430Z, CANTON 1530Z, JOHNSTON 1100Z, MIDWAY 0845Z, WAKE 0930Z, KWAJALEIN 1430Z, GUAM 1315Z, TOKYO 1030Z, SITKA 0530Z, SAN PEDRO 0930Z, LA JOLLA 1000Z, BALBOA 2330Z, ACAPULCO 1300Z, CHRISTMAS 1230Z, CRESCENT CITY 0800Z, LEGASPI 1430Z, NEAH BAY 0730Z, SAN FRANCISCO 0915Z, TAHITI 1430Z, TOFINO B.C. 0730Z, VALPARAISO 2200Z, HONOLULU 9000Z, HUALEIN TAIWAN 1430Z, LA PUNTA 1900Z, MARCUS 1100Z, HONG KONG 1530Z, SHIMIZU 1130Z, HACHINOHE 1000Z. ALL TIMES ARE FOR 28 MARCH.*
0530	HO	KH6ESL	SHORT WAVE CONTACT WITH YAKATAGA, ALASKA.
0531	HO	HONOLULU	CHECKED OPERATION OF HONOLULU GAGE.
0539	UNALASKA T.O.	HO	INSPECT TIDE RECORDS BETWEEN 0600Z AND 0700Z. REPORT ANY UNUSUAL ACTIVITY IMMEDIATELY OR REPLY NEGATIVE AT 0700Z. ACK. RECEIPT OF THIS MSG. IMMED.
0540	HO	CINCPAC	REPORTED EVACUATION OF KODIAK.
0541	KODIAK T.O.	HO	INSPECT TIDE RECORDS BETWEEN 0530Z AND 0630Z. REPORT ANY UNUSUAL ACTIVITY IMMEDIATELY OR REPLY NEGATIVE AT 063OZ. ACK. RECEIPT OF THIS MSG. IMMED.
0543	ADAK T.O.	HO	INSPECT TIDE RECORDS BETWEEN 0630Z AND 0730Z. REPORT ANY UNUSUAL ACTIVITY IMMEDIATELY OR REPLY NEGATIVE AT 0730Z. ACK. RECEIPT OF THIS MSG. IMMED.
0544	ATTU T.O.	HO	INSPECT TIDE RECORDS BETWEEN 0715Z AND 0815Z. REPORT ANY UNUSUAL ACTIVITY IMMEDIATELY OR REPLY NEGATIVE AT 0815Z. ACK. RECEIPT OF THIS MSG. IMMED.
0548	HO	SITKA OBS.	IP 033759Z. STRONG LOCAL FELT AT SITKA. MADE SOME INSTRUMENTS INOPERATIVE.
0550	SITKA OBS.	HO	INSPECT TIDE RECORDS BETWEEN 0500Z AND 0600Z. REPORT ANY UNUSUAL ACTIVITY IMMEDIATELY OR REPLY NEGATIVE AT 0600Z. ACK. RECEIPT OF THIS MSG. IMMED.
0552	CRESCENT CITY T.O.	HO	INSPECT TIDE RECORDS BETWEEN 0730Z AND 0830Z. REPORT ANY UNUSUAL ACTIVITY IMMEDIATELY OR REPLY NEGATIVE AT 0830Z. ACK. RECEIPT OF THIS MSG. IMMED.
0555	HO	KODIAK T.O.	EXPERIENCE SEISMIC SEA WAVE AT 280435Z. WATER LEVEL 10-12 FT. ABOVE MSL. WILL ADVISE.
0555	TOFINO T.O.	HO	INSPECT TIDE RECORDS BETWEEN 0700Z AND 0800Z. REPORT ANY UNUSUAL ACTIVITY IMMEDIATELY OR REPLY NEGATIVE AT 0800Z. ACK. RECEIPT OF THIS MSG. IMMED.

Seismic Sea Wave Warning Log—Continued

HONOLULU OBSERVATORY

G.M.T.	TO	FROM	EVENT OR REMARKS
0558	CD	HO	ADVISED OF TIDAL ACTIVITY AT KODIAK.
0601	HO	WAKE	TIDAL WAVE (SEISMIC SEA WAVE) ADVISORY 280502Z RECEIVED 280530Z.
0602	HO	TAHITI	IP 034814.5.
0606	HO	WAKE	YOUR 280530Z RECEIVED 280551Z.
0610	HO	NPM	REQUEST RERUN OF BULLETIN NO. 2 TO AIG 158.
0611	HO	KODIAK T.O.	WATER LEVEL STARTED RISING AT 280435. ROSE 15.
0615	HO	FAA	REPORTED COMMUNICATIONS RESUMED WITH ANCHORAGE.
0618	CD	HO	ADVISED OF LATEST ACTIVITY AT KODIAK.
0620	AIG 158	HO	RERUN OF BULLETIN NO. 2.
0625	HO	MARINE PAPEETE	BULLETIN NO. 2 RECEIVED 280618Z.
0625	HO	AP	REPORTED 6 DEAD AT ANCHORAGE.
0630	HO	KODIAK T.O.	WATER LEVEL STARTED RISING AT 280435Z. ROSE 15-20 FT. ABOVE MSL BY 280445Z. EBB TIDE STARTED 280445Z. WATER LEVEL 15-18 FT. BELOW MSL AT 280507Z.
0635	HO	KODIAK	WATER LEVEL STARTED RISING AT 280435Z. ROSE 15.
0637	NAVCOMMSTA HONO AND FAA HONO FOR AIG 158	HO	ISSUED BULLETIN NO. 3 AS FOLLOWS: *THIS IS A TIDAL WAVE (SEISMIC SEA WAVE) WARNING. A SEVERE EARTHQUAKE HAS OCCURRED AT LAT 61 N LONG 147.5 W VICINITY OF SEWARD, ALASKA AT 0336Z 28 MAR. A SEA WAVE HAS BEEN GENERATED WHICH IS SPREADING OVER THE PACIFIC OCEAN. THE ETA OF THE FIRST WAVE AT OAHU IS 0900Z 28 MAR. THE INTENSITY CANNOT REPEAT CANNOT BE PREDICTED. HOWEVER THIS WAVE COULD CAUSE GREAT DAMAGE IN THE HAWAIIAN ISLANDS AND ELSEWHERE IN THE PACIFIC AREA. THE DANGER MAY LAST FOR SEVERAL HOURS. OTHER ETA INFORMATION IS AS FOLLOWS:* [SAME ETA'S AS THOSE LISTED IN ADVISORY BULLETIN ISSUED AT 0530].
0638	CINCPAC	HO	ISSUED BULLETIN NO. 3.
0638	KUNIA DUTY FORECASTER	HO	ISSUED BULLETIN NO. 3.
0640	CD	HO	ISSUED BULLETIN NO. 3.
0644	HAWSEAFRON	HO	ISSUED BULLETIN NO. 3.
0645	W.B. DUTY FORECASTER	HO	ISSUED BULLETIN NO. 3.
0646	HO	CANTON T.O.	YOUR 280502Z RECVD. STAFF READING NEGATIVE DISTURBANCE.
0646	HO	SITKA OBS.	IP 033759Z. STRONG LOCAL FELT. HAVE SOME INSTRUMENTS INOPERATIVE. STANDING BY TIDE GAGE.
0648	HDO	HO	ISSUED BULLETIN NO. 3.
0651	HO	ADAK T.O.	YOUR 280543Z RECVD. 280617Z.
0656	BALBOA T.O.	HO	CORRECT ETA 2000Z, REPEAT 2000Z.
0700	HO	FIJI POLICE SUVA	280530Z RECVD. BY FIJI POLICE SUVA AT 280638Z.
0701	HO	UNALASKA	5.2 AT 1929. 4.6 AT 1933.
0704	HO	WAKE	YOUR 280637Z RECVD. 280655Z.

Seismic Sea Wave Warning Log—Continued

HONOLULU OBSERVATORY

G.M.T.	TO	FROM	EVENT OR REMARKS
0706	HO	ADAK T.O.	YOUR 280544Z RECVD. 280615Z.
0708	HO	KODIAK	SEA WAVES AT 0435Z 32 FT. AT 0540Z 35 FT. AT 0630Z 30 FT. SEAS DIMINISHING WATER RECEDING. EXPECT SIX MORE WAVES. NO EMERGENCY EXISTS.
0710	CD	HO	INFORMED OF LATEST TSUNAMI INFORMATION.
0711	HO	SITKA	UNUSUAL TIDAL ACTIVITY BEGAN 0510Z. FLUCTUATIONS LARGE. STILL OCCURRING.
0715	CD	HO	GAVE FOLLOWING ETA'S FOR HAWAIIAN ISLANDS: KAUAI 2215, OAHU 2300, MAUI 2300, HAWAII 2315, HST.
0725	HO	MARINE PAPEETE	YOUR BULLETIN NO. 3 RECVD. 280716Z.
0725	HO	KWAJALEIN	REQ. VERIFY ETA KWAJ AT 1430Z.
0730	HO	HVO	IP 28034403.6. REMAINING DATA OBSCURED.
0730	KWAJALEIN T.O.	HO	REVISED ETA 1200Z, REPEAT 1200Z.
0732	HO	CRESCENT CITY T.O.	NO DISTURBANCE AT 280705. WILL STAND BY.
0738	RAF	HO	ADVISED ETA FOR CHRISTMAS ISLAND.
0739	CD	HO	ADVISED OF LATEST INFORMATION.
0750	HO	FIJI POLICE SUVA	REF. 280637 RECVD. BY FIJI POLICE SUVA AT 280740Z.
0810	HO	KODIAK	HIGH WATER LEVELS REACHED 280435Z ABT 15 FT. ABV MSL. 280540Z HIGH WATER ABT 18 FT. ABV MSL. 280630Z ABT 16 FT. ABV MSL. 280644Z HIGH WATER ABT 6 FT. ABV MSL. AMPLITUDE RAPIDLY DECREASING. TIDE GAGE INOPERATIVE SINCE 280332Z. FURTHER COMMUNICATIONS PENDING RESTORATION MAJOR COMMUNICATION LINKS. 280715Z WAVE ACTION ONLY SLIGHT. APPEARS TO BE DAMPED OUT COMPLETELY.
0816	HO	TOFINO	YOUR 280555Z RECVD. 280709Z.
0822	HO	COAST GUARD	FOLLOWING INFORMATION ON WAVE HEIGHTS REPORTED BY COAST GUARD. BULL HARBOR, CANADA 12 FT. AT 0722Z; TOFINO 8 FT. AT 0710Z; CORDOVA 30 FT.; HUMBOLDT BAY HIGH NOW.
0825	HO	CG	NAWILIWILI GAGE NORMAL AT 0821Z.
0826	HO	TOFINO	TOFINO OPERATION FIRST SURGE 0710Z REACHED PEAK OF 8 FT.
0830	CD	HO	REPORTED LATEST WAVE ACTIVITY.
0837	HO	CD	EXCHANGE OF INFORMATION.
0842	HO	SITKA	WATER ROLLED 16 FT. IN 30 MIN. JUST PRIOR TO 0700Z. FELL 9 FT. 0700/0745 NOW RISING FAST. WILL REPORT FURTHER.
0848	HO	ATTU	STAFF READING 2.2 AND 1.6. NEGATIVE UNUSUAL DISTURB.
0851	HO	ADAK	YOUR 280543Z RECVD. 280615Z. STAFF READING 4.8 NEGATIVE DISTURBANCE.
0851	HO	CG	NAWILIWILI GAGE RECORDED 1 FT. WAVE AT 0845Z.
0905	HO	JMA	REQUEST YOUR DATA OF TSUNAMI OBSERVATIONS. ESPECIALLY AT HAWAII IS. AND ALEUTIAN IS.
0911	HO	CG	3 FT. WAVE REPORTED AT FRENCH FRIGATE SHOALS.
0915	HO	CD	FOLLOWING WAVE HEIGHTS REPORTED IN HAWAIIAN IS. KAHULUI, MAUI 1 FT. OVER BRIDGE, ¼ MI. INLAND; HILO 6 FT. AT 1107Z; WAIALUA 4 FT.; LANIKAI 5 FT.

Seismic Sea Wave Warning Log—Continued

G.M.T.	TO	FROM	EVENT OR REMARKS
0917	HO	TAIPEI	TAP P 034718Z S 5630 TAU P 034723Z HWA P 034728Z S 5628 HEN P 034737Z.
0923	JMA	HO	WAVE HEIGHTS REPORTED BY VARIOUS MEDIA: KODIAK 30 FT., CORDOVA 30 FT., TOFINO 8 FT., CRESCENT CITY 12 FT., LOCAL WAVE HEIGHTS JUST BEGINNING TO BE RECORDED AT 28/0920Z. ACCURATE REPORTS FOR HAWAII WILL FOLLOW WHEN KNOWN.
0928	HO	KODIAK	QUAKE HAS GENERATED SEA WAVES AT IRREGULAR INTERVALS FROM 30 TO 35 FT.
0934	HO	CG	LATEST NAWILIWILI WAVE HEIGHTS.
0942	HO	CD	SECOND WAVE AT HILO 7¼ FT. SIXTH WAVE AT KAUAI 2½ FT.
0948	HO	CG	NAWILIWILI NOW EXPERIENCING DIMINISHING RECESSIONS AND WAVE ACTION. MAX. WAVE HEIGHT 3 FT.
0953	HO	CG	NO WAVE OBSERVED AT KURE ISLAND.
1002	HO	HDO	NAWILIWILI 1½ FT. AT 0938Z.
1002	HO	HDO	1½ FT. WAVE REPORTED AT MIDWAY.
1009	HO	CD	THIRD WAVE AT HILO 1½ FT. FOURTH WAVE AT 1008Z 2 FT FOLLOWED BY NORMAL RECESSION.
1014	HO	CIVIL DEFENSE WELLINGTON	REQUIRE DETAILS OF WAVE HEIGHTS HONOLULU AND ELSEWHERE IF AVAILABLE.
1020	HO	HONOLULU T.O.	FIRST WAVE ACTIVITY AT 0855Z. 1½ FT.
1023	HO	KWAJALEIN	REQ. FURTHER INFO. TIDAL WAVE EFFECTS KWAJ.
1026	HO	CG	LATEST WAVE HEIGHTS NAWILIWILI.
1029	HO	SITKA	EXPECTED TIDE STAGE BETWEEN 0925 AND 0955. UNUSUAL TIDE ACTIVITIES CONTINUE.
1033	HO	HAWSEAFRON	MIDWAY EXPECTS 1 FT. AT 0847. SINCE 0900Z, HAVE STEADY 0.2 FT. TO 0.3 FT. SEICHE.
1040	HO	CD	4 FT. RISE AT HILO AT 1017. 7TH WAVE 3 FT. AT 1030.
1049	HO	CG	LATEST WAVE HEIGHTS AT NAWILIWILI.
1050	HO	WAKE	AT 1033Z RISE OF 0.8 [FT.] NOTED.
1100	HO	CD	EIGHTH WAVE AT HILO 2.5 FT. RECOMMENDED 1100Z FOR ALL CLEAR HAWAII.
1100	NAVCOMMSTA HONO AND FAA	HO	ISSUED BULLETIN NO. 4 AS FOLLOWS: *THIS IS A TIDAL WAVE (SEISMIC SEA WAVE) INFORMATION BULLETIN. THE LARGER WAVES HAVE APPARENTLY PASSED HAWAII. AN ALL CLEAR STATUS FOR HAWAII CAN BE ASSUMED AT 1100Z. ALL PARTICIPANTS IN THE SSWWS SHOULD ASSUME THE ALL CLEAR STATUS 2 HOURS AFTER THEIR PARTICULAR ETA UNLESS LOCAL CONDITIONS WARRANT THE CONTINUANCE OF THE ALERT STATUS. MAXIMUM WAVE HEIGHTS REPORTED BY VARIOUS MEDIA ARE: OAHU 8 FT., HAWAII 6 FT., KODIAK 30 FT., MIDWAY 1.5 FT., KAUAI 3 FT., CRESCENT CITY 12 FT., CORDOVA 30 FT., TOFINO 8 FT.*
1108	HONO FOR AIG 158 HO	TOFINO	0850Z DIAGRAM READ 16 FT. RUNOUT STARTED AT THIS POINT. THIS IS THE SECOND WAVE.
1111	HO	HONOLULU T.O.	FIFTH WAVE 2½ FT. PEAK TO PEAK PERIODS OF ½ HOUR.
1122	HO	WAKE	YOUR 281100Z RECVD. 281112Z.
1123	HO	MARINE PAPEETE	RECVD. YOUR BULLETIN NO. 4. 281117Z.

Seismic Sea Wave Warning Log—Continued

G.M.T.	TO	FROM	EVENT OR REMARKS
1124	HO	RAF	REQUESTED INFO. ON CHRISTMAS ISLAND.
1126	HO	CG	LATEST WAVE HEIGHTS NAWILIWILI.
1134	HO	CINCPAC	REQUEST INFO. ON ALL CLEAR FOR ISLAND OF HAWAII.
1203	HO	ADAK	YOUR 280544Z RECVD. 280615Z. STAFF READING 4.2. SLIGHT DISTURBANCES.
1225	HO	JMA	TSUNAMI BEGAN AT 1020Z EASTERN COAST OF HOKKAIDO, AT 1038Z PACIFIC COAST OF NE HONSHU, ALL INITIAL MOTIONS ARE PUSH.
1226	HO	KWAJALEIN	NO UNUSUAL DISTURBANCES NOTED.
1230	HO	CINCPAC	AT SAN DIEGO 5 FT. RECESSION FOR 1 HOUR. THEN RETURN TO NORMAL. 10 FT. WAVE AND MINOR DAMAGE AT CATALINA ISLAND.
1252	HO	KWAJALEIN	SMALL DISTURBANCES TO TIDE RECORD BEGAN ABOUT 281230Z. WATER FELL 0.3 FT. WILL REPORT FURTHER.
1258	HO	TOFINO	FIRST WAVE AT 0710 DIAGRAM 15 FT. AT PEAK, SECOND WAVE AT 0850 DIAGRAM 16 FT. AT PEAK, THIRD WAVE PEAK AT 0955. NO READING. TIDE GAGE DAMAGED.
1306	HO	HONG KONG	REQ. EXPECTED INTENSITY AND REVISED ETA HONG KONG.
1306	HO	KWAJALEIN	WATER FELL 0.5. BEGAN RISE AT 281245Z.
1315	HONG KONG	HO	HO CANNOT PREDICT THE INTENSITY OF A TIDAL WAVE (SEISMIC SEA WAVE). ETA HONG KONG IS 28/1530Z BASED ON INFORMATION AVAILABLE.
1425	HO	NAVSTA GUAM	AT 291315Z NEGATIVE DISTURBANCES.
1428	HO	KWAJALEIN	RISE OF 1.3 BETWEEN 281345Z AND 281357Z. FELL 0.3 AT 281400Z. NOW RISING.
1613	HO	CIVIL DEFENSE WELLINGTON	CAN YOU ADVISE WAVE HEIGHT AT CANTON ISLAND.
1622	CIVIL DEF. WELLINGTON	HO	NO WAVE HEIGHT REPORT RECEIVED FROM CANTON ISLAND AS OF 1620Z. HO WILL SEND INFO. IF RECEIVED.
1743	HO	VALPARAISO	PLS. INFORM AS SOON AS POSSIBLE INTENSITY OF SEA WAVE AT HAWAIIAN IS.
1813	VALPARAISO	HO	SENT BULLETIN NO. 4.
1841	HO	VALPARAISO	YOUR MESSAGE 28/0600Z RECVD. 28/1240Z.
1923	HO	CHRISTMAS ISLAND	UNUSUAL DISTURBANCES OCCURRED 281130. RAISED TENTH OF A FOOT AND FELL THE SAME.
1927	HO	ADAK T.O.	TIDE IS 5 FT. NORMAL. ADAK IS NORMAL. SHEMYA IS NORMAL.
1932	HO	SAMOA	TIDAL ACTION COMMENCED AT 1400Z WITH SLIGHT RISE AND FALL. ROSE 6 IN. AT 1415Z FOR A PERIOD OF 6 MIN. FALL OF LESS THAN 6 IN. OVER A PERIOD OF 5 MIN. AT 1447Z.
2050	HO	CANTON	NO TIDAL WAVE ACTION OBSERVED AT CANTON. OBSERVATIONS STILL BEING TAKEN.
2143	HO	LA PUNTA	WAVE BEGAN 1910 TIDE RECORD SHOWS WATER ROSE 3 FT. IN 7 MIN. AND FELL 3.4 FT. IN 9 MIN. 2ND WAVE SAME HEIGHT AND SAME PERIOD. 3RD WAVE ROSE 3.6 FT. AND FELL 5 FT. IN 17 MIN.
2145	HO	SUVA T.O.	TIDE RECORD SHOWS WATER ROSE 0.6 FT. AND FELL 0.4 FT. IN 10 MIN. AT FOLLOWING TIMES: 281910Z, 281945Z, 282020Z STILL IRREGULAR.

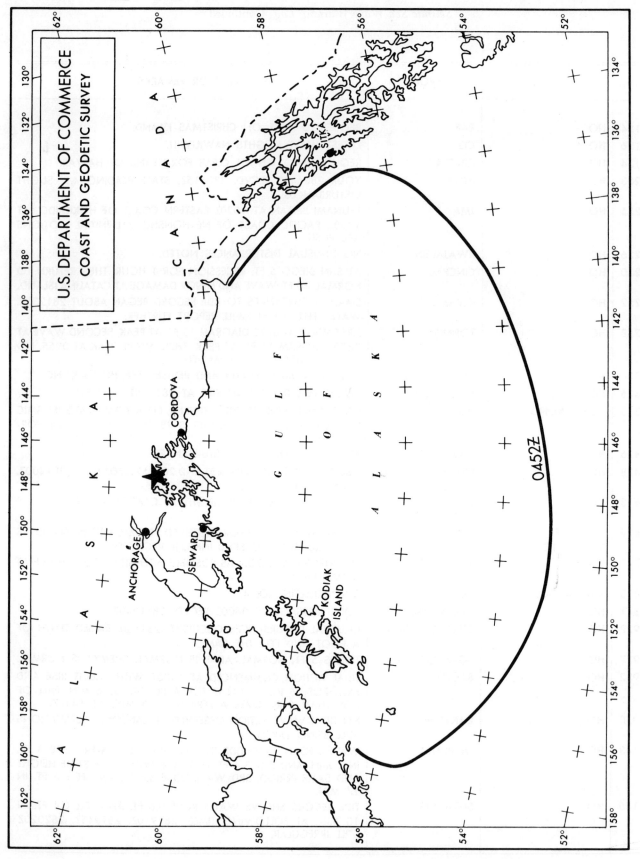

FIGURE 5 Approximate tsunami wave front at 0452Z when the epicenter was determined.

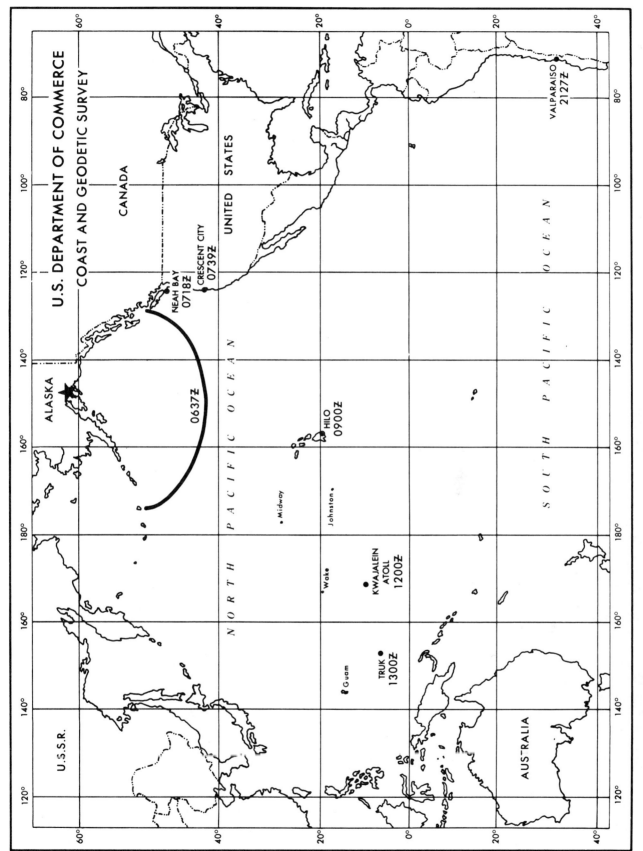

FIGURE 6 Approximate tsunami wave front at 0637Z when the warning message was issued. The arrival times of the tsunami at selected stations are indicated.

55

Beyond Cape St. Elias, damage in Alaska was limited to a dock which collapsed at Sitka, and there were minor disruptions of floats and log rafts at logging camps in the Ketchikan area. The nearest tide gage to the epicenter which survived the tsunami was at Yakutat. It recorded a maximum rise of 7.6 ft beginning at 1007, near the time of the predicted high tide. The Sitka tide gage recorded a 14.3-ft rise on the third wave of the tsunami beginning at 0624.

The Alaska Peninsula and the Aleutian Islands were shielded by the Kodiak Island group from the direct action of the tsunami. In Shelikof Strait, as in Cook Inlet, maximum amplitudes were on the order of 5 ft. Maximum amplitude in the Aleutian Islands, as recorded on tide gages, was under 3 ft.

The city of Kodiak and Kodiak Naval Station were the only places in Alaska that received advance warning of the tsunami. The U.S. Fleet Weather Central at Kodiak Naval Station, which participates in the Seismic Sea Wave Warning System by maintaining a tide station and by serving as a dissemination agency, provided this local warning.

The earthquake, strongly felt at the Fleet Weather Central, put out of commission the tide gage and all available communication circuits (except telephone) and caused damage to the hangars, aprons, and ramps at the Naval Station. The damage was caused mainly by differential settlement of pile- and fill-supported structures.

At 0410, after a report of a 30-ft tsunami was received from Cape Chiniak, the Commanding Officer of the Fleet Weather Central, failing to reach the Naval Station Officer of the Day, called the Armed Forces Radio Station and had a warning broadcast. This broadcast resulted in an extremely smooth, orderly, prompt, and complete evacuation of the Naval Station and Federal Aviation Agency personnel on Woody Island. Reports indicate that the evacuation of the city of Kodiak was reasonably prompt, but it was not as complete or as well carried out. This difference was undoubtedly due to the better discipline of the military and government personnel and their dependents and to the emergency procedures that had been prepared in advance for the Naval Station.

About 10 minutes after the warning was issued, the tsunami, similar in appearance to a swiftly rising flood, arrived at Fleet Weather Central. By 0435, the first wave had crested at 22 ft above the tide staff zero, giving a rise of about 16 ft on the first wave. The highest crest in the tsunami reached about 30 ft above the tide staff zero, and the maximum amplitude (crest to trough) was about 35 ft.

Under extreme handicap, the personnel at Fleet Weather Central continued to supply information on the tsunami to the Honolulu Observatory. With all radio circuits in the tower building inoperative, a telephone message was passed to a remote Navy radio station for relay via Naval Communication Station, San Francisco, giving information on the first crest. At 0447, all electric power in the tower was lost, due to

flooding of the main power station. Auxiliary power was supplied at 0503, and an additional message was sent to the HO, giving more detail on the first wave. Since there was doubt about the delivery of the first two messages, a third message was sent over Coast Guard circuits at 0726, shortly after the Coast Guard Radio Station NOJ, located in the tower building, returned to operation and contacted Ketchikan. This message gave details on crest heights and arrival times.

The Kodiak Naval Station suffered heavy damage from the tsunami and minor damage from the earthquake. Estimates of approximately $10 million tsunami damage by Public Works, Kodiak Naval Station (Tudor, 1964), include complete destruction of the cargo dock and heavy damage to roads and bridges, the central power plant and the Holiday Beach generator, the microwave installation, the runway ends and shoulders, the marginal pier, the public works maintenance shop, the hobby shop, and the bowling alley. Because of the advance warning, there were no fatalities or serious injuries among military personnel at the Naval Station.

The tsunami caused 19 deaths in and near the city of Kodiak. These included 8 dead at Kodiak, 3 at Kaguyak, 6 at Kalsin Bay, 1 at Old Harbor, and 1 at Spruce Cape. (In an unpublished letter, Don Lowell, Director of the Alaska Disaster Office, reported the unexplained loss of 3 at Spruce Cape.) The low-lying areas of the Kodiak waterfront suffered extreme damage. All float docks in the area that were protected by breakwaters were broken up and cast ashore or were washed away. All wharves and piers on the waterfront were destroyed, except for the City Dock. A preliminary Civil Defense survey listed 58 structures in a five-block section of the business district as demolished or so badly damaged as to make demolition necessary. Seven more structures in the same five-block area were so badly damaged as to make their salvage questionable, and an additional 23 were damaged. Overall, Civil Defense estimated damage to Kodiak at $31,279,000 (Tudor, 1964). This includes damage of $2,165,000 to harbor facilities; $19,346,000 to business and industry; $5,400,000 to other public property; $2,440,000 to the fishing fleet; and $1,928,000 to dwellings. Comdr. Alfred Stroh, Civil Engineer Corps, U.S. Navy, reported 158 dwellings destroyed and 20 severely damaged (Stroh, 1964). The Alaska Department of Public Health (1964) lists 71 business firms that were heavily damaged or destroyed.

The city of Kodiak was fortunate in that it had approximately 30 minutes of warning before the arrival of the first crest. The first wave was a gentle flood followed by a gradual ebb. The second wave advanced as a cresting 30-ft wall that thundered through the channel and pushed 50- to 100-ton boats over the breakwater as far as three blocks into the city.

Small villages in the area also suffered heavily. The nine houses and the Russian Orthodox Church that comprised Kaguyak were swept away. All of the 35 homes in Old Harbor were floated from their foundations; however, six or seven probably were salvageable. The old school and the new school suffered minor damage, and the church was undamaged. Ouzinkie had five houses, a grocery store, and a cannery destroyed. At Afognak, four homes, the community hall, and a grocery were washed away and destroyed. Several other homes moved on their foundations, and most of the 26 autos in the town sustained water damage.

CANADA

Since the Canadian dissemination agency had withdrawn from the Seismic Sea Wave Warning System in July 1963, no official warning of the tsunami was provided to Canada. The earthquake, however, was felt in the Yukon Territory and northern British Columbia.

The tsunami struck the Canadian coast near the time of high tide (Wigen and White, 1964). It was higher than any previously recorded in British Columbia. The earliest recorded arrival was 0533 at Tasu Sound. Damage was extensive and widespread, although the majority of the damage occurred at the twin cities of Alberni and Port Alberni. The highest wave reported in Canada was at Shields Bay, on the west coast of Graham Island. This crest was reported to be 17 ft above spring high water (32 ft above tidal datum), and the wave severely damaged a logging camp.

The twin cities of Alberni and Port Alberni are about 35 mi from the open ocean, near the head of the long and narrow Alberni Inlet. The tsunami period apparently matched the natural frequency of the inlet, causing amplification of the waves. According to the Port Alberni tide gage, the first wave arrived shortly before 0800 and swept into the towns, equaling the worst flooding conditions ever recorded there. The second crest was the highest of the series. It reached 20.9 ft above tidal datum, as determined from water marks on buildings. The period from the first to the second crest was approximately 97 minutes. The initial wave served to alert the inhabitants of the most heavily damaged areas of Alberni and Port Alberni. Many evacuated their houses, and almost all had dressed and were alert when the second wave arrived. As a consequence, there were no fatalities or serious injuries. Fifty-eight properties, including individual homes, stores, and multiple auto courts, were completely destroyed. In addition, 320 dwellings suffered damage ranging from minor to severe; 694 persons were driven from their homes until repairs or replacements could be made.

Damage near Alberni was centered on the low-lying areas along the north bank of the Somass River. Buildings not bolted to their foundations were swept inland as far as 1,000 ft. Log booms and boats in the inlet were carried high on shore, causing heavy damage. Total damage in the Alberni–Port Alberni area, excluding damage to heavy industry and private autos, was about $5 million. The forest industries

complex of MacMillan, Bloedel, and Powell River, Ltd., suffered much damage, but the amount was not made public.

An attempt to compute the natural period of Alberni Inlet was made, by using the formula for a rectangular harbor open at one end,

$$T = 4l/\sqrt{gh},$$

where l is the length of the harbor, h the depth, and g the gravitational constant. In using this formula, the effects of the meandering path of the channel, the numerous constrictions in the channel, and the effects of friction were all neglected. The natural period of Alberni Inlet from Chup Point was 70 minutes, based on an average depth of 91 fathoms and a path length of 23 mi. The natural period of Trevor Channel and Alberni Inlet was computed as 110 minutes, based on an average depth of 82 fathoms and a path of 34 mi. It is probable that the 90- to 100-minute period, as recorded on the Port Alberni tide record, is the natural period of the 23-mi path.

Other locations also suffered major damage. The village of Hot Springs Cove had 16 of its 18 houses destroyed. At Zeballos, 30 homes were knocked from their foundations, and considerable damage to personal property was caused by silt and salt water. In the small logging community of Amai, where the tsunami caused considerable damage to 10 buildings, 37 people were made homeless. The tsunami also destroyed the radio telephone communication system at Amai.

WASHINGTON

Some damage was done on Lake Union, Seattle, Washington, by seiching caused by the earthquake vibration. The disturbance caused minor damage to the gangway of the USC&GS ship *Patton* and snapped a mooring line on the USC&GS ship *Lester Jones*. Minor damage was also caused to several pleasure craft, houseboats, and floats which broke their moorings.

Of the four bulletins issued by the Honolulu Observatory during the tsunami, three were received by the Washington State Department of Civil Defense. At 0642, the second advisory was received, giving an estimated arrival time of 0730 for Neah Bay. The warning was received at approximately 0713. By 0718, all coastal counties had been advised that the tsunami warning had been received. The final advisory was received by the Washington Civil Defense about 1130, at which time the coastal counties were advised that the emergency had ended. Damage in the State of Washington included the destruction of one small bridge at Copalis and one at Iron Springs, near Pacific Beach. A mile of ocean shore bulkhead was taken out at Moclips. Minor damage was reported to houses at Moclips and Pacific Beach; four mobile campers were overturned, and a sheriff's car was lost in the Ocean Shores and Pacific Beach area (R. R. Robinson, April

10, 1964, and June 20, 1966, personal communication). The tsunami struck the outer coast of Washington between 0715 and 0755. Maximum heights were approximately 4 to 5 ft. The Neah Bay tide gage recorded a maximum wave of 4.7 ft.

OREGON

Reception times of the first two bulletins were not reported by the Oregon State Civil Defense Agency. The warning bulletin, filed at 0637, was received at 0700 and immediately disseminated to the coastal areas. U.S. Coast Guard stations along the coast reported that the initial wave arrived between 0730 and 0800. The only tide station in Oregon, that at Astoria, recorded a maximum wave of 2.4 ft. The Coast Guard stations reported much greater heights, ranging up to 14 ft at Umpqua River, 12 ft at Siuslaw River; and 10 to 11½ ft at Nehalem River, Depoe Bay, Yaquina Bay, and Coos Bay.

The Oregon State Civil Defense Agency reported that four children who were camping with their parents on the beach near Newport were drowned. Damage estimates, supplied by Oregon State Civil Defense, are given below.

Bandon—negligible
Cannon Beach—city, $50,000; private, $180,000
Chetco—negligible
Coos Bay—negligible
Depoe Bay—$5,000
Florence—$50,000
Port Orford—negligible
Rogue River—$3,000
Seaside area—city, $41,000; private, $235,000
Tillamook—negligible
Umpqua—$5,000
Waldport-Alsea area—port facilities, $145,000; private, $15,000
Warrenton—negligible
Yaquina—$5,000

Much of the damage in Oregon occurred away from the oceanfront. For example, in Seaside (Figure 7), all damage occurred along the banks of the Necanicum River and Neawanna Creek. At the north end of town, the wave overflowed the banks of Neawanna Creek, damaging four house trailers and 10 to 12 houses, and washing out a railroad trestle over the creek. Along the Necanicum River, flooding occurred in the downtown section of Seaside in the area bounded by Broadway, Downing Street, Second Avenue, and the river. The Fourth Avenue Bridge was washed out, and the Avenue G Bridge was so badly damaged that it had to be closed. Logs and debris were scattered all over the low-lying areas.

Much the same pattern of damage occurred at Cannon

Beach where the wave penetrated to Elk Creek, washing out the old Highway 101 bridge and damaging the new one.

CALIFORNIA

The first advisory bulletin issued by the Honolulu Observatory was received by the California Disaster Office (CDO) at 0536. The second advisory was received at 0644 and disseminated via the State Department of Justice Teletype System to all sheriffs, chiefs of police, and civil defense directors of coastal counties and cities at 0703. The California Disaster Office received the warning at 0713 and relayed it to the coastal counties and cities at 0725. Some discrepancy exists in these reported dissemination times, since all coastal jurisdictions reporting stated that Bulletin 2 was received at 0708, and the warning bulletin was received at 0750.

The tsunami reached record heights along the coast of northern California and was disastrous at Crescent City. The large amplitude of the waves at Crescent City was probably due to focusing caused by bottom topography. J. A. Roberts and Chen-Wu Chien (1965) have ascribed this focusing primarily to the topography in the vicinity of Cobb Seamount, approximately 400 mi northwest of Crescent City, and have prepared refraction diagrams to illustrate this.

California had a longer time to prepare for the onslaught of the tsunami than the other Pacific Coast states did, but, due to much larger wave amplitudes and lack of proper response and knowledge among the public, the death and damage totals were much greater than in any other place, except Alaska. The California Disaster Office reported 11 killed and 35 injured in Crescent City, and between $7,939,000 and $8,789,000 damage in the state. An additional $1 million in Marin County, which was not included in the CDO estimate, brought the total damage in California to almost $10 million.

At Crescent City (Griffin, 1964) where the bulk of the damage occurred, the county sheriff immediately contacted county and city civil defense authorities upon receipt of the advisory at 0708. The low-lying and coastal areas were warned, and evacuation began immediately. Evacuation was reasonably prompt, but not complete. The first two waves caused minor flooding in the business district, and many people returned to the area to clean up their places of business, since past experience showed that Crescent City normally experienced one or two surges with minor flooding during a tsunami. This premature return to the evacuation area was the cause of most of the fatalities. The third and fourth waves caused most of the destruction and the casualties; they caught the people who returned to the area after the second wave, and others who had failed to evacuate. Seven people, including the owner and his wife, returned to the Long Branch Tavern to remove the money from the building. Since everything appeared normal, they stopped to

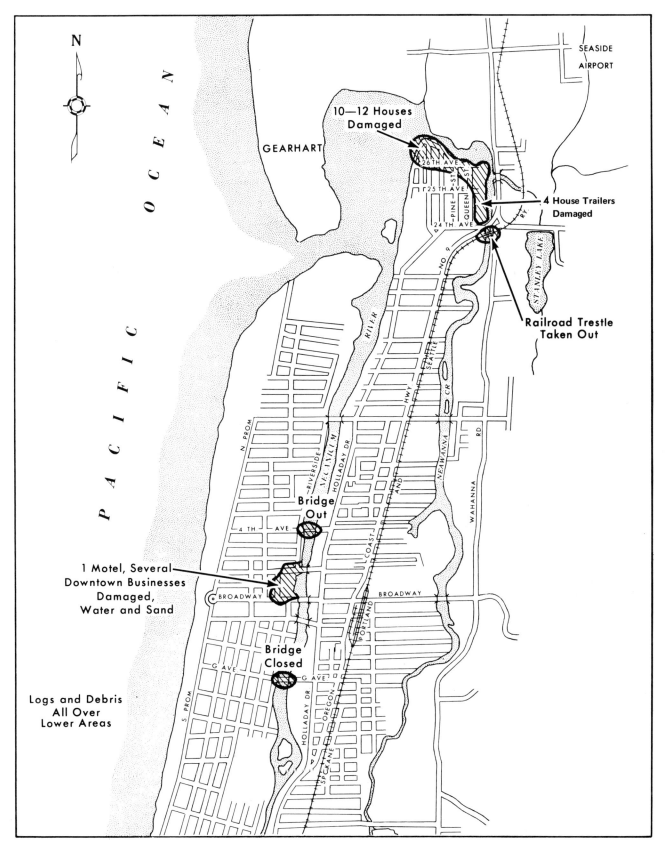

FIGURE 7   Location of major tsunami damages in Seaside, Oregon.

drink beer and were trapped by the third wave. Five of these seven were drowned when the boat in which they were attempting to escape was sucked into Elk Creek by the recession and was smashed against the steel grating of the bridge over the mouth of the creek.

Approximately 30 blocks were devastated in Crescent City. The California Disaster Office reported damage (excerpted from a report of the California Department of General Services) as follows: 54 residences, total loss; 13 residences, major damage; 24 residences, minor damage; 21 commercial fishing boats, lost (sunk or beached); 12 house trailers, total loss; and 172 business houses, severely damaged or destroyed.

Estimated cost to replace and repair:

Public property	$ 473,000
Private utilities	68,000
Private property	6,873,000
Total estimated cost	$7,414,000

The streets of Crescent City were strewn with rubble from demolished buildings and with logs which were swept in from the beaches. Automobiles were heaped in scattered piles, and stock from damaged stores was scattered throughout the area. The third wave picked up a gasoline tank truck parked at the Texaco station and slammed it through the garage door of the Nickols' Pontiac Building. An electrical junction box just inside the door was knocked loose by the impact, and a fire started. The fire destroyed the building and spread back to the Texaco tank farm which burned for 3 days.

The greatest height reached by the tsunami at Crescent City was 20.70 ft above mean sea level. This height was determined from the water marks on the flag pole near the Harbor Master's office at Citizens dock.

Crescent City was not the only place where the inhabitants placed themselves in jeopardy. Newspapers estimated that 10,000 people jammed beach areas at San Francisco to watch the tsunami arrive. In San Diego, an attempt was made to evacuate the beach areas, but curious citizens created a problem. Had large-amplitude waves struck these places, the casualty lists would have been much greater.

Reaction by county and city civil defense organizations varied considerably. In Humboldt County, the second advisory issued by the Honolulu Observatory was received at 0708 at the county sheriff's office. All agencies were mobilized by 0718, evacuation of all persons in danger areas was completed by 0740, and roadblocks were established under the direction of the sheriff's office to guarantee and enforce against any return to the threatened area. In Marin County, internal weaknesses in the county disaster organization were emphasized in reports submitted by cities and districts. San Francisco attempted to evacuate ocean beaches immediately upon receipt of the advisory, but, as noted above, efforts were unsuccessful. Los Angeles County made no attempt to evacuate waterfront areas.

The tsunami did not spare other areas of the California coast. Mendocino County reported that approximately 100 fishing boats in Noyo Harbor suffered damage, with 10 being sunk. A dredge in the harbor was carried upstream about one-fourth mile and grounded on a sandbar. Estimates of the damage ranged from $250,000 to $1 million. In Marin County, approximately $1 million worth of damage was done to small boats and berthing facilities, mostly by tsunami-induced currents in Loch Lomond Harbor in San Rafael. Los Angeles County Civil Defense reported $100,000 to $200,000 damage to six small-boat slips, pilings, and the Union Oil Company fuel dock; $75,000 damage due to scouring action on the harbor sides in Los Angeles County Harbor; and eight docks with a value of $100,000 destroyed in Long Beach Harbor. Only negligible damage was reported elsewhere in the state.

HAWAII

At 0401, the Honolulu Observatory notified the Assistant Tsunami Advisor to the State of Hawaii that a major earthquake had occurred. The same information was provided the Civil Defense Vice Director at 0405. The Vice Director passed the information to the Director, key staff members, and the civil defense administrators in all counties. At 0425, Civil Defense activated its emergency operating center. At 0643, after receipt of the tsunami warning from the HO, the decision was made to sound all coastal sirens and to activate the Civ-Alert Radio Broadcast System. At 0700, the sirens and the Civ-Alert System were activated simultaneously in all counties. The sirens were sounded again at 0800 and 0830, and the Civ-Alert System remained continuously active after 0700. Evacuation was fairly complete, and no casualties resulted from the tsunami. The earliest recorded arrival was 0833, at Nawiliwili.

Damage was light in Hawaii, although wave heights in excess of 12.5 ft were recorded at Hilo and waves in excess of 11.0 ft were recorded at Kahului. In Hilo, four restaurants and a residence were flooded near the head of Reeds Bay. The highest of the flooded restaurants had a floor approximately 6 ft above sea level. This floor was flooded to a depth of 1 ft. The west end of the Waiakea Bridge over the Wailoa River was partially undermined, and the sidewalk collapsed, creating a hole approximately 9 by 10 ft. Civil Defense estimated the total damage to be $15,000.

Considerable damage was reported from Maui where Civil Defense reported estimated damages of $52,590. The major damage was limited to facilities at Kahului Harbor, and all damage, resulting mainly from flooding, was restricted to the immediate waterfront area. The Kahului Railroad Company, which suffered the majority of the tsunami damage, reported that damage occurred primarily to freight and to the wooden supports of concrete piers. The complete listing of the damage on Maui is given below.

Aloha Bar and Restaurant	$ 50
Camp 1 Beach, Spreckelsville	600
Full Gospel Church	500
Kahului Railroad Company	42,500
Kaiser Permanente Cement	60
Agrifino Cortez, Kualapuu	100
Maui Frontier Restaurant	4,000
Maui Savings and Loan Company	100
Standard Oil Company	1,000
State and County	1,620
Ulupalakua Cold Storage	1,060
Y. Hata and Company	1,000
Total damage	$52,590

CHILE

The warning issued by the Honolulu Observatory was received by the Departamento de Navegación e Hidrografía in Valparaiso at 1210. By 1440, all maritime authorities along the Chilean coast had been alerted and supplied with estimated arrival times of the tsunami.

Since time was available, the Departamento de Navegación e Hidrografía instructed its tide observers to install 5-m staffs and make photographs of the maximum and minimum sea-level oscillations to provide more exact records of wave amplitudes than those provided by the tide gages. Maximum amplitudes reported were 11.3 ft at Valparaiso and 16.4 ft at Huasco.

Because beaches and harbors were cleared, there were no deaths or injuries resulting from the tsunami. Slight damage was done at Iquique, Coquimbo, Huasco, and San Vincente, primarily to shipping.

MISCELLANEOUS

Reports received from other dissemination agencies in the Warning System indicate that the response to the warning was adequate and timely. No damage was reported by any of the dissemination agencies, except as noted above. A report was received from Honiara in the Solomon Islands, indicating that a boat had been beached there by the tsunami.

TIDE-GAGE DATA

The U.S. Coast and Geodetic Survey has published reports based on tide records of the tsunamis of April 1, 1946; November 4, 1952; March 9, 1957; and May 22, 1960. This paper provides observational data on the fifth major tsunami of recent years.

The earthquake of March 28, 1964, and the resulting tsunami caused more damage than any of the other four, except the May 22, 1960, disturbance. In 1964, damage in the United States exceeded the total for the other four disturbances.

A further comparison of the five tsunamis is through the amplitude of the greatest wave recorded for each. In Table 2,

TABLE 2.—*Maximum recorded rise or fall*

Station	1946	1952	1957	1960	1964
	Feet	*Feet*	*Feet*	*Feet*	*Feet*
Massacre Bay, Alaska	......	8.0	3.8	11.0+	2.8
Sweeper Cove, Alaska	......	6.9	.....	7.0+	1.9
Yakutat, Alaska	......	1.8	2.2	5.2	7.6
Sitka, Alaska	2.6	1.5	2.6	3.0	14.3
Prince Rupert, British Columbia, Canada	......	....	....	0.4	8.9
Tofino, British Columbia, Canada	1.9	2.0	.....	4.6	8.1
Neah Bay, Wash	1.2	1.5	1.0	2.4	4.7
Crescent City, Calif	5.9	6.8	4.3	10.9	13.0+
San Francisco, Calif	1.7	3.5	1.7	2.9	7.4
Santa Monica, Calif	......	3.6	3.0	9.1+	6.5
Los Angeles, Calif	2.5	2.0	2.1	5.0	3.2
La Jolla, Calif	1.4	0.8	2.0	3.3	2.2
San Diego, Calif	1.2	2.3	1.5	4.6	3.7
Ensenada, Mexico	......	......	3.4	8.1	7.8+
Salina Cruz, Mexico	......	4.0	1.2	5.2	2.8
La Libertad, Ecuador	......	6.2	3.5	6.3	4.2
La Punta, Callao, Peru	......	6.4	0.9	7.2	6.4
Antofagasta, Chile	5.9	4.7	3.0	4.6	3.3
Valparaiso, Chile	5.0	5.9	6.7	5.6	6.2
Talcahuano, Chile	......	12.0+	4.6	16.6	5.4
Hilo, Hawaii	......	7.9	8.9	9.6+	12.5+
Honolulu, Hawaii	4.1	4.4	3.2	5.5+	2.7
Midway Island	......	6.6	2.7	2.0	0.9
Johnston Atoll	......	1.4	0.7	3.4	1.0
Pago Pago, American Samoa	......	6.0	1.4	5.2	1.3
Wake Island	......	1.7	2.4	3.3	0.5
Ft. Denison, Sydney Harbour, Australia				2.7	1.0
Coffs Harbour, New South Wales, Australia				3.3	0.2
Miyako Jima, Japan				10.2	1.1
Aburatsu, Japan				6.6	2.4
Shimizu (Tosa), Japan				8.9	1.8
Kushimoto, Japan				10.5	2.6
Toba Ko, Japan				5.9	0.8
Mera, Japan				7.9	1.9
Hanasaki, Japan				8.2	2.2

statistics are given on maximum wave heights (maximum heights of rise or fall) recorded at several tide stations which were in operation during at least two of the tsunamis. Where the maximum wave exceeded the gage limit (indicated by + in the table), the figures may be misleading. For example, Hilo, Hawaii, was devastated in 1960, although the height indicated is only 9.6+ ft. The 1964 height, however, was 12.5+ ft, and Hilo suffered only minor flooding.

This report presents the data gathered through an examination of the curves from 108 stations in the Pacific Ocean area. Statistical information is presented primarily in Table 4; it includes certain data relative to the time and height of the initial and maximum waves. In relation to the data compiled in Table 4, there are 107 prints of tide curves showing the arrival and initial stages of the tsunami which may be studied for variations in wave period, amplitude, etc., for many locations. The Marcus Island tide curve is not reproduced, since the tsunami cannot be distinguished on it. The 107 tide curves, a map locating the 108 tide stations, and Table 4 appear in the Appendix to this paper. As elsewhere in the report, Greenwich Mean Time is used.

Data included in Table 4 and the accompanying tide curves illustrate some of the difficulties encountered in analyzing the tide curves, because interpretation of the various statistics is often subjective. In the majority of cases, the initial disturbance is clearly defined, but for other stations it is obscure and not well determined. This is due, at least in part, to one or more of the following factors: screening effects of continental masses or island groups between the source and the tide gage; location of the tide gage in an area protected from the action of the open ocean; poor response of the tide gage to waves of tsunami periods; and masking of the tsunami effects by a large tidal range, local seiche action, or both.

WAVE TRAVEL

Wave-travel data are given in Table 3 for stations where the initial arrival time of the tsunami is fairly well determined. Since the epicenter of the earthquake was on land, distances are measured from a point with coordinates 60°N, 147°W. Distances of wave travel are computed for the great-circle arc from this point to the tide station. In almost all cases, the great-circle route is shorter than the actual path traveled by the initial wave. The great-circle routes from this point to

TABLE 3.—*Wave travel*

[Station numbers are identical with those in table 4. Locations are on figure 11. Distances are measured from a point with coordinates 60° N., 147° W.]

Tide station	Great-circle distance	Time		Average speed
	Nautical miles	*Hours*	*Minutes*	*Knots*
1. Massacre Bay, Attu, Alaska.	1,365	3	51	355
2. Sweeper Cove, Adak, Alaska.	1,098	3	24	323
3. Unalaska, Alaska	733	2	30	293
5. Yakutat, Alaska	222	1	24	159
6. Sitka, Alaska	405	1	30	270
8. Ketchikan, Alaska	564	2	49	200
10. Tasu Sound, Canada	658	1	57	337
15. Tofino, Canada	973	3	24	286
24. Neah Bay, Wash	1,042	3	42	282
27. Astoria (Tongue Pt.), Oreg.	1,165	4	20	269
28. Crescent City, Calif.	1,380	4	03	341
29. San Francisco (Presidio), Calif.*	1,626	5	06	319
31. Avila Beach, Calif.*	1,805	5	08	352
32. Rincon Island, Calif.*	1,877	5	41	330
33. Santa Monica, Calif.*	1,917	5	39	339
34. Los Angeles (Berth 60), Calif.*	1,937	5	48	334
35. Alamitos Bay, Calif.*	1,939	6	00	323
36. Newport Bay, Calif.*	1,952	5	50	335
37. La Jolla, Calif.*	2,006	5	48	346
38. San Diego, Calif.*	2,015	6	14	323
39. Ensenada, B.C., Mexico*	2,074	6	06	340
40. La Paz, B.C., Mexico	2,635	8	51	298
41. Mazatlàn, Sin., Mexico*	2,782	8	24	331
44. Manzanillo, Col., Mexico*	3,056	8	39	353
45. Acapulco, Gro., Mexico	3,286	9	29	347

TABLE 3.—*Wave travel*—Continued

Tide station	Great-circle distance	Time		Average speed
	Nautical miles	*Hours*	*Minutes*	*Knots*
46. Salina Cruz, Oax., Mexico*.	3,447	10	34	326
47. San José, Guatemala*	3,685	11	16	327
48. Acajutla, El Salvador*	3,730	11	42	319
50. Corinto, Nicaragua*	3,862	12	24	311
51. Puntarenas, Costa Rica*	4,061	12	47	318
52. Quepos, Costa Rica*	4,109	12	24	331
53. Puerto Armuelles, Panama*	4,206	12	48	329
55. Bahia Solano, Colombia*	4,470	14	09	316
58. San Cristobal, Galapagos Islands, Ecuador*	4,510	12	51	351
59. La Libertad, Ecuador*	4,816	14	33	331
60. Talara, Peru*	4,932	14	20	344
61. La Punta, Callao, Peru*	5,442	15	35	349
62. San Juan, Peru*	5,672	15	54	357
63. Matarani, Peru*	5,843	16	21	375
64. Arica, Chile*	5,970	16	54	353
65. Antofagasta, Chile*	6,237	17	03	366
66. Caldera, Chile*	6,403	17	19	370
67. Valparaiso, Chile*	6,689	17	51	375
68. Talcahuano, Chile*	6,839	18	39	367
69. Corral, Chile*	6,991	19	03	367
71. Bahia Esperanza, Palmer Peninsula, Antarctica	8,445	22	34	374
72. Argentine Islands, Palmer Peninsula, Antarctica	8,368	21	49	384
73. Easter Island	5,546	13	54	399
74. Christmas Island	3,515	7	45	454
75. Hilo, Hawaii Island, Hawaii	2,441	5	24	452
76. Kahului, Maui Island, Hawaii.	2,380	5	11	459
77. Mokuoloe Island, Oahu Island, Hawaii	2,359	5	09	458
78. Honolulu, Oahu Island, Hawaii	2,368	5	17	448
79. Nawiliwili, Kauai Island, Hawaii	2,342	4	57	473
80. Midway Island	2,271	4	51	468
81. Johnston Atoll	2,773	6	03	458
82. Canton Island, Phoenix Islands	3,944	8	39	456
83. Pago Pago, American Samoa	4,602	10	15	449
84. Lyttelton, New Zealand	6,524	18	34	351
87. Fort Denison, Sydney Harbour, Australia	6,397	17	09	373
88. Camp Cove, Sydney Harbour, Australia	6,394	16	54	378
90. Rabaul, New Britain Island	4,778	11	49	404
91. Moen Island, Truk Islands, Caroline Islands	4,165	9	24	443
92. Kwajalein Atoll, Marshall Islands	3,682	8	24	438
93. Eniwetok Atoll, Marshall Islands	3,673	8	09	451
94. Wake Island	3,138	6	45	465
96. Apra Harbor, Guam, Mariana Islands	4,058	9	12	441
99. Aburatsu, Japan	3,536	10	27	338
102. Toba Ko, Japan	3,235	11	24	284
104. Ofunato, Japan	2,874	7	04	406
105. Hanasaki, Japan	2,569	6	39	386
106. Yuzhno Kurilsk, Kuril Islands, U.S.S.R	2,540	6	24	397
108. Petropavlovsk, Siberia, U.S.S.R	1,793	5	34	322

*The great-circle lines to stations on the west coast of North and South America intersect the continents. Therefore, the true wave-travel distances for these stations are greater than the computed distances. Computed speeds are similarly distorted, and are less than their real values.

most stations on the west coast of North and South America intersect the continents. Because of greater ocean depths, longer routes may provide earlier arrival than the great-circle route, even where there is no intervening land mass or island group. Since wave speed varies during the travel period and the travel time to each station is the only factor that is fairly well determined, the computed speed is an average for the distance from the source to the tide stations. These computed speeds are generally less than the actual velocity, since the true travel distances for the wave are greater than the computed distances.

Because tsunami wave lengths (distance between successive crests) are very much longer than the oceanic depths over which they travel, their speed is controlled by the water depth and is computed by the shallow-water wave formula $S = \sqrt{gd}$, where d is the water depth and g is the acceleration due to gravity. For computing speed in knots with the depth in fathoms, this equation becomes $S = 8.23 \sqrt{d}$.

WAVE PERIOD AND LENGTH

Wave period for a tsunami is difficult to determine, and the wide variation in this time interval for the stations given in Table 4 will illustrate the confusion encountered. The period between the first and second wave crests, as recorded, varies from 7 minutes to 2 hours. The deep-ocean period of the tsunami is almost impossible to determine from records of coastal tide stations, although the majority of the energy of the tsunami was probably contained in a single wave formed by drainage from the uplifted portion of the Gulf of Alaska (Malloy, 1965). The natural period of the local basin, harbor, or shelf area should be evident shortly after the arrival of the initial wave. However, interference caused by refracted or reflected arrivals commences and is indicated on the tide curve quite early; this confuses the identity of the true period.

OTHER FEATURES

The tsunami was highly directional, being focused by the shape of the generating area and the surrounding land masses toward the south and southeast. Maximum wave heights in the Aleutians and Japan, except at Ofunato, were under 3 ft. Chilean stations, on the other hand, generally had maximums in excess of 6 ft.

The tide gage maintained by the U.S. Coast and Geodetic Survey at Seward, Alaska, was destroyed by the earthquake and tsunami. However, the wreckage of the gage and the tide house was later found on the deck of a tanker which had been tied up at the dock where the tide gage was installed. The tide record was salvaged, and, although it did not show the tsunami, an analysis was made to extract available water-level information. Figures 8 and 9 show the daily sea-level variations for the months of March 1964 and March 1965 for

Seward and two other Alaskan tide stations. The values for each day are the mean of the hourly heights for the date. The dates for these three stations are based on local (+10 hours) time. The value for March 27, 1964, is based on data to 1800 hours.

No unusual variations in sea level were found to have occurred prior to the earthquake. The control stations were deliberately chosen outside of the area of crustal deformation; however, all three stations show the same direction and order of variation. The magnitude of the variation prior to the earthquake did not exceed the maximum variations noted on other days.

REGIONAL TSUNAMI WARNING SYSTEMS

Since the Honolulu Observatory is unable to provide warnings to areas close to the source of a tsunami, regional tsunami warning systems are being organized by the U.S. Coast and Geodetic Survey. These regional systems are designed to provide tsunami warnings on the basis of seismic data alone, within 15 minutes of the occurrence of any large earthquake in the area they are protecting. The warnings normally will be based solely on the fact that an earthquake with a magnitude great enough to generate a tsunami has occurred in an area where tsunami generation is possible. The first regional system is designed to provide warning information for Alaska and the Aleutian Islands. Its headquarters will be at the Palmer Observatory, Palmer, Alaska.

Seismic data for the system will be provided by a tripartite network of seismographs, with remote recording at the Palmer Observatory. Short-period seismographs will be installed at two outposts—Palmer West and Palmer South—approximately 25 and 28 mi, respectively, from the Palmer Observatory. In addition, data will be telemetered to Palmer from short-period seismographs at the Adak, College, and Sitka Observatories. All telemetered seismic data and the data from the short-period seismographs at Palmer will be recorded on helicorders, thus providing the personnel at Palmer with instantaneous visual readout of seismic data from six locations, three at Palmer and one each at Adak, College, and Sitka.

Since the Adak and Sitka Observatories will have limited warning responsibility in their immediate areas, expanded seismic capabilities are being provided at these two locations. At Sitka, a short-period vertical seismometer is being installed on Biorka Island, and the data will be telemetered to the Sitka Observatory. Adak will have a small tripartite network with legs 1 to 2 mi long. In addition, Adak will have telemetered tide data available from Shemya.

Palmer, as the center of the Alaska Tsunami Warning Center, will have an extensive communication network (Figure 10). The basic network will be supplied by the Defense Com-

TABLE 4.—*The tsunami of March 28, 1964, as recorded by tide gages*

[Earthquake epicenter 61.04° N., 147.73° W., on coast of northern Prince William Sound, Alaska. Wave generating area is shown on figure 2; station locations are on figure 11. Symbols are defined at the end of this table. All times are Greenwich Mean Time.]

Tide station	Latitude ° '	Longitude ° '	Initial wave: Time of arrival Day	Hour	Minute	Period 1st to 2nd crest Minute	Initial rise Feet	Following fall Feet	Maximum rise or fall: Time of beginning Day	Hour	Minute	Duration Minute	Height Feet
	North	East											
1. Massacre Bay, Attu, Alaska.........	52 50	173 12	28	07	27	72	0.7	1.0	28	19	46	14R	2.8
	North	West											
2. Sweeper Cove, Adak, Alaska.........	51 51	176 39	28	07	00f	54	0.6	0.8	29	04	17	21F	1.9
3. Unalaska, Alaska....................	53 53	166 32	28	06	06	36	0.3	1.0	28	15	15	13R	2.6
4. Homer, Alaska......................	59 38	151 27	28	03	45f	g	3.0	2.0	28	03	50	g	3.5
5. Yakutat, Alaska....................	59 33	139 44	28	05	00	7	4.6	2.8	28	10	07	23R	7.6
6. Sitka, Alaska......................	57 03	135 20	28	05	06	50	5.8	11.6	28	06	24	35R	14.3
7. Juneau, Alaska.....................	58 18	134 25	28	06	49	81	2.7	7.5	28	07	22	32F	7.5
8. Ketchikan, Alaska.................	55 21	131 39	28	06	25	29	1.6	1.2	28	09	22	30R	3.7
9. Prince Rupert, Canada.............	54 19	130 20	28	06	52	92	1.4	5.8	28	08	12	56R	8.9
10. Tasu Sound, Canada...............	52 45	132 01	28	05	33	70	2.9	6.3	28	05	52	22F	6.3
11. Bella Bella, Canada..............	52 10	128 08	28	06	53	39	3.2	6.3	28	07	24	20F	6.3
12. Ocean Falls, Canada..............	52 21	127 41	28	08	00	32	7.2	12.5	28	08	25	15F	12.5
13. Alert Bay, Canada................	50 35	126 56	28	07	39	29	3.8	5.7	28	07	53	18F	5.7
14. Port Alberni, Canada.............	49 14	124 49	28	08	00	87 (est.)	......	......				17+F	......
15. Tofino, Canada...................	49 09	125 55	28	07	00	20	3.4	5.1	28	08	50	24F	8.1
16. Pitt Lake, Canada................	49 26	122 31	28	12	00	g	......	......				......	......
17. Point Atkinson, Canada...........	49 20	123 15	28	09	07	90	0.3	0.7	28	12	50	52R	0.8
18. Vancouver, Canada................	49 17	123 07	28	09	20	120	0.2	0.5	28	11	05	45R	0.6
19. Fraser North Arm, Canada.........	49 12	123 05	28	10	15	g	......	......				......	......
20. New Westminster, Canada..........	49 12	122 54	28	10	30	g	......	......				......	......
21. Steveston, Canada................	49 07	123 12	28	09	45	g	......	......				......	......
22. Fulford Harbour, Canada..........	48 46	123 27	28	08	35	40	1.3	1.4	28	13	53	22R	2.0
23. Victoria, Canada.................	48 25	123 24	28	08	02	50	2.2	4.8	28	08	18	39F	4.8
24. Neah Bay, Wash...................	48 22	124 37	28	07	18	22	2.9	2.4	28	08	44	21R	4.7
25. Friday Harbor, Wash..............	48 33	123 00	28	08	30	19	0.8	0.2	28	09	50	60R	2.3
26. Seattle, Wash....................	47 36	122 20	28	09	12	48	0.4	0.3	28	11	39	20F	0.8
27. Astoria (Tongue Pt.), Oreg.......	46 13	123 46	28	07	56	20	1.7	1.3	28	09	44	9R	2.4
28. Crescent City, Calif.............	41 45	124 12	28	07	39	29	4.8+	13.0+	I	I	I	......	......
29. San Francisco (Presidio), Calif..	37 48	122 28	28	08	42	39	2.3	3.9	28	09	35	24F	7.4
30. Alameda (NAS), Calif.............	37 46	122 18	28	09	06	42	1.5	2.5	28	09	57	24F	5.4
31. Avila Beach, Calif...............	35 10	120 44	28	08	44	15	4.4	5.0	28	10	00b	14F	10.4+
32. Rincon Island, Calif.............	34 21	119 26	28	09	17	37	2.4	4.1	28	11	33b	22F	5.9+
33. Santa Monica, Calif..............	34 00	118 30	28	09	15	39	2.5	4.2	28	11	20	15R	6.5
34. Los Angeles (Berth 60), Calif....	33 43	118 16	28	09	24	27	0.5	0.4	28	10	08	24F	3.2
35. Alamitos Bay, Calif..............	33 45	118 07	28	09	36	37	1.7	2.8	28	09	56	24F	2.8
36. Newport Bay, Calif...............	33 36	117 54	28	09	26	24	1.0	1.3	28	10	06	14F	1.8
37. La Jolla, Calif..................	32 52	117 15	28	09	24	33	1.9	2.2	28	09	36	16F	2.2
38. San Diego, Calif.................	32 43	117 10	28	09	50	9	0.7	0.4	28	11	31	27R	3.7
39. Ensenada, Baja California, Mexico.	31 51	116 38	28	09	42	46	4.7	7.8+	28	09	52	18F	7.8+
40. La Paz, Baja California Sur, Mexico..	24 10	110 19	28	12	27	39	0.3	0.3	30	05	39	42F	1.8
41. Guaymas, Sonora, Mexico..........	27 55	110 54	28	12	30	180	0.2	0.3	28	14	00	60F	0.3
42. Topolobampo, Sinaloa, Mexico.....	25 37	109 03	28	11	59	......	S						0.1
43. Mazatlán, Sinaloa, Mexico........	23 11	106 26	28	12	00	38	0.6	0.5	28	22	56	22F	1.6
44. Manzanillo, Colima, Mexico.......	19 03	104 20	28	12	15	31	1.3	2.4	29	07	20	6R	3.9
45. Acapulco, Guerrero, Mexico.......	16 51	99 55	28	13	05	30	0.8	1.2	29	04	09	13F	3.5
46. Salina Cruz, Oaxaca, Mexico......	16 10	95 12	28	14	10	31	0.8	1.0	29	02	07	10R	2.8
47. San José, Guatemala.............	13 55	90 50	28	14	52	48	0.4	0.3	29	03	00	18F	0.6
48. Acajutla, El Salvador...........	13 35	89 51	28	15	18	48	0.5	0.3	29	22	15	17F	1.0
49. La Union, El Salvador...........	13 20	87 49	c	c	c	......	S					......	......
50. Corinto, Nicaragua..............	12 28	87 12	28	16	00	g	0.1	0.1	......			......	......
51. Puntarenas, Costa Rica..........	09 58	84 50	28	16	23	42	0.2	0.3	29	03	50	7R	1.0
52. Quepos, Costa Rica..............	09 24	84 10	28	16	00	g	0.3	0.2	29	05	17	8F	1.5
53. Puerto Armuelles, Panama........	08 16	82 52	28	16	24	g	0.2	0.1	29	01	12	7F	0.6

See footnotes at end of table.

TABLE 4.—*The tsunami of March 28, 1964, as recorded by tide gages*—Continued

[Earthquake epicenter 61.04° N., 147.73° W., on coast of northern Prince William Sound, Alaska. Wave generating area is shown on figure 2; station locations are on figure 11. Symbols are defined at the end of this table. All times are Greenwich Mean Time.]

Tide station	Latitude		Longitude		Initial wave			Period 1st to 2nd crest	Initial rise	Following fall	Maximum rise or fall			Duration	Height
					Time of arrival						Time of beginning				
	°	′	°	′	Day	Hour	Minute	Minute	Feet	Feet	Day	Hour	Minute	Minute	Feet
	North		*West*												
54. Naos Island, C.Z.	08	55	79	32	c	c	c	......	......	S	......	......	......	......	......
55. Bahia Solano, Colombia	06	14	77	24	28	17	45	11	0.2	0.1	29	02	54	5F	1.2
56. Buenaventura, Colombia	03	54	77	05	......	......	......	......	......	S	......	......	......	......	......
57. Tumaco, Colombia	01	50	78	44	c	c	c	......	......	......	29	03	31	15R	0.3
	South		*West*												
58. San Cristobal, Galapagos Islands, Ecuador	00	54	89	37	28	16	27	14	1.7	2.7	28	17	18	6R	3.8
59. La Libertad, Ecuador	02	13	80	55	28	18	09	23	0.7	0.9	28	19	49	8R	4.2
60. Talara, Peru	04	35	81	17	28	17	56	15	1.8	2.9	28	19	03	6F	3.5
61. La Punta, Callao, Peru	12	03	77	09	28	19	11	16	2.0	2.3	28	21	09	12	6.4
62. San Juan, Peru	15	21	75	09	28	19	30	16	2.0	3.9	28	19	40	10F	3.9
63. Matarani, Peru	17	00	72	07	28	19	57	12	0.9	1.2	29	04	22	4R	2.9
64. Arica, Chile	18	28	70	20	28	20	30	15	1.4	1.3	29	05	09	10R	7.0
65. Antofagasta, Chile	23	39	70	25	28	20	39	19	1.5	1.7	28	23	09	6F	3.3
66. Caldera, Chile	27	04	70	50	28	20	55	19	2.4	4.1	I	I	I	......	......
67. Valparaiso, Chile	33	02	71	38	28	21	27	31	2.8	3.8	28	22	52	14R	6.2
68. Talcahuano, Chile	36	42	73	06	28	22	15	12	2.3	1.0	29	00	00	6R	5.4
69. Corral, Chile	39	52	73	26	28	22	39	27	4.3	6.3	28	22	54	20F	6.3
70. Ushuaia, Tierra del Fuego, Argentina	54	49	68	13	c	c	c	......	......	......	29	03	03	36F	0.8
71. Bahia Esperanza, Palmer Peninsula, Antarctica	63	24	57	00	29	02	10	g	0.1	0.1	......	......	......	......	0.2
72. Argentine Islands, Palmer Peninsula, Antarctica	65	15	64	16	29	01	25	17	1.9	1.0	29	03	40	9F	3.2
73. Easter Island	27	09	109	27	28	17	30	4	0.6	0.2	28	19	28	3R	2.0
	North		*West*												
74. Christmas Island	01	59	157	29	28	11	21	12	0.3	0.1	28	11	21	13R	0.3
75. Hilo, Hawaii Island, Hawaii	19	44	155	03	28	09	00	19	5.7	11.3+	28	09	22	8R	12.5+
76. Kahului, Maui Island, Hawaii	20	54	156	28	28	08	47	23	6.8	11.0+	28	09	00a	12	11.0+
77. Mokuoloe Island, Oahu Island, Hawaii	21	26	157	48	28	08	45	57	1.0	1.1	28	11	51	46R	1.9
78. Honolulu, Oahu Island, Hawaii	21	18	157	52	28	08	53	21	1.5	2.6	28	10	04	16F	2.7
79. Nawiliwili, Kauai Island, Hawaii	21	57	159	21	28	08	33	13	1.2	2.4	28	08	46	7F	2.4
80. Midway Island	28	13	177	22	28	08	27	15	0.2	0.1	28	08	51	7F	0.9
81. Johnston Atol[1]	16	45	169	31	28	09	39	26	0.9	1.0	28	10	02	18F	1.0
	South		*West*												
82. Canton Island, Phoenix Islands	02	48	171	43	28	12	15	24	0.2	0.1	28	12	15	19R	0.2
83. Pago Pago, American Samoa	14	17	170	41	28	13	51	20	0.4	0.3	29	12	34	7R	1.3
	South		*East*												
84. Lyttelton, New Zealand	43	37	172	43	28	22	10	12	0.2	0.2	29	06	00	40F	4.1
85. Greymouth, New Zealand	42	26	171	13	c	c	c	......	......	......	29	05	27	20R	1.2
86. Nelson, New Zealand	41	16	173	16	c	c	c	......	......	......	I	I	I	......	......
87. Fort Denison, Sydney Harbour, Australia	33	51	151	14	28	20	45	33	0.1	0.1	29	02	52	33R	1.0
86. Camp Cove, Sydney Harbour, Australia	33	48	151	16	28	20	30	g	0.1	0.1	29	04	50	17R	0.6
89. Coffs Harbour, Australia	30	18	153	09	c	c	c	......	......	......	......	......	......	......	0.2
90. Rabaul, New Britain Island	04	12	152	12	28	15	25	30	0.3	0.3	29	03	24	15F	2.0
	North		*East*												
91. Moen Island, Truk Islands, Caroline Islands	07	27	151	51	28	13	00	33	0.3	0.1	28	17	50	25F	0.6
92. Kwajalein Atoll, Marshall Islands	08	44	167	44	28	12	00	41	0.6	0.6	28	13	39	18R	1.0
93. Eniwetok Atoll, Marshall Islands	11	22	162	21	28	11	45	......	0.1	0.1	......	S	......	......	......

See footnotes at end of table.

TABLE 4.—*The tsunami of March 28, 1964, as recorded by tide gages*—Continued

[Earthquake epicenter 61.04° N., 147.73° W., on coast of northern Prince William Sound, Alaska. Wave generating area is shown on figure 2; station locations are on figure 11. Symbols are defined at the end of this table. All times are Greenwich Mean Time.]

Tide station	Latitude		Longitude		Initial wave						Maximum rise or fall				
					Time of arrival			Period 1st to 2nd crest	Initial rise	Following fall	Time of beginning			Duration	Height
					Day	Hour	Min-ute	Min-ute	Feet	Feet	Day	Hour	Min-ute	Min-ute	Feet
	°	'	°	'											
	North		East												
94. Wake Island....................	19	17	166	37	28	10	21	15	0.5	0.5	28	10	21	14R	0.5
95. Marcus Island..................	24	17	153	58	c	c	c	g	....	....	....	....	....	....	....
96. Apra Harbor, Guam, Mariana Islands.	13	26	144	39	28	12	48	42	0.2	0.3	28	20	15	24R	0.4
97. Hong Kong.....................	22	18	114	10	c	c	c	....	....	....	....	....	....	....	0.1
98. Miyako Jima, Jpaan.............	24	48	125	17	c	c	c	....	....	....	28	22	13	17R	1.1
99. Aburatsu, Japan................	31	35	131	25	28	14	03	23	0.4	0.5	29	04	43	12F	2.4
100. Shimizu (Tosa), Japan.........	32	47	132	58	c	c	c	....	....	....	28	20	40	11R	1.8
101. Kushimoto, Japan.............	33	28	135	46	c	c	c	....	....	....	29	11	58	8F	2.6
102. Toba Ko, Japan..............	34	29	136	51	28	15	00	g	0.2	0.2	28	21	45	13R	0.8
103. Mera, Japan.................	34	55	139	50	c	c	c	....	....	....	29	03	00	10R	1.9
104. Ofunato, Japan..............	39	04	141	43	28	10	40	40	0.5	0.5	28	21	20	23F	4.5
105. Hanasaki, Japan.............	43	17	145	35	28	10	15	g	0.3	0.1	30	01	00	25F	2.2
106. Yuzhno Kurilsk, Kuril Islands, U.S.S.R......	44	00	145	30	28	10	00	45	0.3	0.5	30	01	40	18R	2.5
107. Poronaysk, Sakhalin Island, U.S.S.R..	49	12	143	05	c	c	c	....	....	....	29	18	03	58R	1.1
108. Petropavlovsk, Siberia, U.S.S.R......	53	01	158	39	28	09	10	g	0.1	0.1	....	....	....	....	0.1

I—Incomplete record.
S—Only slight evidence on record.
+—Gage limit exceeded.
R—Rise.
F—Fall.

a.—Four waves exceeded gage limit.
b.—Small part of record missing.
c.—Arrival time indefinite.
f.—Initial oscillation was a fall.
g.—Indeterminate.

munication Agency (DCA) and supplemented by facilities of the FAA and Office of Civil Defense.

One circuit will bring seismic data to Palmer from Adak, and tide data from Shemya, Adak, Unalaska, Cold Bay, and Kodiak. Bridging facilities at Adak will permit the Adak Observatory to monitor Shemya tide data transmitted on this circuit. A second circuit will be used to bring seismic and tide data from Sitka to Palmer (future plans call for the transmission of tide data from Yakutat on this circuit as well). Palmer also will have a continuous record of Seward tide data, and an additional circuit will be used to telemeter seismic data from College to Palmer.

A full-time voice circuit will connect the observatories at Palmer, Sitka, and College. A full-time teletype circuit will link Palmer and Adak. In addition, the Palmer Observatory will have teletype circuits into the FAA ES-3 switch at Anchorage and the Defense Communications System.

The primary means for disseminating watch and warning information to the people of Alaska will be through the National Warning System (NAWAS) which is being extended to the Palmer Observatory.

It is anticipated that a similar regional system will be developed for western United States. The Honolulu Observatory would serve as a regional warning center in the event of a major earthquake in the Hawaiian Islands.

ACKNOWLEDGMENTS

Tide observers are responsible for the original records reproduced in this report. Services of these individuals and local organizations cooperating in maintenance of tide stations and furnishing records used in this report are greatly appreciated. Special acknowledgment is extended to the following organizations in other countries for providing tide records and pertinent information, thus permitting a more complete coverage of the region affected.

Departamento de Navegación e Hidrografía de la Armada, Chile;
Canadian Hydrographic Service;
Inter-American Geodetic Survey and the several countries in Central and South America that regularly furnish tide records to this Bureau;
Instituto de Geofísica, Universidad Nacional de México;
The Royal Observatory, Hong Kong;
Republic of the Philippines, Coast and Geodetic Survey;
Earthquake Research Institute, University of Tokyo, Japan;
Oceanographic Institute, Wellington, New Zealand;
Naval Hydrographic Office, Taiwan, Republic of China;
Naval Hydrographic Service, Australia;
Bureau of Mineral Resources, Geology and Geophysics, Australia;
Institute of Aeroclimatology, USSR;
National Institute of Oceanography, England; and
Servicio de Hidrografía Naval Secretaría de Marina, Argentina.

Special thanks are due also to the many civil defense organizations and dissemination agencies that participated in the Seismic Sea Wave

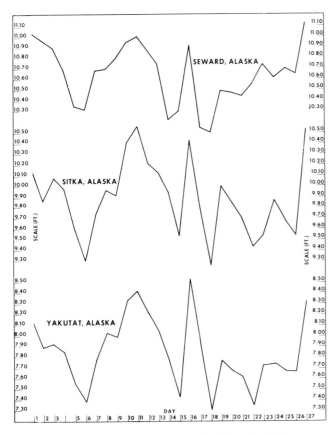

FIGURE 8   Daily variations in sea level for March 1964.

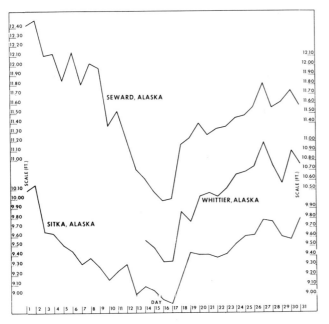

FIGURE 9   Daily variations in sea level for March 1965.

Warning System and submitted reports on the tsunami in their respective areas.

REFERENCES

Alaska Department of Health and Welfare, 1964. Preliminary report of earthquake damage to environmental health facilities and services in Alaska. Mimeographed Report of Alaska Department of Health and Welfare, Division of Public Health. Juneau: Branch of Environmental Health, April. 47 p.

Anchorage Daily News, 1964. Quake damage total over $500 million. *Anchorage Daily News*, April 18.

British Columbia Civil Defense, 1964. Tidal wave. British Columbia Civil Defense Circular, Summer edition. Victoria: British Columbia Civil Defense. p. 1–38.

Grantz, Arthur, George Plafker, and Reuben Kachadoorian, 1964. Alaska's Good Friday earthquake, March 27, 1964: A preliminary geologic evaluation. U.S. Geological Survey Circular 491. Washington: U.S. Geological Survey. 35 p.

Griffin, Wallace, editor, 1964. Crescent City's dark disaster: tsunami; March 28, 1964. Crescent City [California]: Crescent City American. 64 p.

Malloy, Richard J., 1965. Gulf of Alaska: seafloor upheaval. *Geo-Marine Technology*, 1 (May–June), 22–26.

Plafker, George, and L. R. Mayo, 1965. Tectonic deformation, subaqueous slides and destructive waves associated with the Alaskan March 27, 1964 earthquake: an interim geologic evaluation. U.S. Geological Survey Open-File Report. Menlo Park: U.S. Geological Survey. 34 p.

Roberts, James A., and Chen-Wu Chien, 1965. The effects of bottom topography on the refraction of the tsunami 27–28 March 1964: the Crescent City case *in* Ocean Science and Ocean Engineering 1965 (Volume 2): Transactions of the Joint Conference and Exhibit, Washington, D.C., June 14–17, 1965. Washington: Marine Technology Society. p. 707–716.

Stroh, Alfred, Jr., 1964. Navy operations at Kodiak. *Military Engineer*, 56 (July–August), 254–255.

Tudor, W. J., 1964. Tsunami damage at Kodiak, Alaska, and Crescent City, California, from Alaskan earthquake of 27 March 1964. U.S. Naval Civil Engineering Laboratory Technical Note N-622. Port Hueneme [California]: U.S. Naval Civil Engineering Laboratory, November. 131 p.

U.S. Coast and Geodetic Survey, 1965. Assistance and recovery, Alaska/1964: a report covering the activities of the U.S. Coast and Geodetic Survey in conjunction with the Prince William Sound, Alaska, earthquake of 1964 for the period March 27–December 31, 1964. Washington: U.S. Department of Commerce. 45 p.

Van Dorn, William G., 1965. Source mechanism of the tsunami of March 28, 1964 in Alaska. Proceedings of the Ninth Conference (1964) on Coastal Engineering (Chapter 10). New York: American Society of Civil Engineers. p. 166–190. Also *in* The Great Alaska Earthquake of 1964: Oceanography and Coastal Engineering. NAS Pub. 1605. Washington: National Academy of Sciences, 1972.

Wigen, S. O., and W. R. H. White, 1964. Tsunami of March 27–29, 1964, west coast of Canada. Canada Department of Mines and Technical Surveys Duplicate Report. Victoria: Canada Department of Mines and Technical Surveys, August. 12 p.

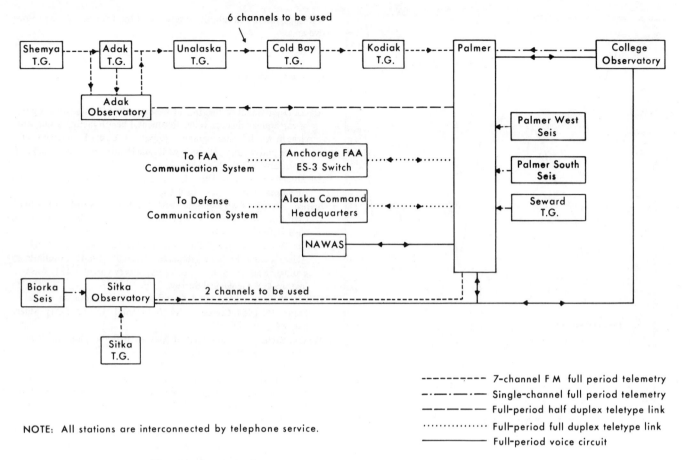

FIGURE 10   Alaska Seismic Sea Wave Warning System Communication Network.

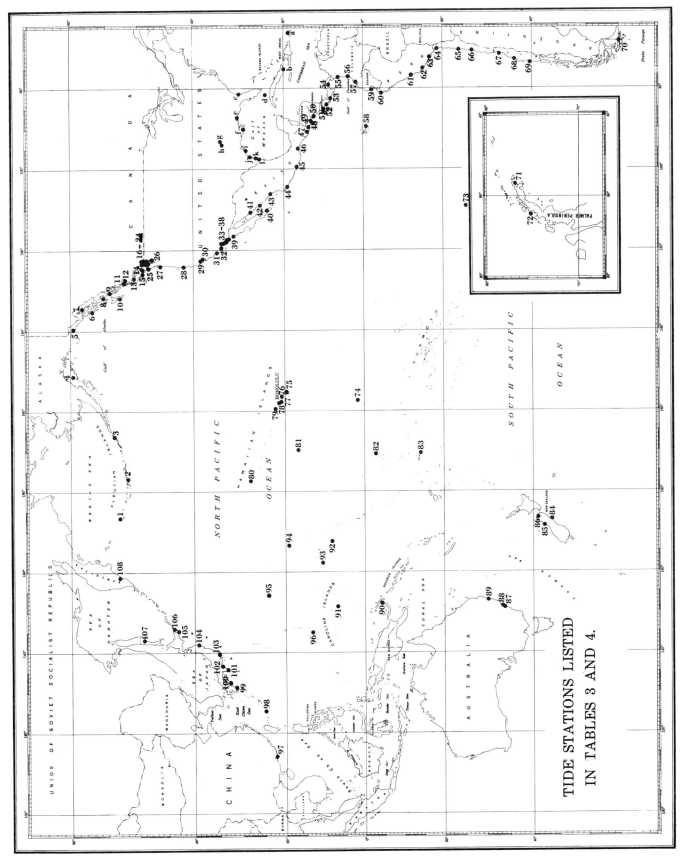

TIDE STATIONS LISTED
IN TABLES 3 AND 4.

FIGURE 11 Locations of tide stations.

69

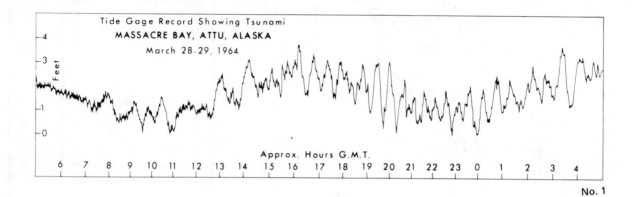

Tide Gage Record Showing Tsunami
MASSACRE BAY, ATTU, ALASKA
March 28-29, 1964

No. 1

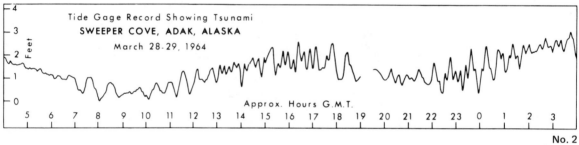

Tide Gage Record Showing Tsunami
SWEEPER COVE, ADAK, ALASKA
March 28-29, 1964

No. 2

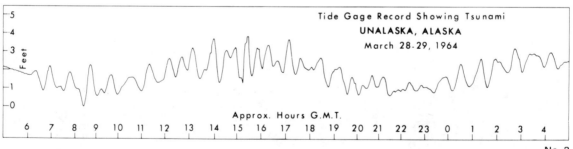

Tide Gage Record Showing Tsunami
UNALASKA, ALASKA
March 28-29, 1964

No. 3

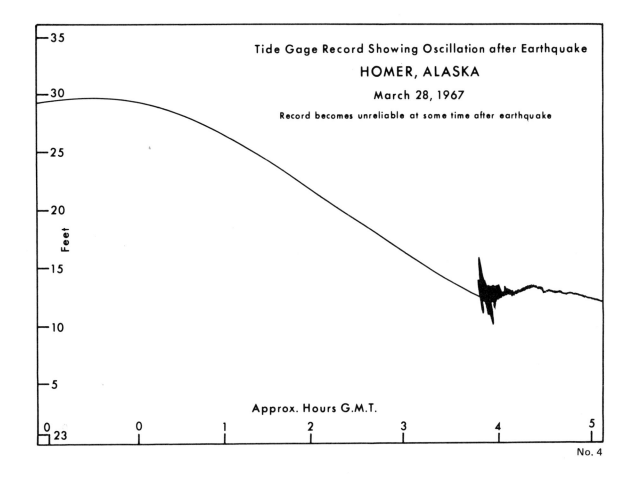

Tide Gage Record Showing Oscillation after Earthquake

HOMER, ALASKA

March 28, 1967

Record becomes unreliable at some time after earthquake

Approx. Hours G.M.T.

No. 4

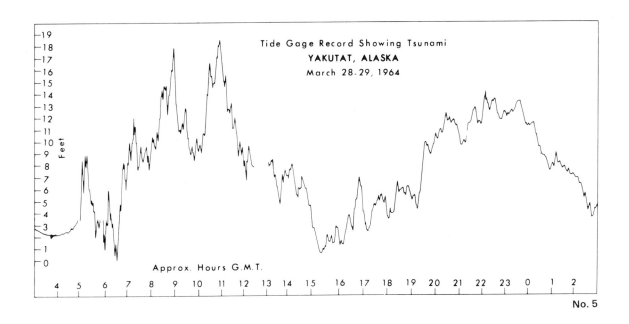

Tide Gage Record Showing Tsunami

YAKUTAT, ALASKA

March 28-29, 1964

Approx. Hours G.M.T.

No. 5

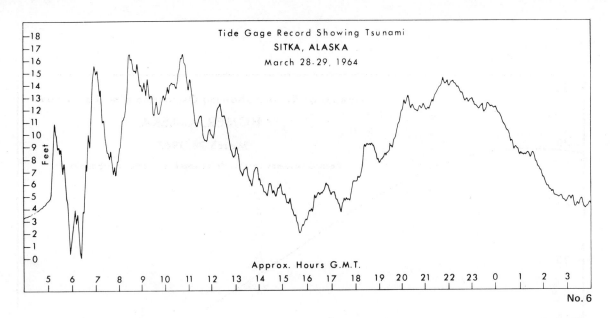

Tide Gage Record Showing Tsunami
SITKA, ALASKA
March 28-29, 1964

Approx. Hours G.M.T.

No. 6

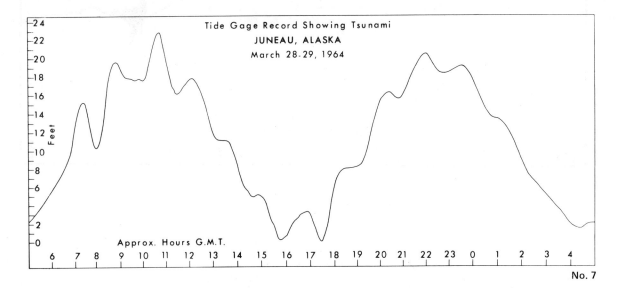

Tide Gage Record Showing Tsunami
JUNEAU, ALASKA
March 28-29, 1964

Approx. Hours G.M.T.

No. 7

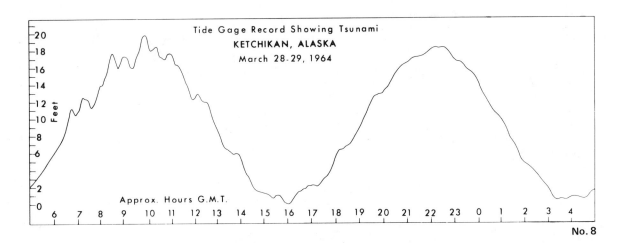

Tide Gage Record Showing Tsunami
KETCHIKAN, ALASKA
March 28-29, 1964

Approx. Hours G.M.T.

No. 8

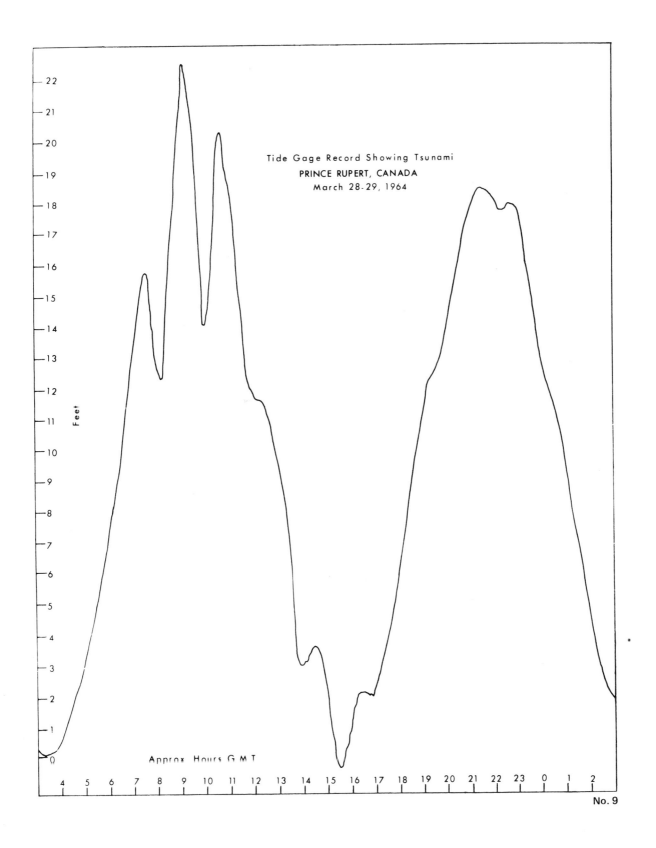

Tide Gage Record Showing Tsunami
PRINCE RUPERT, CANADA
March 28-29, 1964

Feet

Approx. Hours G M T

No. 9

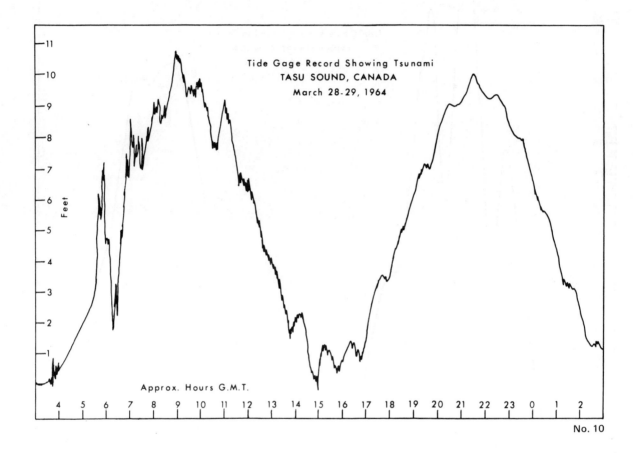

Tide Gage Record Showing Tsunami
TASU SOUND, CANADA
March 28-29, 1964

Feet

Approx. Hours G.M.T.

No. 10

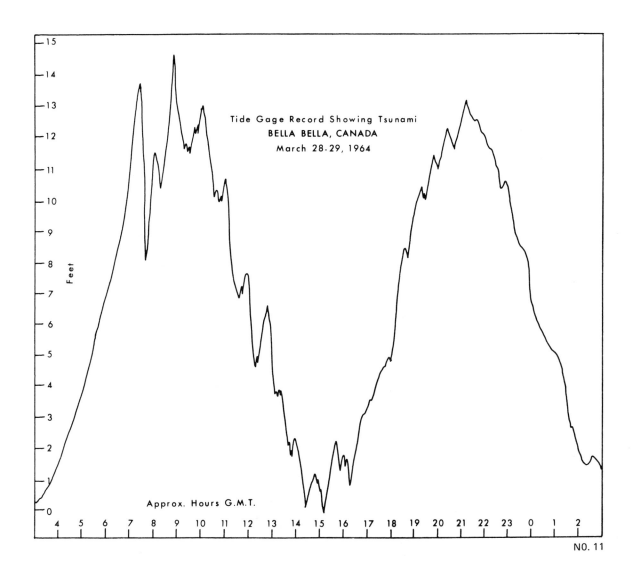

Tide Gage Record Showing Tsunami
BELLA BELLA, CANADA
March 28-29, 1964

Feet

Approx. Hours G.M.T.

NO. 11

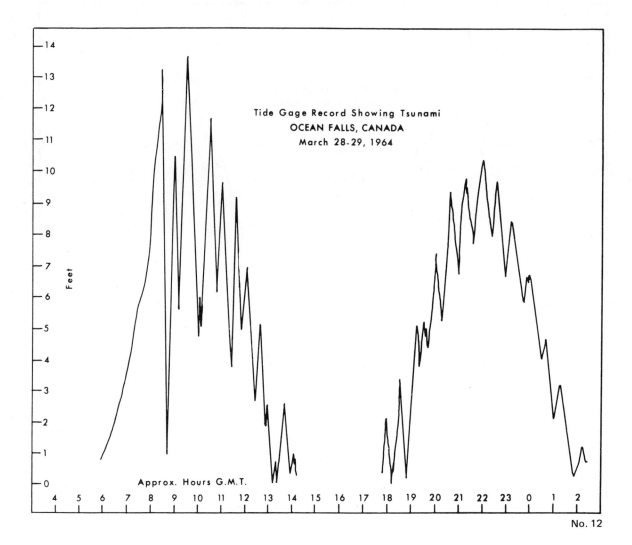

No. 12

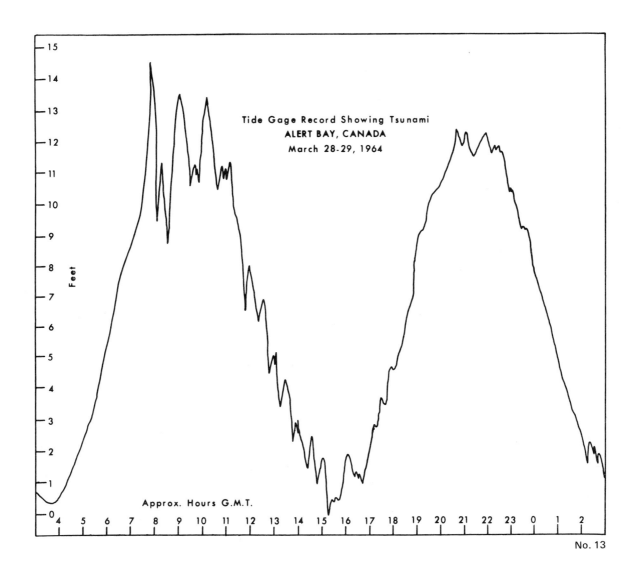

Tide Gage Record Showing Tsunami
ALERT BAY, CANADA
March 28-29, 1964

No. 13

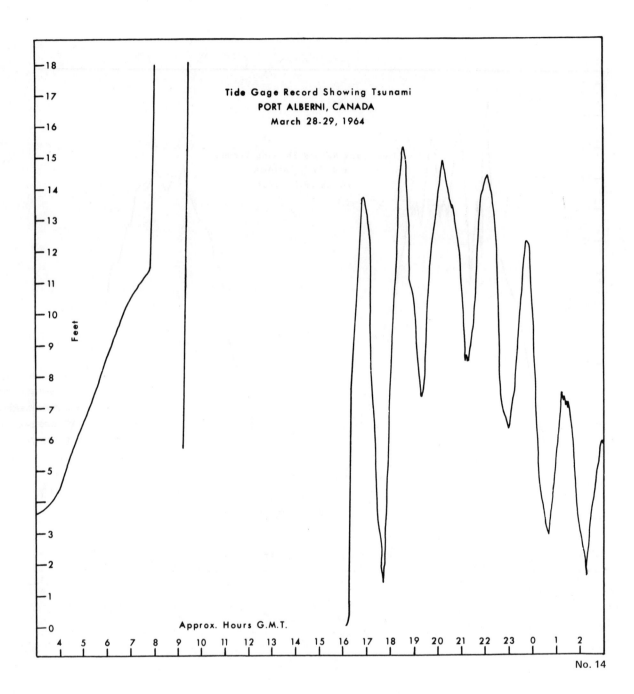

Tide Gage Record Showing Tsunami
PORT ALBERNI, CANADA
March 28-29, 1964

Feet

Approx. Hours G.M.T.

No. 14

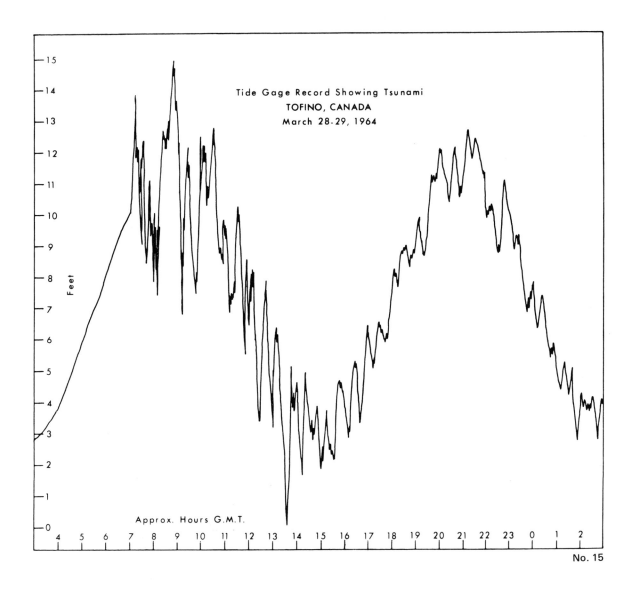

Tide Gage Record Showing Tsunami
TOFINO, CANADA
March 28-29, 1964

Approx. Hours G.M.T.

No. 15

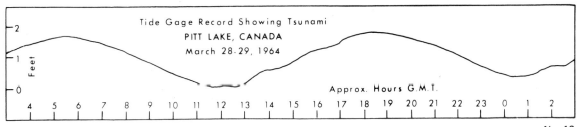

Tide Gage Record Showing Tsunami
PITT LAKE, CANADA
March 28-29, 1964

Approx. Hours G.M.T.

No. 16

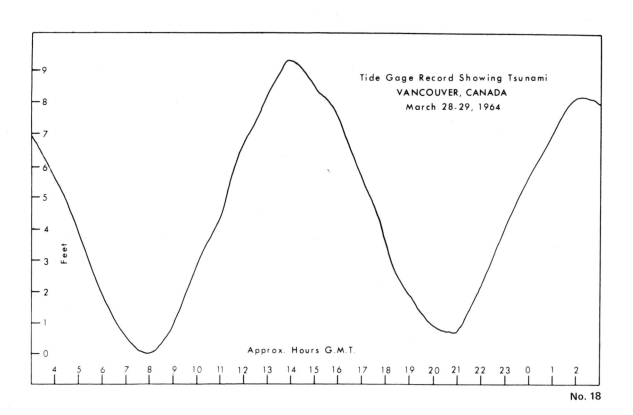

Tide Gage Record Showing Tsunami
POINT ATKINSON, CANADA
March 28-29, 1964

Approx. Hours G.M.T.

Feet

No. 17

Tide Gage Record Showing Tsunami
VANCOUVER, CANADA
March 28-29, 1964

Approx. Hours G.M.T.

Feet

No. 18

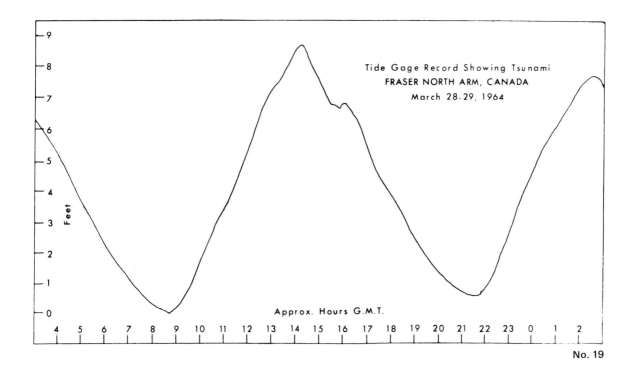

Tide Gage Record Showing Tsunami
FRASER NORTH ARM, CANADA
March 28-29, 1964

Approx. Hours G.M.T.

No. 19

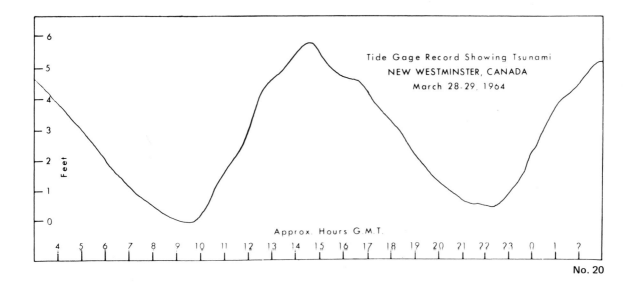

Tide Gage Record Showing Tsunami
NEW WESTMINSTER, CANADA
March 28-29, 1964

Approx. Hours G.M.T.

No. 20

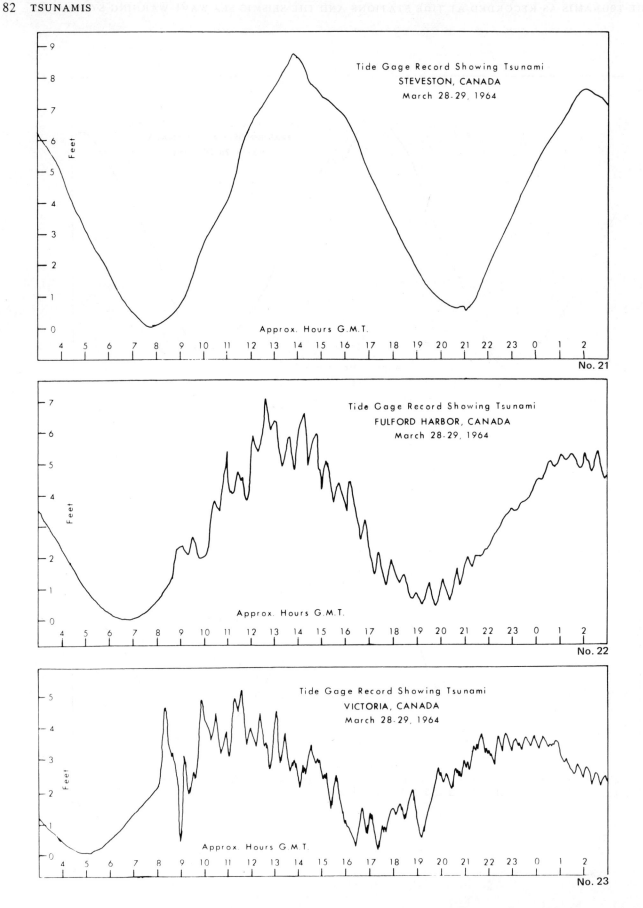

Tide Gage Record Showing Tsunami
STEVESTON, CANADA
March 28-29, 1964

Approx. Hours G.M.T.

No. 21

Tide Gage Record Showing Tsunami
FULFORD HARBOR, CANADA
March 28-29, 1964

Approx. Hours G.M.T.

No. 22

Tide Gage Record Showing Tsunami
VICTORIA, CANADA
March 28-29, 1964

Approx. Hours G.M.T.

No. 23

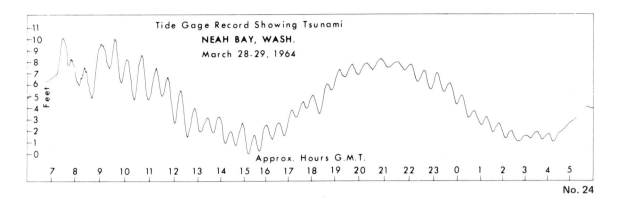

Tide Gage Record Showing Tsunami
NEAH BAY, WASH.
March 28-29, 1964

No. 24

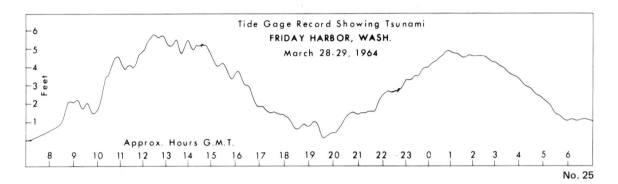

Tide Gage Record Showing Tsunami
FRIDAY HARBOR, WASH.
March 28-29, 1964

No. 25

Tide Gage Record Showing Tsunami
SEATTLE, WASH.
March 28-29, 1964

No. 26

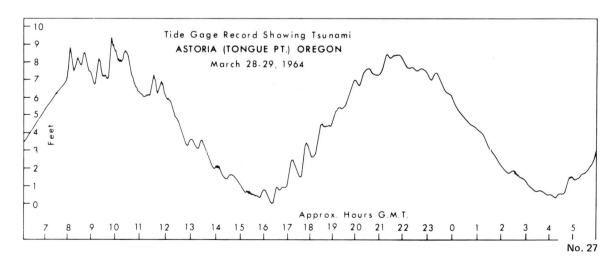

Tide Gage Record Showing Tsunami
ASTORIA (TONGUE PT.) OREGON
March 28-29, 1964

No. 27

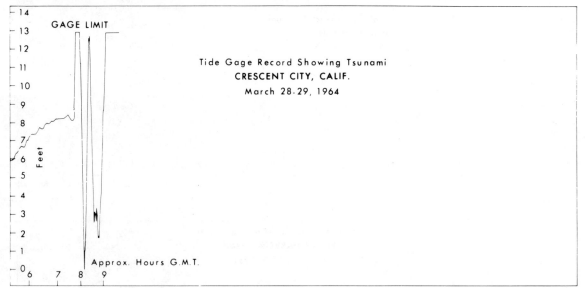

Tide Gage Record Showing Tsunami
CRESCENT CITY, CALIF.
March 28-29, 1964

No. 28

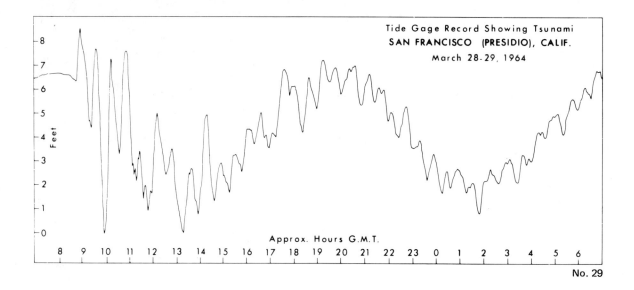

Tide Gage Record Showing Tsunami
SAN FRANCISCO (PRESIDIO), CALIF.
March 28-29, 1964

No. 29

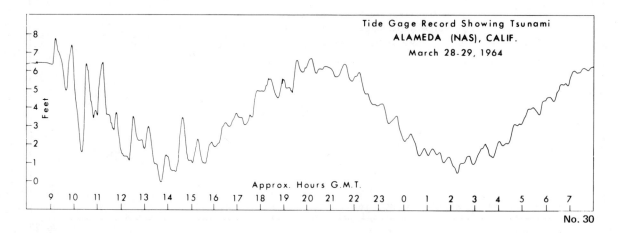

Tide Gage Record Showing Tsunami
ALAMEDA (NAS), CALIF.
March 28-29, 1964

No. 30

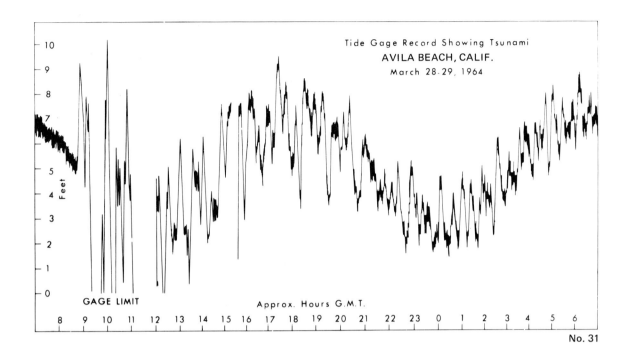

Tide Gage Record Showing Tsunami
AVILA BEACH, CALIF.
March 28-29, 1964

No. 31

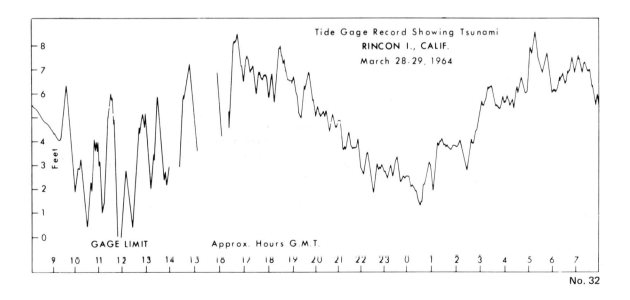

Tide Gage Record Showing Tsunami
RINCON I., CALIF.
March 28-29, 1964

No. 32

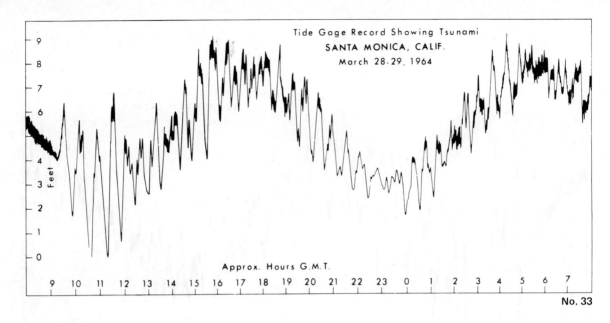

Tide Gage Record Showing Tsunami
SANTA MONICA, CALIF.
March 28-29, 1964

Approx. Hours G.M.T.

No. 33

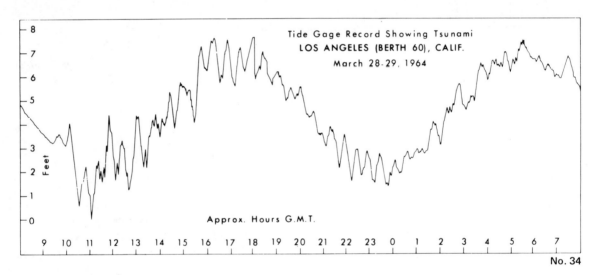

Tide Gage Record Showing Tsunami
LOS ANGELES (BERTH 60), CALIF.
March 28-29, 1964

Approx. Hours G.M.T.

No. 34

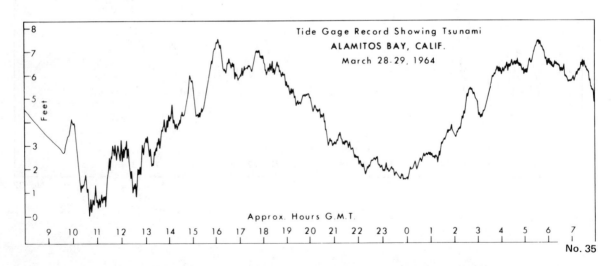

Tide Gage Record Showing Tsunami
ALAMITOS BAY, CALIF.
March 28-29, 1964

Approx. Hours G.M.T.

No. 35

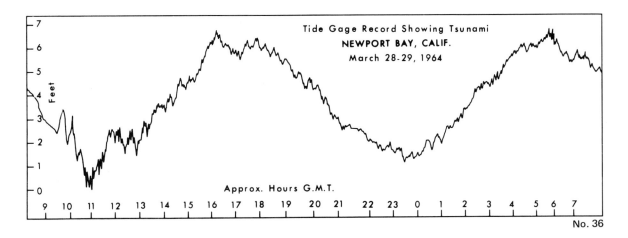

Tide Gage Record Showing Tsunami
NEWPORT BAY, CALIF.
March 28-29, 1964

Approx. Hours G.M.T.

No. 36

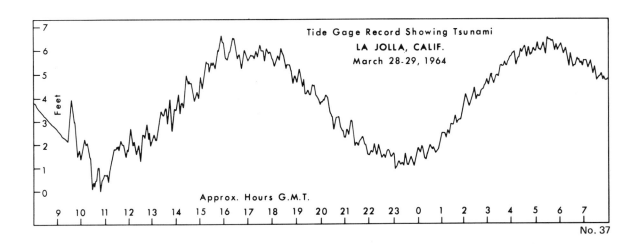

Tide Gage Record Showing Tsunami
LA JOLLA, CALIF.
March 28-29, 1964

Approx. Hours G.M.T.

No. 37

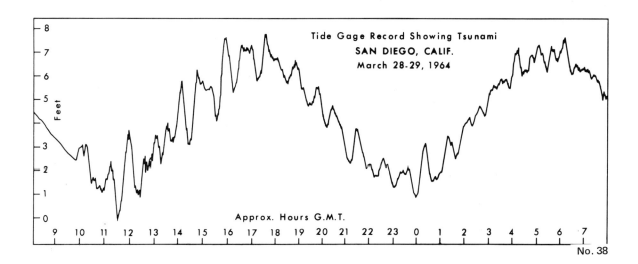

Tide Gage Record Showing Tsunami
SAN DIEGO, CALIF.
March 28-29, 1964

Approx. Hours G.M.T.

No. 38

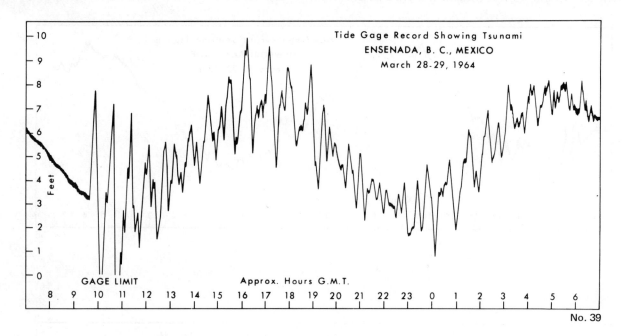

Tide Gage Record Showing Tsunami
ENSENADA, B. C., MEXICO
March 28-29, 1964

No. 39

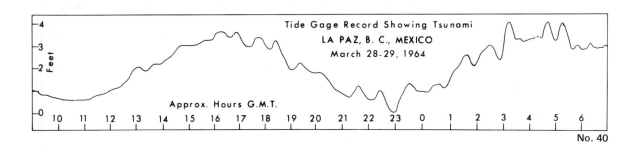

Tide Gage Record Showing Tsunami
LA PAZ, B. C., MEXICO
March 28-29, 1964

No. 40

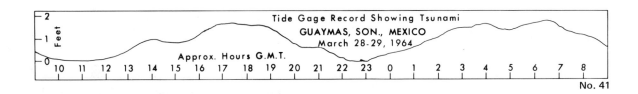

Tide Gage Record Showing Tsunami
GUAYMAS, SON., MEXICO
March 28-29, 1964

No. 41

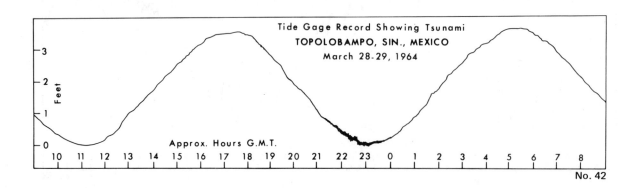

Tide Gage Record Showing Tsunami
TOPOLOBAMPO, SIN., MEXICO
March 28-29, 1964

No. 42

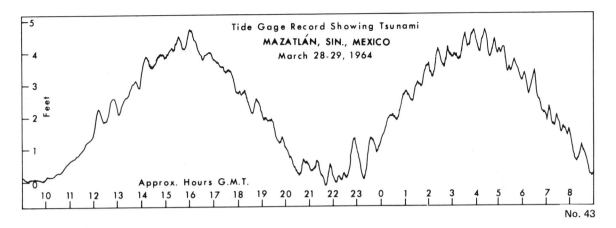

Tide Gage Record Showing Tsunami
MAZATLÁN, SIN., MEXICO
March 28-29, 1964

No. 43

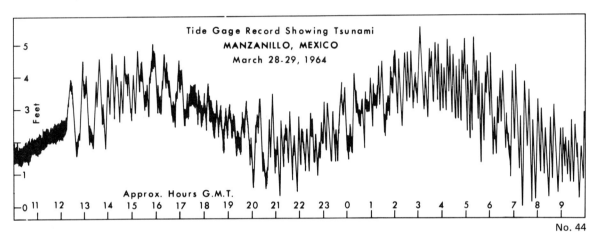

Tide Gage Record Showing Tsunami
MANZANILLO, MEXICO
March 28-29, 1964

No. 44

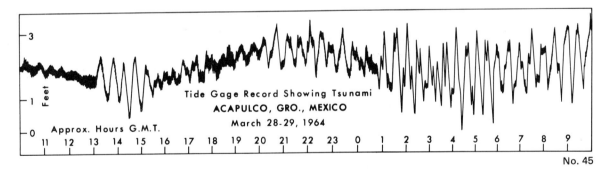

Tide Gage Record Showing Tsunami
ACAPULCO, GRO., MEXICO
March 28-29, 1964

No. 45

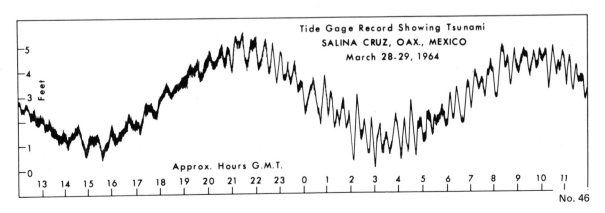

Tide Gage Record Showing Tsunami
SALINA CRUZ, OAX., MEXICO
March 28-29, 1964

No. 46

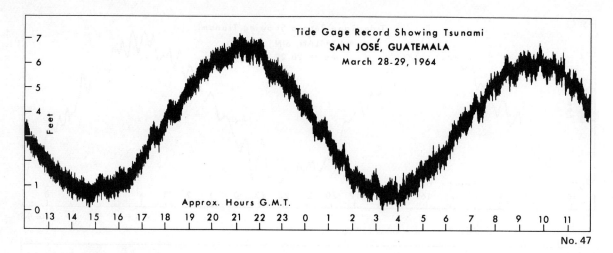

Tide Gage Record Showing Tsunami
SAN JOSÉ, GUATEMALA
March 28-29, 1964

No. 47

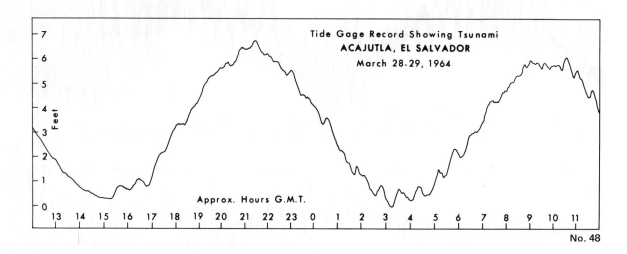

Tide Gage Record Showing Tsunami
ACAJUTLA, EL SALVADOR
March 28-29, 1964

No. 48

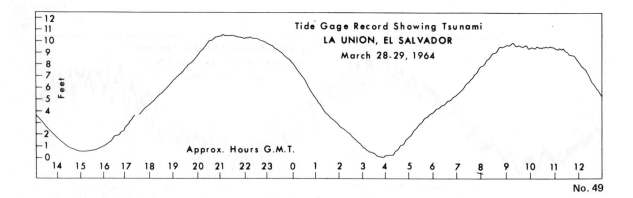

Tide Gage Record Showing Tsunami
LA UNION, EL SALVADOR
March 28-29, 1964

No. 49

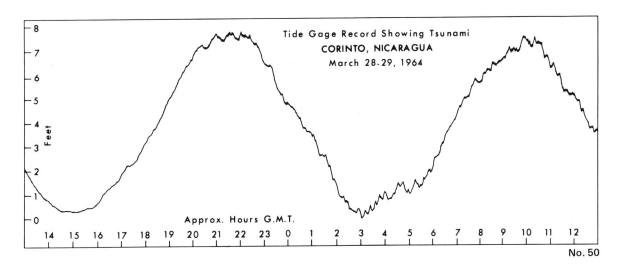

Tide Gage Record Showing Tsunami
CORINTO, NICARAGUA
March 28-29, 1964

Approx. Hours G.M.T.

No. 50

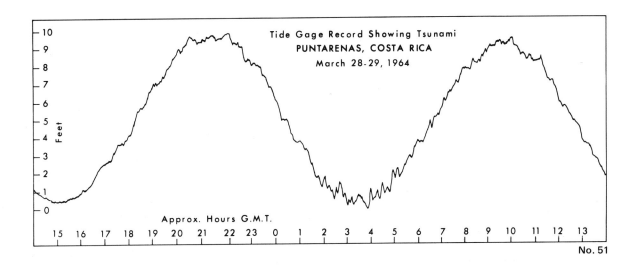

Tide Gage Record Showing Tsunami
PUNTARENAS, COSTA RICA
March 28-29, 1964

Approx. Hours G.M.T.

No. 51

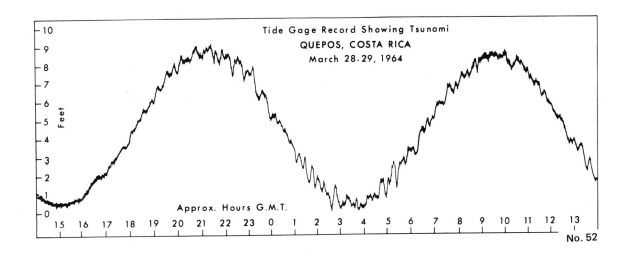

Tide Gage Record Showing Tsunami
QUEPOS, COSTA RICA
March 28-29, 1964

Approx. Hours G.M.T.

No. 52

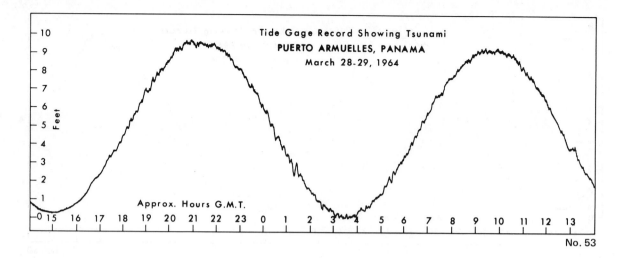

Tide Gage Record Showing Tsunami
PUERTO ARMUELLES, PANAMA
March 28-29, 1964

No. 53

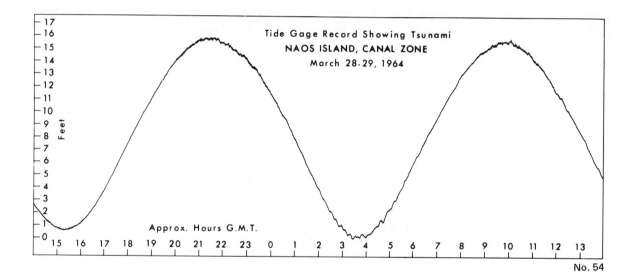

Tide Gage Record Showing Tsunami
NAOS ISLAND, CANAL ZONE
March 28-29, 1964

No. 54

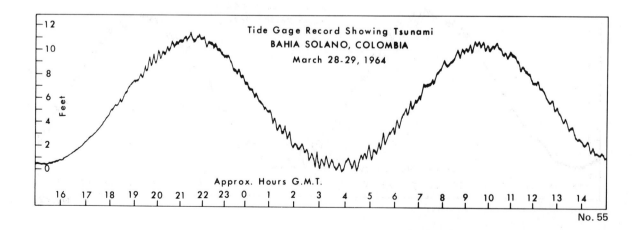

Tide Gage Record Showing Tsunami
BAHIA SOLANO, COLOMBIA
March 28-29, 1964

No. 55

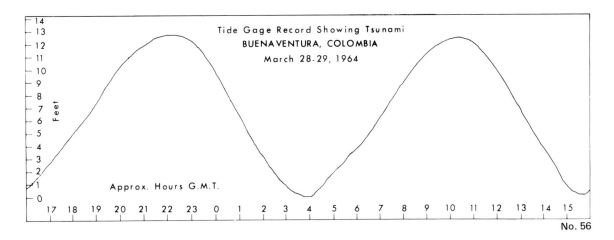

Tide Gage Record Showing Tsunami
BUENAVENTURA, COLOMBIA
March 28-29, 1964

No. 56

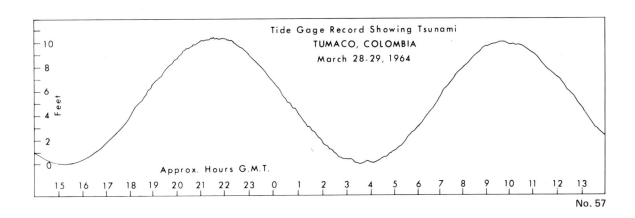

Tide Gage Record Showing Tsunami
TUMACO, COLOMBIA
March 28-29, 1964

No. 57

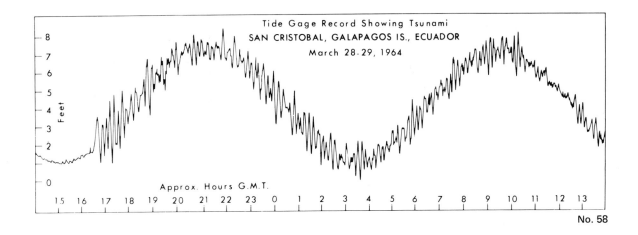

Tide Gage Record Showing Tsunami
SAN CRISTOBAL, GALAPAGOS IS., ECUADOR
March 28-29, 1964

No. 58

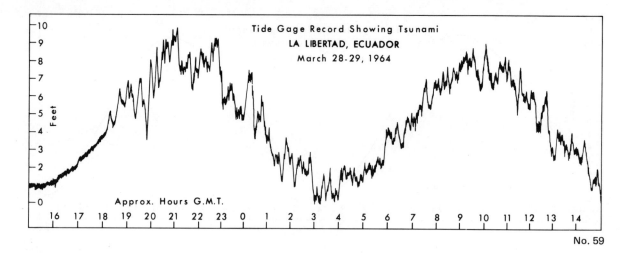

Tide Gage Record Showing Tsunami
LA LIBERTAD, ECUADOR
March 28-29, 1964

No. 59

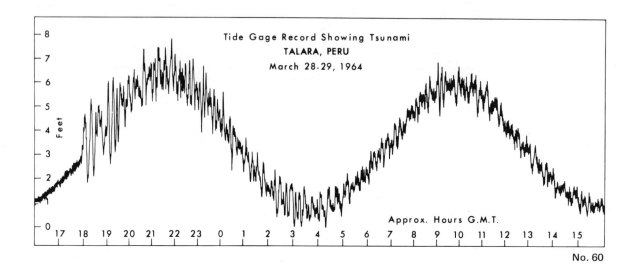

Tide Gage Record Showing Tsunami
TALARA, PERU
March 28-29, 1964

No. 60

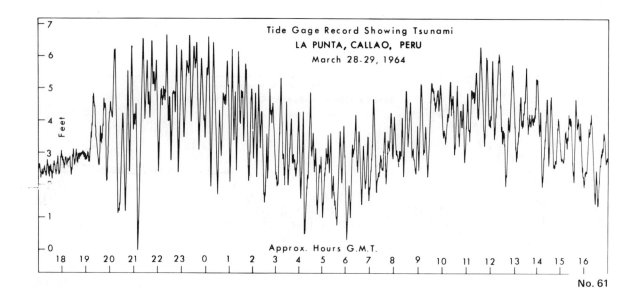

Tide Gage Record Showing Tsunami
LA PUNTA, CALLAO, PERU
March 28-29, 1964

No. 61

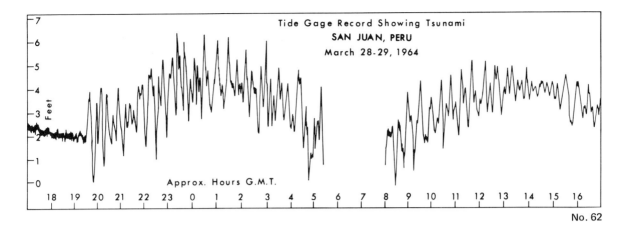

Tide Gage Record Showing Tsunami
SAN JUAN, PERU
March 28-29, 1964

No. 62

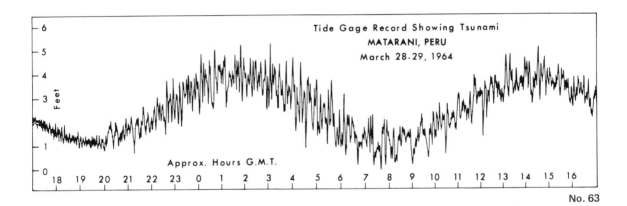

Tide Gage Record Showing Tsunami
MATARANI, PERU
March 28-29, 1964

No. 63

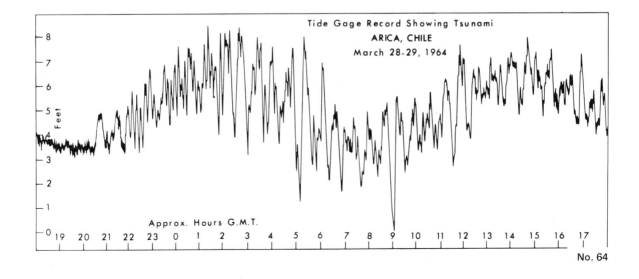

Tide Gage Record Showing Tsunami
ARICA, CHILE
March 28-29, 1964

No. 64

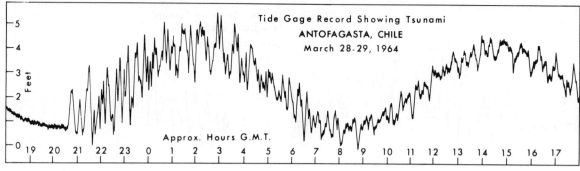

Tide Gage Record Showing Tsunami
ANTOFAGASTA, CHILE
March 28-29, 1964

Approx. Hours G.M.T.

No. 65

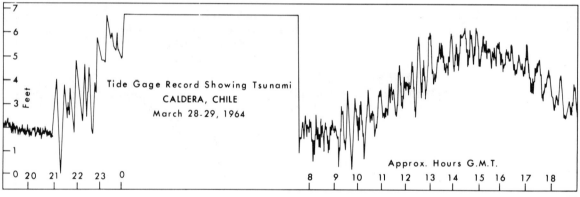

Tide Gage Record Showing Tsunami
CALDERA, CHILE
March 28-29, 1964

Approx. Hours G.M.T.

No. 66

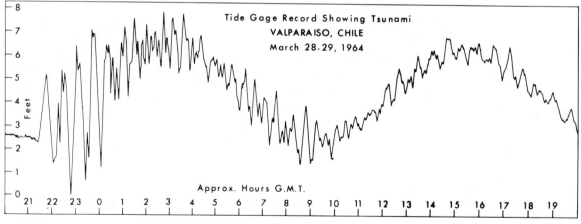

Tide Gage Record Showing Tsunami
VALPARAISO, CHILE
March 28-29, 1964

Approx. Hours G.M.T.

No. 67

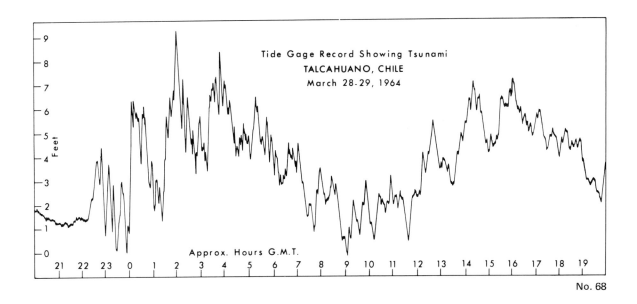

Tide Gage Record Showing Tsunami
TALCAHUANO, CHILE
March 28-29, 1964

Approx. Hours G.M.T.

No. 68

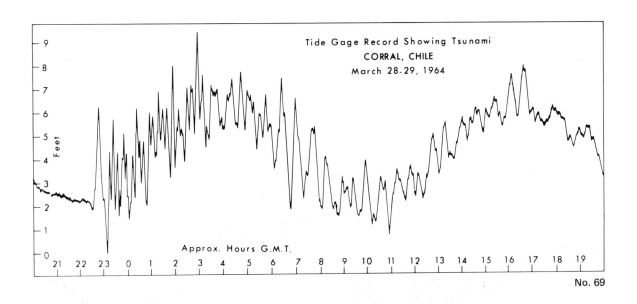

Tide Gage Record Showing Tsunami
CORRAL, CHILE
March 28-29, 1964

Approx. Hours G.M.T.

No. 69

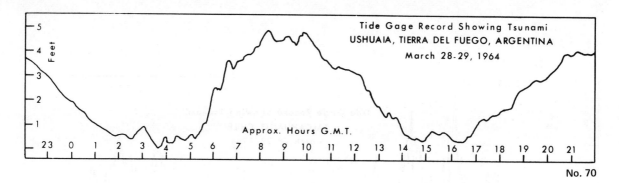

Tide Gage Record Showing Tsunami
USHUAIA, TIERRA DEL FUEGO, ARGENTINA
March 28-29, 1964

Approx. Hours G.M.T.

No. 70

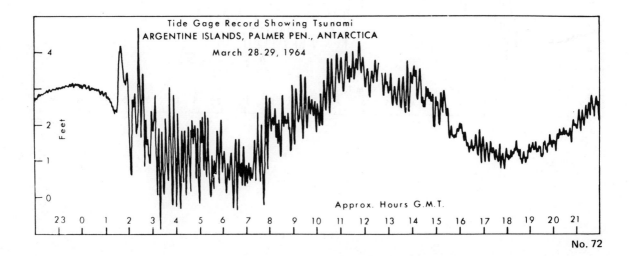

Tide Gage Record Showing Tsunami
BAHIA ESPERANZA, PALMER PEN., ANTARCTICA
March 28-29, 1964

Approx. Hours G.M.T.

No. 71

Tide Gage Record Showing Tsunami
ARGENTINE ISLANDS, PALMER PEN., ANTARCTICA
March 28-29, 1964

Approx. Hours G.M.T.

No. 72

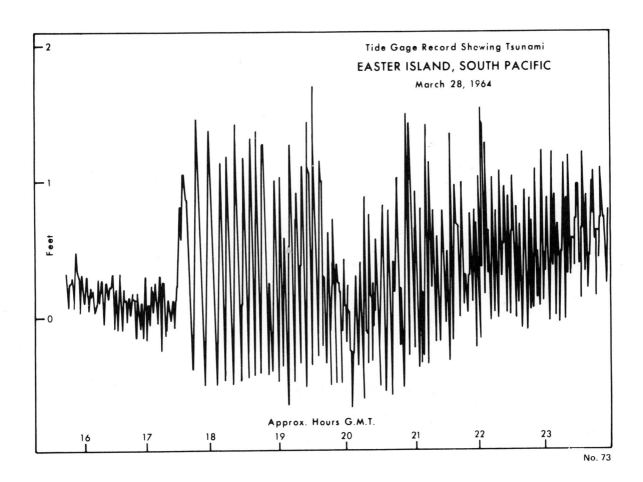

Tide Gage Record Showing Tsunami
EASTER ISLAND, SOUTH PACIFIC
March 28, 1964

No. 73

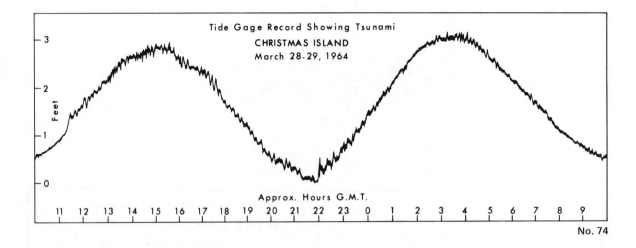

Tide Gage Record Showing Tsunami
CHRISTMAS ISLAND
March 28-29, 1964

No. 74

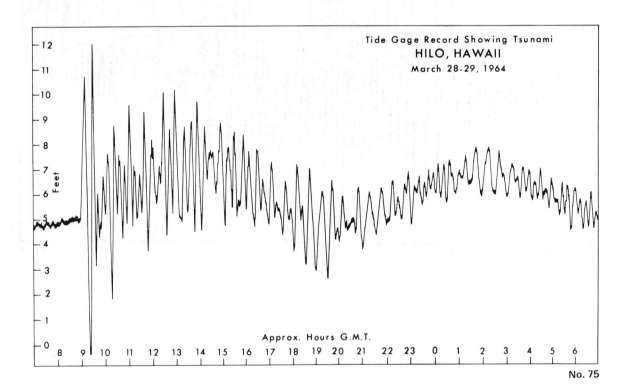

Tide Gage Record Showing Tsunami
HILO, HAWAII
March 28-29, 1964

No. 75

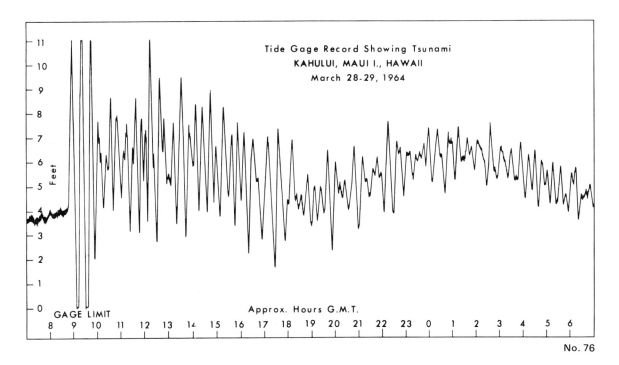

Tide Gage Record Showing Tsunami
KAHULUI, MAUI I., HAWAII
March 28-29, 1964

No. 76

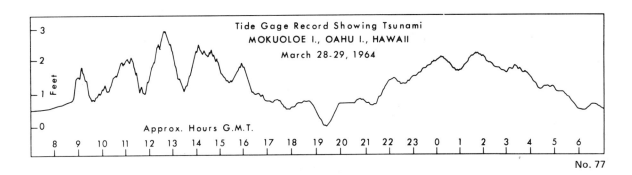

Tide Gage Record Showing Tsunami
MOKUOLOE I., OAHU I., HAWAII
March 28-29, 1964

No. 77

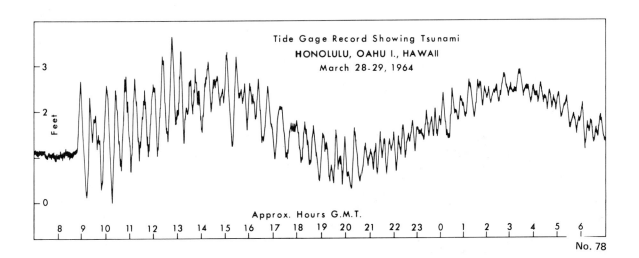

Tide Gage Record Showing Tsunami
HONOLULU, OAHU I., HAWAII
March 28-29, 1964

No. 78

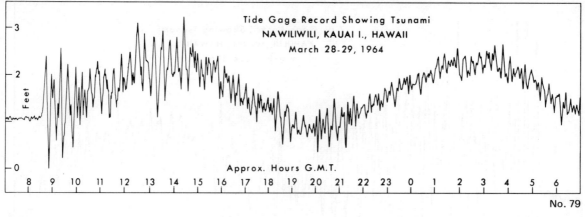

Tide Gage Record Showing Tsunami
NAWILIWILI, KAUAI I., HAWAII
March 28-29, 1964

Approx. Hours G.M.T.

No. 79

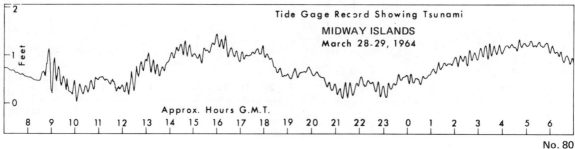

Tide Gage Record Showing Tsunami
MIDWAY ISLANDS
March 28-29, 1964

Approx. Hours G.M.T.

No. 80

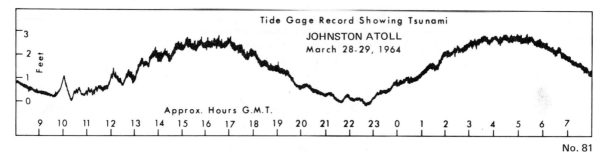

Tide Gage Record Showing Tsunami
JOHNSTON ATOLL
March 28-29, 1964

Approx. Hours G.M.T.

No. 81

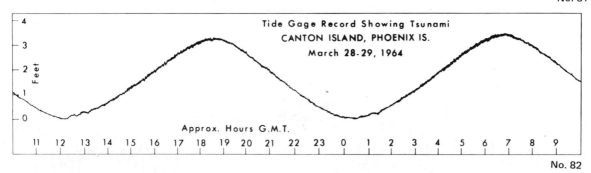

Tide Gage Record Showing Tsunami
CANTON ISLAND, PHOENIX IS.
March 28-29, 1964

Approx. Hours G.M.T.

No. 82

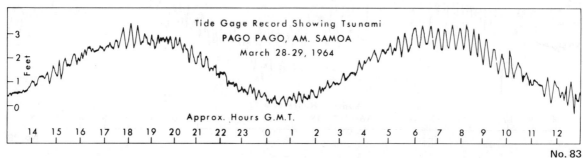

Tide Gage Record Showing Tsunami
PAGO PAGO, AM. SAMOA
March 28-29, 1964

Approx. Hours G.M.T.

No. 83

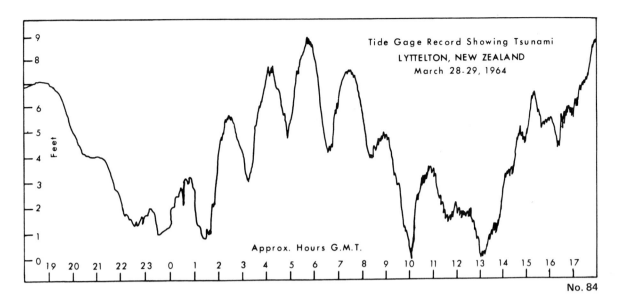

Tide Gage Record Showing Tsunami
LYTTELTON, NEW ZEALAND
March 28-29, 1964

No. 84

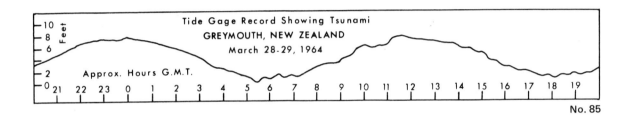

Tide Gage Record Showing Tsunami
GREYMOUTH, NEW ZEALAND
March 28-29, 1964

No. 85

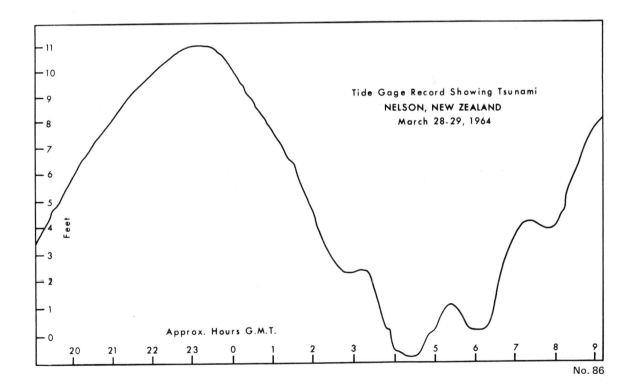

Tide Gage Record Showing Tsunami
NELSON, NEW ZEALAND
March 28-29, 1964

No. 86

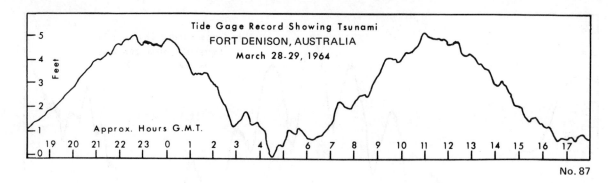

Tide Gage Record Showing Tsunami
FORT DENISON, AUSTRALIA
March 28-29, 1964

Approx. Hours G.M.T.

No. 87

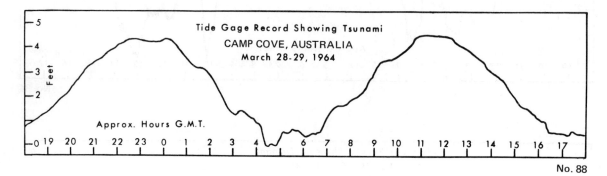

Tide Gage Record Showing Tsunami
CAMP COVE, AUSTRALIA
March 28-29, 1964

Approx. Hours G.M.T.

No. 88

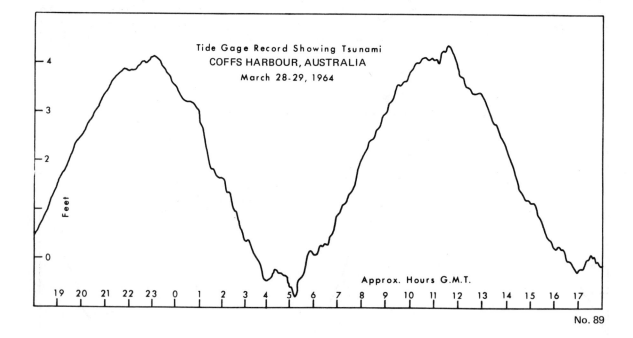

Tide Gage Record Showing Tsunami
COFFS HARBOUR, AUSTRALIA
March 28-29, 1964

Approx. Hours G.M.T.

No. 89

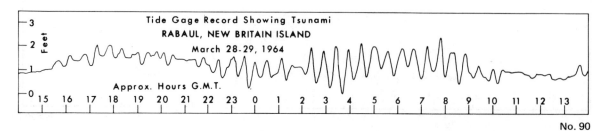

Tide Gage Record Showing Tsunami
RABAUL, NEW BRITAIN ISLAND
March 28-29, 1964

Approx. Hours G.M.T.

No. 90

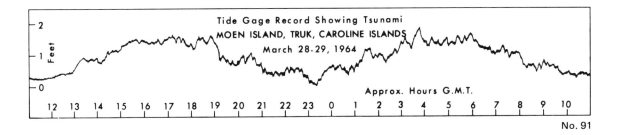

Tide Gage Record Showing Tsunami
MOEN ISLAND, TRUK, CAROLINE ISLANDS
March 28-29, 1964

Approx. Hours G.M.T.

No. 91

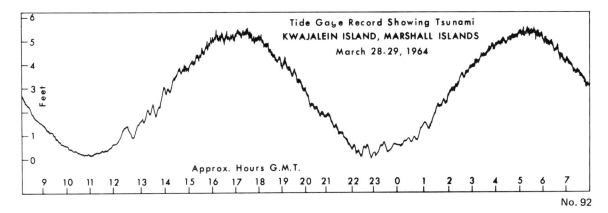

Tide Gage Record Showing Tsunami
KWAJALEIN ISLAND, MARSHALL ISLANDS
March 28-29, 1964

Approx. Hours G.M.T.

No. 92

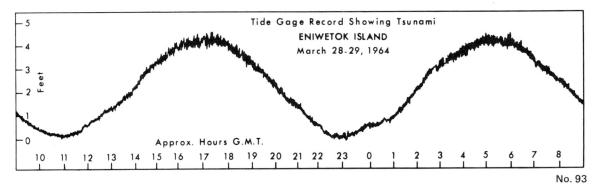

Tide Gage Record Showing Tsunami
ENIWETOK ISLAND
March 28-29, 1964

Approx. Hours G.M.T.

No. 93

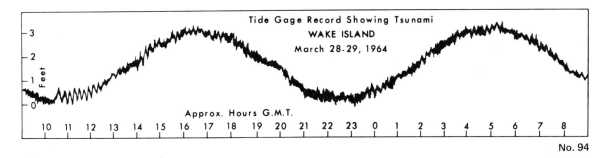

Tide Gage Record Showing Tsunami
WAKE ISLAND
March 28-29, 1964

Approx. Hours G.M.T.

No. 94

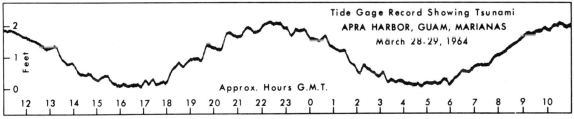

Tide Gage Record Showing Tsunami
APRA HARBOR, GUAM, MARIANAS
March 28-29, 1964

Approx. Hours G.M.T.

No. 96

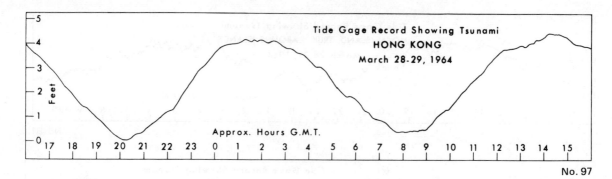

Tide Gage Record Showing Tsunami
HONG KONG
March 28-29, 1964

Approx. Hours G.M.T.

No. 97

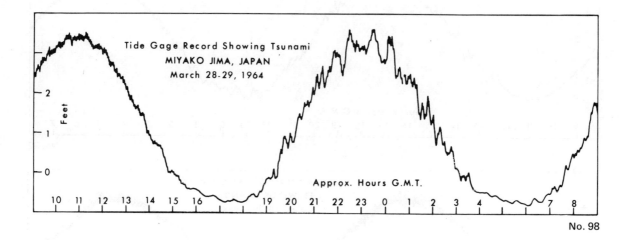

Tide Gage Record Showing Tsunami
MIYAKO JIMA, JAPAN
March 28-29, 1964

Approx. Hours G.M.T.

No. 98

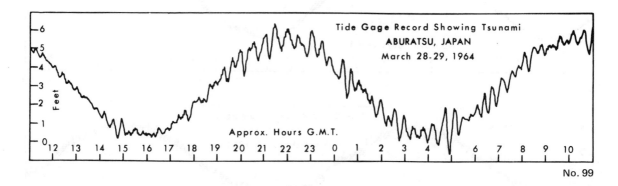

Tide Gage Record Showing Tsunami
ABURATSU, JAPAN
March 28-29, 1964

Approx. Hours G.M.T.

No. 99

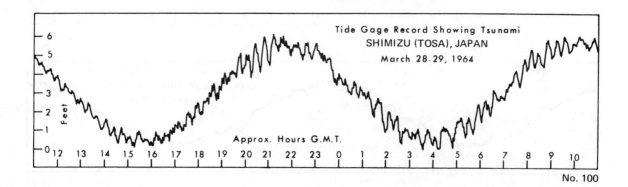

Tide Gage Record Showing Tsunami
SHIMIZU (TOSA), JAPAN
March 28-29, 1964

Approx. Hours G.M.T.

No. 100

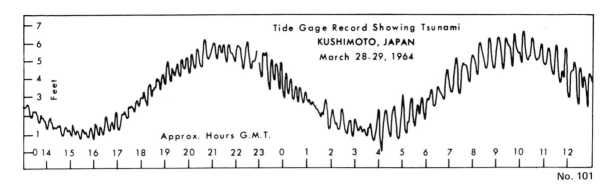

Tide Gage Record Showing Tsunami
KUSHIMOTO, JAPAN
March 28-29, 1964

Approx. Hours G.M.T.

No. 101

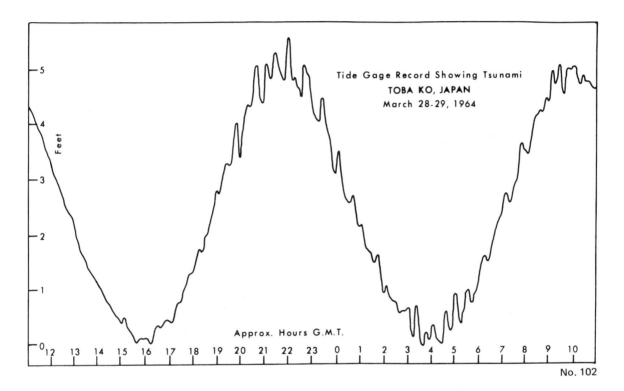

Tide Gage Record Showing Tsunami
TOBA KO, JAPAN
March 28-29, 1964

Approx. Hours G.M.T.

No. 102

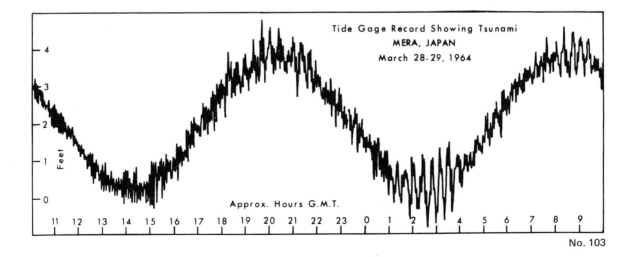

Tide Gage Record Showing Tsunami
MERA, JAPAN
March 28-29, 1964

Approx. Hours G.M.T.

No. 103

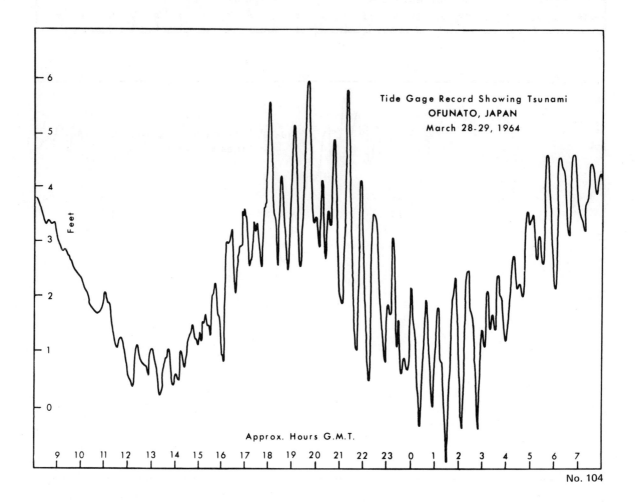

Tide Gage Record Showing Tsunami
OFUNATO, JAPAN
March 28-29, 1964

Feet

Approx. Hours G.M.T.

No. 104

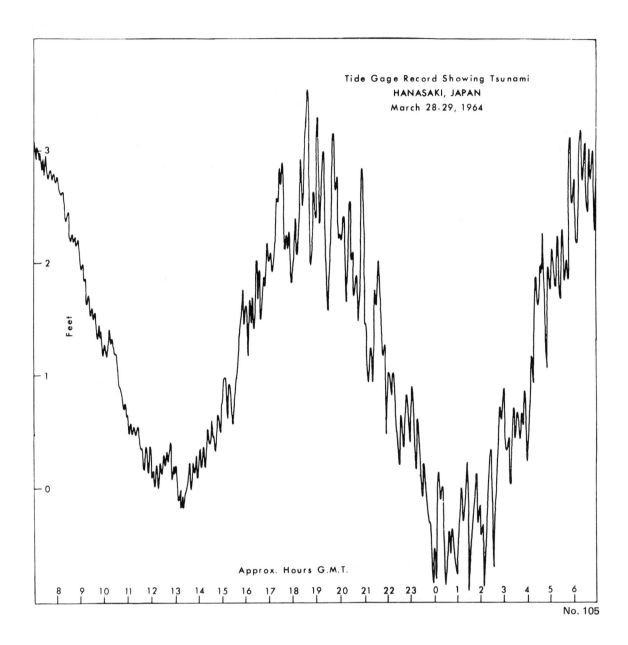

Tide Gage Record Showing Tsunami
HANASAKI, JAPAN
March 28-29, 1964

No. 105

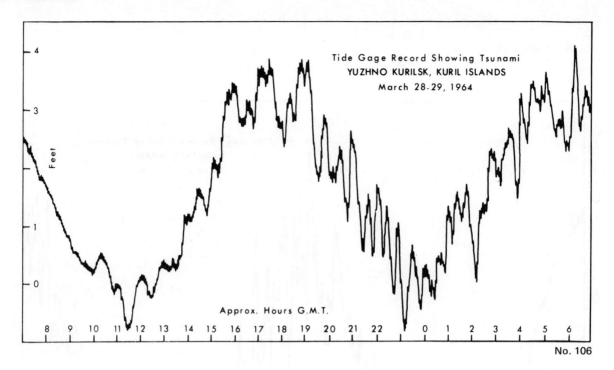

Tide Gage Record Showing Tsunami
YUZHNO KURILSK, KURIL ISLANDS
March 28-29, 1964

No. 106

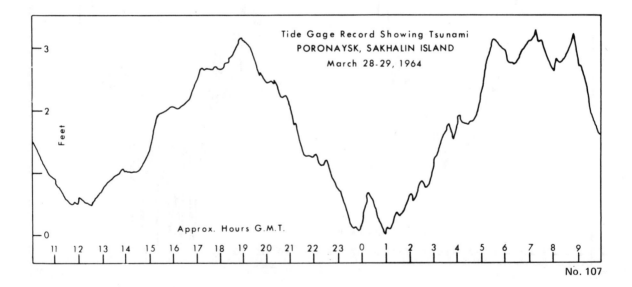

Tide Gage Record Showing Tsunami
PORONAYSK, SAKHALIN ISLAND
March 28-29, 1964

No. 107

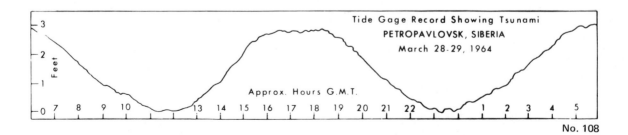

Tide Gage Record Showing Tsunami
PETROPAVLOVSK, SIBERIA
March 28-29, 1964

No. 108

WILLIAM G. VAN DORN
SCRIPPS INSTITUTION OF OCEANOGRAPHY

Reprinted with minor changes from
Proceedings of the Ninth Conference on Coastal Engineering,
"Source Mechanism of the Tsunami of March 28, 1964 in Alaska"

Source Mechanism of the Major Tsunami

INTRODUCTORY NOTE: The following paper was submitted for publication in the *Proceedings of the Ninth Conference on Coastal Engineering*, American Society of Civil Engineers, less than 2 months after the Alaska earthquake. Thus, many of the conclusions therein depend upon preliminary evidence, a large part of which was collected personally by the author within a week after the earthquake.

Nevertheless, except for the fact that subsequent detailed surveys have shown that the amplitude of the ground motion in the immediate vicinity of Montague Island was substantially greater (40–50 ft) than that reported in the present paper (8 ft), none of the vast amount of subsequent survey information obtained within the past 5 years substantially alters the general pattern of the crustal deformations apparent soon after the earthquake. Thus, the conclusions relevant to tsunami generation in this paper remain substantially unchanged.

Of some interest among the subsequent studies is a paper by Mikumo (1968), who, acting on a suggestion made in the present paper, investigated the Fourier spectra of the atmospheric pulse from the Alaska earthquake recorded at several barometric stations. Mikumo finds general agreement between these barograms and a theoretical model for surface displacements that appears to be consistent with the observed deformations. He concludes that the time scale of the deformations could not have been longer than 3 minutes without seriously affecting the agreement obtained.

ABSTRACT: The distribution of permanent, vertical crustal dislocations, the times and directions of early water motion in and around the generation area, and the unusual, low-frequency character of the tsunami record obtained from Wake Island, all suggest that the tsunami associated with the great Alaska earthquake of March 28, 1964, was produced by a dipolar movement of the earth's crust, centered along a line running from Hinchinbrook Island (Prince William Sound) southwesterly to the Trinity Islands. The positive pole of this disturbance encompassed most of the shallow shelf bordering the Gulf of Alaska, while the negative pole lay mostly under land. Thus, the early effect was the drainage of water from the shelf into the Gulf, thus generating a long solitary wave, which radiated out over the Pacific with very little dispersion.

Tilting of Prince William Sound to the northwest produced strong seiching action in the deep, narrow adjacent fiords, thus inundating inhabited places already suffering from earth shock and slumping of the deltas on which they were situated.

Preliminary calculations indicate that the potential energy of the initial water displacement for the tsunami was about 2.3×10^{21} ergs, as compared with 2.7×10^{22} ergs computed for the tsunami of March 9, 1957, in the Andreanof Islands.

The dipolar dislocation also produced a "tsunami" in the atmosphere which was recorded in La Jolla, indicating that the dislocations must have occurred during the period (about 2–6 min) of strong ground motion near the epicenter.

INTRODUCTION

On March 28, 1964, at 0336 GMT, the largest North American earthquake of this century occurred in south central Alaska. The epicentral coordinates for the principal shock (Richter magnitude 8.4) are currently (as of May 1964) taken as $61.05°$N, $147.5°$W, focal depth less than 20 km, although these coordinates may be subject to later revision, owing to the long-continuing nature of the seismic signals and the fact that lesser shocks occurred as much as 2 hours earlier in the same vicinity. The great strength and shallow depth of this earthquake were visibly manifested by violent dynamic earth motions over a radius of more than 200 km in all directions. The duration of these motions, during which time it was difficult or impossible for people to run or even stand erect, was reported to be from 3 to 8 minutes in various localities. Deep ground fissures, snow and rock avalanches, and permanent changes in land elevations relative to sea level also occurred in most of the areas of strong ground motion, and, presumably, over a similar period of time. Closely following the principal shocks, tsunami waves were reported in many areas of the Gulf of Alaska and adjacent Prince William Sound. The main tsunami, which subsequently spread out over the Pacific Ocean, appears to have been of rather moderate intensity, generating oscillations of several feet in amplitude in bays and harbors around the Pacific, but causing relatively little damage beyond the immediate area of generation.

There is no doubt that the severity of this tsunami was substantially mitigated because it occurred near the time of low tide in all areas where the waves were largest.

This great natural catastrophe was the immediate focus of attention of earth scientists from all over the world. To the author, it represented an unprecedented opportunity to reconstruct the generation mechanism for a tsunami, because the earthquake epicenter was located in a region where fairly precise geodetic control has existed for some decades, and because it was probable that enough local eyewitness accounts of the water-wave chronology might be obtained to put together a systematic picture of the generation process. Although it is apparent at this writing that many months will elapse before the land-elevation changes relative to sea level will be known in detail, obvious vertical displacements occurred in many places along the seacoast and islands in the Gulf of Alaska of sufficient magnitude to be easily distinguishable (by the trained eye) from the normal tide range. Thus, it is already possible to draw some fairly firm qualitative conclusions regarding the generation process, although its quantitative aspects must await more accurate data. An essential feature of this reconstruction is the wave record obtained at a special recording station installed at Wake Island in 1960 (Van Dorn, 1960). Because this record can be used within limits as an indicator of the deepwater nature of this tsunami, it serves as a check on the mode of generation hypothesized from other considerations.

BACKGROUND

There have been several attempts to estimate the generation mechanism of tsunamis. Most of these are inconclusive for lack of specific evidence of the sea-floor readjustment, although Nagata (1950) has shown in the case of the great Nankaido earthquake of December 21, 1946, near Shikoku that the dislocations on land can be quite complex. Miyabe (1934) attempted to compute the size of the tsunami-generation area for the Sanriku earthquake (March 3, 1933) by projecting wave fronts back toward the epicenter from observation stations along the shore. According to Takahasi (personal communication), the generation areas determined by such constructions generally agree with those delimiting the areas of earthquake aftershocks obtained from seismic evidence. Van Dorn (1963) computed the equivalent axisymmetric source which could have produced the wave spectrum observed for the tsunami of March 1957 at Wake Island. Kajiura (1963) has pointed out that, aside from explosions, seismic sources cannot be expected to be axisymmetric, and he has given solutions for asymmetric sources of various types. Never before, however, has a sufficiently detailed knowledge been obtained of seafloor motion, type of wave

action, and the deep-water spectrum offshore, to permit a convincing reconstruction of the generation mechanism.

GEOMORPHOLOGY

According to the U.S. Coast and Geodetic Survey (1964), the substructure of the region affected by the earthquake consists of a blanket of Cretaceous sediments which have subsequently been uplifted and deformed into a series of geanticlines and geosynclines, having a vertical relief as great as 10,000 ft. The axes of this accordion-like structure have been mapped from the Trinity Islands through Kodiak, up the Kenai Peninsula, and identified as outcrops at elevations as high as 5,000 or 6,000 ft in the Chugach Mountains (Figure 1). The entire structure is bent in an arc around the Gulf of Alaska, essentially paralleling the coast. Although the old tectonic history of this region appears to have been very complex, its present general appearance gives the impression that it is a coastline of submergence (Twenhofel, 1952) which has undergone recent, gradual uplift, except for small areas in the Prince William Sound and Copper River Delta areas. Figure 2 shows the general pattern of uplift as evidenced by a series of exposed marine terraces. Twenhofel reports that such secular changes have, in fact, been observed since the turn of the century in several areas where geodetic control exists, and rates of uplift as high as 7 or 8 ft per century have been recorded.

SEISMOLOGICAL HISTORY

The Gulf of Alaska, in common with the Aleutian Arc and the entire western border of North America, has a long history of repeated seismic activity and associated volcanism. The epicenters of earthquakes larger than magnitude 6 which have occurred since 1900 are shown in Figure 3, and it is apparent that several of the largest earthquakes occurred in the immediate region of Prince William Sound. Thus, the present earthquake was not particularly anomalous, from the standpoint of either magnitude or frequency of occurrence, since the most recent previous earthquake of this magnitude (8.4) occurred in nearby Yakutat Bay in 1899.

St.-Amand (1957) has probably made the most thorough study of the fault system of this region, which tends to follow the synclinal substructure parallel to the coast. Aftershocks from the present earthquake (Figure 4), however, are clustered in two loci—one in the vicinity of Hinchinbrook Island (A) and the other southeast of Kodiak (B), with scattered aftershocks in the region between them. The aftershock activity appears to have been essentially confined to the region of the westerly geanticline of the Cretaceous substructure, being mostly underwater beneath the shallow coastal shelf and bounded to the southeast by the Aleutian trench.

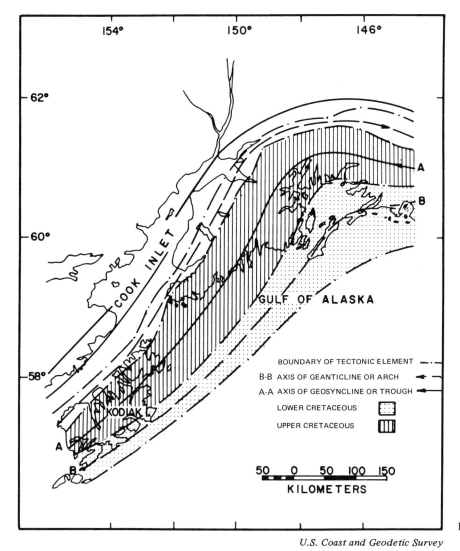

FIGURE 1   Tectonic map of epicentral area.

U.S. Coast and Geodetic Survey

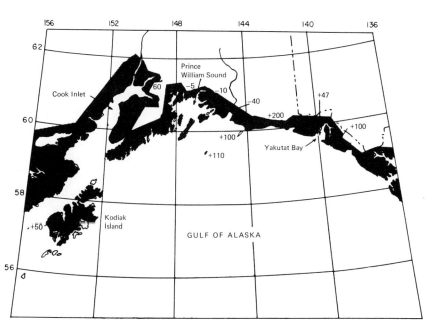

FIGURE 2   Recent land-elevation changes in Gulf of Alaska (after Twenhofel).

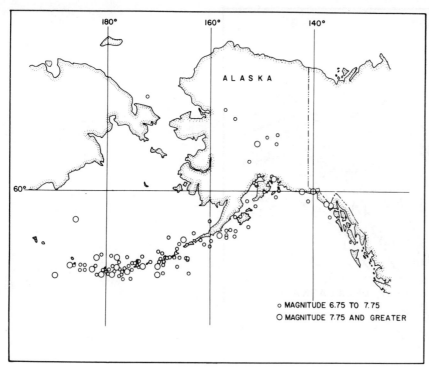

○ MAGNITUDE 6.75 TO 7.75
◯ MAGNITUDE 7.75 AND GREATER

FIGURE 3 Distribution of large earthquakes in Gulf of Alaska since 1899.

U.S. Coast and Geodetic Survey

NATURE OF THE GROUND MOTION

A remarkable feature of this earthquake, which became apparent very early during the field survey, was the enormous extent of the areas that had undergone relatively large vertical changes in elevation relative to sea level. Virtually the entire Kenai Peninsula, from the Turnagain Arm of Cook Inlet, including the Kenai–Kodiak Ridge and Kodiak Island itself, appears to have subsided by 2 to 6 ft. At the same time, most of the land areas along the seacoast from the Yakutat area to the center of Prince William Sound have been elevated by similar amounts. The time rates of these displacements are unknown, but they appear to have been of the same order as that of the intense ground motion (2-6 min), since many observers reported immediate water withdrawal from the elevated regions. Additionally, an atmospheric gravity wave transient was recorded on a special microbarograph at the Scripps Institution of Oceanography, beginning at 280655Z (Figure 5). Such atmospheric pulsations are a common feature associated with the detonation of large nuclear explosions, but, to the author's knowledge, have not previously been observed in connection with earthquake motions. Pressure pulses from the explosions outside the region of hypercompression propagate at acoustic velocity in the lower atmosphere (about 1,050 ± 30 ft per second). Therefore, the initiating disturbance—if it originated in the vicinity of the reported epicenter—occurred at about the same time as the principal shock. Such a pressure disturbance in this case

could only have been produced by vertical motions of the earth over a very large area and in a time of the order of that required for an acoustic wave to propagate across dimensions of the generator. Thus, a substantial fraction of the net motion inferred from relative sea-level changes must have occurred very rapidly.

The present picture of the areas of permanent dislocation is shown in Figure 6. It should be borne in mind that most of these figures are tentative, some being obtained on the basis of preliminary surveys by the U.S. Coast and Geodetic Survey, while others are only estimated by measurements to local sea level at some later time and are largely based on the long-term experience of local inhabitants. Such observations as these, carried on over a period of several weeks, are probably accurate to about 1 ft, although smaller changes are readily apparent to fishermen and mariners who have had long experience with the tides in a particular area. The tentative distribution of these dislocations is included, for the most part, within the same perimeter that circumscribes the earthquake aftershocks. Also shown in this figure are the axes of the synclinal ridges and troughs of the Cretaceous substructure, transferred from Figure 1, and a schematic profile section *M-M*. Significantly, perhaps, the general trend of surface dislocations is well mapped by the "contour lines" of the substructure: negative elevation changes lie to the west and north of the line *P-P* dividing the Kodiak geosyncline from the shelf geanticline, and all the areas of positive elevation lie to the south and east of this line. It almost appears as if the observed dislocations could have been produced by slight increase in

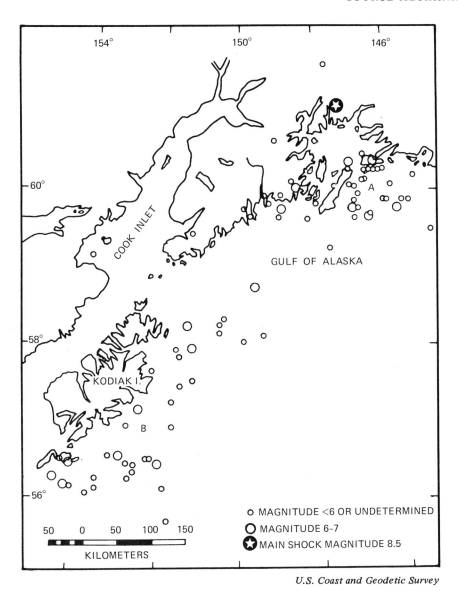

U.S. Coast and Geodetic Survey

FIGURE 4 Distribution of aftershocks occurring during first 9 days after earthquake of March 28, 1964.

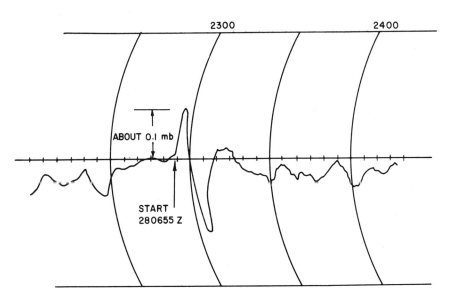

FIGURE 5 Microbarograph record from La Jolla, showing atmospheric tsunami from Alaska earthquake (signature is typical of that for large dipole source).

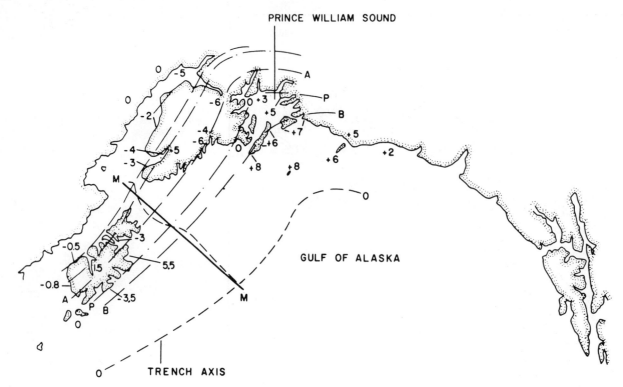

FIGURE 6   Tentative distribution of land dislocations (in feet) relative to sea level in Gulf of Alaska after earthquake of March 28, 1964.

the subsurface deformation. It is certainly beyond the author's training and experience to comment on this seeming coincidence, but, as will be shown, this interpretation permits an extrapolation of the pattern of surface dislocations out under the sea, which is quite consistent with that obtained from interpretation of the surface-wave history.

THE PATTERN OF EARLY WATER MOTION

During the field survey, a strenuous attempt was made to obtain information on the chronology and direction of early water motion, particularly in Prince William Sound, since it was felt that the key to the tsunami-generation problem might hinge on the decision as to whether the tsunami originated close to the reported epicenter or in some other region outside the Sound. As it turned out, the region of wave generation was very much larger than the Sound, encompassing most of the shelf bordering the Gulf of Alaska.

The hydrodynamic situation in Prince William Sound at early times after the principal shock is shown in Figure 7. Land-elevation changes (in feet) are shown by the numerals in this figure. As already mentioned, the positive and negative changes are separated into two regions by a line of zero change in elevation. Within the Sound, this line runs through Point Elrington, up the Knight Island Passage, through Perry

Island, and curves away toward the east—possibly through Port Valdez. So far, no specific data on change of elevation at Valdez are available. The reported subsidence there was probably due to the settling of the alluvial delta on which the town is built. The pattern of earthquake and wave damage at Valdez is typical of what occurred also at Seward, Whittier, and numerous uninhabited areas of the Sound. Such glacial deltas possess very steep angles of repose (approximately 45°) beneath the water level. During the violent earthquake motion, the edges of these deltas simply slumped into the fiords, carrying with them any indigenous waterfront structures. Alluvial slumping also precipitated local seiche action which, in turn, was large enough in some cases to cause inundation of waterfront areas.

The pattern of elevation changes indicates that the entire Prince William Sound region was tilted about the axis (P-P) of zero elevation change. This tilting action caused an immediate flux of water in the direction of the tilt gradient. Prince William Sound is a very deep basin (200–300 fathoms), compared with the broad Continental Shelf outside (50–100 fathoms). It is also of complex shape, containing many mountainous islands and radiating into numerous deep fiord-like inlets, some of which are more than 100 miles in length. The hydrodynamic motions of this body of water were extremely complicated, and it is not always easy to predict details of the initial motion, except to state that the water withdrew from elevated areas almost immediately and began to rise in depressed areas very soon after the earthquake. Large seiches were set up in the main basin and the adjacent fiords, although it appears that there was relatively little exchange of energy between Prince William Sound and the Gulf of Alaska. The Sound is virtually cut off from the Gulf by a cluster of islands, the largest of which are Montague and Hinchinbrook islands, as well as by the extreme shoalness of the shelf outside. The general early flow of water within the Sound was northwest, as indicated by the arrows in Figure 7. Strong northerly currents and violent seiching action were observed immediately in the Knight Island Passage. Water was observed to drain southerly and easterly out of Unakwik Inlet. A large wave was seen to propagate out of Valdez Narrows into the Sound immediately after the principal shock. Strong seiching action within the Sound continued for at least 12 hours after the earthquake. In many regions the greatest inundation damage occurred about 5 to 6 hours after the earthquake, at the time of high tide.

Although the details of the wave activity within Prince William Sound are of great practical interest because of the extensive damage to habitation, it is apparent that this activity is of only secondary importance to the tsunami generated outside of the Sound.

In the Gulf of Alaska (Figures 6 and 7), the general picture is the same, except that much less specific detail is available: immediate water withdrawals were reported at Boswell Bay (Hinchinbrook Island), Cape St. Elias, and Middleton Island, all of which were regions of uplift, while similar withdrawals were reported at Rocky Bay and Nuka Bay, at the end of the Kenai Peninsula, and in Marmot Bay, Afognak Island, all of which are located on the northwest side of the axis of major depression. No early water motion was reported from regions on the synclinal axis running from Chiniak Bay, Kodiak Island, to just easterly of Resurrection Bay on the Kenai Peninsula. Aside from local turbulence and seiching generated by the earthquake motions, no wave action or water motions were reported anywhere within Cook

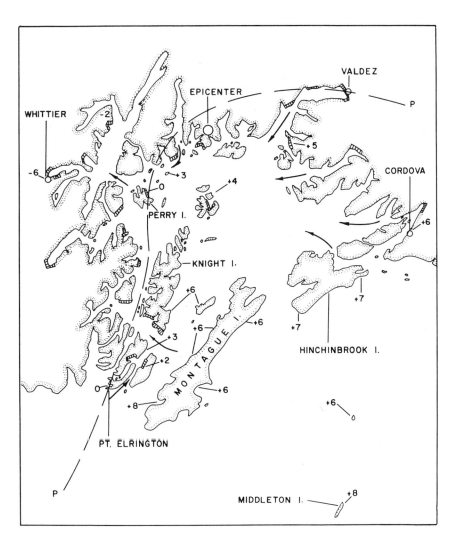

FIGURE 7 Land-elevation changes within Prince William Sound.

Inlet until several hours after the earthquake. This pattern of water motion is again consistent with the concept of uplift along the shelf geanticline and subsidence along the Kodiak geosyncline; the pattern suggests that the tsunami was produced by drainage of water away from the anticlinal ridge running from the Trinity Islands southwest of Kodiak through Montague and Hinchinbrook islands in Prince William Sound. As will be shown, this view is also supported by the wave observations.

WATER-WAVE OBSERVATIONS

Reproductions of tide-gage records were obtained from the U.S. Coast and Geodetic Survey for tide stations at Sitka, Yakutat, Hilo (Hawaii), and Unalaska. In addition, fairly complete early chronologies of wave motion were available from Cape Yakataga and Chiniak Bay, Kodiak (U.S. Naval Station). Less reliable, but useful, information of the time of arrival and sense of first wave motion was also reconstructed from eyewitness accounts at numerous places along the Gulf of Alaska. Pertinent data on initial wave motion are given in Table 1. It is significant that, outside of the immediate area of tsunami generation, the sense of the initial wave motion was everywhere positive, being strongly upward at all points in the southeasterly quadrant and weakly positive westerly along the Aleutian Chain.

In order to obtain some concept of the size of the tsunami-generation area, I projected imaginary wave fronts, according to Huygens' principle, back toward the epicenter at velocity $c = \sqrt{gh}$ (h = depth) from each of the several points of wave observations over time intervals equal, respectively, to the time intervals between the main shock and the observed times of arrival of the first wave motion at these stations. The most recent analysis of the nature of the leading wave of a tsunami (Kajiura, 1963) points out that the toe of the leading wave actually precedes the wave front, which travels at $\sqrt{gh}$ velocity. The correction term is approximately given by

$$\left(\frac{6}{t\sqrt{gh}}\right)^{1/3}\left(\frac{r}{h} - t\sqrt{g/h}\right) = 4,$$

where h is the effective depth over the travel path (Van Dorn, 1963), r = distance, g = gravitational acceleration, and t = time of arrival of first disturbance. These corrections (also listed in Table 1) increase as the cube root of travel time and were subtracted from the observed arrival times for first motion at all stations.

For accuracy, these graphical-numerical constructions were commenced on very small-scale charts in the immediate vicinity of each station, and the coordinates successively transferred to larger-scale charts, until deep water was reached. Such constructions are carried out routinely by Japanese scientists in tracking tsunamis and can be considered accurate to about 2 percent in time. The results are shown in Figure 8 by the heavy curves, each of which is connected to its source station by dashed lines. The best representation of the area of tsunami generation is construed to be the region circumscribed by an envelope which touches each of these heavy curves. It seems clear from the distribution of these curves that the origin of the tsunami was a broad region of uplift somewhere near the central part of the Continental Shelf in the Gulf of Alaska; the waves that radiated to the northwest appear to have originated from a line source which coincides with the presumed axis of the geanticline, while the wave system traveling toward the south and east seems to have originated along the northeasterly end of the Aleutian trench itself.

Since the wave-front constructions depend on the assumption that the ground motion took place instantaneously at

TABLE 1   Tsunami Travel Times to Observation Stations, March 28, 1964

Station	Arrival Time of First Motion (GMT)	Sense of First Motion	Travel Time (min)	Travel Distance (nautical mi)	Effective Depth (ft)	Travel Time Correction (min)	Corrected Travel Time (min)
Old Harbor	0424[a]	Up	48	29	117	0	48
Chiniak Bay	0420	Up	44	26	111	0	44
Seward	0411[a]	Up	35	45	510	0	35
Controller Bay	0415	Up	39	51	530	0	39
Cape Yakataga	0425	Up	45	78	930	1	44
Yakutat	0450	Up	74	169	1,630	2	72
Sitka	0508	Up	92	347	4,420	3	89
Unalaska	0613	Up	157	840	8,900	5	152
Hilo, Hawaii	0900	Up	324	2,440	17,600	8	316

[a]These times are the average of two or more estimates.

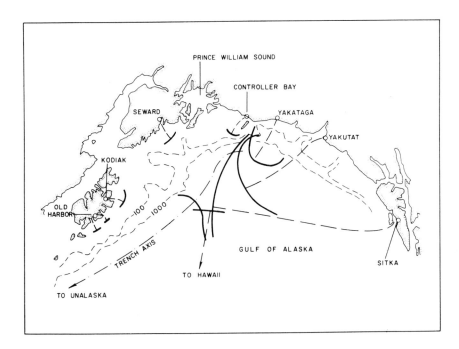

FIGURE 8 Projection of imaginary wave fronts from observation stations back toward tsunami source.

the time of the principal shock, it is apparent that any finite time required for this action would modify this picture somewhat, pushing back the constructed wave fronts toward their sources by distances corresponding to travel times equal to the appropriate time delay in each case. For example, the time of the principal shock is listed by the U.S. Coast and Geodetic Survey as 0336Z, while the inception of strong ground shocks in Kodiak (Navy Weather Central) is given as 0342Z, or about 6 minutes after the first shock.

THE TSUNAMI IN THE OPEN SEA

The tsunami generated by the earthquake of March 28 was recorded at Wake Island, 3,050 nautical miles from the source region, at a station specifically constructed for this purpose in 1960. A portion of this record, showing the first 2 hours of the tsunami, is shown in Figure 9. The recording element of this station is an absolute pressure transducer on the bottom in 50 ft of water; it is connected to a plastic garden hose extending to a depth of 800 ft offshore on the south side of Wake Island. The hose depth, together with an electrical low-pass filter, restricts the excursions of ordinary wind waves to negligible amplitudes. For wave periods longer than about 40 seconds, the response is unity, and the resolution of the record is about 0.02 ft of water. The tsunami begins with a slow increase in sea level to a height of about 4 in. over a period of 15 minutes, followed by a normal dispersive wave train of rather small amplitude. The remarkable feature of this record is that it does not return to normal tide level—as indicated by the dashed line in this figure—for more than an

hour. At the time of the tsunami, the local wind velocity was about 7 knots and extremely steady; therefore, the record obtained can be considered to be a reasonably accurate representation of the actual tsunami characteristics in deep water.

From the general appearance of this record, one has the impression that a large fraction of the energy of the tsunami was contained in a single, long solitary wave formed in the Gulf of Alaska by drainage of water from the coastal shelf. The small amplitude of the dispersive signature attests to the lack of sudden or discontinuous variations in the rate of drainage. Kajiura (1963) has investigated in some detail the theoretical aspects of the leading wave of a tsunami for a variety of source conditions. But the theory applies only to tsunamis generated and propagating in water of uniform depth, and thus it cannot be applied directly to the present situation without some suitable modification of the initial conditions and consideration of the effect of depth variations along the travel path. Some speculations in this connection, and the results of model tests in the author's wave channel at the Scripps Institution, will be reported later.

A broad solitary wave of the type observed at Wake can only be produced by the net (albeit temporary) addition of water to the ocean. The nature of the tsunami source described above appears to fulfill this condition, if the gross ground motion is considered to be dipolar, as evidenced by the signature of the barometric wave recorded at La Jolla. As judged by the pattern of ground dislocations, the positive pole was mostly on the shelf, under water, while the negative pole was largely on land. This circumstance would not be expected to influence the barometric wave, which was fairly symmetric, but it implies that the net signature in the Gulf

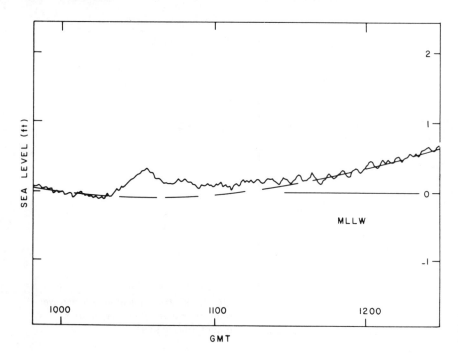

FIGURE 9   Wave record from Wake Island, showing arrival of tsunami (initial motion is positive and remains above normal tide curve for more than an hour).

was strongly positive, as shown by the initial motion at all coastal observation stations. The later stages of the Wake record (not shown in Figure 9) exhibit slow, lesser oscillations of both above and below the local tide stage; these are probably due to readjustments of sea level in the Gulf to the initial outflow of water from the shelf, and reflection from the Kenai-Kodiak Ridge produced by subsidence of the Kodiak geosyncline.

RECONSTRUCTION OF THE TSUNAMI ORIGIN – A HYPOTHESIS

The tsunami of March 28, 1964, is construed to have originated from a dipolar dislocation of the earth's crust centered about the axis *P-P* in Figure 6. The dipole appears to have had positive and negative extrema along the axes *B-B* and *A-A*, respectively, on which severe bending or ground rupture occurred. The dislocations probably took place within 6 minutes after the initial shock, beginning in the region of maximum dislocation, in the vicinity of Hinchinbrook Island, and propagating southwesterly along these axes to a point of zero dislocation southeast of Kodiak.

In Figure 10, the entire, quasi-rectangular area of the coastal shelf between the lines *A-A* and *B-B* is considered to have been uplifted in a pattern indicated by the dotted gradients between these lines. Water motion toward the south and east commenced concurrently with the uplift at all points within this region and parallel to the direction of the gradients. Successive wave fronts, constructed from the topography, are shown for 5-minute intervals out to 25 minutes, as is the wave front at 50 minutes, which encompasses most of the Gulf of

Alaska. Also shown in this figure is a positive front propagating northwest 25 minutes after the earthquake. The negative wave, presumably generated within the small negative dipole region over the subsiding geosyncline, would not be observed within the generation area and was probably immediately reflected by the shallow ridge connecting Kodiak with the Kenai Peninsula.

Within Prince William Sound, no negative phase was generated, and the local tsunami was caused by tilting of the entire region of the Sound toward the northwest, followed by extensive seiching in the deep, complex basin, with little exchange of energy with the Gulf.

Outside the region of generation, the tsunami radiated into the Pacific basin, principally as a solitary wave, followed, some hours later, by lesser slow oscillations, as described above. Judging by the circumpacific distribution of reported tide-gage heights, the tsunami source was somewhat directional, radiating energy preferentially toward the southeast. Local shoreline-wave heights were larger at similar distances all along the coast of North America than along the Aleutian Islands. A maximum height of 4 ft was reported from the Palmer Peninsula in Antarctica while heights in Japan were only a foot or so. Despite the long-continuing nature of the disturbance observed at Wake, tide records around the Pacific exhibited their usual strong periodicities, characteristic of the local environment, showing that such records cannot be depended upon to give much information about the nature of a tsunami in the open sea.

A preliminary estimate of the total energy for this tsunami can be obtained by consideration of the potential energy of the dipole uplift over the shelf. Taking the source dimensions as 240 by 100 nautical miles, and the uplift as

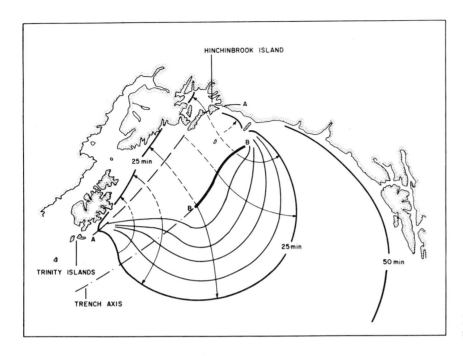

FIGURE 10 Hypothetical model of tsunami source.

6 ft at the northeasterly end of the long axis and zero at the southwesterly end, the total energy E is

$$E = \frac{1}{2}pgh^2A = \frac{35 \times 36 \times 100 \times 240 \times 6080^2}{2 \times 6} =$$

$$1.7 \times 10^{14} \text{ ft-lb} = 2.3 \times 10^{21} \text{ ergs},$$

which is about 10 percent of that (2.7×10^{22} ergs) computed for the tsunami of March 9, 1957, in the Andreanof Islands (Van Dorn, 1963). This calculation, of course, ignores the energy of wave motion within Prince William Sound but is consistent with the general magnitude of shoreline heights reported around the Pacific, relative to those from the previous tsunami.

ACKNOWLEDGMENTS

Contributors to the fund of information were numerous; particular advice and assistance was provided by Dr. Pierre St.-Amand, Navy Ordnance Test Station, China Lake, California, and by Lt. Delmer L. Brown, U.S. Army Engineers, who cooperated with the author during his survey and later remained for some weeks to collect additional data under the terms of his temporary assignment for this purpose. The tide-gage data and the bulk of the seismic evidence presented herein were obtained through the auspices of the U.S. Coast and Geodetic Survey, whose representatives were among the first scientific personnel to arrive after the earthquake. The author was considerably impressed by the number of people who, with no official concern for the collection of data, had the initiative and interest to keep detailed logs of information as it became available. Among these were Lt. Barney, U.S. Fleet Weather Central, Kodiak; Jim Reardon, Area Biologist, Alaska Department of Fish and Game, Homer Alaska; and C. R. Bilderback, fisherman and 10-year resident of remote Cape Yakataga. The conclusions drawn herein depend heavily upon such detailed information.

REFERENCES

Kajiura, Kinjiro, 1963. The leading wave of a tsunami. *Bulletin of the Earthquake Research Institute*, University of Tokyo, 41 (September), 535-571.

Mikumo, Takeshi, 1968. Atmospheric pressure waves and tectonic deformation associated with the Alaskan earthquake of March 28, 1964. *Journal of Geophysical Research*, 73 (March 15), 2009-2025.

Miyabe, Naomi, 1934. An investigation of the Sanriku tsunami based on mareogram data. *Bulletin of the Earthquake Research Institute*, University of Tokyo, Supplemental Vol. 1, p. 112-126.

Nagata, Takesi, 1950. Summary of the geophysical investigations on the great earthquake in southwestern Japan on December 21, 1946. *Transactions, American Geophysical Union*, 31 (February), 1-6.

St.-Amand, Pierre, 1957. Geological and geophysical synthesis of the tectonics of portions of British Columbia, the Yukon Territory and Alaska. *Geological Society of America Bulletin*, 68 (October), 1343-1370.

Twenhofel, W. S., 1952. Recent shore-line changes along the Pacific coast of Alaska. *American Journal of Science*, 250 (July), 523-548.

U.S. Coast and Geodetic Survey, 1964. Preliminary report—Prince William Sound, Alaskan earthquakes March–April 1964 (second printing). Seismology Division Report. Washington: U.S. Coast and Geodetic Survey, 101 p.

Van Dorn, William G., 1960. A new long-period wave recorder. *Journal of Geophysical Research*, 65 (March), 1007-1012.

Van Dorn, William G., 1963. The source motion of the tsunami of March 9, 1957 as deduced from wave measurements at Wake Island. Proceedings of the Tenth Pacific Science Congress, Honolulu, Hawaii, August–September 1961. Doak C. Cox, editor. IUGG Monograph 24. Paris: International Union of Geodesy and Geophysics. p. 39-48.

EDUARD BERG
UNIVERSITY OF ALASKA

DOAK C. COX
UNIVERSITY OF HAWAII

AUGUSTINE S. FURUMOTO
UNIVERSITY OF HAWAII

KINJIRO KAJIURA
UNIVERSITY OF TOKYO

HIROSI KAWASUMI
UNIVERSITY OF TOKYO

ETSUZO SHIMA
UNIVERSITY OF TOKYO

Reprinted in part with minor changes from the section entitled
"The Source of the Major Tsunami"
in "Field Survey of the Tsunamis of 28 March 1964 in Alaska
and Conclusions as to the Origin of the Major Tsunami,"
Hawaii Institute of Geophysics Report HIG 70-2

Source of the Major Tsunami

ABSTRACT: From results of a field survey conducted shortly after the Alaska earthquake of 1964 in the area of maximum disturbance, and from the results of subsequent studies, it is clear that the major tsunami associated with the earthquake was caused by tectonic uplift of the Continental Shelf.

Measurements of shore elevations and depressions relative to sea level, supplemented by subsequent leveling, indicate a bipolar pattern of vertical crustal displacement. An area of the Continental Shelf about 750 km long and averaging about 150 km wide, together with Prince William Sound and adjacent land areas, was uplifted on the average about 2 m. Locally, blocks southwest of Montague Island were uplifted as much as 17 m. To the northeast and northwest of the uplifted area there was a belt of depression, mainly in land areas. The area of aftershocks of the earthquake agrees closely with the area of vertical displacement, and lines of crustal rupture estimated from seismological analyses lie within the area of displacement.

The origin area of the major tsunami, as defined by inverse travel-time diagrams, agrees closely with the area of uplift of the Continental Shelf and the oceanic portion of the aftershock area, confirming relationships obtained previously from tsunamigenic earthquakes occurring near Japan. The area of crustal disturbance and tsunami generation is, however, larger in relation to earthquake magnitude than Japanese experience would have suggested.

The shape of the first wave of the tsunami at Wake Island, a crest with a duration of about 1.3 hours, has been related to the drainage of water from the uplifted Continental Shelf area. Contemporary microbarographic disturbances have been related similarly to the total pattern of vertical crustal displacement.

The energy of the tsunami is estimated from the potential energy of the body of water uplifted on the Continental Shelf at 2.2×10^{22} ergs. Horizontal displacement may have been significant in generating relatively short-period waves, but could not have contributed significantly to the energy of the major tsunami.

INTRODUCTION

A connection between tsunamis and earthquakes has been recognized for many centuries. That the nature of the relationship may be different for different tsunamis has been generally recognized also, but there has been some divergence of opinion concerning the general nature of the relationship for the large tsunamis. The majority of students have held that tsunamis are usually generated directly by vertical displacements of the submarine crust accompanying the earthquakes; the minority have held that the usual cause is submarine sliding triggered by the earthquakes. Even among those who have considered crustal displacements the direct cause, some divergence of opinion still persists—the Americans generally conceiving of the displacements as well organized about faults or fault systems, and the Japanese tending to conceive of the displacements as more irregular in pattern (Cox 1963, 1965).

From the first surveys of the effects of the waves associated with the Alaska earthquake of 1964 (Brown, 1964; Van Dorn, 1965, and this volume; Berg and others, 1965), it was obvious that the waves represented not just one tsunami, but several tsunamis. The effects of most of the tsunamis were local, being largely restricted to the single fiord, sound, or channel in which the tsunami in question was generated, usually by submarine slumping. This paper deals with the source and general character of the major tsunami that was responsible for the damage and loss of life at Kodiak, contributed to the disastrous effects at Seward, swept out across the Pacific to cause additional damage and loss of life in Crescent City, California, and was even recorded noticeably on the shores of Antarctica. It is based on the results of a field survey conducted by the authors in Alaska during the period from 2 to 4½ weeks after the earthquake, and on a review of available information up to the end of 1969.

FAULT LOCATION, ORIENTATION, AND LENGTH OF CRUSTAL RUPTURE

If a tsunami is generated by a vertical displacement of the crust bounded by a fault, the generating area of the tsunami should have some connection with the location and extent of the fault, irrespective of whether the fault retains its integrity to the surface or degenerates in sedimentary rocks at the surface to a sharp flexure.

The epicenter of the Alaska earthquake was early located by the Honolulu Observatory at 61°N, 147½°W (Spaeth and Berkman, 1967, and this volume), and later more precisely at 61.1°N, 147.7°W ± 15 km (Hansen and others, 1966). It is to be noted that the epicenter was located on land, but much of the displaced area was under the sea, as shown in the investigations discussed below.

In 1961, Ben-Menahem developed a method for determining the direction, speed, and length of the rupture spreading from an epicenter by using seismic surface waves of an earthquake as recorded on long-period seismographs. Toksöz and others (1965) applied this method to Love waves from the Alaska earthquake and found that the crustal rupture propagated in the direction S50°W for about 600 km at about 3 km per second. Furumoto (1967, and Seismology and Geodesy volume), considering Rayleigh waves from the earthquake recorded on a strain seismograph at the Kipapa Station, Hawaii, found that the rupture was 800 km long and propagated in the direction S30°W at 3.0 km per second. Wyss and Brune (1967, and Seismology and Geodesy volume) analyzed *P*-wave records of 80 low-magnification stations in the distance range from 40° to 90°. They found evidence of a series of earthquakes spreading simultaneously in three directions from the original epicenter at a velocity of 3.5 km per second. The directions of spread from the original epicenter were northeast, south, and southwest.

A map showing the results of the several analyses of crustal rupture is shown in Figure 1. The rupture zone of Toksöz and others passes through Shelikof Strait; that of Furumoto cuts more or less diagonally across the area of earthquake uplift (compare Figures 1 and 7). The solid circles denoted as A, B, C, X, Y, and Z are separate rupture events identified by Wyss and Brune.

AFTERSHOCK AREA

Iida (1963) has shown that, for earthquakes and tsunamis in the vicinity of Japan, there are fairly well-defined relationships among earthquake magnitude, aftershock area, and area of tsunami generation as outlined by inverse travel-time diagrams (see section on tsunami arrival times). Using the relationships between aftershock area and earthquake magnitude and between earthquake magnitude and the diameter of

a circle equivalent to the tsunami source area, he obtained the relation

$$\text{(a)} \quad \log_{10} A_a = 1.56 \log_{10} L_t + 0.82,$$

where A_a is the aftershock area in square kilometers and L_t is the diameter (in kilometers) of circular equivalent to tsunami source. For a small number of events for which both aftershock and tsunami source areas could be determined, Iida obtained the relation

$$\text{(b)} \quad \log_{10} A_a = 1.95 \log_{10} L_t + 0.56.$$

Converting diameters to areas, with rearrangement, these relations are, respectively, equivalent to

$$\text{(a)} \quad A_t = 0.07 A_a^{1.28}$$

$$\text{(b)} \quad A_t = 0.21 A_a^{1.02},$$

where A_t is the tsunami source area.

For earthquakes with large aftershock areas, the estimates of tsunami source area derived from these two relations would be quite different, but averaging the estimates obtained for aftershock areas of about 5×10^5 km² would yield the result $A_t = A_a$ (approximately). Kajiura (1967) took the stand that, within the limits of error imposed by the scanty data, this last relationship is as useful as can be derived.

The locations of aftershocks of the 1964 Alaska earthquake are plotted in Figure 2. Because the density of distribution of aftershocks of an earthquake decreases gradually at the borders of the zone of aftershocks, the aftershock area is a somewhat arbitrary parameter. Press (1965, and Seismology and Geodesy volume) estimated the zone of densest distribution of aftershocks of the Alaska earthquake to be 800 km long and 250 km wide, with an azimuth of about 40°. On the assumption that the zone had an elliptical shape, the aftershock area was 1.6×10^5 km². Recognizing that, unlike most tsunami-generation areas off Japan, about half the area of vertical crustal movement associated with the Alaska earthquake was on land, the value for the tsunami source area associated with the Alaska earthquake seems more likely to be of the order of 0.8×10^5 km².

EARTHQUAKE MAGNITUDE

Kajiura (1967) has found that areas of aftershocks and tsunami origin for tsunamigenic earthquakes in the vicinity of Japan are both related to earthquake magnitude (Figure 3). If the relations for earthquakes in Japan held true elsewhere, the potential area of tsunami origin indicated by the 8.3 mag-

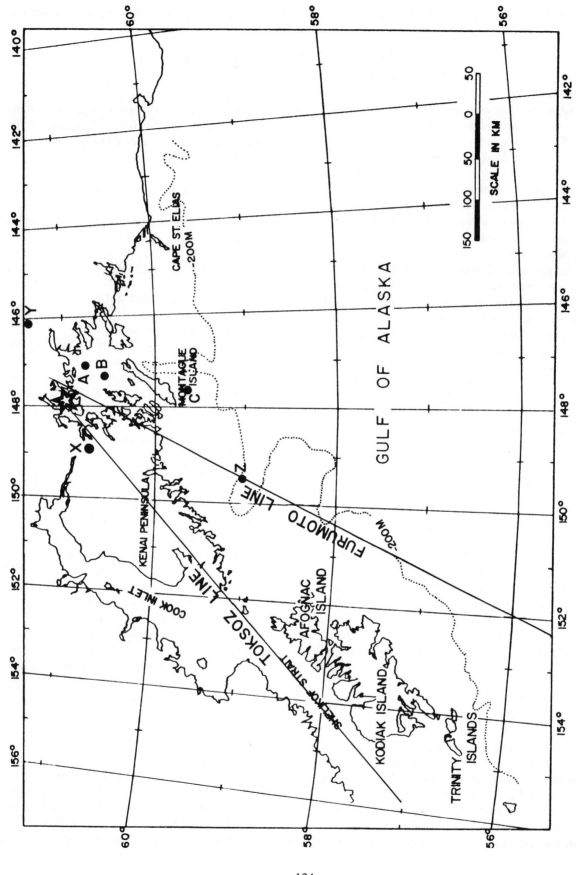

FIGURE 1 Crustal rupture lines of the Alaska earthquake as determined by Toksöz and others (1965) and by Furumoto (1967), with rupture events (A, B, C, X, Y, Z) determined by Wyss and Brune (1967).

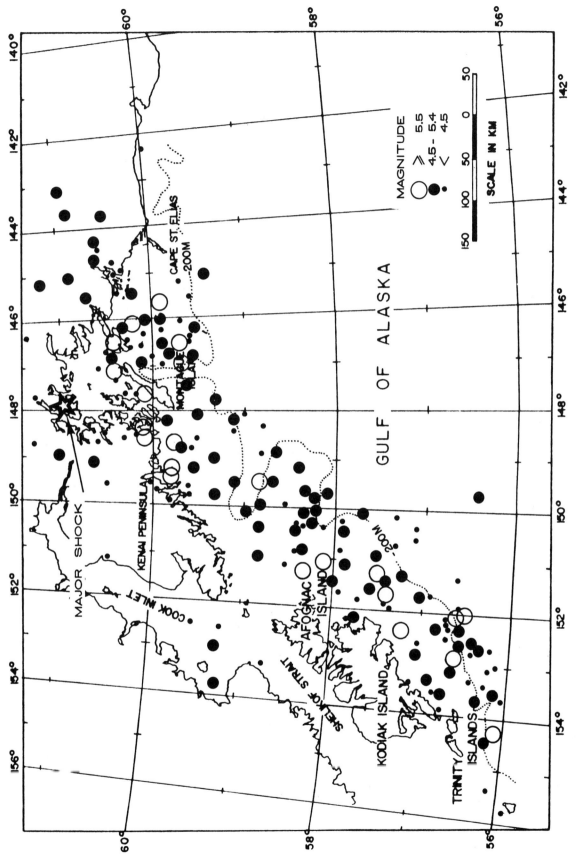

FIGURE 2   Aftershocks (through April 2, 1964) associated with the Alaska earthquake (after Algermissen and others, 1969).

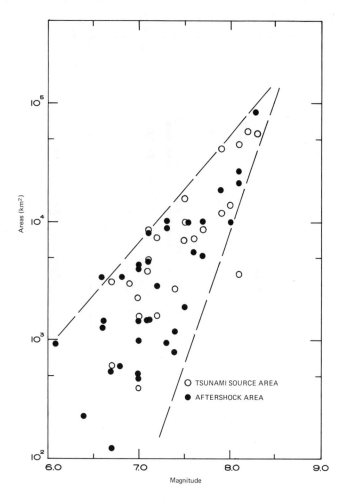

FIGURE 3   Relation of aftershock and tsunami origin areas to magnitude for earthquake in Japan (after Kajiura, 1967).

VERTICAL CRUSTAL DISPLACEMENT

At the time of our survey, the places for which estimates of vertical crustal displacement (Table 1) were made probably represented a significant sample of all the places for which changes in coastal level were known. From them we arrived at the same conclusion that others had reached, namely, that the displacements were bipolar, that a large area involving the southeastern part of Prince William Sound and the shelf beyond had been elevated 1 m or more, and that another large area involving the western coast of Prince William Sound, the Kenai Peninsula, and Afognak and Kodiak islands had been depressed a similar amount (Berg and others, 1965). It was apparent that the positive displacement tapered off eastward and the negative displacement westward, but that the areas of positive and negative displacement were joined by a very sharp double flexure (Figure 4). (Both the line of zero displacement and the line of inflection in the middle of the double flexure have frequently been referred to as "hinge lines.") The double flexure appeared to be so sharp that we kept a lookout for fault scarps during our survey. We saw from the air the evidences of faulting on Montague Island, and members of our party measured on land the large vertical displacement at Patton Bay; but elsewhere we saw no evidences of faulting. We speculated whether the tendency for the negative displacement to taper off more gradually than the positive displacement was an indication that the couple might, in depth, be inclined to the northwest, as shown in the figure. Our measurements suggested that the medial line of zero displacement passed from the vicinity of Valdez along the western coast of Prince William Sound and out under the Gulf of Alaska, east of Seward, bearing perhaps S15° to 20°W.

By now, of course, a great many more measurements of vertical crustal displacement are available, including more accurate measurements at places where we made estimates. Most significantly, evidences of uplift have been found on the southeasternmost tip of Narrow Cape, Kodiak Island (Plafker and Kachadoorian, 1966, and Geology volume), indicating that the medial flexure is located just to the north and has an average bearing between the south coast of the Kenai Peninsula and Kodiak Island of about S35°W.

The work of the Geological Survey on land (Plafker, 1967, and Geology volume) and of the Coast and Geodetic Survey at sea (Malloy, 1964) has outlined distinct fault blocks on and extending southwest from Montague Island, with maximum uplifts of more than 10 m on land and 17 m on the sea floor. Figure 5 indicates the changes in crustal level in general.

HORIZONTAL CRUSTAL DISPLACEMENT

In addition to the vertical crustal displacements, substantial horizontal displacements have been found by comparisons of

nitude of the Alaska earthquake would be between 0.5 and 1.0×10^5 km²; again, because about half the area is mostly land, the actual area would be only about 0.4×10^5 km².

Mogi (1968) has since shown that there are significant regional differences in the relationship between earthquake magnitude and the dimensions of aftershock area; these probably apply also to the relationship between earthquake magnitude and tsunami origin areas. He showed that the long dimensions of the aftershock areas of earthquakes in the Kuril Islands, Kamchatka, the Aleutian Islands, Alaska, and Chile were four times as great, in relation to earthquake magnitude, as they were for earthquakes in the vicinity of Japan. His data indicate that the aftershock areas differ also by about the same factor. With the assumption that the relations of tsunami origin areas to earthquake magnitude differ regionally in the same way, the tsunami origin area computed on the basis of the magnitude of the Alaska earthquake might be of the order of 1.6×10^5 km².

TABLE 1 Measurements of Crustal Displacement and Tsunami Runup

Location	Vertical Displacement (meters)[a]	Runup Heights (meters)				
		Measured Inundation Height above Tide Level	Tide Level at Measurement	Height above MLLW[b]	Approximate Arrival Time (AST)	Height of Wave above Contemporaneous Tide Level
Cape Yakataga	0	—	−0.06	(3.66)	18:45	3.72
Cordova	+1.83	—	—	(6.40)	00:15	2.50
	+1.92	—	—	(7.94)	01:30	4.18
Tatitlek	+1.07 to +1.22	3.40	2.25	5.65	21:00	4.12
				(3.96)	21:45	1.62
Valdez	0	—	—	(5.49)	17:38	5.64
		—	—	(5.95)	17:45	6.10
	(−0.27)	2.75	3.54	6.29 ⎫		2.69 ⎫
		3.46	3.54	7.00 ⎬ 01:45		3.40 ⎬ 3.15
		3.50	3.54	7.04		3.44
		3.12	3.54	6.66 ⎭		3.06 ⎭
Peak I.	+1.31	Small	—	—	—	Small
Perry I.	+0.46	6.7	0.92	7.6	17:40 to 18:00	7.8
Whittier	−1.58	8.55	0.52	9.07	17:40 to 18:00	9.22
Chenega	+0.92	16.46	0	16.46	17:40 to 18:00	16.61
Pt. Oceanic	+1.71	7.88	−0.06	7.82	17:40 to 18:00	7.97
San Juan	((+2.90))	—	—	—	—	—
Zaikof Bay	+2.96	6.30	1.95	8.25	—	—
Patton Bay	+6.0 (+4.55)	—				
Seward	(−1.10)	3.96	2.46	6.42		
		6.15	2.10	8.25		
		6.30	0.67	6.97		
		4.10	2.62	6.72		
		3.90	2.56	6.46		
		4.65	2.01	6.66		
		6.08	1.31	7.39		6.98
		3.00	1.10	4.10		
Homer	−1.13 (−1.65)					
Seldovia	−1.10 (−1.19)	7.94	−1.10	6.84	02:00	1.22
Pt. Lock	−1.00?	2.85	2.28	5.13		
Pt. Williams	−0.43?		0.60	5.00?		
Afognak	−0.40 to −0.55	4.58	1.28	5.86		

TABLE 1 (Continued)

Location	Vertical Displacement (meters)[a]	Runup Heights (meters)			Approximate Arrival Time (AST)	Height of Wave above Contemporaneous Tide Level
		Measured Inundation Height above Tide Level	Tide Level at Measurement	Height above MLLW[b]		
Raspberry I.	−0.92					
Pt. Bailey	−0.31	6.82	−0.52	6.30		
Ouzinkie	−1.07	4.42	2.13	6.55	19:30 to 20:00	6.45
Kodiak	((−1.68))	5.09	1.16	6.25 ⎫		
		4.97	1.16	6.13 ⎬		6.07
		5.22	1.16	6.38		
		4.35	1.16	5.51 ⎭		
Womens Bay	((−1.65))			(3.87)	19:40	3.87
	(−1.71)			(5.70)	23.16	3.56
Lagoon	−	6.55	1.71	8.26		
Beatty Ranch	−	11.16	1.84	13.00		
Narrow Cape	−	18.30	1.95	20.25		
Pasagshak Bay	−	7.38	2.02	9.40		
Saltery Cove	−1.53 to −1.83	4.95	2.07	7.02		
		5.25	2.07	7.32		
Ugak Bay	to −0.3	6.84	1.37	8.21		
McCord Bay	to −0.3 to −0.9	5.36	1.71	7.07	00:00 01:00	4.45
Old Harbor	((−0.61 to −1.22))	6.71	0.06	6.77	21:27	5.80 ⎫
						⎬ 7.34
		8.95	0.06	9.01	21:27	8.04
		9.10	0.06	9.16	21:27	8.19 ⎭
Kaguyak	−	8.92	0.0	8.92 ⎫		
				⎬ 9.32		
		9.71	0.0	9.71 ⎭		
Sitkinak I.	±0?	−				
Lazy Bay	±0 (−0.12)	5.04	0.67	5.71 ⎫	00:00 to 01:00	2.04 ⎫
		4.48	0.70	5.18 ⎬		1.52 ⎬ 1.86
		4.75	0.92	5.67 ⎭		2.02 ⎭
Olga Bay	±0.18	−				Small
Larsen Bay	−0.64 (−0.76)	−				
Zacher Bay	((−0.3 to −0.5))			6.10		
Pt. O'Brien	to −0.27 (−1.10)		−0.70	5.35	01:25	0.79
						1.25
			−0.70	5.60	02:30	1.00

TABLE 1 (Continued)

Location	Vertical Displacement (meters)[a]	Runup Heights (meters)				
		Measured Inundation Height above Tide Level	Tide Level at Measurement	Height above MLLW[b]	Approximate Arrival Time (AST)	Height of Wave above Contemporaneous Tide Level
Karluk	±0					
Shearwater		5.85	1.38	7.23		

[a]Crustal displacements in parentheses from Small and Wharton (1969) or from earlier listing in USC&GS (1965); those in double parentheses from other sources of information.
[b]Heights above MLLW in parentheses were indirectly estimated.

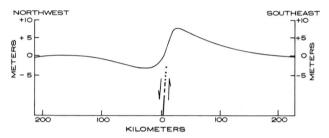

FIGURE 4 Diagrammatic profile of vertical displacements across the disturbed zone of the Alaska earthquake.

preearthquake and postearthquake triangulation (Parkin, 1966). Although there is no proof of the exact time when these displacements occurred, other than that it was subsequent to the original triangulation, it is assumed that they accompanied the earthquake. Some doubt has been cast on the significance of the measurements as indicators of general crustal movement as distinct from displacements of the mountaintop triangulation stations due to local tilting. However, since tilts of the order of 1° would be necessary to account for the displacements indicated and because there is no evidence of such extreme tilting except in the vicinity of the Montague Island faults, there seems little reason to believe that, in general, the crustal displacements are very different from those estimated.

From Parkin's vectors of crustal displacement, assuming that a station near Palmer had not changed position, Wilson and Tørum (1968) prepared a map of the northern part of the disturbed area, showing streamlines and contours of magnitude of horizontal movements (see Figure 6). It will be seen that horizontal movements of as much as 24 m (80 ft) are inferred. The direction of the movement over Prince William Sound and the Kenai Peninsula was mostly southeastward, but the direction changed over the shelf so that at Middleton Island the edge of the shelf was displaced parallel to itself. The maximum displacement, southwest of Montague Island, may have been as much as 25 m southward. As far as is

known, the area of horizontal displacements coincides generally with that of vertical displacements.

TSUNAMI ARRIVAL TIMES

As is well known, tsunami waves, long with respect to the maximum depth of the ocean, travel with velocities close to shallow-water wave velocity:

$$C = \sqrt{gh},$$

where g is acceleration of gravity and h is depth. Although the shorter-period waves may have substantially lower velocities and thus fall to the rear of the wave train, the waves of longer periods travel essentially at the $\sqrt{gh}$ speed. Wave-front diagrams indicating the propagation of a tsunami may be drawn by assuming the $\sqrt{gh}$ velocity of propagation and using Huygens' principle to account for the complicated refraction arising from irregular bottom topography and hence variable velocity. Such diagrams have been constructed for many tsunamis, and the indicated arrival times of the tsunami front at various marigraphic stations generally agree very well with actual arrival times.

Inverse wave-front diagrams, used for predictive purposes in the Seismic Sea Wave Warning System (Spaeth and Berkman, 1967, and this volume), are drawn as though the position of some marigraphic station was also the position of origin of a tsunami. The wave fronts corresponding to various travel times are the loci of points from which tsunamis would reach the station with respective travel times. Miyabe (1934), Omote (1947), and Iida (1963) used such inverse travel-time charts to define the finite area of origin of actual tsunamis. Assuming that a particular tsunami originated at the same time as the earthquake, they computed travel times to various marigraphic stations from the arrival times of the tsunami front at those stations. The inverse-diagram wave front that corresponds to the tsunami's travel time to a particular

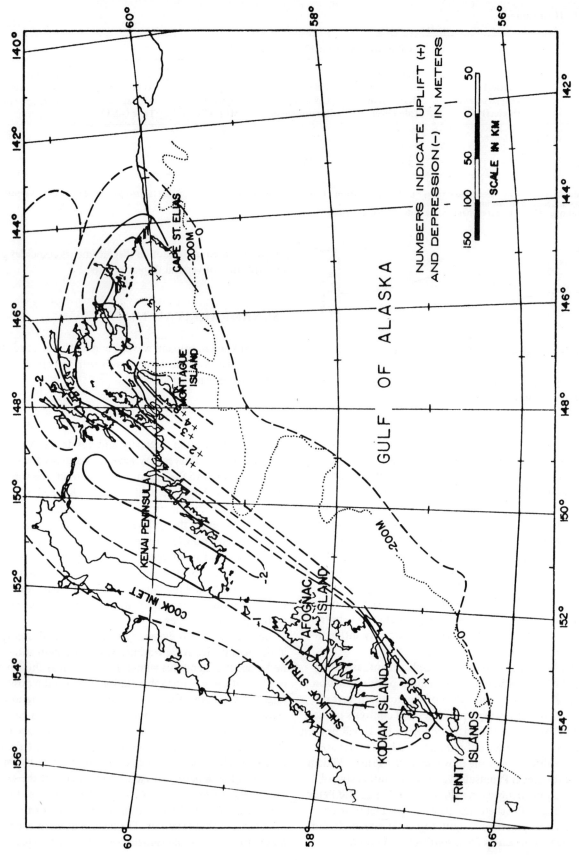

FIGURE 5 Vertical crustal displacement associated with the Alaska earthquake (after Plafker, 1965).

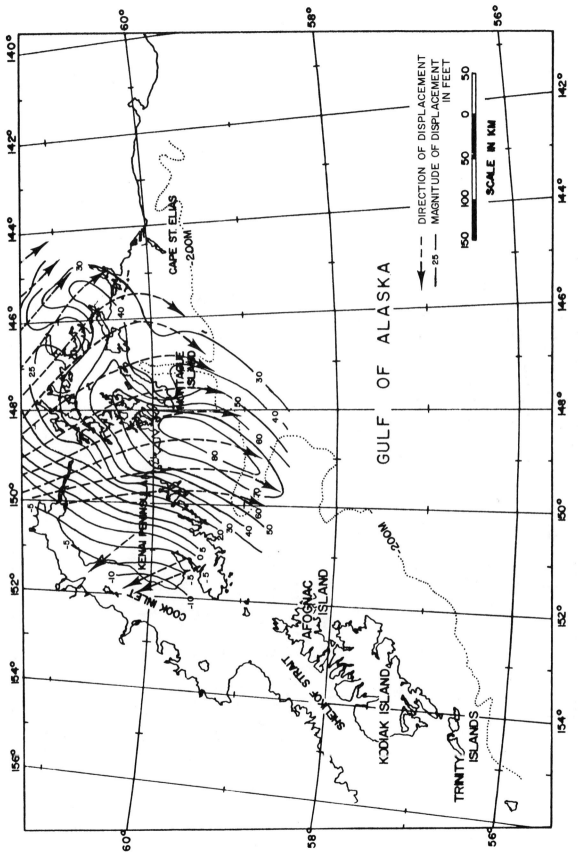

FIGURE 6   Horizontal crustal displacements associated with the Alaska earthquake (after Wilson and Tørum, 1968).

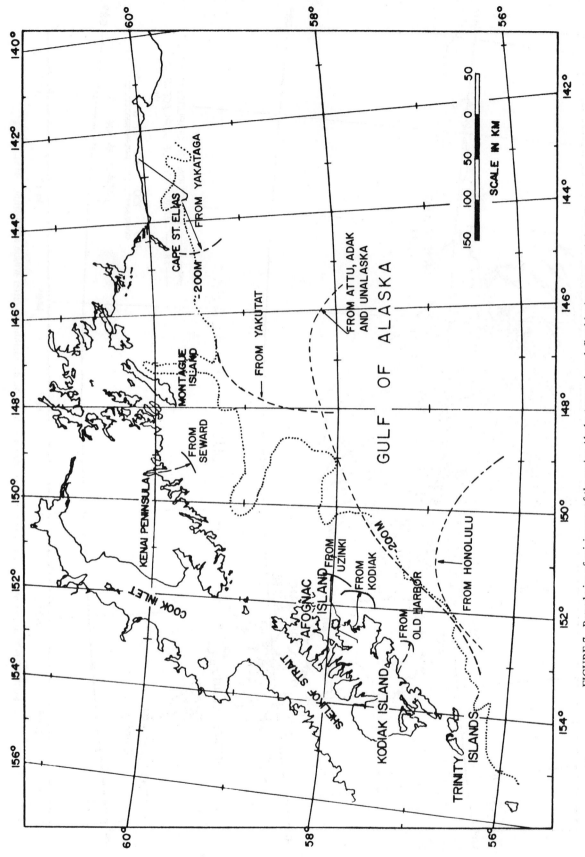

FIGURE 7 Boundaries of origin area of the major Alaska tsunami, as defined by inverse travel-time diagrams.

station represents the locus of the point (on the edge of the real tsunami's origin area) from which the travel time to the station is least. From inverse travel-time diagrams from several favorably located stations, the entire edge of the source area may be interpolated. The origin times of the earthquake and tsunami are assumed to be the same for this purpose.

For long travel paths a small correction to the travel time indicated by $\sqrt{gh}$ propagation is appropriate. Kajiura (1963) has shown that there is a leading edge of exponential shape which propagates ahead of the part of the first wave that moves with $\sqrt{gh}$ velocity in such a way that the difference, over a given path, between the travel time of a point on the front and the travel time according to $\sqrt{gh}$ velocity, is

$$t = t_o - t_f = a \left(\frac{ht_o}{6g}\right)^{1/3}$$

where

t_o = travel time according to $\sqrt{gh}$ velocity,
t_f = actual travel time of a point on the leading edge,
h = effective depth = l^2/gt_o^2,
g = acceleration of gravity,
l = distance from origin,
a = constant, depending on choice of point on the leading edge, equal to about 3 or 4 (in practice).

For a tsunami originating from the area of vertical crustal displacement associated with a very long fault, an additional correction to travel times computed from earthquake origin times is necessary because of the finite velocity, about 200 km per minute, by which the crustal displacements propagate from the epicentral area to distant parts of the disturbed zone.

Kajiura's correction and that arising from rupture velocity, although both large enough to be taken into account in the construction of conventional wave-front diagrams, are of doubtful significance when we consider travel-time errors arising from inadequacies in bathymetry and from uncertainties in identifying the wave front on marigraphs.

For the definition of the origin area of the major tsunami of the Alaska earthquake, Pararas-Carayannis (1967, and Seismology and Geodesy volume) has constructed inverse wave-front diagrams from several tide-gage stations and other places for which arrival times were obtained by Berg and others (1971). The results are shown in Figure 7.

CHARACTERISTICS OF THE INITIAL WAVE AT WAKE ISLAND

Because of the wave distortions that are introduced in coastal waters, the characteristics of a tsunami as it propagates across the open ocean cannot satisfactorily be determined from ordinary marigrams. As has frequently been noted, there is more general resemblance between marigrams of different tsunamis at the same station than between those of the same tsunami at different stations. Small, steep-sided islands should, however, have smaller effects on the character of a train of long waves passing it than other coasts would have; for this reason, Van Dorn (1960) has maintained a tsunami gage recorder offshore at Wake Island.

The Wake Island record of the Alaska tsunami was initiated by a crest about 10 cm higher than normal water level and with a duration of about 1.3 hours. As shown by Van Dorn (1965, and this volume), this behavior can be accounted for only by displacement of water from the source area continuing over a comparable time.

At the $\sqrt{gh}$ shallow-water wave velocity, this interval corresponds to a travel distance of about 140 km in water depths averaging about 100 m on the Continental Shelf in the source area. Because this is approximately the width of the Continental Shelf, it strongly suggests that the source area included the entire width of the Continental Shelf.

ATMOSPHERIC PRESSURE WAVES

Large high-frequency pressure oscillations and somewhat smaller low-frequency oscillations were noted soon after the earthquake on the records of a microbarograph operated by Berg at College, Alaska. Van Dorn in 1964 called attention to the similarity between waves of the low-frequency type that were recorded on a microbarograph at La Jolla, California, and those of the tsunami; in his interpretation, both were generated by the vertical crustal displacements accompanying the earthquake. Bolt (1964) and Donn and Posmentier (1964) estimated the group velocity of the same sort of waves recorded at Berkeley, California, and Mikumo (1968) has since published an extensive analysis of the waves observed at the places mentioned and also at San Diego, California.

The results of the analysis indicate that the waves are dispersive, but are coherent between stations for periods of more than a few minutes, with group and phase velocities of about 310 m per second for periods greater than about 5 minutes.

Theoretical barograms were computed for atmospheric pressure oscillations, including the fundamental gravity mode and the fundamental, first, and second acoustic modes. The theoretical barograms computed for point sources do not match the actual records, but those computed for a model involving finite sources resembling the real vertical crustal displacements (see Figure 8) did match the actual records quite closely. Row (1966) analyzed a number of records of long-period ionospheric disturbances that propagated at the speed of sound in the neutral atmosphere at F-region heights. No evidences of these ionospheric waves were found in

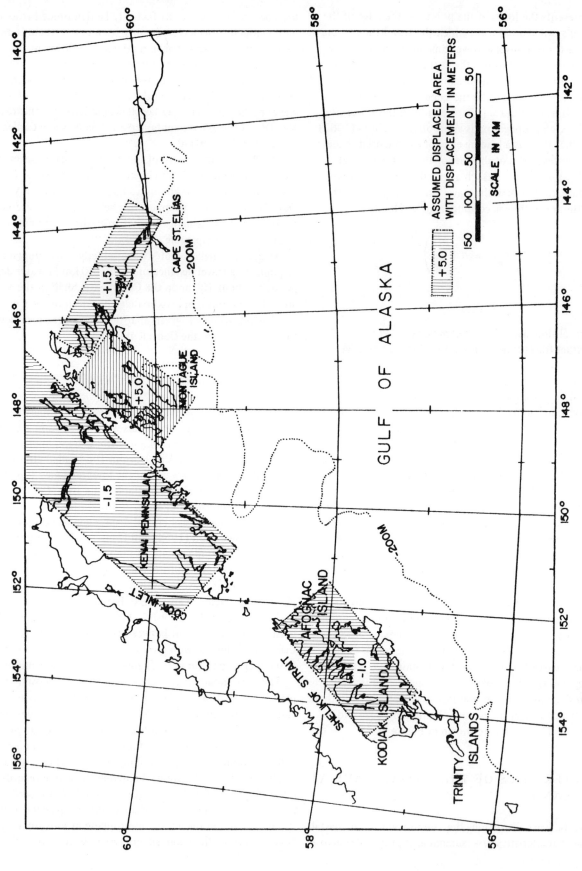

FIGURE 8 Model source providing theoretical barograms best fitting the 1964 macrobarometric disturbance (after Mikumo, 1968).

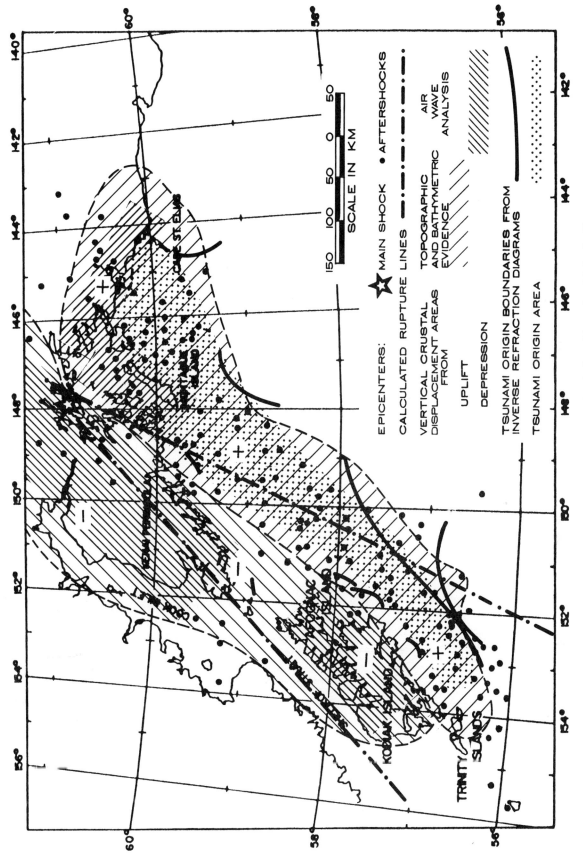

FIGURE 9 Source area of the major Alaska tsunami, as indicated by various kinds of evidence.

SCALE IN KM

EPICENTERS: ☆ MAIN SHOCK • AFTERSHOCKS

CALCULATED RUPTURE LINES

VERTICAL CRUSTAL DISPLACEMENT AREAS FROM

UPLIFT

DEPRESSION

TOPOGRAPHIC AND BATHYMETRIC EVIDENCE

AIR WAVE ANALYSIS

TSUNAMI ORIGIN BOUNDARIES FROM INVERSE REFRACTION DIAGRAMS

TSUNAMI ORIGIN AREA

ST. ELIAS

KODIAK ISLAND

TRINITY ISLANDS

ground-level microbarographic records. Row considers that the evidences of such long-period *F*-region waves may prove useful as a further means for determining ground motion associated with an earthquake.

SUMMARY AND SYNTHESIS

Probably for no previous tsunami have so many different kinds of evidence as to the source been available. The agreement as to location and character of the source from most of the different kinds of evidence is remarkable (Figure 9). Clearly, the tsunami was generated mainly by the broad uplift of a portion of the Continental Shelf in the Gulf of Alaska, extending in length from the Copper River Delta at the northeast to a point off Sitkinak Island on the southwest (a distance of about 750 km) and in width from the Kenai Peninsula and Kodiak Island on the northwest nearly to the edge of the shelf on the southeast (a distance of about 150 km on the average). The total area uplifted, including land areas, was somewhat larger. The northwestern and western edges of this uplifted area and the amount of uplift near them are indicated by the changes in shoreline elevation. These changes and bathymetric observations indicate also the amount of uplift in the northernmost part of the area and suggest that the

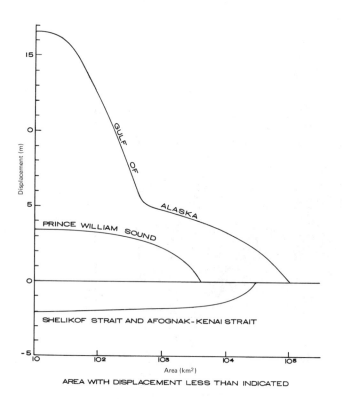

FIGURE 10 Hypsographs of vertical displacements in the disturbed zone of the Alaska earthquake.

average uplift over the entire area of about 200,000 km² was about 2 m. Locally, however, southwest of Montague Island, there was a narrow horst in which the uplift was as much as 17 m.

To the north and northwest of the major area of uplift there was a belt of depression which was mainly in land areas. Water areas included only the strait between Kodiak Island and the Kenai Peninsula together with the connecting Shelikof Strait and Cook Inlet, a total area of about 40,000 km² with an average depression of about 1 m.

The part of the area of uplift in Prince William Sound (about 4,000 km²) with an average uplift of about 1.5 m was fairly well isolated from the major part on the Continental Shelf by Hinchinbrook and Montague islands.

The atmospheric pressure waves recorded at distant stations are explicable by a model of vertical crustal displacement corresponding reasonably closely to the actual displacements measured.

The origin area of the tsunami as defined by the inverse travel-time charts constructed from various marigraph stations agrees very closely with the area of uplift on the Continental Shelf and in fact probably provides the best evidence for the location of its southeastern edge. The source area of the crest of the first tsunami wave, as defined by inverse travel-time charts, agrees approximately with the zone of maximum uplift extending southwestward from Montague Island.

The 1.3-hour duration of the surge at Wake Island corresponds, at $\sqrt{gh}$ velocity in the 100-m average water depth on the Continental Shelf, to a distance of about 150 km, which is the average width of the area of uplift on the shelf across which the tsunami was generated.

The aftershock area of the main earthquake agrees very closely with the total area of vertical displacements, but only a part of this area was under water, and part of the water areas were poorly connected with the ocean, so that only a part of the aftershock area was involved in tsunami generation.

The line of rupture as determined by seismic analysis falls near the major axis of the aftershock area, and its length corresponds very closely to the length of the tsunami-generating area.

Although the area of the tsunami source estimated from the earthquake magnitude on the basis of relations derived from tsunamigenic earthquakes in Japan is only about half as large as the actual area, as indicated by other evidence, it has already been shown that the long dimensions and areas of aftershock activity, and hence presumably of tsunami origin, are considerably larger, relative to earthquake magnitude, for north- and east-Pacific-rim earthquakes not in Japan than for those occurring in Japan.

Clearly, the crustal uplift on the Continental Shelf in the Gulf of Alaska was responsible for the generation of the major tsunami that swept across the ocean.

TSUNAMI ENERGY

The energy of the tsunami may be estimated from the potential energy of the body of water uplifted on the Continental Shelf

$$E_p = (\tfrac{1}{2})\, \rho\, gAh^2,$$

where

ρ = density of water,
g = acceleration of gravity,
A = area,
h = elevation of the water surface.

The total uplifted water area may be taken as about 1.1×10^5 km^2. Over this area the uplift heights appear to be distributed approximately as shown in Figure 10. The average uplift height over the whole area is about 1.8 m, and the average square of the height about 4.1 m^2 (of which only about 0.1 m^2 is due to the extreme heights southwest of Montague Island). The potential energy involved in this uplift is about 2.2×10^{22} ergs. This is about 3½ times the energy estimated by Pararas-Carayannis (1967) and nearly 10 times the energy estimated by Van Dorn (1965, and this volume) on the basis of more limited evidence.

The depressed area between Afognak Island and the Kenai Peninsula and in Shelikof Strait and Cook Inlet amounts to about 4.5×10^4 km^2. From the distribution of the depression depths (Figure 10), the average depression depth in this area is about 0.8 m and the average square of the depression depth is about 0.9 m^2. Waves must have been generated in this body of water as the result of the differential water levels at the west end of Shelikof Strait and the larger differential at the east end of the Afognak–Kenai Strait. However, because of the small width of the Afognak–Kenai Strait, as compared to the length of the generating area on the shelf, the contribution of the energy of this body of water to the tsunami propagating from the shelf must have been small, and it is unlikely that the wave generated in it would have been in phase with those generated on the shelf. In Prince William Sound, an area of about 4×10^3 km^2 was uplifted an average of 1.5 m. The greatly restricted connection between the shelf and the Sound must have prevented a significant contribution of energy to the major tsunami.

Wilson and Tørum (1968) have suggested that the horizontal displacement of the shelf and its margins contributed to the major tsunami. Consideration of the mechanics involved casts doubt on that hypothesis, however. Because of the low viscosity of water, the effects of a sudden horizontal shift of a flat plane bottom would be felt at best only a few centimeters above the bottom. Any significant effects on the water column from horizontal bottom movement must be related to the vertical relief of the bottom.

The energy produced by the horizontal motion of a sloping bottom lifting the water column may be calculated by

$$E = \tfrac{1}{2}\, \rho\, gLW\,(sd)^2,$$

where

ρ = water density,
g = acceleration of gravity,
L = length of sloping bottom,
W = width of sloping bottom,
s = slope or gradient of bottom,
d = horizontal displacement.

With a simple model involving three segments—the shore, the Continental Shelf, and the continental slope descending to the Aleutian Trench—in which each segment has a length of 700 km and is displaced 25 m, the results of applying the energy equation are:

Segment	Depth (m)	Width (km)	Slope	Energy (ergs)
Shore	0– 50	5	0.01	0.1×10^{20}
Shelf	50– 150	100	0.001	0.02×10^{20}
Continental slope	150–3,500	80	0.04	3×10^{20}

The total energy, 3×10^{20} ergs, is about 1½ percent of that estimated as resulting from the vertical uplift. However, even this is a gross overestimate. The major energy component in the estimate is that for the continental slope. As shown by the vectors of horizontal displacement (Figure 6), the actual horizontal displacement at the edge of the continental slope was far less than the 25-m maximum, and furthermore the displacement there was nearly parallel to the slope, not normal to it. Hence, although the horizontal displacement may have been of importance in generating relatively short-period waves in areas of steep bottom topography subject to maximum displacements, it could not have contributed much to the major tsunami.

ACKNOWLEDGMENTS

Our field survey was supported by grants from the National Science Foundation and from the Japan Society for the Promotion of Science. The persons who assisted with the survey are named in our detailed report (Berg and others, 1971); their number is too great to permit individual acknowledgment here, but we wish to recognize especially the help of Keith Mather, Director of the Institute of Geophysics, University of Alaska, who made possible the logistic arrangements without which the survey could not have been made, and of our three pilots, Warren Wright of Sea Air Motive in Anchorage, James Osborne of Cordova Airlines in Cordova, and Woodford Seiber of Harvey's Air Service in Kodiak, who offered more than normal cooperative service.

George Pararas-Carayannis of the Hawaii Institute of Geophysics prepared a number of refraction diagrams used in the study; the Water Resources Research Center, University of Hawaii, provided extensive typing assistance; and Richard Rhodes and Ethel McAfee of the Hawaii Institute of Geophysics rendered drafting and editorial services, respectively.

This is contribution 310 of the Hawaii Institute of Geophysics, and contribution B-192 of the Geophysical Institute, University of Alaska.

REFERENCES

Algermissen, S. T., W. A. Rinehart, R. W. Sherburne, and W. H. Dillinger, Jr., 1969. Preshocks and aftershocks of the Prince William Sound earthquake of March 28, 1964 *in* Volume II-B,C: The Prince William Sound, Alaska, earthquake of 1964 and aftershocks. Environmental Science Services Administration, U.S. Coast and Geodetic Survey. Washington: Government Printing Office. p. 79–130. Also *in* The Great Alaska Earthquake of 1964: Seismology and Geodesy. NAS Pub. 1602. Washington: National Academy of Sciences, 1972.

Ben-Menahem, Ari, 1961. Radiation of seismic surface-waves from finite moving sources. *Bulletin of the Seismological Society of America*, 51 (July), 401–435.

Berg, Eduard, Doak C. Cox, Augustine S. Furumoto, K. Kajiura, H. Kawasumi, and E. Shima, 1965. The tsunami of 27 March 1964 in Alaska *in* Science in Alaska, 1964: Proceedings Fifteenth Alaskan Science Conference, College, Alaska, August 31 to September 4, 1964. George Dahlgren, editor. College: Alaska Division American Association for the Advancement of Science, March 15. p. 91.

Berg, Eduard, Doak C. Cox, Augustine S. Furumoto, Kinjiro Kajiura, Hirosi Kawasumi, and Etsuzo Shima, 1971. Field survey of the tsunamis of 28 March 1964 in Alaska, and conclusions as to the origin of the major tsunami. Report HIG-70-2. Honolulu: University of Hawaii, Institute of Geophysics. 57 p.

Bolt, Bruce A., 1964. Seismic air waves from the great 1964 Alaskan earthquake. *Nature*, 202 (June 13), 1095–1096.

Brown, Delmer L., 1964. Tsunamic activity accompanying the Alaskan earthquake of 27 March 1964. Technical Report, U.S. Army Engineer District, Alaska. Anchorage: U.S. Army Corps of Engineers, April 23. 31 p.

Cox, Doak C., 1963. Status of tsunami knowledge. Proceedings of the Tenth Pacific Science Congress, Honolulu, Hawaii, August–September 1961. Doak C. Cox, editor. IUGG Monograph 24. Paris: International Union of Geodesy and Geophysics. p. 1–6.

Cox, Doak C., 1965. Tsunami research in Japan and in the United States *in* Studies on oceanography. K. Yoshida, editor. Seattle: University of Washington Press. p. 403–412.

Donn, William L., and Eric S. Posmentier, 1964. Ground-coupled air waves from the great Alaskan earthquake. *Journal of Geophysical Research*, 69 (December 15), 5357–5364.

Furumoto, Augustine S., 1967. A study of the source mechanism of the Alaska earthquake and tsunami of March 27, 1964: Part II, Analysis of Rayleigh wave. *Pacific Science*, 21 (July), 311–315. Also *in* The Great Alaska Earthquake of 1964: Seismology and Geodesy. NAS Pub. 1602. Washington: National Academy of Sciences, 1972.

Hansen, Wallace R., Edwin B. Eckel, William E. Schaem, Robert E. Lyle, Warren George, and Genie Chance, 1966. The Alaska earthquake, March 27, 1964: field investigations and reconstruction effort. U.S. Geological Survey Professional Paper 541. Washington: Government Printing Office. 111 p.

Iida, K., 1963. Magnitude of tsunamigenic earthquake, aftershock area, and area of tsunami origin *in* Geophysical papers dedicated to Professor Kenzo Sassa. Kyoto: Kyoto University. p. 115–124.

Kajiura, Kinjiro, 1963. The leading wave of a tsunami. *Bulletin of the Earthquake Research Institute*, University of Tokyo, 41 (September), 535–571.

Kajiura, Kinjiro, 1967. Tsunami. *Zisin* (Journal of the Seismological Society of Japan), 20 (No. 4), 219–222.

Malloy, Richard J., 1964. Crustal uplift southwest of Montague Island, Alaska. *Science*, 146 (November 20), 1048–1049.

Mikumo, Takeshi, 1968. Atmospheric pressure waves and tectonic deformation associated with the Alaskan earthquake of March 28, 1964. *Journal of Geophysical Research*, 73 (March 15), 2009–2025.

Miyabe, N., 1934. An investigation of the Sanriku tsunami based on mareogram data. *Bulletin of the Earthquake Research Institute*, University of Tokyo, Supplemental Vol. 1, p. 112.

Mogi, Kiyoo, 1968. Development of aftershock areas of the great earthquakes. *Bulletin of the Earthquake Research Institute*. University of Tokyo, 46 (No. 2), 175–203.

Omote S., 1947. On the central area of seismic sea waves. *Bulletin of the Earthquake Research Institute*, University of Tokyo, Vol. 25, p. 15.

Pararas-Carayannis, George, 1967. A study of the source mechanism of the Alaska earthquake and tsunami of March 27, 1964: Part I, Water waves. *Pacific Science*, 21 (July), 301–310. Also *in* The Great Alaska Earthquake of 1964: Seismology and Geodesy. NAS Pub. 1602. Washington: National Academy of Sciences, 1972.

Parkin, Ernest J., 1966. Alaskan surveys to determine crustal movements: Part II–horizontal displacement. Proceedings of the American Congress on Surveying and Mapping, Washington, D.C., March 10. Rockville, Maryland: U.S. Coast and Geodetic Survey. 15 p.

Plafker, George, 1965. Tectonic deformation associated with the 1964 Alaska earthquake. *Science*, 148 (June 25), 1675–1687.

Plafker, George, 1967. Surface faults on Montague Island associated with the 1964 Alaska earthquake. U.S. Geological Survey Professional Paper 543-G. Washington: Government Printing Office. 42 p. Also *in* The Great Alaska Earthquake of 1964: Geology. NAS Pub. 1601. Washington: National Academy of Sciences, 1971. p. 135–176.

Plafker, George, and Reuben Kachadoorian, 1966. Geologic effects of the March 1964 earthquake and associated seismic sea waves on Kodiak and nearby islands, Alaska. U.S. Geological Survey Professional Paper 543-D. Washington: Government Printing Office. 46 p. Also *in* The Great Alaska Earthquake of 1964: Geology. NAS Pub. 1601. Washington: National Academy of Sciences, 1971. p. 177–226.

Press, Frank, 1965. Displacements, strains, and tilts at teleseismic distances. *Journal of Geophysical Research*, 70 (May 15), 2395–2412. Also *in* The Great Alaska Earthquake of 1964: Seismology and Geodesy. NAS Pub. 1602. Washington: National Academy of Sciences, 1972.

Row, Ronald V., 1966. Evidence of long-period acoustic-gravity waves launched into the *F*-region by the Alaskan earthquake of March 28, 1964. *Journal of Geophysical Research*, 71 (January 1), 343–345.

Small, James B., and Lawrence C. Wharton, 1969. Vertical displacements determined by surveys after the Alaskan earthquake of March 1964 *in* Volume III: The Prince William Sound, Alaska, earthquake of 1964 and aftershocks. Environmental Science Services Administration, U.S. Coast and Geodetic Survey. Washington: Government Printing Office. p. 21–33. Also *in* The Great Alaska Earthquake of 1964: Seismology and Geodesy. NAS Pub. 1602. Washington: National Academy of Sciences, 1972.

Spaeth, Mark G., and Saul C. Berkman, 1967. The tsunami of March 28, 1964, as recorded at tide stations. Environmental Science Services Administration Technical Report C&GS 33. Washington: Government Printing Office. 86 p. Also *in* The Great Alaska Earthquake of 1964: Oceanography and Coastal Engineering. NAS Pub. 1605. Washington: National Academy of Sciences, 1972.

Toksöz, M. Nafi, Ari Ben-Menahem, and David G. Harkrider, 1965. Source mechanism of Alaska earthquake from long-period seismic surface waves (Abstract). *Transactions, American Geophysical Union*, 46 (March), 154.

U.S. Coast and Geodetic Survey, 1965. Assistance and recovery, Alaska/1964: A report covering the activities of the U.S. Coast and Geodetic Survey in conjunction with the Prince William Sound, Alaska, earthquake of 1964 for the period March 27–December 31, 1964. Washington: U.S. Department of Commerce. 45 p.

Van Dorn, William G., 1960. Tsunamis. *Transactions, American Geophysical Union*, 41 (No. 2), 265–266.

Van Dorn, William G., 1965. Source mechanism of the tsunami of March 28, 1964 in Alaska. Proceedings of the Ninth Conference (1964) on Coastal Engineering (Chapter 10). New York: American Society of Civil Engineers. p. 166–190. Also *in* The Great Alaska Earthquake of 1964: Oceanography and Coastal Engineering. NAS Pub. 1605. Washington: National Academy of Sciences, 1972.

Wilson, Basil W., and Alf Tørum, 1968. The tsunami of the Alaskan earthquake, 1964: Engineering evaluation. Coastal Engineering Research Center Technical Memorandum No. 25. Washington: U.S. Army Corps of Engineers, May. 444 p.

Wyss, Max, and James N. Brune, 1967. The Alaska earthquake of 28 March 1964: A complex multiple rupture. *Bulletin of the Seismological Society of America*, 57 (October), 1017–1023. Also *in* The Great Alaska Earthquake of 1964: Seismology and Geodesy. NAS Pub. 1602. Washington: National Academy of Sciences, 1972.

WILLIAM G. VAN DORN
SCRIPPS INSTITUTION OF OCEANOGRAPHY

Reprinted with minor changes from
Proceedings of The International Symposium on Tsunamis and
Tsunami Research,
Honolulu, October 7–10, 1969,
"A Model Experiment on the Generation of the Tsunami of
March 28, 1964, in Alaska"

A Model Experiment on the Generation of the Major Tsunami

INTRODUCTION

In a previous paper (Van Dorn, 1965, and this volume), the source mechanism of the tsunami of March 28, 1964, in Alaska was discussed in a qualitative fashion. On the basis of observed land-elevation changes and patterns of early water motion, the tsunami was construed to have resulted from a dipolar deformation of a large sector of the shallow coastal shelf bordering the Gulf of Alaska, resulting in immediate flow away from the uplifted pole (largely under water), both southeasterly toward the open Gulf and northwesterly toward the depressed pole (largely above water). This latter flow was presumed (Wilson and Tørum, 1968) to have soon been arrested by land and reflected back out into the Gulf as a second pulse about 1.8 hours later.

This paper attempts to show, by more detailed analysis of the wave record obtained at Wake Island and by a one-dimensional model experiment, that the above interpretation is essentially correct, except that there appears to be no evidence of significant reflection from the coastline.

SOURCE CONDITIONS

The earlier geometrical reconstruction of the region of uplift (Figure 1) was shown as comprising that area between the dipole axis A–A and the northerly end of the Aleutian Trench B–B, which borders the Continental Shelf. This figure shows a diagrammatic progress of the reconstructed wave front radiating out into the Gulf of Alaska at 5-minute intervals. By 25 minutes after the major earthquake, the wave front has filled the Gulf, and by 50 minutes it has already traveled one third of the way to Hawaii. The great-circle direction to Wake Island, where this tsunami was recorded at a special offshore station, is shown as nearly tangent to the trench axis, as well as to the dipole hinge-axis. Other reconstructions have been given (Wilson and Tørum, 1968; Pararas-Carayannis, 1967), but they do not differ enough from that given here to affect the substance of the following. The significant feature of the motion described is that, although the

ABSTRACT: Analysis of the wave record for the tsunami of March 28, 1964, obtained from a special tsunami recording station at Wake Island, suggests that the tsunami originated from a line source in the form of a monopolar uplift of half-breadth about 20–30 km. Dispersive waves superimposed on the broad uplift are predicted by theory for such an uplift.

A laboratory experiment is described to show that the essential features of such a source can be represented by a one-dimensional model.

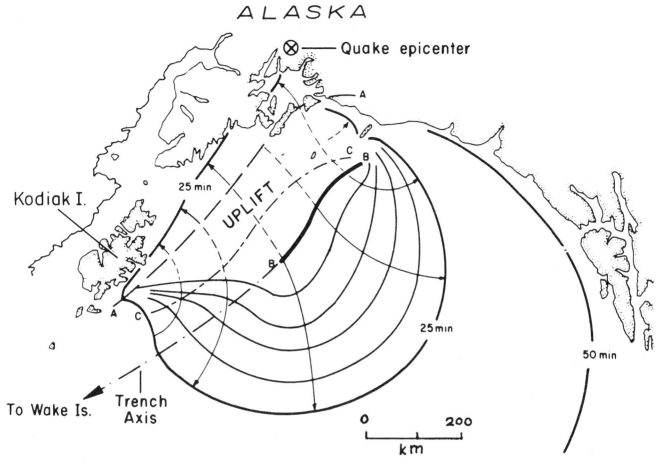

FIGURE 1   Gulf of Alaska, showing wavefront reconstruction of the region of uplift.

uplifted region was rather long and narrow and apparently radiated its principal energy in a southeasterly direction normal to the dipole axis, the wave front became rapidly circular in deep water. Tide-gage records from Eniwetok and Truk atolls (Spaeth and Berkman, 1965), both of which lie in almost the same direction as Wake Island, substantiate the Wake record in indicating that the first motion of the tsunami was a rise in sea level, thus ensuring that the wave motion reaching Wake came from the positive (uplifted) sector of the dipole source, as a result of strong refraction in the source region. Because most of the uplifted region was under water, while a large fraction of the depressed sector was on land, the net effect of the dipolar ground motion was to add water to the ocean. Thus the oceanic effect was essentially a monopolar uplift.

ANALYSIS OF THE WAKE RECORD

The pertinent section of the Wake record (Figure 2) consists of a sudden increase in elevation above the local tide datum by about 12 cm, followed by several cycles of decreasing amplitude and duration before the record finally returns to the tidal datum after 70–80 minutes. The theory of shallow-water wave generation (Kajiura, 1963) provides a means of distinguishing between one- and two-dimensional sources consisting of a uniform uplift of the sea floor along a line, or over a rectangular area, respectively. When viewed at a great distance, the leading wave from a line source will be the highest wave of the train, whereas with a radial source it will be some succeeding wave, depending upon the distance. Moreover, the crest of the leading wave will be retarded further behind the wave front—traveling at velocity $c = \sqrt{gh}$ (g = gravity, h = depth)—for the line source than for the radial source, if they have the same width in the direction of interest and that width is large compared with the depth of water at the source. These relative characteristics remain unchanged irrespective of variable water depth over the travel path if it is the same in both cases.

From Figure 2 it is clear that the leading crest is the highest, and thus it is appropriate to think of the Alaska earthquake displacement as a long line source, despite the

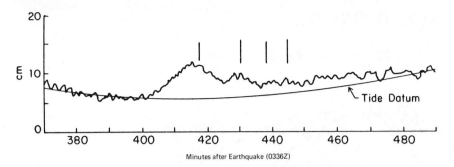

FIGURE 2   Tide-gage recording at Wake Island for the 1964 earthquake.

subsequent distortion of the wave pattern by refraction. Correspondingly, any calculations involving energy conservation or behavior should take refraction effects into account. The functions governing the wave train characteristics predicted by the shallow-water theory are shown in Figure 3 for line sources (left) and two-dimensional sources (right). The upper traces refer to wave systems produced by abrupt monopolar uplift, the center traces to dipolar motions with zero net displacement, and the bottom pair to impulsive sources initiated from rest. Clearly, the Wake record most closely resembles the upper left trace, the further quantitative correspondence with which can be demonstrated as follows:

The functions of Figure 3 are plotted to a common abscissa scale in units of a parameter

$$p = (6/T)^{1/3} (R - T), \qquad (1)$$

where $R = r/h$ is dimensionless distance from the origin of the disturbance to a remote observation point, $T = t\sqrt{g/h}$ is dimensionless time from the instant of source occurrence, g is gravity, and h is the water depth (assumed constant) over the travel path between source and observation point. Thus p is a dimensionless time scale that increases like $T^{1/3}$ at great

distances ($R \approx T$). Although the position of the first positive maximum of each of these functions depends in a different way upon the dimensionless source parameter

$$p_a = (6/T)^{1/3} (a/h),$$

representing the time (in units of p) for a long gravity wave to propagate across the half-breadth of a source of dimensionless width a/h, the respective spacings of subsequent crests depend also upon the nature of the source. Specifically, the functions $-T_p$ and T_{pp} are successive derivatives of

$$T_{(p)} \equiv \int_p^\infty Ci_3 (p/3) \, dp,$$

where

$$Ci_3 (p/3) = \frac{1}{2\pi} \int_0^\infty \cos (m^3 + pm) \, dm, \qquad (2)$$

is an Airy integral, and $m - m^3/6 \approx \gamma$ approximates the wave frequency $\gamma = (m \tanh m)^{1/2}$ for small values of the wave number $m = 2\pi h/\lambda \ll 1$.

For the uniform uplift Hb of a line source of width $2a$,

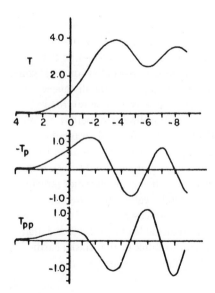

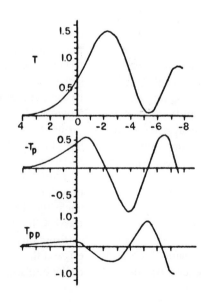

FIGURE 3   Functions for wave-train characteristics predicted by shallow-water theory (line sources on the left and two-dimensional sources on the right). (After Kaijura.)

the surface elevation η at $R \gg 1$ is given by Kajiura (1963, p. 59) as

$$\eta(p) = \frac{Hb}{2\pi}[T(p-p_a) - T(p+p_a)], \qquad (3)$$

and the source breadth can be determined from the arrival time of the leading wave ($p = p_1$), where p_1 is the first maximum of the function $T(p)$. Equation (3) shows that the principal spectral contributions to the wave form at a distance result from delta functions representing the abrupt leading and trailing edges of the disturbance. If the source is very broad ($p_a > 4$), $T(p + p_a) \to 0$, and only the leading edge contributes to the wave form; if it is narrow ($p_a \sim 0$), the wave amplitude is smaller and the wave form is given by

$$\eta = \frac{Hb}{2\pi}(6/T)^{1/3}/(-T_p). \qquad (4)$$

For extremely broad sources ($p_a \gg 4$), $m^3/6 \ll 1$, and $\gamma \approx m$, and the wave form approximates the sea-floor deformation in shape, increasing only in length in proportion to $T^{1/3}$. If a broad source is anywhere discontinuous in uplift, it will have superimposed upon it a wave form of the type given by equation (4).

From the general character of the observed ground motions in Alaska, the ratio a/h may be presumed to be of order 10^3, such that $p_a \gg 1$ for any possible values of $(6/T)^{1/3}$. Thus we can reasonably suppose that the wave form recorded at Wake conforms to the model of an extremely broad source with a local discontinuity. This view is supported by the large local uplift reported along the major uplift axis southwest of Montague Island (Plafker, 1965).

For the Alaska tsunami, however, conditions are complicated by the fact that the source was in very shallow water (< 200 m) compared with the range of depths (4,000–6,000 m) over the remainder of the travel path to Wake Island, nor is it clear which point along the source axis constituted the effective origin of the wave system. Nevertheless, a test of the dispersion predicted by (4) can be obtained without knowing p_a by matching the observed wave-arrival times to an equivalent source disturbance propagating in water of uniform effective depth h given by Van Dorn (1961):

$$h^{-1/2} = \frac{1}{n}\sum_1^n h_i^{-1/2}, \quad i = 1, 2 \ldots n,$$

where the h_i represent local water depths assumed constant over small, equal increments of the least-time (refracted) travel path to Wake Island. The effective depth from Wake over the 5,800-km travel path to the center of the line B-B (Figure 1) giving the deep-water boundary of the reconstructed source is $h = 5,400$ m.

If we now let T_i represent the arrival time of the ith crest from a localized uplift at a remote point $R = T_o \gg 1$, we can write, from (1) and (4)

$$T_o = T_1 + p_1(T_1/6)^{1/3} = T_i + p_i(T_i/6)^{1/3}, \text{ etc.,} \quad (5)$$

where the p_i correspond to consecutive positive maxima of $-T_p = Ci_3(p/3)$. For $R \gg 1$, we can let $T_i = T_1(1 + \delta)$, $\delta \ll 1$, and (5) becomes

$$\Delta T_i \equiv T_1 - T_i \doteq (p_1 - p_i)(T_1/6)^{1/3} - p_i(T_1/6)^{1/3}(\delta/3), \quad (6)$$

the last term of which can be neglected. Thus the crest intervals can be approximated when only the first-crest arrival time T_1 is known. The pertinent data and results for the first four crests at Wake Island are given in the following table, and the computed crest arrivals are shown in Figure 2 as vertical lines directly above the wave trace, showing that the approximate theory adequately predicts both the form and phase of the observed record.

Crest No.	$p*$	$p_1 - p_i$	ΔT_i	Δt_i (min)	Arrival time $417 + \Delta t_i$ (minutes)
1	−1.47				417
		5.70	32.2	12.6	
2	−6.97				430
		9.17	51.8	20.3	
3	−10.64				437
		12.28	69.5	27.2	
4	−13.75				444

*The p_i are taken as the positive maxima of $\pi/3^{1/3}Ai(p/3^{1/3}) = Ci_3$, tabulated by Miller (1946), and $T = 417 \times 60\sqrt{g/h} = 1085$.

MODEL EXPERIMENT

To test further the one-dimensional source hypothesis and to obtain an estimate of the source width, a model experiment was conducted in a wave channel constructed for studying the behavior of waves of very small amplitude. The experimental setup (Figure 4) consisted of a shallow-water section 5 m long and 3.3 cm deep at one end of the channel, terminated in a 1/10 slope to the full depth of 31.5 cm over the remaining 19-m channel length. On a scale of 1:17,000, this model represents a section of the Continental Shelf normal to the fault axis 90 km in half-breadth and 565 m deep, descending at the appropriate slope to the uniform depth of 5,400 m, corresponding to the effective depth computed for the travel path to Wake Island. In lieu of tilting the shallow shelf section to form the model tsunami, a long plunger A, hinged at B, and suspended from an automatic cycling mechanism C was lowered into the water. The plunger consisted of three wooden boards with spacers between them, with their lower edges slightly curved, such that when fully raised they just cleared the surface, and when fully lowered

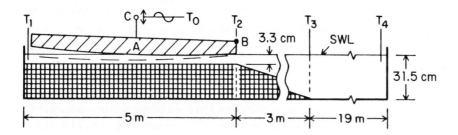

FIGURE 4 Setup of model experiment.

they were immersed full length to a maximum depth of 1 cm. The total effective plunger width was only 16 percent of the channel width of 40 cm. Thus, when lowered rapidly, the plunger produced a positive half-wave 5 m long with a maximum height of about 0.25 cm at the head end of the tank.

Surface elevations as a function of time were measured to an accuracy of 0.001 cm by pressure transducers $T_1 - T_4$, as shown, and the plunger motion was monitored by a separate displacement transducer T_o. Details of the tank instrumentation are given by Van Dorn (1966). The plunger and lowering mechanism are shown in Figure 5.

Of a number of similar experimental runs performed with various plunger speeds and initial conditions, the two considered to resemble the Wake record most closely are shown in Figures 6 and 7. In Figure 6, the plunger (trace T_o) was started from its bottom-center position and cycled roughly sinusoidally to its initial position during an elapsed time of about 8 seconds, thus simulating an initial depression of the

sea floor followed by an uplift of equal displacement. The other traces give the time history of surface elevation at the transducer stations, including reflections from the far end of the channel. Trace T_2 shows that the tsunami at the edge of the Continental Shelf consisted of a leading trough, followed by a double pulse (A). The reflected train at the same station (B) exhibits a shallower trough and a dispersive train rather like the Wake record.

The result of a single, rapid plunger depression, corresponding to a simulated shelf uplift, is shown in Figure 7. In this case, the outgoing (A) and reflected (B) disturbances consist of single intumescences that have roughly the same amplitude but that gradually develop a dispersive profile. The vertical lines over the crest of pulse B were computed with the same method as that for the Wake record, by using the observed first-crest arrival time (34 seconds) and an effective depth $h = 21.3$ cm to account for the increased travel time over the continental slope. Again, the agreement be-

FIGURE 5 Plunger and lowering mechanism for model experiment.

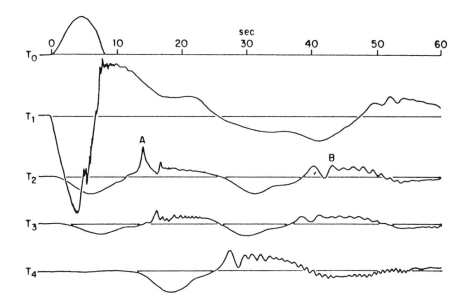

FIGURE 6   Recording in model experiment for plunger started from bottom-center position and cycled for 8 seconds.

tween the computed and observed arrivals supports the use of a one-dimensional dispersion model for the Alaskan source.

Making use of the known model source dimensions, we can now estimate the source half-breadth for Alaska. With reference to Figure 7, let t_1 be the arrival time of the first crest at the shelf edge $(T_2 - A)$, and t_2 be its arrival time at any later station, say, T_4. The pulse duration at $t = t_1$ will be $2t_1$, since it consists of its direct and reflected image from the tank end at T_1. Letting Δt = pulse duration at T_4, we have, according to the theory for very long waves,

$$2t_1 (t_2/t_1)^{1/3} = \Delta t. \tag{7}$$

But $t_1 = a/(gh_1)^{1/2}$, where a is the shelf half-breadth between T_1 and T_4, and (7) can be written

$$a = (\Delta t/2)^{3/2} (g h_1/t_2)^{1/2}. \tag{8}$$

Taking, from Figure 7, $\Delta t = 24.5$ seconds, $t_1 = 8.5$ seconds, $t_2 = 21.5$ seconds, and $h = 3.3$ cm, we obtain $a = 525$ cm, which is to be compared with the known shelf width

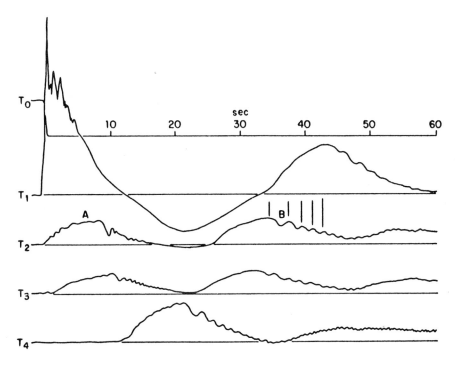

FIGURE 7   Recording in model experiment for single, rapid plunger depression, corresponding to a simulated shelf uplift.

(500 cm). This computation assumes that $p_a \sim 0$, so that the first crest propagates at the velocity $c = \sqrt{gh}$. This can be shown to be a good approximation for all traces.

Similarly, for Alaska, from the Wake record, we take $\Delta t = 80$ minutes, $t_2 = 417$ minutes, and $h_1 = 100$-200 m, as reasonable mean depths for the Continental Shelf, giving

$$a = 23 \text{ km } (h_1 = 100 \text{ m})$$
$$= 33 \text{ km } (h_1 = 200 \text{ m}).$$

These estimates are comparable to the width (~ 30 km) between the smoothed 200-m contour C-C and the presumed axis of maximum uplift A-A (Figure 1), albeit only about half as wide as the zone extending to the trench axis B-B, previously defined by wave travel times (Van Dorn, 1965, and this volume). Because of the agreement between the above analysis and the model experiments, the latter estimates appear to be more convincing.

ACKNOWLEDGMENTS

This work was supported by the Office of Naval Research under contracts Nonr 2216 (16) and 2216 (20).

REFERENCES

Kajiura, Kinjiro, 1963. The leading wave of a tsunami. *Bulletin of the Earthquake Research Institute*, University of Tokyo, 41 (September), 535–571.

Miller, J. C. P., 1946. The Airy integral. British Association for the Advancement of Science. Cambridge: University Press. 56 p.

Pararas-Carayannis, George, 1967. A study of the source mechanism of the Alaska earthquake and tsunami of March 27, 1964: Part I, Water waves. *Pacific Science*, 21 (July), 301–310. Also *in* The Great Alaska Earthquake of 1964: Seismology and Geodesy. NAS Pub. 1602. Washington: National Academy of Sciences, 1972.

Plafker, George, 1965. Tectonic deformation associated with the 1964 earthquake. *Science*, 148 (June 25), 1675–1687.

Spaeth, M. G., and S. C. Berkman, 1965. The tsunami of March 28, 1964, as recorded at tide stations. U.S. Coast and Geodetic Survey Publication. Rockville, Maryland: U.S. Coast and Geodetic Survey. 59 p.

Van Dorn, William G., 1961. Some characteristics of surface gravity waves in the sea produced by nuclear explosions. *Journal of Geophysical Research*, 66 (November), 3845–3862.

Van Dorn, William G., 1965. Source mechanism of the tsunami of March 28, 1964 in Alaska *in* Proceedings of the Ninth Conference (1964) on Coastal Engineering (Chapter 10). New York: American Society of Civil Engineers. p. 166–190. Also *in* The Great Alaska Earthquake of 1964: Oceanography and Coastal Engineering. NAS Pub. 1605. Washington: National Academy of Sciences, 1972.

Van Dorn, William G., 1966. Theoretical and experimental study of wave enhancement and runup on uniformly sloping impermeable beaches. SIO Report 66–11. La Jolla: University of California, Scripps Institution of Oceanography. 101 p.

Wilson, Basil W., and Alf Tørum, 1968. The tsunami of the Alaskan earthquake, 1964: Engineering evaluation. Coastal Engineering Research Center Technical Memorandum No. 25. Washington: U.S. Army Corps of Engineers, May. 444 p.

WILLIAM G. VAN DORN
SCRIPPS INSTITUTION OF OCEANOGRAPHY

DOAK C. COX
UNIVERSITY OF HAWAII

Oceanic Character, Propagation, and Coastal Modification of the Major Tsunami

ABSTRACT: Many of the marigrams of the 1964 Alaska tsunami show low-frequency components of some consistency with a modal period of 1.7 or 1.8 hours. The radiation from the source of a train of coherent, nondispersive waves seems negated by the variation in periods from 1.5 to 2.0 hours without systematical geographic distribution and by the lack of any significant coherent energy peaks associated with the corresponding part of the spectrum in the records from the Hawaiian Islands. It is uncertain, however, whether the low-frequency components represent selective amplification in the coastal area from a broad low-frequency spectrum continuing to be radiated from the source or are the result of energy conversion in the coastal area from a high-frequency part of the spectrum.

Arrival times of the tsunami at most marigraphic stations agree well with long-wave speeds, although apparent arrival times at some stations in the southwest Pacific seem to pertain to reflected waves. The tsunami energy appears to have been preferentially radiated in a southeast direction, as is expectable from the northeast–southwest elongation of the source data.

Such frequency-dependent processes as reflection, wave-trapping, and amplification prevent exact analysis of the modifications of a tsunami in affected coastal regions. The runup of a tsunami has been shown to exhibit both regional variation due to refraction and random variation following a log-normal distribution.

OCEANIC CHARACTER

As in the case of all earlier tsunamis, there were no records of the 1964 Alaska tsunami in the open ocean. Its oceanic character can only be estimated qualitatively from what is known of its generation mechanism, the magnitude and distribution of coastal runup heights, and the records of coastal gages, which, with one exception, were ordinary tide gages (see Spaeth and Berkman, 1967, and this volume). The most unambiguous record, from a special tsunami recording station at Wake Island, has been discussed by Van Dorn (1965a, and this volume).

On the basis of observed and inferred coastal displacements over an area circumscribed by the zone of strong aftershocks, and by projecting wave fronts backward from remote points of observation of first wave arrivals, Van Dorn (1965a, and this volume) estimated the total potential energy of wave motion capable of radiating to the open seas as 2.3×10^{21} ergs.

Later estimates based on similar methods but with successively more complete data have given the higher values 5.7×10^{21} ergs (Pararas-Carayannis, 1967) and 2.2×10^{22} ergs (Berg and others, 1971, and this volume) or about the same as the energy of the tsunami of March 9, 1957, which originated in the Fox Islands about midway along the Aleutian chain (Van Dorn, 1963).

Comparative records of these two tsunamis at Wake Island (Van Dorn, 1965b) suggest substantial differences in their open-sea character. While both records exhibit one or more low-frequency oscillations of durations in excess of 1 hour, in the 1957 record these oscillations were superimposed upon a long-continuing dispersive wave train of much larger amplitude; the dispersive phase was nearly absent from the Alaskan record. This difference implies that the source of the former tsunami contained abrupt discontinuities in the local surface deformation not present in the motion in Alaska. Both the general monotonic character of the Wake record and the apparent absence of a discontinuous fracture in the zone of uplift on the Alaskan shelf suggest that the latter tsunami was produced by the smooth and orderly drainage of water from the shallow shelf into the relatively deep Gulf of Alaska. A small, discontinuous horst uplifted more than 15 m extending southwest from Montague Island (Malloy and Merrill, 1969, and this volume) forms a likely source for a short series of waves several meters in height and about 2 minutes in duration (as reported by observers at Middleton Island); Wilson and Tørum (1968) describe these waves as "parasitic oscillations."

The difficulty of interpreting tide-gage records in terms of the open-sea spectrum of tsunamis is well recognized. Not only does the water overlying the offshore shelves, comprising the continental margin, tend to oscillate at modal frequencies characteristic of their local topography, but the bays and harbors in which most tide stations are located act as additional filters through which the offshore wave system must pass (Munk, 1962). Despite the variability of these natural filters, the 1964 Alaska tsunami, as recorded at shore stations, seems to have contained low-frequency components of some consistency, as may be noted even by casual inspection of the marigrams (see, for example, those shown by Spaeth and Berkman, 1967, and this volume). From a simple process of fitting 10-point dividers to major long-period oscillations, it appears that strong periodicities in the range of 1.5 to 2.0 hours are present in the records from most stations.

The significance of these low-frequency oscillations is uncertain. The following interpretations are discussed: (1) according to Wilson and Tørum (1968), these oscillations indicate the existence of a train of coherent, nondispersive, low-frequency waves emanating from the tsunami source; (2) alternatively, they may indicate selective amplification, from a spectrum of low frequencies (broadly peaked at about 0.6 cycles per hour), whose radiation from the source somehow continued for several hours, of certain natural frequencies that happened to be similar because of similarities of coastal configuration and bathymetry in the recording areas; or (3) they may represent the result of some coastal process of energy conversion from high frequencies that continued to be radiated from the source to low frequencies that again happened to be similar because of similarities of coastal configuration and bathymetry in the recording areas.

Wilson and Tørum (1968) identified the long-period components in the marigrams by subtracting the tide from the tsunami records and then fitting to them, by eye, apparent underlying long-period oscillations. The periods that they calculated at the various stations by using averages over the first three waves at each station clustered closely about 1.8 hours. From this they concluded that the tsunami as it crossed the ocean from its source involved a coherent, nondispersive wave train with a period of approximately 1.8 hours. Further, on the basis of similarities among many of the records in the shapes of the modulation envelopes of

these long-period oscillations, they speculated that these similar envelope shapes had some simple connection with the shape of the source.

Some doubt is cast on the Wilson-Tørum interpretation by the fact that the periods measured, although similar, vary somewhat from station to station. Using the average period of nine waves at each station as determined by fitting 10-point dividers to the records, we find a somewhat greater variation to the periods than Wilson and Tørum's estimates indicate (see Table 1 and Figure 1). Plots of the periods measured by Wilson and Tørum and by us suggest that they are not distributed systematically in space. Hence, coherence seems questionable.

More doubt is cast by the fact that, although results of the subjective analyses of Wilson and Tørum have purportedly been substantiated by objective techniques of spectrum analysis in the case of several stations on continental coasts, they have not been confirmed in the case of the critical mid-ocean record from Hilo, Hawaii. Power spectra of the tsunami marigrams from San Francisco and several stations near Los Angeles, California, computed by Basil Wilson (1969, and personal communication), indicate peaks at 1.8 hours in all records as well as shorter-period peaks related to local resonant behavior. Spectra computed by Murty and Boilard (1970) for certain Canadian stations show a peak at about 1.9 hours at Port Alberni, and one at about 1.5 hours at Tofino. However, the cross spectrum of these stations has low coherence, and no spectral peak in the vicinity of 1.8 hours is shown in the record for Tasu, a station on the Pacific coast of the Queen Charlotte Islands. Spectra computed by Hatori (1967) at Miyagi-Enoshima and Onahama, Japan, not far from Ofunato, show peaks at about 2.0 hours. Spectra computed by Loomis (this volume) from the records from Hilo, Kahului, and Honolulu, Hawaii, and from Midway Island contained no significant low-frequency spectral peaks, and no minor peaks that were coherent even between the records of Midway and Kahului whose spectra appeared qualitatively most similar. The spectra, rather, were typical of those to be expected from a broad spectral continuum modified by independent local response factors.

If the seeming evidence for a single, long period does not, on close examination, support the hypothesis that the tsunami consisted of a simple train of long-period waves, an alternative hypothesis suggested by the same evidence is that the tsunami in the ocean involves a broad spectrum in which energy continues to be radiated from the source at low frequencies. Cox (1963) suggested such broad continuing spectra for tsunamis generally, noting that tide-station records commonly showed increases in amplitude of long-period oscillations that could not be accounted for by concentration of the low-frequency energy at the front of the wave train.

Takahasi (1963a) showed that the spectra of five tsunamis recorded by a Van Dorn long-wave recorder at Miyagi-

TABLE 1 Long-Period Oscillations on Alaska Tsunami Marigrams, March 28, 1964

Place	Period (hr) Wilson and Tørum (1968, Table III) (3 Waves)	Cox and Van Dorn (9 Waves)	Place	Period (hr) Wilson and Tørum (1968, Table III) (3 Waves)	Cox and Van Dorn (9 Waves)
Yakutat	1.9	1.9	Ushuaia	1.9	–
Juneau	1.7	1.6	Argentine I.	1.6	–
Sitka	1.8	1.7	Hilo	1.8	–
Prince Rupert	1.8	1.7	Mokuoloe	1.8	1.9
Port Alberni	1.7	–	Midway I.	1.8	1.9?
Victoria	1.6	1.6	Johnson I.	–	1.5
Crescent City	1.8	–	Apia	–	0.8 (1.5?)
San Francisco	1.7	1.7	Lyttleton	1.8	–
Rincon I.	1.7	1.8	Moen I.	1.8	1.8
Santa Monica	–	1.7	Massacre Bay	1.9	2.3 (1.3?)
San Diego	1.6	1.0 (1.7?)	Poronuysk	1.8	1.8
Ensenada	–	1.7	Yuzhno	1.8	1.7
Manzanillo	–	1.6	Hanasaki	2.3	1.7
Talcahuano	1.8	1.8	Ofunato	1.9	–
Corral	1.9	0.6			

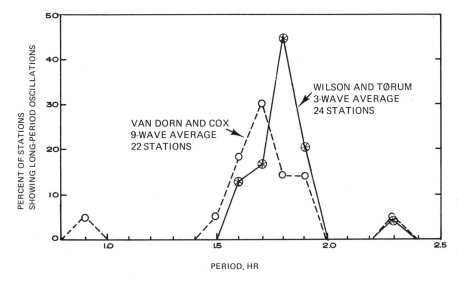

FIGURE 1 Frequency distribution of long-period oscillations in tsunami marigrams of the Alaska tsunami.

Enoshima Island, off the coast of Honshu, Japan, are consistent with the concept of broad spectra, modified by the excitation of preferred resonant modes that are present in the ordinary daily background spectrum. Smooth curves fitted to the spectra define broad spectral peaks equivalent to effective periods whose logarithms Takahasi found to be linearly related to the magnitudes of the associated earthquakes.

Takahasi and Aida (1961, 1963) estimated the spectra of several tsunamis incident on the shelf from the spectra recorded at various tide stations and transfer functions for the same tide stations calculated as average spectra from several tsunamis. Even though the records of various tsunamis at a single station may superficially resemble each other more closely than the records of a single tsunami at various stations, the incident spectra for a single tsunami, estimated from the records of several stations, showed close similarities. The incident spectra were all broad, some peaking at low frequencies and some at high.

Even from work with unsmoothed spectra, Hatori (1963, 1967) reported evidence that spectral peaks define characteristic periods related to the dimensions of tsunami sources and their orientation relative to the propagation path to the recording station and to earthquake magnitude and distance.

However, neither hydrodynamic theory nor hydraulic-model experiments support the hypothesis of continuing radiation of low-frequency wave energy from a tsunami source. Momoi (1964), examining the time history of water motion near the source in the case of broad uplifts or depressions, found that it involves one or two long oscillations of decaying amplitude on which shorter oscillations are later superimposed. However, his analysis is pertinent only to generation on an essentially flat bottom and extends to a time only a little more than twice the travel time of a wave across the generating area. Takahasi's (1963b) hydraulic-model experiments gave similar results, although he described the nondispersive wave form underlying the dispersive waves as a wave train rather than a single or double oscillation.

Momoi's and Takahasi's investigations involved bottom configurations quite different from those in the generating area of the Alaskan tsunami, notably in having no possibly resonating platform comparable in size to that of the uplifted area. It is therefore of interest to examine the Alaskan source as an approximation to a Helmholtz resonator which may be capable of sustained oscillation on a longer period of time in the manner implied by Wilson and Tørum (1968). Assuming that a transverse section of the Continental Shelf extending southeast from Afognak Island was initially tilted tectonically about a hinge at the margin, oscillations would be set up that would radiate energy to the Gulf of Alaska at the rate

$$E = E_0\, T^{t/\tau},$$

where E_0 and E are the initial and final energies, respectively, t is time, τ is the period of oscillation, and T is the transmission coefficient at the depth transition from the shelf to the much deeper Gulf of Alaska. But $T = \sqrt{1 - R^2}$ is the conjugate of the reflection coefficient R, for periodic waves advancing in the opposite direction from deep to shallow water. For the long waves in the latter context, Kajiura gives curves of R versus a parameter $a = (\pi/l)\,(h_1 - h_2)$ for several values of the dimensionless wave frequency $\omega^2 h_2/g$ and the ratio h_1/h_2 of the depths across a transition of width l. Taking, for Alaska, $l = 20$ km, $\tau = 1.8$ hours, $h_1 = 200$ m, and $h_2 = 4,000$ m, so that $h_1/h_2 = 0.05$, $a = 0.6$, and $\omega^2 h_2/g = 4\pi^2 h^2/\tau^2 g = 4 \times 10^{-4}$, we obtain $R \approx 0.63$ and $T \approx 0.78$. Thus, about 78 percent of the energy will be radiated on the first oscillation and little energy will be left for subsequent oscillations.

Van Dorn (1970, and this volume) has reported on a hydraulic-model experiment on the generation of the 1964 Alaska tsunami which showed, propagating away from the shelf, a first wave directly generated by the deformation and a second wave reflected from the shoreline in a manner consistent with the resonant behavior postulated above. The original oscillograms cut off quite abruptly in the record at the far end—an indication of no significant energy beyond the first oscillation. However, the length of the flume used was such that the existence and relative amplitude of possible additional waves could not be studied because of the interference of reflections.

It is quite clear that as a result of dispersion, the dependence of the group velocity of waves on the frequency, wave energy propagating directly from an impulsive source will continue to arrive at a distant station over a protracted period. However, in a purely dispersive wave train the energy continuing to arrive after the first wave arrival will be associated with higher and higher frequencies (for example, see Van Dorn, 1965b). Still unexplained are the ways in which the low frequencies observed at distant coasts are generated, and particularly the means by which their relatively high amplitudes of oscillation are so long maintained or even increased through several cycles as the result of late, high-frequency arrivals from the ocean.

In summary, although it appears unlikely that the long-period (1.8 hours) oscillations observed at many stations represent a train of coherent long-period waves emanating from the source, it is not clear whether they represent selective amplification from a spectrum broadly peaked at about this period or are the result of conversion of energy propagating from the sources as shorter-period waves.

TRAVEL TIMES

Although the phase velocities associated with the high frequencies ($>$ 1 cycle per kilosecond) of a tsunami are significantly less than the long-wave velocity, and their group velocities are still lower, leading to dispersive effects (Van Dorn, 1965b), the front of the tsunami and any low-frequency oscillations travel at essentially the long-wave velocity

$$C = \sqrt{gh},$$

where g = acceleration of gravity and h = depth of water.

Using this velocity-depth relation and working backward from the arrival times of the wave front at tide gages that recorded the tsunamis (Spaeth and Berkman, 1967), Wilson and Tørum (1968) constructed a refraction diagram showing the position of the wave front at hourly intervals (Figure 2) from 04:00 GMT, March 28, 24 minutes after the earthquake, to 01:00 GMT, March 29, 25 minutes before the front arrived at the Argentine Islands, Antarctica.

Pararas-Carayannis (1967) constructed a refraction diagram in greater detail but generally in agreement with that of Wilson and Tørum for the sector of waves propagating to the Hawaiian Islands, Marshall Islands, and Line Islands.

Average speeds, tabulated by Spaeth and Berkman, ranged from 159 knots for propagation to Yakutat, Alaska, over a path that was mostly on the Continental Shelf, to 473 knots to Nawiliwili, Kauai, Hawaii, over a path mainly at oceanic depths.

Braddock (1969) has calculated travel times for the Alaska tsunami to 15 tide stations distributed about the Pacific by

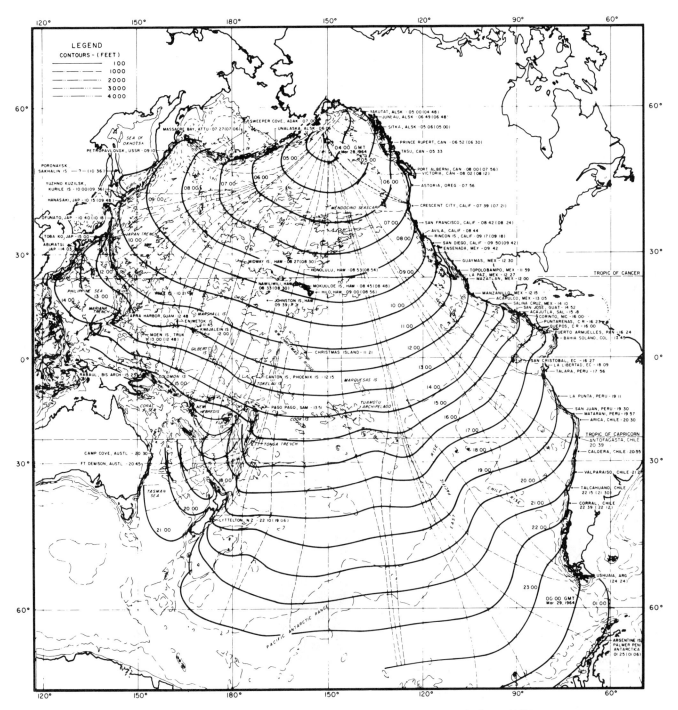

FIGURE 2 Refraction diagram for the Alaska tsunami (from Wilson and Tørum, 1968).

an iterative procedure employing discrete methods to obtain convergent sequences of approximation to optimal paths and corresponding travel times. Assuming direct paths, he found agreement between calculated and observed travel times within 1 to 19 minutes (Figures 3 and 4), except in the case of stations on the west coast of New Zealand, for which the observed travel times might be explained by waves reflected from the east coast of Australia.

DIRECTIONAL EFFECTS

Although the crustal movement associated with the Alaska earthquake was dipolar, the depressed area was mostly on land, and the source of the tsunami was essentially a unipolar uplift elongated northeast-southwest (see Berg and others, 1971, and this volume). It was to be expected that the wave energy would be preferentially radiated in a direction normal

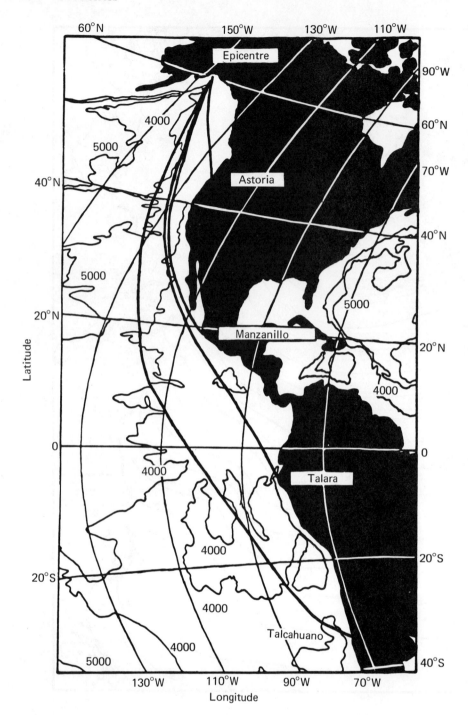

FIGURE 3 Calculated ray paths for the Alaska tsunami to Astoria, Manzanillo, Talara, and Talcahuano (from Braddock, 1969).

to the long axis of the area of uplift, even though the wave front became nearly circular at a distance several times the length of the long axis area.

For the Alaska tsunami, the refracted wave front was nearly circular by the time it emerged from the Gulf of Alaska, about 50 minutes after the earthquake (Van Dorn, 1965a, and this volume). Nevertheless, present evidence suggests that the tsunami energy leaving the Gulf of Alaska was

preferentially radiated in a southeast direction.

Any quantitative attempt to resolve directional differences in tsunami intensity, however, must take into consideration not only the expected attenuation of maximum wave amplitude in the open sea, but also the compound effects of refraction, shoaling, and interference produced by irregular topography between the source and points of observation, none of which can be easily assessed. For example, runup

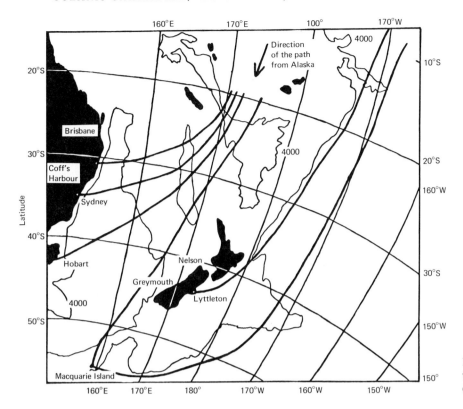

FIGURE 4   Approximate travel paths for the Alaska tsunami in the southwest Pacific (from Braddock, 1969).

heights alone at sensibly equal distances from remote sources have been shown to vary by a factor of 3 above and below their local log-normal mean height along a short stretch of coastline (Van Dorn, 1965b). Tide-gage records suffer from the difficulties of interpretation mentioned in connection with frequency characteristics, and even large coastal regions differ markedly in their inherent susceptibility or insensitivity to tsunami effects (for example, Hawaii and Japan in contrast to southern California, respectively).

Probably the most meaningful (but only qualitative) directional comparison that can be made for the available data from the Alaska tsunami consists of differences occurring between the maximum reported tide-gage heights from continental stations at equal distances from Alaska in different directions. Such data are shown in Table 2 for directions nearly parallel, and nearly normal, respectively, to the long axis of the source as a function of source distance. Despite the irregular trend of data with distance, it is apparent that the runup heights to the southeast of the source are generally higher than those to the southwest, in accord with the geometrical orientation of the source. It appears that, for warning purposes, useful weighting might be given to directional differences in the severity of probable tsunami effects if the orientation of the source can be established sufficiently early. It also seems likely that the geologic structure or previous history of known tsunami-producing regions might provide advance information in this regard.

COASTAL MODIFICATION

As a tsunami approaches a coast after crossing the ocean, it becomes subject to a large number of important modifications.

1. As it crosses the continental slope, much of the energy may be reflected back to the ocean. As shown by Kajiura (1963), the amplitude and phase of the transmitted waves are critically dependent upon a number of factors such as the ratio of the depths across the discontinuity, the ratio of the incident component of wavelengths to the transition width, and the angle of approach. For multiple wave systems, multiple reflections must be considered. For strongly oblique reflections, a nonlinear Mach stem, which cannot be treated analytically, may develop (Perroud, 1957). Thus, there is a lack of generalized analytic solutions to account for the variation in "intensity" or other characteristics of a tsunami even at the margin of the Continental Shelf. For additional information, see Wiegel (1965).

2. The Continental Shelf acts as a wave guide, as shown by Munk and others (1964), tending to trap energy at wavelengths of the order of the shelf width and to reradiate preferentially (leak) shorter waves back to sea.

3. As already noted, harbors or embayments along the perimeter of the shelf constitute a set of additional filters

TABLE 2 Alaska Tsunami Comparative Tide-Gage Maxima, March 28, 1964[a]

Station SE	Station SW	Distance (Nautical Miles)	H_{max} (Ft)	$H_{max}SE/H_{max}SW$
Neah Bay, Washington	Sweeper Cove, Adak	1,098 1,042	1.9 4.7	2.5
Crescent City, California	Massacre Bay, Attu	1,365 1,380	2.8 13+	4.7+
Avila Beach, California	Petropavlovsk, Siberia	1,793 1,805	0.1 10.4+	100+
Mazatlán, Mexico	Hanasaki, Japan	2,569 2,782	2.2 1.6	0.7
Manzanillo, Mexico	Ofunato, Japan	2,874 3,056	4.5 3.9	0.9
Acapulco, Mexico	Toba Ko, Japan	3,235 3,286	0.8 3.5	4.4
Salina Cruz, Mexico	Aburatsu, Japan	3,536 3,447	2.4 2.8	1.2

[a]Data from Spaeth and Berkman (1967, and this volume).

through which the already modified tsunami spectrum must be viewed, since each will possess individual preferred modes of oscillation that can be excited by shelf oscillations of corresponding frequencies. Moreover, both the amplification and phase response of a tide gage within a harbor may depend on the precise location of the gage for all frequencies higher than the lowest modal frequency for that harbor.

To the extent that the local shoreline oscillations during tsunamis are periodic, as suggested by the duration of sustained oscillations on tide records, they can be discussed (W. H. Munk, personal communication) in the light of elementary linear filter theory. Groves and Harvey (1967) suggest the use of bilinear operations. The incoming tsunami signature can be likened to an energy pulse $f(t)$ propagating through a parallel array of black boxes (each determined by local harbor characteristics coupled to those of the shelf outside, within one or two tsunami wavelengths) with individual responses to a spike input designated by $k_i(T)$. The output of any box i

$$g_i(t) = \int_0^\infty f(t - \tau) k_i(\tau) d\tau \qquad (1)$$

depends on its response kernel k, whose Fourier transform is the frequency-dependent admittance. The problem of interpreting tide-gage records then is to determine their respective admittances; there are a number of conceivable ways of doing this, but none have yet been accomplished. The methods are to

1. measure tsunamis offshore and cross-correlate them with the tide-gage records; 2. measure low-frequency background noise spectra; 3. use bottom topography to compute theoretical admittance functions; or 4. build and analyze hydraulic models.

Method 1 may soon become possible if bottom-mounted offshore pressure recorders, currently under development, prove successful. Method 2 would also require special instrumentation because the ambient low-frequency noise is smaller than the digitizing errors for most tide gages. Method 3 may very shortly become possible with the use of a new theoretical approach and computer program developed by Hwang and Tuck (1970). While the present program deals only with uniform depth, the case of arbitrary depth contours is now near solution. Until now, hydraulic modeling has been the only practical method of obtaining "engineering" answers to specific harbor problems, but similitude laws require large models that are very expensive and time-consuming to construct and operate. Even the large model of Hilo Harbor (Palmer and Funasaki, 1966; Cox and others, 1965; Palmer and others, 1967) could not reproduce the observed frequency characteristics to the point where the tsunami signature could be determined, although reasonable approximations to the observed inundation patterns for several tsunamis were obtained by experimentally determined (albeit unrealistic) adjustment of input and dissipation conditions.

In summary, the complexity of the nearshore hydrodynamics proscribes simple analysis and generalization, and each local region must be studied on its own basis. Because of their great expense and questionable results, present modeling techniques will probably be replaced later by new and rapid numerical methods.

Certain simple cases of linear wave motion in two dimensions over variable topography have already been successfully treated by analytical and numerical methods. The experiments of Williams and Kartha (1966) quantitatively support the theory of Webster and Perry (in press) concerning wave amplification and refraction around circular islands with analytical profiles, except for wavelengths smaller than the island base diameters, where diffractive effects begin to obliterate the fine structure predicted by theory. Vastano and Reid (in press) developed a conformal coordinate-mapping technique that permits numerical computation of long, periodic wave behavior around real islands and have obtained convincing agreement with model results by Van Dorn (1970, and this volume) for Wake Island. This technique is not restricted to islands but requires large computer storage for complex topography. Such results support the conclusion that, except for nonlinear effects very near the shore, linear techniques probably suffice to describe the gross motions of actual tsunamis.

RUNUP

Runup, of course, is the end product of the nearshore oscillations—however produced—just as the capability of predicting its probable occurrence and extent is the desired end product of tsunami research. An understanding of the runup mechanism presupposes an equal understanding of all the above-mentioned antecedent offshore motions, most of which have not yet been elucidated.

Historically the most perplexing feature of tsunami runup has been the great vertical extent of water encroachment on the shoreline, relative to the maximum wave height in the open sea, as inferred from observations at small islands, despite the fact that most tsunami damage resulted from extensive inundation of low-lying areas more favorable for habitation.

From a comparison between runup observations in Hawaii and corresponding wave heights recorded at Wake Island for four tsunamis, Van Dorn (1965b) concluded that the logarithmic mean runup in Hawaii exceeded the offshore wave height by a factor of 16. From statistical analyses of several hundred runup observations on three Hawaiian Islands from the tsunamis of 1946 and 1957, he concluded that the regional logarithmic mean on the incident sides of the islands was about three times as great as on the lee sides and that the scatter of individual heights about the regional mean had a log-normal Gaussian distribution with a standard deviation

of 1.8 times the mean (that is, a 5 percent probability of heights as great as three times the mean value). A similar distribution for runup heights in Japan implies a generally similar amplification process and magnitude.

By analogy to light or sound waves, such a normal Gaussian distribution suggests that the local runup variation is random and due to noncoherent, energy-scattering processes along a shoreline having roughness elements (bays and promontories, submarine valleys, and ridges) separated by less than an incident wavelength. Such scattering represents a "noise" that limits severely the accuracy of predictions since it is not amenable to calculation.

The incident-to-leeward differences in mean runup may be explicable by refractive effects around islands, since differences of this order clearly show up in the experiments of Williams and Kartha (1966). But the very large logarithmic mean enhancement (16 times) observed in Hawaii has yet to be successfully demonstrated in theory or model experiments (Van Dorn, 1966), probably because of scaling problems such as boundary-layer dissipation and surface contact resistance at the very small slopes and wave steepnesses characteristic of tsunamis (Perry, 1963; Van Dorn, 1966).

Probably the most careful theoretical study of tsunami runup is that by Carrier (1966), who considered very long, slightly dispersive plane waves of height H propagating in water of depth h and having a runup R_s on a small slope a, after traveling a dimensionless distance x_0/h given by

$$R_s/H \approx 2.1 \, a^{-1/2} \, (x_0/h)^{-1/6}.$$

Taking for the tsunami of March 9, 1957, in Hawaii, the representative values $a = 0.025$, $x_0/h = 600$, one obtains $R_s/H \doteq 4.6$, which is only about $\frac{1}{3}$ of the mean observed runup ratio, based on the maximum offshore wave height at Wake Island (Van Dorn, 1965b).

These results suggest that the abnormal runup of tsunamis is not simply due to enhancement of individual waves in shallow water but is possibly the result of complex interactions between edge waves set in motion by the broad offshore spectrum. Clearly, any physical or numerical model of tsunami effects should resolve this discrepancy as a prerequisite.

REFERENCES

Berg, Eduard, Doak C. Cox, Augustine S. Furumoto, Kinjiro Kajiura, Hirosi Kawasumi, and Etsuzo Shima, 1971. The source of the major tsunami in Field survey of the tsunamis of 28 March 1964 in Alaska, and conclusions as to the origin of the major tsunami. Report HIG-70-2. Honolulu: University of Hawaii, Institute of Geophysics. p. 38–49. Also in The Great Alaska Earthquake of 1964: Oceanography and Coastal Engineering. NAS Pub. 1605. Washington: National Academy of Sciences, 1972.

Braddock, R. D., 1969. On tsunami propagation. *Journal of Geophysical Research*, 74 (No. 8), 1952–1955.

Carrier, G. F., 1966. Gravity waves in water of variable depth. *Journal of Fluid Mechanics*, 24 (Pt. 4), 641–659.

Cox, Doak C., 1963. Status of tsunami knowledge. Proceedings of the Tenth Pacific Science Congress, Honolulu, Hawaii, August–September 1961. Doak C. Cox, editor. IUGG Monograph 24. Paris: International Union of Geodesy and Geophysics. p. 1–6.

Cox, Doak C., Masashi Hom-ma, Masatsugu Suzuki, Ryutaro Takahasi, and Robert L. Wiegel, 1965. Physically feasible means for protecting Hilo from tsunamis. Third Report of the Hilo Technical Tsunami Advisory Council to the Board of Supervisors, Hawaii County, through its Tsunami Advisory Committee, December 31. Hilo: Hilo Technical Tsunami Advisory Council. 38 p.

Groves, G. W., and R. R. Harvey, 1967. Representation of nearshore distortion of tsunamis by bilinear operators. Report HIG–67–4. Honolulu: University of Hawaii, Institute of Geophysics, March. 23 p.

Hatori, Tokutaro, 1963. Directivity of tsunamis. *Bulletin of the Earthquake Research Institute*, University of Tokyo, 41 (No. 1), 61–81.

Hatori, Tokutaro, 1967. The wave form of tsunami on the Continental Shelf. *Bulletin of the Earthquake Research Institute*, University of Tokyo, 45 (No. 1), 79–90.

Hwang, Li-San, and E. O. Tuck, 1970. On the oscillation of harbours of arbitrary shape. *Journal of Fluid Mechanics*, 42, Part 3 (July 9), 447–464.

Iida, Kumizi, and Yutaka Ohta, 1963. On the heights of tsunamis associated with distant and near earthquakes. Proceedings of the Tenth Pacific Science Congress, Honolulu, Hawaii, August–September 1961. Doak C. Cox, editor. IUGG Monograph 24. Paris: International Union of Geodesy and Geophysics. p. 105–123.

Kajiura, Kinjiro, 1963. On the partial reflection of water waves passing over a bottom of variable depth. Proceedings of the Tenth Pacific Science Congress, Honolulu, Hawaii, August–September 1961. Doak C. Cox, editor. IUGG Monograph 24. Paris: International Union of Geodesy and Geophysics. p. 206–230.

Loomis, Harold G., 1972. The major tsunami in the Hawaiian Islands *in* The Great Alaska Earthquake of 1964: Oceanography and Coastal Engineering. NAS Pub. 1605. Washington: National Academy of Sciences.

Malloy, Richard J., and George F. Merrill, 1969. Vertical crustal movement of the sea floor associated with the Prince William Sound, Alaska, earthquake *in* Volume II-B, C: The Prince William Sound, Alaska, earthquake of 1964 and aftershocks. Environmental Science Services Administration, U.S. Coast and Geodetic Survey. Washington: Government Printing Office. p. 327–338. Also *in* The Great Alaska Earthquake of 1964: Oceanography and Coastal Engineering. NAS Pub. 1605. Washington: National Academy of Sciences, 1972.

Momoi, Takao, 1964. Tsunami in the vicinity of a wave origin. *Bulletin of the Earthquake Research Institute*, University of Tokyo, 42 (No. 1), 133–146; (No. 2), 369–381.

Munk, Walter H., 1962. Long ocean waves *in* The Sea. M. N. Hill, editor. Volume 1, Physical Oceanography. New York: Interscience Publishers. p. 647–663.

Munk, Walter H., Frank Snodgrass, and Freeman Gilbert, 1964. Long waves on the Continental Shelf: an experiment to separate trapped and leaky modes. *Journal of Fluid Mechanics*, 20 (No. 4), 529–554.

Murty, T. S., and Lise Boilard, 1970. The tsunami in Alberni Inlet caused by the Alaska earthquake of March 1964 *in* Tsunamis in the Pacific Ocean. Proceedings of the International Symposium on Tsunamis and Tsunami Research, Honolulu, Hawaii, October 7–10, 1969. W. M. Adams, editor. Honolulu: East-West Center Press. p. 165–187.

Palmer, Robert Q., and Gerald Funasaki, 1966. The Hilo Harbor tsunami model. State of Hawaii, James Look Laboratory of Oceanographic Engineering, Technical Report No. 1. 10 p.

Palmer, Robert Q., Michael E. Mulvahill, and Gerald T. Funasaki, 1967. Study of proposed barrier plans for the protection of the city of Hilo and Hilo Harbor, Hawaii. Corps of Engineers Technical Report No. 1, November. Honolulu: U.S. Army Corps of Engineers. 76 p.

Pararas-Carayannis, George, 1967. A study of the source mechanism of the Alaska earthquake and tsunami of March 27, 1964: Part I, Water waves. *Pacific Science*, 21 (July), 301–310.

Perroud, P. H., 1957. The solitary wave reflection along a straight vertical wall at low oblique incidence. Institute of Engineering Research Technical Report, Series 99, Issue 3. Berkeley: University of California.

Perry, Byrne, 1963. On the use of small-scale hydraulic models in tsunami research. Proceedings of the Tenth Pacific Science Congress, Honolulu, Hawaii, August–September 1961. Doak C. Cox, editor. IUGG Monograph 24. Paris: International Union of Geodesy and Geophysics. p. 231–234.

Spaeth, Mark G., and Saul C. Berkman, 1967. The tsunami of March 28, 1964, as recorded at tide stations. Environmental Science Services Administration Technical Report C&GS 33. Washington: Government Printing Office. 86 p. Also *in* The Great Alaska Earthquake of 1964: Oceanography and Coastal Engineering. NAS Pub. 1605. Washington: National Academy of Sciences, 1972.

Takahasi, Ryutaro, 1963a. On the spectra and the mechanism of generation of tsunamis. Proceedings of the Tenth Pacific Science Congress, Honolulu, Hawaii, August–September 1961. Doak C. Cox, editor. IUGG Monograph 24. Paris: International Union of Geodesy and Geophysics. p. 19–25.

Takahasi, Ryutaro, 1963b. On some model experiments on tsunami generation. Proceedings of the Tenth Pacific Science Congress, Honolulu, Hawaii, August–September 1961. Doak C. Cox, editor. IUGG Monograph 24. Paris: International Union of Geodesy and Geophysics. p. 235–248.

Takahasi, Ryutaro, and Isamu Aida, 1961. Studies on the spectrum of tsunamis. *Bulletin of the Earthquake Research Institute*, University of Tokyo, 39 (No. 3), 523–535.

Takahasi, Ryutaro, and Isamu Aida, 1963. Spectra of several tsunamis observed on the coast of Japan. *Bulletin of the Earthquake Research Institute*, University of Tokyo, 41 (No. 1), 299–314.

Van Dorn, William G., 1963. The source motion of the tsunami of March 9, 1957, as deduced from wave measurements at Wake Island. Proceedings of the Tenth Pacific Science Congress, Honolulu, Hawaii, August–September 1961. Doak C. Cox, editor. IUGG Monograph 24. Paris: International Union of Geodesy and Geophysics. p. 39–48.

Van Dorn, William G., 1965a. Source mechanism of the tsunami of March 28, 1964 in Alaska. Proceedings of the Ninth Conference (1964) on Coastal Engineering (Chapter 10). New York: American Society of Civil Engineers. p. 166–190. Also *in* The Great Alaska Earthquake of 1964: Oceanography and Coastal Engineering. NAS Pub. 1605. National Academy of Sciences, 1972.

Van Dorn, William G., 1965b. Tsunamis. *Advances in Hydroscience*, 2 (Annual), 1–47.

Van Dorn, William G., 1966. Theoretical and experimental study of wave enhancement and runup on uniformly sloping impermeable beaches. SIO Report No. 66–11. La Jolla: University of California, Scripps Institution of Oceanography. 101 p.

Van Dorn, William G., 1970. A model experiment on the generation of the tsunami of March 28, 1964, in Alaska *in* Tsunamis in the Pacific Ocean. Proceedings of the International Symposium on Tsunamis and Tsunami Research, Honolulu, Hawaii, October 7–10, 1969. W. M. Adams, editor. Honolulu: East-West Center Press. p. 33–45. Also *in* The Great Alaska Earthquake of 1964: Oceanography and Coastal Engineering. NAS Pub. 1605. Washington: National Academy of Sciences, 1972.

Vastano, A. C., and R. O. Reid, in press. Tsunami response at Wake Island: Comparison of the hydraulic and numerical approaches. *Journal of Marine Research*.

Webster, David L., and Byrne Perry, in press. Amplification of tsunamis by oceanic islands. Civil Engineering Technical Report 67. Palo Alto: Stanford University.

Wiegel, Robert L., 1965. Water wave equivalent of mach-reflection. Proceedings of the Ninth Conference (1964) on Coastal Engineering. New York: American Society of Civil Engineers. p. 82–102.

Williams, John, and Krishna Kartha, 1966. Model studies of long wave amplification by circular islands and submarine seamounts. Report HIG–66–19. Honolulu: University of Hawaii, Institute of Geophysics, November. 46 p.

Wilson, Basil W., 1969. Tsunami responses of San Pedro Bay and Shelf, California: Civil Engineering in the Oceans II. Proceedings of the American Society of Civil Engineers, Waterways and Harbors Division, Miami Beach, Florida, December 1969. New York: American Society of Civil Engineers. p. 1099–1133.

Wilson, Basil W., and Alf Tφrum, 1968. The tsunami of the Alaskan earthquake, 1964: Engineering evaluation. Coastal Engineering Research Center Technical Memorandum No. 25. Washington: U.S. Army Corps of Engineers, May. 444 p.

BASIL W. WILSON*
CONSULTING OCEANOGRAPHIC ENGINEER, PASADENA

ALF TØRUM*
TECHNICAL UNIVERSITY OF NORWAY, TRONDHEIM

Adapted from Section III (Chapters 2 and 9) of
Coastal Engineering Research Center Technical Memorandum 25,
"The Tsunami of the Alaskan Earthquake, 1964:
Engineering Evaluation"

Runup Heights of the Major Tsunami on North American Coasts

ABSTRACT: A great many accounts of local effects of the Alaska tsunami in different areas have been published. These are assembled and assimilated with interpretive additions to give a macroscopic view of the inundations from the main tsunami along the central Alaskan and western seaboard of the United States. The emergent picture is of an initially elevated wave, linked to an uplift of the seabed, propagating seaward from the Continental Shelf of Alaska. Initial withdrawals of water, reported at some places along the central Alaskan coastline, would have been consistent with subsidence of the seabed, known to have occurred northwest of the hinge line of vertical earth movement in the earthquake. In the Alaskan area, runup heights were often from 30 to 40 ft above the low-tide level prevailing at the time of the event. The observations confirm quite well an empirical relationship, based on Pacific Ocean data, which indicates a statistical dependence of maximum tsunami wave height near the source region on the earthquake magnitude. Along the North American coastline from Alaska to Oregon, the largest tsunami waves tended to be concurrent with the peak of the high spring tide, leading to very high runup. Some of the highest waves appear to have attacked the Washington and Oregon coastlines. In particular areas of coastline, resonance effects probably accentuated runup level and account for the rather disparate runup heights reported. South of Oregon and northern California, the tsunami waves reached the coast on a falling tide and the flooding was less.

*Formerly with Science Engineering Associates, San Marino, California.

RUNUP NEAR THE SOURCE

Tide-gage records of the major tsunami generated on the Continental Shelf by the Alaska earthquake, outside the immediate area affected by the earthquake, show an initial rise of water, indicating a positive sea wave resulting from the upward motion of the sea bed (Brown, 1964; Spaeth and Berkman, 1967, and this volume; U.S. Coast and Geodetic Survey, 1964). The initial water movement within the Gulf of Alaska and along its coast is less well known because no tide gages were in operation in the area between Yakutat and Kodiak and in Prince William Sound. In the region of uplift, immediate water withdrawals were reported at Boswell Bay (Hinchinbrook Island), Cape St. Elias, and Middleton Island (Van Dorn, 1965, and this volume), and also at Cape Yakataga (Berg and others, 1971; Brown, 1964; Chance, 1966); see Figure 1 for locations.

Middleton Island on the edge of the Continental Shelf (see Figure 2 for bathymetric details) occupies a rather unique position in relation to the tsunami wave-generating area. According to Brown (1964), the initial regression of the sea there was observed to be 2–3 ft and to last 15 to 20 minutes (Chance, 1966). A wave arrived some 20 minutes after the earthquake but rose no higher than the tectonically elevated higher high-water line (Chance, 1966). St.-Amand, on the other hand, found swash marks at an elevation 10 ft above the latter level (Brown, 1964). Wilson and Tørum (1968) have attempted to explain these observations on the basis of a long wave caused by general uplift and tilt of the shelf with the water over it, especially in the vicinity of Montague Island (Wilson and Tørum, this volume), of the uplift of Middleton Island itself, and of secondary oscillations.

At Cape Yakataga the arrival of the waves was recorded by Charles Bilderback, and their levels were noted in relation to reference marks from which he was able to assess their runup height (compare Berg and others, 1971; Pararas-Carayannis, 1965; Chance, 1966). Figure 3 is a plot of Bilderback's observations, which suggest that the underlying dominant wave had a period of about 1.4 hours and a height of about 4 m (13 ft).

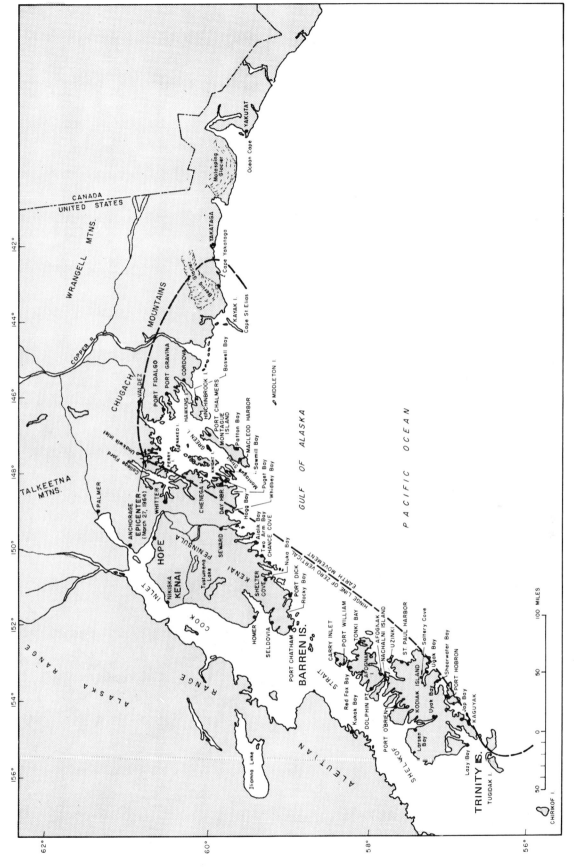

FIGURE 1 General map of south central Alaska, covering the area most affected by the earthquake and containing place-names referred to in the text.

159

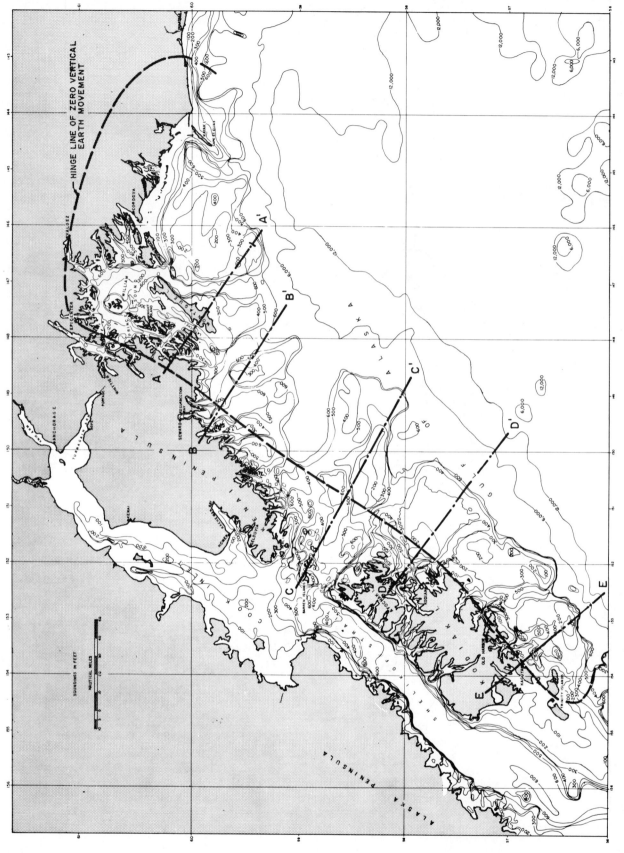

FIGURE 2 General bathymetry of the Continental Shelf, Gulf of Alaska, Prince William Sound, and Cook Inlet. (Note: The section lines AA' to EE' relate to discussions of the bathymetry given in Wilson and Tørum, 1968; they are not referred to in the present text.)

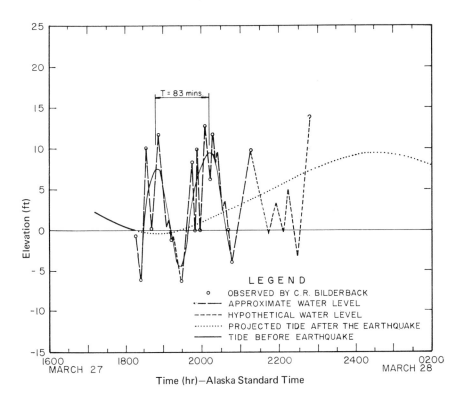

FIGURE 3   Observed tsunami wave activity at Cape Yakataga (adapted from Pararas-Carayannis, 1967).

Local oscillations in the period from 5 to 20 minutes increased the height by almost 1 m, as is evident in this record.

At Puget Bay and Whidbey Bay on the Kenai Peninsula (Figure 1) quite close to the hinge line of zero vertical earth movement, about 18 to 20 minutes after the earthquake, waves up to 35 ft (runup) rolled in (Chance, 1966). The lack of recession of the water here may be imputed to the probability that both land and water were uplifted to about the same extent in the same time. Further to the southwest, however, along the greatly indented southeast coast of the Kenai Peninsula, which lies on the subsidence side of the hinge line, initial withdrawals of water were reported for such places as Rocky Bay and Nuka Bay (Van Dorn, 1965, and this volume; Chance, 1966).

Seward, at the head of Resurrection Bay, experienced very remarkable early effects from waves which resulted from submarine and shoreline slumping of the fronts of deltas (Berg and others, 1971; Brown, 1964; Chance, 1966; Grantz and others, 1964; Plafker and Mayo, 1965; Lemke, 1967, and Geology volume; Wilson and Tørum, 1968, and this volume) and perhaps also from faulting along the axis of Resurrection Bay; this was intimated to the authors by Captain Watkins of the Coast and Geodetic Survey ship *Hodgson* and by Gene Rusnak of the U.S. Geological Survey. According to Lemke, the first wave of the main tsunami, however, rolled in on Seward some 25 minutes after the earthquake and was estimated to be 30 to 40 ft high as it neared the bayhead.

Still further to the southwest, in the Kodiak Island region (Figure 1), initial drawdown of the water table was reported for Port Williams, Afognak, and Ouzinkie (Berg and others, 1971). No initial regression of water seems to have occurred, on the other hand, along the southeast coast of Kodiak Island at such places as Saltery Cove, Old Harbor, and Kaguyak.

Kodiak is the only place within the earthquake area where a fairly detailed knowledge of the wave sequence and wave height is available, due to a log kept by Lt. C. R. Barney of the U.S. Fleet Weather Central at the Naval Base, Womens Bay, some 7 mi southwest of Kodiak City. Lt. Barney's log is now well documented, and various plots of his data have been made (compare Brown, 1964; Berg and others, 1971; Tudor, 1964; Chance, 1966; Pararas-Carayannis, 1965, and Seismology and Geodesy volume; Plafker and Kachadoorian, 1966, and Geology volume; Kachadoorian and Plafker, 1967; Spaeth and Berkman, 1967, and this volume); the log is also recorded here in Appendix A. Because the above authors disagree on certain details, whenever different interpretations have been applied to parts of the data that seem ambiguous, we have studied these interpretations rather carefully and evolved our own record of Barney's data in Figure 4, indicative of the fluctuations of sea level in Chiniak Bay on the northern coast of the entrance to Womens Bay, Kodiak, after the earthquake.

The basis for Figure 4 is the premise that mean lower low water (MLLW) at Kodiak, as a tide level, referenced to mean sea level (MSL), has remained unaffected by the earthquake.

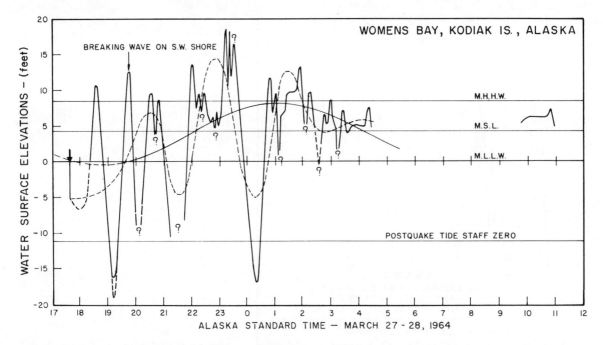

FIGURE 4 Reconstructed marigram from water-level fluctuations in Womens Bay, Kodiak, observed and logged by Lt. C. R. Barney, U.S. Naval Station, Kodiak. Indicated in the diagram are the astronomic tide curve (full line) and apparent long-period tsunami waves (short dashed line). At the commencement of the disturbances, the sea is presumed to have dropped suddenly with subsidence of the land. The minor additional drop preceding the first rise of water level is hypothetical but inserted as a probable inertial effect of the water mass adjusting to the dynamic phenomenon.

The only way in which it could be affected would be through a complete change of tidal range in the area; by all accounts, this has not been altered. Since astronomical tide level is presumed to be unaffected at the time of the earthquake, the record must show, in regard to mean water level at any time, the essential continuity of the tide. Barney's readings were referenced to a tide staff zero, which from later observation (Bryant, unpublished letter, 1964) is related to sea level (as indicated in Figure 4).

Wilson and Tørum (1968) suggested that the Kodiak record may be resolved into three major components: the astronomic tide; a modulated wave system with a period of about 2½ hours (evident in Figure 4), which they related to the half-wave length of the wave generated on the uplifted shelf to the southeast; and an oscillation of about 80 minutes, representing the second mode of the free oscillation (fundamental period about 5 hours) of the water on the Continental Shelf.

At various places along the coast of the Gulf of Alaska in the earthquake zone, accounts have indicated runup heights of waves to 60–100 ft. The greatest heights, 90 to 100 ft above mean lower low water near the head of Aialik Bay, are attributed by Rusnak (personal communication) to waves locally generated by submarine landslides. However, the debris line measured by Berg and others (1971) west of Narrow Cape on Kodiak Island could only have been left by the major

tsunami. This line was 67 ft above mean lower low water and 58 ft above the high tide in the early morning of March 28 indicating a runup of at least the latter amount. Other fairly well-documented measurements on the Kodiak Island coast between Cape Chiniak and Narrow Cape (see Berg and others, 1971; Plafker and Mayo, 1965; Chance, 1966; Plafker and Kachadoorian, 1966) indicate that waves there reached some 30 to 40 ft above the low-tide level soon after the earthquake (Figure 5).

The effects of the main tsunami within Prince William Sound are described in a later section of this volume (Wilson and Tørum, 1972).

It is of interest to note that the general maximum runup height above still-water level along the Alaskan seaboard (at least 10 m and perhaps something in excess of 20 m), falls near the upper bound of maximum heights for tsunamis defined empirically by Wilson (Wilson and others, 1962; Wilson, 1964, 1969) as a function of the magnitude M of the associated earthquakes. The relationship (Figure 6)

$$\log_{10} H_{max} = 0.75\,M - 5.06,$$

where H_{max} = maximum anticipated tsunami height (crest to trough), may be expected to give a rough idea of the maximum tsunami height (at a coastline) to be expected from an earthquake of a given magnitude occurring within a range of

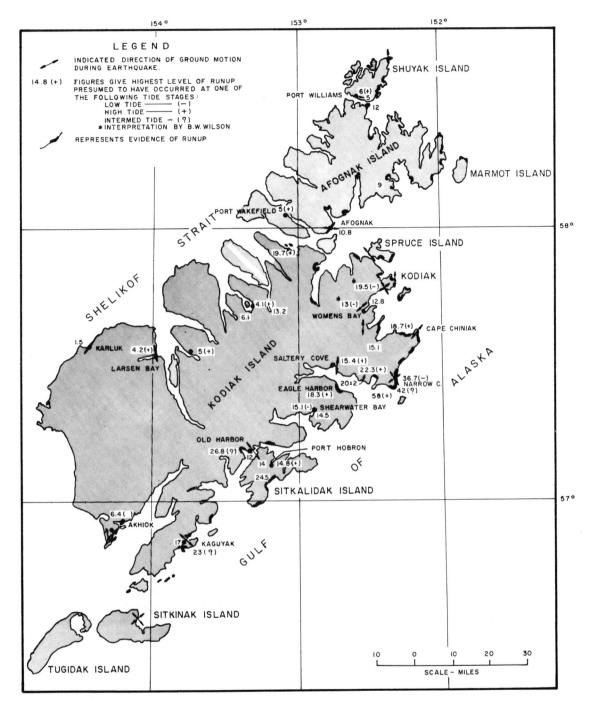

FIGURE 5   Observed tsunami runup along the coasts of Kodiak and Afognak Islands (based on data of Plafker and Kachadoorian, 1966, and of Berg and others, 1971).

about 500 mi. Cox (personal communication, 1970) reports that work he accomplished on tsunami records for Hilo, Hawaii, led him to the conclusion that maximum runup observed in Hilo harbor was generally about 2½ times the maximum amplitude (~1¼ times maximum wave height) recorded on the Hilo tide gage. He is of the opinion that actual runup

heights above prevailing mean sea level would be from 1 to 1.5 times the actual wave height of the tsunami waves recorded on a tide gage in the vicinity, this factor being a function of location, period of waves, and damping characteristics of tide gages. On this basis, maximum runup heights R_{max} could be construed to be from 1.0 to 1.5 H_{max} for values of

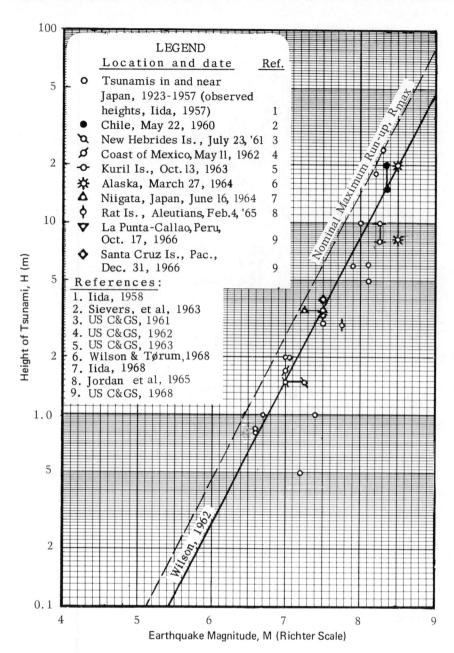

FIGURE 6   Approximate maximum height of tsunami to be expected at or near the source from a shallow-focus earthquake of given magnitude (adapted from Wilson, 1969).

H_{max} given by the full-line curve of Figure 6. In this figure, data of Iida (1958) are runup heights measured from the contemporary sea level at the time of the event. The range of wave heights for Chile (based on data from Sievers and others, 1963) is for some of the largest waves, observed by several witnesses to have formed about 800 m from the coast off the Playa Chauman near Ancud. Various observations by U.S. Coast and Geodetic Survey (1961, 1962, 1963, 1968) are the range or heights of highest tsunamis measured or reported from the affected areas. The observation for Rat Island (Jordan and others, 1965) is the tide-gage wave height at the island of Attu; that for Niigata (Iida, 1968) is the mean maxi-

mum wave height measured at numerous stations nearest the earthquake source (actual peak runup heights ranged to about 6 m). In general, the data of Figure 6 may be considered to represent maximum wave heights H_{max} (double amplitudes) of tsunamis close to a coast and near an earthquake source.

RUNUP ALONG THE NORTH AMERICAN COAST

As they impinged on the North American coast, the tsunami waves were recorded at a large number of tide stations. From the marigraphic records may be measured the maximum rise or fall of water level, the maximum wave height—maximum rise or fall corrected for the local change in astronomic tide level as reported by Spaeth and Berkman (1967, and this volume), the maximum crest height above predicted tide level at the time, or the maximum crest height above mean sea level or some other statistical tide level.

In addition, at a large number of points measurements were made of the maximum runup of the tsunami waves as indicated by swash marks, debris lines, and so on. Such measurements may be made with reference to various levels—for example, still-water level at the time of measurement (Berg and others, 1971)—and adjusted to other levels such as mean sea level or statistical tide levels.

Figure 7 (adapted from Wilson and Tørum, 1968) gives an interpretation of the expansion of the tsunami wave front, at hourly intervals, as the waves traveled across the Pacific and arrived along the coastline of North America. These wave fronts are reproduced in Figures 8, 10, and 12 as an indication of the approximate position of the tsunami train in relation to the astronomical tide wave along the North American seaboard.

In Figure 8, the equivalent height (crest to trough) of the highest tsunami wave recorded on the marigrams of tide stations along the United States and Canadian coastline from Alaska to Vancouver Island is registered as a number with a qualifying letter—R (for Rise) or F (for Fall). The qualification R means that the wave height is estimated on the basis of a *rise* of water level from trough to crest; likewise, the letter F indicates that the wave height has been estimated on the basis of a *fall* of water level from crest to trough. The data are derived from the marigrams reproduced by Spaeth and Berkman (1967, and this volume; 1969) and from Wigen and White (1964) and White (1966) (Table B-1, Appendix B).

Figure 9 provides added detail for the Vancouver Island region.

It should be noted that the waves of highest equivalent height in the tsunami wave train (given in Figures 8 and 9) are not necessarily the waves that gave highest runup, which was often caused by lesser tsunami waves occurring on the crest of the astronomical tide wave. Of particular interest is the height of the largest waves, independent of the tide, which rolled in on a given coastal area. Values from Spaeth and Berkman (1969) are those that they tabulated as "maximum rise or fall"; values from Wigen and White (1964) and White (1966) are double the difference shown in Table B-1 between tsunami crest and higher high-water heights.

In general, Figures 8 and 9 show that the tsunami penetrated deeply into the farthest reaches of the embayed coastline, making its presence felt even at Pitt Lake, about 135 nautical miles from the mouth of the Juan de Fuca Strait at the south end of Vancouver Island. On the seaward side of Vancouver Island, wave heights registered from 8 to 17 ft according to location. Port Alberni suffered the highest waves of all, along with Shields Bay, Queen Charlotte Islands.

Figure 8 shows the approximate positions (on the hour) reached by the tsunami wave front, as well as the approximate positions (on the hour) of the crest of the spring tide sweeping in toward the Gulf of Alaska. The tsunami front reached the coast between Prince Rupert and Vancouver Island at about 07 hours GMT of March 28, 1964. The crest of the high tide reached approximately the same position 2 hours later at 09 hours GMT. Since the tsunami wave period may be considered nominally 2 hours, the second tsunami wave crest would occupy the frontal position (07 hours) at about 09:30 GMT, or very near the peak of the high astronomical tide. This circumstance accounts for the high runup encountered in this area.

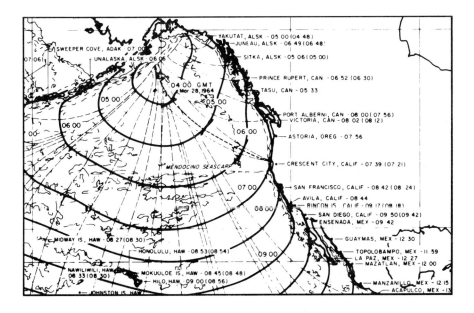

FIGURE 7 Approximate locations of tsunami wave front at 1-hour intervals (GMT) in the northeast Pacific ocean, based on arrival times of tsunami at tide stations and refraction of waves by water depths (adapted from Wilson and Tørum, 1968).

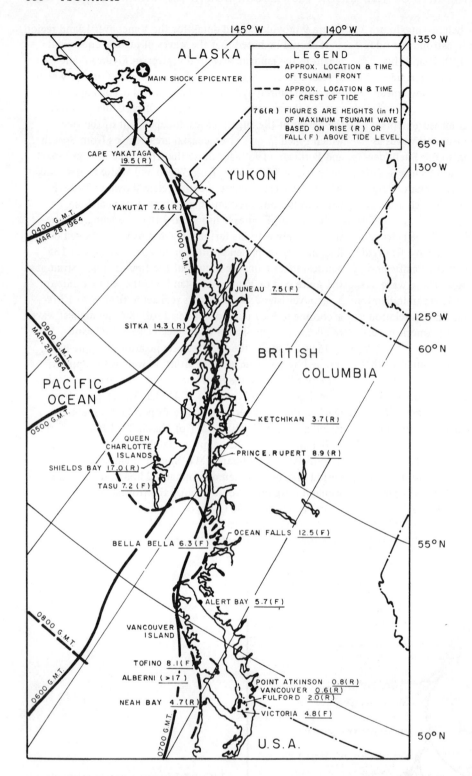

FIGURE 8 Maximum heights of tsunami waves recorded at tide stations along the North American seaboard from Alaska to Vancouver Island.

Farther to the south below the Canadian–United States border the tsunami waves, as also the tide wave, rolled in almost normally to the coastline. In this area the concurrence of high tsunami waves with high spring tide again made the runup along the coastline of serious proportions. Wave heights for the Washington coastline (Figure 10) accord with figures (multiplied by 2) given in Table B-2 (column 4) and represent measurements made by the Corps of Engineers, Seattle (Hogan and others, 1964; Whipple and Lundy, 1964). It has been thought best to reproduce unchanged in Figure 10

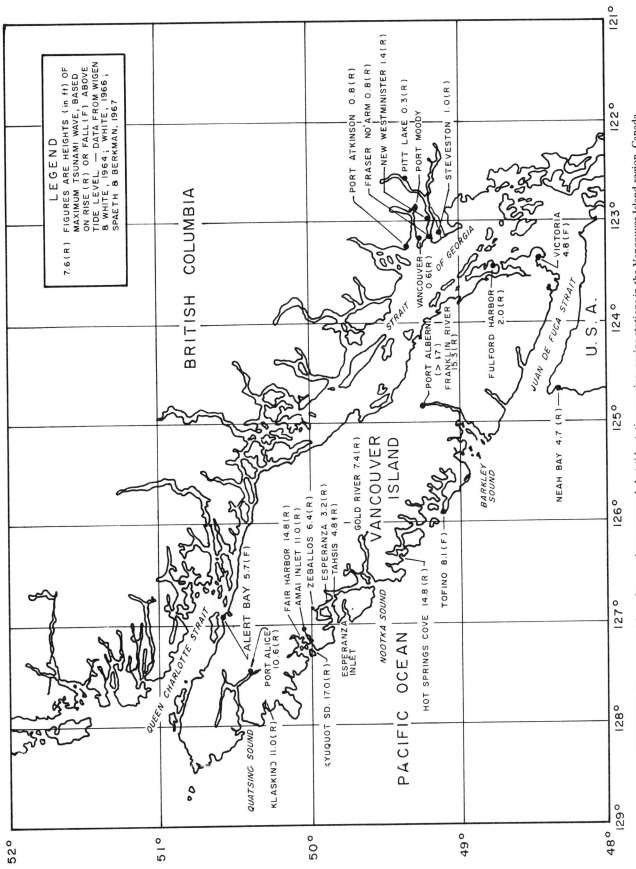

FIGURE 9   Maximum heights of tsunami waves recorded at tide stations or river-gaging stations in the Vancouver Island region, Canada.

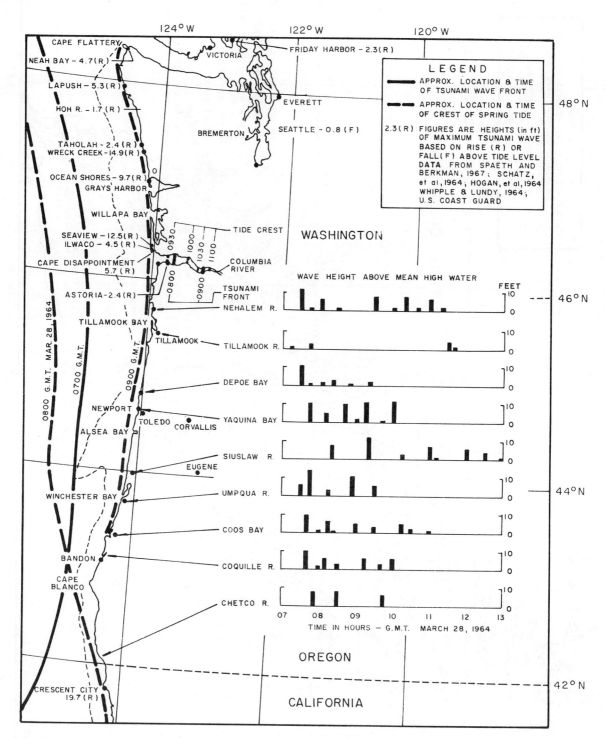

FIGURE 10 Maximum heights of tsunami waves recorded at tide stations or by observation along the Washington–Oregon coastline.

the Oregon coastline data of Schatz and others (1964), represented by the series of bar diagrams drawn on a horizontal time scale. The implication of Figure 10 is that some of the highest waves along the entire North American seaboard battered the Washington and Oregon coastlines.

Both the tide wave and the tsunami ran straight up the Columbia River, with the tsunami front preceding the tide crest by about 1.5 hours. Because of the vast size of the tide wave, however, this ensured that the leading waves of the tsunami rode majestically on the top of the tide wave and propagated upriver in this virtually interlocked fashion (see Wilson and Tørum, 1968, and this volume). The situation is of particular interest inasmuch as the effects were recorded at tide-gage stations spaced over some 90 nautical miles of estuary from the mouth of the Columbia River (Figure 11).

South of the Columbia River along the Oregon coast, no well-established pattern of wave arrivals can be determined from the data of Schatz and others (1964). The approximate tsunami wave-front and tide-crest positions and times show that the leading waves of the tsunami would have occurred everywhere along this coast on the top of the high spring tide. Runup generally is seen to be some 10 to 15 ft above the high-tide line (Figure 10), a fact confirmed in August 1966 by one of the authors (Wilson), who observed that long debris lines along this entire coast are to be found at about this level.

The height of the maximum tsunami wave given in Figure 10 for Crescent City is based on an interpretation of the brief marigram recorded before the tide gage failed, when this is taken in conjunction with the known runup heights of the highest waves measured against fixed objects (see Wilson and Tørum, 1968).

The data presented in Figure 12 are drawn from the extensive survey of the Corps of Engineers, San Francisco (Magoon, 1966), and indicate that runup along this part of the North American coast (south of Crescent City) was generally much less than farther north. The Corps of Engineers data are all referred to MLLW datum (see Table B-3, Appendix B). These data were plotted here in preference to maximum wave heights (see column 5, Table B-3) because they were more numerous in coverage of the coastal area involved.

Figure 12 suggests that south of Crescent City and Fort Bragg the tsunami waves were arriving 1 to 2 or more hours after the occurrence of high tide, when the tide would have been falling, so that a natural lessening of the runup potential was ensured. The approximate range of the tide along the coast from Monterey to Crescent City is shown on the cotidal lines in Figure 12.

The fact that Crescent City experienced such high damaging waves from the tsunami (Figures 10 and 12) led Wilson and Tørum (1968) to seek an explanation in terms of resonance of the waves on the Continental Shelf in that area.

Their conclusion that shelf resonance was probably important in developing dynamic amplification of the waves is supported by subsequent analysis of Harrison and Keulegan (1968).

Wilson and Tørum (1968) also described the behavior of the tsunami in San Francisco Bay in terms of the resonant periods of the Bay. In Monterey Bay, about 60 nautical miles south of San Francisco, the tsunami produced quite widely different effects at the north and south extremities—Santa Cruz and Monterey, respectively. Santa Cruz experienced a runup almost twice that of Monterey despite its apparently protected setting in relation to the approach direction of the tsunami. This may perhaps be ascribed to the deep canyon that virtually bisects the bay and favors refraction of more wave energy entering the bay toward the north than toward the south (Wilson and others, 1965). Wilson and Tørum (1968) analyzed the behavior of the waves, as recorded by the Monterey tide gage and three additional wave sensors (Marine Advisers, 1964) in terms of various resonant modes in Monterey Bay.

Runup of the tsunami along the California coast south of Monterey appears not to be documented. Marigrams reproduced by Spaeth and Berkman (1967, and this volume), however, show that the tsunami, although drawing powerful response from such places as Santa Monica, arrived on the low spring tide and therefore failed to reach higher than the normal range of tide.

REFERENCES

Berg, Eduard, Doak C. Cox, Augustine S. Furumoto, Kinjiro Kajiura, Hirosi Kawasumi, and Etsuzo Shima, 1971. Field survey of the tsunamis of 28 March 1964 in Alaska, and conclusions as to the origin of the major tsunami. Report HIG-70-2. Honolulu: University of Hawaii, Institute of Geophysics. 57 p.

Brown, Delmer L., 1964. Tsunamic activity accompanying the Alaskan earthquake of 27 March 1964. Technical Report, U.S. Army Engineer District, Alaska. Anchorage: U.S. Army Corps of Engineers, April 23. 31 p.

Chance, Genie, 1966. Chronology of physical events of the Alaskan earthquake (unpublished). Anchorage: University of Alaska. 176 p.

Grantz, Arthur, George Plafker, and Reuben Kachadoorian, 1964. Alaska's Good Friday earthquake, March 27, 1964: a preliminary geologic evaluation. U.S. Geological Survey Circular 491. Washington: U.S. Geological Survey. 35 p.

Harrison, J., and G. H. Keulegan, 1968. Probability of occurrence of tsunamis of various amplitudes at Crescent City (California) (unpublished manuscript). Vicksburg: U.S. Army Corps of Engineers, Waterways Experiment Station, August.

Hogan, D., W. W. Whipple, and C. Lundy, 1964. Tsunami of 27 and 28 March 1964, State of Washington coastline (unpublished file report). Seattle: U.S. Army Corps of Engineers.

Iida, K., 1958. Magnitude and energy of the earthquakes accompanied by tsunami, and tsunami energy. *Journal of Earth Sciences* (Nagoya University), 6 (December), 101–112.

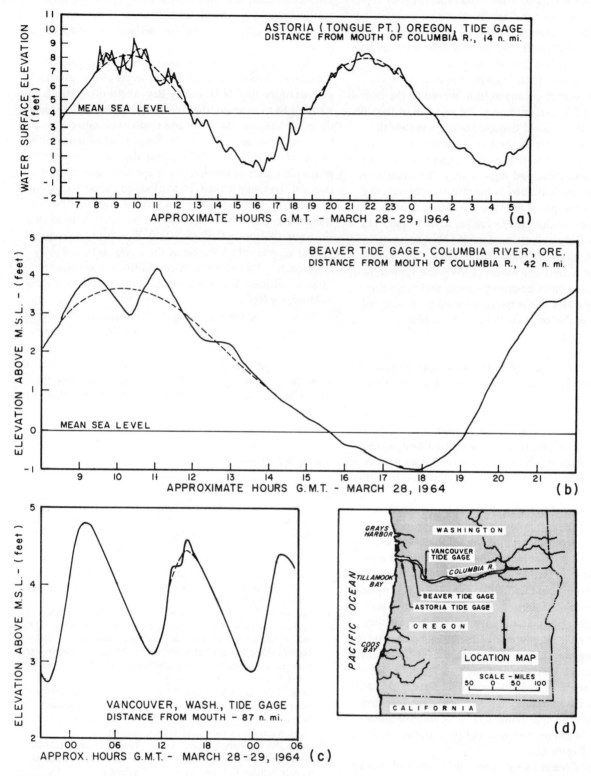

FIGURE 11 Sample tide-gage records from stations along the Columbia River, showing progression of the tide wave and tsunami.

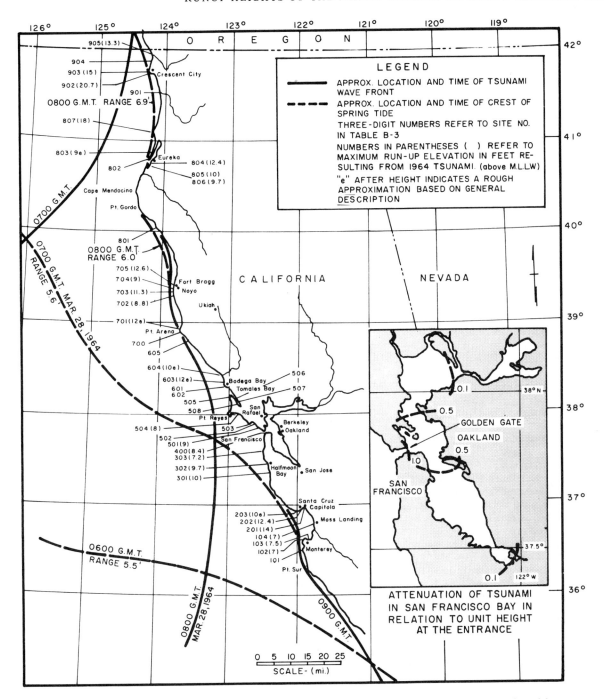

FIGURE 12   Maximum runup heights of tsunami waves observed along the north central California coast (adapted from Magoon, 1965).

Iida, K., 1968. The Niigata tsunami of June 16, 1964 in General Report on the Niigata Earthquake of 1964. H. Kawasumi, editor-in-chief. Tokyo: Electrical Engineering College Press. p. 97–127.

Jordan, J. N., J. F. Lander, and R. A. Black, 1965. Aftershocks of the 4 February, 1965 Rat Island earthquake. *Science*, 148 (June 4), 1323–1325.

Kachadoorian, Reuben, and George Plafker, 1967. Effects of the earthquake of March 27, 1964 on the communities of Kodiak and nearby islands. U.S. Geological Survey Professional Paper 542-F. Washington: Government Printing Office. 41 p. Abstract in The Great Alaska Earthquake of 1964: Geology. NAS Pub. 1601. Washington: National Academy of Sciences, 1971. p. 539–540.

Lemke, Richard W., 1967. Effects of the earthquake of March 27, 1964, at Seward, Alaska. U.S. Geological Survey Professional Paper 542-E. Washington: Government Printing Office. 43 p. Also in The Great Alaska Earthquake of 1964: Geology. NAS Pub.

1601. Washington: National Academy of Sciences, 1971. p. 395–437.

Magoon, Orville T., 1966. Structural damage by tsunamis. Proceedings of the Specialty Conference (1965) on Coastal Engineering, Santa Barbara, California, October 11. New York: American Society of Civil Engineers. p. 35–68.

Marine Advisers, 1964. A broad-frequency-band wave study at Monterey Harbor, California. Report to U.S. Army Corps of Engineers, San Francisco. La Jolla: Marine Advisers, July. 19 p.

Pararas-Carayannis, George, 1965. Water waves, Part I *in* Source mechanism study of the Alaska earthquake and tsunami of 27 March 1964. Report HIG-65-17. Honolulu: University of Hawaii, Institute of Geophysics, December. p. 1–30.

Plafker, George, and Reuben Kachadoorian, 1966. Geologic effects of the March 1964 earthquake and associated seismic sea waves on Kodiak and nearby islands, Alaska. U.S. Geological Survey Professional Paper 543-D. Washington: Government Printing Office. 46 p. Also *in* The Great Alaska Earthquake of 1964: Geology. NAS Pub. 1601. Washington: National Academy of Sciences, 1971. p. 177–226.

Plafker, George, and L. R. Mayo, 1965. Tectonic deformation, subaqueous slides and destructive waves associated with the Alaskan March 27, 1964 earthquake: an interim geologic evaluation. U.S. Geological Survey Open-File Report. Menlo Park, California: U.S. Geological Survey. 34 p.

Schatz, Clifford E., Herbert Curl, Jr., and Wayne V. Burt, 1964. Tsunamis on the Oregon coast. *The Ore Bin* (Publication of the Oregon Department of Geology and Mineral Industries), 26 (December), 231–232.

Sievers C., Hellmuth A., Guillermo Villegas C., and Guillermo Barros, 1963. The seismic sea wave of 22 May 1960 along the Chilean coast. *Bulletin of the Seismological Society of America*, 53 (December), 1125–1190.

Spaeth, Mark G., and Saul C. Berkman, 1967. The tsunami of March 28, 1964, as recorded at tide stations. Environmental Science Services Administration Technical Report C&GS 33. Washington: Government Printing Office. 86 p. Also *in* The Great Alaska Earthquake of 1964: Oceanography and Coastal Engineering. NAS Pub. 1605. Washington: National Academy of Sciences, 1972.

Spaeth, Mark G., and Saul C. Berkman, 1969. The tsunami of March 28, 1964, as recorded at tide stations *in* Volume II-B, C: The Prince William Sound, Alaska, earthquake of 1964 and aftershocks. Environmental Science Services Administration, U.S. Coast and Geodetic Survey. Washington: Government Printing Office. p. 223–307.

Tudor, W. J., 1964. Tsunami damage at Kodiak, Alaska, and Crescent City, California, from Alaskan earthquake of 27 March 1964. U.S. Naval Civil Engineering Laboratory Technical Note N-622. Port Hueneme, California: U.S. Naval Civil Engineering Laboratory, November. 131 p.

U.S. Coast and Geodetic Survey, 1961, 1962, 1963, 1968. Tsunamis *in* United States Earthquakes, 1945–1968 (published annually). Environmental Science Services Administration, U.S. Coast and Geodetic Survey. Washington: Government Printing Office.

U.S. Coast and Geodetic Survey, 1964. Preliminary report: tidal datum plane changes, Prince William Sound, Alaskan earthquakes March–April, 1964. Office of Oceanography Report. Rockville, Maryland: U.S. Coast and Geodetic Survey. 5 p.

Van Dorn, William G., 1965. Source mechanism of the tsunami of March 28, 1964 in Alaska. Proceedings of the Ninth Conference (1964) on Coastal Engineering (Chapter 10). New York: American Society of Civil Engineers. p. 166–190. Also *in* The Great Alaska Earthquake of 1964: Oceanography and Coastal Engineering. NAS Pub. 1605. Washington: National Academy of Sciences, 1972.

Whipple, W., and C. Lundy, 1964. Damage reconnaissance (unpublished file report). Seattle: U.S. Army Corps of Engineers, Tidal Hydraulics Unit, April.

White, W. R. H., 1966. The Alaska earthquake—its effect in Canada. *Canadian Geographical Journal*, 72 (June), 210–219.

Wigen, S. O., and W. R. H. White, 1964. Tsunami of March 27–29, 1964, west coast of Canada. Technical Report. Victoria, British Columbia: Canada Department of Mines and Technical Surveys, August. 12 p.

Wilson, Basil W., 1964. Generation and dispersion characteristics of tsunamis *in* Studies on oceanography. Tokyo: University of Tokyo Press. p. 413–444. (See also University of Washington Press, Seattle, Washington, 1965.)

Wilson, Basil W., 1969. Earthquake occurrence and effects in ocean areas. Technical Report CR 69-027 to U.S. Naval Civil Engineering Laboratory. Port Hueneme: U.S. Naval Civil Engineering Laboratory, February. 141 p.

Wilson, Basil W., J. A. Hendrickson, and R. E. Kilmer, 1965. Feasibility study for a surge-action model of Monterey Harbor, California. Waterways Experiment Station Contract Report No. 2-136. Vicksburg: U.S. Army Corps of Engineers, October. 166 p.

Wilson, Basil W., and Alf Tørum, 1968. The tsunami of the Alaskan earthquake, 1964: Engineering evaluation. Coastal Engineering Research Center Technical Memorandum No. 25. Washington: U.S. Army Corps of Engineers, May. 444 p.

Wilson, Basil W., and Alf Tørum, 1972. Effects of the tsunamis: An engineering study *in* The Great Alaska Earthquake of 1964: Oceanography and Coastal Engineering. NAS Pub. 1605. Washington: National Academy of Sciences.

Wilson, Basil W., L. M. Webb, and J. A. Hendrickson, 1962. The nature of tsunamis: their generation and dispersion in water of finite depth. NES Technical Report No. SN 57-2. Pasadena: National Engineering Science Company, August. 150 p.

APPENDIX A

U.S. FLEET WEATHER CENTRAL, KODIAK, ALASKA

RÉSUMÉ OF ACTIVITIES, 27 MARCH–4 APRIL 1964

Local
time AST

March
271732   Moderate to severe earthquake commenced.

1740   Sustained earthquake ceased. Electrical equipment in tower out of commission. Power OK. C.O. arrived.

1750   Tide Station inoperative due to earthquake damage. HO advised via seismo message D T G 280350Z which was passed to FWC Alameda for relay. FAA Circuits inoperative.

1805   Seismo N R 2 D T G 280415Z to HO via FWC Alameda after trying FAA Circuits.

1810   Cape Chiniak reports 30-ft tsunami. Unable to contact Station O O D, called Armed Forces Radio Station and had "Tidal Wave" warning broadcasted, resulting in evacuation to higher ground of base and city personnel. Advised Station O O D of actions later.

1820   Water rising rapidly. No recession has previously occurred within sight of tower.

1835   Water crested 22 ft above tide staff zero. Tsunami N R 1 to HO prepared, D T G 280445Z, passed via telephone to remote transmitter site for relay to HO via NAVCOMSTA San Francisco.

1836   Water ebbing.

1847   Lost electrical power.

1903   Auxiliary power supplied to tower.

1907   Maximum low ebb, estimated 15 to 18 ft below mean sea level. Tsunami N R 2 to HO prepared, D T G 280512Z handled same as Tsunami N R 1.

1930   Water rising.

1940   Water crested at 24 ft above staff zero.

2000   Water maximum low level—elevation unknown.

2030   Water crested at 21 ft above staff zero.

2044   Water crested again at less than 21 feet. Oscillation appears to be superimposed on tsunami period.

2100   FAA Woody Island called. Discussed wave times, damages, etc.

2115   Sent Tsunami N R 3 D T G 280726Z to HO via Coast Guard Radio N O J.

2130   Water started to rise again, minimum level unknown.

2132   Slight tremor felt.

2200   Water crested 25 ft above staff zero.

2210   Water slowly ebbing. Heights unknown, small amplitude, believe seiche.

2215   Water slowly rising. ⎫ Heights unknown, small
2219   Water slowly ebbing. ⎬ amplitude, believe seiche.
2225   Water slowly rising. ⎭

2227   Water crested at 21 ft above staff zero. Intervening minimum height not observed.

2232   CO NAVSTA KODIAK and COMALSEAFRONT/COM17 relocated their base operations to Fleet Weather Central in tower.

2240   Slight tremor felt.

2248   Water rapidly rising and falling. Small amplitude, believe seiche.

2300   Preliminary inspection reveals tide station inundated, having been inoperative from 1740. Record lost. G M D Bldg. inundated repeatedly. All equipment on first deck washed away or damaged and immersed.

2316   Water crested 30 ft above staff zero.

2317   Water ebbing rapidly.

2319   Water rising rapidly, crest 30 ft again. Intervening ebb level unknown.

2322   Water ebbing.

2324   Water has risen and crested at unknown level, but below 30 ft above staff zero.

280015   Minimum low water estimated about 5 ft below staff zero.

0034   Slight tremor.

0037   Stronger tremor. Water 18 ft above staff zero and rising.

0045   Water crested at 23 ft above staff zero.

0050   Water receding.

0100   Water rising. Crested at less than 23 ft above staff zero.

0102   Water receding rapidly.

0110   Water has risen to 18 ft above staff zero, holding steady.

0120   Water rising further to 21 ft above staff zero, then holding steady.

0144   Water rising again.

0145   "Rumble" reported, water rising rapidly.

0154   Water crested at 25 ft above staff zero.

0159   Water receding rapidly. Ebb water level unknown.

0213   Water level crested 21 ft above staff zero.

Local
time AST

0219	Water level steady at 21 ft.
0222	Slight tremor felt, water receding.
0240	Water starting to rise.
0243	Water crested at 18 ft above staff zero.
0247	Water receding rapidly.
0258	Water still receding—about 2 ft above normal.
0305	Water still receding—rate about 1 ft per minute.
0312	Sudden drop in water level.
0316	Strong sound of surf. Water appears to be being drawn from Small Boat Harbor. Moving observation party to higher ground for safety.
0318	Water rising in Crash Boat Harbor.
0320	Gradual increase in water level.
0323	Water ebbing rapidly. No crest estimated.
0347	Water rising slowly.
0355	Water appears normal. No change in height.
0408	Water rising.
0410	Water rose about 3 more ft. Now steady, just over seawall in Crash Boat Harbor.
0415	Water back to normal level.
0422	Water receding.
0434	Light tremor.
0440	Light tremor.
0517	Strong current from northeast toward Nyman Peninsula. No apparent rise in water level.
0535	Observation party secured. Watch with field glasses posted in Tower Building.
0615	Water level steady.
0634	Water rising.
0641	Water ebbing.
0718	Water rising.
0815	Water ebbing.
0900	Water rising.
0942	Water ebbing.
1000	Tide staff reading 17.5 ft, water temperature 36°F.
1045	Water rising.
1047	Water just over 18 ft on tide staff. Start ebb.
1200	Water rising.
1227	Water ebbing.
1300	Water rising.
1346	Water ebbing. Crest reached 22.8 ft above staff zero.
1438	Water rising.
1530	Tide gage overhauled and placed back in operation. Staff reading 18.7 ft.
1659	Slight tremor.
1902	Slight tremor, continuing at intervals until 1930.
2030	Slight tremor.
2217	Slight tremor.
2230	Tide staff reading 16.3 ft.

Local
time AST

290125	Received report that Cape Hinchinbrook sustained large tremors of 5-second duration in last hour. Severe shock wave reported in Prince William Sound area.
0845	Tide staff reading 12.1 ft.
1810	Received HO tsunami DTG 300351Z.
1835	Replied to HO. Staff 13.8 ft. Maximum height past 6 hours 20.6 ft at 291400 AST.
300144	High tide estimated 22 ft above staff zero.
0212	Slight tremor.
0410	Slight tremor (rolling motion).
1700	Irregular marigram. Staff reading 17.5 ft.
310015	Coast Guard Cutter *Sedge* reports tides 6 to 8 ft below normal at Cape Hinchinbrook.
0815	Staff reading 11.1 ft.

April

010825	Staff reads 12.4 ft.
1543	Staff reads 18.3 ft.
2200	Staff reads 13.8 ft.
020330	Coast and Geodetic Survey set up a seismograph in Tower Bldg.
0350	Staff reads 20.0 ft.
1020	Staff reads 12.7 ft.
1031	Staff reads 12.5 ft.
031234	AST recorded earthquake on seismograph.
1245	Recorded earthquake on seismograph.
1415	Tsunami of 6-in. amplitude started on marigram.
2312	Light tremor, duration, 1 minute and 40 seconds. Seismograph indicated local quake.
040030	Tsunami of 6-in. amplitude started on marigram.

Notes

1. Unless otherwise indicated, all times are Alaska Standard Time (+10).

2. Heights were referred to staff zero in the following manner. After each crest, a pencil mark was made at the resultant water line in a building very near the water. When it was impossible to make a pencil mark, the water level was referred to the nearest identifying feature on the building and marked in pencil after the water had ebbed. The highest mark was then measured in reference to the tide staff at the Tide Gage and the heights of all other wave heights in the building where the pencil marks were made were subtracted from this height. The building mentioned is *not* in the immediate vicinity of the Tide Gage. [The building in question is on the north coast of the entrance to Womens Bay from Chiniak (Berg and others, 1971).]

3. Other highest water marks on cliffs and buildings were measured along a 3-mile area from Nyman Peninsula to about ½ mile northeast of the mouth of Buskin River. All were within 2 ft of the highest water mark at the Tide Gage.

4. The Tide Gage is located on Marginal Pier, Nyman Peninsula, U.S. Naval Station, Kodiak, Alaska, and is in Womens Bay.

5. All tidal bench marks were connected by spirit leveling on 5–7 April and the relative elevations of the tide staff and bench marks are unchanged from previous values.

6. An analysis of the Tide Station hourly heights for the 5-day period 2–6 April gives a mean value for the tide level of 15.8 ft referred to zero of the tide staff. With the assumptions that this short record is a reasonable approximation of mean sea level (MSL) and that MSL differs a negligible amount from the half-tide level, it is the opinion of USC&GS that a subsidence of 5.5 ft has occurred in the Nyman Peninsula area.

7. Hydrographic surveys by USC&GS in the Kodiak area indicate increased depths of 4 to 6 ft and give support to Note 6.

8. All heights mentioned refer to the tide staff in its new elevation relative to half-tide level.

9. When water level could not be measured with any degree of accuracy, its level was estimated and is so stated, or the height was listed as unknown. Few low water levels could thus be tabulated.

10. Tides since the event of 27 March 1964 indicate that there is no change in tidal period or amplitude and that the tides are the same in all respects as they were prior to 27 March 1964. The Tide Tables therefore are still considered accurate.

11. TIDES 27 March 1239, 9.0 ft; 1853, −0.2 ft
        28 March 0101, 8.9 ft; 0710, −0.1 ft

12. SUNRISE   SUNSET   MOON RISE   MOON PHASE
    27 March 0522   1840   1817   Full
    28 March 0519   1842   1935

13. Cloud cover 271800 to 280000 AST 8/10, 280000 to 280500 AST Clear. Wind velocity (true light and variable 271800 to 280800 AST). Visibility unrestricted 271800 to 280800 AST.

APPENDIX B

WATER LEVELS OF THE TSUNAMI OF MARCH 27–28, 1964, ALONG THE CANADIAN, WASHINGTON, AND NORTHERN CALIFORNIA COASTS

TABLE B-1   Maximum Crest Levels of the Tsunami along the Canadian Coast[a], March 28, 1964

The heights reached by the maximum tsunami wave crest at a number of Vancouver Island ports where no tide gages were operating are compared to the elevations of higher high water, large tide. Elevations at some permanent gaging stations, showing normal and extreme recorded high waters, are also included for comparison.

Port	Latitude	Longitude	Tsunami Crest (ft)	Higher High Water (HHW) (ft)	Difference (ft)	Extreme High Tide (ft)
Port Alice	50 23	127 27	19.3	14.0	+5.3	—
Klaskino	50 18	127 44	19.2	13.7	+5.5	—
Fair Harbour	50 04	127 07	21.0	13.6	+7.4	—
Amai Inlet	50 06	127 05	19.0	13.5	+5.5	—
Zeballos	49 59	126 51	16.8	13.6	+3.2	—
Esperanza	49 52	126 44	15.2	13.6	+1.6	—
Tahsis	49 55	126 40	16.4	14.0	+2.4	—
Gold River	49 41	126 07	17.7	14.0	+3.7	—
Hot Springs Cove	49 22	126 16	20.5	13.1	+7.4	—
Tofino	49 09	125 55	14.0	13.2	+0.8	15.60
Franklin River	49 06	124 49	20.6	13.0	+7.6	—
Port Alberni	49 14	124 49	20.9	12.2	+8.7	14.8
Victoria	48 25	123 24	8.4	9.6	−1.2	12.10
Prince Rupert	54 19	130 20	25.2	24.6	+0.6	26.18

[a]Reproduced from Wigen and White (1964).

TABLE B-2   Water Levels and Damage along Pacific Coast of Washington[a], March 28, 1964

Location	Elevation of Highest Wave above MLLW (ft)	Elevation of Highest Wave above MSL (ft)	Height of Wave above Predicted Tide (ft)	Monetary Value of Damage (dollars)	Damage
La Push	13.7	9.3	5.3	–	Several boats and a floating dock broke loose from moorings.
Mouth of River Hoh	10.1	5.6	1.7	–	None
Tahola	11.0	6.3	2.4	1,000	Loss of several skiffs and fish nets in inlet at mouth of Quinault River.
Wreck Creek State Hwy., 109 Bridge	23.5	18.8	14.9	500	Erosion of fill at bridge approach; debris on bridge deck and nearby highway.
Town of Copalis, Copalis River	–	–	–	5,000	Damage to buildings
Copalis River State Hwy., 109 Bridge	–	–	–	75,000	Loss of one timber bent and two timber spans near the bridge center and one piling in a four-pile timber bent.
Joe Creek State Hwy., 109 Bridge					Loss of five-pile bent, damage to two pile bents (loss of three pilings) and loss of two 20-ft reinforced concrete spans.
Copalis River State Hwy.	–	–	–	5,000	Shoulder erosion and deposition of debris on highway.
Town of Moclips	19.7	14.9	11.1	6,000	Damage to ocean side of buildings by floating logs; one building moved off foundation. Timber pile bulkheads and fills extensively damaged. Water over some floors from 6 in. to several feet. Heavy debris scattered over yards.
Ocean Shore Development ¾ mile south of Oylust	18.1	13.3	9.7	–	Deposition of debris on streets near Central Motel Office. Debris on streets and yards in vicinity of break in sand dune dike about ¾ mi south of Central Motel Office.
Town of Pacific Beach	–	–	–	12,000	Medium-sized house lifted off the foundation and partly torn apart; total loss. Several sheds moved off foundations. A second building partly damaged. Yards eroded and covered with debris.
Town of Sea View	19.5	14.8	12.5	–	None
Town of Ilwaco	10.7	7.1	4.5	–	Minor damage
U.S. Coast Guard Station Cape Disappointment	11.9	8.3	5.7	–	None

[a]Reproduced from Hogan, Lundy, and Whipple (1964).

TABLE B-3 Summary of Three Recent Tsunamis along Northern California Coast in 1946, 1960, and March 27–28, 1964*

Site No.	Site	Coastal Description	Maximum Water Elevation above MLLW[a] (ft)			Maximum Wave Height[b] (ft)			Time of Maximum Water Level[c] (PST)			Damage ($1,000)			Remarks
			46	60	64	46	60	64	46	60	64	46	60	64	
101	Point Lobos	Exposed coast	–	–	x	–	–	–	–	–	–	–	–	x	
	Point Lobos to Carmel (3)	Exposed coast	–	–	x	–	–	x	–	–	–	–	–	x	
102	Pacific Grove (2)	Open cove	10.3	+7	+7	–	6	6	–	–	–	–	–	x	1964 damage: one tier of small boats broke loose, only minor damage.
103	Monterey Harbor (2)	Protected harbor (breakwaters)	–	+8	+7.5	–	5	9	–	0940	0330	x	x	1	1946 and 1964: whirlpools at seaward end of Monterey breakwater, no damage. Special analysis made of 1964 tsunami from pressure gage by Marine Advisers[1] and analysis and discussion of float and pressure gage records by Wilson.[2]
104	Moss Landing Harbor (2)	Protected harbor (jetties)	x	–	+7	x	5	9	–	–	–	x	x	0.2	1964 damage: one skiff broke apart; strong currents in channels.
	Moss Landing to Capitola	Exposed coast	–	–	–	–	–	–	–	–	–	–	–	x	At Seacliff Beach State Park maximum wave from +5 to –1 MLLW. At New Brighton Beach State Park, maximum wave from +5 to –12 MLLW (1964)
201	Capitola Pier (1)	Cove open to south	–	–	–	–	–	14	–	–	0130	–	–	x	
202	Santa Cruz Harbor (1)	Protected harbor (jetties)	–	–	12.4	0	0	10	–	–	–	0	0	100	(Constructed 1962.) 1964 damage consisted of the loss of a dredge and cabin cruiser which broke loose during tsunami. Major effect was strong currents. Wave gage recorded wave not less than 7.5 ft; observers reported 10-ft wave with minimum elevation about –8 MLLW. Most boats and facilities in harbor undamaged.
203	Santa Cruz (1)	Cove open to south	12.4	–	–	10	6	10[e]	–	1000	–	x	x	x	1964 and 1946, one life lost due to person being trapped in cave during tsunami and subsequently drowned.
	Santa Cruz (3) to Martin's Beach	Exposed coast	–	–	x	–	–	x	–	–	–	–	–	x	

177

TABLE B-3 (Continued)

Site No.	Site	Coastal Description	Maximum Water Elevation above MLLW[a][b] (ft)			Maximum Wave Height (ft)			Time of Maximum Water Level[c] (PST)			Damage ($1,000)			Remarks
			46	60	64	46	60	64	46	60	64	46	60	64	
301	Martin's Beach (1)	Very small exposed cove	–	–	10	–	–	20	–	–	–	–	x	x	Tsunami always higher at north end of cove. Minimum elevation –10 MLLW.
	Martin's Beach to Half Moon Bay (4)	Exposed coast	–	–	–	–	–	–	–	–	–	–	–	x	1946; two observers reported unusual lows reached by tsunami.
302	Half Moon Bay Harbor (1)	Protected harbor (breakwaters)	15	11.5	10.1	17.3	–	–	–	–	–	–	–	1	Low wave height in 1964 probably caused by construction of harbor.
303	Pacifica (Shelter Cove) (1)	Very small exposed cove	–	6.5	7.2	–	8	9	–	–	–	–	–	x	
400	Golden Gate (Presidio)	Entrance to Bay	5.8	6.5	8.4	1.7	2.9	7.4	1000	1200	0100	–	–	–	San Francisco Bay Area
501	Muir Beach (1)	Coves open to south	13.4	–	9	–	–	–	–	–	–	–	–	–	1946; wave cut through lagoon bar.
502	Stinson Beach (1)	Coves open to south	–	–	–	–	10	–	–	–	–	–	–	x	
503	Bolinas (1)	Coves open to south	–	–	–	–	–	–	–	–	–	–	–	–	1964; one life lost by drowning on Duxberry Reef, March 28, 1964.
504	Drakes Beach Bay (1)	Cove open to south	–	–	8	–	–	–	–	–	–	x	–	x	
505	Tomales Bay (entrance) (1)	Bay with Entrance Restricted	–	–	–	–	–	6.5	–	–	–	–	–	6	1964; 25 mph current reported. 1960 and 1946; strong currents reported. 1964; damage to "Lawson's Pier," located inside entrance.
506	Marshall (1)	Protected bay	–	–	–	–	–	2	–	–	–	–	–	x	
507	Jensen Oyster Beds (1)	Protected bay	–	–	–	–	–	2	–	–	–	–	–	x	
508	Inverness Yacht Club (1)	Protected bay	–	–	–	–	–	1	–	–	–	–	–	x	
601	Bodega Bay inside entrance (1)	Bay with entrance jetties	–	–	–	–	2	5	–	–	0100	–	–	2	1964; damage to navigational aids. 1946, 1960, 1964, strong currents reported in entrance; 1964, reported 8 knots.
602	Bodega Bay, N.E. side (2)	Bay with entrance jetties	–	–	–	x	x	1	–	–	–	x	x	x	
603	Salmon Creek Beach (1)	Exposed beach	–	–	12[e]	–	–	–	–	–	–	–	–	x	1964; fisherman on beach reported that wave reached elevation higher than usual high tide plus runup

178

No.	Location	Description													Remarks
604	Jenner Beach (1)	Exposed shallow cove	—	10^e	—	—	—	—	—	—	—	—	—	x	x	1964; no effect in Russian River.
	Jenner to Gualala (3)	Exposed coast	—	—	—	—	—	—	—	—	—	—	—	x	x	
605	Gualala River Bar (1)	Exposed shallow cove	—	—	—	—	—	—	—	—	—	—	—	x	x	1960; two waves washed over bar at mouth into Gualala River.
700	Arena Cove (1)	Exposed cove	14	—	16	—	12	—	—	—	—	x	x	x	x	
701	Point Arena Light Station (1)	Exposed point	—	12^e	—	—	—	—	—	—	—	—	—	x	x	
702	Van Damme State Park (1)	Protected cove	—	8.8	—	—	—	—	—	—	—	—	—	x	x	1964; maximum wave progressed about 500 yd into Little River (from mouth at beach).
703	Russian Gulch State Park (1)	Protected cove	—	11.3	—	—	—	—	—	—	—	—	—	x	x	
704	Albion River (2)	Coastal river; 100-ft-wide mouth	—	9	—	—	—	—	0002	—	—	—	—	—	0.5	1964: Observers reported four or five low bores traveled upriver making a loud noise. Currents scoured out river mouth. Effect of wave was felt at least 1¼ mi upriver from entrance. Damage was due to delays to fishing vessels.
705	Noyo River (4)	Coastal river; 150-ft-wide entrance	11.2	12.6	—	—	13	—	1140	—	—	—	—	—	124	1964: Observers reported that 2nd and 3rd waves progressed upriver from mouth like a bore with the forward face consisting of a series of small steplike jumps. Waves traveled about 35 mph. Damage to boats and floating structures.
801	Shelter Cove	Protected cove	—	—	—	4^e	—	—	—	—	—	—	—	x	x	
802	Humboldt Bay	Bay with entrance jetties	—	—	—	—	—	—	—	—	—	—	—	—	—	
803	USGS Station North spit (1)		—	9^e	—	—	12	—	—	—	—	—	—	—	x	1964; 14 (estimated) knot current and 6-ft change in water level in about 20 minutes in channel opposite station.
804	Municipal Marina (1)		—	12.4	—	—	—	—	—	—	—	—	—	x	x	Strong currents in entrance 1960 and 1964.
805	King Salmon (Entrance to King Slough) (1)		—	—	—	—	—	—	—	—	—	—	—	—	—	
806	P.G. & E. Power Plant (0.6-mi upstream of entrance to King Slough) (1)		—	9.7	—	—	—	—	0005	—	—	—	—	—	x	

Site No.	Site	Coastal Description	Maximum Water Elevation above MLLW[a][b] (ft) 46	60	64	Maximum Wave Height (ft) 46	60	64	Time of Maximum Water Level[c] (PST) 46	60	64	Damage ($1,000) 46	60	64	Remarks
807	Trinidad (1)	Protected cove	–	–	18	–	–	–	–	–	–	–	–	–	–
	Trinidad to Klamath River (5)	Exposed cove	–	–	–	–	–	–	–	–	–	–	–	x	
901	Klamath River Requa Boat Dock (0.7 mi above mouth) (1)	Coastal river with restricted entrance	–	–	–	–	–	–	–	–	–	–	–	4	1964: Damage to boat dock and boats; strong currents.
	Panther Creek Lodge (1 mi from mouth) (1)		–	–	–	–	–	–	–	–	–	–	–	x	1964: Strong currents; water level 3 ft above normal high tide.
	Chinook Trailer Court (1.6 mi above mouth) (1)		–	–	–	–	–	–	–	–	–	–	–	0.2	1964: Damage to boat dock and boats.
	Deans Camp (0.7 mi south of entrance) (1)		–	–	–	–	–	–	–	–	–	–	–	x	1964: Water level "2 feet above normal high tide."[3]
902	Crescent City	Improved harbor	–	18.5	20.7	–	10+	28[e]	–	–	–	–	30	11,000	From information compiled by State of California, communicated by Paul Clifton.
903	Pebble Beach (2)	Exposed beach	–	–	15	–	–	–	–	–	–	–	–	x	
904	Pelican Beach (1)	Exposed beach	–	–	–	–	–	–	–	–	–	–	–	x	Driftwood stranded on beach back-shore not moved by tsunami.
905	Smith River (0.3 mi above mouth) (1)	Coastal river; 300-ft-wide mouth	–	–	13.3	–	–	–	–	–	–	–	–	6	Damage to floating structures, strong currents in river, water level higher on right bank than on left.

*Reproduced from O. T. Magoon (1965).

– No data available.

x Observers noted no effects or damage.

( ) Number of interviews (1964).

[a]Maximum high water elevations shown to the tenth of a foot have a probable accuracy of ± 1 foot.

[b]Maximum high water elevations shown to the whole foot have a probable accuracy of ± 1 foot.

[c]Times given are in Pacific Standard Time. 46 is actually 1 April 1946; 60 is 23 May 1960; 64 is 28 March 1964.

[e]Estimated from very general description.

[1]Marine Advisers, a Broad-Frequency-Band Wave Study at Monterey Harbor, California, July 1964 (U.S. Army Contract No. DA-04-04-203-CIVENG-64-7).

[2]Wilson, Basil W., Progress Reports, Surge Study for Monterey Bay and Harbor, California (U.S. Army Contract No. DA-22-079-CIVENG-65-10).

[3]Clifton, Paul, Personal Communication from information compiled by State of California, 1964.

HAROLD G. LOOMIS
ENVIRONMENTAL SCIENCE SERVICES
ADMINISTRATION*

The Major Tsunami in the Hawaiian Islands

INTRODUCTION

The tsunami generated by the Alaska earthquake of March 28, 1964 (0336 GMT), caused slight damage in the Hawaiian Islands and no loss of life. The highest water levels reported were generally about 10 ft above mean lower low water on the northern shores of Maui and Oahu and in Hilo Bay. High-water marks of 15 and 16 ft were observed at isolated places on the northern shore of Oahu. The highest water level measured at Kahului, Maui, was 12 ft, and on Kauai, 6 ft. There was some intrusion of water beyond the usual limits of high water and occasional high seas at these places. In Hilo, the floors of several restaurants and houses at the water's edge were flooded; this was the basis for newspaper stories about damage, but the author knows of no serious damage to structures in the Hawaiian Islands caused by this tsunami. The previous tsunamis of 1946, 1952, 1957, and 1960 had washed out vulnerable areas at Hilo so that there remained little that could be damaged by a moderate tsunami; under a redevelopment agency, the section of Hilo that had been severely damaged in 1946 and in 1960 was mostly clear of buildings by March 1964. Even so, the highest wave did not come over the road into that portion of town.

ABSTRACT: The March 28, 1964, tsunami caused little damage and no loss of life in Hawaii. The highest water levels were generally about 10 ft on the northern or exposed shores of the islands, locally up to 16 ft. Maps of runup heights are shown. The successive crests of the tsunami quickly became out of phase with natural modes of Hilo Bay so that the "Hilo tsunami problem" did not materialize. Energy, coherence, and quadrature spectra of the tsunami at Midway, Honolulu, Kahului, and Hilo are shown. The low coherence between these stations does not support the hypothesis that a coherent source of waves was emanating from the Gulf of Alaska. The energy decay curve has several peaks that can be identified with reflections from North America, Kamchatka, Mexico, and Australia. The mean frequency of the incoming energy changes with time in a peculiar way, but not so as to support the hypothesis that energy is being converted from lower to higher frequencies, at least during the initial phase of the tsunami.

*Now, in part, the National Ocean Survey, NOAA.

TIDE-GAGE RECORDS

The GMT tide-gage records of this tsunami at Hawaiian Island stations (Spaeth and Berkman, 1965) are shown in Figure 1. The local (–10 hours) arrival times of the first wave on March 27 were as follows: Nawiliwili, Kauai—2230 HST; Kahului, Maui—2248 HST; Honolulu, Oahu—2250 HST; and Hilo, Hawaii—2300 HST. The state Civil Defense had called an alert on the advice of the Seismic Sea Wave Warning System of the Coast and Geodetic Survey, and coastal regions were evacuated except for parts of Honolulu, particularly the Waikiki area, where there is less cooperation in evacuations.

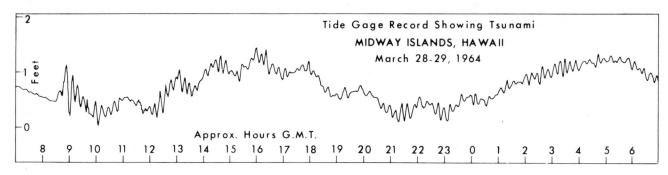

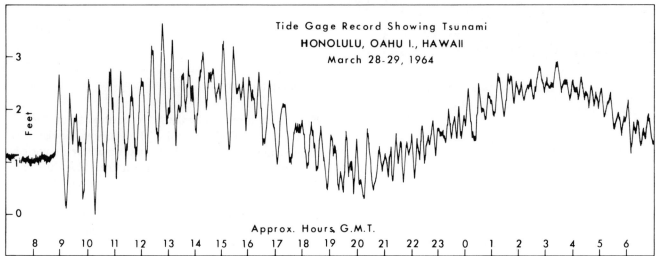

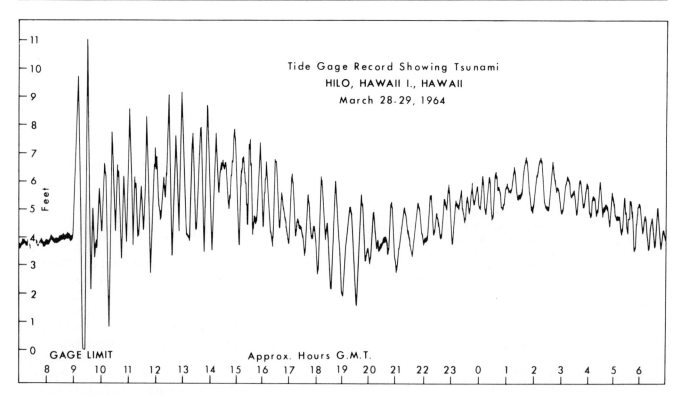

FIGURE 1   Tide-gage records showing the tsunami of March 28, 1964, for Midway Islands, Honolulu, Hilo, Kahului, Nawiliwili, and Mokuoloe, Hawaii. (From Spaeth and Berkman, 1965.)

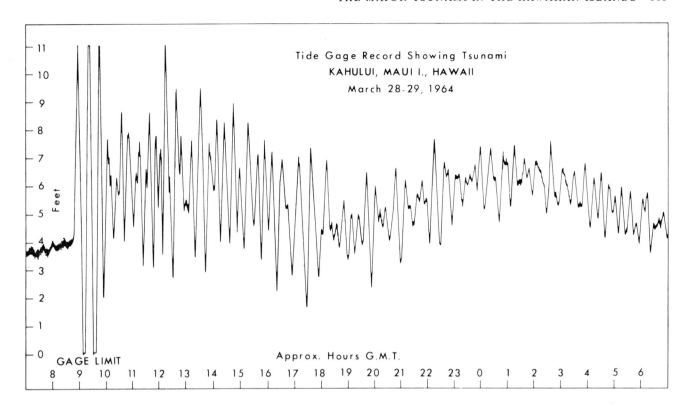

Tide Gage Record Showing Tsunami
KAHULUI, MAUI I., HAWAII
March 28-29, 1964

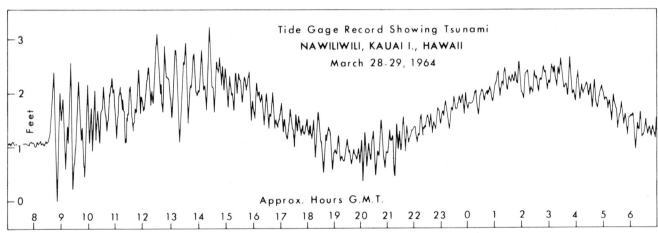

Tide Gage Record Showing Tsunami
NAWILIWILI, KAUAI I., HAWAII
March 28-29, 1964

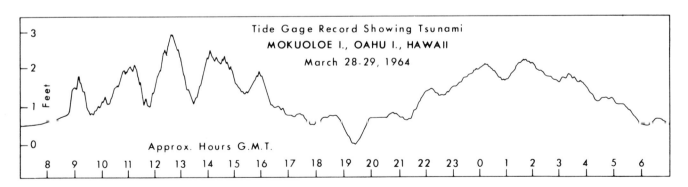

Tide Gage Record Showing Tsunami
MOKUOLOE I., OAHU I., HAWAII
March 28-29, 1964

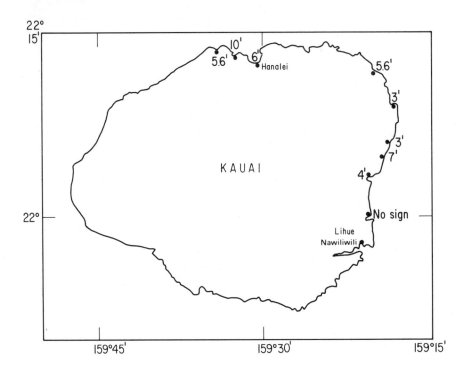

FIGURE 2   Runup of tsunami of March 28, 1964, on Kauai.

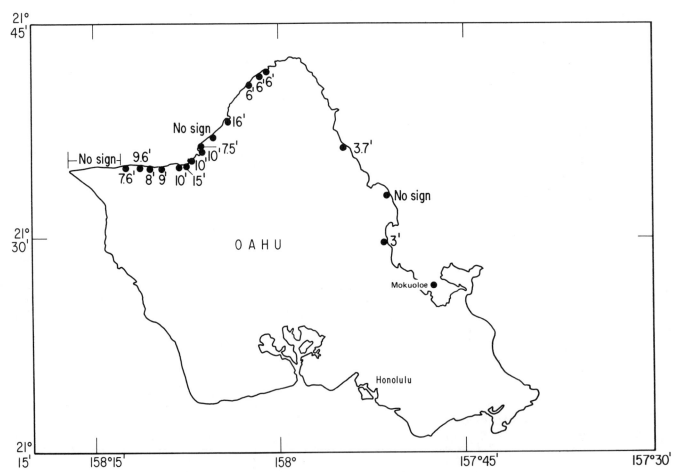

FIGURE 3   Runup of tsunami of March 28, 1964, on Oahu.

Runup measurements were made by teams from the University of Hawaii at most places on the islands of Hawaii, Maui, Oahu, and Kauai where waves were sufficiently high to leave a measurable high-water mark. The height of the high-water marks was measured in some cases by surveyor's staff and hand level and was estimated in others. Some information was obtained by questioning people about their observations during and immediately after the tsunami. Most of the staff of the Tsunami Research Program at the University of Hawaii happened to be out of the state on the day of the tsunami, and the runup measurements (Figures 2 through 6) were therefore made 2 or 3 days after the tsunami occurred.

WATER LEVELS

The highest water levels occurred on the north sides of the islands as expected. The U.S. Coast and Geodetic Survey tide-gage records of the tsunami (Figure 1) present the following interesting features. The record from Mokuoloe Island, Oahu, shows the effect on the tsunami of a low-pass filter produced by the large shallow bay enclosed by a reef. This record shows five large waves with crests separated by about 1 hour and 40 minutes; this pattern was also found in several of the Alaska tide-gage records. It is inferred from these observations that this tsunami had a large low-frequency component in the open ocean. The records from Hilo, Honolulu, and Kahului all begin with wave crests 23 minutes apart. At Kahului, this appears to be near to a natural resonance; three large crests occurred before an incoming crest and a cycle of a natural mode of oscillation were out of phase, and destructive interference occurred. In the case of Hilo, the lowest natural mode of oscillation of the triangular bay is closer to 30 minutes, and the incoming waves thus were quickly out of phase with oscillations in this mode. The second trough and third crest that followed showed destructive interference.

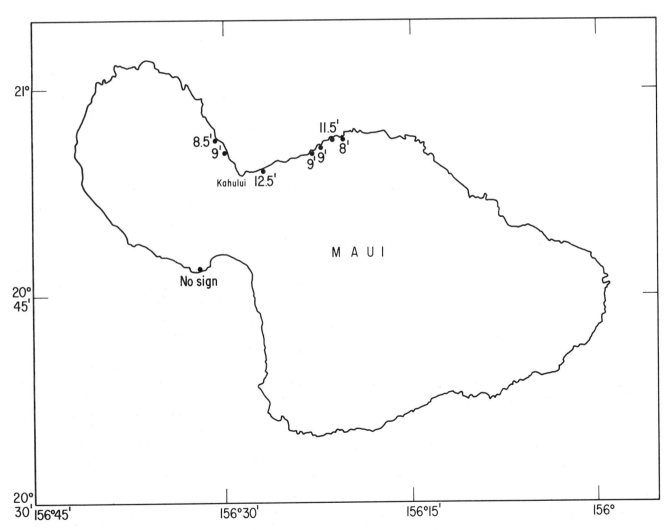

FIGURE 4   Runup of tsunami of March 28, 1964, on Maui.

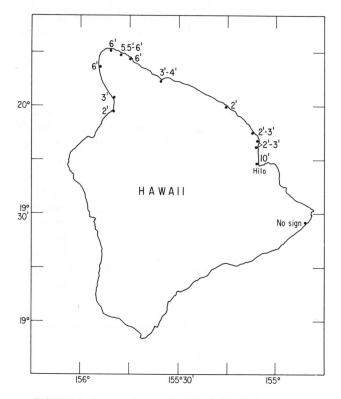

FIGURE 5   Runup of tsunami of March 28, 1964, on Hawaii.

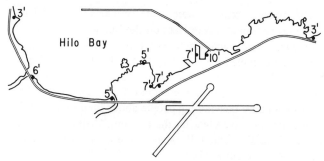

FIGURE 6   Runup of tsunami of March 28, 1964, at Hilo.

Such considerations may account for the greater amplification in Kahului than in Hilo. One might have expected a larger wave in Hilo than the one that actually occurred, but apparently the time spacing of the leading crests was "wrong" for Hilo.

ANALYSIS OF SPECTRA

A considerable amount of work (Loomis, 1966) was required for the examination of spectral characteristics of this and other tsunamis. It was thought that in the open ocean there is some wave pattern which is selectively amplified at various harbors and coastal regions according to some frequency response pattern peculiar to each location. If this response pattern could be learned by analyzing many records at one station, then one could work backward to undo the local effect and determine the open-ocean characteristics of the tsunami as well as to predict amplifications of future tsunamis at coastal points when their measured characteristics in the open ocean are given.

Although common sense and experience have indicated that in a general way things are as described above, it has not been possible in specific cases to extrapolate from the shore records to any certain or detailed knowledge of the tsunami in the open ocean. Miller (1964), after detailed study, devised

a general classification of certain tsunamis according to whether their spectra are weighed toward higher or lower frequencies.

One small part of the work mentioned above is shown here. Figure 7 gives spectra of this tsunami as calculated from U.S. Coast and Geodetic Survey tide-gage records from Midway, Honolulu, Kahului, and Hilo. The records were digitized by sampling at 2-minute intervals. In these particular spectra, 1,024 points were used to represent a record length of 34.1 hours. The diurnal and semidiurnal tides were removed by fitting the proper tidal functions to the data by the best least-squares fit, and the residual series was analyzed by a Cooley–Tukey algorithm to produce the Fourier coefficients. The squared coefficients were then summed by 4's to produce these spectra, which are taken to be a compromise between a desirable resolution on the frequency scale and excessive variance of the estimate on the ordinate. Less variability in the ordinate could be achieved by averaging further. A further summing by 2's of adjacent estimates would cut the length of the 95 percent confidence interval by a third. This can be done by eye, if desired.

The main information contained in these spectra, however, is a description of the potential energy versus frequency at a particular place in a harbor during a period when it is strongly excited by long-period wave energy; that is, the particular placing of the gage in a harbor and the natural modes of oscillation of the harbor and surrounding coastal regions are the determining factors in such spectra.

I tested the hypothesis that the water in the Gulf of Alaska was set into oscillation by the earthquake which then fed energy at a constant frequency (or frequencies) into the Pacific Ocean as the oscillations of the Gulf decayed. In order to test the "coherent source" hypothesis, the coherence and quadrature spectra between all pairs of the stations at Midway, Honolulu, Kahului, and Hilo were calculated from a 24-hour record beginning 6 hours after first arrival. If the source were coherent, then the coherence between two stations at the driven frequency, or set of discrete frequencies, or band of frequencies would be significantly high. In addition, the phase that is quite sensitive to coherent sources

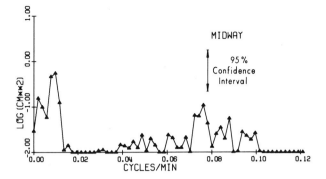

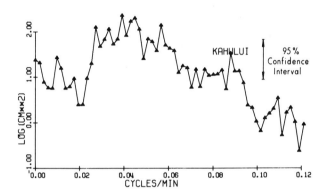

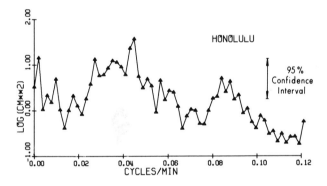

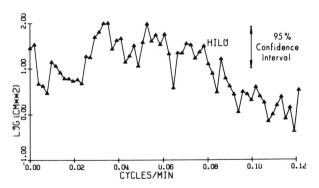

FIGURE 7 Potential energy spectra for the tsunami of March 28, 1964, at Honolulu, Hilo, Kahului, and Midway.

would change linearly as a function of frequency. The four coherence and quadrature spectra shown in Figure 8 are representative of the lot and show discouragingly little coherence or systematic change of phase.

The problems seem to be that (1) the tsunami characteristics being transient and changing are overshadowed in these time-averaging processes by continuing local oscillations and, more seriously, that (2) the simple black-box, linear-system analogy used here does not apply. There is a two-dimensional geometry to deal with—namely, that which is displayed in a plan view. Even without oscillations and standing waves, one can see that a given wave train that arrives at a tide gage by different paths might have destructive interference at some frequencies, constructive interference at other frequencies, and every case in between. The frequencies where constructive or destructive interference occur will depend on the travel-time relations of the multiple paths and very much on the directional aspects of the incident energy. At least part of this problem could be overcome by measuring the potential and kinetic energy—that is, total energy—at a point in the ocean. Much of the confusing and irrelevant complexity of the potential energy spectrum would be eliminated and there would be more hope of learning something about the actual spectral characteristics of a tsunami and the harbor response to tsunamis.

ENERGY DECAY

The energy decay curves of the tsunami of March 28, 1964, at Honolulu and Hilo are shown in Figure 9. In order to focus on the energy most closely related with the tsunami, only the wave energies with periods between 11 and 33 minutes are used. Honolulu and Hilo Harbors both have many resonances with periods shorter than 11 minutes, and it was felt that sustained harbor oscillations could mask the incoming tsunami energy. The upper limit of 33 minutes was chosen because it is well away from tidal periods and because this is about the longest period that can be contained in a window of effective width 1 hour which was necessary to give the detailed time dependence of energy decay that was desired. The decay constant for Hilo is $(12.2 \text{ hours})^{-1}$ and for Honolulu $(12.5 \text{ hours})^{-1}$ for the first part of the decay curve. After about 20 hours, the rate of decay becomes about 1/20 of its initial value, if, indeed, one still chooses to refer to this part of the curve as exponential!

It is interesting to try to identify the source of the energy peaks in the decay curves. The travel time from Honolulu to Hilo is 1 hour, so that reflections arriving on the Hilo-Honolulu axis would be separated by 1 hour. Reflections arriving on a perpendicular to the axis would arrive simultaneously. With this in mind, it seems that the peak at Honolulu (0216) and Hilo (0300) could be a reflection from the

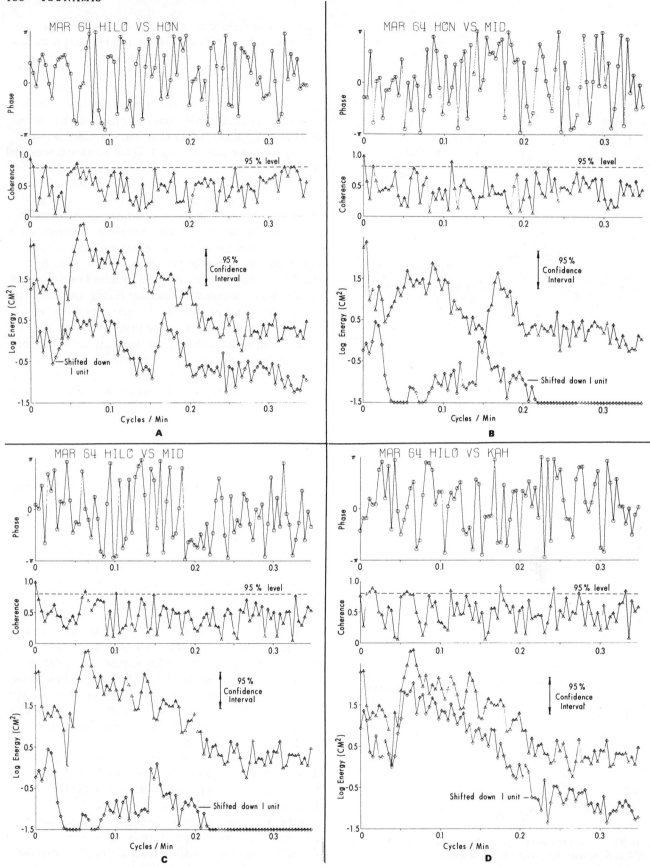

FIGURE 8 Coherence and quadrature spectra for the tsunami of March 28, 1964, between (*A*) Hilo and Honolulu; (*B*) Honolulu and Midway; (*C*) Hilo and Midway; and (*D*) Hilo and Kahului.

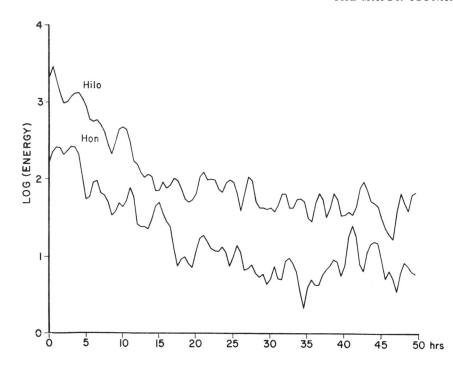

FIGURE 9 Energy decay at Hilo and Honolulu for the tsunami of March 28, 1964. Energy is in square centimeters in the frequency band of 0.03–0.09 cycle per minute, averaged over a cosine window of effective width 1 hour.

Alaskan coast. The peaks at Honolulu (0530) and Hilo (0530) could be from the Washington–Oregon coast. The peaks at Honolulu (0830) and Hilo (0900) could be energy from northern Japan and Kamchatka. The peaks at Honolulu (1000) and Hilo (0900) could be energy reflected from some place off the coast of Mexico. The peak at Honolulu (2000) and Hilo (2000) could come from Australia–New Guinea. The peak at 1600 on March 29, 1964, at both Honolulu and Hilo could be energy from Antarctica. Not all peaks are accounted for, and this listing of possibilities merely attempts to identify some peaks with reflecting areas.

Figure 10A shows how the frequency content of the spectrum at Hilo shifts with time. With the tides removed, the mean frequency is calculated from the energy over an 8.3-hour interval. The starting time of the interval is advanced by steps of 2.1 hours. Figure 10B gives similar information for Honolulu.

It was expected that there would be a continual shift in the spectrum toward higher frequencies. This would be caused by the increasingly closer spacing of zero-crossings of the wave train at a given point from an impulsively generated wave. Also, various nonlinear processes would tend to convert low-frequency energy to harmonics. However, it is shown in Figure 10 that each successive spectrum centered at $T = 4.2$, $T = 6.3$, $T = 8.4$ has a lower average frequency than its predecessor. The spectra centered at $T = 10.5$ and $T = 12.6$, however, have considerably higher average frequencies than earlier spectra. They also contain consider-

able amounts of energy reflected from North America, Asia, and Australia–New Guinea. This tends to support the second mechanism of spectral shift mentioned above, but not the first.

CONCLUSIONS

The tsunami of March 28, 1964, caused little damage in Hawaii. However, it was of sufficient amplitude to be recorded on U.S. Coast and Geodetic Survey tide gages with good tsunami-to-noise ratio, so that it has been a good tsunami on which to test various theories and concepts. As a result of this work, it was concluded that no simple theory explains the nearshore behavior or possibly even the open-ocean characteristics of this tsunami. The complexities introduced by reflections and local resonances are considerable.

REFERENCES

Loomis, Harold G., 1966. Spectral analysis of tsunami records from stations in the Hawaiian Islands. *Bulletin of the Seismological Society of America*, 56 (June), 697–713.

Miller, G. R., 1964. Tsunamis and tides (PhD dissertation). La Jolla: University of California, San Diego.

Spaeth, Mark G., and Saul C. Berkman, 1965. The tsunami of March 28, 1964, as recorded at tide stations. Rockville, Maryland: U.S. Coast and Geodetic Survey, April. 59 p.

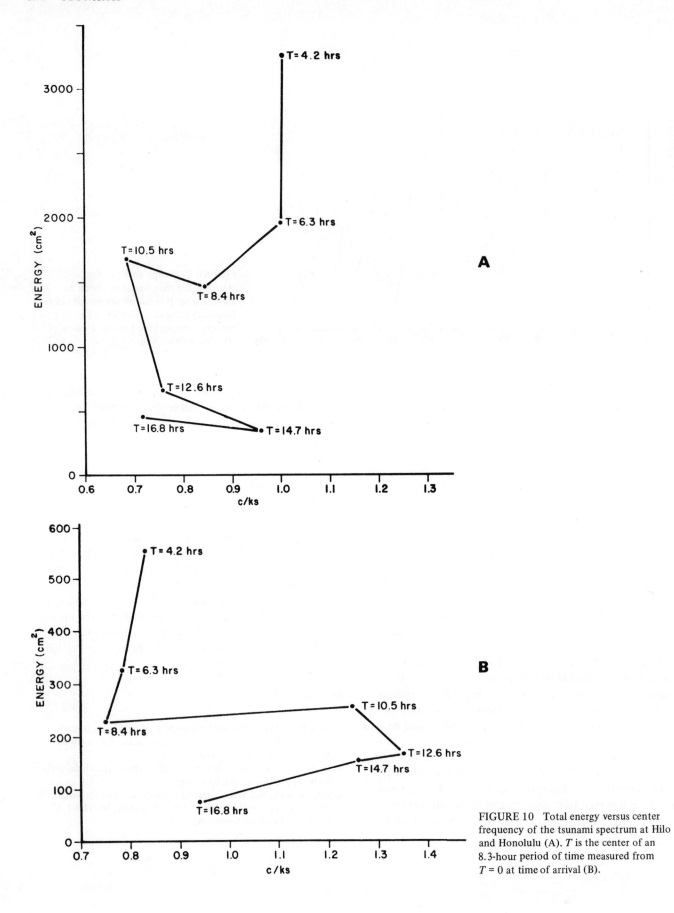

FIGURE 10 Total energy versus center frequency of the tsunami spectrum at Hilo and Honolulu (A). T is the center of an 8.3-hour period of time measured from $T = 0$ at time of arrival (B).

LI-SAN HWANG
DAVID DIVOKY
TETRA TECH, INC., PASADENA, CALIFORNIA

A Numerical Model of the Major Tsunami

INTRODUCTION

The Alaska earthquake of 1964 is, as evidenced by this series of volumes, among the best documented seismic events of record. In particular, the degree of documentation of submarine displacements permits an attempt to model the generation and propagation of the associated tsunami by deterministic methods. We shall first outline a numerical model that relates an arbitrary pattern and time history of bottom motion to the consequent surface disturbance. A somewhat idealized model of the Alaska displacement history is then postulated and used as input for the computer program. From this, we compute a reconstruction of surface wave effects and make a comparison with available data.

The preliminary results are quite encouraging, in view of the many simplifications and inferences made in this first attempt at a numerical model. The major limiting factor is lack of knowledge of the detailed time history of the bottom displacement. Extensive information concerning permanent displacement is available; however, the manner in which those values were attained might significantly influence the resultant wave system. A further limitation on the results shown here is the use of a Cartesian system for reasons of economy, thereby restricting numerical computations to a zone not much larger than the immediate generation region. The outgoing wave system was followed by ray-tracing procedures in its propagation across the Pacific. Work is currently in progress to perform more reliable propagation computations within a spherical coordinate system encompassing most of the Pacific basin.

Our findings should nevertheless be satisfactory near the source region and show a number of interesting features, among which are a strong preferential radiation of energy in a direction normal to the major axis of the elongated source and a great complexity of the surface elevation history at any point, showing short (~ 10-minute) waves superposed on a larger and longer (~ 1.5-hour) system.

Comparison will be made with both a near-source runup

ABSTRACT: A numerical model of tsunami generation is applied to the case of the 1964 Alaska earthquake. The procedure makes possible the determination of surface wave effects resulting from an arbitrary bottom-displacement history through a finite-difference computation. In the application given here, the bottom displacement was inferred from postearthquake bathymetry and from the aftershock distribution pattern; the hypothetical time history incorporates separate rates of horizontal "rupture" and vertical displacement. The numerical results include surface wave behavior near the source for more than 2 hours; considerable complexity is found, although a comparison with a runup record at Cape Yakataga shows general agreement. Transocean propagation was computed with the aid of ray-tracing techniques; although of limited accuracy, these results also show general agreement with records obtained at several Pacific tide-gage stations. A significant finding is that the elongation of the source region causes a preferential radiation of tsunami energy in a direction roughly normal to the source major-axis. Further work is in progress to extend the zone of numerical computations to include transoceanic propagation and to investigate effects of local topography in wave transformation.

observation and tide-gage records of Pacific atolls. The diffi-culty with any such comparison is that records are invariably distorted by effects of local topography to some degree, ranging from extreme (at coastal stations within bays or harbors) to moderate (at relatively open atoll stations). Procedures to consider such local modification are available (Hwang and Tuck, 1970; Le Méhauté and Hwang, 1970) but are not incorporated here. Nevertheless, the general features of computations and records are in encouraging agreement, showing both proper trends and magnitudes. After comple-tion of trans-Pacific propagation computations by using the spherical numerical code, this work will be extended to account for local transformation of the wave system at regions of special interest such as Hilo, Hawaii, and Crescent City, California. In other words, numerical calculations will continue up to the shorelines of interest to define accurately the incident wave system which will then be treated region-by-region to determine the further effects of resonance in bays, runup, and so on.

Ichiye (1958), Honda and Nakamura (1951), Webb (1962), Momoi (1964), and Kajiura (1963) investigated the surface disturbance resulting from a sea-bed motion under restric-tions of constant depth and simplified bottom displacement. Van Dorn (1965) presented an analytical formulation based upon Kajiura's (1963) work for the distant amplitude from an arbitrary source in constant depth; adaptation to the real environment and solution of the integral equations involved is difficult for practical application, however. Van Dorn (1963) discussed the inverse problem of deducing the source motion (for the tsunami of March 1957) from wave measure-ments at Wake Island; this procedure appears to be somewhat uncertain, however. Most recently, Aida (1970) adopted an approach similar to that used here. Some of the present re-sults were also reported by Hwang and Divoky (1970) and Hwang, Divoky, and Yuen (1970).

GENERATION MODEL

GOVERNING EQUATIONS

The equations of motion in a Cartesian system are written as

$$u_t + uu_x + vu_y + g\eta_x = 0 \qquad (1)$$

$$v_t + uv_x + vv_y + g\eta_y = 0 \qquad (2)$$

where

η is wave elevation from mean level,
u, v are vertically averaged x- and y-components of water-particle velocity,
t means time,

x, y are Cartesian coordinates in the horizontal plane, and
g is acceleration of gravity.

The continuity equation takes the following special form

$$(\eta - \xi)_t + [(h + \eta)u]_x + [(h + \eta)v]_y = 0, \qquad (3)$$

in which ξ is the time-dependent vertical bottom displace-ment measured from the initial bottom and h is the water depth, which includes ξ.

These equations are solved by a multistep, finite–difference procedure. During the first half-time step, η and u are com-puted implicitly and v explicitly; in the second half-time step, η and v are computed implicitly and u explicitly.

A staggered space mesh is employed with h given at $(i + \frac{1}{2}, j + \frac{1}{2})$, η at (i,j), u at $(i + \frac{1}{2}, j)$, and v at $(i, j + \frac{1}{2})$. The finite–difference equations follow in a straightforward manner. [See Leendertse (1967) and Dronkers (1969) for a detailed development of numerical schemes.]

A particular problem arises in the treatment at the open boundaries. Owing to considerations of computing time and cost, the region over which calculations are made is limited to a small multiple of the earthquake region. In this way, the computer program provides an initial wave condition, which is then followed over oceanic distances by other methods. In truncating the domain for computer calculations, some con-ditions must be specified at these "open boundaries." In par-ticular, one wishes to specify complete transmission at those points. Of course, one might also simply move the open boundaries to a sufficient distance such that the calculations are completed over the time range of interest before the wave front (traveling at speed $\sqrt{gh}$) arrives; that is, conditions are always null at the open boundaries. This procedure is in-efficient, however. We have chosen the artifice of selecting Δx, the space step, and Δt, the time step, such that $\Delta x = V \Delta t$, V being the wave speed at the boundary, and with the assumption that u and η at $x_E + 1$, $t_{\tau+1}$ equal u and η at x_E, t_τ modified by any necessary refraction or dispersion decay, that is, that a wave property is preserved over a dis-tance Δx during a time $\Delta t = \Delta x/V$. This is approximately true, so that only a small numerical reflection is introduced from this fictitious outer boundary. We have also, however, tended to minimize this problem further by choosing the boundaries far enough away to prevent their interference before a certain time.

The size of the generation region is such that the earth's curvature becomes of distinct importance. Therefore, the numerical grid can only be approximately Cartesian, although the procedure in this study minimizes the discrepancy. This procedure first establishes two great-circle arcs intersecting at right angles at the center of the region of interest. Each is then divided into segments of equal length (earth length, not map length) and, at each segment, a perpendicular great-circle is drawn. The resulting grid deviates negligibly from orthogonality and uniformity of size over distances of 1,000 to 2,000 mi. The grid spacing is determined by considerations of computer size as well as accuracy.

As has been noted, work is currently under way to utilize a computational grid covering the Pacific basin; this requires that equations (1) to (3) be recast into a spherical coordinate system. If the Coriolis force is neglected, the appropriate form is:

$$u_t = \frac{-g}{a} \eta_\theta \qquad (4)$$

$$v_t = \frac{-g}{a \sin \theta} \eta_\phi \qquad (5)$$

$$\eta_t = \frac{1}{a \sin \theta} \left\{ \frac{\partial}{\partial \theta} \left[(h+\eta)u \sin \theta \right] + \frac{\partial}{\partial \phi} \left[(h+\eta)v \right] \right\} + \xi_t \qquad (6)$$

where

  a is the radius of the earth,
  θ is latitude,
  ϕ is longitude,
  u is wave-velocity component in the θ-direction, and
  v is wave-velocity component in the ϕ-direction.

GROUND-MOTION MODEL

The essential input is the nature of the forcing disturbance, the ground motion ξ. In general, this is quite complex, and its transient history may never be reliably known for a given tsunami. We have therefore adopted a somewhat idealized model of the disturbance although, of course, the subsequent numerical development could be as easily utilized with the real history, were it specifiable.

The bottom motion is assumed to result from changes in depth, whether by horizontal or vertical motion. The area over which the disturbance occurs is given by the distribution of aftershock epicenters (Benioff, 1951). It is envisioned that motion begins at the epicenter of the main shock and that the leading tip of disturbance propagates radially from that point at a constant velocity V. This "rupture" velocity may be of the order of 3 to 4 km/sec (Plafker and Savage, 1970). Vertical motion at a given point begins upon passage of this radial front; that is, if (a, b) and (i, j) denote Cartesian coordinates of main shock epicenter and an arbitrary point within the generation area, respectively, then vertical motion is assumed to commence at (i, j) at a time t, given by

$$t_{ij} = (\Delta x/V) \left\{ (a-i)^2 + (b-j)^2 \right\}^{\frac{1}{2}} , \qquad (7)$$

with Δx the coordinate spacing.

The vertical displacement is known to be quite irregular in time and may be somewhat as shown by the solid curve in Figure 1, evidencing overshoot and random oscillation ending in a permanent displacement value ξ_{ij}'. Because the time scale of the fine structure is small in comparison to that of the tsunami period and since the waves generated by the fine structure will vanish from the leading waves after a long distance of propagation, the introduction of a simplified monotonic displacement history (dashed curve in Figure 1) is justified. In particular, we have chosen the following expressions for bottom displacement:

$$\xi_{ij}(t) = 0 \qquad t \leqslant t_{ij}$$

$$\xi_{ij}(t) = \xi_{ij}' \sin^2 \left[\frac{\pi(t - t_{ij})}{2\tau} \right]$$

$$t_{ij} \leqslant t \leqslant t_{ij} + \tau \qquad (8)$$

$$\xi_{ij}(t) = \xi_{ij}' \qquad t \geqslant t_{ij} + \tau$$

The parameter τ is a characteristic time of ground motion that is difficult to specify; records of horizontal displacement of earthquakes in the western United States (Berg and Housner, 1961) indicate that $\tau = 10$ seconds is a reasonable value. The controlling factor for tsunami height at a distance is the permanent displacement ξ_{ij}', which may be obtained by extensive survey of the region and a degree of inference assisted by the assumption of zero motion along the periphery of the aftershock region. It is noted that horizontal displacement of a sloping bottom will also generate waves; to a first approximation, however, such a motion can be interpreted as an appropriate pattern of purely vertical displacement.

APPLICATION TO THE ALASKA EARTHQUAKE

INPUT DATA

The primary method of determining the areal extent of the source disturbance is through the distribution of aftershock epicenters, the assumption being that the regions are congruent.

Figure 2 shows the distribution of major aftershocks (of magnitude greater than 4) occurring from March 27 to December 31, 1964. An enclosing curve would approximate the source region of the tsunami.

Within this region, the permanent displacement $\xi'(x,y)$ has also been summarized by Plafker (1969). The presence of

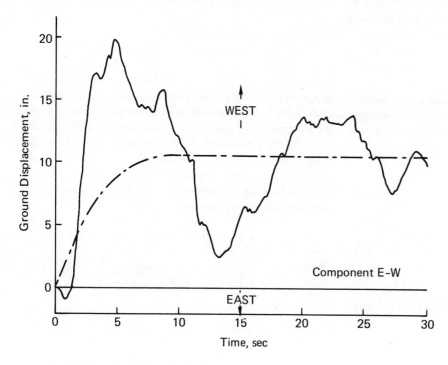

(a) El Centro, California, 1940

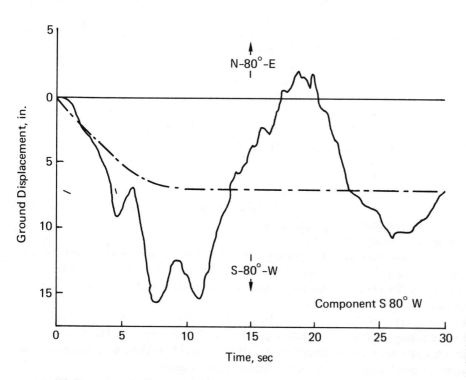

(b) Olympia, Washington, 1949

FIGURE 1 Typical recorded ground-displacement histories for two earthquakes in the western United States (from Berg and Housner, 1961, with the average ground motion, as shown in broken lines, adopted by Wilson, 1969).

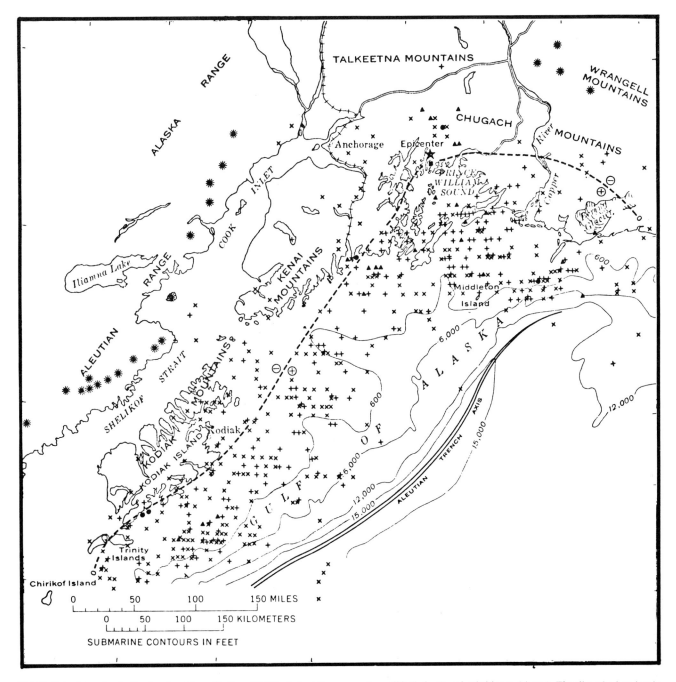

FIGURE 2   Aftershock distribution (from Plafker, 1969); dashed line separates uplift (below) and subsidence (above). The disturbed region is approximately 525 mi long and 225 mi wide.

islands (showing displaced shorelines), good preearthquake bathymetry, and considerable commerce provide the basis for extensive reconstruction of the disturbance. The pattern in Figure 3 is consistent with Plafker's data and differs only in that contour lines have been interpolated where missing across submerged regions. This is somewhat arbitrary but, in any case, must be nearly correct.

The computational grid was established (Figure 4); the grid spacing is 16.1 km. We have chosen $\tau = 10$ seconds and $V = 3.5$ km/sec. The time step was taken to be 2 seconds during ground motion and 100 seconds thereafter. Depths, read at each grid point from a nautical chart, were key-punched for computer; displacements were similarly prepared by using Figure 3.

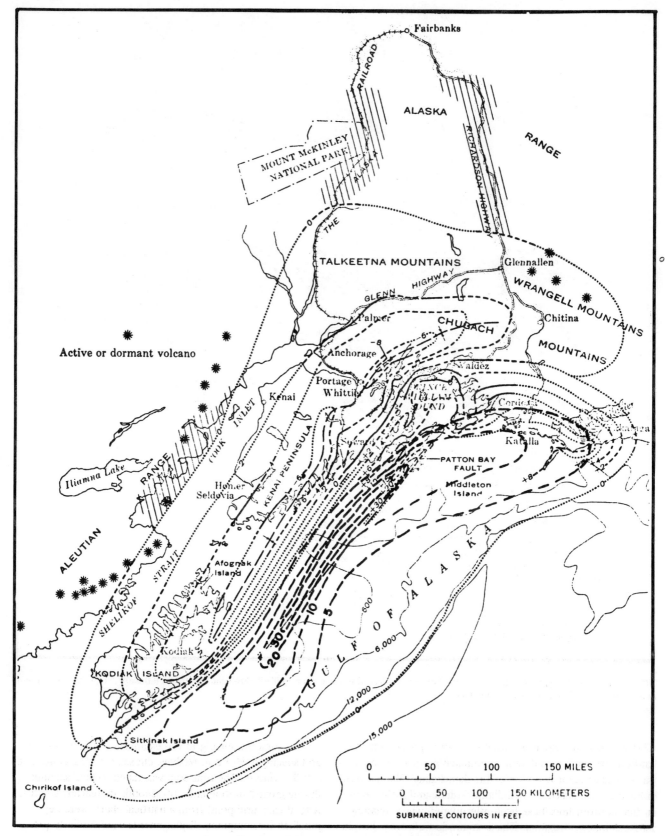

FIGURE 3 Assumed bottom displacement (in feet) (inferred from Plafker, 1969).

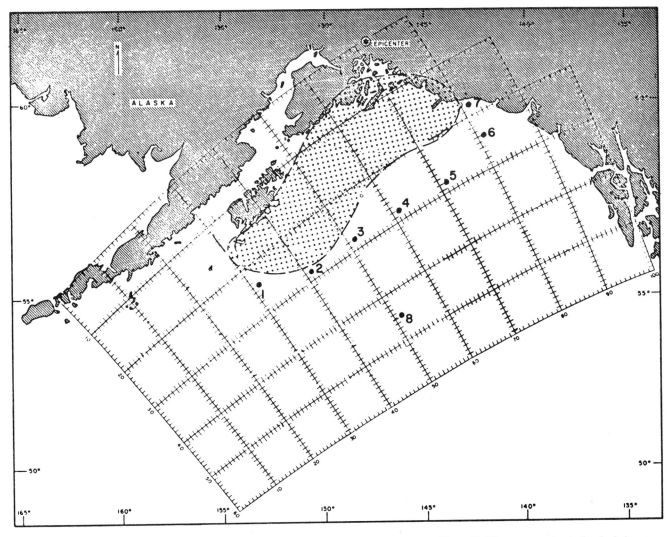

FIGURE 4 Computational grid and locations of points at which wave history is shown (see Figure 7). The source region is the shaded area.

NEAR-SOURCE WAVE SYSTEM

Figure 5 shows contours of equal water-surface displacement from equilibrium at cited time intervals from 100 to 1,000 seconds after the initial major earthquake (5:36 p.m. AST). The pattern grows rapidly toward the southwest, following the major rupture axis, which propagated from Prince William Sound toward Kodiak Island at a speed of about 3.5 km/sec. At the same time, it spread seaward and shoreward—the latter motion soon being reflected by the coastline. An important feature is the complex topography of the sea surface even at early times.

These figures are most useful in showing the pattern of propagation of the leading disturbance, summarized in Figure 6. Most interestingly, the shape of the source region is generally preserved.

To allow a better appreciation of the wave time history, results at eight points indicated in Figure 4 are shown in Figure 7. Again, considerable complexity is apparent. The wave forms shown are the superposition of many components traveling in various directions, including not only the fundamental wave due to the ground upthrust, but also components scattered randomly by reflection from the Alaska coast. The underlying long wave seems to have a period on the order of 1.5 hours (Figures 7c through 7g). This is in accord with reports of many observers (for example, Wilson and Tørum, 1968). In addition, there is a superposed higher-frequency system due to geometric complexity; this is particularly evident in Figures 7b through 7d and appears to be dominantly in the 10-minute-period range. Interestingly, Van Dorn (1970) reports such higher-frequency components in measurements that he obtained at Wake Island, components with periods of roughly 12 or 13 minutes.

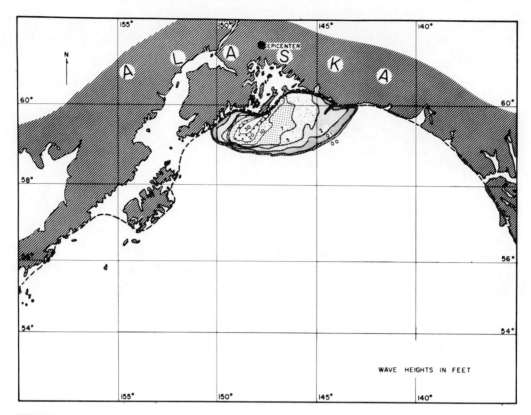

FIGURE 5 (*a*) Computed water surface elevations 100 seconds after initiation of ground motion.

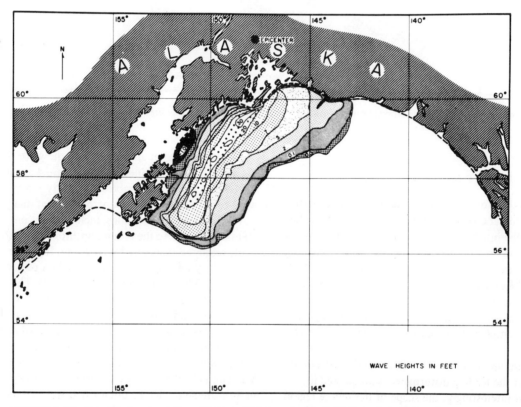

FIGURE 5 (*b*) Computed water surface elevations 200 seconds after initiation of ground motion.

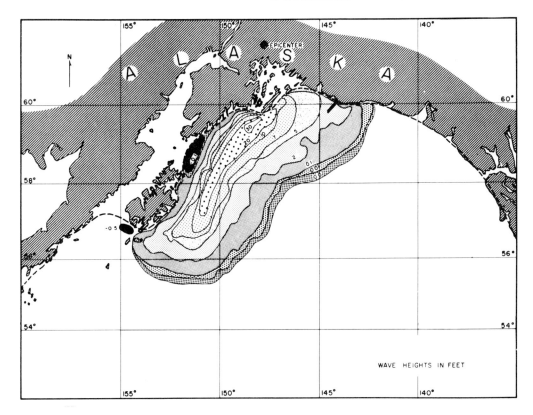

FIGURE 5 (c) Computed water surface elevations 300 seconds after initiation of ground motion.

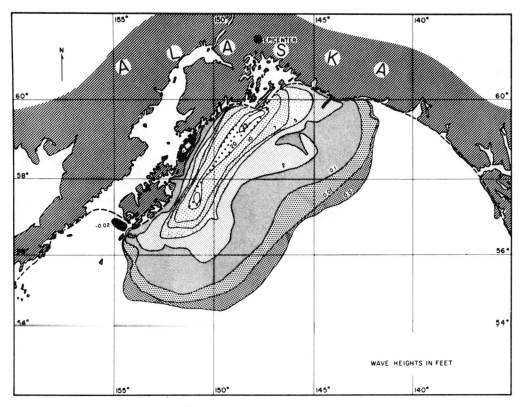

FIGURE 5 (d) Computed water surface elevations 500 seconds after initiation of ground motion.

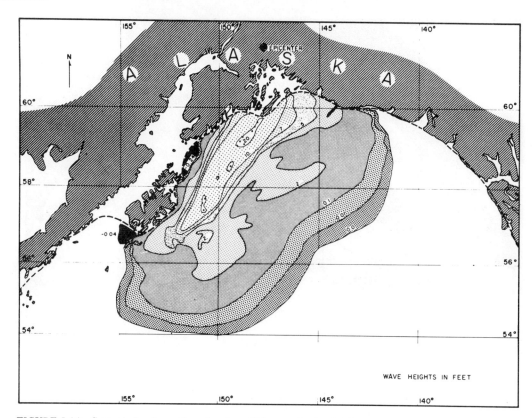

FIGURE 5 (*e*)   Computed water surface elevations 700 seconds after initiation of ground motion.

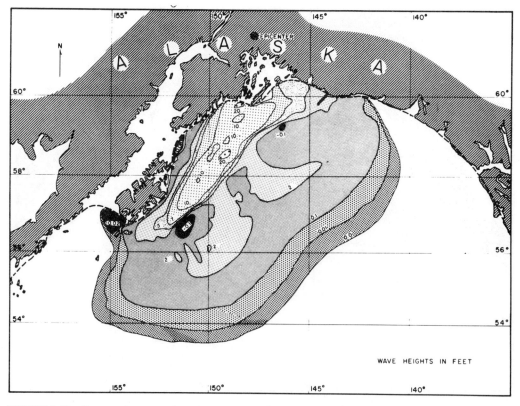

FIGURE 5 (*f*)   Computed water surface elevations 900 seconds after initiation of ground motion.

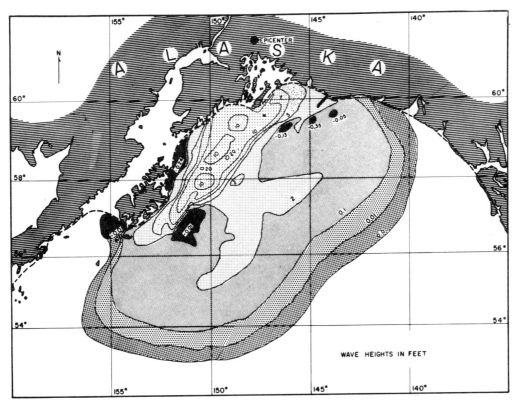

FIGURE 5 (*g*)   Computed water surface elevations 1100 seconds after initiation of ground motion.

TRANSOCEAN PROPAGATION

Because of time and cost limitations in the work reported here, the numerical grid method could not be extended over oceanic distances and the greatly simplified and approximate method of ray optics was employed to propagate the wave system across the Pacific. By this method, long waves are assumed to travel at speeds $c = \sqrt{gh}$, where g is gravity and h is the local water depth. Moreover, a wave front is considered to travel always normal to itself. From the initial patterns shown in Figure 6, successive wave fronts were constructed for equal increments of time, and orthogonals (rays) were then drawn as curves intersecting consecutive wave fronts normally. The method is somewhat subjective and tends to accumulate errors, but provides some estimate of topographic modification of the developing wave train. Such a refraction diagram is shown in Figure 8.

Under the assumption of conservation of energy between orthogonals, one obtains the relation

$$H_1^2 b_1 = H_2^2 b_2,$$

where H is wave height and b is the separation of orthogonals. The refraction coefficient is defined as

$$K_R = \sqrt{\frac{b_1}{b_2}},$$

which includes, of course, depth-independent radial spreading.

By beginning with an initial wave height from Figure 7, for example, the height elsewhere in Figure 8 can be evaluated approximately through multiplication by K_R. Of course, many other effects, such as shoaling and diffraction, are operative and should be included in a detailed evaluation. Such modifications are implicit in the numerical transocean computations currently under way.

Beyond considerations of arrival times and the like, the pattern given in Figure 8 enables investigation of the preferential direction of wave energy radiation. It has been speculated that tsunami sources, being typically quite elongated in shape, may tend to radiate the bulk of wave energy in some directions and much less energy in others. For example, Hatori (1963), investigating a number of Japanese tsunamis, found that the wave heights tended to peak in a direction near $90°$ from the source major axis. This is seen clearly in Figure 9, the height normal to the major axis being typically an order of magnitude greater than that emanating parallel to it.

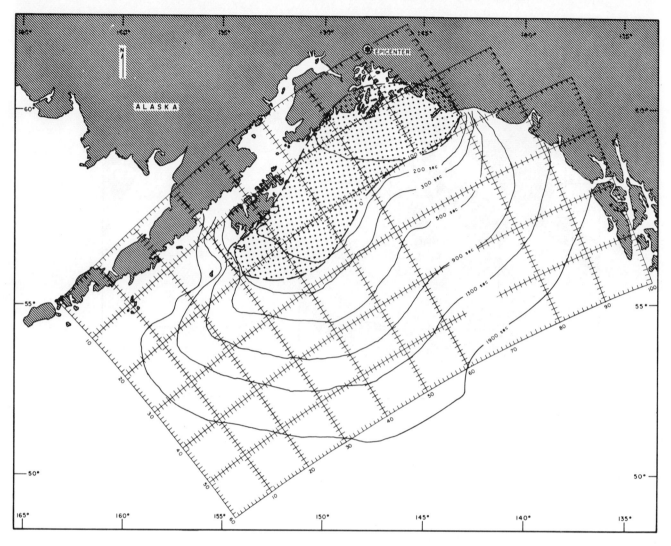

FIGURE 6   Computed position of leading disturbance at successive times; region of ground displacement is shaded area.

In the present case, the amplitude variation near the source is deduced from computations such as those shown in Figure 7. Figure 10, for example, shows the variation along the 0.5-hour front. It is apparent that the largest amplitudes will be seen to the southeast of the source. At later times, refraction alters this pattern somewhat. Figure 11 shows the distribution along the 5-hour front and indicates that the largest waves pass just to the east of Hawaii, whereas the Asian and lower American coasts are less affected. A correlation with damage patterns is not justified, however, without consideration of the very dominant local wave modifications.

COMPARISON WITH OBSERVATIONS

It has been noted that observations are always distorted by local effects to some degree through the processes of shoal-ing, breaking, diffraction, resonant amplification, and so on. To make truly valid comparisons with predictions therefore requires assessment of all such processes for each station at which observations are made. In principle all such effects are either implicit in the numerical code or are easily added. On the other hand, a finely spaced computing grid would be needed to resolve local behavior, so that in any case special treatment is needed. This has not been attempted in the comparisons to be given here; these should therefore be considered schematic and indicative only of trends and magnitudes.

A near-source comparison is provided by a record of personal observations made by a resident of Cape Yakataga, C. R. Bilderback (see Pararas-Carayannis, 1965). This is apparently a record of the time sequence of successive peaks of runup and rundown with height estimated by comparison with local landmarks. The shoreline observation point lies relatively near our computation point 7 so that Figure 7g is

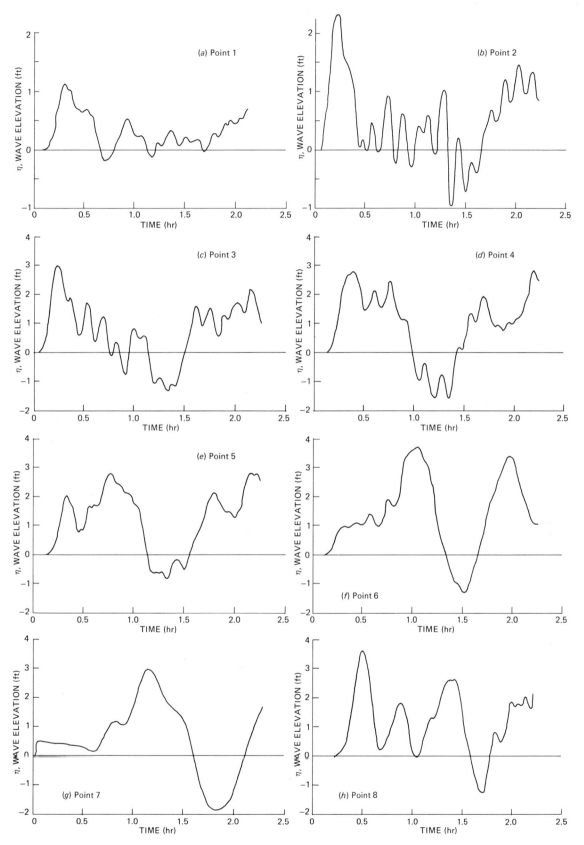

FIGURE 7 Computed wave history at points indicated in Figure 4.

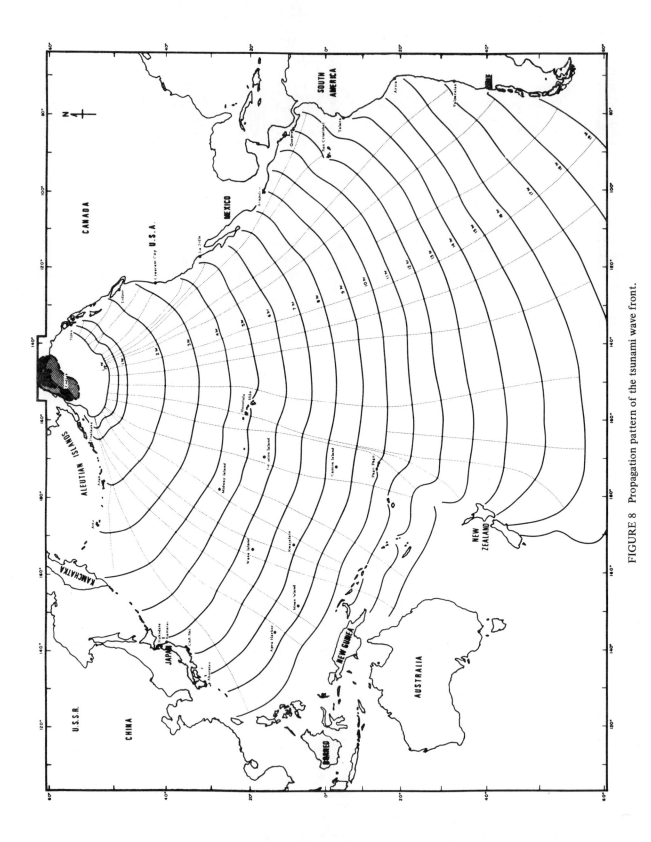

FIGURE 8 Propagation pattern of the tsunami wave front.

204

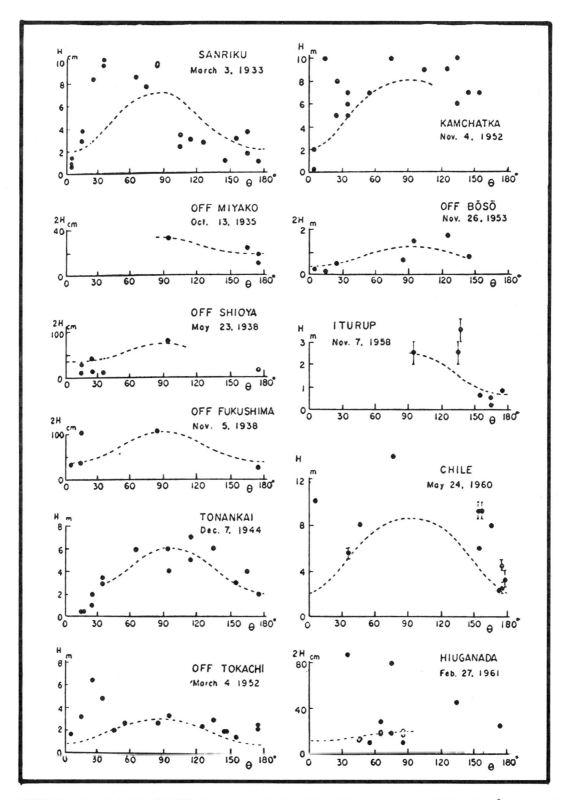

FIGURE 9   Records by Hatori (1963), showing variation in heights of Japanese tsunamis with direction; θ is measured from the major axis of the source.

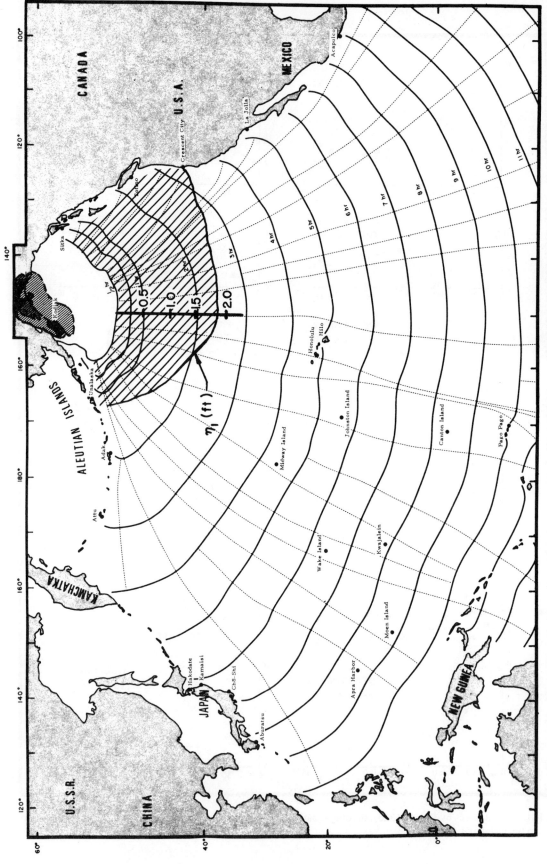

FIGURE 10 Wave amplitude along a crest near the source, Alaska 1964.

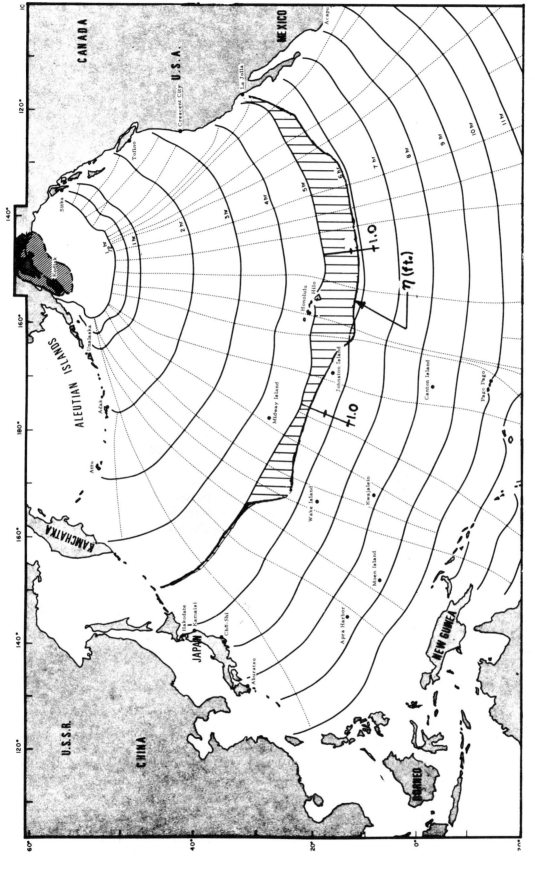

FIGURE 11 Amplitude along a crest near Hawaii, indicating the directional pattern of energy radiation.

207

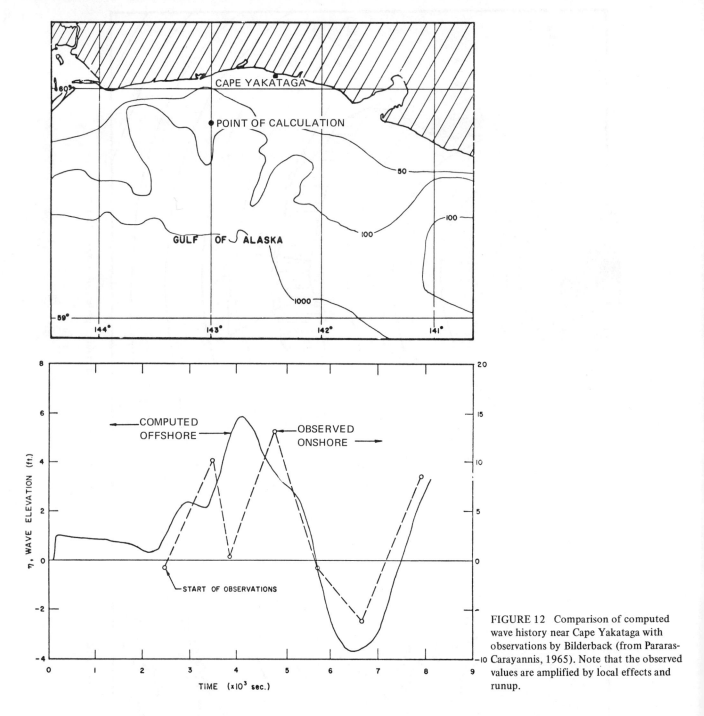

FIGURE 12 Comparison of computed wave history near Cape Yakataga with observations by Bilderback (from Pararas-Carayannis, 1965). Note that the observed values are amplified by local effects and runup.

the appropriate "prediction." Figure 12 shows both a regional map and the runup record. The phase and amplitude coherence are generally good with the exception of the third data point. There is a runup amplification of just more than two, which is not at all unreasonable for a sloping beach. When one takes into account the coarseness of the computational grid (16 km) and the sensitivity of shoreline action to local topography, this comparison appears quite satisfactory and encouraging.

For a second sort of comparison, tide-gage records at atolls were chosen. Atolls are relatively open to such long waves and therefore introduce much less modification than large islands do. In addition to records taken at four atolls, one taken at Wake Island (Van Dorn, 1965) is included; the gage here, located far offshore in moderately deep water, should also show a minimum of local transformation. The results are summarized in Table 1. The predicted amplitudes were obtained through ray-tracing procedures discussed in conjunction with Figure 11. They contain correction only for the gross refractive effects derived from Figure 8; all effects of

TABLE 1 Comparison of Predicted Incident and Recorded Amplitudes at Five Stations for the 1964 Alaska Tsunami

Location	Predicted Amplitude[a] (cm)	Recorded Amplitude (cm)
Johnston Island 16°45′N, 169°31′W	18.9	30.5
Midway Island 28°13′N, 177°22′W	13.7	27.4
Wake Island 19°17′N, 166°37′E	19.2	15.2
Canton Island 02°49′S, 171°43′W	16.5	6.1
Kwajalein 08°44′N, 167°44′E	14.0	30.5

[a]Without consideration of local effects.

shoaling, diffraction, dispersion, and dissipation are absent. It is seen that, for three of the records, the observed amplitude is roughly twice that predicted. Such a factor is reasonable for the unconsidered local effects. At Canton Island, the situation is reversed, the predicted value being greater than observed; this may be because this gage is on the lee side of the island. Van Dorn's (1965) record at Wake Island shows the best agreement, doubtless owing to placement of the gage considerably offshore in moderately deep water. Of course, a major limitation for all tide-gage records is the ray-tracing procedure used, because this is somewhat subjective and subject to accumulation of error with propagation distance.

DISCUSSION

This initial application of deterministic methods to the problem of tsunami generation has revealed a number of interesting features and promising directions of future research. It will be of special value to extend the zone of numerical computations to more distant coasts and thereby avoid the ray-tracing procedure resorted to here. At that time it will also be of prime interest to refine the grid resolution and investigate local wave transformation at all regions for which reliable observations are available.

Among the items requiring investigation, wave instability seems particularly important. If there is a consistent tendency for a single large wave to split into two or more shorter undulations under certain conditions of bottom topography, for example, the entire character of local response will be changed. This problem has been discussed by Madsen and Mei (1969) and Mei (1970), who have developed a numerical procedure that gives the step-by-step transformation of a wave profile traveling over variable depth. It is shown that wave disintegration occurs naturally for a range of conditions

which appear pertinent to the tsunami problem. In particular, if a dispersion parameter, D, defined as the ratio of amplitude dispersion rate to frequency dispersion rate

$$D = \eta \frac{\lambda^2}{h^3},$$

is of order unity or greater, disintegration is to be expected, given sufficient time. In this relation η represents a maximum wave amplitude and λ is a horizontal length scale such as wave length.

If suitable approximations are adopted, it is readily found that this parameter is of order unity in the deep ocean for a large tsunami and increases rapidly with decreasing depth. For this reason, a more detailed investigation of the practical importance of higher-order terms in equations (4) to (6) is being made in the work currently under way. One might speculate, for example, that the discrepancy between computation and observation found in Figure 11 could result from this source or that the observations of Van Dorn (1970) at Wake Island show such a disintegration.

A second major topic for further investigation is the directionality of tsunamis generated by elongated sources. Figures 9 and 10 indicate such behavior, as do similar results reported by Hwang and Divoky (in press) for the Chilean, Andreanof, and Rat Island tsunamis of 1960, 1957, and 1965, respectively. If it is envisioned that the earth's crust is separating along the midocean ridges and that this movement is compensated by a downward "flow" of discrete "blocks" along active island arcs and ocean trenches, it may be practical to characterize the directionality of potential sources in terms of past behavior. In other words, the general shape of the source displacement and hence its tsunami radiation pattern may be relatively fixed by the block tectonics of the region. If "typical" tsunami sources could be specified in this manner for the active periphery, a step would be taken toward eventual establishment of tsunami-protection design criteria.

ACKNOWLEDGMENTS

This work was supported by the U.S. Atomic Energy Commission under contract AT(26-1)-289(M006). We wish to thank the following individuals for their contributions, advice, and encouragement: Bernard Le Méhauté, William Van Dorn, Arthur Cox, Kenneth Olsen, Gaylord Miller, Ernest Tuck, Basil Wilson, Ron Ballard, and Lee Butler.

REFERENCES

Aida, I., 1970. A numerical experiment for the tsunami accompanying the Kanto earthquake of 1923. *Bulletin of the Earthquake Research Institute*, University of Tokyo, 48 (No. 1), 73–86.

Benioff, Hugo, 1951. Earthquakes and rock creep. *Bulletin of the Seismological Society of America*, 41 (January), 31–62.

Berg, G. V., and G. W. Housner, 1961. Integrated velocity and displacement of strong earthquake ground motion. *Bulletin of the Seismological Society of America*, 51 (April), 175–189.

Dronkers, J. J., 1969. Tidal computations for rivers, coastal areas and seas. *Journal of Hydraulics* (American Society of Civil Engineers), 95 (No. 1), 29–77.

Hatori, Tokutaro, 1963. Directivity of tsunamis. *Bulletin of the Earthquake Research Institute*, University of Tokyo, 41 (No. 1), 61–81.

Honda, H., and K. Nakamura, 1951. The waves caused by one-dimensional deformation of the bottom of a shallow sea of uniform depth. *Scientific Report*, Tohoku University, 3 (No. 3), 133–137.

Hwang, Li-San, and David Divoky, 1970. Tsunami generation. *Journal of Geophysical Research*, 75 (November 20), 6802–6817.

Hwang, Li-San, and David Divoky, in press. Tsunami directionality. *Journal of Waterways and Harbors* (American Society of Civil Engineers).

Hwang, Li-San, David Divoky, and Albert Yuen, 1970. Amchitka tsunami study. Tetra Tech Report TC-177. Las Vegas: U.S. Atomic Energy Commission. 84 p.

Hwang, Li-San, and E. O. Tuck, 1970. On the oscillation of harbours of arbitrary shape. *Journal of Fluid Mechanics*, 42, Part 3 (July 9), 447–464.

Ichiye, T., 1958. A theory on the generation of tsunamis by an impulse at the sea bottom. *Journal of the Oceanographic Society of Japan*, 14 (No. 2), 41–44.

Kajiura, Kinjiro, 1963. The leading wave of a tsunami. *Bulletin of the Earthquake Research Institute*, University of Tokyo, 41 (September), 535–571.

Leendertse, J. J., 1967. Aspects of a computational model for long-period water wave propagation. RAND Corporation Memorandum RM-5294-PR. p. 53–70.

Le Méhauté, B., and Li-San Hwang, 1970. Harbor design: scale model or computer *in* Topics on Ocean Engineering. C. I. Bretschneider, editor. Houston: Gulf Publishing Company.

Madsen, O. S., and C. C. Mei, 1969. The transformation of a solitary wave over an uneven bottom. *Journal of Fluid Mechanics*, 39 (No. 4), 781–791.

Mei, C. C., 1970. Evolution of solitary and periodic long waves with dispersion. Symposium on Long Waves, University of Delaware, September 1970.

Momoi, Takao, 1964. Tsunami in the vicinity of a wave origin. *Bulletin of the Earthquake Research Institute*, University of Tokyo, 42 (No. 1), 133–146.

Pararas-Carayannis, George, 1965. Water waves, Part I *in* Source mechanism study of the Alaska earthquake and tsunami of 27 March 1964. Report HIG-65-17. Honolulu: University of Hawaii, Institute of Geophysics, December. p. 1–30.

Plafker, George, 1969. Tectonics of the March 27, 1964, Alaska earthquake. U.S. Geological Survey Professional Paper 543-I. Washington: Government Printing Office. 74 p. Also *in* The Great Alaska Earthquake of 1964: Geology. NAS Pub. 1601. Washington: National Academy of Sciences, 1971. p. 47–122.

Plafker, George, and J. C. Savage, 1970. Mechanism of the Chilean earthquakes of May 21 and 22, 1960. *Geological Society of America Bulletin*, 81 (April), 1001–1030.

Van Dorn, William G., 1963. The source motion of the tsunami of March 9, 1957, as deduced from wave measurements at Wake Island. Proceedings of the Tenth Pacific Science Congress, Honolulu, Hawaii, August–September 1961. Doak C. Cox, editor. IUGG Monograph 24. Paris: International Union of Geodesy and Geophysics. p. 39–48.

Van Dorn, William G., 1965. Tsunamis. *Advances in Hydroscience*, 2 (Annual), 1–47.

Van Dorn, William G., 1970. A model experiment on the generation of the tsunami of March 28, 1964, in Alaska *in* Tsunamis in the Pacific Ocean. Proceedings of the International Symposium on Tsunamis and Tsunami Research, Honolulu, Hawaii, October 7–10, 1969. W. M. Adams, editor. Honolulu: East-West Center Press. p. 33–45. Also *in* The Great Alaska Earthquake of 1964: Oceanography and Coastal Engineering. NAS Pub. 1605. Washington: National Academy of Sciences, 1972.

Webb, L. M., 1962. Theory of waves generated by surface and sea-bed disturbances: Appendix 1 *in* The nature of tsunamis: Their generation and dispersion in water of finite depth. Technical Report SN-37-2. Pasadena: National Engineering Science Company.

Wilson, Basil W., 1969. Earthquake occurrence and effects in ocean areas. Technical Report CR 69-027 to U.S. Naval Civil Engineering Laboratory. Port Hueneme: U.S. Naval Civil Engineering Laboratory, February. 141 p.

Wilson, Basil W., and Alf Tørum, 1968. The tsunami of the Alaskan earthquake, 1964: Engineering evaluation. Coastal Engineering Research Center Technical Memorandum No. 25. Washington: U.S. Army Corps of Engineers, May. 444 p.

ROLAND VON HUENE
U.S. GEOLOGICAL SURVEY

DOAK C. COX
UNIVERSITY OF HAWAII

Locally Generated Tsunamis and Other Local Waves

ABSTRACT: Locally generated waves devastated coastal communities during or immediately after the Alaska earthquake. These waves caused more destruction and loss of life than the major tsunami that was generated on the Continental Shelf. Mechanisms that caused local waves are somewhat obscure in spite of much research. The known or suspected mechanisms fall into two main classes: impulsive generation and resonant coupling. Impulsively generated waves are known to have occurred as the result of the displacement of water by large, rapidly moving masses of sediment that resulted from sudden failure of steep delta fronts. Two other mechanisms of impulsive generation have been suggested in cases where evidence for submarine slides has not been found: waves may have been generated (1) by tilting or (2) by a large horizontal translation of the land during the earthquake. However, these mechanisms are not well known because the critical evidence for them consists of dynamic parameters that were not measured during the earthquake. Impulsive generation was sometimes responsible not only for progressive waves but also for systems of standing waves or seiches. Seiches may also have been produced by the second class of mechanisms, a resonant coupling of the water with earthquake waves. There are suggestions that harmonics of the fundamental resonant periods of basins were contained in the train of seismic waves from the earthquake. These would produce seiches that cannot be distinguished from waves caused by impulsive generation but that are believed to be of less importance. Evidence from the area deformed by the Alaska earthquake rarely allows a distinction among the four possible mechanisms that may have caused local waves. Because the dominant modes of deformation vary in coastal areas, assessment of hazards from local waves requires first of all a greater understanding of the mechanisms involved.

INTRODUCTION

In Alaska's coastal communities, damage and casualties related to the 1964 earthquake resulted mainly from inundation by waves that were components of two types of tsunamis, which are differentiated by their mode of generation. One kind resulted from uplift of a large area of the Continental Shelf, producing trains of major, long-period waves that first struck the coast about 20 minutes after the earthquake began. The other kind consisted of trains of shorter-period waves generated locally in semiconfined waters near the shore, each set being largely restricted to a single fiord or strait.

Local waves were singularly devastating because they often struck with little warning either during or shortly after the earthquake. At many places in Alaska where there was tsunami damage, local waves were responsible for initial heavy damage and loss of life, whereas the main tsunami, which followed later, contributed little to the overall destruction. The sudden and violent local waves were often generated at the heads of fiords where deltas are commonly formed. Deltaic areas provide the most attractive sites for towns and harbors, but they also proved to be unstable during earthquakes and prone to underwater slides that caused direct damage as well as the generation of disastrous waves. The importance of understanding local waves is further underscored by the fact that local tsunamis associated with the 1964 earthquake claimed the greatest number of lives (Plafker and others, 1969, and Geology volume; Weller, this volume).

This paper summarizes published information concerning the origin, character, and effects of local tsunamis accompanying the 1964 Alaska earthquake. It is a substitute, but not a replacement, for a larger and more informative study by G. A. Rusnak, who was unable to complete his work for this volume because of illness.

Local waves resulting from the earthquake are attributed to two general types of generative mechanisms. The first type

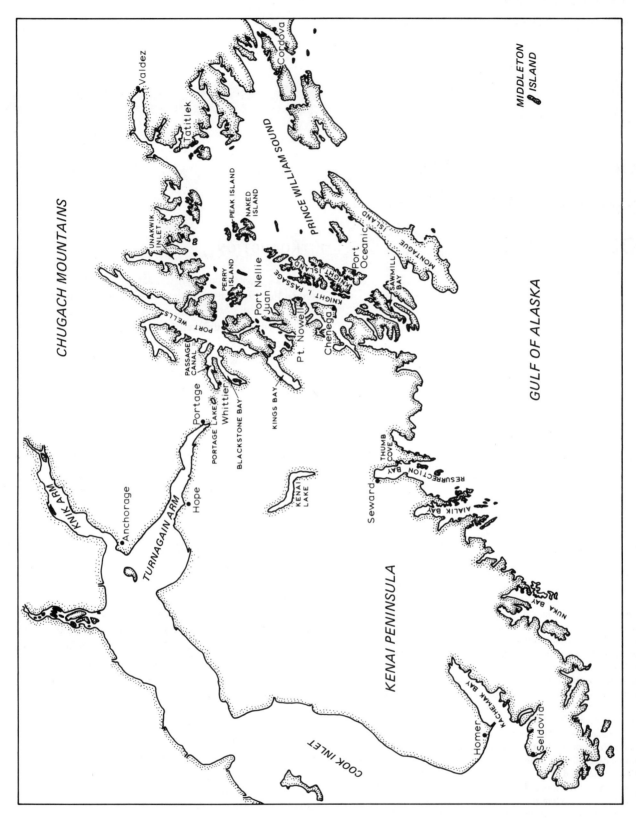

FIGURE 1 Map showing location of towns, islands, lakes, and bays where local waves or the effects of local waves were reported. Kodiak Island is not shown.

212

was impulsive generation, in which the wave energy was imparted to the water in a single impulse. The best-understood example of impulsive generation involved rapid sliding of unconsolidated sediment at or below the water line. Impulsive generation may also have resulted from sudden permanent tilting of a basin and from sudden horizontal translation of the land. Impulsively generated progressive waves or trains of waves are tsunamis (Cox, 1963; Van Dorn, 1965).

In the second type of mechanism, the energy was imparted from the sides of a basin to the water by resonant coupling over an interval probably equivalent to several water-wave periods. Such a mechanism could only be effective in a body of water with a well-defined natural period of oscillation, such as a lake or a fiord whose natural period or some harmonic of it matched some significant period of the earthquake waves. The standing waves resulting from resonant coupling are seismic seiches. At the time of the Alaska earthquake, seismic seiches were observed far beyond the limits of permanent displacement of the crust (McGarr and Vorhis, 1968, and Hydrology volume), indicating the effectiveness of the resonant coupling mechanism. In the area of permanent crustal displacement, seiches may have resulted not only from resonant coupling but also from impulsively generated waves. In many places it was difficult or impossible to distinguish between waves of impulsive origin and those due to resonant coupling.

LOCAL WAVE OBSERVATIONS

The following descriptions of local waves in the area of permanent crustal deformation, drawn from the observations of a number of authors, emphasize aspects that suggest causative mechanisms. Places referred to (excepting Kodiak Island) are shown in Figure 1.

KODIAK ISLAND

The town of Kodiak was severely damaged by the major tsunami generated on the Continental Shelf, with the first wave striking at a time variously reported as 6:20 or 6:47 p.m. and estimated by Wilson and Tørum (1968) to have been between 6:40 and 6:45 p.m. However, several witnesses, notably Jerry Tilley who was loading ice onto a shrimp boat at the city dock, reported earlier wave phenomena. He reported that at 5:35 or 5:36 p.m., "During the shaking, a huge boil of reeking black water rose from under the boat moving west and rooodod oast nearly severing our line" (Kachadoorian and Plafker, 1967, p. F22). After the earthquake, the water gradually rose 13 ft, cresting at 5:45 p.m., and then dropped 23 ft. Kachadoorian and Plafker have suggested the possibility that the boil resulted from local sliding, but they preferred to consider it a local upwelling. They considered the subsequent

wave a seiche or a surge resulting from permanent tilting or horizontal displacement of the area. Wilson and Tørum (1968, p. 146) have analyzed the events and have also suggested a relationship to tilting or horizontal displacement of the land. They explained localization of noticeable seiches in the harbor of Kodiak in terms of the shape of the harbor and its partial separation from the main bay. Berg and others (1971) agreed that the early wave must have had a local mechanism of generation, and they considered horizontal displacement of the earth's crust most probable.

COOK INLET

From persons at Homer, there were various reports of wave action during and immediately after the earthquake. Berg and others (1971) reported the observations of the wharfinger at the end of Homer Spit that an initial 4- to 5-ft withdrawal of water about 30 minutes after the earthquake was followed by three waves from 4 to 6 ft high at 5-min intervals. According to Waller (1966a, p. 3–4, and Geology volume), three persons noticed that an estimated 9-ft swell about a mile offshore came from the southwest about 5 minutes after the earthquake began. A news account of unknown origin reported that there were 10-ft waves at 2-minute intervals at about the time the shock was felt (U.S. Coast and Geodetic Survey, 1964, p. 82). The waves in these somewhat differing accounts may be explained by impulsive generation from an unknown amount of permanent horizontal crustal displacement, although Waller did not dismiss the possibility of submarine slumping despite the shallow depth here (Waller, 1966a, and Geology volume). The origin of a complex pattern of 4-ft waves, reported in Kachemak Bay (Stanley, 1965; Waller, 1966a), is largely unexplained, Wilson and Tørum (1968, p. 199), however, have noted that the earthquake motion was favorable for the development of a seiche in the bay. Waves observed at Homer and Seldovia after 7:00 p.m. were those of the major tsunami generated on the Continental Shelf (Berg and others, 1971).

In other parts of Cook Inlet no significant local tsunamis were reported. However, in the Turnagain Arm of Cook Inlet a 40-ft tide was reported at Hope shortly after the earthquake (Chance, in Wilson and Tørum, 1968). Wilson and Tørum suggested that tilting of the land caused this wave, but it was not reported by others and hence its existence is considered questionable.

KENAI AND PORTAGE LAKES

Although Kenai and Portage lakes are not arms of the ocean, observations of their behavior are among the most informative in regard to local waves. At Kenai Lake, McCulloch (1966, and Hydrology volume) found evidence for seiches as well as surges from impulsively generated waves. He differentiated two kinds of slide-generated surge waves: a "backfill wave" that fills the void caused by the slide and a "farshore wave" resulting from water pushed ahead of the slide. The seiches, recorded on a limnograph, were compared with the calculated fundamental period for Kenai Lake, as well as with shorter-period harmonics. A long-period seiche had the same period as the calculated fundamental period for Kenai Lake, but shorter-period seiches did not coincide with simple harmonics of the fundamental. Surges had maximum runup heights as great as 70 ft, and seiches generally had runup heights of 3 to 5 ft, although the maximum initial runup height was 30 ft. McCulloch attributed the seiches to permanent tilting of the lake basin, and Plafker (1969, p. 39, and Geology volume) offered an alternative explanation involving permanent horizontal translation of the region.

Arthur Kennedy of the U.S. Forest Service recorded his experiences on the ice covering Portage Lake at the time of the earthquake (Waller, 1966b, p. 5–6, and Geology volume). He reported oscillations of the ice as high as 5 ft at 2- to 5-minute intervals. Waller concluded that Kennedy "apparently experienced the direct seismic motion as an intense vibration and then felt the secondary effect as an oscillation (seiche) of the water body which continued almost 2 hours."

RESURRECTION BAY

At Seward, near the head of Resurrection Bay, a devastating local tsunami was generated by widespread failure of the delta front upon which the town is built. Lemke (1967, p. 4–5, and Geology volume) reported that, 30 to 45 seconds after shaking began, slice after slice of the delta began to slide until eventually the front of the delta had receded 50 to 500 ft. A tanker alongside the dock dropped some 20 to 30 ft, probably into the void at the head of a slide, and part of the dock collapsed onto it.

As the sea withdrew from shore, a large mound of water formed several hundred yards down the bay. A wave radiating from this mound inundated the waterfront of the town about 1½ or 2 minutes after the shaking began. After initially striking the waterfront, the wave split and ran north and south along the shore. The wave running north was estimated to be 30 ft high; upon reaching the head of the fiord, it seemed to be complicated by waves from other local submarine slides. Wilson and Tørum (1968, p. 222–227) produced photographic evidence from two independent sources which recorded the north and south components of the initial wave.

A number of other waves, causing additional damage, subsequently washed into the town during the next hour. The various accounts of witnesses differ considerably as to the number and times of these later waves (Brown, 1964; Grantz and others, 1964; Van Dorn, 1965; Lemke, 1967; Wilson and Tørum, 1968; Berg and others, 1971). Wilson and Tørum

(1968, p. 216) have reconstructed from several reports a marigram with six wave arrivals during the hour after the initial local tsunamis, but the greatest number of waves reported by any single observer was four.

At Thumb Cove, about 8 mi from the head of Resurrection Bay, observers reported the development of another large slide and ensuing waves (Chance, in Wilson and Tørum, 1968). At the head of the cove this wave had a runup of 30 ft, and it may have been responsible for the runup in excess of 40 ft in Resurrection Bay opposite the cove (Plafker and others, 1969).

Unquestionably, the submarine slide of unconsolidated delta sediments was largely responsible for the early waves observed in Resurrection Bay. A high degree of certainty is warranted by the vivid description of delta-front collapse, the sudden lowering of the sea at the head of the slide, the rise of a mound of debris-laden water in the bay presumably at the toe of the slide, and the radiation of a wave from the water mound. The second wave at Seward may have been generated at Thumb Cove. Other observed waves may have resulted from reflected waves or a complex system of oscillations related to the natural modes of the bay, as discussed by Wilson and Tørum (1968, p. 226–227). Horizontal displacement and tilting may have contributed significantly to the waves observed.

AIALIK BAY

In Aialik Bay, wave runups as great as 100 ft were observed on both sides of the bayhead (Rusnak, personal communication; Plafker and others, 1969). The wave forces were sufficient to break off spruce trees 18 in. in diameter. The locations of the observed runup were such as to indicate wave action transverse to the fiord, generated presumably by submarine slides, and not effects of the major tsunami entering from the Gulf.

KNIGHT ISLAND PASSAGE AND CONNECTING BAYS AND PASSAGES

Local waves occurred in various places along the complex system of waterways east and south of Knight Island. The distribution of waves as determined by runup, debris distribution, destruction of vegetation, and erosion or deposition has been mapped by Plafker and others (1969). Eyewitnesses observed the waves at three locations. At Chenega a wave rose gently up the beach 1 to 1½ min after the earthquake had begun. The water then withdrew rapidly, exposing a large part of the ocean floor, and returned in a 30-ft wave before or soon after the earth vibration had stopped. The runup height of the wave was measured as 54 ft above the tide level at the time of the earthquake (Berg and others, 1971). Runup similar to that in Chenega Cove occurred in three adjoining coves. No evidence for a submarine slide was found in Fathometer records near Chenega (Plafker and others, 1969). They suggested that the waves were generated by a 55-ft southerly horizontal translation of Chenega Island. Alternatively, Berg and others (1971) attributed the waves to a northerly tilt of Knight Island Passage.

At Sawmill Bay, the water rose smoothly for about 1 minute and then withdrew in a few seconds, leaving the bottom of the bay exposed. The sea then rushed back and rose to as much as 10 ft above the high-tide level. All these events occurred before shaking had stopped (Plafker and others, 1969). Smaller surges continued for about 5 hours.

A similar wave at Port Oceanic on Knight Island arrived 2 to 3 minutes after the shaking started, rising about 3 ft above high-tide level. Although the origin of this wave is uncertain, it could have been generated by a larger slide in the bay (Plafker and others, 1969).

Unobserved waves with runups and damaging effects similar to those reported in the above locations were mapped by Plafker and others (1969) on both coasts of southern Knight Island Passage, and south of Knight Island in Latouche Passage, Elrington Passage, Prince of Wales Passage, Bainbridge Passage, Whale Bay, Icy Bay, Dangerous Passage, and in a few places along northern Knight Island Passage, notably Pt. Nowell. More than one source of waves in this area is suggested by the wave directions and irregular distribution of wave damage. Completely submerged slides, horizontal translation (Plafker and others, 1969), or regional tilt (Berg and others, 1971) may have been responsible for the wave generation.

KINGS BAY AND PORT NELLIE JUAN

Large waves destroyed part of the cannery at Port Nellie Juan. Plafker and others (1969) presumed that the waves struck suddenly at the time of the earthquake because all three of the residents were missing after the earthquake. Additional evidence of the waves has come from a description of violent currents surging back and forth in Culross Passage soon after the earthquake (Chance, in Wilson and Tørum, 1968). The passage opens into Port Nellie Juan opposite the cannery. Toward the head of Port Nellie Juan and in the interconnected Kings Bay, the shores were inundated by large waves. Massive slides at the head of Kings Bay were at least partially responsible for wave runups as great as 113 ft (Mayo and McCulloch, in Plafker and others, 1969).

PASSAGE CANAL AND BLACKSTONE BAY

The only witnesses to waves in Passage Canal and Blackstone Bay were at the port of Whittier, near the head of Passage Canal. The number of waves and their sequence differ somewhat in the reports given to various investigators (Chance, in Wilson and Tørum, 1968; Berg and others, 1971; Kachadoorian, 1965, and Geology volume). The sequence of events described here is essentially that reported by Kachadoorian (1965) and modified somewhat from the accounts of others.

A glassy hump of clear water, reported by two witnesses, developed offshore during the earthquake. From it a runup no higher than high tide resulted within a minute after the earthquake began; 1 to 1½ minutes later, a large turbulent wave broke on the shore and ran up to a height of about 35 ft at the railroad depot. A recession of about 30 ft reported by one witness probably preceded this wave. The first turbulent wave was followed by another wave not quite so high. Subsequent wave runup measurements (Kachadoorian, 1965; Plafker and others, 1969) indicated a maximum runup of 43 ft in Whittier and a maximum runup of 104 ft opposite Whittier on the north shore of Passage Canal.

Postearthquake surveys indicated submarine landslides of delta sediments at the head of Passage Canal, at Whittier, and perhaps on the north side of the canal (Kachadoorian, 1965). Most investigators consider these to be the primary source of the waves.

Toward the mouth of Passage Canal there were signs of high wave runups in the form of debris-line levels and damage to vegetation. These runups were seen in the mouth of Blackstone Bay and on the adjoining south shore of Passage Canal (Plafker and others, 1969).

PORT WELLS, UNAKWIK INLET, AND NORTHWEST PRINCE WILLIAM SOUND

The water initially receded at Pigot Bay and Hobo Bay, two small bays opening into Port Wells. The recession at Hobo Bay was reported to have begun during the earthquake, and at Pigot Bay withdrawal occurred soon afterward. A similar initial withdrawal was reported by a witness on a fishing vessel in Port Wells. The water returned at Pigot and Hobo bays in a wave that rose quietly to a level 5 to 8 ft above high tide.

The initial withdrawal of water in Port Wells can be explained as resulting from the northwestward tilt of the region (Berg and others, 1971). Because its opening to Prince William Sound is constricted, Port Wells may have been drained as water flowed to fill the northwesterly interconnected fiords (College and Harriman fiords); the subsequent wave may have been a backwash of water from the fiords. Observations made from the fishing boat in Port Wells, particularly the time of recession which was estimated to have been 20 minutes after the earthquake, cannot be explained satisfactorily without knowledge of the boat's location. Possibly the boat was in the fiord area, and its occupants did not notice the initial flow but began observing at the time of the subsequent outflow.

On the south shore of Perry Island, in the north part of Prince William Sound, there was a withdrawal of the sea during the earthquake that may (Plafker and others, 1969) or may not (Berg and others, 1971) have been preceded by a wave. About 8 minutes after the earthquake, there was a large wave. Berg and others (1971) have suggested that this wave came from Knight Island Passage, but high runups elsewhere on Perry Island and adjacent islands (Plafker and others, 1969) suggest at least one wave source north of Knight Island.

At Peak Island the water was reported to have "boiled furiously" as it rose along the shore. Subsequently the water receded almost 15 ft lower than low tide; about 4 to 5 minutes after the earthquake, a wave 5 ft higher than normal moved in and struck the shore (Wilson and Tørum, 1968).

Fishermen in Unakwik Inlet reported that the water oscillated east–west during the earthquake, washing high onshore and withdrawing an unusually great distance offshore (Chance, in Wilson and Tørum, 1968). Perhaps this resulted from horizontal crustal displacement. At one of the boats the oscillation was said to have been followed by a rapid outflow of water from the bay which continued for almost 2½ hours. This report is difficult to reconcile with the observations of the regional tilt after the earthquake, because the mouth of the inlet was about 7 ft higher than the head.

At Tatitlek, a village on the east shore of Valdez Arm, the sea withdrew during the earthquake and then returned to 17 or 18 ft above mean lower low water, according to witnesses quoted by Plafker and others (1969). Witnesses interviewed by Berg and others (1971) mentioned only waves that arrived much later—from 9:00 p.m. on. The later waves probably represent crests of the main Gulf of Alaska tsunami. The earlier wave, if it existed, must have had a local source.

PORT VALDEZ

Although there were many witnesses to the waves at Valdez, their experiences were very traumatic and consequently their accounts differ in important details.

The first motions of the water, beginning during the earthquake, were especially well noted by the awesome gyrations of the Liberty ship *Chena*, which had moored at one of the two large docks (Coulter and Migliaccio, 1966, and Geology volume; Wilson and Tørum, 1968; Berg and others, 1971). The ship was violently thrown astern and ahead; it rolled and pitched and it rose and fell, bottoming several times in a sequence with details related differently by various observers. Finally the ship managed to get away from shore with the help of a wave that returned from land and struck the bow. In the meantime, the delta front failed, carrying away the dock and the people on it.

During this time, one or perhaps two waves ran up into the town. Then, 10 minutes later, another wave entered the town and reached an elevation of 20 ft above mean lower water. Witnesses differed as to whether it was higher or lower than the wave that preceded it. Additional waves arriving later had lower runups until between 11:00 and 12:00 p.m., when a wave on the rising tide reached an elevation of 20 ft or more above mean lower low water and was followed by a 23-ft-high wave at the 1:45 a.m. high tide.

Submarine sliding of nearly 100 million yd³ of delta front, including the dock area, is indicated as the cause of the first wave with measured runup in the town (Coulter and Migliaccio, 1966). However, the exact causal relation between the preceding complex waves that first hit the *Chena* and the subsequent waves is not clear. Many of the witnesses' accounts, confirmed by motion pictures taken from the *Chena*, indicate that some of the *Chena*'s tossing about occurred before the collapse of the dock and the failure of the delta front (Wilson and Tørum, 1968; Berg and others, 1971).

The main dock had just disappeared when the *Chena* was thrown into the area occupied by the dock moments earlier. Perhaps this was the first large wave which entered the town, at about the time the adjacent dock was just beginning to collapse. It is possible that the drawdown between the waves helped induce failure of the delta front.

Wilson and Tørum (1968, p. 298) have developed a possible sequence of events in which initial waves, generated by sliding of the southern delta front or by permanent horizontal regional displacement, oscillated transversely across the head of the fiord and harbor area two or three times before the major submarine slide occurred. They believe that these waves helped induce failure of the delta front. Wilson and Tørum (1968) and Berg and others (1971) have discounted the opinion of Coulter and Migliaccio (1966) that the initial large wave was reflected to strike Valdez a second time; they considered that the wave 10 minutes after the earthquake was the result of the slumping in the western end of Port Valdez. Evidence for this was described by Plafker and others (1969); it is further supported by the account from a fishing boat just outside western Port Valdez and also by debris lines and trim lines indicating maximum runups of 78 ft on the south shore of western Port Valdez and 170 ft on the north shore.

MECHANISMS OF LOCAL WAVE GENERATION

As stated in the Introduction, mechanisms of local wave generation can be classified as impulsive generation or resonant coupling. The preceding summary shows agreement among most investigators that one impulsive mechanism—that of submarine slides—is well established. Other impulsive generation mechanisms are the horizontal displacement and tilt of fiords, bays, or straits during the permanent tectonic movement associated with the earthquake. The second class of generative mechanisms presumes the possibility of resonant coupling between earthquake waves and natural periods of oscillation in bodies of water.

GENERAL CONSIDERATIONS

Three submarine slides were well documented because they occurred at towns, involved waterfront land areas, and destroyed harbor facilities. Detailed bathymetry confirmed the expectation that large volumes of material below the water were involved in the slides. The essentially simultaneous occurrence of slides and waves left little question as to the causal relationships between the submarine slides and the local tsunamis.

The gross picture of permanent horizontal displacements was determined after the earthquake by triangulation, and tilting was locally established in remarkable detail because of the intricate convolution of the Alaskan shorelines. There were, however, no direct observations of accelerations or velocities associated with either oscillatory or permanent horizontal displacements or with permanent tilts. No strong-motion seismographs to provide quantitative instrumental data were operating in Alaska. Furthermore, no marigraphic records were recovered in Alaska, and indeed at most places the only evidences of waves were the aftereffects of the inundation. Hence, where submarine sliding was not the obvious mechanism responsible for the generation of local waves, other mechanisms that are not as well established might have been involved.

Ascription to a preferred mechanism, where possible, depended heavily on eyewitness accounts, but there were many discrepancies among such accounts and among interpretations based on them. The observers were, of course, under great stress, and were generally unaware of the scientific importance of their observations—particularly as to temporal relationships. Unavoidably some biases were probably introduced in the recording of these accounts through the preconceptions of the collators, but the discrepancies persisting in the final record are assurances that the effects of such biases are not serious.

On the basis of available evidence from eyewitness accounts, interpretations of scientists, and photographic evidence, Wilson and Tørum (1968) have constructed hypothetical marigrams for several places that were inundated by local and major tsunami waves. Although the uncertainties are large and their interpretations may not always be close to reality, a consistent pattern emerges. In almost all cases where damage was severe, local sea waves were of considerable amplitude (heights of 30 to 40 ft) and of comparatively short period (generally 2 to 10 minutes). The local waves differed from the major tsunami waves, which had periods in excess of an hour. In most of Alaska, with the exception of Kodiak,

the principal damage came from the local waves that occurred during and immediately after the earthquake. In areas with direct access to the sea, local waves were followed by long-period major tsunami waves that caused extensive flooding.

SUBMARINE SLIDES

Submarine slides occurred on deltas where large quantities of poorly stratified sand, silt, and gravel were deposited. McCulloch (1966) found that at Kenai Lake local protrusions from the face of deltas were most susceptible to failure. He attributed the localization of such failures to the fact that protrusions have "the largest amount of material bounded by the shortest possible surface of rupture."

Coulter and Migliaccio (1966) and Lemke (1967) postulated essentially the same mechanism for the development of the slides at Valdez and Seward, respectively. Deltaic material was saturated with water up to a few feet below the ground surface. At low tide the pore pressure within these materials was probably increased because of the loss of buoyant force. The bedding planes, which were incipient slip planes, dipped toward the sea. Man-made structures and waterfront earth fill (particularly at Seward) were additional loads. Thus, conditions that were nearly optimum for slope failure were already in existence before the earthquake. Ground vibration caused further increase in pore pressure and decrease in shear strength so that failure occurred. At Valdez and Seward the first water motion was away from shore, further decreasing the buoyancy and shear strength and increasing the tendency to failure. As sliding began, more water was withdrawn in front of the disrupted delta face. This may have contributed to successive smaller slides observed at Seward (Lemke, 1967) and the progressive sliding inferred by McCulloch at Kenai Lake. Thus, a combination of factors preceding and during the earthquake produced slides of large proportions.

Submarine slides were most easily identified in cases where their heads included part of the waterfront, as at Seward and Valdez, but changes in bathymetry were also used to identify submarine slides that did not extend to shore.

The wave effects to be expected from a dipolar disturbance like a waterfront slide would depend upon the size of the sliding mass, as well as its speed and the distance that it moved. McCulloch (1966) has interpreted the wave runup evidence at Kenai Lake as indicating the existence of two primary waves: (1) a "backfill wave" caused by water rushing in to fill the depression left at the head of the slide and inundating especially the shore back of the slide, and (2) a "farshore wave" originating in the bulge of water over the toe of the slide and propagating across the lake to inundate especially the opposite shore. Kachadoorian (1965) explained wave observations at Whittier by essentially the same mechanisms, except that he emphasized that the wave generated over the toe of the slide spread toward the near shore as well as away from it. The observations of a wave radiating in all directions from the dome of water formed presumably over the toe of a slide at Seward conforms to the observations at Whittier.

Differences in wave character reported at the different fiords can be easily explained as a function of differences in the size of each body of water and slide sediment types as well as slide volume, rate of travel, and dispersal.

Quantitative relationships among size of sliding body, angle of slide, depth of water, and wave period and amplitude have been developed from laboratory experiments by Wiegel (1955) for simple models of slides, but no attempt seems to have been made to fit any of the Alaska observations to Wiegel's results.

HORIZONTAL TRANSLATION

Rusnak (personal communication, 1967), Wilson and Tørum (1968), and Plafker (1969) have suggested that permanent or transitory horizontal displacement of the crust at the time of the earthquake may have been rapid enough to pile water against one side of a basin and start a seiche. This is an appealing explanation for many waves that cannot be attributed to slides, especially for sudden rises of water observed during the earthquake.

Net horizontal translation of a large area in the region affected by the earthquake was measured by reoccupying a 1933 triangulation network after the earthquake (Parkin, 1969, and Seismology and Geodesy volume). With the assumption of the stability of a point north of Knik Arm at the head of Cook Inlet, the measurements indicated crustal displacements of 42 to 55 ft southward at Resurrection Bay, 23 to 25 ft southeastward at Port Valdez, 24 to 26 ft southeast near Passage Canal, and 70 ft southward at Evans Island. It is generally supposed that most, if not all, of the translation occurred during the earthquake, but there is no direct evidence of the velocity. Plafker (1969, p. 32) suggested that the bulk of the horizontal translation occurred during the period of most violent shaking, which lasted between 1½ and 5 minutes. If a period of as long as a few minutes were required for the permanent horizontal displacements, the velocities of displacement would have been too small to have been of much significance in generating waves. However, if the displacements occurred primarily within periods of 10 seconds or less, the velocities of translation would have exceeded the water-particle velocities for waves with heights of the order of 10 ft even in waters of midfiord depth and hence might well have been effective in generating waves. Plafker noted the lack of evidence of systematic horizontal shifting from fallen bodies or the sensation of those who experienced the earthquake, and so, presumably, the accelerations associated with the horizontal movement were considerably smaller than the acceleration of gravity. The horizontal shifts, how-

ever, might still have been accomplished within periods of 10 seconds or less.

It is difficult to be more definite than to suggest that horizontal translation contributed significantly to the generation of local waves at some places. There is no evidence of a correlation between measured tectonic deformation and the intensity of wave runup (Plafker, 1969; Plafker and others, 1969, Plate II). The seeming lack of correlation may be due to differences from place to place in the rate at which the permanent deformation occurred. Such differences are easily entertained in light of the evidence for complex multiple rupture along the causative fault zone (Wyss and Brune, 1967). The concentration of observed runup around the southern Knight Island Passage area is near the second in a sequence of fault ruptures producing the main earthquake as proposed by Wyss and Brune. However, the seeming lack of correlation may simply be due to the very great variety of configurations of the bottoms and shores of the fiords and sounds and the effects of interactions with local waves generated by other mechanisms. As far as is known, the horizontal translation mechanism has not been quantitatively tested by hydraulic modeling, a test that would seem very worthwhile.

REGIONAL TILTING

Several authors, including Van Dorn (1965), have used regional tilting as an explanation for local waves; Wilson and Tørum (1968) have used it to explain seiching in Prince William Sound, Berg and others (1971) to account for waves in the Knight Island Passage, and McCulloch (1966) to explain the waves in Kenai Lake. Plafker (1969) determined regional tilt in the area of uplift (outside the belt of extreme uplift on Montague Island) as averaging 1 ft per 2.1 mi with local maxima reaching 1 ft in 185 ft. Roland von Huene and others (1972, this volume) estimate a maximum local tilt of 1 ft in 515 ft near Middleton Island.

Tilts of the magnitudes mentioned would certainly be great enough to produce waves. Presumably the sharp local tilts, not reflected in Plafker's regional contours of vertical deformation, must be proposed to account for the heights and steepness of observed waves if they were generated by tilt alone. It must be acknowledged, however, that the overall behavior of an irregular semienclosed body of water, such as Prince William Sound, must have been quite complex and that waves activated by the gross regional tilt could have been amplified in some of the fiords and channels.

RESONANT COUPLING

Seismic seiches produced by resonant coupling of the water with seismic surface waves in the crust were recorded in lakes and channels across much of North America and as far away as Australia (McGarr and Vorhis, 1968, and Hydrology volume). In Alaska, within the area of deformation, seismic seiches were produced by impulsively generated waves as well as by resonant coupling. Therefore, the role of resonant coupling in the area of deformation cannot be evaluated from reports of standing waves alone. The heights (double amplitudes) of the seismic seiches outside the area of deformation were generally less than a foot. In channels along the Gulf of Mexico coastline, however, remarkable and even damaging waves were generated approximately 25 to 40 minutes after the occurrence of the earthquake in Alaska (Spaeth and Berkman, 1965). The delay corresponds to the travel time of Love and Rayleigh waves from the epicenter to the Gulf of Mexico seaboard; Donn (1964) and McGarr (1965, and Hydrology volume) have accounted for the transverse seiches in the mouth of the Old Brazos River at Freeport, Texas, by coupling with Rayleigh waves of 16-second period.

Seiching in Alaskan fiords and passages associated with the Alaska earthquake has been noted by many authors, and seiching in Kenai Lake was clearly evidenced by limnograph records (McCulloch, 1966). Coupling with long-period seismic waves in the crust has even been suggested in the past as a possible mode for tsunami generation (St.-Amand, 1961). Hence, resonant coupling merits consideration as a generating mechanism for seiches in Alaskan fiords and passages at the time of the Alaska earthquake.

A consideration of periods indicates, however, that resonant coupling cannot account satisfactorily for the local waves described by witnesses or recorded in Alaska. For resonant coupling to occur, there must be a match between the period of some seismic surface wave component and a natural period of oscillation in the body of water (not necessarily the fundamental period but some harmonic). There is remarkably little information on the periods of the seiches developed in North American lakes and channels by the Alaska earthquake, but McGarr and Vorhis (1968) indicated from energy considerations that they must have been excited by the horizontal acceleration of seismic waves in the period range from 5 to 15 seconds. Despite the fact that there would have been larger horizontal oscillations in longer-period surface waves closer to the epicenter, it still seems unlikely that such oscillations (as distinct from the permanent or transitory tectonic horizontal displacement) could have been effective in generating seiches with a period of more than a minute or two. This conclusion is based on the fact that the total duration of felt motion during the earthquake was estimated in the range of 4½ to 7 minutes, that strong motion in Anchorage was limited to 3 minutes (Steinbrugge, 1967), but that observed seiches had periods ranging from a few minutes to a few tens of minutes. The earthquake periods are therefore much shorter than the natural periods of water bodies where large destructive waves were observed. Wilson and Tørum (1968, p. 218), for example, postulated from observations at Seward a transverse seiche at the head of Resurrection

Bay with a 3.6-minute period. Spectral analysis of the seiche limnogram at Kenai Lake indicated periods ranging from 1.4 to 36.4 minutes (McCulloch, 1966).

McCulloch (1966) theorized that the Kenai seiche resulted from permanent crustal tilt, and Plafker (1969) suggested horizontal translation as an alternative explanation. The observed seiches in fiords and passages may have had similar origins in impulsive disturbances. Seiches suggested solely from effects or a sequence of events cannot be convincingly attributed to a particular mechanism. However, from considerations of energy and frequency the resonant coupling mechanism was probably only effective in generating water oscillations of less than a minute or two in period and generally only a few feet in height.

SUMMARY

The significance of understanding the generation mechanisms of local waves observed in Alaska is in knowing the hazards from waves to be expected as accompaniments of similar earthquakes, the places they are most likely to occur, and means of detection so that warnings may be issued. The wave effects in Alaska would have been much more disastrous if the earthquake had occurred during high tide or if there had been a greater population density along the shores of Prince William Sound.

Submarine sliding was the most clearly demonstrated mechanism that generated damaging local tsunamis. Many slides have probably not been recognized, and hence many waves of slide origin may not have been identified. Slide-generated local waves were particularly devastating along the waterfronts at the heads of slides and on opposite facing shores. The wave runup on shores adjacent to the area of generation was generally smaller. The understanding of the slide-generation mechanism is sufficient to permit an estimate of the hazard from slide-generated waves elsewhere if the regional seismicity, the stability of deltaic deposits, and the general hydrodynamics of local basins are known. The magnitude of slide-generated waves would, expectably, be less in other kinds of water bodies than the fiords of Alaska, because steep and unstable deltas in deep waters are generally restricted to glaciated coastal terrains. However, some local wave damage might occur wherever there are deltas or other unstable rock masses.

The importance of the other generating mechanisms is more difficult to evaluate. Generation of local tsunamis by tilting and by horizontal translation were invoked by most authors when the slide mechanism seemed inadequate. Tilt-generated waves could be expected in areas where vertical tectonic displacement occurs, just as waves generated by horizontal translation might form wherever horizontal tectonic displacement occurs. Waves generated by horizontal displacement in Alaska may have been at least 10 ft high and possibly 30 to 40 ft high. Therefore, any moderately deep harbor or bay along the California coast, where large strike-slip faulting occurs, might be subject to destructive local waves during a strong earthquake.

The amplitude of waves caused by a resonant coupling between seismic oscillations and a body of water has not been quantitatively established in the area of tectonic deformation. Outside the area of deformation, such waves occasionally had amplitudes of slightly more than 1 ft. In the area of deformation, however, resonant coupling may have produced higher waves and may have enhanced local waves from other causes. Therefore, this mechanism warrants consideration and should be further evaluated. Critical to such an evaluation would be a power spectral-density analysis of the full range of seismic waves from a large earthquake.

It is practically impossible to issue warnings of local waves because they occur during or shortly after an earthquake. Under such circumstances, the hazard to life can best be reduced by first assessing the possibility of local wave generation at individual coastal towns and then conducting a program of local education. Many lives would have been saved in Alaska if people had immediately evacuated waterfront areas at the onset of the earthquake.

There is still much to be learned about local waves from further studies of Valdez, Whittier, Seward, Chenega, and the Knight Island Passage areas. Evaluation of the local tsunami hazards in a coastal area requires a multidisciplinary effort including seismology, marine geology and geophysics, and hydrodynamics and coastal engineering.

ACKNOWLEDGMENTS

The authors appreciate the extensive insightful suggestions of Dr. Basil Wilson and are grateful to Dr. David McCulloch for many comments and stimulating discussions.

REFERENCES

Berg, Eduard, Doak C. Cox, Augustine S. Furumoto, Kinjiro Kajiura, Hirosi Kawasumi, and Etsuzo Shima, 1971. Field survey of the tsunamis of 28 March 1964 in Alaska, and conclusions as to the origin of the major tsunami. Report HIG-70-2. Honolulu: University of Hawaii, Institute of Geophysics. 57 p.

Brown, Delmer, L., 1964. Tsunamic activity accompanying the Alaskan earthquake of 27 March 1964. Technical Report, U.S. Army Engineer District, Alaska. Anchorage: U.S. Corps of Engineers, April 23. 31 p.

Coulter, Henry W., and Ralph R. Migliaccio, 1966. Effects of the earthquake of March 27, 1964, at Valdez, Alaska. U.S. Geological Survey Professional Paper 542-C. Washington: Government Printing Office. 36 p. Also in The Great Alaska Earthquake of 1964: Geology. NAS Pub. 1601. Washington: National Academy of Sciences, 1971. p. 359-394.

Cox, Doak C., 1963. Status of tsunami knowledge. Proceedings of the Tenth Pacific Science Congress, Honolulu, Hawaii, August-September 1961. Doak C. Cox, editor. IUGG Monograph 24. Paris: International Union of Geodesy and Geophysics. p. 1-6.

Donn, William L., 1964. Alaskan earthquake of 27 March 1964: remote seiche stimulation. Science, 145 (July 17), 261-262.

Grantz, Arthur, George Plafker, and Reuben Kachadoorian, 1964. Alaska's Good Friday earthquake, March 27, 1964: a preliminary geologic evaluation. U.S. Geological Survey Circular 491. Washington: U.S. Geological Survey. 35 p.

Kachadoorian, Reuben, 1965. Effects of the earthquake of March 27, 1964, at Whittier, Alaska. U.S. Geological Survey Professional Paper 542-B. Washington: Government Printing Office. 21 p. Also in The Great Alaska Earthquake of 1964: Geology. NAS Pub. 1601. Washington: National Academy of Sciences, 1971. p. 439-459.

Kachadoorian, Reuben, and George Plafker, 1967. Effects of the earthquake of March 27, 1964 on the communities of Kodiak and nearby islands. U.S. Geological Survey Professional Paper 542-F. Washington: Government Printing Office. 41 p. Abstract in The Great Alaska Earthquake of 1964: Geology. NAS Pub. 1601. Washington: National Academy of Sciences, 1971. p. 539-540.

Lemke, Richard W., 1967. Effects of the earthquake of March 27, 1964, at Seward, Alaska. U.S. Geological Survey Professional Paper 542-E. Washington: Government Printing Office. 43 p. Also in The Great Alaska Earthquake of 1964: Geology. NAS Pub. 1601. Washington: National Academy of Sciences, 1971. p. 395-437.

McCulloch, David S., 1966. Slide-induced waves, seiching, and ground fracturing caused by the earthquake of March 27, 1964, at Kenai Lake, Alaska. U.S. Geological Survey Professional Paper 543-A. Washington: Government Printing Office. 41 p. Also in The Great Alaska Earthquake of 1964: Hydrology. NAS Pub. 1603. Washington: National Academy of Sciences, 1968. p. 47-81.

McGarr, Arthur, 1965. Excitation of seiches in channels by seismic waves. Journal of Geophysical Research, 70 (February 15), 847-854. Also in The Great Alaska Earthquake of 1964: Hydrology. NAS Pub. 1603. Washington: National Academy of Sciences, 1968. p. 133-139.

McGarr, Arthur, and Robert C. Vorhis, 1968. Seismic seiches from the March 1964 Alaska earthquake. U.S. Geological Survey Professional Paper 544-E. Washington: Government Printing Office. 43 p. Also in The Great Alaska Earthquake of 1964: Hydrology. NAS Pub. 1603. Washington: National Academy of Sciences, 1968. p. 196-236.

Parkin, Ernest J., 1969. Horizontal crustal movements determined from surveys after the Alaskan earthquake of 1964 in Volume III: The Prince William Sound, Alaska, earthquake of 1964 and aftershocks. Environmental Science Services Administration, U.S. Coast and Geodetic Survey. Washington: Government Printing Office. p. 35-98. Also in The Great Alaska Earthquake of 1964: Seismology and Geodesy. NAS Pub. 1602. Washington: National Academy of Sciences, 1972.

Plafker, George, 1969. Tectonics of the March 27, 1964, Alaska earthquake. U.S. Geological Survey Professional Paper 543-I. Washington: Government Printing Office. 74 p. Also in The Great Alaska Earthquake of 1964: Geology. NAS Pub. 1601. Washington: National Academy of Sciences, 1971. p. 47-122.

Plafker, George, Reuben Kachadoorian, Edwin B. Eckel, and Lawrence R. Mayo, 1969. Effects of the earthquake of March 27, 1964, on various communities. U.S. Geological Survey Professional Paper 542-G. Washington: Government Printing Office. 50 p. Also in The Great Alaska Earthquake of 1964: Geology. NAS Pub. 1601. Washington: National Academy of Sciences, 1971. p. 489-538.

St.-Amand, Pierre, 1961. Los terremotos de Mayo—Chile 1960—an eyewitness account of the greatest catastrophe in recent history.

Technical Article 14. China Lake, California: U.S. Naval Ordnance Test Station, Michelson Laboratory. 39 p.

Spaeth, M. G., and S. C. Berkman, 1965. The tsunami of March 28, 1964, as recorded at tide stations. U.S. Coast and Geodetic Survey Publication. Rockville, Maryland: U.S. Coast and Geodetic Survey. 59 p.

Stanley, Kirk W., 1965. Effects of post-earthquake conditions on the Homer Spit, Alaska (Abstract) *in* Science in Alaska, 1964: Proceedings Fifteenth Alaskan Science Conference, College, Alaska, August 31 to September 4, 1964. George Dahlgren, editor. College: Alaska Division American Association for the Advancement of Science, March. p. 89–90.

Steinbrugge, Karl V., 1967. Introduction to the earthquake engineering of the 1964 Prince William Sound, Alaska, earthquake *in* Volume II-A: The Prince William Sound, Alaska, earthquake of 1964 and aftershocks. Environmental Science Services Administration, U.S. Coast and Geodetic Survey. Washington: Government Printing Office. p. 1–6.

U.S. Coast and Geodetic Survey, 1964. Preliminary report—Prince William Sound, Alaskan earthquakes March–April 1964 (second printing). Seismology Division Report. Washington: U.S. Coast and Geodetic Survey. 101 p.

Van Dorn, William G., 1965. Tsunamis. *Advances in Hydroscience*, 2 (Annual), 1–47.

von Huene, Roland, George G. Shor, Jr., and Richard J. Malloy, 1972. Offshore tectonic features in the affected region *in* The Great Alaska Earthquake of 1964: Oceanography and Coastal Engineering. NAS Pub. 1605. Washington: National Academy of Sciences.

Waller, Roger M., 1966a. Effects of the earthquake of March 27, 1964, in the Homer area, Alaska (*with a section on* Beach changes on Homer Spit by Kirk W. Stanley). U.S. Geological Survey Professional Paper 542-D. Washington: Government Printing Office. 28 p. Also *in* The Great Alaska Earthquake of 1964: Geology. NAS Pub. 1601. Washington: National Academy of Sciences, 1971. p. 461–488.

Waller, Roger M., 1966b. Effects of the March 1964 Alaska earthquake on the hydrology of south-central Alaska. U.S. Geological Survey Professional Paper 544-A. Washington: Government Printing Office. 28 p. Also *in* The Great Alaska Earthquake of 1964: Hydrology. NAS Pub. 1603. Washington: National Academy of Sciences, 1968. p. 12–39.

Weller, Jack M., 1972. Human response to tsunami warnings *in* The Great Alaska Earthquake of 1964: Oceanography and Coastal Engineering. NAS Pub. 1605. Washington: National Academy of Sciences.

Wiegel, R. L., 1955. Laboratory studies of gravity waves generated by the movement of a submerged body. *Transactions, American Geophysical Union,* 36 (October), 759–774.

Wilson, Basil W., and Alf Tørum, 1968. The tsunami of the Alaskan earthquake, 1964: Engineering evaluation. Coastal Engineering Research Center Technical Memorandum No. 25. Washington: U.S. Army Corps of Engineers, May. 444 p.

Wyss, Max, and James N. Brune, 1967. The Alaska earthquake of 28 March 1964: A complex multiple rupture. *Bulletin of the Seismological Society of America,* 57 (October) 1017–1023. Also *in* The Great Alaska Earthquake of 1964: Seismology and Geodesy. NAS Pub. 1602. Washington: National Academy of Sciences, 1972.

JACK M. WELLER*
THE OHIO STATE UNIVERSITY

Human Response to Tsunami Warnings

INTRODUCTION

This brief summary of the warnings of tsunamis associated with the 1964 Alaska earthquake and of human responses to these warnings is not intended to be comprehensive or particularly detailed. Its focus is on the general description of the range of warnings and of responses among the several communities in Alaska and elsewhere which were struck by the tsunamis or warned of possible tsunami effects. Greater detail may be found in the Human Ecology volume of this series; in that volume Norton and Haas (1970) discussed the warnings and responses in various Alaskan communities, and Anderson (1970) compared the warnings and responses at Crescent City, California, and Hilo, Hawaii.

WARNINGS AND RESPONSES IN ALASKA

The earthquake struck at 03:36, March 28, 1964, Greenwich Mean Time (GMT) (5:36 p.m. March 27, Alaska Standard Time). For some Alaskan communities where local subaqueous slides generated tsunamis in the immediate vicinity, the earthquake was the only possible warning of the coming waves. For others, more remote from tsunami origin areas, there was a little more time. In no case did an Alaskan community have sufficient time before initial impact to profit from Seismic Sea Wave Warning System (SSWWS) messages. The Honolulu Observatory completed its preliminary location of the epicenter at 04:52 GMT and issued its first advisory message of a possible tsunami at 05:02 GMT (Spaeth and Berkman, 1967, and this volume). Before then, all the damage caused by the tsunamis generated locally in Alaskan fiords and straits had already occurred, and at least the initial waves of the major tsunami generated in the Gulf of Alaska had struck all the Alaskan communities that it was to affect (Wilson and Tørum, 1968; Berg and others, 1971).

For many Alaskans, there was no warning. For others, experience with the sea provided visual cues sufficient to make

ABSTRACT: The Seismic Sea Wave Warning System (SSWWS) issued a first advisory message (indicating the possibility of a tsunami) not quite 1½ hours after the Alaska earthquake and a formal tsunami warning just over 3 hours after the earthquake.

By the time the initial advisory message was issued, all affected Alaskan communities had already been struck by the locally generated tsunamis or the initial waves of the major tsunami. Unofficial warnings saved some lives, but more could have been saved if the earthquake itself or the initial waves had been perceived as warnings. However, at some places the waves arrived too soon for any warning to have been effective.

At affected communities outside of Alaska, SSWWS warnings were received early enough to have induced appropriate response (except in Canada which was not part of the system). The responses varied greatly, however, from community to community, depending on the experience and understanding of system officials and of the public.

Fatalities from the tsunamis totaled 103 in Alaska and 16 elsewhere.

---

*Now with Connecticut College, New London.

escape possible. In several cases the nature of the first wave action was mild enough to provide warning of subsequent, more powerful action. Rarely did communications technology provide warning either through mass media or private broadcasts. For the most part, public officials and public organizations, which were intermediate agents in the warning process at points farther from the epicenter, did not have sufficient time to assist in evacuation and other precautionary actions.

At Valdez, a town of 1,200, 45 mi east of the epicenter of the earthquake and at the head of Valdez Arm, which opens on Prince William Sound, there was no possibility of warning. Before the earthquake there were 28 people on the dock watching or participating in the unloading of the coastal freighter *Chena*. As the earthquake reached its highest intensity, a huge land mass slid from the face of the delta on which Valdez was situated, carrying away the dock area and generating severe destructive water action in the harbor. All 28 persons on the dock perished. Four other deaths occurred in the vicinity of Valdez. Of the 32, apparently only one, a resident who left Valdez by small boat after the initial wave, could have been saved. (One Valdez resident drowned near Port Ashton and is not considered in the above totals.)

Similarly, at Chenega, a native village of 76 residents on Chenega Island in Prince William Sound, there was hardly any opportunity to escape a massive wave that arrived no more than 10 minutes after the onset of the earthquake. There was a slight recession of sea level before the wave, but it was followed so quickly by an inward flood that few could react to the warning. Caught in their homes or along the beach, 23 Chenegans were killed.

About 40 mi southwest of the epicenter of the earthquake on a long narrow bay off Prince William Sound was the rail and harbor installation of Whittier. At the time of the disaster, there were only 70 people in the once-larger, Army-built installation. At Whittier three tsunami waves struck within minutes after the earthquake. The first was low and not particularly destructive, but the second and third that immediately followed were 30 to 40 ft high, according to local witnesses. No warning was possible. Thirteen residents among those closest to the waterfront were killed, all but one as a result of the waves.

The city of Seward with a population of about 2,300 was another community that was hit almost without warning. A rail and harbor facility located on the southeastern coast of the Kenai Peninsula at the head of Resurrection Bay, Seward suffered immediate damage as the earthquake caused the collapse of a fuel storage complex on the waterfront, leading to explosions and fire. As the shock ended, sections of the waterfront and dock facilities slid into the bay. These and other local slides set the water in the bay into a circular motion, culminating in a wave which struck the already damaged waterfront of the town, causing some additional damage but

no reported loss of life. The townspeople for the most part took warning and left low areas, but after another 20 minutes a second wave estimated at 30 to 40 ft in height swept into the city. Eleven of the 12 people who lost their lives in Seward were swept away by this wave (the other death was not attributed to wave action). Tsunami action continued for about 5 hours, but security measures taken by local officials prevented return of the townspeople to the lower, dangerous areas of the city.

On the southeastern shore of Kodiak Island at the head of small Kaguyak Bay, the 45 people of the native village of Kaguyak were more furtunate. One member of the community foresaw the possibility of a tsunami resulting from the earthquake. While there was no immediate attempt to evacuate to higher ground, he did communicate his fears to a few others. Soon he sighted a seismic swell approaching the village. Warnings were shouted as others became aware of the danger. The height and force of the first wave were not sufficient to reach even those who were slowest to respond. At intervals of about 50 minutes there was subsequent wave action of similar mild effect. Warned, but lulled, by the low power of the waves, some people began moving to their boats, homes, and other low-lying areas. The fourth wave, however, was more powerful. It was estimated to have been between 30 to 50 ft high and caught many who had left high ground, killing three, while others narrowly escaped.

A few miles northeast of Kaguyak along the shore of Kodiak Island, the 200 residents of Old Harbor had more complete warning. After the earthquake, a few of the villagers told others to anticipate "tidal" waves. Additionally, two warning messages were received over shortwave radio from Kaguyak and a nearby cannery, both of which were hit before Old Harbor. Shortly after the radio messages, the first wave action occurred, being more similar to a swift, high tide than a wave. It caused little damage and no injury. The second wave was stronger, but still weak enough to serve more as warning than threat. After this wave, the last of the people left for higher ground. The village, finally emptied after several "warnings," was nearly destroyed by the third [8:00 p.m. Alaska Standard Time (AST)] and fourth (10:00 p.m. AST) waves. No one in the village was killed, although one person on Sitkalidak Island across a narrow strait was drowned (Kachadoorian and Plafker, 1967).

North of Kodiak Island on small Spruce Island is Ouzinkie, another native village of about 200. Shortly after the earthquake, Ouzinkie's inhabitants noticed the water offshore begin to act strangely, and within half an hour a cycle of surging waves and ebbs began. No deaths occurred in the village despite the eventual destruction of several homes and the local cannery. The highest crests were not experienced until 11:00 p.m. AST; thus, the action of the water served as sufficient warning, the natives having long since evacuated the village for higher ground.

Afognak, a village of some 180 natives, was located on Afognak Island, another larger island north of Kodiak Island. There, as in most native villages, damage from the earthquake was slight, and, after the shaking stopped, the people went about their planned activities for the evening. A few soon noticed a great recession of the water in the bay before the village. Additionally, radio reports of "tidal" waves at nearby points were received and, while there was no organized or systematic warning, many began to evacuate the village. Within a half hour of the earthquake, a low wave hit the beach and came into the village. Only a few of the slowest to leave were caught by the wave, and all escaped safely. Subsequent wave action was stronger, but the people were safe, since, for the most part, they remained on high ground until the next morning.

The 4,200 people who lived in the area in and around Kodiak on the northeastern coast of Kodiak Island received a variety of warnings. However, there is wide disagreement over the relative utility of the particular warning cues in persuading the inhabitants to take precautionary action. For some minutes after the earthquake, people were occupied partly by contending with the moderate earthquake damage and partly with returning to routine activities of the day. The city telephones were out of order, as was electrical power. Events related to warning are somewhat confused and therefore cannot be given in strict chronological order. Between the time of the earthquake and the arrival of the first tsunami, however, several warning events took place.

Evidence shows that some Kodiak residents, including some city officials, were aware of the potential tsunami-generating power of the earthquake. However, no warning action was taken solely on this basis. Kodiak's mayor, city manager, and police chief met shortly after the earthquake to discuss the possibility of issuing a warning, but no action was taken until radioed warnings were received.

At approximately 6:10 AST (04:10 GMT), an Air Force installation at Cape Chiniak, about 20 mi southeast along the shore of Kodiak Island, experienced a tsunami. This information was radioed by shortwave and was received by Fleet Weather Central on Kodiak Naval Station and by an undetermined number of shortwave sets in Kodiak City, including one at police headquarters. The officer at Fleet Weather Central telephoned the Armed Forces radio station on the base, which in turn broadcast the warnings. An orderly and successful evacuation of the naval base followed (Spaeth and Berkman, 1967, and this volume). Because electrical power was off in Kodiak City, receipt of the warning was limited to those with auxiliary or battery-powered radio sets.

In addition to the direct reception of warning from Cape Chiniak and Armed Forces radio, Kodiak residents were warned by the sound of fire sirens. Upon receiving the warning from Cape Chiniak, city officials at police headquarters sounded the sirens even though no prearranged tsunami warning procedure was in effect. People generally responded by going to the streets to see why the sirens were being sounded. A police cruiser and a Shore Patrol truck (manned by a civilian) went into the lower areas of the city to spread the tsunami warning orally.

Response to these warnings was not uniform. In many cases, people were slow to leave dangerous areas, and, when the first wave reached Kodiak, many were caught. Fortunately, the water action was not violent, and all were able to wade from the rising water.

Even after the first wave, with the various radio sources and public agencies continuing to warn of subsequent waves, many remained in dangerously low areas. Fishermen, particularly, remained in danger as they went to the harbor in an attempt to save their boats. Although several rode out all the waves in their boats, more than half of the 15 deaths in and near Kodiak occurred among those on boats in the harbor or at nearby Spruce Cape.

In addition to the fatalities in Alaskan communities already noted, there were five other deaths attributable to tsunamis in Prince William Sound and its connecting fiords, one at Crab Bay near Port Ashton on Evans Island, one at Point Nowell on Knight Island Passage, and three at Port Nellie Juan in McClure Bay, as well as two deaths on the coast of the Gulf of Alaska, one at Cape St. Elias on Kayak Island, and one at Point Whitshed west of Cordova. It is improbable that the majority of these people received any warning.

WARNINGS AND RESPONSES OUTSIDE ALASKA

For communities along coasts of the Pacific other than Alaska, greater distance from the area of generation of the tsunamis allowed time for adequate warning to threatened populations. However, the variation in warnings and responses to tsunami threats indicates that preservation of life is not predicated solely on the availability of time and the issuing of SSWWS warnings.

The first bulletin of the SSWWS (issued at 05:02 GMT) that indicated the possibility of tsunamis was followed by a second (at 05:30 GMT) that reiterated the possibility and gave estimated arrival times for each locale, and by a third (at 06:37 GMT) that reported that a tsunami had been generated and repeated estimated arrival times (Spaeth and Berkman, 1967, and this volume). These messages were transmitted to states and participating nations bordering the Pacific. Although the warnings received were identical for all participants, there were wide variations in the responses they elicited.

Canada was no longer a participating member of the Seismic Sea Wave Warning System (Spaeth and Berkman, 1967, and this volume), but approximately 25,000 people of the twin cities of Alberni and Port Alberni on Vancouver Island, British Columbia, had mass media reports that tsunamis generated by the Alaska earthquake might strike the Canadian coast (Office of Provincial Civil Defense Coordinator [1964], p. 7). The twin cities are located 40 mi from the open sea at the head of narrow Alberni Inlet. Thus, normal danger from tsunami action on the open ocean might seem negligible, but the tsunami's period "apparently matched the natural frequency of the inlet, causing amplification of the waves" (Spaeth and Berkman, 1967, p. 39; Wilson and Tørum, 1968, p. 91-92). Accordingly, Alberni and Port Alberni were unprepared for the series of tsunamis commencing at approximately 08:00 GMT (12:00 p.m. local time) (Spaeth and Berkman, 1967, p. 39). Soon after the first crest, the Royal Canadian Mounted Police (RCMP), a local volunteer rescue squad, and a number of citizens were at the scene of the impact. There was no certain knowledge that further crests were expected, but those at the scene were aware of this possibility. At the request of the RCMP, the rescue squad and others went from house to house, waking people and warning them to be ready for further emergency. Ninety-seven minutes after the first crest, a second, the largest to hit the Albernis, struck. Tsunami activity recurred for approximately 18 hours. Although damage amounted to millions of dollars, none were killed and few were injured. The initial crest coupled with rapid local response was sufficient warning (Office of Provincial Civil Defense Coordinator [1964], p. 7).

The third tsunami bulletin released by Honolulu Observatory at 06:37 GMT was received by the Washington State Department of Civil Defense at about 07:13 GMT and by the Oregon State Civil Defense at 07:00 GMT. Both immediately disseminated warning for the first time to all their coastal counties (Spaeth and Berkman, 1967, p. 40-43). The response of local officials in these states prior to the passage of the tsunami front between 07:15 and 08:00 GMT is unknown. Tsunami damage was comparatively light in both Washington and Oregon. No reports indicate that local warning took place where tsunamis did occur. Spaeth and Berkman (1967) state: "By 07:18 all coastal counties (Washington) had been advised that the tsunami warning had been received."

In Grays Harbor County at resort areas west of Aberdeen, Washington, tsunamis flooded a trailer court area, some permanent residences, and a shopping center. Several people who had retired for the night awakened to find themselves surrounded by water. The only warning before the wave reported by newspaper accounts was received over shortwave radio on the marine band. A man who heard the marine-band radio broadcast telephoned a local fire department that, in turn, sounded its sirens. Apparently, the sirens sounded almost concurrently with the arrival of the wave, alerting those not already aware of the cresting water (*The Seattle Sunday Times*, March 29, 1964, vol. 87, no. 89, sec. A, p. 14, col. 1).

In Oregon, wave crests of 10 to 15 ft were reported in several places, but no details are available on local warning (Spaeth and Berkman, 1967, p. 41). Four children who were sleeping with their parents in a state park near Depoe Bay, Oregon, were killed when struck by a tsunami without warning (*The Seattle Sunday Times*, March 29, 1964, sec. A, p. 2, col. 3). No other deaths were reported, but at Seaside, Oregon, low areas were flooded, damaging 10 to 12 houses and 4 trailers (Spaeth and Berkman, 1967, Figure 7).

The California Disaster Office (CDO) in Sacramento received its first tsunami advisory information via the National Warning System (NAWAS) from the 28th Warning Center, Hamilton AFB, at 05:36 GMT, March 28 [local time was 9:36 p.m. Pacific Standard Time (PST), March 27]. The CDO received the second bulletin at 06:44 GMT (10:44 p.m. PST) and the third at 07:13 GMT (11:13 p.m. PST) from the same source. Presumably because of the tentative nature of the first dispatch, CDO did not disseminate the information to areas in California vulnerable to tsunamis. However, the second and third messages were transmitted via the State Department of Justice (DOJ) Teletype System as an "All Points Bulletin" to all sheriffs, chiefs of police, and Civil Defense directors of coastal counties and cities. They were transmitted by DOJ Teletype at 07:03 GMT (11:03 p.m. PST) and 07:25 GMT (11:25 p.m. PST), respectively. The second and third messages, those communicated to the localities, contained the Honolulu Observatory's estimates of arrival times for various points along the California coast (California Disaster Office [1964], p. 1). The two "All Points Bulletins" transmitted for CDO via DOJ Teletype were received by local officials of the several coastal political subdivisions simultaneously at 07:08 GMT (11:08 p.m. PST) and 07:50 GMT (11:50 p.m. PST). Additionally, Los Angeles and San Diego counties received the second transmission sent by the 28th Warning Center directly via NAWAS at 07:25 GMT (11:25 p.m. PST).

The bulk of California's tsunami damage, as well as nearly all its deaths, occurred in Crescent City. There, local Civil Defense officials and the Del Norte County sheriff were notified and arrived at the sheriff's office by 11:20 p.m. PST. Although the first message estimated the time of arrival for Crescent City as 12:00 p.m. PST, no action was taken to notify the public until the second formal warning arrived at 11:50 p.m. PST. Then sheriff's deputies and local police were sent into waterfront areas to warn residents. Before they had completed their door-to-door alert, the first crest reached Crescent City on schedule at about 12:00 p.m. PST. Fortunately, it was a mild surge causing little damage. Subsequently, two other mild crests were experienced at 12:40 a.m. and 1:20 a.m. PST. In the meantime the door-to-door warning was completed and, using fire-department personnel, policemen, specially deputized volunteers, and his deputies, the sheriff set up a cordon to guard damaged areas. This was successful in keeping away the people from outside the water-front area, but, because of the mild action of the water, some residents, businessmen, and tourists returned to lower areas (Yutzy, 1964).

At about 1:45 a.m. PST, the fourth wave hit Crescent City. It was by far the most destructive, catching many of those who had returned to the waterfront area. Twelve verified deaths and 35 injuries or illnesses, for which 14 people were hospitalized, were attributed to the disaster (California Disaster Office [1964], p. 3).

The measured response of public officials to the tsunami warnings that they received was reportedly based on (1) the fact that warnings indicated that tsunamis were only probable, (2) the lack of information about how large a wave was to be expected, and (3) information that coastal areas to the north with earlier estimated arrival times had not experienced tsunamis (Yutzy, 1964, p. 5-6). That these considerations had little predictive value for determining whether destructive waves would occur in Crescent City was apparently not known by public officials responsible for deciding the nature and extent of local warning. Further, local residents assumed that this tsunami danger would be comparable to past experiences in alerts where Crescent City received only mild surges. Thus, loss of life in Crescent City can be attributed in part to public and private actions based on inadequate knowledge of tsunamis.

In California, local decisions were crucial in determining response to SSWWS warnings. Despite the fact they received the same warning, local officials responded quite differently in various coastal areas. For instance, officials in Humboldt County reacted immediately to the first message received at 11:08 p.m. PST. Fire and police personnel in various municipalities and county government personnel were notified and responded according to their "standard operating procedures for tidal wave alerts" (California Disaster Office [1964], p. 3). By 11:40 p.m., evacuation of beaches and homes in low-lying areas had been completed and road blocks to the areas were established. No tsunami action was reported. Elsewhere, responses ranged from partial evacuation similar to that in Crescent City to almost no response. Public response also varied. Some counties reported no difficulty in gaining public cooperation with precautionary measures, but in San Diego curious citizens created problems as they came to observe the sea (California Disaster Office [1964], p. 6). In San Francisco where no deaths and slight damage occurred, a reported 2,500 persons were evacuated from low areas (*The Seattle Sunday Times*, March 29, 1964, sec. A, p. 2, col. 7). However, efforts to protect the population were thwarted by an estimated 10,000 curious inhabitants who went into dangerous areas in hopes of seeing a tsunami (Spaeth and Berkman, 1967, citing newspaper estimates).

Hawaii, unlike the states on the western coast of the continental United States, is supplied with tsunami warnings

directly from Honolulu Observatory. Shortly after 04:00 GMT, the Observatory notified the Acting Tsunami Advisor of the State of Hawaii and the Vice Director of the Hawaii State Civil Defense about the earthquake. These officials in turn notified other members of their organizations, including the Civil Defense officials of all Hawaiian counties; within half an hour the state Emergency Operations Center was activated. At 06:43, following receipt of the third tsunami bulletin (the formal warning), personnel at the Emergency Operations Center decided to sound all coastal sirens and activate the state's Civ-Alert Radio Broadcast system: accordingly, this was done at 07:00 GMT in all counties. Again at 08:00 and 08:30 GMT, the sirens were sounded. The earliest recorded crest reached the islands at 08:33 (Spaeth and Berkman, 1967). Fixed siren signals were supplemented by police-car sirens. Also, the police supervised the evacuation and prevented return to dangerous areas. The public cooperated with the efforts of agencies responsible for the evacuation. All communities on the Hawaiian coast were reported to have been evacuated by 8:28 GMT (Hawaii State Civil Defense Division, through D. C. Cox, personal cummunication). Although there was only slight damage from the generally mild tsunamis that struck the Hawaiian shore, the response of both the officials and the public would have prevented loss of life in even a greater disaster (Anderson, Human Ecology volume, p. 116).

Elsewhere on the perimeter of the Pacific, other participating members of the SSWWS responded to warnings. At Vera Cruz, Mexico, warning reportedly led to the evacuation of parts of the city at 3:00 a.m. local time. At Mazatlán, Mexico, 80,000 were reported evacuated (*The Seattle Sunday Times*, March 29, 1964, sec. A, p. 2, col. 6). Low areas on the Chilean coast were evacuated prior to the arrival of weak tsunamis (Spaeth and Berkman, 1967, p. 49). The eastern shores of the Philippine Islands were evacuated, but only small, undestructive waves were experienced (*The Seattle Sunday Times*, March 29, 1964, sec. A, p. 2, col. 7). Likewise, Kushiro on the island of Hokkaido was evacuated for a 4-hour alert, but again the tsunami action was mild (*The Seattle Sunday Times*, March 29, 1964, sec. A, p. 2, col. 3; and *The New York Times*, March 29, 1964, no. 38, sec. 1, p. 48, col. 8). In Japan the responsibility for evaluation of warning messages and implementation of local alerts and protective actions based on SSWWS warnings is given to a national agency; thus, response is more uniform than in the United States where various local officials have the responsibility.

CONCLUSIONS

Although tsunami warnings were issued by the Seismic Sea Wave Warning System and by unofficial sources on the occasion of the Alaska earthquake of 1964, the tsunamis caused 119 fatalities—103 in Alaska and 16 in California and Oregon. The distribution by place and by type of tsunami is shown in Table 1.

In general there was little possibility of warning for most Alaskan communities struck by the tsunamis. Since all these communities experienced the earthquake first, some lives could have been saved if the earthquake itself had been perceived as a warning. Except at Valdez, Chenega, and Whittier, which were immediately hit by locally generated tsunamis, most loss of life could have been avoided if, once they had been warned by initial wave action, radio, or public officials, the public had uniformly responded by going to high ground and staying there.

Despite the availability of SSWWS warnings in all communities outside Alaska (except those in Canada), wide variations in response were found. Apparently the most crucial variable involved in determining the nature of the warning received by the public was the judgment and experience of officials responsible for determining the measure of response

TABLE 1   Fatalities due to Tsunamis and Other Causes Associated with the Alaska Earthquake[a], March 27–28, 1964

Place	Earthquake Fatalities		
	Local Tsunamis	Major Tsunami	Other Causes
Alaska			
Prince William Sound and connecting fiords			
Crab Bay (near Port Ashton), Evans I.[b]	1		
Chenega, Chenega I.	23		
Point Nowell, Knight I. Passage	1		
Port Nellie Juan, McClure Bay	3		
Whittier, Passage Canal[c]	12		1
Valdez, Port Valdez[d]	30		1
Anderson Bay, Port Valdez[e]	1		
Kenai Peninsula			
Seward, Resurrection Bay[f]	11		1
North coast of Gulf of Alaska			
Cape St. Elias, Kayak I.		1	
Point Whitshed, W. of Cordova		1	
Kodiak Island group[g]			
Kodiak (incl. Spruce Cape), Kodiak I.[h]		9	
Kalsin Bay, Kodiak I.		6	
Sitkalidak I. (near Old Harbor, Kodiak I.)[i]		1	
Kaguyak, Kodiak I.		3	
Cook Inlet			
Anchorage			9
Totals for Alaska	82	21	12
	103		

TABLE 1   (Continued)

Place	Earthquake Fatalities		
	Local Tsunamis	Major Tsunami	Other Causes
Oregon			
Depoe Bay (N. of Newport)[j]		4	
California			
Crescent City[k]	16	10	
Klamath[l]		1	
Bolinas Bay[m]		1	
Totals, all states	82	37	12
Total, all tsunamis	119		
Grand total, all fatalities	131		

[a]Compilation by Doak C. Cox, University of Hawaii. Enumerations and attribution to specific causes for Alaska are based on manuscript tabulations from death certificates by Margaret Lantis, University of Kentucky, and by Francis E. Kester, Alaska State Registrar of Vital Statistics, Juneau, Alaska, for the Panel on Geography, Committee on the Alaska Earthquake, and on other sources cited below. Enumerations outside Alaska are based on sources cited. Fatalities attributed to tsunamis include all those who were drowned and those missing and presumed to have drowned.
[b]The presumed drowning of a Valdez resident identified in many reports as having occurred at Port Ashton actually occurred at Crab Bay (Plafker and others, 1969, p. 30).
[c]At Whittier the total of 13 tsunami fatalities given in several reports includes one fatality due to other causes, according to the death certificate.
[d]At Valdez the total of 33 fatalities given in several reports probably includes one person missing and presumed drowned at Crab Bay (note b), one missing and presumed drowned at Anderson Bay (note e), and one killed by skull fracture on the dock and listed here as a fatality by other sources. Twenty persons missing in the collapse of the dock and presumed drowned, one death (on the ship) from heart failure, and one death (on the ship) from a broken neck are included here in deaths from the tsunami.
[e]The presumed drowning of one of the Valdez residents, commonly included among Valdez fatalities, actually occurred at Anderson Bay (Plafker and others, 1969, p. 13).
[f]At Seward a total of 13 fatalities is given by some sources. Of the 12 fatalities listed by the Registrar of Vital Statistics, one resulted from causes other than the tsunami.
[g]The fatality totals reported for Kodiak and vicinity have varied widely, apparently because of incomplete lists used by some authors and double listings by others.
[h]At Kodiak, estimates of fatalities have ranged from 9 to 11, including 8 or 9 drowned, or missing and presumed drowned, from boats in the small boat harbor or at Spruce Cape.
[i]A death presumed to be by drowning and included in most lists as occurring at Old Harbor actually occurred on Sitkalidak I. (Kachadoorian and Plafker, 1967, p. 36).
[j]At Depoe Beach the four fatalities were deaths by drowning of members of a family camped on the beach (Hansen and others, 1966, p. 37; Spaeth and Berkman, 1967; Cloud and Scott, 1969, p. 46).
[k]At Crescent City, California, the fatality total of 10 deaths by drowning has been verified from death certificates filed with the California Department of Public Health. Reports of 11 or 12 fatalities seem to have resulted from inclusion of the victim at Klamath and of a supposed victim at Crescent City who was later found alive.
[l]At Klamath the death by drowning has been verified from a death certificate filed with the California Department of Public Health.
[m]At Bolinas the fatality included was a death by drowning of a man swept from a reef by a "tidal surge," according to a Marin County, California, coroner's report, on the afternoon of March 28 about 1 hour after high tide while tsunami waves were still moderately high.

to be taken within their political subdivisions. Similarly, the response of the public to measures taken by officials seemed to depend on their experience with and understanding of tsunamis and tsunami warnings.

ACKNOWLEDGMENT

This research is supported in part by the National Institutes of Health, Grant Number MH 11558-01.

REFERENCES

Anderson, William A., 1970. Tsunami warning in Crescent City, California, and Hilo, Hawaii in The Great Alaska Earthquake of 1964: Human Ecology. NAS Pub. 1607. Washington: National Academy of Sciences. p. 116–124.

Berg, Eduard, Doak C. Cox, Augustine S. Furumoto, Kinjiro Kajiura, Hirosi Kawasumi, and Etsuzo Shima, 1971. Field survey of the tsunamis of 28 March 1964 in Alaska, and conclusions as to the origin of the major tsunami. Report HIG-70-2. Honolulu: University of Hawaii, Institute of Geophysics. 57 p.

California Disaster Office [1964]. Receipt and dissemination of sea-wave warning. Sacramento: California Disaster Office.

Cloud, William K., and Nina H. Scott, 1969. Distribution of intensity, Prince William Sound earthquake of 1964 in Volume II-B, C: The Prince William Sound, Alaska, earthquake of 1964 and aftershocks. Environmental Science Services Administration, U.S. Coast and Geodetic Survey. Washington: Government Printing Office. p. 5–48. Also in The Great Alaska Earthquake of 1964: Seismology and Geodesy. NAS Pub. 1602. Washington: National Academy of Sciences, 1972.

Hansen, Wallace R., Edwin B. Eckel, William E. Schaem, Robert E. Lyle, Warren George, and Genie Chance, 1966. The Alaska earthquake, March 27, 1964: field investigations and reconstruction effort. U.S. Geological Survey Professional Paper 541. Washington: Government Printing Office. 111 p.

Kachadoorian, Reuben, and George Plafker, 1967. Effects of the earthquake of March 27, 1964 on the communities of Kodiak and nearby islands. U.S. Geological Survey Professional Paper 542-F. Washington: Government Printing Office. 41 p. Abstract in The Great Alaska Earthquake of 1964: Geology. NAS Pub. 1601. Washington: National Academy of Sciences, 1971. p. 539–540.

Norton, Frank R. B., and J. Eugene Haas, 1970. The human response in selected communities in The Great Alaska Earthquake of 1964: Human Ecology. NAS Pub. 1607. Washington: National Academy of Sciences. p. 248–399.

Office of Provincial Civil Defense Co-ordinator [1964]. Report on the Alberni tidal wave disaster, Part II. Vancouver (?): Province of British Columbia.

Plafker, George, Reuben Kachadoorian, Edwin B. Eckel, and Lawrence R. Mayo, 1969. Effects of the earthquake of March 27, 1964, on various communities. U.S. Geological Survey Professional Paper 542-G. Washington: Government Printing Office. 50 p. Also in The Great Alaska Earthquake of 1964: Geology. NAS Pub. 1601. Washington: National Academy of Sciences, 1971. p. 489–538.

Spaeth, Mark G., and Saul C. Berkman, 1967. The tsunami of March 28, 1964, as recorded at tide stations. Environmental Science Services Administration Technical Report C&GS 33. Washington: Government Printing Office. 86 p. Also in The Great Alaska Earthquake of 1964: Oceanography and Coastal Engineering. NAS Pub. 1605. Washington: National Academy of Sciences, 1972.

Wilson, Basil W., and Alf Tørum, 1968. The tsunami of the Alaskan earthquake, 1964: Engineering evaluation. Coastal Engineering Research Center Technical Memorandum No. 25. Washington: U.S. Army Corps of Engineers, May. 444 p.

Yutzy, Daniel, 1964. Aesop, 1964: Contingencies affecting the issuing of public disaster warnings at Crescent City, California. Disaster Research Center Research Note 4. Columbus: The Ohio State University, Disaster Research Center. 8 p.

DOAK C. COX
UNIVERSITY OF HAWAII

HARRIS B. STEWART, JR.
ENVIRONMENTAL SCIENCE SERVICES
ADMINISTRATION*

Technical Evaluation of the Seismic Sea Wave Warning System

ABSTRACT: The objective of the Seismic Sea Wave Warning System is taken to be to minimize the hazards of tsunamis, especially hazards to human life and health, through issuance of timely warnings for dissemination by participating agencies. A tsunami warning was issued by the system on the occasion of the 1964 Alaska earthquake; nevertheless, loss of life suggests room for improvement.

Means of increasing the speed of seismic analyses and their data, the speed of wave detection, and the information from hydrodynamic analyses used in the system are discussed. Many of these have been adopted since the Alaska earthquake. In the reduction of hazard on a particular coast, not only the timeliness and accuracy of the warning issued on a single instance are important, but also the record of successes and failures of previous warnings on that coast. A policy of regional evaluation, adopted in 1966, will permit an increased ratio of successes to failures on each coast.

A special regional warning system has been established for Alaska since the earthquake. Even with the special system, there will be difficulties connected with the high frequency of earthquakes, low frequency of significant tsunamis, and short travel times to vulnerable coasts from areas of potential tsunami generation.

*Now, in part, the National Ocean Survey, NOAA.

OBJECTIVES OF THE SSWWS

The performance of the Seismic Sea Wave Warning System (SSWWS) in relation to the threat of tsunamis accompanying the great 1964 Alaska earthquake has been described in detail by Spaeth and Berkman (1967, and this volume). Any evaluation of this performance must depend on the objectives assumed for the system. In terms of the simple objective of issuing warnings of tsunamis, which has sometimes been considered to be the objective of the SSWWS (for discussion of the various objectives stated for the SSWWS, see Cox, 1968), the system of course functioned perfectly. This is, however, neither the final nor the most important objective.

A requirement of the SSWWS that distinguishes it from other tsunami warning systems is that the generation of a tsunami be confirmed, if possible, by marigraphic evidence before a warning is issued. Because of unavoidable imperfections in the array of marigraphic stations participating in the system and the communications system linking them with the Honolulu Observatory, which serves as the control center of the SSWWS, this requirement introduces the significant probability that some small tsunamis will occur without warning. The SSWWS was, however, rightfully considered as constituting a considerable improvement over an earlier system that had used only seismographic information (Finch, 1924; Cox, 1964). That system, which had previously been discontinued, could have been more certain of issuing warnings of every tsunami by a suitable choice of threshold seismic magnitude, but there would have been less certainty of tsunami generation for every warning issued. The greater importance attached to issuing warnings more likely to be followed by tsunamis than to issuing warnings of all possible tsunamis is an indication of a humanitarian intent involving human response. As stated by Comdr. (later Capt.) Elliott B. Roberts of the U.S. Coast and Geodetic Survey, under whose leadership the SSWWS was initially planned, the operation of the system was intended to be effective ". . . so that the people of seacoast towns such as Hilo could be warned and escape death" (Roberts, 1950).

229

The U.S. Coast and Geodetic Survey has never actually been responsible for the dissemination of warnings directly to the public. It has relied on state and local Civil Defense and police organizations for dissemination of warnings in the United States and its territories, and on foreign agencies for reevaluation and dissemination in foreign countries. In view of the essential cooperation of these other agencies, the real objective of the SSWWS apparently is to minimize the hazards of tsunamis—especially hazards to human life and health—through the issuance of timely warnings for dissemination by participating agencies.

In relation to this goal, the performance of the SSWWS on the occasion of the great earthquake of March 1964 should be evaluated not only in itself but also in relation to the capabilities of the agencies to which the warning information was issued and the understanding of the public whose appropriate response was intended to be induced by the warnings.

The capabilities and performance of the agencies responsible for the dissemination of the warnings and the understanding and response of the public to the warnings are summarized by Weller (1972, this volume) and are treated in detail elsewhere (Norton and Haas, 1970; Yutzy, 1964; Anderson, 1970). Hence, these topics will not be discussed at length here, except for the preconditioning of the public by the performance of the SSWWS prior to 1964; their essential importance must, however, be kept in mind.

MARCH 1964 OPERATIONS

For convenience in the evaluation of the operation of the SSWWS at the time of the March 1964 earthquake and tsunami, an abbreviated chronology, compiled from the detailed log of the Honolulu Observatory (HO) (Spaeth and Berkman, 1967, and this volume) and from tide-gage and other reports, is given below:

Time (GMT) March 28, 1964	Event
03:36	Occurrence of earthquake [March 27, 17:36 Alaska Standard Time (AST)]. First waves of local tsunamis arrived within minutes at Valdez, Whittier, and Seward.
03:44	Seismograph alarm triggered at HO.
04:10±	Tsunami warning, based on reports of Coast Guard at Cape Chiniak, informally spread in town of Kodiak (March 27, 18:10 AST).
04:05	HO informally notified Coast and Geodetic Survey and Civil Defense (CD) personnel in Hawaii.
04:13–04:18	HO requested readings from cooperative seismograph stations.
04:19–04:59	Seismic readings, except from Alaska, received by HO.

Time (GMT) March 28, 1964	Event
04:20–04:35	Rise of first tsunami wave at Womens Bay, Kodiak (March 27, 18:20–18:35 AST). Tide observer sent message to HO at 04:35.
04:32	HO received report on quake felt and damage to tide gage on Kodiak.
04:49	Seismic readings sent by HO to Japan Meteorological Agency
04:36–04:54	HO received Federal Aviation Agency reports of Alaskan communications failures.
04:52	Epicenter and magnitude determined by HO.
05:01	HO received report of tsunami headed for Kodiak.
05:02	HO issued advisory bulletin giving estimated time of arrival (ETA) at Honolulu if tsunami generated.
05:30	HO issued second advisory bulletin giving ETA's at other places, including Alaska.
05:39–05:50	Marigraphic readings requested from Alaska stations.
05:50+	Maximum inundation by second wave in town of Kodiak (March 27, 19:50+ AST).
05:52–05:55	Marigraphic readings requested from British Columbia and California.
05:55	HO received 04:35 report on tsunami from Kodiak tide observer. Information passed to CD at 05:58.
06:11	HO received beginning of second message on tsunami from Kodiak tide observer.
06:30	HO received complete second message on tsunami from Kodiak tide observer. (Message apparently originated not long after 05:07.)
06:37–06:45	HO issued warning, repeating original ETA's.
07:15	HO provided CD with ETA's for other Hawaiian ports besides Honolulu.
07:39	First rise began at Crescent City, California [March 27, 23:39 Pacific Standard Time (PST)].
08:10	HO received report from Kodiak that by 07:15 wave action had decreased and was only slight.
08:22	HO received report from Coast Guard on tsunami heights at various points between Alaska and northern California.
08:26	HO received report from Tofino, Canada, on first crest at 07:10 (March 27, 23:10 PST).
08:42	HO received Sitka report of waves to 07:45.
09:00	First rise began at Hilo, Hawaii [March 27, 23:00 Hawaiian Standard Time (HST].
09:15	CD passed first Hawaiian wave reports to HO.
09:23	HO passed various wave reports to Japan Meteorological Agency.
09:42	Highest wave (second) hit Hilo (March 27, 23:42 HST).
09:45	Highest wave (fourth) hit Crescent City, California (March 28, 01:45 PST).
11:00	HO issued all clear for Hawaii, and advised all-clear status elsewhere 2 hours after local ETA's in absence of local contraindications.

WARNING

The first and most important comment to be made on the SSWWS operation on the occasion of the March 1964 earthquake is that it issued a warning which reached many coasts on the borders and on islands of the Pacific Ocean, resulting unquestionably in a reduction of casualties at Crescent City, California, and perhaps at other places in Washington, Oregon, California, and Hawaii. Clearly, then, the Warning System fulfilled its mission in part, even though the loss of life that did occur suggests that the risk had not been reduced to a minimum and that further improvement should be sought.

One limitation of the effectiveness of the warning lay in its timing. As shown by Table 1, the warning was issued by the sswws at 06:37 GMT about 3 hours after the occurrence of the earthquake, almost the same length of time after the attack of the first of the local, slump-generated tsunamis at some Alaska towns such as Valdez, Seward, and Whittier, and 2¼ hours after the arrival of the front of the major tsunami at Kodiak and probably about ¾ hour after the arrival of the highest crest there.

The warning of the sswws was issued ¾ hour before the arrival of the tsunami late at night on the coast of Washington, and over 1 hour before its arrival at the coasts of Oregon and northern California. The relay of the warning information to the public consumed most of the lead time on these coasts, however, so that warnings were publicly disseminated at about the time of arrival of the tsunami. The highest crests, however, came after midnight 1½ to 2 hours after the warning had been given to the public. The tsunami front arrived in Hawaii 2 hours after the warning had been issued by the sswws and 1½ hours after the public dissemination of the warning.

The timeliness of warnings has always been a problem for the sswws, particularly in the case of tsunamis from the Aleutian Islands, which may arrive in the Hawaiian Islands in not much over 4 hours. Because the Hawaii State Civil Defense Division believes that it needs 1 hour, and preferably should have 2 hours, to make certain that a warning is disseminated as well as possible, the sswws has in recent years agreed to issue any warning for Hawaii not later than 70 minutes before the earliest estimated Hawaiian time of arrival, even if tsunami generation cannot be confirmed by then. Ordinarily, however, confirmation can be obtained in less than 3 hours,

In the case of the March 1964 tsunami, although the 3-hr interval from the time of the earthquake until issuance of the warning by HO did not exceed the elapsed intervals in some previous Aleutian tsunami warnings, it deserves comment. An interval of this length between the earthquake and the issuance of the tsunami warning becomes important when one realizes that (1) local tsunamis washed on shore at populated places almost immediately after the earthquake, (2) the major tsunami was observed at Cape Chiniak, Kodiak, only about half an hour after the earthquake, with a local warning being given in the town of Kodiak not long after, and (3) a report of the waves at Kodiak was received by HO less than 2⅓ hours after the earthquake. The slowness with which reports of the early waves in Alaska reached the Honolulu Observatory was, of course, due to the failure of most of the conventional lines of communication in Alaska.

Undoubtedly the Observatory did not issue a warning at the time of its receipt of the first report of a tsunami approaching Kodiak, because this report had come through an unusual channel. The Observatory had had considerable experience with reports from agencies and through channels other than those officially connected with the sswws; many of these had proved to be highly exaggerated or even totally false.

It is not clear, however, why a warning was not issued 2½ hours after the earthquake, following the receipt (at 05:55 GMT) by the Observatory of the first official message from

TABLE 1   Times (GMT) of Issuance and Dissemination of Alaska Earthquake Tsunami Warnings, March 28, 1964

Time of Issuance of Warning by HO	State	Time of Receipt of Warning by State CD	Time of Local Warning Dissemination	Earliest Arrival of Tsunami		Highest Waves	
				Time	Place	Time	Place
06:37	Alaska	–	–	03:40[a]	Valdez, Whittier, Seward	–	–
		–	04:10[b]	04:20	Womens Bay, Kodiak	05:50	–
	Washington	07:13	07:18+	07:18	Neah Bay	–	–
	Oregon	07:00	07:00+	07:56[c]	Astoria	–	–
	California	07:13	07:25–07:50	07:39	Crescent City	09:00–09:50	Crescent City
	Hawaii	06:43	07:00	08:33	Nawiliwili	09:28	Hilo

[a] Local slump-generated tsunamis, during or immediately after the main shock.
[b] Warning originated locally, not from HO.
[c] The Coast Guard reported arrivals between 07:00 and 08:00.

the Kodiak tide observer that a seismic sea wave was experienced at 04:35 GMT. There are several possible explanations, which may well have reinforced each other. The Observatory personnel had computed and broadcast an estimated arrival time of 05:30 GMT at Kodiak for the tsunami. They were probably skeptical of a report that a significant water-level change could have begun almost an hour earlier. The message did not give a measure of the change in water level, as is prescribed in tsunami reporting, but instead reported a height 10 to 12 ft above mean sea level.

Actually, a water level that high above preearthquake mean sea level would not have been beyond the range of the normal tide, because of the subsidence of 5 ft at Kodiak, but the Observatory personnel could not have known of the subsidence; if the Kodiak tide range had been known, the excursion reported should have been recognized as excessive. The picture was complicated by the fact, known to the Observatory, that the Kodiak tide gage had been damaged and that any readings reported must have been based on visual observations. In hindsight, then, the Kodiak report received at 05:55 GMT should have served as the basis for issuance of a warning under the officially accepted criterion that a tsunami, of however small magnitude, had been observed.

The beginning of the second message from the Kodiak tide observer, originating a little after 05:07, was received by HO at 06:11, but the transmission was cut off before any information additional to that of the first message had been received. The full message was not received until 06:30, and the warning was issued only 7 minutes later. The message delays point up the inadequacy of the communication equipment to handle the incoming and outgoing traffic during the peak period of an actual emergency.

It appears probable that earlier issuance of the warning would not actually have made any sigificant difference in the number of casualties from the tsunami. The warning from Honolulu could not have reached any of the Alaska communities in time to effect shoreline evacuation, and in Oregon and California the disastrous high waves came some time after the warning had been disseminated.

Special comment is due on the warning of Alaska communities. The tsunami warning services serving Japan and the Soviet Union are designed to issue warnings, on the basis of seismographic information alone, in time for them to be of value in the case of tsunamis generated locally offshore. The SSWWS, with its requirement of the marigraphic confirmation necessary to reduce false alarms, could not be expected to operate with sufficient speed to provide for local warnings. The manual of the system (Spaeth, 1962) specifically cautions against reliance on SSWWS warnings in the case of locally generated tsunamis on foreign coastlines; the caution would have been just as pertinent to domestic coastlines. It is somewhat questionable whether a local warning system is practicable on a coastline such as that of Alaska, with its sparse population, attenuated communications, and

low frequency of tsunamis, although the U.S. Coast and Geodetic Survey has now established a regional warning system in Alaska to do what it can.

In any case, the earthquakes themselves provide natural warnings, and there will always be a place for the kind of intelligent local initiative that must certainly be credited with a significant reduction in casualties from the 1964 tsunami at the town of Kodiak.

ADVISORY BULLETINS

While considering the timing of bulletins issued by HO, we should note (1) that the Civil Defense personnel in Hawaii were informally notified by HO of the occurrence of the earthquake less than half an hour after the earthquake and only 21 minutes after the seismograph alarm was triggered at the Observatory, and (2) that an official advisory bulletin was issued less than 1½ hours after the earthquake and 1½ hours before the tsunami warning was issued. With the advance notice that a warning might be issued, the Hawaii State CD and its various cooperating county agencies could be fully mobilized and capable of coordinating the siren warnings, radio broadcasts, and police action all along the Hawaiian shores.

Warning-dissemination agencies in areas other than Hawaii probably did not begin to mobilize until after the issuance of the first official advisory bulletin by the Observatory about 1½ hours after the earthquake and 1½ hours before tsunami warning. It seems probable that the advisory bulletin was delayed pending determinations by the Observatory of an epicentral location and a magnitude for the earthquake, proof that the quake was of such size and location as to be of concern. These determinations were made 1¼ hours after the earthquake, and the bulletin was issued 10 minutes later.

SEISMOGRAPHIC AND MARIGRAPHIC ANALYSIS

The length of time required for determining epicentral location and magnitude deserves some comment. It should be recognized, of course, that no analysis could begin until after the seismograph alarm was triggered in the Observatory, which was 8 minutes after the earthquake began in the Prince William Sound area of Alaska. Still, over an hour was required for the analysis. Cause of some of the delay probably lies in part in the sophistication of the seismographic equipment used. There was a visual recorder in the Observatory, but only the onset of the primary (P) phase of the earthquake could be distinguished on that. Other, more sensitive instruments recorded photographically, and the records had to be removed and developed before they could be used. To some extent, this sophistication was a needless handicap. For the major earthquakes of principal concern to the SSWWS, high magnification of the seismic wave does nothing but confuse the recording, but simple, low-magnification, visual-recording seismographs, available decades before the modern precise equipment was developed, are no longer used.

Another source of slowness in epicentral determination lies in the method of *P*-phase-arrival analysis ordinarily used. This method has advantages in precision and in lack of ambiguity, but it requires reports of arrival times of the *P*-phase of an earthquake from several stations. Reports from stations around the Pacific began to arrive at HO within 45 minutes after the beginning of the earthquake. However, an epicentral distance, at least, probably could have been computed from the difference in arrival times of successive phases of an earthquake on the records of the Honolulu Observatory alone, if the clutter of the traces on the records had been reduced by low magnification. Local estimates of the direction of the epicenter and of the earthquake magnitude could also have been made after the photographic records were developed.

A potentially serious result of slowness of epicentral determination is a delay in the request for marigraphic data. A request to a tide station has to indicate an approximate ETA at the station. Travel times to every participating tide station have been worked out in advance, but it is necessary to know earthquake time and epicentral location. It should be noted that several tide stations in the system, including three in the Aleutian Islands, are equipped with automatic tsunami detectors and alarms, so that queries from HO are not necessary in the case of large waves. However, waves that are damaging elsewhere are commonly too small at these stations to trigger the detector alarms.

COMMUNICATIONS

Of course, the major contributor to delays in all the operations of the warning system was the partial failure of the most important communications links. Those who would compare the transmission times of March 1964 SSWWS messages with the times for normal transocean or transcontinental telephone communication should recognize, first, that most of the stations reporting to HO, especially the tide stations, are in isolated localities far from normal communication lines. Indeed, a system of communications, very ingenious and intricate but inevitably requiring multiple relaying, has had to be worked out. At the time of a major catastrophe, even though alternate routes were prearranged, considerable delays were to be expected; indeed, considering the general collapse of communications in Alaska immediately after the 1964 earthquake, it is a wonder that any of the initial messages were successfully transmitted.

ESTIMATED TIMES OF ARRIVAL

It is of interest to look into some other deficiencies of the warning information. The error in estimate of arrival of the tsunami at Kodiak and its possible importance in HO's eval-

TABLE 2   Comparison of Estimated and Actual Times (GMT) of Arrival of the 1964 Tsunami

	Estimated	Actual
Kodiak	05:30	04:20
Unalaska	06:30	06:06
Adak	07:00	07:00
Attu	07:45	07:27
Sitka	05:30	05:06
Tofino	07:30	07:00
Neah Bay	07:30	07:18
Crescent City	08:00	07:39
Midway	08:45	08:27
Honolulu	09:00	08:53

uation of Kodiak's early reports has already been mentioned. Other estimated arrival times were also in error, although not so seriously (Table 2).

The discrepancies were due to the assumption of a point source for the tsunami. The epicenter determined by HO at 61°N, 147½°W was near northern Prince William Sound, about 100 mi from the coast. The tsunami travel times were computed from a point on the coast near Seward. However, the uplifted portion of the Continental Shelf that served as the tsunami-generating area extended some 600 km to the south, 100 km to the east, and 500 km to the west of the assumed source, giving the wave front in all directions a considerable lead.

WAVE-HEIGHT INFORMATION

The possible importance of the nonstandard height parameter used in the first official report of the tsunami from Kodiak has already been mentioned. It is worth noting that other wave reports received by HO, including some transmitted by HO to other warning agencies, used nonstandard parameters, in general not identified. Initial rise, double amplitude or range, runup height on land, and height above mean sea level were all used in reports to HO, and these four at least were passed on to other agencies.

It is unlikely that the confusion of wave-height parameters, rarely involving errors exceeding a factor of two, made any significant difference in the effectiveness of the warning in March 1964, with the exception already noted. However, such confusion has caused problems in earlier warnings, and it must certainly be eliminated before even generalized quantitative tsunami forecasting is attempted. The recently revised wave-reporting manual for tide observers, which gives explicit instructions on scaling and reporting wave heights, should reduce this confusion.

MANPOWER AND EQUIPMENT LIMITATIONS

Without a doubt, the few possibly serious deficiencies in the operation of the SSWWS and some deficiencies that might have proved serious under other circumstances are due, in very large measure, to limitations in manpower and equipment. The system was originally established by the U.S. Coast and Geodetic Survey through improvisation without specific authorization and without special funding. The Honolulu Observatory has assumed its tsunami-warning duties in addition to its pre-1948 duties with no significant increase in manpower. A crew ranging from two to four is responsible during a tsunami alert for developing and reading seismograph records, analyzing seismic data, sending data requests and receiving data from distant stations, transmitting advisory and warning bulletins, and consulting with civil and military warning authorities, as well as making judgments of an obviously critical nature. Improvement in the recording, communication, and analytical equipment available has been slow because of financial limitations. Under the circumstances, the degree of success of the SSWWS must be judged remarkable.

PAST PERFORMANCE OF THE SSWWS

Undoubtedly, the effectiveness of the warning issued for the 1964 Alaska tsunami was influenced by the experience that the agencies and the public had had with previous warnings and the degree of confidence felt by both the officials and the public. According to Yutzy (1964), the relative ineffectiveness of the warning in Crescent City was due largely to a low level of confidence resulting from previous experience with false or seemingly false alarms; a qualitatively similar limitation in effectiveness could probably have been demonstrated at most other places for which warnings were issued.

The performance of the SSWWS from its initiation in August 1948 through August 1967 has been discussed at length in a report by Cox (1968). In the 15½ years from September 1, 1948, through February 1964, there occurred in and on the borders of the Pacific 224 earthquakes of sufficient magnitude to have been accompanied by tsunamis (Table 3). At least 45 of these earthquakes were, in fact, accompanied by tsunamis, including 16 large enough (generally, near their origins) to have been capable of doing damage (that is, with maximum runup heights of 2 m or more). In the same period, 14 warnings were issued by the SSWWS. The correlation between warnings and significant tsunamis was far from perfect, however, as will be shown.

Table 4 summarizes data for all Pacific tsunamis that had maximum runups greater than 2 m and all SSWWS warnings for the period September 1948 through March 1964. This table shows that no tsunami causing significant damage on United States coasts had occurred without warnings and, indeed, that warnings had been issued for the only three tsunamis that were readily observable on any United States coast after crossing the ocean. These three were that of 1952 from Kamchatka, 1957 from the Aleutians, and 1960 from Chile. That casualties had been reduced by the operation of the SSWWS prior to the Alaska earthquake seems beyond question.

However, warnings had also been issued on the occasion in 1958 when the only significant wave motion occurred within Lituya Bay in southeastern Alaska, and on 10 other occasions when no significant wave activity was observed on any United States coastline, including two when the waves did not run up on any Pacific coastline as high as 2 m, another occasion when the generation of a tsunami is ques-

TABLE 3   Summary of SSWWS Action in Relation to Pacific Tsunamis and Large Pacific Earthquakes, from August 1948 through February 1964[a]

Tsunamis or Earthquakes	SSWWS Action[b]			Total
	None	Watch	Warning	
Moderate to large tsunamis (magnitude ⩾ 1)	5	2	9[c]	16
Small tsunamis (magnitude < 1)	26[d]	2	1	29
Total of certain tsunamis	31	4	10	45
Questionable tsunamis	5[e]	0	1	6
Earthquakes without tsunamis	164	6	3	173
Total	200	10	14	224

[a]Tsunami magnitude as defined by Iida and others (1967) = $\log_2 H_{max}$, where H_{max} is the maximum runup in meters at a coastline near the origin.

[b]The "warning" column includes events for which warnings were issued by the Honolulu Observatory; the "watch" column, those for which advisory bulletins, but not warnings, were issued by the Honolulu Observatory; the "none" column, those for which no public releases were made by the Honolulu Observatory, although there may have been much diagnostic activity.

[c]An enormous tsunami within Lituya Bay, Alaska, resulting (in July 1958) from a quake-triggered landslide, is included as a large tsunami, although the tsunami tectonically generated on the Alaska Continental Shelf on the same occasion was very small.

[d]53 small tsunamis generated by volcanic explosions in the Bonin Islands in 1952–1953 are omitted.

[e]Questionable tsunamis occurring without earthquakes at Midway Island in October 1957 and in Dixon Entrance, British Columbia, in March 1963 are omitted.

TABLE 4 Moderate and Large Pacific Tsunamis and SSWWS Warnings, from August 1948 through March 1964[a]

Date		Origin	Magnitudes		Coast with Highest Runup	U.S. Coasts with Runup ≥ 1 m		Foreign Coasts with Runup ≥ 1 m	Warnings Issued
			Earthquake	Tsunami		Maximum Runup (m)	Location		
1948	September 3	Tonga	7.8	1	Samoa	—	—	—	W
1949	December 29	Philippines	7.2	1	Philippines	—	—	Philippines	—
1952	March 4	Japan	8.3	2	Japan	—	—	Japan	W
	March 18	Hawaii	?	1	Hawaii	2½	Hawaii	—	—
	November 4	Kamchatka	8¾	4	Kamchatka	6.1 / 1.5 / 1.4 / 1.0	Hawaii / Aleutians / California / Amer. Samoa	Kamchatka / Kurils / Okhotsk / Sakhalin / Japan / New Zealand / Peru / Chile	W
1953	March 17	Kurils	5¾	1	Kurils	—	—	Kurils	—
	September 14	Fiji	6¾	1	Fiji	—	—	Fiji	—
	November 25	Japan	8.0	1½	Japan	—	—	Japan	W
1957	March 9	Aleutians	8.3	3½	Hawaii	16 / 4[b] / 1.7	Hawaii / Aleutians / California	Chile / Japan	W
1958	July 28	Mexico	7.9	1½	Mexico	—	—	Mexico	—
	January 19	Ecuador	7.8	2	Ecuador	—	—	Ecuador	W
	July 10	Alaska	7.9	c	Alaska	525[c]	Alaska	—	W
	November 6	Kurils	8.7	2	Kurils	—	—	Kurils / Japan	W
	November 12	Kurils	7.3	?	—	—	—	—	W
1959	May 4	Kamchatka	8	0	Aleutians	—	—	—	—
1960	May 22	Chile	8½	4½	Chile	10½ / 3.7 / 1.8 / 1.0	Hawaii / California / Aleutians / Amer. Samoa	Chile / Peru / Ecuador / Easter Island / Samoa / Japan / Kurils	W

235

TABLE 4 (Continued)

Date	Origin	Magnitudes		Coast with Highest Runup	U.S. Coasts with Runup ≥ 1 m		Foreign Coasts with Runup ≥ 1 m	Warnings Issued
		Earthquake	Tsunami		Maximum Runup (m)	Location		
1960 May 25	Chile	6¾	None	—	—	—	—	W
November 13	Aleutians	7	None	—	—	—	—	W
1962 December 20	Aleutians	6½	None	—	—	—	—	W
1963 March 30–31	British Columbia	None	?[d]	British Columbia	—	—	British Columbia	—
October 13	Kurils	8¾	2	Kurils	—	—	Kurils Japan	W
October 20	Kurils	6¾–7	3½	Kurils	—	—	Kurils	W
1964 March 28	Alaska	8.5	[e]	Alaska	30	Alaska	—	—
			4¼	Alaska	20	Alaska	British Columbia Mexico Peru Chile	W
					6.3	California		
					4.8	Hawaii		

[a] Information mainly from Cox (1968), with additions from Iida and others (1967). Earthquake magnitudes are Pasadena determinations quoted in the U.S. Coast and Geodetic Survey annual issues of "United States Earthquakes." Tsunami magnitudes are generally approximate estimates and are rounded to the nearest half unit.

[b] A 12-m runup was reported at Scotch Cap, Unalaska, immediately after the earthquake. The height seems exaggerated and the waves could not have represented the main tsunami, but might have constituted a tsunami locally generated by a submarine slump.

[c] Tsunami magnitude not assigned to large landslide-generated wave in Lituya Bay, Alaska, because of special circumstances of its generation. An accompanying tectonically generated tsunami on the Continental Shelf was of very small magnitude.

[d] A 5-m runup was reported in Dixon Entrance, B.C. Origin of tsunami, if it was one, is unknown.

[e] Tsunami magnitudes not assigned to slump-generated tsunamis in various sounds and inlets in Alaska; 4¼ magnitude is that of tectonically generated tsunami in Gulf of Alaska.

tionable, and three more occasions when there was no tsunami. In contrast, warnings were not issued on the occasions of seven tsunamis that had runups equal to or exceeding 2 m somewhere in the Pacific, including one generated immediately off the coast of Puna, Hawaii, which had a very local runup of 2½ m.

All the false warnings (those of May 25, 1960; November 13, 1960; and December 20, 1962), as well as the warning on November 12, 1958, on the occasion of a questionable tsunami, were the result of faulty marigraphic reporting. The water-level changes on which the warnings were based were probably not greater than the normal background oscillations at the stations in question on all these occasions except that of May 25, 1960, when the abnormal oscillations probably represented the tail of the major tsunami that had been generated 3 days before. The importance of the problem of faulty marigraphic reporting was noted in a Natural Disaster Warning Survey in 1965 (Keutschenreuter, 1965), which ascribed it in part to inadequate training of frequently rotated personnel at the tide stations.

The actual false warnings are, however, not the only ones that cause a loss of public confidence. So far as the populace of any particular coast is concerned, a warning seems false if it is not followed by tsunami effects at least readily visible on that coast. Because every tsunami varies greatly in its effects from one coastal region to another (and even in short distances on the same coast), it will never be possible to eliminate completely these seemingly false warnings.

Of the 16 tsunamis that occurred from September 1, 1948, through February 1964 and that had runups anywhere in the Pacific as much as 2 m, only five had runups as great as 1 m outside the immediate region of their generation. Table 5 includes two tsunamis that have occurred since: in March 1964 and in February 1965.

Table 5 indicates the distribution of the significant effects (runups $\geq$ 1 m) of these seven in 13 coastal regions of the Pacific. It will be seen that, of the seven, only two had significant effects in as many as half the regions listed (not counting respective regions of generation). These were the Kamchatka tsunami of November 1952 and the Chile tsunami of May 22, 1960. Alaska and Kamchatka were, as far as is known, not significantly affected by any tsunami not generated off their own coastlines. In contrast, Peru and Chile were each significantly affected by three distant tsunamis, the Washington-Oregon-California coast by four, and Japan and Hawaii each by five of the seven tsunamis of interregional significance.

With a policy of issuing a warning uniformly to all coasts of the Pacific whenever a tsunami had been generated, regardless of its size in the area of generation or the location of the generating area, the Seismic Sea Wave Warning System must inevitably have continued to issue a large number of seemingly false warnings to most coasts of the Pacific.

In Crescent City, Yutzy (1964) found that false alarms had contributed greatly to the lack of response to the warning of the March 1964 Alaska tsunami. Yet Crescent City had been damaged by a runup of 3.7 m from the May 1960 Chile tsunami. How much poorer a response might have been expected in Alaska, which had never had any significant effects from a distant tsunami!

IMPROVEMENTS

Since the Alaska earthquake, a considerable number of improvements have been made in the SSWWS, some resulting from deficiencies disclosed by the performance of the system at the time of the earthquake and some made possible by

TABLE 5   Distribution of Known Significant Runups of Tsunamis outside Their Areas of Origin, 1948–1965[a]

Area	1952 November 4	1957 March 9	1958 November 6	1960 May 22	1963 October 13	1964 March 28	1965 February 4
Japan	X	X	X	X	X	–	–
Kuril Islands	X	–	O	X	O	–	–
Kamchatka	O	–	–	–	–	–	O
Aleutian Islands	X	O	–	X	–	–	O
Alaska	–	–	–	–	–	O	–
British Columbia	–	–	–	–	–	X	–
Washington-Oregon-California	X	X	–	X	–	X	–
Mexico	–	–	–	X	–	X	–
Ecuador	–	–	–	X	–	–	–
Peru	X	–	–	X	–	X	–
Chile	X	X	–	O	–	X	–
Hawaii	X	X	–	X	–	–	X
Samoa	X	–	–	X	–	–	–

[a]Only tsunamis that had runups of 1 m or more outside their regions of origin are listed. O, the region of origin of each tsunami; X, other regions in which the tsunami had a runup of 1 m or more.

special appropriations for reconstruction after the earthquake.

The most important change, as far as Alaska is concerned, is the creation of the Alaska Regional Tsunami Warning System, supplementing the original Seismic Sea Wave Warning System and primarily intended to cope with the problem of issuing warnings of tsunamis generated locally in Alaska. The operating center of the new system is at Palmer, Alaska, where a tripartite seismograph array has been constructed. Additional arrays have been constructed at other Alaska seismograph stations, a two-part array at Sitka, and a small tripartite array on Adak Island. All the participating seismograph and marigraph stations in Alaska and the Aleutian Islands (except Attu) are now required to report information useful in tsunami warning to the Palmer Observatory as well as to the Honolulu Observatory. This service has been further improved by telemetering seismic and marigraphic data from several Alaska stations to Palmer; this permits rapid determination of earthquake epicenters and early detection of tsunamis generated in Alaska.

Another array, a quadripartite one, has been constructed on the island of Oahu, Hawaii. The records of the array, telemetered to the Honolulu Observatory, increase the capability of HO for rapid determination of earthquake epicentral location.

In the network of seismographic and marigraphic stations reporting to the SSWWS, 3 new seismographs and 10 new marigraph stations have been added. However, the Canton marigraph station has been withdrawn, owing to the closing of communications facilities on Canton Island. Two additional teletype machines have been installed at the Honolulu Observatory. This added capability in communications should aid in the more rapid receipt and transmission of tsunami information and warning bulletins.

The major change, as far as U.S. Pacific coasts other than Alaska's are concerned, is the institution of a new policy of selective cancellation of warnings in which warnings may be kept in force for selected coastal regions and canceled early in other regions where significant tsunami effects are not expected. The idea that regional selectivity in warning was not only needed but was already probably feasible, at least for Hawaii, emerged during a tsunami symposium sponsored by the Panel on Oceanography of the Committee on the Alaska Earthquake and held in Menlo Park in May 1965. The time seemed propitious for a change in policy. The U.S. Coast and Geodetic Survey, with its competence in managing the SSWWS, and the U.S. Weather Bureau, with its regional approach to forecasting and warning, had just been merged to form the new Environmental Science Services Administration (ESSA). The Governor of the State of Hawaii recommended in June 1965, and more explicitly in September of that year, the creation of a capability for regional evaluation of tsunami risk for Hawaii. The matter was thoroughly discussed by Hawaiian tsunami scientists with ESSA officials through conferences and correspondence. In April 1966, the U.S. Coast and Geodetic Survey and Hawaii Civil Defense Division announced a new policy whereby regional evaluation would be involved in the issuance and particularly in the cancellation of tsunami warnings in Hawaii. In May 1966, the U.S. Coast and Geodetic Survey had arranged to supply the necessary competence for regional evaluation from its newly established tsunami research group at the University of Hawaii. In June 1966, the following new specification was issued in the Communication Plan for the Warning System (Spaeth, 1962) (Change 18 to Communication Plan for SSWWS): "A watch will be canceled when HO determines that a wave has not been generated. A warning will be canceled if it is issued on the basis of erroneous data or if HO determines from subsequent information that only an insignificant wave has been generated. In addition, a warning may be canceled on a selective basis when a significant wave which has been generated clearly poses no threat to one or more of the areas HO warns, either because of intervening continents or islands which screen them or because the orientation of the generating area causes the tsunami to be directed away from the areas warned." This specification still does not explicitly provide for regional selectivity in the original issuance of warnings; but if a warning can be canceled in some areas immediately after issuance, on the basis that the tsunami poses no threat in those areas, then presumably nonissuance for those areas is implied.

The adoption of the principle of regional selectivity in issuance and cancellation of warnings is not of great consequence on coastlines served by foreign national tsunami warning systems, because those systems are capable of evaluating and free to evaluate for those coasts the warnings of remotely generated tsunamis which the SSWWS supplies. More important for foreign areas are the improvements in international coordination for which firm plans were first made by a working group established by the Intergovernmental Oceanographic Commission meeting in Honolulu in April 1965 (Stewart, 1965). Most significantly, the group recommended the establishment in Honolulu of a permanent International Tsunami Information Center to augment the services of the Honolulu Observatory and the appointment of an International Coordinating Group to effect technical liaison, to ensure the due exchange of information, and to coordinate efforts with concerned international bodies. Although hampered by a lack of funds, the U.S. Coast and Geodetic Survey began in 1967 the collection and collation of records to initiate the International Tsunami Information Center, and a first meeting of the International Coordinating Group was held in the spring of 1968.

Perhaps indicative of its undertaking of increased international responsibilities, the name of the Seismic Sea Wave Warning System was changed in 1967 to one that was more in accord with international technical usage, the Tsunami

Warning System (Change 24 to Communications Plan for sswws).

SPECIAL PROBLEMS WITH TSUNAMI WARNING IN ALASKA

Some problems of tsunami warning in Alaska deserve special attention, particularly in consideration of the establishment of the Alaska Regional Tsunami Warning System with headquarters at Palmer. This system was developed explicitly to handle regional analysis for Alaska in connection with warnings of tsunamis of local origin. The most serious problems are: (1) how to provide, in time to be of use, warnings of significantly greater reliability than natural warnings afforded by the earthquakes; and (2) how to maintain public confidence and public understanding in spite of the low-recurrence frequency of actual hazard. A thorough analysis of these problems would require a much better record of Alaska tsunamis and their effects than is available, but the historical data at hand are adequate to indicate their severity.

The history of tsunamis in Alaska has been examined in detail by Cox and Pararas-Carayannis (1969), and the record of tsunamis generated in Alaska is summarized in Table 6. As noted by these authors, the record was unquestionably quite incomplete prior to the 20th century because of the paucity of civilized settlements. In fact, it approaches adequacy only for the period after 1946 when several new tide gages were established as components in the Seismic Sea Wave Warning System of the U.S. Coast and Geodetic Survey. Tsunamis locally generated by landslides, submarine slumps, and icefalls in the isolated straits, sounds, and fiords of Alaska, and even major tsunamis tectonically generated off the Aleutian Islands might easily have escaped the historic record. However, there is little reason to believe that tsunamis other than those historically recorded had any significant effects at the few old and continuously occupied settlements. These old settlements include Old Harbor, established in 1784, Kodiak in 1792, Sitka in 1799, Wrangell in 1834, Juneau in 1880, Cordova about 1890, Valdez in 1898, and Seward in 1902.

On 12 (or 13) of the 20 to 23 occasions of Alaska and Aleutian tsunami generation listed in Table 6, the tsunamis were generated off the coast in connection with earthquakes. Seven of these tsunamis were generated off the Aleutian Islands, and the other five off the Alaska mainland. Only half of these offshore tsunamis are known to have had significant runup heights anywhere (equal to or exceeding 1 m), four originating off the Aleutian Islands (1878, 1946, 1957, and 1965) and two off the mainland (1788 and 1964).

On the occasions of two of the earthquakes associated with offshore tsunamis (1958 and 1964) and on the occasions of four or perhaps six other earthquakes, tsunamis were generated in straits, sounds, or fiords. On the six occasions when

tsunamis were certainly generated locally, they were reported to have had significant runup heights (>1 m) to distances of a few tens of miles at the most from the points of generation. Some of the tsunamis were tectonically generated (the Yakutat tsunami of 1899, the tectonovolcanic Augustine tsunami of 1883, and the possible tectonovolcanic tsunami of 1901). Others were generated by landslides or submarine slumps (several additional tsunamis in 1899, the Lituya tsunami of 1958 that occurred at the same time as a small tectonic offshore tsunami, and several tsunamis occurring at the same time as the major offshore tsunami in 1964).

On four occasions, significant tsunamis (runup height > 1 m) were generated in fiords by icefalls or by landslides without earthquakes. On none of these occasions was the tsunami of any consequence outside of the fiord in which it was generated.

Table 7 contains the record of tsunamis generated elsewhere for which measurements or observations have been reported in Alaska. The records of the 1868 Chilean tsunami were taken from a tide gage established at Kodiak soon after the United States assumed sovereignty over Alaska. Unfortunately the records appear to be lost, and the amplitude is not known. All the other records resulted from the modern program of tide gaging. Of the 10 or 11 tsunamis recorded in Alaska since the beginning of 1944, only two had amplitudes exceeding 1 m. These, from Kamchatka in 1952 and Chile in 1960, had recorded amplitudes between 1 and 2 m both at Massacre Bay, Attu, and at Sweeper Cove, Adak, but no amplitudes or runups of as much as 1 m were recorded elsewhere. There is no record of damage from a distant tsunami in either Alaska or the Aleutians.

Since the beginning of 1946, 17 or 18 tsunamis, of which six have been of practical consequence, have been observed in Alaska and the Aleutians. Of these six, two were of Aleutian origin, two of Alaskan origin, and two of distant origin. This frequency of six significant tsunamis in 22 years is essentially the same as that in Hawaii (7 in the same period). However, the combined Aleutian-Alaskan coastline is much too long to treat as a single region, as far as public warning is concerned. A resident of Sitka would surely consider false a warning of a tsunami whose runup exceeded 1 m on no shore closer than Unalaska.

In Table 8, the distribution of significant tsunamis—those with runup heights of 1 m or more—is shown in relation to four Alaska-Aleutian coastal segments, each about 1,000 km long. It will be seen that only four earthquakes were accompanied by tsunamis that had significant effects in more than one of these segments, and none were accompanied by tsunamis with such effects in more than two segments. The 1788 tsunami had significant effects on coasts (totaling no more than a few hundred kilometers in length) that happened to span the arbitrary boundary between the eastern Aleutian and western Alaska segments. The 1957 tsunami, originating

TABLE 6 Tsunamis Reported Generated on the Coasts of Alaska and the Aleutian Islands, 1788–1965, with Maximum Runups

Date	Area of Generation	Maximum Runup and Other Runups > 1 m in Alaska	Place	Effects
1788 July 27	Alaska Peninsula	?	Shumagin Island	Effects uncertain
		?	Unga Island	Many natives drowned
		?	Sanak Island	Hogs drowned
		?	Alaska Peninsula	Effects uncertain
		?	Kodiak Island	Ship cast ashore and cabins washed away
?1792 —	Near Kodiak Island	?	Kodiak Island	Abnormal waves
(1827 —)	(Unimak) (Probably confused report)			
1845 —	Yakutat Bay	?	Yakutat Bay	Local tsunami generated by ice fall; 100 drowned
1853–1854	Lituya Bay	120	Lituya Bay	Local tsunami
?1856 July 26	Unimak Strait		(Perhaps a tsunami generated by submarine volcanic eruption)	
1874 —	Lituya Bay	24	Lituya Bay	Local tsunami
1878 August 29	Fox Islands	?	Unalaska	Village of Makushin destroyed by quake and tsunami
1883 October 6	Mt. Augustine eruption	7½ to 9	Port Graham	—
(1899 September 3)	(Lynn Canal) (Probably a seiche)			
1899 September 10	Yakutat Bay	10	Yakutat Bay	Local tsunami
		1	Controller Bay	Perhaps an independent tsunami
		2	Valdez	Probably an independent tsunami
		60	Lituya Bay	Independent local landslide-generated tsunami
?1901 December 30	Eruption on Cook Inlet	?	Kenai Peninsula	Possibly confused report
1905 July 4	Yakutat Bay	35	Yakutat Bay	Local tsunami generated by ice fall
(1908 February 14)	(Port Valdez) (Probably a seiche)			
(1911 September 21)	(Wells Bay) (Probably a seaquake)			
1925 February 23	Port Valdez	?	Valdez	Local tsunami
1929 March 6	Fox Islands		Not observed in Alaska	—

240

Year	Date	Location	Height	Place	Remarks
1936	October 27	Lituya Bay	150	Lituya Bay	Local landslide-generated tsunami; no quake
1938	November 10	Shumagin Island and Alaska Peninsula	0.2	Sitka	—
1946	April 1	Fox Islands	30	Scotch Cap, Unimak Island	—
1949	August 22	South Alaska	0.1	Ketchikan	—
(1949	September 27)	(Seward) (Report referred to a shaken tide gage)			
1957	March 9	Andreanof Islands	12	Scotch Cap, Unimak Island	Doubtful record
			4	Sweeper Cove, Adak	
1958	July 10	Lituya Bay	525	Lituya Bay	Local tsunami
		Off Lituya Bay	0.2	Yakutat	General tsunami
(1962	December 22)	(Fox Islands) (Confused report)			
1964	March 28	Valdez Inlet	30	Valdez	Local tsunami; great damage
		Passage Canal	9.2	Whittier	Local tsunami; great damage
		Prince William Sound	16.6	Chenega	Local tsunami; village destroyed
		Resurrection Bay	7.0	Seward	Local tsunami; great damage
		Gulf of Alaska	20	S.E. Kodiak Island	⎫
			9	Kaguyak	⎪
			9.2	Old Harbor	⎪
			6.1	Kodiak	⎬ General tsunami; great damage
			6.1	Womens Bay	⎪
			?	Afognak Island	⎪
			1.2	Seldovia	⎪
			4.2	Cordova	⎪
			3.7	Cape Yakataga	⎪
			2.2	Yakutat	⎪
			1.1	Juneau	⎪
			2.4	Sitka	⎭
1965	February 4	Rat Islands	10	Shemya Island	
			3.2	Massacre Bay, Attu	
1965	March 29	Rat Islands	0.2	Massacre Bay, Attu	
1965	July 2	Fox Islands	0.1	Dutch Harbor, Unalaska	

Dates are Greenwich date of generation. Entries in parentheses are events reported as tsunamis that are considered *not* to be tsunamis. Entries preceded by a question mark are doubtful tsunamis. Heights shown for the 1964 tsunami are selected examples from a much longer list. Runup is measured above contemporaneous sea level.

TABLE 7 Distant Tsunamis Reported Observed in Alaska, 1868–1966

Date		Area of Origin	Maximum Runup (m)[a]	Place	Maximum Runup and all Runups ≥ 1 m in Alaska (m)	
					Runup	Place
1868	August 13	Chile	14 to 21	Arica	Small	Kodiak
(1883	August 27)	(Indonesia, Krakatoa volcano eruption)	–	–	Small	Kodiak[b]
1944	December 7	Japan	7.5	Kumanoura	0.3	Massacre Bay, Attu
1952	March 4	Japan	3.8	Kiritappu	0.2	Massacre Bay, Attu
1952	November 4	Kamchatka	4 to 18.4	Paramushir Island	1.5	Massacre Bay, Attu
					1.1	Sweeper Cove, Adak
1953	November 25	Japan	3	Choshi	0.2	Massacre Bay, Attu
1956	March 30	Kamchatka	?	–	0.3	Massacre Bay, Attu
1958	November 6	Kuril Islands	3 to 4	Shikotan	0.2	Massacre Bay, Attu
?1958	November 12	Kuril Islands	?	–	0.2	Massacre Bay, Attu
1959	May 4	Kamchatka	?	–	0.2	Massacre Bay, Attu
1960	May 22	Chile	20 to 25	Isla Mocha	1.5	Sweeper Cove, Adak
					1.8	Massacre Bay, Attu
1963	October 13	Kuril Islands	4.4	Urup	0.4	Massacre Bay, Attu
1966	October 17	Peru	1.1	Callao	0.1	Massacre Bay, Attu

[a]Runup is measured above contemporaneous sea level.
[b]Small waves observed at Kodiak were generated by atmospheric-pressure disturbances and did not represent the tsunami that caused damage in the Sunda Strait.

in the Andreanof Islands, was reported to have had a 12-m runup at Scotch Cap, Unalaska, although this seems questionable. There were several separate tsunamis generated in inlets as accompaniments of the 1899 Yakutat earthquake. Only the major tsunami accompanying the 1964 earthquake had significant effects certainly extending across major parts of of two coastal segments—all the way from the Trinity Islands in the south central Alaska segment to the southern boundary of Alaska (and far south of that).

As with the local tsunamis accompanying the 1964 earthquake, which were disastrous at Valdez, Whittier, Chenega, and Seward, the effects of tsunamis accompanying the 1899 Yakutat Bay earthquake were practically restricted to the individual bays, Yakutat Bay, Lituya Bay, and Valdez Arm. The tsunami accompanying the 1958 Lituya Bay earthquake, three other tsunamis generated by landslides in Lituya Bay, and two tsunamis generated by icefalls in Yakutat Bay were restricted to the bays in which they originated.

What may be deduced concerning recurrence intervals for significant tsunamis on the four coastal segments and at settlements with long histories may be summarized as follows. (It will be recognized that the probable error of most of the estimates is very great.)

Western Aleutian Islands: Two tsunamis generated locally offshore and two distant tsunamis of significance have occurred in the last 20± years, that is, the average recurrence interval seems to be about 5 years. No damage has been recorded.

Eastern Aleutian Islands: One or two significant and damaging tsunamis locally generated offshore but no significant distant tsunamis have occurred in the last 20± years, that is, the recurrence interval seems to be on the order of 10 to 20 years. (This is probably more reliable than the 45- to 50-year recurrence interval indicated by the record since 1788.) At Unalaska, no damage or casualties have occurred in 192 years.

South central Alaska: In the last 20± years, only one significant and damaging tsunami of local offshore origin has occurred, that of 1964. On the same occasion, several separate tsunamis generated in inlets had significant effects confined to those inlets. Other tsunamis generated in inlets occurred 69 and 84 years ago. A distant tsunami 100 years ago had observable effects but, so far as is known, did no damage. The only other significant and damaging tsunami of local offshore origin occurred 179 years ago. The recurrence interval of damaging offshore and distant tsunamis appears to be at least 20 years and perhaps as much as 90 years. At Kodiak, only one tsunami causing damage and casualties has occurred in 184 years. At Valdez, two damaging or potentially damaging tsunamis have been locally generated in less than 70 years. One damaging tsunami has occurred in the 78-year record at Cordova.

Southeastern Alaska: Only one offshore or distant tsunami has occurred in the last 20± years or in the historical record. However, one damaging tsunami was generated in Lituya Bay in the period of 20± years and at least four damaging or potentially damaging tsunamis have occurred in the last 115 years, suggesting a recurrence frequency of less than 30 years. Local tsunamis have similarly affected Yakutat Bay, with an average recurrence interval of less than 45 years. Wrangell has

TABLE 8   Distribution of Tsunami Runup Heights of 1 Meter or More in Alaska and Aleutian Islands, 1788–1965

Date		Western Aleutians (Near Islands to Andreanof Islands)	Eastern Aleutians (Fox Islands to Shumagin Islands)	Southcentral Alaska (Alaska Peninsula to Prince William Sound)	Southeastern Alaska (Cape St. Elias to Ketchikan)
1788	July 27	–	O	O	–
1845		–	–	–	I
1853–1854		–	–	–	I
1868	August 13	–	–	D	–
1874	?	–	–	–	I
1878	August 29	–	O	–	–
1883	October 6	–	–	I	–
1899	September 10	–	–	I	I
1905	July 4	–	–	–	I
1936	October 27	–	–	–	I
1946	April 1	–	O	–	–
1952	November 4	D	–	–	–
1957	March 9	O	O?	–	–
1958	July 10	–	–	–	I
1960	May 22	D	–	–	–
1964	March 28	–	–	OI	O
1965	February 4	O	–	–	–

I, tsunami or tsunamis generated in inlet, fiord, or strait in Alaska or the Aleutians;
O, tsunamis generated offshore in Alaska or the Aleutians;
D, distant tsunami.

not experienced tsunami damage or casualties in 133 years. At Sitka a dock collapsed in the 1964 tsunami, but otherwise there have been no tsunami damage or casualties in 163 years.

Very long recurrence intervals for the tsunamis generated by vertical crustal displacements associated with the largest earthquakes are suggested by the record, in the stratigraphy of the Copper River Delta and the terrace history of Middleton Island, of but three major sudden uplifts during the last 1,700 years (Reimnitz, this volume).

Considering the difficulties in maintaining public understanding in Hawaii, where there are considerably higher recurrence frequencies of significant tsunamis, the region to be served by the recently established Alaska Regional Tsunami Warning System should expect even greater difficulties because of the lower recurrence frequencies in Alaska, as indicated above.

Further, to be successful, the Tsunami Warning System will have to provide warnings more reliable than those provided naturally by the public's direct observation of the earthquakes themselves. Although the probability of tsunami generation by crustal displacement may in some cases be better indicated by the Warning System's epicentral location and magnitude determination than by the simple observation of the earthquake in coastal areas, it must be recognized that, at least for a major earthquake like that of 1964, the epicentral location may be quite misleading as to the probability of tsunami generation. Further, the epicentral location would give no indication of the extent of the area in which tsunamis might be locally generated by submarine slumps. In particular,

tsunamis generated by slumps might very well cause serious inundation within minutes after the earthquake (as was the case in 1964), far too soon for a warning to be formulated and disseminated by the Warning System. In addition, as demonstrated in 1964, there is a high probability that damage caused by a large earthquake will seriously interfere with the communications required by the system for the receipt of information and for the dissemination of warnings.

The observation of earthquakes is, of course, of no value in warning of tsunamis that occur independently of earthquakes—for example, the tsunamis locally generated by landslides, as in Lituya Bay, or by icefalls, as in Yakutat Bay. However, the warning system will be of no value in these cases either, because the system is normally triggered by earthquake recording.

It would seem that the practical feasibility of operation of a regional tsunami warning system for Alaska should be closely re-examined in the light of the low-recurrence frequencies of significant tsunamis in any of the Alaskan or Aleutian coastal segments and the difficulties of producing warnings more reliable than those provided by the simple observation of earthquakes.

CONCLUSIONS

In the light of the objective of issuing timely warnings of impending tsunamis, the operation of the Seismic Sea Wave Warning System in relation to the tsunami associated with the Alaska earthquake was an unqualified success. However, some qualifications should be made in the light of the perhaps more appropriate objective of minimizing the hazards of tsunamis, especially hazards to human life and health, through the issuance of warnings for dissemination by cooperating agencies. As far as the operation of the system at the time of the Alaska earthquake is concerned, the principal deficiency was in the time of the issuance of the warning and earlier bulletins. Considering the system's requirement of marigraphic confirmation before issuance of a warning, no warnings could have been issued in time to be of value in the macroseismic area of the earthquake. Although warnings for the coasts of Washington, Oregon, and California were somewhat delayed, they reached residents on those coasts an hour and a half or more before arrival of the highest crests of the major tsunami. The major deficiency in the effectiveness of the system arose not through its operations at the time of the Alaska earthquake, but from confusion and lack of confidence (stemming from earlier operations) on the part of those receiving the warnings.

To speed the seismological analysis with which the warning process usually begins, maximum use should be made of seismographic information available at the Honolulu Observatory. The quadripartite seismographic installation, established on Oahu by ESSA since the earthquake, should be of considerable assistance, especially if and when arrangements can be made to analyze its output by computer. However, the utility of simple equipment, especially visibly recording seismographs of low magnification, for speedy determination of the most essential data, should not be overlooked.

In connection with the Alaska tsunami warning, there was some confusion in marigraphic data; in the history of the Warning System, faulty marigraphic data have been a major contributor to false alarms. Since 1964, the U.S. Coast and Geodetic Survey has taken a number of steps to increase the speed of transmission, reliability, and significance of marigraphic information by installation of additional sensors on exposed coastlines; arrangement for remote recording from some sensors to communication centers; arrangement for long-distance telemetering in the Alaska Regional System; and general improvement and simplification of communications.

Further improvement in each of these areas should be promoted. On-call telemetering direct to the Honolulu Observatory should be arranged wherever feasible. Parameters and units used in transmitting marigraphic information should be standardized or explicitly indicated. The vulnerability of the communications system to earthquake damage, clearly demonstrated during the Alaska earthquake, must be taken into account in estimating the reliance to be placed on marigraphic data from the macroseismic zone of an earthquake.

The development of midocean tsunami gages, which has been under way for several years, should be pushed to completion as rapidly as possible; installation of such gages in midocean makes it possible for them to record tsunamis undistorted by coastal effects.

To avoid errors in estimated times of arrival of a major tsunami generated on the Continental Shelf, such as occurred in the case of the Alaska tsunami, propagation should be assumed from the edge of a hypothetical generating area whose size depends on the earthquake magnitude and whose location is suggested by the local geologic structure considered in relation to the epicenter of the earthquake.

The policy whereby regional evaluation of the risk from a tsunami is involved in the issuance of tsunami warnings in Hawaii will assist greatly in the elimination of the seemingly false alarms that have contributed so heavily to lack of public confidence in the warning system. Presumably the Palmer Observatory will serve the same function with respect to regional analysis for Alaska that the Honolulu Observatory does for Hawaii. Provision must still be made, however, for the analyses of regional risk that should be made before warnings are issued in Washington, Oregon, or California.

In addition, it must be recognized that the existence of a certain probability of tsunami arrival in a region is not in itself a sufficient basis for the issuance of a warning. The hazard from the tsunami must at least be sufficient basis for the issuance of a warning. The hazard from the tsunami must at least be sufficient to balance the unquestionable hazards that stem from the warning operations, including the future jeopardy that may occur through the destruction of confidence if the warning later appears to have been unjustified. Logically the whole Tsunami Warning System, as it is now known, should be subjected to an economic justification. The benefits of the system are clearly the values associated with the reduction of casualties together with the reduction of damage to movable property. The costs include those of the equipment and operation of the official parts of the system with the seismic and marigraphic detection and analysis, communications, and decision-making component, as well as the public dissemination and evacuation-policing component. They also include the cost to the public of the disruption of normal activities during warning periods, whether or not the damaging waves arrive. This includes the costs of accidents attributable to the disruption.

The issuance of a warning should involve a similar analysis or at least estimation of (1) the values associated with the probable reduction in casualties to be achieved on the immediate occasion, and (2) the costs both of the potential warning and of the future jeopardy that such a warning might induce.

In Alaska, the low frequency of tsunami recurrence makes the successful operation of a formal warning system appear very difficult, both from the standpoint of economics and from that of maintaining public confidence. In order to be judged successful, the formal system would have to provide warnings more reliable than those naturally provided by the direct observation of the earthquakes by the public. The vulnerability of communications systems in the macroseismic area is a contributory problem.

It is important to guard against the rejection of authorization or support for those components of the Tsunami Warning System that are effective and economically feasible, while at the same time withholding authorization for other components that are not effective.

REFERENCES

Anderson, William A., 1970. Tsunami warning in Crescent City, California, and Hilo, Hawaii *in* The Great Alaska Earthquake of 1964: Human Ecology. NAS Pub. 1607. Washington: National Academy of Sciences. p. 116–124.

Cox, Doak C., 1964. Tsunami forecasting. Report HIG-43. Honolulu: University of Hawaii, Institute of Geophysics. 15 p.

Cox, Doak C., 1968. Performance of the Seismic Sea Wave Warning System, 1948–1967. Report HIG-68-2. Honolulu: University of Hawaii, Institute of Geophysics, March 25. 79 p.

Cox, Doak C., and George Pararas-Carayannis, 1969. Catalog of tsunamis in Alaska. World Data Center A: Tsunami. Washington: Environmental Science Services Administration, U.S. Coast and Geodetic Survey, May. 39 p.

Finch, R. H., 1924. On the prediction of tidal waves. *Monthly Weather Review* (U.S. Weather Bureau), v. 52, p. 147–148.

Iida, Kumizi, Doak C. Cox, and George Pararas-Carayannis, 1967. Preliminary catalog of tsunamis occurring in the Pacific Ocean. Data Report No. 5, HIG-67-10. Honolulu: University of Hawaii, Institute of Geophysics, August. 270 p.

Keutschenreuter, P. H. (Chairman), 1965. A proposed nation-wide disaster warning system. Report of Natural Disaster Warning Survey Group. Washington: Environmental Science Services Administration, October. 113 p.

Norton, Frank R. B., and J. Eugene Haas, 1970. The human response in selected communities *in* The Great Alaska Earthquake of 1964: Human Ecology. NAS Pub. 1607. Washington: National Academy of Sciences. p. 248–399.

Reimnitz, Erk, 1972. Effects in the Copper River Delta *in* The Great Alaska Earthquake of 1964: Oceanography and Coastal Engineering. NAS Pub. 1605. Washington: National Academy of Sciences.

Roberts, Elliott B., 1950. A seismic sea wave warning system for the Pacific. *Journal of the Coast and Geodetic Survey*, v. 3, p. 74–79.

Spaeth, Mark G., 1962. Communication plan for Seismic Sea Wave Warning System. *Journal of the Coast and Geodetic Survey*, 3 (November), 1–85.

Spaeth, Mark G., and Saul C. Berkman, 1967. The tsunami of March 28, 1964, as recorded at tide stations. Environmental Science Services Administration Technical Report C&GS 33. Washington: Government Printing Office. 86 p. Also *in* The Great Alaska Earthquake of 1964: Oceanography and Coastal Engineering. NAS Pub. 1605. Washington: National Academy of Sciences, 1972.

Stewart, Harris B., Jr. (Chairman), 1965. Report of the working group meeting on the International Aspects of the Tsunami Warning System in the Pacific. Honolulu: Intergovernmental Oceanographic Commission, April. 17 p.

Weller, Jack M., 1972. Human response to tsunami warnings *in* The Great Alaska Earthquake of 1964: Oceanography and Coastal Engineering. NAS Pub. 1605. Washington: National Academy of Sciences.

Yutzy, Daniel, 1964. Aesop 1964: Contingencies affecting the issuing of public disaster warnings at Crescent City, California. Disaster Research Center Research Note 4. Columbus: The Ohio State University, Disaster Research Center. 8 p.

III
MARINE AND SHORELINE GEOLOGICAL EFFECTS

Introduction

INTRODUCTION

One need only look at the history of frequent tsunamis that wash up along Pacific shores to realize that continental margins around the Pacific must often be deformed during large disastrous earthquakes. In a recent 5-year period, the aftershock sequences associated with three large earthquakes (Chile, 1960; Alaska, 1964; Aleutian Arc, 1965) covered extensive areas on the Continental Shelf, suggesting submarine deformation. However, because many marine techniques have only recently been developed and are more costly than investigations ashore, submarine crustal deformation has not been studied as extensively as deformation on land. Therefore, important evidence is unavailable for developing an understanding that would help minimize the devastation in coastal areas from earthquakes.

Marine investigations related to the Alaska earthquake provide the most comprehensive data (gathered so far) on sea-floor deformation during a major earthquake. They also reveal geologic structures important for understanding the deformational mechanism and past geologic history. The data significantly limit inference and permit a synthesis of the tectonic setting based mainly on observations rather than on analogy.

The studies reported in this section were made by four institutions: the Scripps Institution of Oceanography, two West Coast Navy Laboratories, the U.S. Coast and Geodetic Survey, and the U.S. Geological Survey.

SEA-FLOOR TECTONIC DEFORMATION

Soon after the Alaska earthquake, it became apparent that a large part of the sea floor had been uplifted, because 20 minutes after the earthquake a major tsunami inundated the coast. The seaward portions of this coast show signs of remarkable uplift. Uplift at sea was subsequently detected by careful marine surveys. Southwest of Montague Island where well-controlled preearthquake bathymetric surveys were available, uplift as great as 14 m was determined by Malloy and Merrill (1969, and this volume). The sea floor around Middleton Island was also uplifted measurably (von Huene and others, 1972, this volume). In both of these areas the uplift configuration suggested a local structure superimposed on the broad regional deformation. Elsewhere, it was difficult to establish the deformation accompanying the earthquake, because changes in depth were often less than the accuracy of preearthquake nautical charts. Nevertheless, a series of pre- and postearthquake depth comparisons off Kodiak Island suggests tilting of the Continental Shelf with a maximum uplift near the shelf edge. Repeated past uplift along the shelf edge is indicated by erosion of a large arch and a sequence of terraces on Middleton Island (Plafker, 1969, and Geology volume).

The marine data reveal scarps on the sea floor and other evidence of recently active and inactive faults, especially off Hinchinbrook and Montague islands and the Kodiak Island group (von Huene and others, 1967; Malloy and Merrill, 1969, and this volume; and von Huene and others, 1972, this volume). Collectively, the faults form a zone paralleling the regional geologic trend, separating the Kenai-Kodiak Mountains from the Continental Shelf. The fault zone is here believed to have been active during the Alaska earthquake because it roughly coincides with the zone of maximum aftershock strain release. But apparently not all faults in the zone were active enough to produce scarps at the sea floor during the earthquake. Surface rupture during the Alaska earthquake can be established locally, but it appears to have been discontinuous along the fault zone—in fact, along some faults only segments show displacement at the sea floor since the last eustatic rise of sea level.

Interestingly, no fault displacement since the last glacial recession was found near the initial earthquake epicenter in Prince William Sound (von Huene and others, 1967). Similar tectonic quiescence was found in Nuka Bay (von Huene, 1966) which coincides with the axis of maximum subsidence accompanying the earthquake (Plafker, 1969, and Geology volume). Evidence of Holocene faulting was also absent between the Kenai Peninsula and the Kodiak Island group (von Huene and others, 1972, this volume). Both marine and terrestrial data suggest that, in the continental block landward of the fault zone, displacement along individual faults was insignificant during the Alaska earthquake or, for that matter, during most of Holocene time.

The tectonic history of the Continental Shelf seaward of the fault zone off Prince William Sound and Kodiak Island is one of active deformation, part of which is well enough known to relate the 1964 earthquake deformation to past tectonism. The zone of faults off Hinchinbrook, Montague, and Kodiak islands forms a fundamental geologic boundary that has probably been active through late Tertiary time. Landward, the area has been uplifted, and since the last major recession of glaciers the landward area appears to have deformed mainly by tilting or flexing. Seaward, a subsiding basin, best known off Kodiak Island, has trapped sediment up to 4 km thick. The seaward flank of the basin, a complex broad arch rising since the Miocene or Pliocene, forms the edge of the Continental Shelf. During this period, the Aleutian Trench has been subsiding (von Huene and Shor, 1969). The trench is partially filled with an undeformed stratified sequence resting upon a gently plunging blanket of deep oceanic sediment. Marine seismic reflection data are obscure where the trench and slope join, but there are some indications that deformed as well as undeformed sediment layers are present along the juncture. The critical information on type and rate of deformation is not available with present marine techniques.

Some deformation associated with the Alaska earthquake may have continued the apparent long-term geologic trend, but other deformation did not. The arch at the shelf break seems to have continued rising as in past geologic time (von Huene and others, 1972, this volume). Along the fault zone off Hinchinbrook and Montague islands and the Kodiak Island group, fault displacement disrupted the sea floor discontinuously, much as in the zone's past history. But certain areas of the Kenai Peninsula that subsided during the earthquake are areas of long-term uplift, and other areas of long-term subsidence, such as the large sedimentary basin offshore, appear to have been uplifted. Perhaps slow deformation during the years between major earthquakes exceeds the magnitude of deformation in an opposite sense that occurs during earthquakes, thus giving an apparent reversal of long- and short-term deformation.

GEOLOGIC PROCESSES ALONGSHORE AND IN FIORDS

Some shoreline and nearshore effects of the Alaska earthquake are a guide to features in the geologic record that indi-

cate earthquakes. Reimnitz (1972, this volume) has explicitly focused attention on this aspect of coastal phenomena accompanying the earthquake, and other authors, in describing phenomena peculiar to the earthquake, implicitly recognized the significance these features have to historical geology. If major earthquakes during Holocene time could be read from the geologic record, estimates of earthquake hazard would be greatly improved.

Most features connected with earthquakes that might be found in the geologic record are associated in one way or another with the sea. Waves associated with the earthquake damaged vegetation, uprooted trees, and carried rocks as large as boulders high onto land (McCulloch, 1966, and Hydrology volume; Plafker and others, 1969, and Geology volume). But geologically more significant were the sudden changes in elevation alongshore (Kirkby and Kirkby, 1969; Stanley, 1968, and Geology volume). Normal geologic processes operating alongshore were greatly accelerated. When the shore subsided, beaches receded shoreward. The bases of sea cliffs, brought closer to the waves, were more vigorously eroded (Stanley, 1968, and Geology volume). The salt water killed a fringe of shoreline vegetation. Stream mouths were drowned, and the lowered stream courses quickly adjusted to new profiles of equilibrium (Kirkby and Kirkby, 1969). Streams along uplifted coasts cut rapidly to adjust to a new profile of equilibrium, beaches were sometimes stranded beyond the reach of normal waves, and new beaches were formed.

Mass movement of sediment, mainly submarine slumps, occurred at deltas. The sediment was dispersed over large areas on the floors of fiords, but little is known about the depositional processes. In Port Valdez, and notably in Nuka Bay, extensive seismic reflection work has shown few obvious slumps (von Huene, 1966; Reimnitz and others, 1970). Sediment must have been widely redistributed by currents after slumping. The evidence for slumping is apparently detectable only with high-resolution seismic techniques or sampling. A high-resolution seismic record made by Reimnitz shows slump structures of the Copper River Delta. From the sedimentary record in the Copper River area, Reimnitz points out some sedimentary structures by which a previous history of seismicity and elevation changes could be established. Such features are changes in lithofacies and biofacies, sand dikes and sand pipes, as well as unconformities and sudden shifts in shorelines. Reimnitz found two sedimentary sequences that suggest major earthquake deformation, about 750 and 1700 years ago, that was similar to deformation during the 1964 Alaska earthquake.

As in any new study, many lessons were learned. The first and most obvious was the need for good preearthquake bathymetry to permit detection of elevation changes. Especially valuable would have been high-resolution geophysical observations immediately after the earthquake to observe features later destroyed by currents or covered by sediment. The need for high-resolution seismic reflection techniques to identify slumped sediment has only recently been realized. This technique could have been used in assessing the probability of waves prior to the earthquake. One can only reflect on the possible saving of lives that might have resulted from a preearthquake awareness that Prince William Sound and Resurrection Bay are areas where local destructive waves are very apt to accompany large earthquakes.

Each investigator considers his study incomplete, but the amount of detail desirable to minimize future damage and casualties will probably be best assessed in the future. The value of marine information when a large portion of the deformed area is below the sea is evident. The sea surface is a readily available elevation datum, and distinctive erosional and sedimentary processes can facilitate an understanding of earthquakes, the places where earthquakes have frequently occurred in the past, and the location in which earthquakes may be expected to produce devastating sea waves. The studies in this section provide some new insights from marine geology, and, although few questions are answered with convincing certainty, some new lines of investigation are opened.

ROLAND VON HUENE
U.S. Geological Survey

REFERENCES

Kirkby, M. J., and Anne V. Kirkby, 1969. Erosion and deposition on a beach raised by the 1964 earthquake, Montague Island, Alaska. U.S. Geological Survey Professional Paper 543-H. Washington: Government Printing Office. 41 p. Abstract in The Great Alaska Earthquake of 1964: Geology. NAS Pub. 1601. Washington: National Academy of Sciences, 1971. p. 281.

McCulloch, David S., 1966. Slide-induced waves, seiching, and ground fracturing caused by the earthquake of March 27, 1964, at Kenai Lake, Alaska. U.S. Geological Survey Professional Paper 543-A. Washington: Government Printing Office. 41 p. Also in The Great Alaska Earthquake of 1964: Hydrology. NAS Pub. 1603. Washington: National Academy of Sciences, 1968. p. 47–81.

Malloy, Richard J., and George F. Merrill, 1969. Vertical crustal movement of the sea floor associated with the Prince William Sound, Alaska, earthquake in Volume II-B, C: The Prince William Sound, Alaska, earthquake of 1964 and aftershocks. Environmental Science Services Administration, U.S. Coast and Geodetic Survey. Washington: Government Printing Office. p. 327–338. Also in The Great Alaska Earthquake of 1964: Oceanography and Coastal Engineering. NAS Pub. 1605. Washington: National Academy of Sciences, 1972.

Plafker, George, 1969. Tectonics of the March 27, 1964, Alaska earthquake. U.S. Geological Survey Professional Paper 543-I. Washington: Government Printing Office. 74 p. Also in The Great Alaska Earthquake of 1964: Geology. NAS Pub. 1601. Washington: National Academy of Sciences, 1971. p. 47–122.

Plafker, George, Reuben Kachadoorian, Edwin B. Eckel, and Lawrence R. Mayo, 1969. Effects of the earthquake of March 27, 1964, on various communities. U.S. Geological Survey Professional Paper 542-G. Washington: Government Printing Office. 50 p. Also in The Great Alaska Earthquake of 1964: Geology. NAS Pub. 1601. Washington: National Academy of Sciences, 1971. p. 489–538.

Reimnitz, Erk, 1972. Effects in the Copper River Delta in The Great Alaska Earthquake of 1964: Oceanography and Coastal Engineering. NAS Pub. 1605. Washington: National Academy of Sciences.

Reimnitz, Erk, Roland von Huene, and F. F. Wright, 1970. Detrital gold and sediments in Nuka Bay, Alaska, in Geological Survey Research 1970. U.S. Geological Survey Professional Paper 700-C. Washington: Government Printing Office.

Stanley, Kirk W., 1968. Effects of the Alaska earthquake of March 27, 1964, on shore processes and beach morphology. U.S. Geological Survey Professional Paper 543-J. Washington: Government Printing Office. 21 p. Also in The Great Alaska Earthquake of 1964: Geology. NAS Pub. 1601. Washington: National Academy of Sciences, 1971. p. 229–249.

von Huene, Roland, 1966. Glacial marine geology of Nuka Bay, Alaska, and the adjacent Continental Shelf. Marine Geology, 4 (August), 291–304.

von Huene, Roland, and George G. Shor, Jr., 1969. The structure and tectonic history of the eastern Aleutian Trench. Geological Society of America Bulletin, 80 (October), 1889–1902.

von Huene, Roland, George G. Shor, Jr., and Richard J. Malloy, 1972. Offshore tectonic features in the affected region in The Great Alaska Earthquake of 1964: Oceanography and Coastal Engineering. NAS Pub. 1605. Washington: National Academy of Sciences.

von Huene, Roland, George G. Shor, Jr., and Erk Reimnitz, 1967. Geological interpretation of seismic profiles in Prince William Sound, Alaska. Geological Society of America Bulletin, 78 (February), 259–268.

RICHARD J. MALLOY*
GEORGE F. MERRILL
ENVIRONMENTAL SCIENCE SERVICES ADMINISTRATION†

Reprinted with minor changes from
*U.S. Coast and Geodetic Survey Volume II-B,C:
Seismology and Marine Geology*,
"Vertical Crustal Movement of the Sea Floor Associated
with the Prince William Sound, Alaska, Earthquake"

Vertical Crustal Movement on the Sea Floor

INTRODUCTION

On March 28, 1964 (local time), the day after the Prince William Sound earthquake, the U.S. Coast and Geodetic Survey (USC&GS) began mobilizing equipment and personnel to assist in the emergency and to conduct scientific and technical investigations of the earthquake and its effects. Hydrographic and oceanographic operations included the inspection and repair of tide-gage stations, reconstruction of portions of the geodetic control network, and geophysical investigations of the Continental Shelf and slope in the vicinity of the earthquake's epicenter. Marine reconnaissance studies included depth soundings, gravity and magnetic measurements, seismic-reflection profiling, core sampling of sea-floor sediments, and bottom photography. To assist in these postearthquake operations and investigations, four Coast and Geodetic Survey ships—the *Hodgson*, *Lester Jones*, *Pathfinder*, and *Surveyor*—were diverted to Alaska.

Soon after work began in the offshore epicentral region, it became apparent that a major task would be the reconstruction of portions of the U.S. Coast and Geodetic Survey's geodetic network to provide accurate vertical and horizontal control. Vertical measurements could not be made on shore until the datum of reference (mean lower low water) was re-established. Offshore, vertical measurements or changes in depth could be made immediately because the datum of sea level had not changed—that is, the eustatic sea level remained fixed. Postearthquake geodetic operations are described in Volume I of *The Prince William Sound, Alaska, Earthquake of 1964 and Aftershocks*, Coast and Geodetic Survey Publication 10-3 (1966).

The USC&GS ship *Hodgson*, after completing her primary mission of installing portable tide gages, reoccupying portions of triangulation schemes, and conducting reconnaissance surveys in Prince William Sound, was directed to the area just off the southwest tip of Montague Island to investigate suspected extension of the faulting and crustal uplift observed

ABSTRACT: In 1965, the U.S. Coast and Geodetic Survey ship *Surveyor* conducted hydrographic and ocean-bottom-scanning sonar surveys southwest of Montague Island, Alaska, to identify vertical crustal movement of the sea floor associated with the March 27, 1964, Prince William Sound earthquake. The 1965 survey was controlled by precision navigation and covered portions of the *Surveyor's* 1965 geophysical reconnaissance investigations during which sea-floor uplift in excess of 15 m was discovered. A 21-kc, conical-beam echo sounder was used for the depth soundings, and a side-scanning sonar—with two laterally directed sonar beams of 150 and 160 kc—for detection of sea-floor features to a range of 366 m to the right and left of the ship's trackline. Fresh fault scarps were traced seaward a distance of 19 km. Data from the 1965 survey were used to prepare a bathymetric map of the uplifted area and, by comparison with preearthquake surveys, to construct profiles and a map showing the amount of sea-floor uplift. Lineaments detected by side-scanning sonar included scarps, strata ridges, and joint patterns. Areas of rock bottom yielded stronger reflections, and more meaningful data, than did areas of sediment.

---

*Now with U.S. Naval Civil Engineering Laboratory, Port Hueneme, California
†Now, in part, the National Ocean Survey, NOAA.

on the island by geologists of the U.S. Geological Survey (Grantz and others, 1964). On June 5, 1964, the *Hodgson* ran traverses across the projected strike of suspected faults and obtained three bottom profiles. Later, seven additional bottom profiles and seven subbottom profiles were obtained by the USC&GS ship *Surveyor* during geophysical survey work southwest of Montague Island, completed July 3, 1964.

Depth soundings by the *Hodgson* and *Surveyor* were compared with those of preearthquake surveys made in 1927–1928. This comparison showed that a large area of the sea floor was uplifted in excess of 9 m and that several areas of maximum uplift exceeded 15 m (Malloy, 1964, 1965). Because significant changes of the sea floor were detected and because the Loran A and radar navigational control of the 1964 surveys provided less precise horizontal control than that of the 1927–1928 surveys, plans were initiated for

a more detailed investigation of the area southwest of Montague Island.

In July 1965, the USC&GS ship *Surveyor* undertook a 1-week study of the sea floor off Montague Island (Figure 1). Raydist stations were erected to provide precise horizontal control for the work. As in 1964, depth soundings were made with a Raytheon DE 723 shallow-water Fathometer. A side-scanning sonar (Westinghouse Ocean Bottom Scanning Sonar, or WOBSS) was used to provide additional detail in the area shown in Figure 2. Southeast of Montague Island visual control—with sextants to measure horizontal angles between prominent points—was used to reoccupy positions of the 1928 survey (lines 1–12 of Figure 3). The side-scanning sonar was not used along these sextant-controlled lines. Corrections were made for sound propagation velocity in the area of the investigation and for the phases of the tide during the field

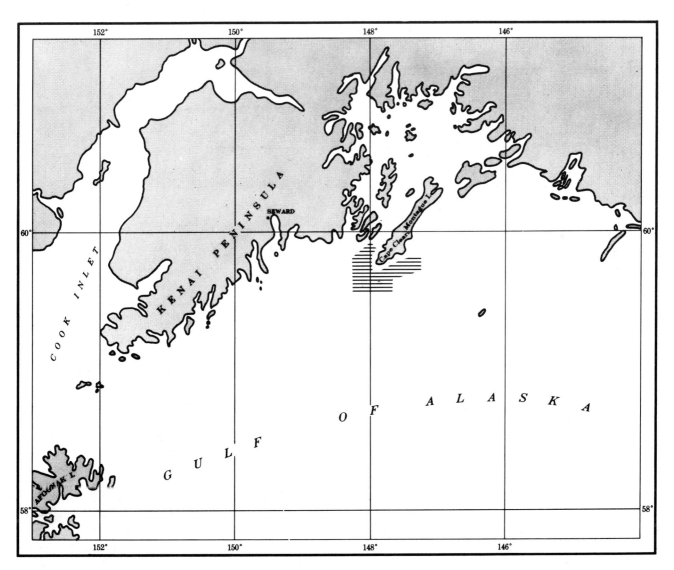

FIGURE 1   Area of 1965 marine geophysical survey by USC&GS ship *Surveyor* southwest of Montague Island, Alaska.

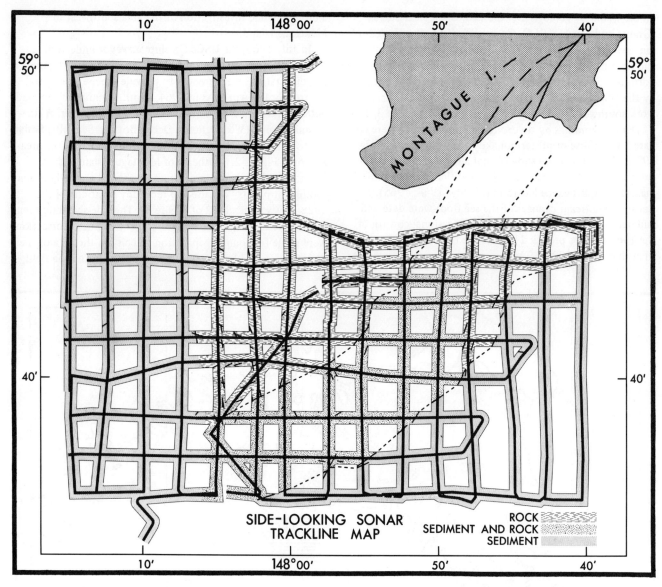

FIGURE 2   Trackline map of side-scanning sonar survey, showing sonar-detected features of the sea floor.

work. The ship's speed was reduced to 3 knots when the large sonar transducers of the WOBSS system were being towed.

This report is primarily concerned with the vertical uplift of the sea floor caused by the earthquake, as determined by depth soundings and side-scanning sonar. Supporting evidence, obtained by seismic-reflection profiling and bottom photography, was previously reported (Malloy, 1964, 1965).

GEOLOGICAL SETTING

The rocks comprising Montague Island have been mapped in some detail on the northwest side of the island, but the southeast side of the island has not received this attention because of the inaccessibility of its coastline. The northwestern side of the island is composed of beds of graywacke, banded argillites, and some arkosic sandstones which probably belong to the Orca Group of the Upper Cretaceous (Moffit, 1954). Since the Prince William Sound earthquake in 1964, a number of geological investigations have been made along the exposed southeastern side of Montague Island, but reports to date suggest that the southeastern side differs little from the better-mapped northwestern side of the island.

In general, Montague Island is composed of Cretaceous metasedimentary rocks. For the most part, these rocks are dark gray to black, and highly folded. Vertical dips are common. From what be learned from the offshore seismic reflections, the rocks are acoustically opaque. Offshore bottom photography shows a well-defined joint pattern devel-

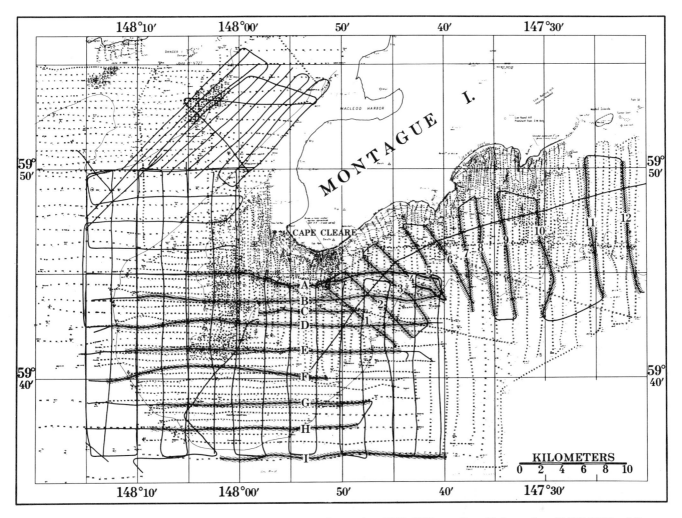

FIGURE 3   Map showing 1965 hydrographic survey tracklines superimposed on 1927–1928 soundings. Hydrography of 1927–1928 and lines 1–12 of the 1965 hydrography were sextant-controlled. All other lines (1965) were Raydist-controlled. (Based on comments and assumed interpretation of text.)

oped in the outcropping bedrock, with two sets of lineaments striking NE–SW and NW–SE (Figure 4).

The pattern of crustal uplift of the sea floor, as contoured from the reconnaissance data (Malloy, 1964, 1965), is similar to that mapped on land, that is, a northwesterly tilted block lies northwest of the northeasterly striking refaulted scarp known on land as the Patton Bay Fault (Plafker, 1965). The two major faults associated with the earthquake were identified at the southwestern end of Montague Island by a combination of aerial reconnaissance and observed vertical displacements of the barnacle line. Both faults strike more or less parallel to the long axis of Montague Island. The one on the southeast has been referred to as the Patton Bay Fault by Plafker (1965). The fault on the northwestern side of the island has been informally designated as the Hanning Bay Fault. The Patton Bay Fault, according to Plafker, has been traced northeastward from the shore for a distance of 16 km and has a vertical displacement of 5.2 m (northwestern side

up) where it intersects the coastline. Presumably, all the displacement is attributable to dip-slip movement. The Hanning Bay Fault has been traced by U.S. Geological Survey geologists for about 5 km; like the Patton Bay Fault, it has its northwestern side upthrown relative to the southeastern side. The maximum displacement along the fault of 5 m occurs on the beach at Hanning Bay (Plafker, 1965). Neither fault exhibits much in the way of strike-slip movement, but Plafker did report 15 cm of left-lateral movement along the Hanning Bay Fault. The attitude of the fault that cuts through Patton Bay seems to be vertical, and that of the Hanning Bay Fault plane is 70°, dipping toward the upthrown side, suggesting compression as the causative force.

Both faults on the southwestern tip of Montague appear to be rejuvenated faults (Plafker, 1965), that is, both occur along scarps that can be traced on preearthquake aerial photographs. The reconnaissance data of Malloy (1964, 1965) show that the Patton Bay Fault strikes into a preearthquake scarp

FIGURE 4 Postearthquake photographs of sea floor southwest of Montague Island. (*A*) Joint pattern (?) in encrusted bedrock; (*B*) angular nonencrusted features of fresh fault surface (?).

at sea. This is shown by the Coast Survey's depth-sounding data of 1927 and 1928. The Hanning Bay Fault apparently follows no preearthquake scarp to sea and may not cut the sea floor to any extent southwest of Montague Island.

PREVIOUS WORK

Prior to the hydrographic and geophysical reconnaissance investigations immediately after the Prince William Sound earthquake, the only significant submarine investigations in the epicentral area were the hydrographic surveys of the U.S. Coast and Geodetic Survey in the late 1920's. In 1927, a detailed hydrographic (bottom-sounding) survey was conducted off the southwest tip of Montague Island by an earlier ship, also named *Surveyor*, using a then-new method of sounding, the sonic Fathometer (the designation of the instrument was the Submarine Signal Corporation Model 312 Sonic Fathometer). Several vertical casts, with lead-line and paraffin inserts to obtain sediment samples, were made to check the relatively new sonic device. Navigational control was obtained by using sextants to measure horizontal angles between prominent features on land. This horizontal control was exceptionally good because of the proximity of the shore with its many clearly visible and prominent peaks, crags, and promontories on which to sight. Figure 3 shows the 1927–1928 soundings and 1965 tracklines off the southwestern end of Montague Island.

Other early hydrographic work over the Continental Shelf and slope in the north central Gulf of Alaska—where the concentration of aftershocks of strain release occurred—was controlled by visual bearings, celestial navigation, and dead reckoning and accomplished with the early-model nonrecording echo sounders; hence, preearthquake fathograms over critical portions of the epicentral and aftershock areas are not available for comparison with postearthquake hydrography made with recording echo sounders. Although many deep-sea tracklines later were made across the Gulf of Alaska, as Coast and Geodetic Survey ships steamed between work areas in Alaska and their home port of Seattle, the tracklines were discontinued when waters of the Continental Shelf were reached. The few tracklines for which fathograms of the shelf are available are considerably west of Montague Island and remote from the center of maximum uplift and sea-floor faulting.

Trackline data collected by the ships of the Coast and Geodetic Survey have been worked into bathymetric maps by Menard and Dietz (1951) and later by Gibson (1960) using additional data. These publications mainly treat the location, delineation, and distribution patterns of submarine volcanoes, the morphology of the Aleutian Trench, and the continental slope to the 100-fathom isobath.

EQUIPMENT AND PROCEDURES

DEPTH SOUNDINGS

Figure 3 shows three different sets of depth sounding data:

1. 1927–1928, individual soundings—navigation control by sextant-measured horizontal angles;

2. 1965, depth-sounding traverses numbered 1 to 12 and intersecting tie line–navigation control by sextant-measured horizontal angles; and

3. 1965, depth-sounding traverses A to I and other tracklines between 147°40'W, 148°15'W and 59°35'N, 59°55'N—navigation control by Raydist.

The 1965 Raydist-controlled sounding data were used to prepare a bathymetric map showing the submarine topography off the southwestern tip of Montague Island (Figure 5). To show the extent and patterns of sea-floor uplift, bottom profiles of preearthquake and postearthquake submarine topography were prepared for traverses A to I (Figure 6) and

1 to 12 (Figure 7). The postearthquake or upper profiles of the cross sections shown in Figures 6 and 7 were prepared from the 1965 fathograms. To provide continuous profiles of preearthquake submarine topography from the individual soundings of the 1927–1928 surveys, the 1965 profiles were fitted to the 1927–1928 sounding data. In the process, all indications of recent faulting and tilting were removed or adjusted to achieve the best fit with the 1927–1928 sounding data. It was assumed in the use of this procedure that the only changes in sea-floor topography between the surveys of 1927–1928 and those of 1965 were brought about by the earthquake of 1964. The validity of this assumption has been reviewed by Malloy (1964, 1965).

Vertical uplift is evident on all the cross sections of Figures 6 and 7. The accuracy of the comparison, however, is believed to be better in the shoaler areas where the 1927–1928 sounding surveys had numerous crosslines to disclose any discrepancies in depths, whereas some of the 1927–1928 offshore survey areas had no crosslines. The 1965 soundings southwest of Montague Island are along tracklines that form an evenly spaced pattern of squares and are considered to be uniformly reliable. However, in that part of the area where the Raydist-controlled tracklines cross the sextant-controlled tracklines, the Raydist-controlled soundings are consistently 3 m deeper, although both surveys were made within a 2-week period by the USC&GS ship *Surveyor*. It is believed that these discrepancies in depths result from discrepancies in position of the Raydist-controlled tracklines, which may have been in the radio-wave shadow of Cape Cleare. One of the Raydist stations was located at 59°56.5'N, 148°3'W, north of Cape Cleare. Signals from this station had to pass over the surface features of the southwest tip of Montague Island before reaching the survey ship. The sextant-controlled soundings were not subject to this type of position error and are preferred wherever the two sets of survey tracklines overlap.

In this paper, emphasis is placed on the pattern of sea-floor uplift rather than on the exact amount of uplift, the details of which require additional hydrographic work. In general, the Raydist-controlled soundings corroborate the findings of the postearthquake reconnaissance surveys of 1964. Figure 8 shows contours of equal uplift and the faults along which movement occurred during the Prince William Sound, Alaska, earthquake.

SIDE-SCANNING SONAR

To obtain greater detail of the sea floor, a Westinghouse Ocean Bottom Scanning Sonar was towed along the Raydist-controlled tracklines southwest of Montague Island (Figure 2). The system consisted of two laterally directed scanning beams, and the instrument was towed above the ocean bottom by an electric-cable towing line, with the recording equipment and power source aboard the ship. The elec-

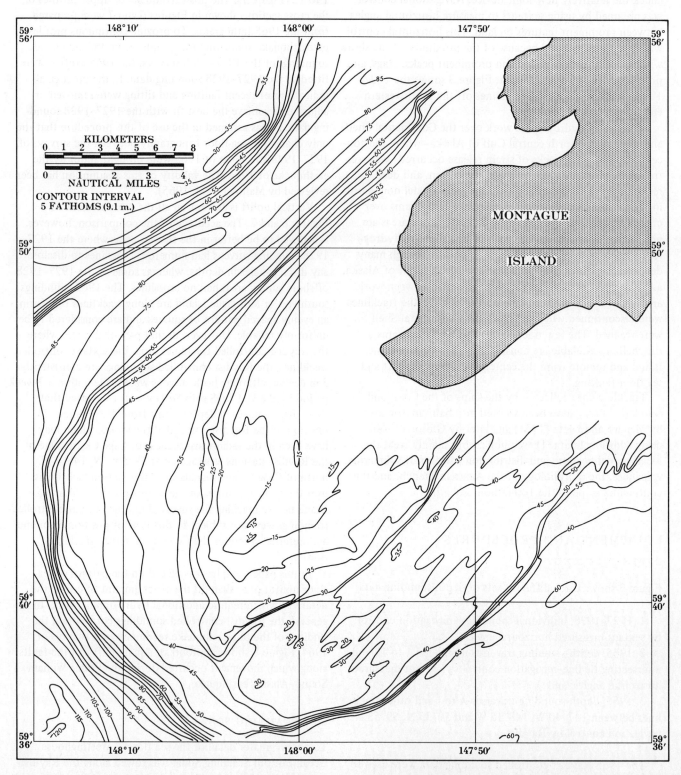

FIGURE 5   Bathymetric map showing submarine topography southwest of Montague Island based on 1965 hydrographic survey by USC&GS ship *Surveyor*.

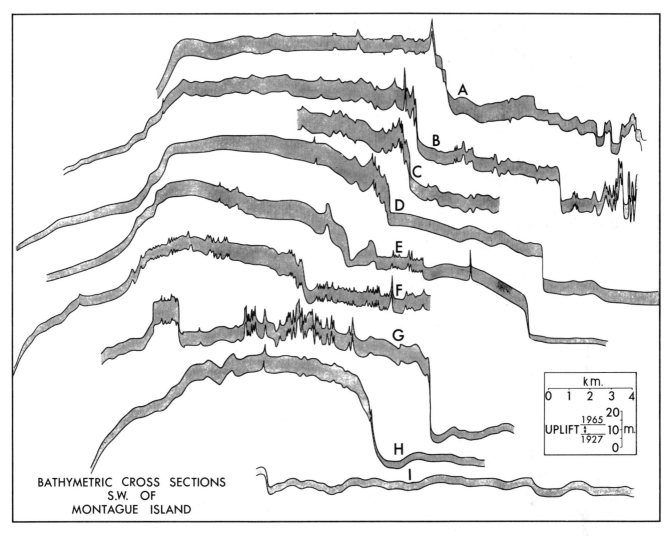

FIGURE 6   Comparison of 1965 and 1927–1928 sea-floor profiles southwest of Montague Island, showing amount of uplift along lines *A* to *I* of Figure 3.

tronics were housed in an instrument case (fish) 3.96 m long, 91 cm high, and 91 cm wide, and weighing about 682 kg in the air. High-frequency transceivers were mounted on the starboard and port sides of the fish to scan the ocean floor both to the right and to the left of the path over which the fish was towed. To identify signals returning from each side-scanning beam, the starboard transceiver was operated at 150 kHz, and the port transceiver at 160 kHz.

The side scanner was towed from the ship by means of a combination strain and electric-cable towline attached to the fish through a metal sleeve fitting and to the ship through an oceanographic winch equipped with heavy-duty slip rings. Extensive shipboard preparation was necessary before the side-scanning sonar equipment could be towed from the *Surveyor*, including installation of the winch on the after-deck and A-frames on the starboard and port sides adjacent

to the winch. To decrease the towing strain on the slightly underpowered winch, the fish was towed at a speed of 3 knots.

The shipboard equipment included a dual-channel amplifier and an Alden dual-channel wet-paper recorder, which provided simultaneous graphic display of the port and starboard transducer return signals.

The swath of ocean floor covered by the side-scanning sonar sweeps was 732 m wide (366 m to each side of the fish) when the fish was towed 68.5 m above the bottom. Side lobes of the main sound pulse were directed vertically, thus allowing the distance of the fish from the bottom to be displayed on both the recorder and the monitoring oscilloscope. The transducers, which were fired simultaneously twice a second, were arranged with their long axes fore and aft to produce a fan-shaped beam of sound with less than a degree of fore and aft width. Each laterally directed beam illumi-

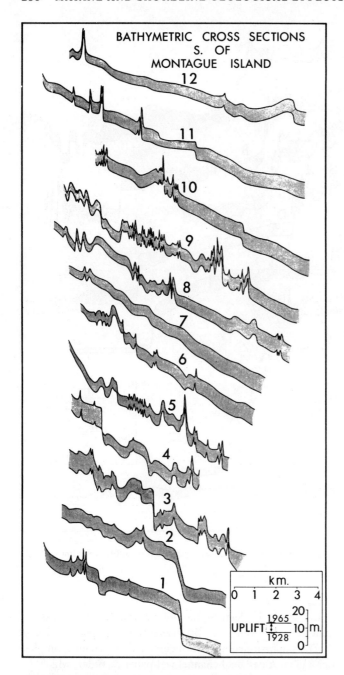

BATHYMETRIC CROSS SECTIONS
S. OF
MONTAGUE ISLAND

12

11

10

9

8

7

6

5

4

3

2

1

km.

0 1 2 3 4

UPLIFT $\begin{array}{c} 1965 \\ \updownarrow \\ \overline{1928} \end{array}$
20
10 m.
0

FIGURE 7 Comparison of 1965 and 1927–1928 sea-floor profiles southwest of Montague Island, showing amount of uplift along lines *1* to *12* of Figure 3.

nated the sea floor in a somewhat trapezoidal pattern that was approximately 1.1 m wide almost directly beneath the ship and 2 m wide at the maximum range of 366 m. In this manner, a new strip of ocean floor was illuminated each time the sonar was pulsed as the towed fish moved forward.

Reflected sound signals were fed from the unfocused receiving transducers into the amplifying and recording system. Variations in signal strength related to transmission geometry were compensated by the receiver circuitry. Distortions that normally would be caused by using a slant-range technique were compensated by equipping the recorder with helices that did not spiral linearly but coiled in such a manner that

the distortions were removed. Speed of the recording paper also was adjusted so that the scale along the width of the paper equaled the scale along the length. The record, therefore, was of equal scale from edge to edge. However, small distortions resulting from changes in the ship's speed remained on the record. These changes in speed were caused by currents and wind, neither of which could be monitored constantly.

The graphic record produced by the side-scanning sonar consists of closely spaced lines that correspond to each scan of the sonar beam. Each line varies in intensity with the strength of the reflected signal. Signals reflected from sea-

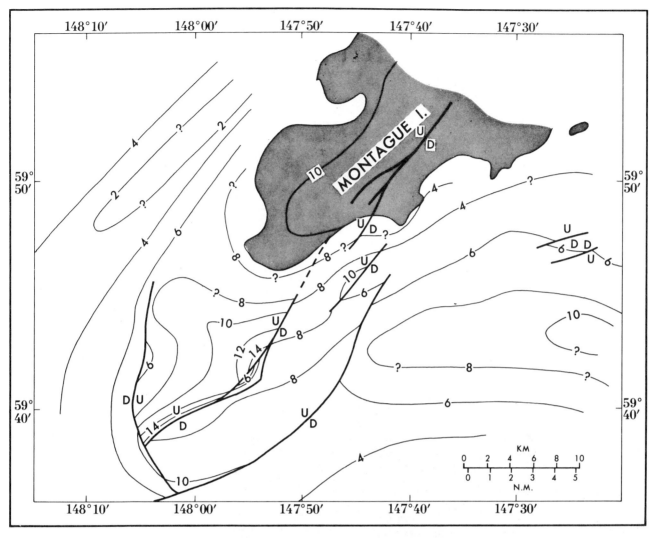

FIGURE 8   Map showing faults and isopleths of equal crustal uplift (in meters).

floor surfaces that are almost perpendicular to the fan-shaped sound beam have strong echoes and appear dark on the record. Areas of no echo remain white on the record and are presumed to be in the shadow zone behind some sea floor prominence. Successive scans of the sea floor produce an image of consecutive lines having a three-dimensional quality of light and shadow as shown in Figure 9. The principle of the side-scanning sonar technique is described in greater detail by Clay and others (1964).

BOTTOM PHOTOGRAPHY

Two camera lowerings were made from the USC&GS ship *Surveyor* during the 1964 survey while searching for the seaward extension of faults observed on Montague Island after the Prince William Sound earthquake. A line of bottom photographs was obtained during each lowering. One line extended from 59°46′N, 147°56′W to 59°40′N,

147°59′W; the other from 59°41′N, 147°56′W to 59°40′N, 147°59′W. A deep-sea stereocamera system from Edgerton, Germeshausen, & Grier, Inc., was used. The camera apparently drifted across a fresh fault scarp, as a number of photographs showed rock debris and surfaces indicative of a fresh break in the sea floor (Figure 4B). Bottom photographs taken northwest of the rejuvenated scarp showed a distinct joint pattern oriented NE–SW and NW–SE (Figure 4A). Color photography was used, but the black-and-white prints (reproduced as Figure 4) show sea-floor features in greater detail than the color photographs do.

DISCUSSION

The salient points concerning the patterns of uplift, as ascertained by the depth-sounding study, are: (1) four NE–SW trending scarps off the southwestern tip of Montague Island appear to have been rejuvenated during the earthquake,

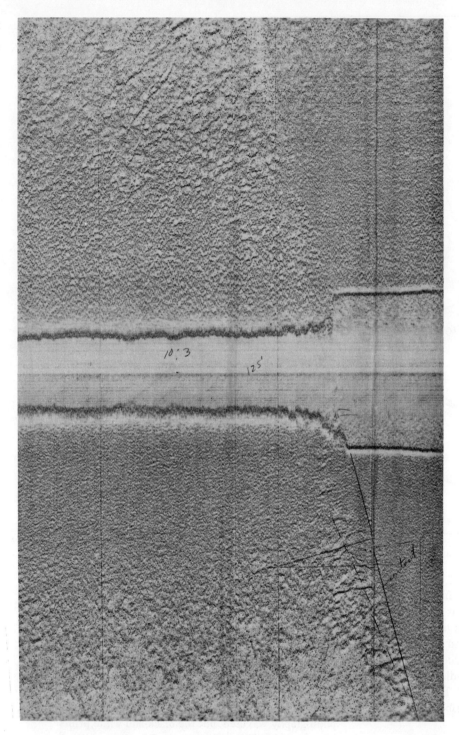

FIGURE 9 Photograph of ocean-bottom-scanning sonar record, showing fault scarp. The traverse runs NW–SE, and the fault scarp strikes NE.

(2) the sea floor northwest of each of the four rejuvenated scarps appears to have been tilted toward the northwest, (3) a moatlike band of lesser uplift surrounds the southwestern end of Montague Island, (4) the Hanning Bay Fault on the northwestern side of Montague Island does not appear to extend into the study area, and (5) the area covered by the study appears to have been uplifted at least 2 m.

The two prominent northeasterly striking scarps off southwest Montague Island (Figure 8) appear to be connected to the Patton Bay Fault complex, as the larger and more southeasterly scarp of the two cannot be traced on strike southeast of Cape Cleare. Also, there is evidence of *en échelon* offset between the southeasterly scarp and its assumed continuation as the Patton Bay Fault on Montague Island.

Most of the uplift profiles in Figures 6 and 7 show north-

westerly tilting of the fault block between the more prominent scarps and of the adjacent fault block to the northwest.
This northwesterly tilting follows the trend of the regional
tilting and the observed local tilting on Montague Island
(Plafker, 1965).

The fault shown at the western edge of the uplift contour
map (Figure 8) with a down-to-the-west relative movement is
anomalous to the other faults on the sea floor and on Montague Island. The evidence for faulting here, however, is not
as clear as for the other faults. Local flexing, which could explain the uplift discrepancies on either side of this gentle
scarp, may have occurred. In either case, this zone of differential disturbance might explain why northeasterly striking
faults are not found southwest of this zone.

The moatlike band of lesser uplift extending around Cape
Cleare can be explained by the fault-and-tilt pattern southeast
of the Cape. The apparent continuation of the moat southwest of Cape Cleare, however, requires a different explanation.
It may be attributed to (1) an artifact of the data, (2) the
isostatic effect of the island mass, or (3) a secondary center
of uplift.

The pattern of uplift on Montague Island (Plafker, 1965)
shows a center of maximum uplift—uplift that decreases toward the shoreline. The presence of this slope and of the
well-established maximum uplift offshore shows rather conclusively that an area of lesser uplift lies between the two
maxima.

The cause of the uplift moat cannot easily be explained
by isostasy. If the vertical forces of uplift as focused on
Montague Island were restrained to any extent by the island's
mass, the uplift maxima would not exist on or near the
island's concentration of mass. Rather, it appears as though
the forces that formed the land mass of Montague Island are
still active.

The cause of the uplift moat is probably the result of the
juxtaposition of two features of uplift minima defined by
common contours. The major portion of the uplift moat,
which lies southeast of Cape Cleare, can be explained by
northeast faulting and northwest tilting. The portion of the
uplift moat southwest of the Cape is probably best explained
by its location between centers of uplift maxima along the
Patton Bay Fault and its submarine extension.

Practically all the depth-sounding comparisons made in
the study area (as outlined in Figure 1) show shoaler depths
after the earthquake. Exceptions totaled less than 1 percent
and suggest that the limit of accuracy of the uplift contour
map is probably as good as the contour interval of 2 m.

The complicated contour pattern immediately southeast
of the northwesternmost scarp may be caused by a narrow
zone of depression that is parallel to the scarp; this can be
observed on the profiles of uplift (Figure 6). It is clearly
brought out on the reconnaissance survey profiles of uplift
described by Malloy (1964, 1965). The depression probably
is fault-controlled, that is, caused by a small down-to-the-

northwest fault running parallel to and southeast of the larger
fault plane.

Rock strata along the major fault scarps were not displaced
sufficiently to show any offset of magnetic anomaly lineaments on maps of magnetic field intensity prepared by the
authors.

Results of the side-scanning (side-looking) sonar survey
are summarized in Figure 2, which shows the trackline pattern
over which the side-scanning sonar fish was towed, the swath
of sea floor covered by the laterally directed sonar beams,
and the sea-floor features within the swath that could be
interpreted from the sonar record—areas of rock bottom and
sediment, and trends of certain topographic features. Features of fine detail, such as lineaments, were best detected in
areas of rock bottom—the strength of the reflected signals
being greater from rock bottom than from sediment-covered
sea floor. Thus, it was possible to record most of the scarps
and associated lineaments on the tabularlike submarine extension of Montague Island where the sea floor was predominantly bedrock with only local lenses of sediment present.

Figure 9, a portion of the side-scanning sonar record,
shows the trend and magnitude of a scarp over which the
sonar fish was towed. The center line represents the path of
the towed sonar fish. The dark reflections immediately to
the right and left of the path give the depth directly beneath
the ship, as detected by the nearly vertical side lobe of the
sonar beam. The variously shaded reflections extending
farther to the right and left on the record depict sea-floor
conditions to the maximum range of the side-scanning sonar
beams. Both the vertical- and side-scanning portions of this
section of the record show a difference in the lithologic character of the sea floor above and below the scarp.

The sea-floor materials shown in Figure 2 are of three
types: bare rock over almost the entire sea floor northwest
of the northwesternmost fault scarp—in the area of shoaler
water over the tabularlike extension of Montague Island; rock
and lenses of sediment in the area between the two prominent fault scarps; and unconsolidated sediment southeast of
the southeasternmost scarp (Figure 10). Many of the lineaments shown in Figure 2 are presumed to be joints, scarps,
and lines of outcropping strata. An interpretation of these
lineaments, other than those that appear to be fault scarps, is
not attempted because the area of investigation belongs, geologically, to the complex structural features of southwestern
Montague Island. On the other hand, the geology of the sea
floor between islands, where fewer forces have interacted
during regional uplift, can be relatively simple compared to
that on land. For this reason, joint patterns—which provide
clues to regional tectonic processes—might be studied to
better advantage in the sediment-free offshore areas. In the
1965 side-scanning sonar survey, however, the detected lineaments did not produce the consistent patterns that one might
expect from studying the orientation of joint patterns on the
bottom photographs. Perhaps outcropping strata deflected

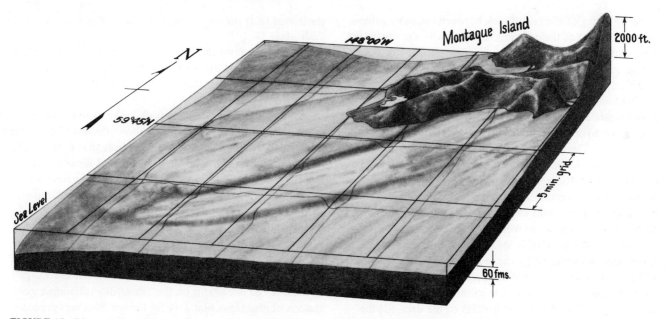

FIGURE 10   Diagram of sea floor southwest of Montague Island, showing two major submarine scarps. Southeasternmost scarp is connected to the island by *en échelon* scarps.

the echo returns and confused the joint-pattern picture.

Very little is known about the details of failure in the earth's crust and the forces of earthquake dimensions that cause crustal deformation, faulting, and vertical crustal changes. Most earthquakes for which epicenter data are available occur around the edge of the Pacific Basin and along the ocean rises and associated fracture zones of the world ocean. Thus, a large number of earthquakes are submarine earthquakes, sometimes called seaquakes. Earthquakes whose hypocenters occur under land areas produce tectonic changes in the earth's surface, but these changes are rarely known in detail because the reference datum, by which land movements are determined, exists only as a series of scattered points or bench marks. Patterns of crustal deformation can be defined only to the extent that the displacement of bench marks, and intervening surface features relative to the bench marks, can be measured. It is conceivable that an earthquake-deformed land surface, which was mapped by photogrammetrically controlled surveys before the earthquake, could be remapped by a similar survey following an earthquake after the disturbed reference points or bench marks were redetermined. This type of study would provide a method whereby an area of land surface could be examined in detail for patterns of uplift. To the writers' knowledge, this type of survey has not been reported.

The problem of determining patterns of crustal uplift on the sea floor differs from that on land in that there are no bench marks. The reference datum is not a series of isolated points; it is the continuous plane of the sea surface. Thus, only in areas where detailed depth soundings were made prior

to crustal deformations can one determine the patterns of crustal deformation on the sea floor. Plafker (1965) has pointed out that the Prince William Sound earthquake was unique in that it not only produced a vast area of subsidence and uplift, but in that so many parts of the area could be measured and contoured because of the irregularity of the Alaska coastline and the numerous islands, all of which served as bench marks in determining the amount of deformation of the sea floor. Modern surveys and techniques will make it possible to extend investigations of submarine crustal deformations over more and more of the zone of earthquake activity surrounding the Pacific. Such studies will contribute to a better understanding of the generation of tsunamis—one of many problems involving the interaction of land and sea in seismically active marine and coastal regions.

The importance of hydrographic work in Alaskan waters has two significant aspects:

1. Each year more ships with deeper drafts use Alaska's vast and complex waterways. This requires many long seasons of bottom-sounding investigations. The task is further complicated by Alaska's geology, as the rugged mountains and many glaciers contribute enough sediment to the rivers, fiords, bays, and estuaries to change bottom-sounding charts radically within a 1-year period (Jordan, 1962). Another cause of frustration to the hydrographic engineer is the continuing tectonic unrest in southern Alaska. During the 1964 earthquake, as much as 90,000 km² of sea floor and islands may have been uplifted (Plafker, 1965), causing dangerous shoaling of the sea floor in many areas.

2. Another aspect of relevancy is the need for continuing detailed hydrographic surveys in areas of crustal deformation. Each time that crustal deformation resulting from earthquake forces is measured, more is learned about the strength and competency of the earth's crust. Among the major authenticated crustal deformations of large magnitude are those resulting from the Yakutat Bay (Alaska) earthquake of 1899 and the Prince William Sound earthquake of 1964, about 420 km apart. The Yakutat Bay earthquake was investigated 6 years after the disturbance. Portions of the earth's crust were calculated to have been uplifted in excess of 14 m, on the basis of new and old barnacle and other sessile organism lines on rocks along the shore (Tarr and Martin, 1912). The 1964 earthquake was accompanied by uplift in excess of 10 m on southwestern Montague Island and, according to detailed bathymetric studies, uplift in excess of 14 m in offshore areas southwest of Montague Island. It may be coincidental that these two maxima of recorded uplift are about equal. It is also possible that these maxima are quantitatively related to local tectonic forces and to the strength of the earth's crust as deformed by a single seismic event.

ACKNOWLEDGMENTS

The authors are grateful for the assistance rendered during the field investigations by Capt. Don A. Jones, Commanding Officer of the USC&GS ship *Surveyor*; Comdr. A. R. Benton, Jr., Navigation and Field Operations Officer; L. A. Weeks, Chief Scientist; and other members of the ship's complement. They also wish to acknowledge the helpful suggestions and critical reading of the manuscript by H. B. Stewart, Jr., R. S. Dietz, G. Keller, L. A. Weeks, and R. N. Harbison, all of the Institute of Oceanography, ESSA.

REFERENCES

Clay, C. S., John Ess, and Irving Weisman, 1964. Lateral echo sounding of the ocean bottom on the continental rise. *Journal of Geophysical Research*, 69 (September 15), 3823–3835.

Gibson, William M., 1960. Submarine topography in the Gulf of Alaska. *Geological Society of America Bulletin*, 71 (July), 1087–1108.

Grantz, Arthur, George Plafker, and Reuben Kachadoorian, 1964. Alaska's Good Friday earthquake, March 27, 1964: a preliminary geologic evaluation. U.S. Geological Survey Circular 491. Washington: U.S. Geological Survey. 35 p.

Jordan, G. F., 1962. Redistribution of sediments in Alaskan bays and inlets. *Geographical Review*, 52 (Winter), 548–558.

Malloy, Richard J., 1964. Crustal uplift southwest of Montague Island, Alaska. *Science*, 146 (November 20), 1048–1049.

Malloy, Richard J., 1965. Seafloor upheaval. *Geo-Marine Technology*, 1 (May–June), 22–26.

Menard, H. W., and R. S. Dietz, 1951. Submarine geology of the Gulf of Alaska. *Geological Society of America Bulletin*, 62 (October), 1263–1285.

Moffit, F. H., 1954. Geology of the Prince William Sound region, Alaska. U.S. Geological Survey Bulletin 989 E. Washington: Government Printing Office. 310 p.

Plafker, George, 1965. Tectonic deformation associated with the 1964 Alaska earthquake. *Science*, 148 (June 25), 1675–1687.

Tarr, Ralph S., and Lawrence Martin, 1912. The earthquakes of Yakutat Bay, Alaska, in September, 1899. U.S. Geological Survey Professional Paper 69. Washington: Government Printing Office. 135 p.

ROLAND VON HUENE
U.S. GEOLOGICAL SURVEY

GEORGE G. SHOR, JR.
SCRIPPS INSTITUTION OF OCEANOGRAPHY

RICHARD J. MALLOY*
ENVIRONMENTAL SCIENCE SERVICES ADMINISTRATION †

Offshore Tectonic Features in the Affected Region

ABSTRACT: Marine geophysical and geological studies show the configuration and distribution of tectonic elements in the offshore area affected by the 1964 Alaska earthquake. Faulting in Holocene time was confined to a linear zone near the shore that parallels regional geologic trends. This zone separates a landward area of uplift from a large subsiding basin as much as 4 km deep. The seaward flank of this basin is a broad complex arch that coincides with the edge of the Continental Shelf; it forms the transition from the shelf to the rugged continental slope. At the base of the slope, there is a zone of stratified rock that is locally deformed, beyond which the sea floor has been downwarped to form the Aleutian Trench. The trench is partially filled with undeformed sedimentary strata.

During the earthquake, the maximum uplift off Kodiak Island occurred on the arch at the edge of the Continental Shelf. At Middleton Island, which is north along the axis of this arch, as much as 8 m of uplift occurred. Episodes of uplift appear to have dominated deformation of the arch during Holocene time. In other areas, however, the direction of deformation during the earthquake was not the same as the Holocene or late Tertiary net direction. A thrust-fault model appears to fit best the deformation during the 1964 earthquake, whereas a steep-fault model best fits the known late Tertiary net deformation. In general, however, the thrust-fault model fits the observed features better than the steep-fault model.

---

*Now with U.S. Navy Civil Engineering Laboratory, Port Hueneme, California.
†Now, in part, the National Ocean Survey, NOAA.

INTRODUCTION

Immediately after the 1964 Alaska earthquake, earth scientists began searching for a surface trace of the causative fault. The area of search was large, very rugged, and for the most part uninhabited. First reports of damage to Alaska's towns and cities left a confused pattern of earthquake intensity, but, as seismological evidence developed, the pattern of aftershock epicenters pointed toward deformation offshore. This was further confirmed by the large tsunami and the obvious uplift of the Gulf of Alaska shoreline, suggesting deformation on the Continental Shelf or possibly in the Aleutian Trench.

Ships with geophysical instrumentation were not available immediately after the earthquake for systematic studies of sea-floor changes caused by the earthquake. In fact, there was no precedent for marine studies of contemporary earthquake effects. But during the following two summers and intermittently in the next 5 years, various marine investigations of the Continental Shelf in the area affected by the earthquake were made. The U.S. Coast and Geodetic Survey (USC&GS) ship *Surveyor* made gravimetric, magnetometric, and continuous seismic-reflection transects between Cape Hinchinbrook and the Trinity Islands during the summer of 1964. The gravity and magnetic observations, combined with previous observations at sea and with observations on land by the U.S. Geological Survey (USGS), have been reported by Barnes and others (1966). Closely spaced seismic and bathymetric transects immediately surrounding Montague Island have been described by Malloy (1964, 1965; and Malloy and Merrill, 1969, and this volume); these show that faults on Montague Island that were active during the 1964 earthquake continue out to sea (Plafker, 1969, and Geology volume). Malloy used a 1,000-joule EG&G-Alpine spark sound source aboard the *Surveyor*. A 20,000-joule Rayflex spark system was employed during the same summer by Shor on the Scripps Institution of Oceanography (SIO) ship *Oconostota*. Two SIO transects extend from the Gulf of Alaska to Kodiak Island where Shor has made seismic-reflection profiles (Shor, 1962, 1965; and

Shor, in preparation); a third SIO transect extends past Middleton Island, through the Hinchinbrook Entrance, and into Prince William Sound. A study of structures and post-glacial sedimentation of the Sound has been published (von Huene, Shor, and Reimnitz, 1967); SIO also made a seismic survey of the Copper River Delta (Reimnitz, 1966; 1972, this volume). Roland von Huene made seven seismic transects across the Continental Shelf and the Aleutian Trench in the summer of 1965, using combined Rayflex and EG&G spark energy systems to obtain as much as 38,000 joules of energy. In 1968 he made some short traverses on the Continental Shelf with a 15,000-joule system, and in 1969 he made two transects across the shelf and trench, using a 120,000-joule system.

This paper summarizes and considers 1964 Alaska earth-quake data gathered by the USC&GS, SIO, the Naval Ord-nance Test Station (NOTS), and the USGS. Many of these observations have been reported elsewhere (von Huene, 1966; von Huene, Shor, and Reimnitz, 1967; von Huene and others, 1967; Malloy and Merrill, 1969, and this volume; von Huene and Shor, 1969), but data gathered in 1968 and 1969 by von Huene are reported here for the first time.

There are great differences in the seismic-reflection data summarized here. Some data are from the Sonoprobe, one of the first commercially available instruments of its kind; others are from far more sophisticated instruments developed 15 years later. Structural detail in higher-frequency records (EG&G-Alpine) was obscured in lower-frequency records (Rayflex), but the depth of information in the low-frequency records was 10 to 20 times greater than in a high-frequency record along the same traverse. We have integrated these data here without describing our comparative evaluation of rec-ords and without presenting all the seismic records.

TECTONIC SETTING OF THE CONTINENTAL MARGIN AFFECTED BY THE EARTHQUAKE

MAJOR TECTONIC UNITS

Strain was released by the Alaska earthquake over an area roughly 80,000 to 100,000 mi^2. Aftershock epicenters were located in this area, deformations in vertical and horizontal directions were measured on land (Plafker, 1969, and Geol-ogy volume), and broad deformation on the Continental Shelf was inferred from development of a major tsunami (Van Dorn, 1965; Plafker, 1969, and Geology volume). In the northeastern end of the area affected by the earthquake, two morphologic and structural trends intersect at an angle of about 105° (Figure 1). For convenience, one trend is here called the Aleutian trend or structural system, and the other is called the Alaska mainland trend or structural system. Between them is the St. Elias transition zone (von Huene and Shor, 1969).

The Aleutian trend strikes N45°E. Major morphologic features that define this trend are the eastern Aleutian Trench and continental slope, the Kenai and Kodiak Mountains, Shelikof Strait, Cook Inlet, and the Alaska Peninsula (Fig-ure 1). The Aleutian trend is also marked by a belt of high seismicity and a chain of volcanic islands (Tobin and Sykes, 1966; Algermissen and others, 1969, and Seismology and Geodesy volume).

The Alaska mainland trend strikes N60°W. In the area affected by the earthquake, it is the western end of the coastal trend along the mainland of the Gulf of Alaska. The Chugach–St. Elias Mountains and the continental slope mark this trend morphologically. In contrast to the Aleutian sys-tem, the Alaska mainland system has a smoother continental slope whose transition to the deep oceanic area is marked by a local shallow trough. Its recorded seismicity has been less than that of the Aleutian system (Algermissen and others, 1969, and Seismology and Geodesy volume).

In a tectonic analysis of the earthquake, it is helpful to differentiate the deformation along each system because the Aleutian system was the primary tectonic system along which the earthquake occurred. Aftershock strain release was con-centrated mostly in an elongate zone paralleling the Aleutian trend (von Huene, Malloy, Shor, and St.-Amand, 1967; Algermissen and others, 1969, and Seismology and Geodesy volume). Contours of tectonic uplift and subsidence trend along the Aleutian system, then bend sharply at the juncture of the Aleutian and Alaska mainland systems, and continue a short distance along the mainland trend (Plafker, 1969, and Geology volume). The initial tsunami wave front paralleled the Aleutian trend (Van Dorn, 1965; Spaeth and Berkman, 1969). Although the role of tectonism along the Alaska trend and its interaction with tectonism along the Aleutian trend are unclear, the Alaska mainland trend probably played a secondary role during the earthquake. In the following dis-cussion, therefore, the tectonic effects along the Alaska main-land system are clearly separated from those of the Aleutian system.

TECTONIC ELEMENTS OF THE ALEUTIAN SYSTEM

The earthquake affected an area whose geology and mor-phology indicate a juncture between the continental and the oceanic crusts. The Kenai–Kodiak Mountains descend to a fiord-indented coast, which becomes increasingly submerged in Prince William Sound and forms mountainous islands sepa-rated by channels. The fiords are deeper than the adjacent topographically subdued Continental Shelf. Marking the sea-ward limit of the shelf is a discontinuous low ridge whose outer flank is the beginning of the rough and complex con-tinental slope. This slope ends at the Aleutian Trench and forms the steep landward trench wall—steep in contrast to the seaward wall, which is a gentle slope (1° to 3°) leading to

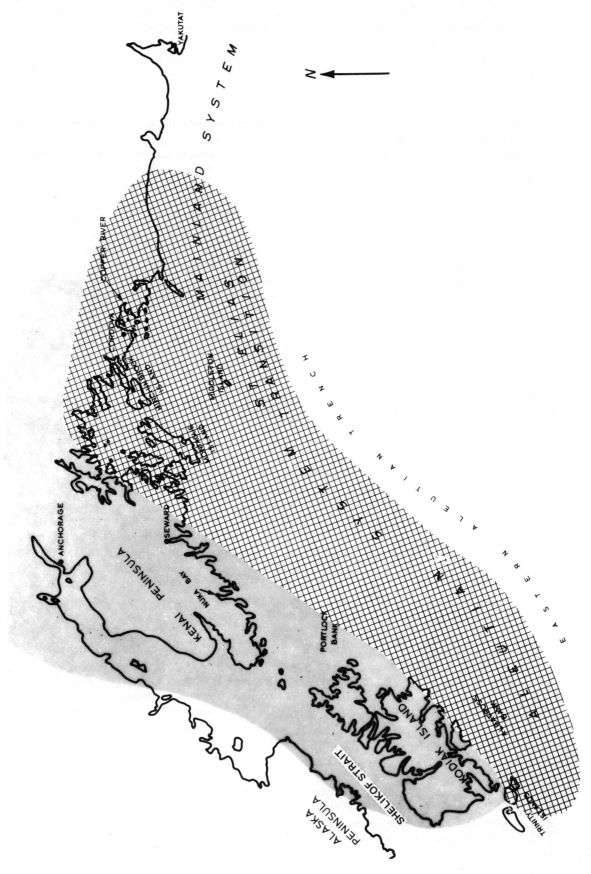

FIGURE 1 Location map of the area affected by the 1964 Alaska earthquake. Shaded areas show uplift and subsidence that occurred during the earthquake (after Plafker, 1969).

the deep Gulf of Alaska sea floor. For convenience of discussion, these tectonic elements are grouped into: (1) nearshore and fiord areas, (2) Continental Shelf, and (3) continental slope and the Aleutian Trench. These groupings are made on a structural or tectonic basis, although it is recognized that the names of each group have a physiographic connotation.

Nearshore and Fiord Areas

Prince William Sound, where the initial epicenter of the earthquake was located, has apparently very little postglacial faulting (von Huene, Shor, and Reimnitz, 1967). Preglacial faults and folds probably influenced the trend of the fiords, which parallel regional structures. These fiords were eroded in rocks of Cretaceous and early Tertiary age by glaciers possibly 2 km thick. During the last recession of the glaciers, morainal debris was deposited upon clean, hard-rock fiord floors and later covered by glacial outwash and sediment. The later sediments have pronounced planar reflecting horizons that would readily show any deformation (Figure 2).

Only four small postglacial faults were found in the Sound (Figure 2C). Records of the postglacial sediments show bending in strata where the faults emerge from the basement. Nowhere does vertical separation exceed 6 m. The deformation is greatest close to the basement and decreases upward, suggesting continuous deformation or possibly some differential compaction. One fault extends upward to the sea floor and is thus the only one located that could have been active during the 1964 earthquake.

In light of the numerous tectonic features seen on land (Condon and Cass, 1958; Condon, 1965), it is surprising to find so little evidence of faulting near the main epicenter of the Alaska earthquake. The postglacial sediments are undeformed where faults recognized on land are projected seaward.

A geologic situation similar to that in Prince William Sound is found further southwest along the Kenai Peninsula in Nuka Bay (von Huene, 1966). The bay is a fiord 70 km long, excavated in steeply tilted Cretaceous graywacke and slate and in Tertiary intrusive rocks. Its parallelism with the regional trend suggests erosion along an older tectonic structure. No faults were observed in a thick sequence of postglacial sediment in the fiord. Nuka Bay subsided 6 ft during the earthquake and is approximately on the axis of maximum subsidence (Plafker, 1969, and Geology volume). Plafker believes that low cirque levels along the coast indicate past subsidence, but no evidence for such subsidence was found in the marine data. On the contrary, a terrace 20 to 30 m deep in sheltered water, that was probably formed by wave action, apparently reflects postglacial sea-level stability (Reimnitz and von Huene, 1969).

South of the Kenai Peninsula on the shallow ocean floor that separates the peninsula from the Kodiak Island group, no large faults with postglacial deformation were found

(von Huene, 1966). The acoustic basement has a rough topography similar to that on land; little, if any, indication of faulting or tight folding is found in sediment strata above basement. Nearshore, sedimentary structures of probable glacial origin are common.

The Kenai Peninsula, the Kodiak Island group, and the intervening Continental Shelf are here grouped into the Kenai-Kodiak structural block. This area has reacted tectonically as a large unit without significant local flexure or displacement along individual faults in Holocene time.

Continental Shelf

The broad Continental Shelf from seaward of the Kenai-Kodiak block to the continental slope is here considered a tectonic unit. Structures found on the shelf parallel the regional trend and can be separated into three major tectonic features. As shown in Figure 3, the shelf has a subsiding Tertiary basin separated from the uplifted Kenai-Kodiak block by a wide fault zone that forms its landward flank. The seaward flank is a broad asymmetric arch that has its axial area where the shelf breaks to form the continental slope. This highly oversimplified picture of the Continental Shelf is adequate in a discussion of the data presently available, but it will probably be modified when more detailed studies are made.

Fault Zone

Many folds and faults were found in seismic records and bathymetric profiles across the Continental Shelf (Figure 4). They are concentrated in a wide zone off Hinchinbrook and Montague islands and the Kodiak Island group. Bathymetric profiles made without concurrent seismic profiles are indicated in Figure 4, and the sense of vertical separation along faults is determined with less certainty where seismic information is absent. Only selected ship tracks south of Montague Island were used in compiling Figure 4; more detailed information can be found in Malloy's work (1965) and in that of Malloy and Merrill (1969, and this volume).

Structures that appear to have formed recently and that may have been active at the sea floor during the 1964 earthquake are denoted by special symbols in Figure 5. The somewhat subjective criterion for judging the recency of a fault scarp is a sharp bathymetric expression of the structure on the sea floor. Such judgment was usually made from fathograms recorded concurrently with the seismic profiles. Activation or rupture at the sea floor in 1964 can be demonstrated only for faults that are on and adjacent to Montague Island (Malloy, 1964, 1965; Malloy and Merrill, 1969, and this volume). These faults cut hard and well-lithified rocks, and therefore they cannot be used as general examples for the durability of other sea-floor scarps that cut softer sediments. Because there are suggestions of both rapid and slow scarp destruction, some of the sharp bathymetric features

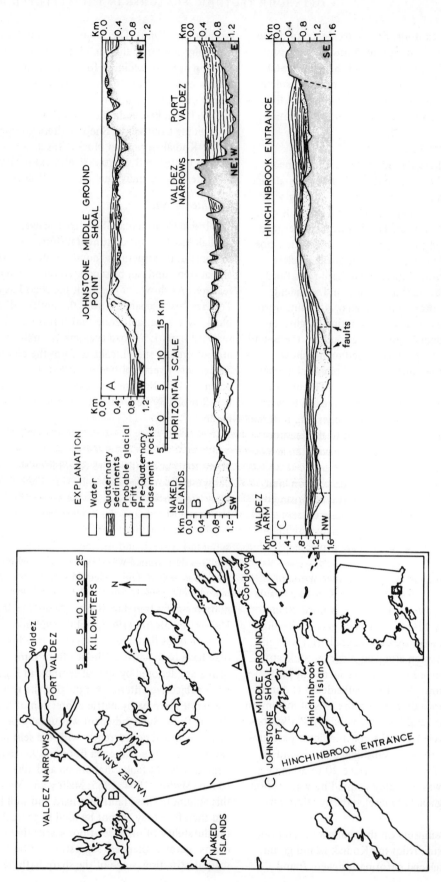

FIGURE 2 Geologic cross sections based on seismic records in Prince William Sound. The vertical scale, five times the horizontal scale, indicates conservative thicknesses of sediments, which could be 20 percent greater. Glacial drift near Johnstone Point may be basement instead. Faults are drawn vertically where their dip is unknown.

270

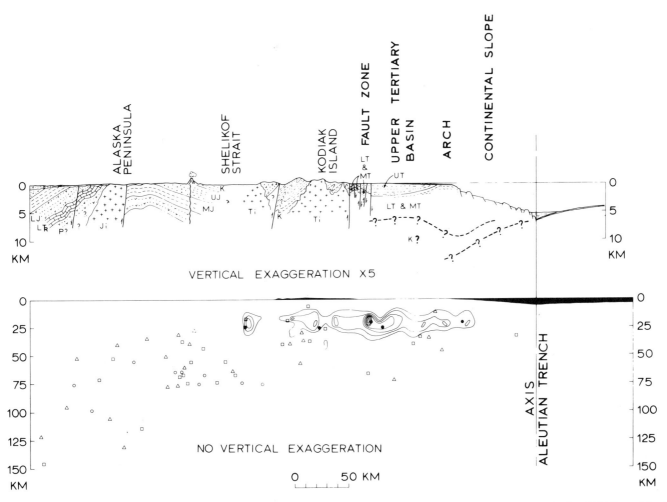

FIGURE 3 Section across the Aleutian structural system, showing a composite of aftershock hypocenters from the latitude of Middleton Island to the southern end of Kodiak Island (from von Huene and Shor, 1969). P – Permian rocks; LT – Lower Triassic rocks; LJ, MJ, UJ – Lower, Middle, and Upper Jurassic rocks; Ji – Jurassic intrusive rocks; K – Cretaceous rocks; LT, MT, UT – lower, middle, and upper Tertiary rocks; Ti – lower Tertiary intrusive rocks. Hypocenters are from Tobin and Sykes (1966): ○ is most accurate, □ is of intermediate accuracy, and △ is least accurate. Contours represent strain release from aftershocks of the 1964 Alaska earthquake in 100-unit intervals of equivalent magnitude– 3 earthquakes per 157 km^2. Individual aftershocks greater than magnitude 6.0 are shown with filled circles. Queried contacts extrapolated from seismic-refraction stations suggest a lower and middle Tertiary thickened section, possibly a continental rise, seaward of a similar Cretaceous feature.

could have been formed at various times before 1964.

Ship tracks along which marine geophysical measurements were made are too widely spaced to allow determination of the length of most faults and folds. Where structures can be identified with confidence in closely spaced seismic transects, they show significant variations along strike. Well-developed faults may change character or die out between records only 4 km apart (Figure 4). One large, broad fold southwest of Middleton Island changes character significantly in an adjacent transect made only a few kilometers away. The longest fault observed at the sea floor extends for at least 50 km. Continuity between structures in adjacent transects is indicated in Figures 4 and 5, where outstanding similarity or very

close transect spacing establishes continuity with a good degree of certainty. Present evidence from the Continental Shelf suggests a few long tectonic features and many that are relatively short, but a much more detailed survey would be required to establish the length and strike of individual faults and folds.

In Prince William Sound, along Hinchinbrook and Montague islands, between Montague and Kodiak islands as well as along Kodiak Island, tectonic structures strike approximately parallel to the continental margin and the Aleutian Trench (Figure 4). However, off the Copper River Delta, where the regional trend changes direction fairly sharply, subparallel structures striking nearly east are separated from

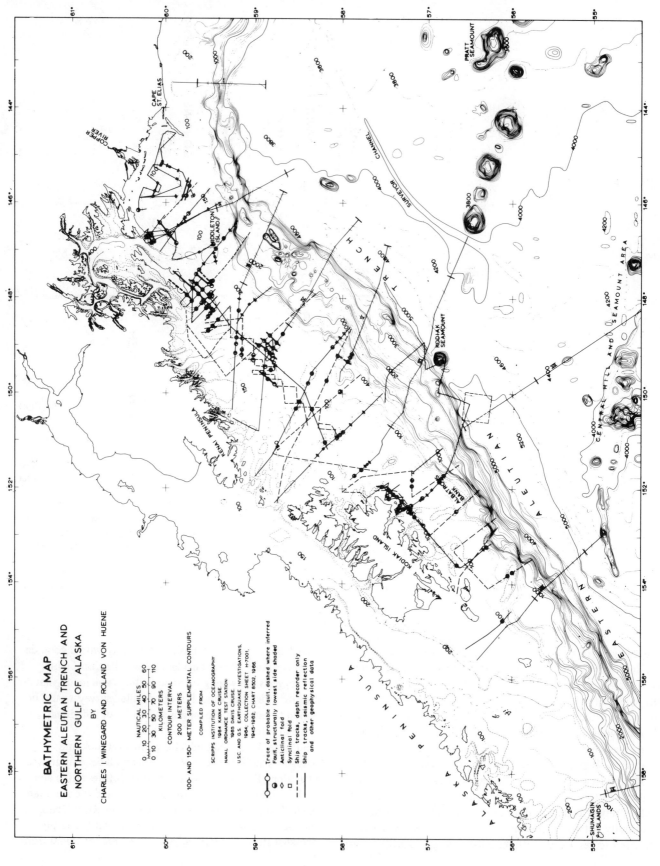

FIGURE 4 Bathymetric map showing, with nondirectional symbols, the location of tectonic features outlined by marine data.

272

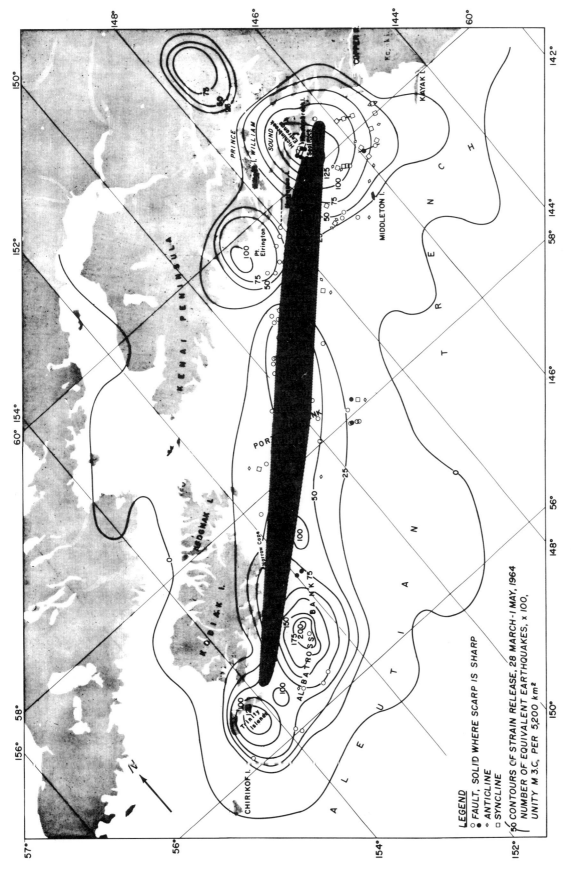

FIGURE 5 Map of strain release and geologic structures found along seismic and bathymetric traverses. Strain release summed over 0.4°-radius circles. Contours are based on preliminary aftershock data from the U.S. Coast and Geodetic Survey and are smoothed graphically. Dark shaded area is the offshore zone of faults inferred from the marine geophysical data.

northeast trending structures by only a short distance, indicating an abrupt change in direction rather than a curved section joining two structural trends. The seismic reflection and bathymetric data indicate extreme structural complexity in the St. Elias transition similar to that established in the Katalla district by Miller (1961).

A large fault zone along Hinchinbrook and Montague islands and the Kodiak group of islands is suggested by the assembled information, especially when the relative quality of each record and other conditions are taken into account. It appears to be well developed from southern Montague Island to Portlock Bank and off Kodiak Island but less clearly defined immediately south of Portlock Bank and north of the southern end of Montague Island. The zone's northern end is probably in the complex deformed region around the Copper River Delta, and its southern end is probably near the Trinity Islands.

Selected tracings of reflection records (Figure 6) show

how faults are concentrated on the landward side of the Continental Shelf. There is little doubt that between southern Montague Island and Portlock Bank the groups of faults belong to a single fault zone. Present data suggest that many faults are shorter than 30 km, the distance between most transects in this area. Along northern Hinchinbrook Island, Reimnitz (1966) inferred a large fault zone near the shore at a contact between upper Tertiary sediments of the shelf and the lithified rocks of the island. Some faults of the zone cross a platform of the harder rock that projects around southern Montague Island. The zone is not as well known from about 25 km southwest of Montague Island to just northeast of the Kodiak Island group because only shallow strata are clearly shown in the records; but at the northern end of Kodiak Island, a seismic-refraction study (Shor and von Huene, in press) shows a large offset of lithified sedimentary rocks across the fault zone. Along Kodiak Island the reflection seismic transects outline a fault zone similar to the one

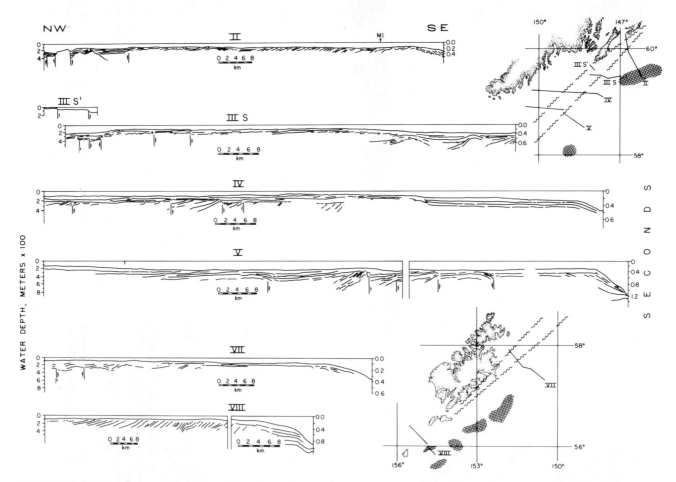

FIGURE 6   Simplified tracings of selected seismic-reflection records across the Continental Shelf between the Kenai Peninsula and Kodiak. The offshore fault zone is indicated on the location maps by a series of wavy lines; observed anticlinal areas at shelf edge whose extent is interpreted from bathymetry are indicated by cross-hatching. All faults are drawn vertically, but dips may be 60° in some cases. *MI* in profile II indicates projection of Middleton Island into the transect.

along Hinchinbrook and Montague islands (Figure 7). A large fault zone has been mapped by Capps (1937) and Moore (1967) along the coast of Kodiak Island.

Seismic records indicate two types of faults. The most common deformational geometry is shown in inset V A of Figure 8. On the northwest flank of this structure, the dip of reflectors increases with depth, indicating that deformation continued over a long period of time. Local unconformities show that the crest of the structure was sometimes elevated to wave base or above sea level. The steepest flank of all such structures is on the southeast side; associated fault scarps all face seaward. The structure changes amplitude significantly in 4 km (inset V B, Figure 8). No sharp surface expression occurs in inset V A of Figure 8, but a 10-m scarp on the sea floor is found 4 km away in inset V B. This type of structure generally appears to have a limited extent along strike. Transects in the fault zone commonly cross two or three of these structures at relatively close intervals, suggesting overlapping shorter faults.

None of the fault planes associated with this type of structure has been directly observed; however, the data indicate attitudes ranging from 60° to vertical. The geometry of these structures would be difficult to produce without a reverse component of slip along a fault that dips steeply landward.

The second type of structure expressed in the records is a sharp fold that must be fault-controlled. All these have a sharp surface expression and adjacent zone of deformed reflectors that is narrower than the zone adjacent to a reverse fault (insets II E and IV F, Figure 8). The scarps, some of which have a 40-m relief, face either northwest (landward) or southeast (seaward). Some of these structures are longer (at least 20 km) and apparently do not have as long a history of activity as the first type, because the deepest strata are deformed about as much as the sea floor. In other words, the faulting has occurred in a short period of time, and the sea floor has not been modified by erosion or sedimentation since then. The sharp flexure and continuity along strike may indicate a thinner sequence of strata through which stresses from the basement are transmitted to the sea floor.

Both the first and second types of structures have approximately the same strike and are separated by distances of 10 km or less. Both types may be reverse faults, and some may dip seaward. However, there is a stronger possibility that those with a seaward dip are normal faults. The absence of deformation in what are presumed to be incompetent strata immediately adjacent to the fault plane is evidence of little horizontal compression. Faults with landward or northwest-facing scarps are too numerous (40 percent of the faults recorded) to be dismissed as local variants. They appear to be intermixed with reverse faults, and the relative effects of normal and reverse faulting are unknown.

The steep faults suggested by marine data also occur along subaerial parts of the Kodiak fault system mapped on land.

Capps (1937) observed that faults along the southeast coast of Kodiak Island are nearly vertical and are accompanied by local severe folding, distortion, and alteration. Moore (in Grantz, 1964; Moore, 1967) describes the faults as a high-angle fault system separating Tertiary from metamorphosed Mesozoic rocks with fault planes dipping either landward or seaward. On southern Montague Island, Plafker (1969, and Geology volume) reported a 55° northwest to vertical dip on faults that broke at the surface in 1964.

Relation of the fault zone to maximum aftershock strain release is shown in Figure 5, where strain is represented in terms of the equivalent number of magnitude 3.0 earthquakes. Each end of the aftershock strain-release field has two distinct maxima. The largest occurs off Hinchinbrook Island and spreads into the area of structural complexity off the Copper River. A smaller maximum occurs to the west in an area of few data and of no known, large, active tectonic feature. At the southern end of the strain field a large maximum is near Albatross Bank, where an anticlinal structure occurs at the continental margin. A linear area of greater strain release between these termini corresponds well to the fault zone between Kodiak and Montague islands, supporting the suggestions from other evidence that the zone was active during the 1964 earthquake.

In summary, the fault zone may be characterized as a system of steep faults, generally shorter than 30 km but sometimes 50 km long in a zone up to 30 km wide extending from Kodiak to Hinchinbrook islands. Fault planes dip both landward and seaward; some are reverse faults and some are probably normal faults. This fault zone separates an uplifted area of deformed metamorphosed Mesozoic sedimentary rocks from a subsiding late Tertiary basin on the Continental Shelf. The zone corresponds roughly to the most intense aftershock seismicity after the 1964 Alaska earthquake.

Tertiary Basin

The late Tertiary basin is formed by depression of the area seaward of the fault zone. This is seen off Kodiak Island (Figure 7, transect ED). To the north, the records were made with older instruments, and the relationship between faults and strata is more obscure (Figure 6).

The thickness and age of sediment in the basin are indicated by various data. Using seismic refraction techniques, Shor (1965) found a section of sedimentary rocks 3 km thick off Kodiak. Between the Trinity and Chirikof islands to the southwest, the apparent thickness of truncated strata at the sea floor is about 4 km (Figure 6, record VIII). A traverse off Kodiak shows an abrupt magnetic dip in the area of the basin (Figure 7, transect EF).

The age of the basin fill is inferred to be late Tertiary, because upper Miocene and Pliocene strata are exposed in a truncated part of the arch forming the seaward flank of the basin (von Huene and Shor, 1969). Older basins must have

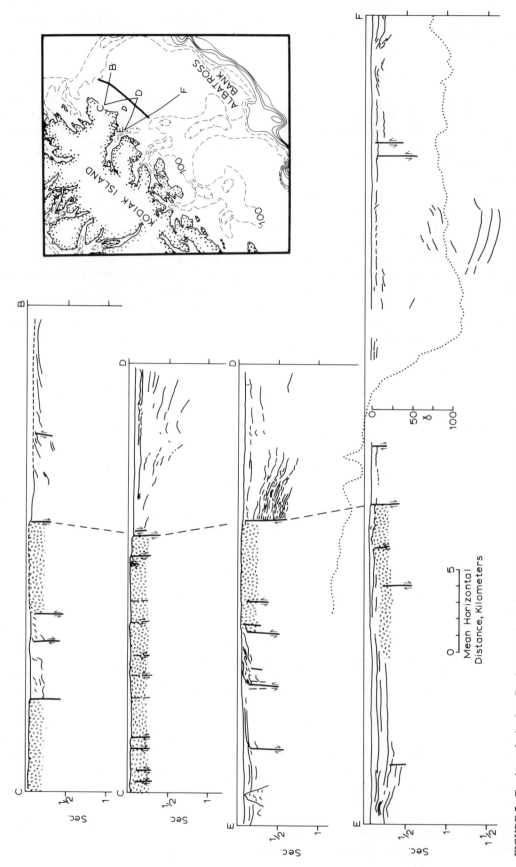

FIGURE 7 Tracings of seismic-reflection records on the Continental Shelf off Kodiak Island (made in 1969 with advanced seismic instrumentation). Acoustic basement is indicated by patterned areas in the tracings. The dashed line between individual tracings connects a continuous major fault shown on the location map by a heavy line across the ship's tracks. Dotted line in transect EF shows simultaneous total field magnetic measurements. Faults are interpreted from the traced records and from high-resolution seismic-reflection records made concurrently. Contour interval on the location map is 200 m with a dashed 100-m contour. Travel times are one-way.

276

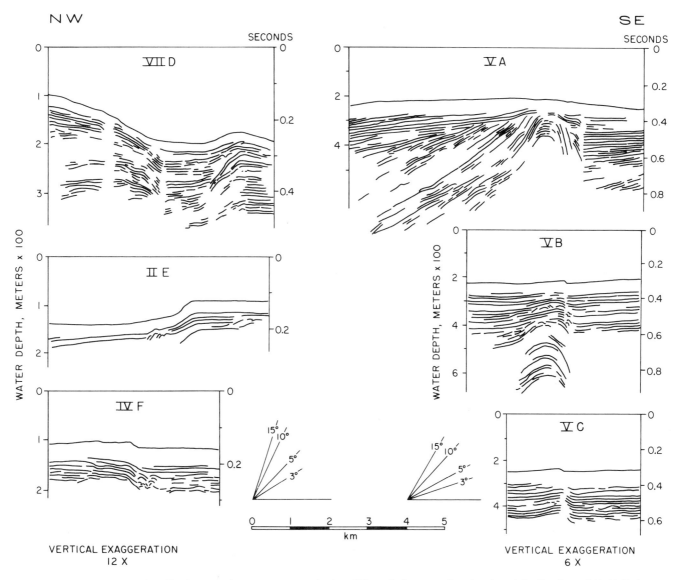

FIGURE 8 Tracing of seismic-reflection records across structures in the offshore fault zone and at the edge of the Continental Shelf. V *A* to V *C* are near 58°50′N latitude and 149°10′W longitude, and V *A* is included on transect V *A* of Figure 6; V *B* is 6 km southwest of V *A*; V *C* is 4 km southwest of V *B*. Inset VII *D* was recorded at 57°55′N latitude and 149°20′W longitude; inset II *E*, recorded at 60°05′N latitude and 146°20′W longitude, is part of transect II of Figure 6; and inset IV *F* was recorded at 59°35′N latitude 147°30′W longitude.

existed in this region, as shown by a thick lower Tertiary section and a deformed section of probable Cretaceous age (Moore, 1967).

The extent of the basin north and south of the Kodiak Island group is not known because of insufficient data. However, from the stratigraphy of Middleton Island (Miller, 1953) and from transect II of Figure 6, it is known that a basin with sediments at least 1 km thick occurs between Middleton Island and the Hinchinbrook Entrance. The hard-rock platform off Montague Island may be a barrier ridge between two separate basins. No expression of a basin was found in magnetic measurements made concurrently with transects IV and

V of Figure 6. The basin off Kodiak may merge into a basin in the St. Elias transition. Although the existence of the basin in not in doubt, its depth configuration, extent, history, and age are not yet well known.

Arch at Edge of Continental Shelf

The broad arch forming one flank of the basin also forms the edge of the Continental Shelf. The arch is absent in some transects and may be discontinuous at moderate depth, but the presence of a more continuous gravity ridge along the continental margin (Barnes and others, 1966) suggests that the arch is continuous, deeper in the earth's crust. The crest

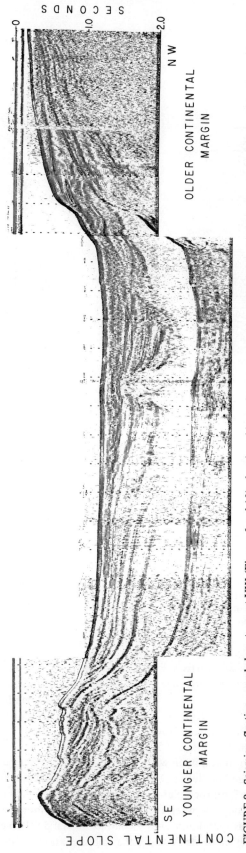

FIGURE 9 Seismic-reflection record along transect VIII (Figures 6 and 10), showing older and younger Continental Shelf edges. Total vertical axis is 2 seconds of recording time (two-way). Timing marks are 12 minutes apart, and the ship's speed was about 6 knots. Note erosion of outer Continental Shelf edge and possible diapiric structures.

of the arch has been locally truncated by erosion. Middleton Island is a present-day example of what must at times have been one or more islands at the shelf break. Some truncated surfaces are deeper than the eustatic lowering of sea level, suggesting at least one episode of uplift followed by subsidence. Repeated deformation and truncation of the arch are also indicated by occasional buried angular unconformities. The net tectonic effect is apparently one of uplift not only because of the geometry of reflections but also because microfossils indicating intermediate oceanic depths are found at 20 fathoms on Albatross Bank at the core of the arch (von Huene and Shor, 1969).

Along one transect (Figure 9; and Figure 6, transect VIII), uplift at the continental margin tilted the Continental Shelf toward the Trinity Islands. After truncation, tilted strata at an older shelf break were covered by prograding sediments which were, in turn, deformed into an irregular anticline at the present shelf break. This younger, outer shelf break was truncated and is now under as much as 0.5 km of water with sediments ponded behind it. The sequence of events suggested here is (1) deposition of a thick sediment sequence on the Continental Shelf (apparent thickness along the transect is more than 4 km); (2) uplift at the continental margin, northwesterly tilting of the whole Continental Shelf, and truncation; (3) contemporaneous with and following step 2, deposition of sediment over the continental margin; (4) uplift of a segment of the continental slope and truncation of upturned strata at the new continental margin; and (5) subsidence of the younger continental margin as well as a probable rise in sea level and ponding of sediment behind the margin. This sequence implies a seaward migration of the shelf break that is not as clearly demonstrated by other data. A similar structure occurs from Middleton Island landward (Figure 6, transect II), where the truncation has exposed 0.7 km of strata. Most of the truncated strata are probably younger than those on Middleton Island where upper Pliocene or lower Pleistocene sediments occur (Miller, 1953). Uplift at Middleton Island has exceeded rates of erosion, as shown by its sequence of terraces; it was uplifted during the 1964 earthquake, forming the most recent terrace of this sequence (Plafker, 1969, and Geology volume).

Two types of structures indicating extension in the crestal area of the arch appeared on some records. The first is small graben (Figure 8, inset D) generally on the seaward flank of the arch. The second is a series of antithetic faults on the arch.

Continental Slope and Aleutian Trench

The continental slope has a rugged morphology composed of benches, peaks, canyons, and steep slopes that are occasionally interspersed with gentler, smooth slopes (Figures 10 and 11). The size of these features varies greatly. Probably the most characteristic morphological features are the benches that are bounded by steep slopes, commonly have raised outer edges, and occasionally have an inner depression. Seismic-reflection records show that these benches are formed by sediment trapped behind raised protrusions or the outer edge of blocks tilted into the slope (see transect IV, Figure 10, and transect XII, Figure 11). Individual blocks have rotated during sedimentation so that the inner or landward edge is depressed and the outer or seaward edge is uplifted. Sediment has collected in the depression, and an increase in landward dip of strata with increasing depth or stratigraphic age indicates continuing rotation. These rotated blocks suggest extension across the continental slope.

Another common feature of the continental slope is the sharp peaks which are not associated with magnetic anomalies. Close inspection of the best seismic records reveals that the peaks may be folded sedimentary rock. In transect XII (Figure 11), clear indications of folded sedimentary rocks are seen beneath strata that covered the rotated blocks. Seismic-refraction studies also indicate that sedimentary rocks make up the continental slope (Shor, 1965; von Huene and Shor, 1969). The tight folding suggested in seismic-reflection records indicates that these sedimentary rocks were once subjected to compression.

At the foot of the continental slope, there is an area critical to the structural interpretation of the continental margin. Hyperbolic reflections in the seismic records commonly mask the juncture of the trench and the slope. However, seismic records made in 1969 with a high-power source (120,000 joules) showed some structures in a wide area of hyperbolic reflections (Figure 11). Transect XII shows a section of seaward-tilted sedimentary strata at least 1 km thick. Also the multiplicity of the hyperbolic reflections suggests that they are caused by reflections from stratified rocks. This has led to a modified interpretation of some records across the trench made in 1964 and 1965 with lower-power and less-sensitive seismic instruments (von Huene and Shor, 1969). The juncture between the trench fill and the continental slope may be either a zone of deformation or an unconformity. In some instances the change in reflective character across the juncture is due to dispersal of the seismic signal by inclined or noncoherent reflectors.

Seismic-reflection records show three distinct rock units in the trench. Lowest in the stratigraphic sequence is the acoustic basement which is in turn overlain by two stratified units, each of a different character (Figure 10).

The acoustic basement has a mildly undulating upper surface that is punctuated by seamounts and is covered by an undeformed sequence of abyssal strata. The uniform thickness, reflective character, and parallel bedding of these strata suggest they are deep-sea sediments of monotonous lithology. In the deep ocean floor of the Gulf of Alaska these strata are horizontal, but they tilt or plunge increasingly toward the continental slope as the abyssal plains gradually give way to

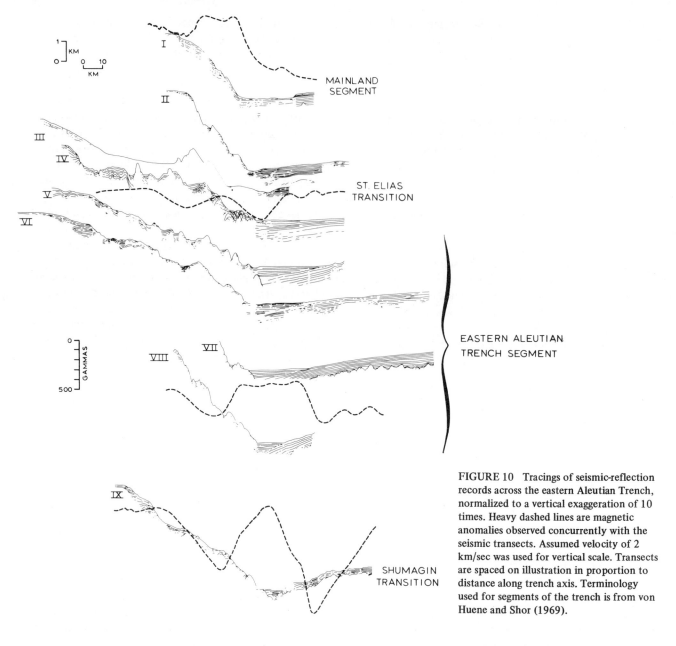

FIGURE 10   Tracings of seismic-reflection records across the eastern Aleutian Trench, normalized to a vertical exaggeration of 10 times. Heavy dashed lines are magnetic anomalies observed concurrently with the seismic transects. Assumed velocity of 2 km/sec was used for vertical scale. Transects are spaced on illustration in proportion to distance along trench axis. Terminology used for segments of the trench is from von Huene and Shor (1969).

the Aleutian Trench. On the seaward side of the trench, the abyssal section tilts between 1° and 3° toward the continental slope. In transects V, VI, and VII (Figure 10), tilting of undeformed strata occurs at a subtle hinge area, but in other transects the seaward limits of the Aleutian Trench are not defined by a sudden increase in tilt. An exception appears in transect V where a small bump, a possible fold or basement high, marks a sharper hinge area.

The upper stratigraphic unit was deposited after the Aleutian Trench had developed (Figure 10, transects V, VIII). It is a wedge of horizontal strata confined seaward by the tilted abyssal strata and landward by the continental slope. No faulting seems to have occurred within the wedge during

its accumulation. Only at Kodiak Seamount (Hamilton and von Huene, 1966) and to the northeast is a very gentle tilting of the trench fill observable. The cross-sectional area of the fill increases from the southwest to the northeast, which reflects differing distances from the large sediment sources to the northeast rather than differential rates of tectonism.

A channel in the sea floor occurs at the juncture of the trench and the continental slope. It is seen in the original records of transects II through VIII and X and XII, but not in transect IX. Hurley (1960) noticed this channel and attributed it to turbidity currents. A similar feature on the seaward side of Kodiak Seamount is attributed to nondeposition or scour (Hamilton and von Huene, 1966).

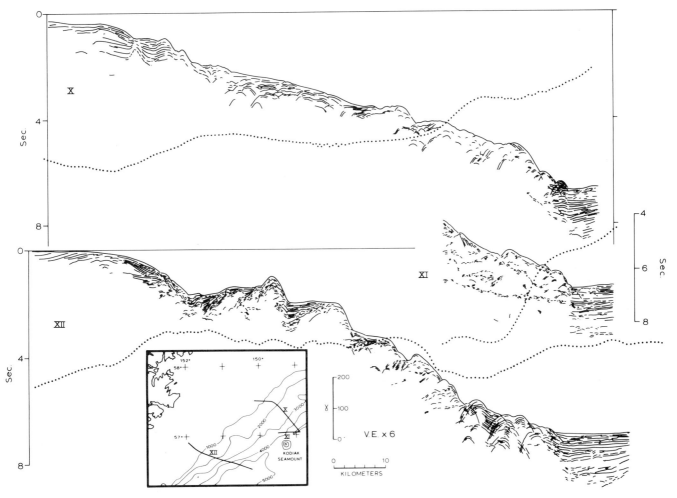

FIGURE 11   Tracings of seismic-reflection records made in 1969 across the eastern Aleutian Trench. Dotted lines are total field magnetic anom-alies observed concurrently with the seismic transects. Travel time is two-way.

ALASKA MAINLAND SYSTEM AND
ST. ELIAS TRANSITION

Seismic records from the mainland system and the St. Elias transition differ from the eastern Aleutian Trench in that the well-defined trench is absent. A single transect across the mainland system shows horizontal strata under a broad trough (Figure 10, transect I). The reflectivity of these strata changes from the trough to the abyssal plain, suggesting a difference in the sediment. The sharp break at the seaward edge of the trough could be formed by sedimentary processes or tectonism, but the quality of the record does not allow a clear choice. The upper strata in the trough are continuous with strata draped over the lower continental slope, and no tectonic or stratigraphic break is seen at the foot of the continental slope.

The continental slope is smooth, probably because of a relatively thick cover of sediment. The juncture between

slope and shelf is marked by a well-developed arch. Structurally, this arch is similar to the arch of the Aleutian system, and it also forms the seaward wall of a large basin. But the shoreward flank of the basin is not a sharp geologic break such as the fault zone off Kodiak, Montague, and Hinchinbrook islands. From the few data available, there appears to be no sharp structural break nearshore but rather a transition from more open structures on the shelf to tighter folds and large reverse faults on land. Structures on land adjacent to the mainland system differ from those adjacent to the Aleutian system; they are dominantly steep reverse faults and thrust faults (Plafker, 1969, and Geology volume; Stoneley, 1967) rather than the nearly vertical fault of the type mapped around Prince William Sound (Condon and Cass, 1958; Condon, 1965) and on Kodiak Island (Moore, 1967).

In the St. Elias transition, some characteristics of the adjacent segments occur, as well as features peculiar to the transition. Transect II (Figure 10) shows more steeply dipping reflections at about 1,000 m below the sea floor in the Aleutian Trench. Above the tilted strata large slumps occur, with northwest, dipping slip planes (not all of which are visible in Figure 10) at about 6, 13, and 23 km seaward of the continental slope. The slumps may have occurred during tilting of the lower strata.

Transect III (Figure 10) and Murray's (1945) profile 10 differ from all other transects. The greatest water depth occurs not against the continental slope, as in the other records, but in a notch about 10 km seaward of the continental slope. Linear parallel reflections, representing sediment about 1 km thick, dip gently from the abyssal plain to the notch. On the landward side of the notch, an abrupt geologic change occurs and the abyssal strata butt against a hard rock that may be stratified.

Structure as well as trend differentiate the Alaska mainland and St. Elias transition from the Aleutian structural systems. This difference and the existence of two intersecting systems may not have been recognized by other authors because it is more apparent at sea than on land. Because the Alaska earthquake occurred along the Aleutian system, structures from the mainland system may be confusing in a tectonic analysis, especially if they are used as an indicator of tectonic mechanism for the earthquake.

DEFORMATION ON THE CONTINENTAL SHELF ASSOCIATED WITH THE EARTHQUAKE

Determination of deformation of the earth surface on the Continental Shelf is limited by the precision of soundings on preearthquake nautical charts. Most soundings on charts of the area affected by the 1964 earthquake were made between 1927 and 1933, before the advent of precision continuous-recording echo sounders. Navigation during these surveys was accomplished without electronic positioning devices. However, comparisons of preearthquake with postearthquake soundings indicate a precision of ±1 fathom in areas of smooth sea floor, especially near land.

Elevation changes caused by earthquake deformation were carefully determined along the shore by Plafker (1969, and Geology volume). Attempts to extend Plafker's measurements seaward were less successful because: (1) the ± 1 fathom reproducibility of depths on the nautical charts is limited to smooth areas of the sea floor, and spot soundings in rough or steep topography were not located well enough to allow good repeated measurements; (2) large slumps and mass movement of sediment made some repeated measurements tectonically nonmeaningful; and (3) the amount of elevation change was commonly less than the precision of preearthquake soundings.

The most dramatic example of sea-floor-elevation changes is reported by Malloy and Merrill (1969, and this volume) who measured the largest known vertical change accompanying the earthquake (greater than 14 m). Their work was facili-

tated by the proximity of this uplift to land and by good preearthquake bathymetric control. They show an extension of the Patton Bay fault offshore and also some of the complexity of vertical deformation in this area, such as an east-west trending ridge of uplift off the southern tip of Montague Island.

Uplift around Middleton Island (Figure 12) is similar to uplift around Montague Island. The preliminary results from a detailed C&GS survey made in 1969 were compared with soundings from 1933. Approximately 5,000 soundings were compared. Locally the sea floor is rough, and the tectonic significance of differences became questionable. But over much of the area there are fields of equal differences larger than 2 km. The differences were averaged over a 3-km circle (generally 100–500 differences) and contoured to produce Figure 12.

Figure 12 suggests that maximum uplift around Middleton Island occurred on a northeast-trending ridge of uplift south of the island. The ridge corresponds approximately with the structural axis of the shelf break arch. A second ridge of uplift north of the island trends east–west and corresponds to a topographic ridge of the same trend. The east–west-trending ridges of uplift near Middleton and Montague islands may signify uplift along structures with the Alaska mainland trend, and they suggest that, in detail, vertical deformation had a complex pattern.

Other comparisons at sea show a 7-m (± 2) uplift of Albatross Bank off Kodiak Island (Figure 13). The soundings, made in 1969, were controlled by Satellite and Loran navigation. The differences in depth between 1933 and 1967 indicate a systematic increase in uplift from the shore to the edge of the Continental Shelf. Other lines in this series were in areas of rougher topography and the depth differences are more scattered, but they suggest both uplift and subsidence adjacent to the coast of Kodiak Island between Chiniak Bay and Ugak Bay.

A surface of deformation projected from Montague to Middleton Island was used by various authors (Press and Jackson, 1965, and Seismology and Geodesy volume; Savage and Hastie, 1966, and Seismology and Geodesy volume; Stauder and Bollinger, 1966, and Seismology and Geodesy volume) in applying the dislocation theory to model the causative fault plane. The surface of deformation seen off Kodiak departs significantly from the one presented by Plafker (Figure 13). The complexities around Middleton Island also depart from the surfaces used in dislocation-theory model studies. The validity of dislocation-theory models is questioned.

Fault scarps formed or rejuvenated during the 1964 earthquake are difficult to separate from scarps produced during previous earthquakes. The most obvious way to identify faults active in 1964 would be to compare pre- and post-earthquake echo-sounding profiles, but no preearthquake continuous fathograms were available. It is conceivable that fault scarps on the sea floor could remain essentially un-

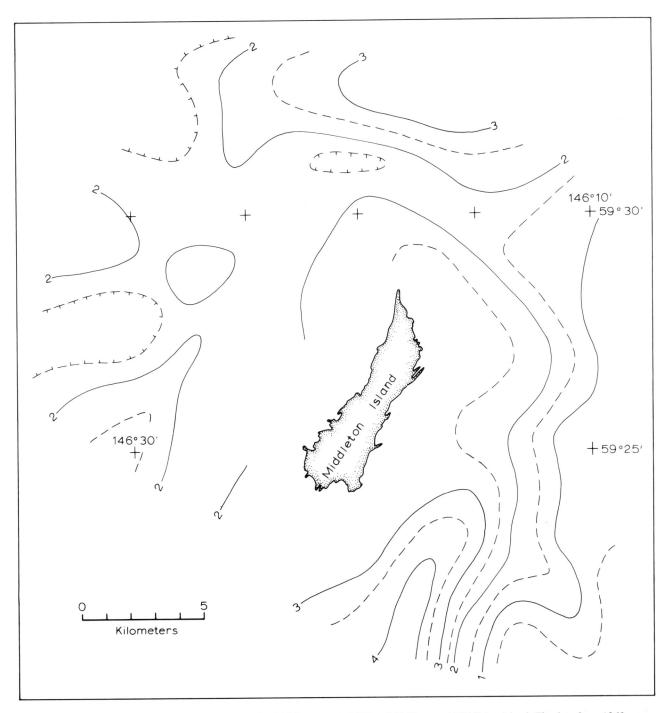

FIGURE 12   Contours of depth differences between USC&GS surveys in 1933 and 1969 around Middleton Island. The data from 1969 are preliminary and not edited. Contours (given in meters) are controlled by readings averaged over a 2.5-km circle. The precision of individual differences on smooth sea floor is estimated to be ±2 m.

modified for thousands of years on parts of the Continental Shelf off Prince William Sound or Kodiak Island. Some areas of the sea floor have not received significant sediment since the last glacial retreat, because most sediment is trapped in fiords (Reimnitz, 1966; von Huene, 1966; von Huene, Shor, and Reimnitz, 1967).

Malloy and Merrill have made a strong case for reactivation of faulting at the sea floor off Montague Island. Elsewhere the data are much less certain. Possible active faults (Figure 5) have a discontinuous distribution, indicating that during the 1964 earthquake the fault zone off Kodiak and Montague Islands did not rupture in a single or continuous series of

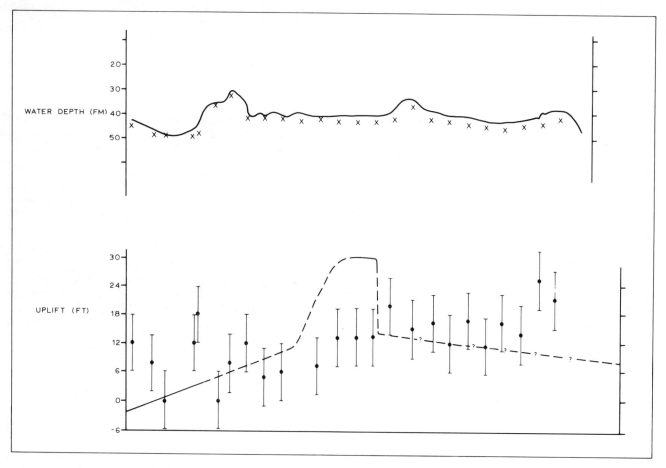

FIGURE 13   Profiles of bathymetry and uplift across the Continental Shelf based on differences in depth between soundings on USC&GS chart 8556 made before 1964 and soundings along line *EF* in Figure 7 and part of transect XII, Figure 11. The differences are plotted as uplift in the lower graph and have bars showing estimate of precision, ±6 ft. The curve of uplift for this region estimated by Plafker (1969, and Geology volume) is shown by the continuous line.

breaks. This has probably been the case for much of Holocene time, because faults in the zone are buried by probable glacial and postglacial sediment. The fault zone may have broken locally in 1964 just as it has throughout Holocene time.

Faulting may also have occurred at the edge of the shelf in conjunction with uplift of the shelf-break arch. The small graben off Portlock Bank may have been reactivated. In high-resolution seismic records, Albatross Bank shows a series of shoreward-facing scarps 4 m high. It seems, however, that surface activity during the 1964 earthquake was primarily confined to the fault zone off Montague and Kodiak islands and that it may have occurred at the shelf-break arch.

LATE TERTIARY AND QUATERNARY TECTONIC DEFORMATION RELATED TO THE 1964 EARTHQUAKE

If deformation associated with the 1964 earthquake was similar to Quaternary and possibly late Tertiary deformation,

the more visible effects accumulating during longer periods of geologic time can be applied in a tectonic analysis of the 1964 earthquake. Plafker (1969, and Geology volume) correlated the deformation associated with the 1964 earthquake with earlier deformation and used certain trends to arrive at a tectonic model. The additional data from marine observations amplify the relation between the 1964 event and past deformation; the data raise further questions as to repetition of long-standing past patterns and variants in deformation associated with the 1964 earthquake.

Near Middleton Island, thick late Tertiary sediments indicate subsidence of the region during that period. After early Pleistocene time the area was deformed and uplifted. Middleton Island and the immediately adjacent sea floor have been continually uplifted before the 1964 earthquake (Plafker, 1969, and Geology volume), as well as during the earthquake. Shoreward of the island, however, upturned strata presumably truncated at the close of Wisconsin Glaciation, or later, now lie with the level of truncation just above the lowest Wisconsin eustatic level of the sea (80-95 m). This suggests that net uplift in Holocene time has been small or that early Holocene uplift was followed by late Holocene subsidence. During the 1964 earthquake the area between Middleton and Montague islands is presumed to have been uplifted (Plafker, 1969, and Geology volume). If this presumption is correct, it indicates a reversal of the Holocene deformational trend during the 1964 earthquake.

A similar but less definite case can be argued for Albatross Bank and the shelf off Kodiak Island. A ridge 15 km shoreward of Albatross Bank is thought to be a terminal glacial feature. If Albatross Bank was beyond Wisconsin glacial advance, it must have been eroded to the lowest Wisconsin eustatic level of the sea. The present depths (16 to 60 m) suggest significant Holocene uplift of the Bank. Here the Holocene trend was continued in 1964 (Figure 13). The rest of the shelf has, however, remained stable or has subsided during the Holocene, and yet uplift was indicated during the 1964 earthquake (Figure 13).

A little information on Holocene vertical changes was obtained in the fiords. There is evidence of recent tectonic stability in Nuka Bay, at least long enough for a small terrace to have developed alongshore (Reimnitz and von Huene, 1969). The terrace is roughly 10 to 30 m deep and very narrow, but it has developed in relatively sheltered water along a steep hard-rock slope. This suggests a long period of stability because surf action cuts slowly under such conditions. However, Nuka Bay lies along the axis of maximum subsidence during the 1964 earthquake (Plafker, 1969, and Geology volume). We offer an alternate interpretation for the features around Nuka Bay that Plafker believes to indicate submergence in Holocene time. Plafker implies that cirques formed above the present level of the sea later subsided at least 300 ft. However, the level of glacial generation may have extended to the lower level of the sea during periods in the Pleistocene, and cirques of this coast could have been drowned by the postglacial rise of sea level. This interpretation is more consistent with the evidence of the wave-cut bench found in Nuka Bay.

Plafker (1969, and Geology volume) has shown that parts of Prince William Sound that were uplifted during the earthquake were subsiding before that time. Presumably, a period of strain accumulation before the earthquake produced vertical deformation in a sense opposite to that occurring during the strain release of the earthquake. Adjacent to the Sound in the Copper River Delta, Reimnitz (1966) found that net subsidence in the last 4,000 years is greater than uplift from isostatic rebound since glaciation, as well as the uplifts resulting periodically from large earthquakes. In other words, the sense of net deformation is subsidence; yet, strong uplift occurred during the 1964 earthquake and previous ones. This kind of complexity seems to characterize the deformational pattern in the area affected by the earthquake. For instance, the Kenai Mountains were probably uplifted in Pliocene time (Burk, 1965). Within the Kenai Mountains,

Girdwood and Kachemak Bay are known to have subsided in Holocene time (Plafker, 1969, and Geology volume), and Nuka Bay appears to have a history of upper Holocene stability (Reimnitz and von Huene, 1969). The Kenai–Kodiak Mountains subsided during the earthquake (Plafker, 1969, and Geology volume).

Deformation in the late Tertiary was complex and at least locally cyclic in the area affected by the earthquake. Deformation directly associated with the earthquake sometimes had a vertical sense opposite to net Holocene deformation. Therefore, not all the available data confirm Plafker's tentative conclusion that "Areas of net Holocene emergence or submergence broadly correspond with those areas in which significant amounts of uplift and subsidence occurred during the 1964 earthquake" (1969, p. 162). In the area around Prince William Sound one of two possibilities occurred: Either (1) net deformation during strain accumulation and the 1964 earthquake strain release was different from net Holocene or net late Tertiary deformation, or (2) a large amount of permanent strain as well as elastic strain accumulated before the 1964 earthquake. The latter possibility seems most reasonable. The 1964 deformation may be misleading in a tectonic analysis unless it is viewed in the perspective of net Holocene deformation.

POSSIBLE TECTONIC MECHANISMS

A simple tectonic mechanism explaining most aspects of the 1964 earthquake does not easily follow from the available data. Because the primary causative fault break either was not exposed or was poorly exposed, the fault plane attitude is assumed from main-shock body wave data (Stauder and Bollinger, 1966, and Seismology and Geodesy volume; Harding and Algermissen, 1969, and Seismology and Geodesy volume). The two alternate solutions are a nearly vertical and a nearly horizontal fault plane. These fault planes are taken as constraints on interpretations in addition to the constraints of the geologic data.

A second basic constraint concerns the relation of the Alaska mainland tectonic trend to the Aleutian trend. The trends are considered individual tectonic systems that intersect on the Continental Shelf. The mainland trend is likely to be secondary with respect to the Alaska earthquake, and most observations north and east of Middleton Island are considered in view of this assumption.

A horizontal fault or megathrust mechanism has been forcefully argued by Plafker (1969, and Geology volume) on the basis of well-documented and careful studies of deformation alongshore as well as on seismological and geodetic data (Stauder and Bollinger, 1966, and Seismology and Geodesy volume; Parkin, 1969, and Seismology and Geodesy volume). Some marine observations and conclusions not available to these authors significantly affect the basic data to be considered, and they are therefore summarized before possible tectonic mechanisms are discussed.

SUMMARY OF DATA

Faults activated on Montague Island during the earthquake are probably part of a much longer fault zone separating an uplifted Kenai–Kodiak mountainous area from a subsiding basin on the Continental Shelf. Active faulting during the earthquake, and probably before it, was concentrated along this zone and not in the adjacent areas landward or seaward. Discontinuous scarps were formed during Holocene time not only by reverse faults but also by presumed normal faults. The zone of maximum aftershock activity associated with the 1964 earthquake corresponds roughly to the fault zone.

Seaward of the fault zone, the Continental Shelf has subsided since at least Pliocene time, forming a basin confined at the edge of the shelf by a rising arch. During the latest tectonic period, step faults formed on the continental slope indicating extension. At the foot of the slope, the oceanic crust subsides to form the Aleutian Trench, and oceanic crust may underlie most of the continental margin. Modification of the interpretation by von Huene and Shor (1969) more readily allows underthrusting from transect IV to transect VIII (Figure 10). North of transect IV (Figure 11), the geometry of reflections is not readily compatible with underthrusting. If underthrusting is assumed, the Pliocene age estimated for the trench must be a minimum age.

Changes in depth off Kodiak Island suggest that uplift was greatest at the shelf-break arch on Albatross Bank with a more or less linear decrease in uplift shoreward. The axis of sharp uplift inferred by Plafker was not seen more than 27 km south of Montague Island. Therefore, there may have been two axes of maximum uplift—one along Montague Island extending southwest for a limited but unknown distance and another corresponding to Albatross Bank.

Around the Copper River Delta and possibly in parts of Prince William Sound, vertical deformation during all of the Holocene, during roughly 800 years of strain accumulation, and during strain release of the 1964 earthquake varies in direction. A reversal of sense during longer and shorter periods of time is also suggested on the Continental Shelf off Montague and Kodiak islands. Short-term events such as the Alaska earthquake may be only part of a complete cycle of strain accumulation and strain release. On the other hand, net deformation over Holocene or Pleistocene time may contain the effects of a changing stress field, but this is difficult to determine without more information on the temporal sequence.

THRUST-FAULT MODEL

The thrust-fault model proposed by Plafker to explain the 1964 earthquake can be modified to account for the shelf-break arch and the subsiding basin on the Continental Shelf (Figure 14). A large megathrust near the base of the crust is the primary feature, and subsidiary steep faults radiate from it through the upper plate. The shelf-break arch may be formed by such a steep subsidiary reverse fault expressed at the earth's surface as a fold. This subsidiary fault is located near the leading edge of the continental plate. In the southwestern part of the region affected by the earthquake, this fault rather than the Patton Bay fault could have been the most active near the earth's surface. The Patton Bay fault would correspond to the fault zone off Kodiak Island (Figure 14). No single master fault is seen in the Aleutian Trench, suggesting that the megathrust does not surface as shown in simple models of the continental margin, and large differential movements may be distributed among subsidiary faults and deformation of the continental slope. Concentration of aftershock activity at depths of about 20 to 30 km just off Kodiak and Montague islands could be explained by major movement at these depths along the fault forming the shelf-break arch. During periods of strain accumulation between large earthquakes, part of the Continental Shelf between the two faults may subside. This model fits well the first-motion studies of Stauder and Bollinger (1966, and Seismology and Geodesy volume), the vertical deformation during the earthquake (Plafker, 1969, and Geology volume), and all but one determination of horizontal deformation reported by Parkin (1969, and Seismology and Geodesy volume). The southwestward shift of Middleton Island reported by Parkin might be attributed to complexities within the St. Elias transition where the Aleutian and Mainland trends intersect.

Observations that are not well explained by the thrust-fault model are the seaward-dipping faults on Kodiak Island (Moore, 1967) and the shoreward-facing fault scarps (interpreted as normal faults) in the same fault zone at sea. It seems difficult to attribute a steep fault zone with roughly 40 percent normal faults to a large thrust fault at depth. It is also difficult to explain how extensional structures can form on the continental slope in a strong compressional environment, without reverting to separate episodes in which stress is reversed. The thrust-fault model explains deformation and seismicity observed to result from the 1964 earthquake, but it does not easily fit the deformation trends since Pliocene time.

STEEP-FAULT MODEL

In a steep-fault model, the fault zone off Montague and Kodiak islands is the major zone of rupture and not a subsidiary fault. Its surface expression is a series of en échelon faults; since only some of the faults broke at the surface in 1964, not much fault displacement reached the surface. This fault zone corresponds roughly to the area of greatest aftershock strain release at a depth of some 20 to 25 km. We consider that the aftershocks located by the U.S. Coast and

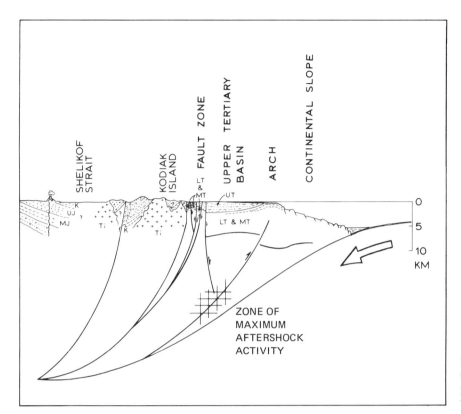

FIGURE 14 Diagrammatic cross section of the thrust-fault model similar to that proposed by Plafker (1969, and Geology volume).

Geodetic Survey indicate a zone of strong aftershock strain release which could be sensed by the available seismograph network. This interpretation does not assume that all strain release after the initial earthquake was recorded, because physical conditions in the crust change with depth. Aki and others (1969, and Seismology and Geodesy volume) and Matumoto and Page (1969, and Seismology and Geodesy volume) recorded numerous microaftershocks below 40 km to depths below the crust-mantle boundary. Possibly physical conditions below 40 km did not allow large aftershocks to occur. The strain-release contours in Figure 3 may only delineate a zone in which the release of strain energy could be recorded; but it is notable that a sharp strain-release maximum occurs at a depth of roughly 25 km and slightly seaward of the fault zone off Kodiak.

The initial epicenter position 100 km landward of the fault zone can be explained by the multiple rupture proposed for the 1964 earthquake by Wyss and Brune (1967, and Seismology and Geodesy volume). The initial shock could have triggered earthquakes along a series of *en échelon* faults in the fault zone.

The steep-fault model is appealing, in that the deformation during the 1964 earthquake could produce structures like those found in the fault zone and on the continental slope. But this model is not compatible with the first-motion studies of Stauder and Bollinger (1966, and Seismology and Geodesy volume) or with most of the horizontal shifts reported by Parkin (1969, and Seismology and Geodesy volume).

The steep-fault model appears to fit better the observations of long-term deformation, whereas the thrust-fault model fits well the observations of 1964 deformation. A thrust-fault model can be linked with the theory of plate tectonics, whereas the steep-fault model cannot be linked well with a unifying theory. The existing data cannot be completely reconciled with a single model, but we think that the thrust-fault model explains the observations best. A better explanation is required if hazards from seismicity in the Gulf of Alaska are to be further evaluated. For instance, based on recent seismicity the next earthquake in the Gulf of Alaska might occur somewhere between Yakutat and Cape St. Elias. If evaluated according to the theory of plate tectonics, a large tsunami is unlikely because the shear between the oceanic and continental plates should be dominantly strike-slip along a large transcurrent fault zone. Pleistocene geologic structures in this area, however, indicate a history of intense overthrusting and large elevation change (Plafker, 1967, 1969). Such deformation on the Continental Shelf would probably generate destructive tsunamis. Resolution of this apparent discrepancy is a challenge to further studies.

POSTSCRIPT

After the 1964–1965 fieldwork that formed the basis for a first version of the preceding report, additional fieldwork on the Continental Shelf (1967, 1968) and in the trench (1969) prompted a revision. As this volume goes to press, data from two additional field seasons have added significantly to knowledge of structure across the continental margin and have further modified conclusions. However, it is not possible to make further revision.

New seismic records (1970) across the continental slope off Kodiak Island indicate that the extensional structures seen in earlier seismic records are probably caused by gravity sliding. Slides are caused in part by oversteepening of the slope in response to uplift at the shelf-break arch. Some slumps come to rest on the lower slope or even travel across the trench floor. These hummocky deposits generally mask reflections from below, including any deformed zones in underlying sediments. The probability of gravity sliding provides an explanation of the seeming paradox that the continental slope shows structures indicating extensional movement while the assumed underthrusting should result in large-scale compression.

Seismic-refraction studies (Shor and von Huene, in press) provide an estimate of maximum underthrust rate by showing the possible volume of deformed abyssal sediments incorporated into the continental margin. The estimated maximum rate is roughly equivalent to the rate derived from the plate tectonic model of Atwater (1970). However, estimated minimum rates show that a static or episodic model cannot be ruled out. Nevertheless, the continental margin crustal structure has a "thin skin" character that intuitively indicates lateral deforming forces.

Drill cores from Leg 18 of the Deep Sea Drilling Project indicate that tectonic processes on the slope and in the trench are more rapid than the estimates given in this paper. They establish that the oldest trench fill seen in seismic records was deposited 0.45 million years ago rather than in Pliocene time (von Huene and others, 1971). Deformed Quaternary sediment which appears as acoustic basement in the seismic records was recovered from a 2000-m-high arch adjacent to the trench on the lower continental slope.

The ideas developed with the additional data are more compatible with the thrust-fault model for the 1964 earthquake than those discussed in this paper.

REFERENCES

Aki, Keiiti, Minoru Hori, and Hideteru Matumoto, 1969. Microaftershocks observed at a temporary array station on the Kenai Peninsula from May 19 to June 7, 1964 in Volume II-B,C: The Prince William Sound, Alaska, earthquake of 1964 and aftershocks. Environmental Science Services Administration, U.S. Coast and Geodetic Survey. Washington: Government Printing Office. p. 131–156. Also in The Great Alaska Earthquake of 1964: Seismology and Geodesy. NAS Pub. 1602. Washington: National Academy of Sciences, 1972.
Algermissen, S. T., W. A. Rinehart, R. W. Sherburne, and W. H.

Dillinger, Jr., 1969. Preshocks and aftershocks of the Prince William Sound earthquake of March 28, 1964 in Volume II-B,C: The Prince William Sound, Alaska, earthquake of 1964 and aftershocks. Environmental Science Services Administration, U.S. Coast and Geodetic Survey. Washington: Government Printing Office. p. 79–130. Also in The Great Alaska Earthquake of 1964: Seismology and Geodesy. NAS Pub. 1602. Washington: National Academy of Sciences, 1972.
Atwater, Tanya, 1970. Implications of plate tectonics for the Cenozoic tectonic evolution of western North America. Geological Society of America Bulletin, 81 (December), 3513–3535.
Barnes, D. F., W. H. Lucas, E. V. Mace, and R. J. Malloy, 1966. Reconnaissance gravity and other geophysical data from the continental end of the Aleutian arc (Abstract). Proceedings, American Association of Petroleum Geologists, 50 (March), 644.
Burk, C. A., 1965. Geology of the Alaska Peninsula–island arc and continental margin. Geological Society of America Memoir 99. New York: The Geological Society of America. 250 p.
Capps, Stephen Reid, 1937. Kodiak and adjacent islands, Alaska. U.S. Geological Survey Bulletin 880-C. Washington: Government Printing Office. p. 111–184.
Condon, William H., 1965. Map of eastern Prince William Sound area, Alaska, showing fracture traces inferred from aerial photographs. U.S. Geological Survey Miscellaneous Geologic Investigations Map I-453. Washington: U.S. Geological Survey.
Condon, William H., and John T. Cass, 1958. Map of a part of the Prince William Sound area, Alaska, showing linear geologic features as shown on aerial photographs. U.S. Geological Survey Miscellaneous Geologic Investigations Map I-273. Washington: U.S. Geological Survey.
Grantz, Arthur, 1964. Committee report in Mineral and water resources of Alaska. 88th Congress, 2nd Session. p. 59.
Hamilton, Edwin L., and Roland E. von Huene, 1966. Kodiak Seamount not flat-topped. Science, 154 (December 9), 1323–1325.
Harding, Samuel T., and S. T. Algermissen, 1969. The focal mechanism of the Prince William Sound earthquake of March 28, 1964, and related earthquakes in Volume II-B,C: The Prince William Sound, Alaska, earthquake of 1964 and aftershocks. Environmental Science Services Administration, U.S. Coast and Geodetic Survey. Washington: Government Printing Office. p. 185–221. Also in The Great Alaska Earthquake of 1964: Seismology and Geodesy. NAS Pub. 1602. Washington: National Academy of Sciences, 1972.
Hurley, R. J., 1960. The geomorphology of abyssal plains in the northeast Pacific Ocean. Scripps Institution of Oceanography Reference 60-7. La Jolla: Scripps Institution of Oceanography.
Malloy, Richard J., 1964. Crustal uplift southwest of Montague Island, Alaska. Science, 146 (November 20), 1048–1049.
Malloy, Richard J., 1965. Gulf of Alaska: seafloor upheaval. Geo-Marine Technology, 1 (May–June), 22–26.
Malloy, Richard J., and George F. Merrill, 1969. Vertical crustal movement of the sea floor associated with the Prince William Sound, Alaska in Volume II-B,C: The Prince William Sound, Alaska, earthquake of 1964 and aftershocks. Environmental Science Services Administration, U.S. Coast and Geodetic Survey. Washington: Government Printing Office. p. 327–338. Also in The Great Alaska Earthquake of 1964: Oceanography and Coastal Engineering. NAS Pub. 1605. Washington: National Academy of Sciences, 1972.
Matumoto, Tosimatu, and Robert A. Page, Jr., 1969. Microaftershocks following the Alaska earthquake of March 28, 1964: Determination of hypocenters and crustal velocities in the Kenai Peninsula-Prince William Sound area in Volume II-B,C: The Prince William

Sound, Alaska, earthquake of 1964 and aftershocks. Environmental Science Services Administration, U.S. Coast and Geodetic Survey. Washington: Government Printing Office. p. 157–173. Also *in* The Great Alaska Earthquake of 1964: Seismology and Geodesy. NAS Pub. 1602. Washington: National Academy of Sciences, 1972.

Miller, Don J., 1953. Late Cenozoic marine glacial sediments and marine terraces of Middleton Island, Alaska. *Journal of Geology*, 61 (January), 17–40.

Miller, Don J., 1961. Geology of the Katalla district, Gulf of Alaska Tertiary Province, Alaska. U.S. Geological Survey Open-File Map, 2 sheets. Scale 1:96,000. Washington: U.S. Geological Survey.

Moore, George W., 1967. Preliminary geologic map of Kodiak Island and vicinity, Alaska. U.S. Geological Survey Open-File Map. Scale 1:250,000. Washington: U.S. Geological Survey.

Murray, H. W., 1945. Profiles of the Aleutian Trench. *Geological Society of America Bulletin*, 56 (July), 757–781.

Parkin, Ernest J., 1969. Horizontal crustal movements determined from surveys after the Alaskan earthquake of 1964 *in* Volume III: The Prince William Sound, Alaska, earthquake of 1964 and aftershocks. Environmental Science Services Administration, U.S. Coast and Geodetic Survey. Washington: Government Printing Office. p. 35–98. Also *in* The Great Alaska Earthquake of 1964: Seismology and Geodesy. NAS Pub. 1602. Washington: National Academy of Sciences, 1972.

Plafker, George, 1967. Geologic map of the Gulf of Alaska Tertiary Province, Alaska. U.S. Geological Survey Miscellaneous Geologic Investigations Map I-484. Scale 1:500,000. Washington: U.S. Geological Survey.

Plafker, George, 1969. Tectonics of the March 27, 1964 Alaska earthquake. U.S. Geological Survey Professional Paper 543-I. Washington: Government Printing Office. 74 p. Also *in* The Great Alaska Earthquake of 1964: Geology. NAS Pub. 1601. Washington: National Academy of Sciences, 1971. p. 47–122.

Press, Frank, and David Jackson, 1965. Alaskan earthquake, 27 March 1964: vertical extent of faulting and elastic strain energy release. *Science*, 147 (February 19), 867–868. Also *in* The Great Alaska Earthquake of 1964: Seismology and Geodesy. NAS Pub. 1602. Washington: National Academy of Sciences, 1972.

Reimnitz, Erk, 1966. Late Quaternary history and sedimentation of the Copper River Delta and vicinity (PhD dissertation). San Diego: University of California. 160 p.

Reimnitz, Erk, 1972. Effects in the Copper River Delta *in* The Great Alaska Earthquake of 1964: Oceanography and Coastal Engineering. NAS Pub. 1605. Washington: National Academy of Sciences.

Reimnitz, Erk, and Roland von Huene, 1969. Bathymetry and isopach map of stratified Holocene sediments of Nuka Bay, Alaska. U.S. Geological Survey Open-File Map, 3 sheets. Washington: U.S. Geological Survey.

Savage, J. C., and L. M. Hastie, 1966. Surface deformation associated with dip-slip faulting. *Journal of Geophysical Research*, 71 (October 15), 4897–4904. Also *in* The Great Alaska Earthquake of 1964: Seismology and Geodesy. NAS Pub. 1602. Washington: National Academy of Sciences, 1972.

Shor, George G., Jr., 1962. Seismic refraction studies off the coast of Alaska: 1956-1957. *Bulletin of the Seismological Society of America*, 52 (January), 37-57.

Shor, George G., Jr., 1965. Structure of the Aleutian ridge, Aleutian Trench, and Bering Sea (Abstract). *Transactions, American Geophysical Union*, 46 (March), 106.

Shor, George G., Jr., and Roland von Huene, in press. Marine seismic refraction studies near Kodiak, Alaska. *Geophysics*.

Spaeth, Mark G., and Saul C. Berkman, 1969. The tsunami of March 28, 1964, as recorded at tide stations *in* Volume II-B, C: The Prince William Sound, Alaska, earthquake of 1964 and aftershocks. Environmental Science Services Administration, U.S. Coast and Geodetic Survey. Washington: Government Printing Office. p. 223-307.

Stauder, William, and G. A. Bollinger, 1966. The focal mechanism of the Alaska earthquake of March 28, 1964, and of its aftershock sequence. *Journal of Geophysical Research*, 71 (November 15), 5283-5296. Also *in* The Great Alaska Earthquake of 1964: Seismology and Geodesy. NAS Pub. 1602. Washington: National Academy of Sciences, 1972.

Stoneley, Robert, 1967. The structural development of the Gulf of Alaska sedimentary province in southern Alaska. *Geological Society of London Quarterly Journal*, 123 (September 15), 25-27.

Tobin, Don G., and Lynn R. Sykes, 1966. Relationship of hypocenters of earthquakes to the geology of Alaska. *Journal of Geophysical Research*, 71 (March 15), 1659-1667.

Van Dorn, William G., 1965. Tsunamis. *Advances in Hydroscience*, 2 (Annual), 1-47.

von Huene, Roland, 1966. Glacial marine geology of Nuka Bay, Alaska, and the adjacent Continental Shelf. *Marine Geology*, 4 (August), 291-304.

von Huene, Roland, L. D. Kulm, J. R. Duncan, J. C. Ingle, S. A. Kling, L. M. Musich, D. J. W. Piper, R. M. Pratt, H. J. Schrader, O. Weser, and S. W. Wise, Jr., 1971. Deep Sea Drilling Project: Leg 18. *Geotimes*, 16 (October), 12-16.

von Huene, Roland, Richard J. Malloy, George G. Shor, Jr., and Pierre St.-Amand, 1967. Geologic structures in the aftershock region of the 1964 Alaskan earthquake. *Journal of Geophysical Research*, 72 (July 15), 3649-3660.

von Huene, Roland, and George G. Shor, Jr., 1969. The structure and tectonic history of the eastern Aleutian Trench. *Geological Society of America Bulletin*, 80 (October), 1889-1902.

von Huene, Roland, George G. Shor, Jr., and Erk Reimnitz, 1967. Geological interpretation of seismic profiles in Prince William Sound, Alaska. *Geological Society of America Bulletin*, 78 (February), 259-268.

Wyss, Max, and James N. Brune, 1967. The Alaska earthquake of 28 March 1964: A complex multiple rupture. *Bulletin of the Seismological Society of America*, 57 (October), 1017-1023. Also *in* The Great Alaska Earthquake of 1964: Seismology and Geodesy. NAS Pub. 1602. Washington: National Academy of Sciences, 1972.

ERK REIMNITZ

U.S. GEOLOGICAL SURVEY

Effects in the Copper River Delta

INTRODUCTION

Seismic motion and large-scale vertical movements of the earth's crust associated with the 1964 Alaska earthquake affected extensive regions of the Continental Shelf in the Gulf of Alaska. These movements also caused a major tsunami and numerous seiches.

An earthquake of magnitude 8.4 is expected to leave both a temporary and a permanent record imprinted on the affected region. The most complete and permanent record should be in the sediments of nearshore basins. It is of interest, therefore, to identify the record of the 1964 earthquake in such a sedimentary basin and to apply the knowledge to the search for evidence of previous seismic events.

Accumulations of Holocene marine sediment are rare in most of the area affected by the earthquake. They are restricted largely to fiord floors and to the Copper River Delta. The delta lies about 130 km east of the major earthquake epicenter; its front extends for a distance of more than 100 km along the Gulf of Alaska (Figure 1). The subaerial and intertidal portion is separated from the open gulf by a string of barrier islands. Landward of these, and in the following order, lie extensive tidal flats, salt marshes and high marshes, and river flood-plain and glacial-outwash fans. The delta also extends into eastern Prince William Sound.

Because the sedimentary regime of the Copper River Delta was being examined when the earthquake occurred (Reimnitz, 1966), pre- and postearthquake information is available for the region. Certain aspects of the earthquake effects on the delta and vicinity have been treated previously by Reimnitz and Marshall (1965, and Geology volume).

The earthquake occurred shortly before low tide when large portions of the tidal flats were exposed. It lasted for 4 to 5 minutes. Shock intensities felt in Cordova—a community built on bedrock near the delta—were severe, but structural damage was negligible. However, along the Copper River Highway, which crosses the delta between Mile 7 and Mile 50, 18 of 52 bridges were totally destroyed, 14 received severe

ABSTRACT: The 1964 Alaska earthquake and related events had pronounced effects on the recent sediments of the Copper River Delta. The sedimentary structures include such features as sand dikes, sand pipes, faults, joints, slumps, and distorted bedding. A unique pattern of low-angle slump scars, dipping 2° 30′ to 5°, was detected in a Sonoprobe profile of the foreset beds. The earthquake record also shows thick accumulations of sediment in certain depressions representing erosion products of tsunamis and seiches in shallow-water areas and a marked unconformity in the latter regions. Mechanisms of redistribution of sediments apparently included turbidity currents in at least one area. Although the immediate effects of the general 2-m uplift were not pronounced, long-range effects probably will include a seaward shift of broad lithofacies and plant zones by as much as 10 km.

Previous strong seismic events should have left a record similar to that of the 1964 earthquake in the sedimentary sequence of the Copper River Delta. Thus, two buried forest horizons in the zone of former salt marshes, dated at about 750 and 1,700 years before the present, apparently formed after sudden uplifts similar to the one of 1964 and were destroyed by continuing slow subsidence. These buried forests may correspond to elevated marine terraces on Middleton Island, over 100 km seaward located on the outer Continental Shelf. Here a new terrace corresponds with uplift of the delta where a forest is presently forming.

Future studies of the Copper River Delta and surrounding areas may enable us to extend the record of strong earthquakes back in time. Extensive sediment ejection during the 1964 earthquake affected the mass physical properties of the upper section. Therefore, horizons related to earlier earthquakes may be identifiable in this otherwise uniform sedimentary environment by changes in the state of packing.

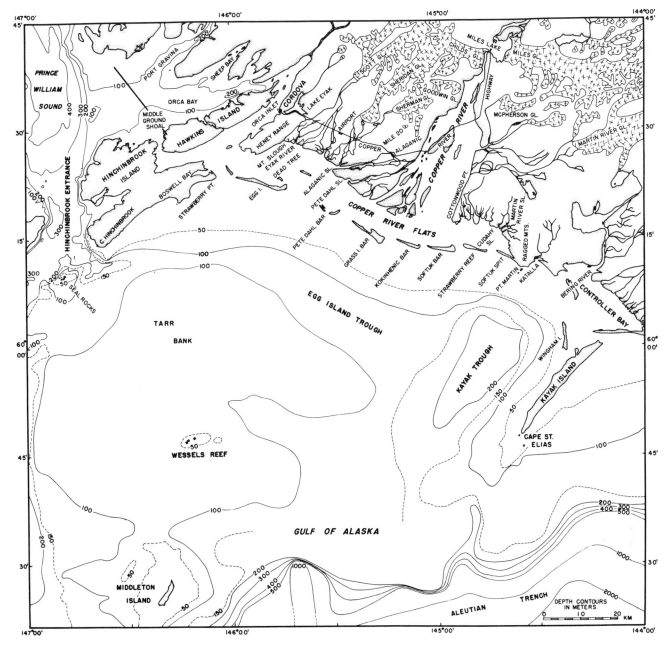

FIGURE 1   Map of the Copper River Delta region. Location of cross section in Figure 3 shown by heavy line.

damage, and 20 suffered lesser to negligible damage (Migliaccio, 1965; Kachadoorian, 1968, and Geology volume). Most of the undamaged bridges were located near bedrock.

At Cordova, nearly 2 m of uplift were associated with the earthquake. At various locations on the delta the uplift was about equal to that at Cordova, but uplift locally may have been as much as 3.5 m.

Uplift and tilting of the Continental Shelf generated water waves. These traveled radially, northwesterly into the coastal regions, and southwesterly across the Pacific Ocean. In Prince

William Sound, the pattern of earthquake-related waves was complicated by local effects of slope failures and fiord configuration (Gene Rusnak, unpublished data).

In Orca Inlet—the eastern, sediment-filled portion of Prince William Sound—seiching was observed. The seiches probably were initiated by a tsunami arriving from the open ocean (Reimnitz and Marshall, 1965, and Geology volume). The rate of advance of the first wave across the exposed tidal flats in Orca Inlet may have been between 35 and 60 km per hour. According to eyewitnesses, this wave was about 8 m high. Passing through Orca Inlet, it was breaking across its entire width and was preceded by a rush of air. Subsequent seiching had a period of about 30 minutes and a maximum amplitude of 7.5 m at Cordova. Seiches on the Copper River Flats in the open gulf had considerably less amplitude than those in eastern Prince William Sound, but data on their amplitude are scant.

GEOLOGICALLY IMPORTANT EFFECTS IN THE DELTA

The considerable effects of the events described above on the deltaic wedge will be discussed under three headings: (1) seismic-shock effects, (2) consequences of the earthquake uplift, and (3) consequences of the tsunami and seiches.

SEISMIC-SHOCK EFFECTS

Onshore

Stresses generated by ground motion during the earthquake caused various types of ground breakage on the subaerial portion of the Copper River Delta. These features have been described by Reimnitz and Marshall (1965, and Geology volume) and by other investigators in nearby areas where thick accumulations of unconsolidated sediments are found (among them, Coulter and Migliaccio, 1966, and Geology volume; Tuthill and Laird, 1966; Foster and Karlstrom, 1967). Therefore, the types of earthquake-shock phenomena and their distribution will not be treated in detail here. It is sufficient to point out that seismic shaking produced numerous sedimentary structures, including sand dikes, sand pipes, slumps, faults, and various types of flow structures within the stratified upper delta section.

Some of the structures were associated with ejection of sediment from below the delta surface. Such ejection is often brought about when grains in the upper section are more tightly packed together thereby releasing pore water. The water mixed with sand, silt, and clay flows to the surface. Sand spouts (also called sand blows, sand vents, silt volcanoes, sand ridges, mud volcanoes, mud spouts, and so forth) were localized either along fissures or at circular vents. In some instances, sand was extruded along fissures without free pore water. Evidence of dry sand extrusion was found especially on the barrier islands, but also on marshes. Ground cracks frequently were marked by ridges of sand, with flanks sloping near the angle of repose. Such ridges could be interpreted as representing either (1) ejecta supplied from depth by the usual mechanism of "sand venting," but originally confined to the upward extensions of ground cracks into the snow cover; or (2) wind-borne materials deposited in cracks in the snow after the earthquake.

I investigated the area a few weeks after the earthquake,

when snow cover was still extensive. If mechanism 1 had been responsible for the ridges in question, evidence for overflowing from the snow gaps should have been found wherever snow cover was relatively thin during the earthquake. Such evidence was not found in certain areas. Furthermore, the sand fill in some of the cracks in the snow, where these were only partly filled, had a sharp crest along the center. Such ridgelike surface features within snow cracks would also rule out mechanism 2. Eolian transport of sediment certainly is an important factor in the sediment dispersal on the Copper River Delta (Reimnitz, 1966), but it would also form thin blankets of sand and silt on the melting snow adjacent to earthquake-produced cracks and would produce laminated deposits within the snow cracks. These characteristics of ridges marking ground cracks may indicate that sand and silt deposits under extreme vibration stresses behave like a fluid even without free pore water. To my knowledge, this mechanism has not been described by other investigators of the Alaska earthquake. Certain features shown by Foster and Karlstrom (1967, p. F23), however, could possibly be so interpreted.

Extensive surficial sand deposits are often formed by sand spouts, but they were relatively rare on the Copper River Delta. Perhaps this can be explained by the frequency of earthquakes in the delta region. Thus, new sedimentary deposits probably do not reach great thickness before the next earthquake occurs, producing widespread compaction.

The phenomenon of sediment ejection probably is most common in, but not restricted to, water-saturated depths above sea level. In fact, an unpublished postearthquake Sonoprobe profile (by Gene Rusnak) of shallow-water deposits in the head of Orca Bay, as well as other evidence, indicates that sediment ejection occurred from submerged deposits. Gill and Kuenen (1957) also present evidence for subaqueous sand venting in the Carboniferous of County Clare, Ireland.

A review of the literature shows that our understanding of the mechanism involved in sand venting, including the type of sediments and thickness affected, is inadequate, although some new information was gained from investigations after the 1964 Alaska earthquake. New approaches in the study of the phenomenon are needed, as Waller (1968) has also pointed out. An outline of suggested future research is presented in a later section.

Offshore

The delta foreset beds, sloping into Prince William Sound and into the Gulf of Alaska, exhibited features indicating that submarine slumping was associated with the 1964 earthquake, as shown by (1) bathymetric surveys and (2) high-frequency (Sonoprobe) and low-frequency (Arcer) continuous sub-bottom profiles of certain areas.

Both the Sonoprobe and the Arcer were used to investigate the sedimentary framework of Middle Ground Shoal

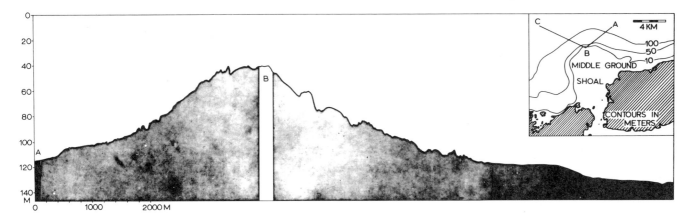

FIGURE 2 Postearthquake bottom profile of Middle Ground Shoal, suggestive of slumping. Bathymetry in inset reflects preearthquake conditions.

(Figure 2), a tidal delta of the Copper River. The Sonoprobe failed to penetrate the bottom, but the Arcer confirmed that the bulge in the contours outlines a wedge of sediments with foreset beds dipping into Orca Bay (Figure 3). This wedge apparently is underlain by glacial drift (von Huene and others, 1967). Pinnacles of bedrock, common elsewhere in the fiord profiles, were not detected. From U.S. Coast and Geodetic Survey chart 8520, the foreset slopes of this delta outside of the 20-m contour were calculated to be 51 to 78 m/km (3°–4.5°) prior to the earthquake. After the earthquake the upper portion of the slope, immediately outside of the lunate bar rimming the shoal, steepened to as much as 120 m/km (nearly 6°).

To a depth of 32 m the slope is covered with silty sand. Beyond that depth, samples are not available. From notations of bottom conditions in Schaefers and others (1955), it appears that the sediments on the floor of Orca Bay consist of blue-gray muds and that mud and sand occur in one place near the foot of the slope.

Figure 2 presents two depth-recorder profiles of the slope leading down to the fiord bottom. The plot of these lines (see inset) shows that the preearthquake 10-m contour should have been crossed in approaching land. The record indicates a depth of 41 m near the end of the profile. This depth could mean that a portion of the delta slumped, but a relatively small navigation error could also account for the discrepancy in soundings in this area of steep slopes.

The bottom configuration of the slope is very irregular and not at all like a slope produced by normal sedimentary processes. Slumping apparently affected the entire delta front. The maximum slope inclination measured was 160 m/km (9°).

Slump features of the Fraser River Delta, described by Mathews and Shepard (1962), were also discussed by Terzaghi in the same publication. He believes that the slumping occurs periodically, locally disturbing the slope and reducing its overall angle. On the foreset beds of this fiord delta, normal sedimentary processes cover former slump features and steepen the slope until another slump takes place. Perhaps the slopes off Middle Ground Shoal behave similarly. The present survey found most of the slope area to be affected by slumping. This observation suggests that recent seismic activity may have played a role.

The foreset beds on the seaward side of the Copper River Delta show slump features of a different nature. Figure 4 is a Sonoprobe record from a depth of 62 m to near the bottom of the slope in Egg Island Trough. Figure 5 is a continuation of the profile with some overlap, as indicated in the inset map. Because a scale change shifted the bottom record into the upper noise band and so obscured the trace, a drawing was prepared for this portion of the record. In the drawing all noise was eliminated and identifiable echoes are shown as dotted patterns. The density and shading of this pattern reproduce the original record as closely as possible.

Figure 4 shows a number of slump scars cutting the seaward-dipping beds. The bottom slope in this area is less than 9 m/km (about 0°30′). From Egg Island Trough landward, the slope of individual scars decreases from nearly 90 m/km (5°) to 45 m/km (2°30′). The thickness of slices

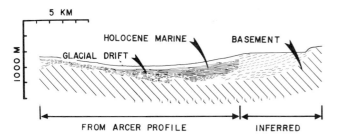

FIGURE 3 Cross section of Middle Ground Shoal (to the right), based on an Arcer profile and local geology. For location refer to Figure 1.

FIGURE 4   Photograph of postearthquake Sonoprobe record, showing slumping of the foreset beds of the delta.

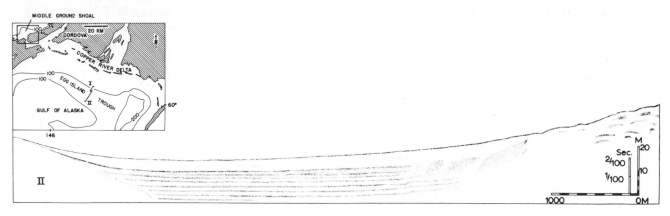

FIGURE 5   Drawing of Sonoprobe record of delta foreset and bottomset beds in Egg Island Trough. Slumping of the foreset beds and recent high rates of deposition on bottomset beds are indicated. I (inset) shows where the Sonoprobe record in Figure 4 was obtained.

between scars varies by as much as a factor of three, with an average of less than 20 m. The dip slip is as much as 34 m.

A gravity core (M-5-C in Figure 4) shows that sediments consist of silty clay interbedded with thin layers of clayey silt. The clayey silt layers are spaced irregularly, but average about 10 cm apart.

The Sonoprobe record of the bottomset beds is poor (Figure 5); nevertheless, two generalizations can be made. First, the uppermost, and thus the most recent, layer is considerably thicker than the underlying uniformly stratified sediments and reflects a change in conditions. Second, this thicker surface layer seems to overlap and smooth out the lowest slump features observed in the foreset beds.

Areas of rapid deposition are subject to failure by slumping even on gentle slopes. For example, slumping is known to occur at the mouth of the Mississippi River on slopes of 10 m/km (Shepard, 1955). Slumping of the Fraser River Delta has already been mentioned. It has also been observed on the Magdalena Delta (Heezen, 1956), and possibly off the Rhone Delta (Van Straaten, 1959). The delta front at Valdez has

failed six times in connection with earthquakes during historic time; three additional failures were not associated with seismic activity (Coulter and Migliaccio, 1966, and Geology volume). Von Huene and Cox (1971, this volume) describe numerous failures of deltaic deposits in fiords of the area affected during the earthquake. Morgenstern (1967) presents a good summary of various types of submarine slope failures.

The mechanism by which delta fronts generally fail seems to be different from that observed on the seaward side of the Copper River Delta. Usually mass movement displaces sections of the delta-front slope, leaving scars and elongate troughs above, and a hummocky topography below. In the case of the Copper River Delta, consecutive slices of the foreset beds, presumably starting from the bottom of the slope upward, failed by dip-slip movement along low-angle fractures. This type of slope failure may be similar to that for retrogressive flow slides in loose sand and silt (Andresen and Bjerrum, 1967).

If related to the 1964 earthquake, the fractures should either meet in a common, nearly horizontal plane or extend downward without deflection but decreasing displacement. If the features were old, but periodically rejuvenated, displacement should increase downward. Because our records do not penetrate deep below the surface layers, it is impossible to determine where the fractures are located. However, periodic rejuvenation might be ruled out on the basis that not all scars would be expected to extend to the sediment-water interface at any one time. To my knowledge, counterparts of these structures have not been observed in similar environments. Because of this and because of the unusual magnitude of the 1964 earthquake, the slumping probably is of seismic origin.

A Sonoprobe record of the foreset beds outside the western extension of the string of barrier islands shows similar but less pronounced features. Arcer traverses of the slumped areas show a distinct irregularity in the reflectors—a characteristic used to detect slumping in other traverses of the delta front. Similar disturbance of stratification was also observed in slightly inclined, thick sedimentary deposits in the deep Prince William Sound (von Huene and others, 1967, sec. 12–15).

If the slumping shown in Figure 4 was caused by the 1964 earthquake, then the anomalously thick upper section of the bottomset beds (Figure 5) must have been deposited during a period of 4 months after the earthquake. Unfortunately, the sediment volume in this section, which apparently represents a greatly increased rate of deposition after the earthquake, cannot be calculated with any degree of confidence.

Three factors may have led to an increased postearthquake rate of sediment supply in this broad trough paralleling the delta front:

1. Tsunamis and seiches associated with earthquakes are known to have planed off over 70 cm of surface sediments in some regions of the tidal flats (Reimnitz and Marshall, 1965, and Geology volume).
2. Regional uplift of 2 m caused erosion of the upper delta and lower river region.
3. Before the earthquake, the Copper River Delta had been subsiding and thereby retained on delta topset beds some portion of the sediment supply. Following the earthquake uplift of the area, the sediment loads bypassed the upper delta and were carried to the offshore regions.

CONSEQUENCES OF THE EARTHQUAKE UPLIFT

Earthquake-related shoaling of extensive tidal flats on the Copper River Delta was very noticeable. The shoaling probably caused changes in tidal harmonic constants and tidal pattern. Without a thorough knowledge of such changes, the exact amount of uplift could not be determined for any one location by measuring changes between a reference horizon and sea level. The regional uplift of the delta was approximated, however, by a number of measurements taken over a

sufficiently large area to minimize error related to local change in tidal pattern. The salt-marsh surface was used as a reference horizon for measurements because it is normally adjusted delicately to the existing tidal regime. In the case of the Copper River Delta, the equilibrium surface of the salt marsh is nearly 4 m above mean lower low water. After the earthquake the average elevation of this surface was almost 6 m, indicating 2 m of uplift, similar to that determined for Cordova. Compensation for uplift by compaction of the delta, which locally is at least 180 m thick (Reimnitz, 1966), surprisingly was not sufficient to be detectable by the methods used.

In any case, the immediate results of the uplift of the delta, in terms of its geology, were minor (Reimnitz and Marshall, 1965, and Geology volume). Important long-range effects, however, are anticipated and should be investigated. Such long-range effects will include changes brought about by a broad seaward shift of the inner salt-marsh boundary (Figure 6)—a shift of nearly 15 km on the central delta.

The extensive intertidal regions and the drainage system, all formerly delicately adjusted to base level, have been undergoing profound changes since the uplift, changes similar to those observed in Prince William Sound (Alaska Department of Fish and Game, 1965; Thorsteinson, 1965; for both articles, see Biology volume). On the upper portion of the delta, where the river channels cut down to base level, flood-plain terraces should develop. The former salt marshes are experiencing a change in vegetation; possibly trees will start to grow. New marshes are forming on uplifted portions of the tidal flats adjacent to the former marsh. Such shifts in plant zones will very likely be paralleled by shifts of lithofacies in adjacent intertidal and shallow-water areas. Other changes may involve channel patterns and possibly a closing off of entire tidal-flat sections from the marsh seaward to the barrier islands.

Two buried forest horizons were investigated on the Copper River Delta. These forest horizons may record previous displacements of plant zones similar to the changes that have been going on since the 1964 uplift, and they may shed light on the frequency of similar earthquakes in the area.

The forest horizons were observed in the cutbanks flanking the sloughs and distributaries that cross the salt-marsh zone. A thin forest horizon, in which the base of the tree trunks lies at a depth of 2.9 to 3.2 m below the marsh surface, can be traced continuously for many kilometers along the sloughs. It is found both along Eyak River in the very western portion of the marsh zone and 60 km to the east along Cudahy Slough at the eastern end of the marsh zone (Figure 1). In the central portion of the delta, below this forest horizon and 4.8 m below the surface of the marsh, another forest horizon, referred to as the "lower forest," is found.

Figure 7 shows a typical exposure of the upper forest horizon. Numerous *in situ* well-preserved tree stumps as much as 1 m in diameter, often with interfingering roots, are

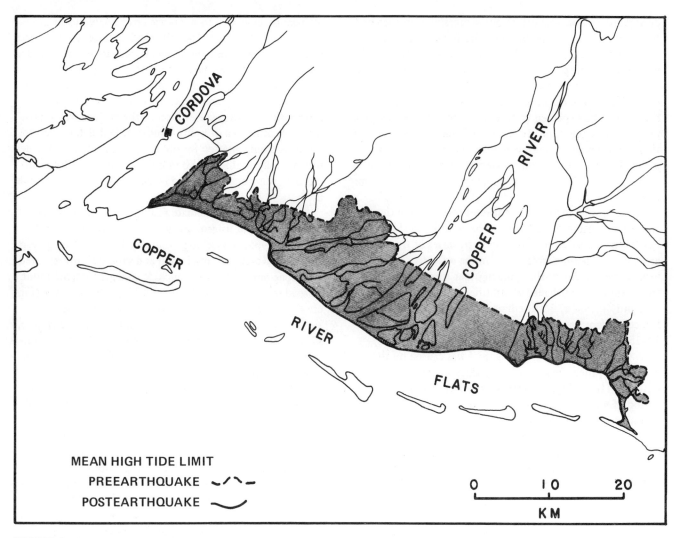

FIGURE 6 Map of the Copper River Delta, depicting seaward shift of the mean high-tide line (generalized) during the 1964 earthquake. Shading indicates areas no longer reached by mean high water. These include the former salt marshes and regions in which buried forests were found. Map modified after Rae E. Baxter and others (Alaska Department of Fish and Game, 1965).

exposed in the cutbanks. No trunks were found in any of the exposures. They seem to have been removed from the stumps immediately above the base of the roots.

Six wood samples were collected from the forest horizons to determine their age and the rates of submergence. Figure 7 shows the locations, amount of submergence, and carbon-14 ages in years before the present, as determined by the La Jolla Laboratory. The amount of submergence was calculated for pre-1964 uplift conditions, assuming that trees would grow at least at +5.8 m, which is 1 m above the level of spring tides. Also shown is the elevation and age of a tree stump from Egg Island near Dead Tree. At that location, a marsh layer 2 to 2.5 m thick covers a number of widely spaced *in situ* tree stumps rooted into a thick substratum of sand.

Table 1 gives depths of trees below the marsh surface, indicated submergence, and the carbon-14 age in years before

the present. The upper forest apparently was killed about 750 years before present (BP). The discrepancy between this age and the 1,360 years indicated for the killing of the tree at Eyak River does not fit the field evidence, which suggests that all belong to the same horizon. The discrepancy may be a laboratory error. The lower forest was killed about 1,700 years BP.

The reason for the death and later burial of the forests appears to be a relative rise of sea level brought about by slow sinking of the land. Organic matter buried within the marsh section is well preserved, as shown by the presence of fine grass roots to a depth of at least 5 m. Driftwood on the marsh surface has been found to decay rapidly. This may explain why the tree trunks could not be found, although the wood of stumps is sound. The continuous section of marsh deposits overlying the lower forest and the lack of evidence for litho-

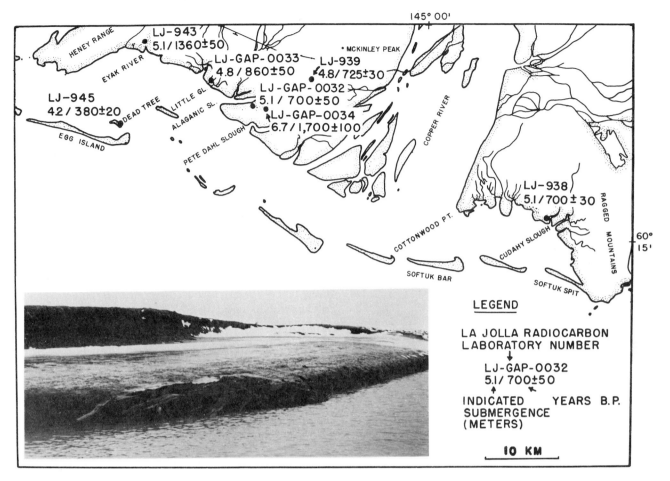

FIGURE 7   Map showing locations and carbon-14 ages of drowned trees from the Copper River Delta. Indicated submergence is related to pre-1964 sea level and is based on the assumption that trees grew at least 1 m above spring tide level, or at +5.8 m. Inset shows the upper forest near the mouth of the Alaganic Slough. A large tree stump is seen in foreground, the high marsh in the background.

logic changes indicate that submergence was not related to catastrophic events or cyclic delta progradation. Submergence after an assumed sudden earthquake-related uplift appears to have been slow enough for marsh accretion to keep pace.

The data presented in Table 1 indicate that the rate of marsh accretion and of subsidence between the growth of the lower and the upper forest may have been about 2 mm per year after the growth of the upper forest about 7 mm per year. These rates correlate reasonably well with the rates of marsh accretion in other comparable environments (Chapman, 1960).

If the subsidence were due to compaction of recent deltaic sediments, the depth of the upper forest below the marsh surface should vary with the thickness of underlying deltaic sediments. This is not the case. At Cudahy Slough, near the thin eastern margin of the deltaic wedge, subsidence indicated by the depth of the forest horizon below the marsh surface was equal to that in the center of the delta (Table 1).

In the eastern portions of the tidal flats, between Cudahy

Slough and the barrier islands and also between Cottonwood Point and the barrier islands (Figure 7), stumps that appear to be in place at nearly the same elevation as the upper forest were noted by Rae Baxter, biologist with the Alaska Department of Fish and Game (oral communication). Thus a forest may have extended southward as far as the present chain of barrier islands.

CONSEQUENCES OF THE TSUNAMI AND SEICHES

The tsunami and subsequent seiches in Orca Inlet, on the Copper River Flats, and in surrounding shallow marine environments, caused abnormally high current velocities. As a result of these strong currents, large amounts of surface sediments were redistributed (Reimnitz and Marshall, 1965, and Geology volume; Barrett, 1966, and Geology volume). Thus large areas of tidal flats in Orca Inlet lost at least 76 cm of surface sediments. Certain areas on the Copper River Flats seem to have lost similar amounts of surface sediment. In

TABLE 1 Radiocarbon Ages, Depth below Marsh Surface, and Indicated Submergence of Drowned Trees from the Copper River Delta

	Depth below Marsh (m)	Indicated Submergence (m)	Age (years BP)[a]
Lower Forest			
Pete Dahl Cutoff (LJ-GAP 0034)	4.8	6.7	1,700±100
Upper Forest			
Eyak River (LJ 943)	3.2	5.1	1,360± 50
Little Glacier (LJ-GAP 0033)	2.9	4.8	860± 50
Pete Dahl Cutoff (LJ-GAP 0032)	3.2	5.1	700± 50
Upper Alaganic Slough (LJ 939)	2.9	4.8	725± 30
Cudahy Slough (LJ 938)	3.2	5.1	700± 30
Dead Tree			
Egg Island (LJ 945)	—	*ca.* 4.2	380± 20

[a]Before present.

some cases, such areas were covered by lag deposits in the form of extensive beds of several species of burrowing molluscs. These lag deposits probably will be preserved in the geologic record.

Because the water waves arrived in the area after the shaking had stopped (Reimnitz and Marshall, 1965, and Geology volume), the erosion surface in the intertidal and surrounding nearshore regions postdates sedimentary structures produced by the seismic shocks. In many cases, therefore, these structures are truncated by an unconformity and are overlain by lag deposits.

The eroded materials were dumped into deep channels and other depressions surrounding the delta to thicknesses of as much as 10 m, as indicated by comparing pre- and postearthquake sounding lines (Reimnitz and Marshall, 1965, and Geology volume). Such thicknesses were also confirmed by the Sonoprobe profiles of G. A. Rusnak (personal communication) in the head of Orca Inlet. The Sonoprobe profile crossing the Egg Island Trough seaward of the chain of barrier islands separating the subaerial portion of the Copper River Delta from the open Gulf of Alaska (Figure 5) shows such a reworked deposit. In this area the apparent lack of postearthquake deposits on the delta foreset beds is hard to explain in view of the increased sediment supply and suggested high rates of sediment accumulation on the bottomset beds. Perhaps the action of turbidity currents accounts for the anomaly.

Because of the lack of cores in the area, nothing is known

regarding the nature of the deposits that accumulated during a period of weeks. The thickness of the deposits precludes the use of standard coring techniques to investigate characteristics such as internal structures and sediment grain-size distribution.

The erosion of the shallow-water areas and deposition in deeper areas probably did not take place with one sweep of a current surge, but instead during a number of such surges that produced the oscillating currents reported by eyewitnesses (Reimnitz and Marshall, 1965, and Geology volume). We believe that the sediments deposited by the seiches, which decreased in intensity over a period of several days, may not only be graded but may also show many features commonly associated with turbidity–current deposits, and that possibly a number of such units make up a channel fill. In the channels and tidal inlets the driving mechanism for the current surges, of course, differed from that for turbidity currents. In the case of the Egg Island Trough, however, true turbidity currents may have been active.

POSSIBLE EVIDENCE FOR PREVIOUS SIMILAR EARTHQUAKES

The 2-m uplift associated with the 1964 earthquake caused extensive shifts of plant zones on the Copper River Delta. The dated record of two similar earlier shifts of plant zones resulting in the burial of forests has been presented above. I believe that the buried forests developed after uplifts related to previous earthquakes. Evidence for this conclusion is found in the history of the late Holocene to pre-1964 vertical crustal movement of the area.

Evidence for Holocene vertical crustal movement has been summarized by Reimnitz (1966) and Plafker and Rubin (1967). Much of the outer coast and Continental Shelf of the Gulf of Alaska has experienced Holocene uplift. Some of this uplift occurred in pulses, as shown by a series of wave-cut terraces on Middleton Island; a new wave-cut terrace was elevated during the 1964 earthquake. The Copper River Delta and portions of Prince William Sound, however, have been subjected to recent subsidence. The trend of emergence on the inner Continental Shelf was reversed to one of gradual submergence 2,000 to 4,000 years ago (Reimnitz, 1966) with a hinge line somewhere along the northern flank of Tarr Bank (Figure 1). Plafker and Rubin (1967) have suggested that the submergence of the Copper River Delta was partly the result of isostatic adjustment of the crust under the sediment load. However, the isostatic effects of post-Wisconsin ice unloading are roughly compensated by those of sediment loading in the Copper River Delta (Reimnitz, 1966). Moreover, the regional trend of submergence also affected areas where there was no large-scale deltaic sedimentation, even though all the area had been recently unloaded of ice. Thus tectonic, rather than isostatic forces, seem to be the dominant factor controlling vertical crustal movement of the area under consideration.

There is an additional point of disagreement with Plafker and Rubin (1967, p. 65). According to their interpretation the evidence suggests gradual submergence of the coast during at least the past 930 years, and probably as long as 1,360 years. I believe that the presence of buried forests in the marsh zones indicates times of uplift. This uplift occurred in pulses, superimposed on the general trend of submergence. The most recent positive pulse may result in a new forest horizon on the former salt marshes. Such a forest horizon would correspond in time to the newly elevated terrace on Middleton Island.

Uplifts recorded in the elevated terraces on Middleton Island and in the submerged forests of the Copper River Delta affected the entire Continental Shelf of the area under consideration just as the sudden uplift of 1964 did. Thus the age of the upper forest (about 700 years) agrees well with a radiocarbon date obtained from the lowest pre-1964 wave-cut terrace on Middleton Island (Ives and others, 1964). Most published radiocarbon dates from Middleton Island (Ives and others, 1964; Levin and others, 1965; Ives and others, 1967; Plafker and Rubin, 1967) do not fit as orderly a sequence as would be expected, possibly because most of these dates were obtained from driftwood rather than from material *in situ*. Such wood could have been carried to the site anytime after the uplift of a particular terrace or could have been in transit along the coast for unknown periods of time.

Based on the evidence presented and on the assumption that the buried forests represent times of sudden uplift corresponding to the elevated terraces on Middleton Island, the following conclusions can be drawn:

1. Three strong earthquakes, each associated with sudden uplift affecting the entire width of the Continental Shelf, occurred during the last 1,700 years. The intervals between the earthquakes were about 1,000 and 700 years.

2. The magnitude of sudden uplift on the outer shelf during the three events was considerably greater than that on the inner shelf.

3. On the outer shelf, a possible combination of gradual and sudden vertical movement resulted in net uplift which extends back in time through possibly all of the Holocene Epoch. On the inner shelf, the effects of sudden uplift were offset by gradual subsidence during the last few thousand years, resulting in the net submergence.

DISCUSSION AND CONCLUSIONS

The marks left by the 1964 Alaska earthquake and associated events on the recent sediments of the Copper River Delta and the changes in pattern of sedimentation are significant. Sedi-

mentary structures related to the earthquake extend to a depth of at least 20 m and probably much deeper. Among the structures are sand dikes, sand pipes, faults, joints, various types of slump features, and distorted bedding. Earthquake-related sedimentary features have been found in the subaerial, the intertidal, and the submarine environment. On the delta-foreset slope an unusual sequence of slump scars was formed. Because of the erosion by the tsunami and seiching, and because of the uplift, these structures are terminated in many areas by an unconformity. On the tidal flats this unconformity is marked locally by accumulations of burrowing clams of mixed species and by other debris. Tidal channels and other depressions on and around the delta collected thick sedimentary deposits representing erosion products from the delta related to the effects of the tsunami and seiches and to the uplift. In the offshore area, and possibly in other areas as well, the mechanism of the redistribution of sediment may have included turbidity currents.

As a result of the 2-m regional uplift, pronounced changes in depositional patterns have occurred. Related to the uplift is a seaward shift of over 10 km for certain lithofacies. In time, these changes will probably also affect plant zonation—a forest may occupy former salt marshes, while salt marsh in turn will occupy former tidal flats.

Two buried forest horizons below the salt-marsh regions are believed to represent a record of former earthquakes, which were also associated with uplift. These periodic uplifts have merely interrupted the gradual subsidence. The buried forests thus probably mark horizons at which earthquake-produced sedimentary structures and features are truncated by an unconformity. The two lowest of a series of elevated wave-cut terraces on Middleton Island on the edge of the Continental Shelf seem to have corresponding horizons on the inner shelf. Higher terraces may also have related features on the Copper River Delta. We seem to have a record of strong earthquakes that affected the entire width of the Continental Shelf.

Most of the features produced by seismic shock that were observed in the Copper River Delta region have also been described in other regions affected by the 1964 earthquake and after previous earthquakes in different parts of the world where thick accumulations of unconsolidated sediments are encountered. Despite the frequent occurrence of various types of ground breakage and despite the damage caused to man-made structures, our understanding of the mechanisms still is very limited (Waller, 1968, and Hydrology volume).

This lack of understanding is also reflected in the loose terminology used by investigators of seismic phenomena. Due recognition, however, should be given to the large amount of new information being obtained by soil engineers in case studies of specific areas, such as the studies of the Anchorage area.

Some of the phenomena commonly described under the

term "ground breakage" are associated with the extrusion of sediment. Generally, the mechanism involves the expulsion of pore water liberated by tighter packing of the grains in water-saturated deposits (Housner, 1958). Laboratory studies by soil-mechanics engineers have supplied much new information concerning the mechanisms involved. However, numerous uncertainties arise when information obtained in laboratory is applied to investigations of natural phenomena. The need for carefully oriented and detailed field studies is apparent. Unfortunately, information furnished by the 1964 Alaska earthquake could not be fully utilized, because accurate subsurface information was lacking in areas where ground breakage, surface deformation, damage to man-made structures, or all three phenomena occurred. The following major problems, among many others, should receive particular attention in future field studies:

1. The stratigraphy of the affected sediment section as related to the various types of ground breakage and sediment deformation;

2. The nature of the materials from which water and sediment are ejected, and certain mass physical properties, both before and after seismic events (in areas of uniform rapid sediment accumulation, preearthquake conditions could be approximated by studying postearthquake deposits);

3. The depth to which sediments are disturbed; and

4. Amplitude, period, direction, and duration of ground motion in relation to the resulting sediment compaction.

Under some conditions, sediment accumulations once compacted by seismic motion probably are not affected to the same extent by a subsequent event with similar characteristics. This has been shown by Dill's (1967, 1969) observations in southern California submarine canyons. The mass physical properties and strength characteristics of disturbed sediments may differ from undisturbed ones. The Snow River Delta north of Seward, Alaska, may illustrate this point: the Alaska Department of Highways found an apparent increase in sediment density after the 1964 earthquake (Lemke, 1967, and Geology volume). Similarly, the average water content (weight of water divided by weight of solids) for 30 postearthquake Copper River Delta bore-hole samples, collected and analyzed by the Materials Section of the Alaska Department of Highways, is 29.4 percent, a value that seems unusually low for the types of materials penetrated. Twelve samples with a silt-plus-clay fraction of less than 20 percent of the total sediment were excluded in this average, because such materials do not retain pore water during the sampling and processing. Inclusion of these samples would lower the average water content to 25.8 percent (Reimnitz, 1966). Unfortunately, preearthquake data from the same locations are not available for comparison.

On the Copper River Delta, the thickness of the surface layer affected by sediment ejection might be expected to correspond to the depth to the horizon affected by the previous earthquake of similar intensity and duration. This horizon should be recognizable by the criteria already described. Areas that have been reworked during that time interval by migrating tidal and river channels, of course, are excepted.

The layer that actually was tapped by the sand vents in one case was at a depth of over 6 m, and in numerous other cases it was at depths in excess of 4 m (Reimnitz and Marshall, 1965, and Geology volume). When one considers calculated rates of subsidence and deposition for the delta in relation to the frequency at which strong earthquakes occur (Reimnitz, 1966), the sediment thickness affected by the last earthquake seems too great. This same excessive depth of disturbance may apply to other areas in which sediment ejection took place in 1964. Much additional information is required in order to gain a better understanding of these relationships.

Some of the needed information undoubtedly could be obtained from investigations of ancient sediment sections in which earthquake-produced features can be identified. So far, there have been very few attempts to relate such features to observations of actual earthquake phenomena. Reports in which possible earthquake-produced features are described include the following: Darton (1899), Oldham (1899), Hobbs (1907), Baker (1916), Hawley and Hart (1934), Simpson (1936), Maxson (1940), Shrock (1948), Dietrich (1952), Niino (1955), Gill and Kuenen (1957), Sutton and Watson (1960), Selly and others (1963), Sutton and Watson (1963), Childers (1964), Myers and Hamilton (1964), Lindström (1967), and Megrue and Kerr (1968).

Strong earthquakes of the past must have left their marks on unconsolidated deposits in the same way as recent sediment accumulations were affected by the 1964 earthquake. Thus records of strong earthquakes are undoubtedly waiting to be deciphered in many areas of the world; this deciphering may shed light on their intensity and duration. From such records it may even be possible to predict future earthquakes. Another application of these studies may be the use of explosives to make unconsolidated sediments relatively safe during an earthquake. Such experiments are currently being carried on in Norway (Kummeneje and Eide, 1961) and in this country by highway engineers, to a limited extent.

ACKNOWLEDGMENTS

The work on which this paper is based was done at the Scripps Institution of Oceanography. It was supported by a grant from the U.S. Steel Foundation and by funds from the Office of Naval Research under contract Nonr 2216 (23). I am very much indebted to Professor Francis P. Shepard for his supervision and guidance. Neil F. Marshall was an able companion during the field investigation. For this, and many valuable discussions, I extend my sincere thanks. G. S. Bien and C. L. Hubbs arranged for the radiocarbon datings. Sonoprobe and Arcer equipment and the necessary ship time were generously made available by J. R. Curray and G. G. Shor, Jr. Acknowledgments also are made to many Cordova people who by their aid and information made the fieldwork much more fruitful than it would otherwise have been. The final writing of this manuscript was done at the U.S. Geological Survey in Menlo Park, California. Roland von Huene, Gene Rusnak, and especially David McCulloch spent considerable time in reading, criticizing, and improving the manuscript. Their help is gratefully acknowledged.

REFERENCES

Alaska Department of Fish and Game, 1965. Post-earthquake fisheries evaluation. An interim report on the March 1964 earthquake effects on Alaska's fishery resources. Juneau: Alaska Department of Fish and Game. 72 p.

Andresen, A., and L. Bjerrum, 1967. Slides in subaqueous slopes in loose sand and silt *in* International Research Conference on Marine Geotechnique. Urbana, Chicago, London: The University of Illinois Press. p. 221–239.

Baker, M. B., 1916. Geology of Kingston (Ontario) and vicinity. *Ontario Bureau of Mines, Annual Report,* 25 (Part 3), 1–36.

Barrett, Peter J., 1966. Effects of the 1964 Alaskan earthquake on some shallow-water sediments in Prince William Sound, southeast Alaska. *Journal of Sedimentary Petrology*, 36 (December), 992–1006. Also *in* The Great Alaska Earthquake of 1964: Geology. NAS Pub. 1601. Washington: National Academy of Sciences, 1971. p. 250–264.

Chapman, Valentine J., 1960. Salt marshes and salt desert of the world. Plant Science Monographs. New York: Interscience Publishers, Inc. 392 p.

Childers, W. Morlin, 1964. Sandstone chimneys of the Imperial Formation. *Pacific Discovery* , 17 (January–February), 29–31.

Coulter, Henry W., and Ralph R. Migliaccio, 1966. Effects of the earthquake of March 27, 1964, at Valdez, Alaska. U.S. Geological Survey Professional Paper 542-C. Washington: Government Printing Office. 36 p. Also *in* The Great Alaska Earthquake of 1964: Geology. NAS Pub. 1601. Washington: National Academy of Sciences, 1971. p. 359–394.

Darton, Nelson H., 1899. Preliminary report on the geology and water resources of Nebraska west of the one hundred and third meridian. 19th Annual Report of the U.S. Geological Survey, Part 4. Washington: Government Printing Office. p. 719–785.

Dietrich, R. V., 1952. Conical and cylindrical structures in the Potsdam Sandstone, Redwood, New York (Abstract). *Geological Society of America Bulletin*, 63 (December), 1244.

Dill, Robert F., 1967. Effects of explosive loading on the strength of seafloor sands *in* International Research Conference on Marine Geotechnique. Urbana, Chicago, London: The University of Illinois Press. p. 291–303.

Dill, Robert F., 1969. Earthquake effects on fill of Scripps Submarine Canyon. *Geological Society of America Bulletin*, 80 (February), 321–327.

Foster, Helen L., and Thor N. V. Karlstrom, 1967. Ground breakage and associated effects in the Cook Inlet area, Alaska, resulting from the March 27, 1964, earthquake. U.S. Geological Survey Professional Paper 543-F. Washington: Government Printing Office. 28 p. Abstract *in* The Great Alaska Earthquake of 1964: Geology. NAS

Pub. 1601. Washington: National Academy of Sciences, 1971. p. 280.

Gill, William D., and Philip H. Kuenen, 1957. Sand volcanoes on slumps in the Carboniferous of County Clare, Ireland. *Geological Society of London Quarterly Journal*, 113 (Part 4), 441–460.

Hawley, J. E., and R. C. Hart, 1934. Cylindrical structures in sandstones. *Geological Society of America Bulletin*, 45 (December), 1017–1034.

Heezen, Bruce C., 1956. Corrientes de turbidez del Rio Magdalena, Colombia. *Boletín de la Sociedad Geográfica de Colombia*, Bogota, 14, p. 135–143.

Hobbs, William H., 1907. Earthquakes; an introduction to seismic geology. New York: D. Appleton-Century Company. 336 p.

Housner, George W., 1958. The mechanism of sandblows. *Bulletin of the Seismological Society of America*, 48 (April), 155–161.

Ives, Patricia C., Betsy Levin, Richard D. Robinson, and Meyer Rubin, 1964. U.S. Geological Survey Radiocarbon Dates VII. *Radiocarbon*, 6, p. 37–76.

Ives, Patricia C., Betsy Levin, Charles L. Oman, and Meyer Rubin, 1967. U.S. Geological Survey Radiocarbon Dates IX. *Radiocarbon*, 9, p. 505–529.

Kachadoorian, Reuben, 1968. Effects of the earthquake of March 27, 1964, on the Alaska highway system. U.S. Geological Survey Professional Paper 545-C. Washington: Government Printing Office. 66 p. Also *in* The Great Alaska Earthquake of 1964: Geology. NAS Pub. 1601. Washington: National Academy of Sciences, 1971. p. 641–703.

Kummeneje, O., and O. Eide, 1961. Investigation of loose sand deposits by blasting *in* Proceedings of the Fifth International Conference on Soil Mechanics and Foundation Engineering, Paris, 1, p. 491–497.

Lemke, Richard W., 1967. Effects of the earthquake of March 27, 1964, at Seward, Alaska. U.S. Geological Survey Professional Paper 542-E. Washington: Government Printing Office. 43 p. Also *in* The Great Alaska Earthquake of 1964: Geology. NAS Pub. 1601. Washington: National Academy of Sciences, 1971. p. 395–437.

Levin, Betsy, Patricia C. Ives, Charles L. Oman, and Meyer Rubin, 1965. U.S. Geological Survey Radiocarbon Dates VIII. *Radiocarbon*, 7, p. 372–393.

Lindström, M., 1967. "Funnel grabens" and early Paleozoic tectonism in South Sweden. *Geological Society of America Bulletin*, 78 (September), 1137–1154.

Mathews, W. H., and F. P. Shepard, 1962. Sedimentation of Fraser River delta, British Columbia. *Bulletin of the American Association of Petroleum Geologists*, 46 (August), 1416–1443.

Maxson, John H., 1940. Gas pits in non-marine sediments. *Journal of Sedimentary Petrology*, 10 (December), 142–145.

Megrue, George H., and Paul F. Kerr, 1968. Alteration of sandstone pipes, Laguna, New Mexico: Reply. *Geological Society of America Bulletin*, 79 (June), 791–794.

Migliaccio, Ralph R., 1965. Earthquake damage to highways in the Valdez district, Alaska *in* Road crown, testing, compaction, soil bitumen; The Alaska earthquake. National Research Council Highway Research Board Record Number 91, NAS–NRC Pub. 1307. Washington: National Academy of Sciences–National Research Council. p. 64–72.

Morgenstern, N. R., 1967. Submarine slumping and the initiation of turbidity currents *in* International Research Conference on Marine Geotechnique. Urbana, Chicago, London: The University of Illinois Press. p. 189–220.

Myers, W. Bradley, and Warren Hamilton, 1964. Deformation accompanying the Hebgen Lake earthquake of August 17, 1959 *in* The

Hebgen Lake, Montana, earthquake of August 17, 1959. U.S. Geological Survey Professional Paper 435. Washington: Government Printing Office. p. 55–98.

Niino, Hiroshi, 1955. Sand pipe from the sea floor off California. *Journal of Sedimentary Petrology*, 25 (March), 41–44.

Oldham, R. D., 1899. Report on the great earthquake of 12 June 1897. *Memoirs of Geological Survey of India*, 49. [Calcutta: Office of the Superintendent of Government Printing.] 379 p.

Plafker, George, and Meyer Rubin, 1967. Vertical tectonic displacements in south-central Alaska during and prior to the great 1964 earthquake. *Journal of Geoscience* (Osaka City University), 10 (March), 53–66.

Reimnitz, Erk, 1966. Later Quaternary history and sedimentation of the Copper River Delta and vicinity, Alaska (unpublished PhD dissertation). La Jolla: University of California, San Diego. 160 p.

Reimnitz, Erk, and Neil F. Marshall, 1965. Effects of the Alaska earthquake and tsunami on recent deltaic sediments. *Journal of Geophysical Research*, 70 (May 15), 2362–2376. Also *in* The Great Alaska Earthquake of 1964: Geology. NAS Pub. 1601. Washington: National Academy of Sciences, 1971. p. 265–278.

Schaefers, E. A., K. A. Smith, and M. R. Greenwood, 1955. Bottom fish and shellfish explorations in the Prince William Sound area, Alaska, 1954. *Commercial Fisheries Review*, 17 (April), 6–28.

Selly, R. C., D. J. Shearman, J. Sutton, and J. Watson, 1963. Some underwater disturbances in the Tooridonian of Skye and Raasay. *Geological Magazine*, 100 (April), 224–243.

Shepard, Francis P., 1955. Delta-front valleys bordering the Mississippi distributaries. *Geological Society of America Bulletin*, 66 (December), 1489–1498.

Shrock, R. R., 1948. Sequence in layered rocks. New York: McGraw-Hill Company. 507 p.

Simpson, George G., 1936. Cylindrical structures in sandstones in Patagonia (Abstract). Proceedings of the Geological Society of America, 1935. New York: The Geological Society of America. p. 106.

Sutton, John, and Janet Watson, 1960. Sedimentary structures in the epidotic grits of Skye. *Geological Magazine*, 97 (March–April), 106–122.

Sutton, John, and Janet Watson, 1963. Structures in shallow-water Precambrian sediments from northwest Scotland. *Sedimentology*, 2 (September), 207–214.

Thorsteinson, Fredrik V., 1965. Aftermaths of the Alaska earthquake in Prince William Sound. *Pacific Fisherman*, 63 (May), 10–11.

Tuthill, Samuel J., and Wilson M. Laird, 1966. Geomorphic effects of the earthquake of March 27, 1964, in the Martin-Bering Rivers area, Alaska. U.S. Geological Survey Professional Paper 543-B. Washington: Government Printing Office. 29 p. Abstract *in* The Great Alaska Earthquake of 1964: Geology. NAS Pub. 1601. Washington: National Academy of Sciences, 1971. p. 284.

Van Straaten, L. M. J. U., 1959. Littoral and submarine morphology of the Rhone delta. Proceedings of the Second Conference on Coastal Geomorphology. Geography Branch of the Office of Naval Research and the National Science Foundation. p. 233–264.

von Huene, Roland, and Doak C. Cox, 1972. Locally generated tsunamis and other local waves *in* The Great Alaska Earthquake of 1964: Oceanography and Coastal Engineering. NAS Pub. 1605. Washington: National Academy of Sciences.

von Huene, Roland, George G. Shor, Jr., and Erk Reimnitz, 1967. Geological interpretation of seismic profiles in Prince William Sound, Alaska. *Geological Society of America Bulletin*, 78 (February), 259–268.

Waller, Roger M., 1968. Water-sediment ejections *in* The Great Alaska Earthquake of 1964: Hydrology. NAS Pub. 1603. Washington: National Academy of Sciences. p. 97–116.

IV
OTHER MARINE
ASPECTS

Introduction

A number of other kinds of marine effects accompanied or might have accompanied the great Alaska earthquake, in addition to the strictly seismic effects, the tsunamis, and the marine geological and geophysical effects already discussed. These include marine biological effects, physical oceanographic effects, chemical oceanographic effects, and effects on marine transportation and fishing. This discussion of these "other" marine aspects will be brief. The marine biological effects, the major topic of the biology volume in this series, provide the basis for a summary by Hanna in this section; the effects on tides are discussed in a paper by Hicks in this section; the bathymetric changes as related to navigation and chart revision are treated in a paper by Wood and Taylor in this section; and the direct effects of the earthquake and tsunamis on ships, small boats, and harbor facilities are matters of engineering more than of oceanography.

MARINE BIOLOGICAL EFFECTS

Fish kills so extensive as to cover large areas with dead fish were reported at the time of the earthquake at several places, including Passage Canal, Valdez Arm, and the vicinity of Chenega Island (Hanna, this section). The fish may have been smothered by the silt churned into the water by the waves and currents, but more likely they were killed by the pressure changes associated with sudden vertical bottom displacements or with large-scale turbulence induced by submarine slides, as postulated by Hanna, or by the rapid pressure fluctuations that constituted the seaquakes (von Huene, this volume).

With the permanent crustal uplift and depression, the flora and fauna in enormous areas of the intertidal zone were killed, and a new intertidal zonation developed, often ecologically unbalanced for the first year or so. Where the coasts were uplifted, the sessile fauna, especially barnacles, died, the lichens began to shift downward, and, after sufficient leaching, other land plants began to invade the former sea floor and intertidal zone. Where the coasts were depressed, the for-

ests with most of their associated invertebrate fauna were killed by saltwater flooding.

The benthic flora and fauna of the fiords and sounds were probably smothered by silt in many areas. Thousands of acres of clam beds were destroyed either by scour or fill.

The mouths of the streams were greatly altered by the vertical crustal displacements and subsequent shoreline adjustments (Reimnitz, this volume), and it was expected that determination of the effects of the changes on salmon spawning would take several years.

PHYSICAL OCEANOGRAPHIC CHANGES

In spite of the vertical crustal displacements occurring at the time of the earthquake, the characteristics of the tides and tidal currents were altered very little. According to Hicks (this section), tide ranges nowhere were changed more than 0.2 ft (in 7 to 9 ft), except at Anchorage where there was a change in range of 1.6 ft (in 25 ft). So far the records have not been analyzed in sufficient detail to indicate whether these apparent changes are significant or whether they fall within the normal variation in range over comparable periods.

The smallness of changes is somewhat surprising at some places such as Cordova, where uplift caused significant shoaling over large areas of the channels through which the tide must propagate, as shown by a comparison of pre- and postearthquake bathymetric surveys (Wood and Taylor, this section). Reimnitz and Marshall (1965, and Geology volume) found that the effects of the shoaling were limited by planing off of the Orca Inlet tide flats by as much as 2½ ft by the currents associated with the tsunamis. The sediments derived from the planing filled the channels by as much as 30 ft.

CHEMICAL OCEANOGRAPHIC CHANGES

No significant chemical oceanographic changes related to the earthquake were expected or observed, except the shifts in the salinity zonation in estuaries resulting from the vertical displacements.

EFFECTS ON BOATS AND NAVIGATION

No major vessel was lost as a result of the Alaska earthquake and tsunamis, although both the tanker *Alaska Standard* at Seward and the freight-passenger vessel *Chena* at Valdez narrowly escaped destruction as the result of shoreline slumps, collapse of the docks, and the initial tsunami waves. The Alaska fishing fleet, however, suffered serious losses from the tsunamis. About 100 boats were lost or damaged at Kodiak alone, and more than 40 were lost elsewhere in the vicinity of Kodiak. Additional losses at several other Alaskan ports, especially Seward and Cordova (Wilson and Tørum, 1968), brought the total to more than 200 (Eckel, 1967, and Geology volume). As usual, boats at sea were safe from the tsunamis, although they may have been jarred by the seaquake (von Huene, this volume).

The major tsunami also resulted in loss of boats at Port Alberni, British Columbia, and at Crescent City, Noyo, and San Rafael, California. Seiches occurring with the earthquake caused damage to boats in Seattle and in several Gulf of Mexico harbors (Wilson and Tørum, 1968; Spaeth and Berkman, 1967, and this volume).

Port facilities at Kodiak, Seward, Whittier, and Valdez were almost entirely destroyed by shoreline slumping or tsunamis, or both, and the facilities were seriously damaged at a large number of other Alaska ports, including Anchorage, Homer, Seldovia, and Chenega. In addition, many dockside canneries in remote places were damaged or washed away (Wilson and Tørum, 1968; Eckel, 1967, and Geology volume). The major tsunami also caused extensive damage to harbor facilities in British Columbia, Oregon, and California, with some damage in Washington and Hawaii; the seiches damaged facilities in Washington and on the coast of the Gulf of Mexico (Wilson and Tørum, 1968; Spaeth and Berkman, 1967, and this volume).

The direct effects of the earthquake on the ships, small boats, and harbor facilities were all accomplished in a few hours. It was apparent immediately, however, that the effects of the vertical crustal displacements and mass movements of sediments had created potential continuing hazards to navigation and, in addition, that a considerable number of aids to navigation had been lost, moved, or put out of commission. The operations of four loran and radio-beacon stations were interrupted by the earthquake, but the Coast Guard restored all of them to service in 3 days or less. Sixteen minor lights and lighted buoys were lost or destroyed by the tsunamis, and one was destroyed by a landslide. Operations at many lighted aids were interrupted by electrical failures. All the lights were rapidly restored to service, except those at ports where bathymetric changes required new surveys or where structures such as breakwaters had to be rebuilt (Steacy Hicks, U.S. Coast and Geodetic Survey, personal correspondence, based on information from Seventeenth Coast Guard District).

Within a month of the earthquake, the Coast and Geodetic Survey had completed preliminary surveys and issued chartlets showing the extensive shoreline retreats due to sliding and associated with hazards at the ports of Valdez, Seward, Whittier, and Kodiak, as well as less extensive changes at Womens Bay and Crescent City (Wood and Taylor, this section). In the next 8 months, the major bathymetric changes had been charted at Resurrection Bay, Valdez, Whittier, Anchorage, and Homer in the area of crustal depression, and at Orca Bay and Inlet and the eastern entrance to Prince William Sound in the uplifted area, as well as more general effects shown by smaller-scale charts. Surveys of the changes have continued since, leading to complete chart revisions and thus gradually merging into the normal resurvey and chart-revision program of the Survey.

DOAK C. COX
University of Hawaii

REFERENCES

Eckel, Edwin B., 1967. Effects of the earthquake of March 27, 1964, on air and water transport, communications, and utilities systems in south-central Alaska. U.S. Geological Survey Professional Paper 545-B. Washington: Government Printing Office. 27 p. Also *in* The Great Alaska Earthquake of 1964: Geology. NAS Pub. 1601. Washington: National Academy of Sciences, 1971. p. 705–731.

Reimnitz, E., 1972. Effects in the Copper River Delta *in* The Great Alaska Earthquake of 1964: Oceanography and Coastal Engineering. NAS Pub. 1605. Washington: National Academy of Sciences.

Reimnitz, Erk, and Neil F. Marshall, 1965. Effects of the Alaska earthquake and tsunami on recent deltaic sediments. *Journal of Geophysical Research,* 70 (May 15), 2363-2376. Also *in* The Great Alaska Earthquake of 1964: Geology. NAS Pub. 1601. Washington: National Academy of Sciences, 1971. p. 265–278.

Spaeth, Mark G., and Saul C. Berkman, 1967. The tsunami of March 28, 1964, as recorded at tide stations. Environmental Science Services Administration Technical Report C&GS 33. Washington: Government Printing Office. 86 p. Also *in* The Great Alaska Earthquake of 1964: Oceanography and Coastal Engineering. NAS Pub. 1605. Washington: National Academy of Sciences, 1972.

von Huene, Roland, 1972. Seaquakes *in* The Great Alaska Earthquake of 1964: Oceanography and Coastal Engineering. NAS Pub. 1605. Washington: National Academy of Sciences.

Wilson, Basil W., and Alf Tørum, 1968. The tsunami of the Alaskan earthquake, 1964: Engineering evaluation. Coastal Engineering Research Center Technical Memorandum No. 25. Washington: U.S. Army Corps of Engineers, May. 444 p.

G DALLAS HANNA
CALIFORNIA ACADEMY OF SCIENCES

Biological Effects

ABSTRACT: Large areas of former sea bottom were uplifted and exposed during the earthquake of March 27, 1964. This destroyed myriads of animals and plants that normally live in shallow waters near shores, the littoral zone. The new land was already beginning to acquire new vegetation in 1965, but it will probably take a century or more for the new forest to become completely merged with that of the preearthquake land area.

After a year, hardly a start had been made in the formation of a new littoral zone. *Verrucaria* had not descended to the new mean high-tide line, but young barnacles, some about a millimeter in diameter, had begun to settle on the rocks.

A great earthquake's effects on the public mind are usually rated in order of importance as (1) loss of human life; (2) loss of property; (3) modification of landscape; and (4) seismological, geological, and other scientific physical aspects. Only rarely is there brief mention of some spectacular loss of animal or plant life. The biological effects of the Alaska earthquake produced by water movement were particularly striking, and it is the purpose of this brief report to describe them and to point out the failure to secure additional information on certain phases of the biological losses—information that could have been obtained immediately after the earthquake but that is no longer available. By August 1967 only three brief reviews of the biological effects of the earthquake had been published (Hansen and Eckel, 1966, p. 34–36, Figures 36 and 37; Hanna, 1964, and Biology Volume; Hanna, 1967).

Two forms of severe dislocation of the earth resulted from the Alaska disturbance. First, there was large-scale vertical movement. Offshore between Montague and Middleton islands, for example, a maximum uplift of about 50 ft was reported (U.S. Coast and Geodetic Survey, 1966, p. 183), and Cape Cleare on Montague Island was uplifted more than 30 ft (Plafker, 1965, p. 1679). Second, submarine landslides of great magnitude occurred in many of the coastal inlets of south central Alaska. Both the vertical movement and the landslides caused giant waves or tsunamis.

Some of the landslide-caused tsunamis were particularly violent. Debris on slopes bordering the deep waters of many fiords and inlets was close to the angle of repose and hence easily dislodged by the severe shaking into huge underwater slides moving downslope at high speeds. Such disturbances under water must produce devastating effects on bottom life.

The huge waves caused by a landslide in Passage Canal, according to eyewitnesses (as reported by Kachadoorian, 1965, p. B6), made the sea "boil," and the second wave of the series became charged with mud, rocks, and much other debris. At some places, waves swept up on the adjacent shores and deposited debris 100 ft and more above sea level. Much

307

of the forest was removed. Residents along Passage Canal reported further that the next morning, after the main shocks of the earthquake and the three successive waves had subsided, many large fish known locally as "red snappers" (but probably rockfish) floated on the surface of the water and that others had drifted ashore. Undoubtedly, the disturbance that caused this catastrophe was also very destructive to other forms of marine life. It is most unfortunate that biologists did not make on-the-spot observations of the biological effects here during the first few critical hours after the earthquake.

At the time of my visit to some of the earthquake-affected areas in 1964, I found the remains of many mollusks and other forms of marine life on land far above the high-tide line; one large rock, with barnacle shells still attached, was 80 ft above sea level. It is doubtful that many of these animals would have survived settling to the bottom in the debris-charged water after the movements of the slides and the shaking had ceased. I know of no reliable estimates of the amount of survival of bottom life in such a sudden disturbance of habitat, but it probably was small in the areas affected by the earthquake. During the action of these seismic sea waves, there was almost continuous and violent shaking that tended to cause loose sediment to go into suspension and be carried away by the great waves. Along the south central Alaska coast, thousands of acres of very prolific beds of clams were destroyed in this way.

In Valdez Arm and the vicinity of Chenega Island as well as in Passage Canal, so many rockfish were killed that they were reported by local residents to have covered the water over large areas. These fishes may have been smothered by suspended silt, but a more plausible explanation is that a sudden uplift of the bottom made adjustment of air-bladder pressure impossible and that they then floated to the surface. A submarine landslide sufficiently violent to produce a surface wave 100 ft high and to cause an entire fiord to acquire a "boiling" appearance would also most certainly cause fishes and other marine life to lose all control of their locomotive processes.

The most spectacular aspect of this earthquake was the sudden tipping of a region of 70,000 to 110,000 mi² (Hansen and Eckel, 1966, p. 14). Some of this region was depressed a maximum of about 7 ft. Large areas were flooded and the forests killed. Associated lower animals would also have been killed, for example, such forms as insects, mites, worms, and snails. Most of the higher animals, birds, and mammals should have been able to escape. No detailed observations of the actions of any of these forms have been found.

In many parts of south central Alaska, there are lakes and lagoons close to shore. The depression of the land caused a change in salinity of the waters in these basins and consequently brought about a change of the aquatic fauna; these variations have not yet been studied in detail. In other areas of depression, partial or complete flooding of some of the low-lying lands deprived large numbers of birds of their accustomed nesting sites. At the beginning of their 1964 nesting season, I observed that the birds were greatly confused by the change in conditions and were apparently reluctant to seek higher ground during that first summer after the earthquake.

In the area that was uplifted a maximum of more than 30 ft, there was total destruction of all animal and plant life between former and resulting mean high tides and also far below the resulting low-water mark. The intertidal zone in that latitude of Alaska is normally extremely rich in sea life. Barnacles extend up to mean high-tide line, and the black lichen *Verrucaria* occupies the splash zone above. Below the mean high-tide line many species of marine algae grow, attached to the rocks. Under normal conditions these plants, which are mostly annuals, tend to grow in groups of species in horizontal bands. The banding or zonation is caused in large part by certain grazing animals, especially such mollusks as limpets and some other gastropods, whose life span is several years. Consequently if the uplift was equal to or greater than the tidal range, which is about 10 ft, the algae in the new littoral zone had no checks after the earthquake, because the grazing mollusks had been destroyed. Even where the uplift of the land was as little as 1 ft, I could readily detect the disturbance of the life zones when I returned to the area in 1965, a year after the earthquake. The number of years required to form a new stable littoral zone has not been determined.

The total extent of the newly formed land area is very large. By the summer of 1965, marine salts had been sufficiently leached out so that 75 species of plants had already started to grow there. No doubt this land will eventually become a part of the adjacent forest, but tree-ring studies in areas of glacier retreat such as around Glacier Bay, Alaska, indicate that a century or more will be required for the forest to be established (Decker, 1966, p. 73).

The uplift of the land altered the mouths of many streams that contain salmon-spawning beds upstream. The newly extended streams commonly spread out into smaller rivulets with the appearance of braided streams on desert fans. Many of these trickles were too small in 1965 for salmon to ascend.

Because catastrophes like the Alaska earthquake are so infrequent, biologists as well as the general populace are not prepared to make immediate assessments of the effects on animals and plants. Mental stress at such a time is so great that other matters occupy most minds. Therefore, this short sketch can do no more than emphasize the loss of information on many important biological phases of the effects of the earthquake, because of absence of on-the-spot trained observers. Some emergency procedure should be set up to avoid such a loss after future earthquakes.

REFERENCES

Decker, Henry F., 1966. Plants *in* Soil development and ecological succession in a deglaciated area of Muir Inlet, southeast Alaska. A. Mirsky, editor. Institute of Polar Studies Report 20. Columbus: The Ohio State University. p. 73-95.

Hanna, G Dallas, 1964. Biological effects of an earthquake. *Pacific Discovery,* 17 (November-December), 24-26. Also *in* The Great Alaska Earthquake of 1964: Biology. NAS Pub. 1604. Washington: National Academy of Sciences, 1971. p. 15-34.

Hanna, G Dallas, 1967. The great Alaska earthquake of 1964. *Pacific Discovery,* 20 (May-June), 25-30.

Hansen, Wallace R., and Edwin B. Eckel, 1966. A summary description of the Alaska earthquake—its setting and effects *in* The Alaska earthquake, March 27, 1964: field investigations and reconstruction effort. U.S. Geological Survey Professional Paper 541. Washington: Government Printing Office. p. 1-37. Also *in* The Great Alaska Earthquake of 1964: Geology. NAS Pub. 1601. Washington: National Academy of Sciences, 1971. p. 5-43.

Kachadoorian, Reuben, 1965. Effects of the earthquake of March 27, 1964, at Whittier, Alaska. U.S. Geological Survey Professional Paper 542-B. Washington: Government Printing Office. 21 p. Also *in* The Great Alaska Earthquake of 1964: Geology. NAS Pub. 1601. Washington: National Academy of Sciences, 1971. p. 439-459.

Plafker, George, 1965. Tectonic deformation associated with the 1964 Alaska earthquake. *Science,* 148 (June 25), 1675-1687.

U.S. Coast and Geodetic Survey, 1966. The Prince William Sound, Alaska, earthquake of 1964 and aftershocks. Fergus J. Wood, editor. Volume I: Operational phases of the Coast and Geodetic Survey program in Alaska for the period March 27 to December 31, 1964. Washington: Government Printing Office. 263 p.

STEACY D. HICKS
U.S. COAST AND GEODETIC SURVEY*

Changes in Tidal Characteristics and Tidal Datum Planes

INTRODUCTION

One of the most interesting geophysical contributions to come out of pre- and postearthquake comparison studies is the discovery that, in spite of large vertical displacements of the crust, the response characteristics of the earth to tide-generating forces do not change.

TIDE PREDICTION

Although tides are caused by precisely known gravitational interactions between the sun, moon, and earth, it is at present impossible to proceed directly from the astronomic tide-generating forces to a prediction of the tide at a specific location with the desired degree of accuracy (generally ± 0.1 ft). This is due to difficulties in the quantitative handling of ocean response factors such as internal and boundary friction, presence of continents and their irregularities in shape and location, relatively shallow water (in comparison to wave length) and irregularities in depth, and the tendency of the tidal waves to reflect and oscillate in oceanic areas demarked by land and critical depths.

It has thus been necessary to adopt an empirical approach, relating astronomic events to the observed tides. The present standard tide-predicting method requires prior observations of the tide at all locations for which predictions are desired. The observations provide data from which empirical constants, called "tidal harmonic constants," can be derived.

HARMONIC CONSTANTS

Because the earth's response to tide-generating forces does not vary, the harmonic "constants" are exceedingly constant. It is therefore possible to predict the tides for hundreds of years in advance with excellent reliability. However, if the ocean configuration is significantly altered by man or nature, obviously it is always prudent to redetermine the harmonic constants. This practice has been followed by the U.S. Coast

ABSTRACT: Comparison of pre- and postearthquake sea-level observations reveals vertical land displacements ranging from a 31.5-ft uplift at MacLeod Harbor, Montague Island, to a 6.6-ft subsidence at Chance Cove, Kenai Peninsula. In spite of these major land movements, changes in tidal harmonic constants remained within the limits of normal variability. Similarly, the nonharmonic tidal characteristics of range, tide level, mean diurnal high-water (and low-water) inequality, and Greenwich mean high-water (and low-water) lunitidal interval did not vary significantly. The observations demonstrate the extreme constancy of the earth in its response to the tide-generating forces.

*Now, in part, the National Ocean Survey, NOAA.

and Geodetic Survey (now, in part, the National Ocean Survey of the National Oceanic and Atmospheric Administration). Redeterminations are conducted whenever extensive engineering alterations are made in harbors and when extended sediment deposition or erosion is evidenced. They are also performed whenever major land movements are recorded—as in the case of the Alaska earthquake of 1964.

As a result of the 6.2-ft uplift observed at Cordova, a redetermination was conducted. In Table 1, the old harmonic constants (based on a 369-day series in 1929–1930) are compared with the new constants (based on a 369-day series in 1965–1966). Sets of harmonic constants for other years are not available. Therefore, comparisons between constants obtained for years with no intervening earthquake are not possible. However, harmonic analyses have been performed on consecutive yearly series from 1899 to 1961 at Seattle. Maximum amplitude differences for the major semidiurnal (M_2) and major diurnal (K_1) constituents were 0.05 ft and 0.07 ft, respectively. Similarly, the maximum phase differences were 3.0° and 1.9°. These figures may be compared with the pre- and postearthquake differences at Cordova of 0.01 ft and 0.2° for both the M_2 and K_1. Although not a

rigorous comparison, this indicates that the changes in the harmonic constants at Cordova due to the earthquake are surprisingly small.

Unfortunately, Cordova was the only station for which tidal harmonic constants had been determined (or could be determined) from preearthquake data. Had an upestuary station been available for the same kind of analysis, changes in the shallow water constituents (such as M_4 and M_6) would have been expected. However, even in that hypothetical case, it should be noted that the upestuary area of Prince William Sound lies along the hinge line (no vertical displacement), thus tending to minimize probable effects.

A similar lack of significant changes was found in comparisons of tidal characteristics determined by nonharmonic treatment of shorter series of observed data. Pre- and postearthquake comparisons are shown in Table 2 for mean range, tide level (mean of heights of high waters and low waters), diurnal high-water inequality, diurnal low-water inequality, and Greenwich mean high-water lunitidal interval and low-water interval. The comparison of series of varying lengths is made for 21 stations, primarily in the Prince William Sound, Cook Inlet, and Kenai Peninsula areas. Again, the similarities are striking, even at upestuary stations! As in the case of the harmonic constants (discussed above), all differences are well within the variability experienced at tide stations during periods of years when major earthquakes do not occur. In fact, the differences even approach the accuracy of the observations and reductions themselves.

For example, MacLeod Harbor, Montague Island, experienced the greatest uplift of the earthquake, 31.5 ft, as accurately determined by tidal datum plane and prediction comparison. Yet, its range decreased by only 0.2 ft, and its High-Water Lunitidal Interval (HWI) decreased by 0.21 hour. Whittier, an upestuary station north of the hinge line at −5.7 ft, had a 0.2-ft increase in range and a 0.12-hour increase in its HWI. Except at Anchorage, where it was 1.6 ft, changes in range throughout the earthquake area amounted to no more than 0.2 ft, and, except at King Cove, where it was +0.39 hour, the maximum change in the HWI was −0.25 hour.

No current measurements are available for comparison of pre- and postearthquake conditions. However, since the tidal current is nothing more than the horizontal component of the particulate motion of the tidal wave and since no significant changes were found in the tidal harmonic constants or nonharmonic characteristics, no significant changes in tidal currents are expected to have occurred.

TIDAL DATUM PLANES

The sea surface, vertically fixed in terms of a specific sampling interval, averaging process, series length, and date of

TABLE 1   Tidal Harmonic Constants at Cordova, Alaska

	369 Days (Series began May 1, 1929)		369 Days (Series began January 1, 1965)	
A_0				
J_1	0.079	136.7	0.087	132.3
K_1	1.621	128.2	1.611	128.0
K_2	0.457	24.6	0.430	26.6
L_2	0.120	20.8	0.119	13.0
M_1	0.068	108.3	0.055	140.0
M_2	4.672	359.4	4.682	359.2
M_3	0.027	182.6	0.027	194.6
M_4	0.130	158.6	0.198	146.9
M_6	0.024	335.2	0.030	342.4
M_8	0.013	167.4	0.008	85.0
N_2	0.942	334.0	0.935	333.3
$2N$	0.125	308.6	0.121	303.2
O_1	0.995	111.2	0.996	111.3
OO	0.043	145.2	0.043	154.0
P_1	0.449	126.3	0.505	124.9
Q_1	0.176	105.8	0.179	101.0
$2Q$	0.026	94.2	0.014	107.0
R_2	0.012	32.1	0.013	198.1
S_1	0.042	243.1	0.043	270.7
S_2	1.577	32.1	1.574	31.0
S_4	0.050	137.7	0.048	126.9
S_6	0.002	268.8	0.006	203.9
T_2	0.093	32.1	0.090	8.4
λ_2	0.004	21.9	0.044	350.9
μ_2	0.105	316.4	0.098	317.8
ν_2	0.177	333.3	0.175	341.9
ρ_1	0.038	103.9	0.027	93.0
S_a	0.303	212.2	0.475	236.8
S_{sa}	0.129	10.2	0.218	120.9

TABLE 2 Nonharmonic Tidal Characteristics Computed from Observations Made before and after the Alaska Earthquake of March 1964

Stations	Length of Series	Range of Tide (ft)	Tide[a] Level (ft)	DHQ[b] (ft)	DLQ[c] (ft)	Greenwich HWI[d] (hr)	Greenwich LWI[e] (hr)
Prince William Sound							
Cordova							
1950–1951	2 yr	10.0	6.50	0.9	1.5	10.19	3.86
1964–1965	10 mo.	10.1	6.44	0.9	1.4	9.94	3.69
Pt. Gravina, Orca Bay							
1913 and 1915	2 mo.	9.4	6.22	1.1	1.5	9.98	3.66
1965	1 mo.	9.5	6.18	0.9	1.4	9.96	3.67
Valdez							
1924–1928	4 yr	9.4	6.20	0.9	1.5	10.12	3.86
1964	3 mo.	9.6	6.26	1.0	1.4	9.91	3.68
Montague Island							
Pt. Chalmers, Wilby Island							
1933	3 mo.	9.3	6.15	0.9	1.5	10.16	3.84
1964	1½ mo.	9.4	6.14	0.9	1.4	10.10	3.73
MacLeod Harbor							
1927	1 mo.	9.0	5.90	0.9	1.4	9.89	3.68
1965	1 mo.	8.8	5.80	0.8	1.4	9.68	3.51
Green Island							
1911	1 mo.	9.4	6.10	0.9	1.4	10.04	3.76
1965	1 mo.	9.5	6.06	0.7	1.3	9.88	3.67
Evans Island							
1927	1 mo.	8.9	5.95	0.9	1.5	10.07	3.78
1965	1 mo.	9.0	5.91	0.9	1.4	9.90	3.63
Chenega Island							
1933	2½ mo.	9.2	6.10	0.9	1.5	10.10	3.84
1964	1 mo.	9.3	6.02	0.9	1.4	10.18	3.78
Whittier							
1948	3 mo.	9.6	6.30	0.9	1.5	9.90	3.77
1964–1965	10 mo.	9.8	6.35	0.9	1.4	10.02	3.70
Seward							
1926–1938	13 yr	8.3	5.51	0.9	1.4	9.92	3.68
1964–1965	17 mo.	8.3	5.42	0.9	1.3	9.88	3.63
Cook Inlet							
Seldovia							
1908 and 1913	9 mo.	15.4	9.33	0.8	1.6	11.27	4.95
1964 and 1965	8 mo.	15.5	9.32	0.8	1.6	11.22	4.92
Homer							
1962	2 mo.	15.9	9.63	0.7	1.6	11.21	4.92
1964–1965	11 mo.	16.0	9.51	0.8	1.5	11.25	4.94
Nikiski							
1961	2 mo.	17.9	11.09	0.7	2.1	1.23	7.78
1964	½ mo.	17.9	11.09	0.7	2.1	0.99	7.54
Anchorage							
1918–1925	28 mo.	26.7	15.55	0.7	2.2	3.64	10.30
1964–1965	1 yr.	25.1	14.70	0.8	2.2	3.59	10.47
Kodiak							
Womens Bay							
1950–1959	10 yr	6.8	4.46	0.9	1.1	10.70	4.32
1964	7 mo.	6.8	4.46	0.9	1.1	10.68	4.29
Lazy Bay							
1929–1931	10½ mo.	9.3	6.25	0.8	1.6	10.67	4.56
1964	1½ mo.	9.2	6.07	0.8	1.5	10.76	4.70
Larsen Bay							
1929	3 days	11.2	7.20	0.8	1.6	11.11	5.01
1964 and 1965	2½ mo.	11.2	7.17	0.9	1.6	11.00	4.90

TABLE 2 (Continued)

Stations	Length of Series	Range of Tide (ft)	Tide[a] Level (ft)	DHQ[b] (ft)	DLQ[c] (ft)	Greenwich HWI[d] (hr)	LWI[e] (hr)
Uganik Bay							
1929	24 days	11.4	7.30	0.9	1.6	11.04	4.90
1964 and 1965	3 mo.	11.4	7.22	0.9	1.5	11.13	5.10
Alaska Peninsula							
Chignik Bay							
1906 and 1920	2 mo.	6.6	4.60	0.8	1.3	11.21	4.99
1964	2 mo.	6.7	4.74	0.8	1.4	11.14	5.01
Sand Pt., Popof Island							
1953–1954	5 mo.	5.2	4.00	0.7	1.4	11.15	4.96
1964	2 mo.	5.2	3.84	0.7	1.3	11.30	4.77
King Cove							
1936–1941	13 mo.	4.8	3.70	0.7	1.3	11.31	4.96
1964	2 mo.	4.8	3.66	0.7	1.3	11.70	5.04

[a] Above Mean Lower Low Water.
[b] Mean Diurnal High-Water Inequality.
[c] Mean Diurnal Low-Water Inequality.
[d] Greenwich Mean High-Water Lunitidal Interval.
[e] Greenwich Mean Low-Water Lunitidal Interval.

TABLE 3 Tidal Datum Plane Changes at Alaska Tide Stations, 1965[a]

Station No.	Location	Period of Tide Observations	Vertical Land Movement (ft)
1	Cordova, Prince William Sound	May–November	+6.2
2	Port Gravina, Prince William Sound	May 16–June 16	+4.2
3	Port Fidalgo, Prince William Sound	June 18–July 17	+2.4
4	Valdez, Prince William Sound	July–November	−3.5
5	Whittier, Prince William Sound	July–November	−5.7
6	Chenega Island, Prince William Sound	July 7–August 4, 1964	+4.8
7	Green Island, Prince William Sound	August	+6.6
8	Port Chalmers, Montague Island, Prince William Sound	July 19–August 23	+10.5
9	Sawmill Bay, Evans Island, Prince William Sound	June 14–July 7	+7.2
10	Hogg Bay, Bainbridge Island, Prince William Sound	July 20–August 16	+5.8
11	Day Harbor, Kenai Peninsula	May 7–June 30	−0.5
12	Seward, Kenai Peninsula	January–September	−3.6
13	Aialik Bay, Kenai Peninsula	May–June	−4.5
14	Two Arm Bay, Kenai Peninsula	May 14–June 30	−5.4
15	Chance Cove, Kenai Peninsula	May 15–June 30	−6.6
16	Shelter Cove, Nuka Bay, Kenai Peninsula	July	−5.4
17	Port Dick, Kenai Peninsula	May 21–June 30	−6.2
18	Port Chatham, Kenai Peninsula	May 22–June 4	−4.6
19	Seldovia, Cook Inlet	April–July	−3.8
20	Homer, Cook Inlet	September–November	−5.8
21	Nikiski, Cook Inlet	June 18–July 31, 1964	−0.9
22	Anchorage, Cook Inlet	April–October	−2.3
23	Carry Inlet, Shuyak Island	July 8–August 7	−3.2
24	Red Fox Bay, Afognak Island	July 1–August 8	−3.4
25	Tonki Bay, Afognak Island	July 10–August 7	−5.2
26	Nachalni Island, Kupreanof Strait	June 14–July 10	−3.9
27	Dolphin Point, Afognak Island	June 7–July 8	−2.9
28	St. Paul Harbor, Kodiak Island	May–November	−5.0
29	Ugak Bay, Kodiak Island	June 12–July 10	−4.2

TABLE 3   (Continued)

Station No.	Location	Period of Tide Observations	Vertical Land Movement (ft)
30	Port Hobron, Sitkalidak Island	July 26–August 27	−0.7
31	Jap Bay, Kodiak Island	July 28–August 24	0.0
32	Lazy Bay, Kodiak Island	July 28–August 15, August 20–24	−0.2
33	Larsen Bay, Kodiak Island	July 18–August 17	−2.4
34	Uyak Bay (Eastern Passage), Kodiak Island	July 22–August 17	−1.9
35	Port O'Brien, Uganik Bay	June 8–July 19	−3.6
36	Kukak Bay, Alaska Peninsula	July 17–August 16	−0.5
37	Chignik, Chignik Bay, Alaska Peninsula	June 19–August 17, 1964	−0.3
38	Humboldt Harbor, Shumagin Islands	June 19–August 18, 1964	+0.2
39	King Cove, Alaska Peninsula	June 21–August 18, 1964	+0.2
40	MacLeod Harbor, Montague Island	b	+31.5
41	Patton Bay, Montague Island	b	+14.9

[a]Except as noted, observations were made in 1965.

[b]Leveled from existing bench marks to predicted water level in 1964.

series, is known as a tidal datum plane. By virtue of their definition, tidal datum planes are recoverable; that is, they can be redetermined at any future date with a new series of observations. Thus, when referenced (by precise leveling) to a bench mark attached to the land, datum planes provide exceedingly accurate comparisons for vertical land movement determinations.

Datum planes were redetermined from series obtained after the earthquake at each station for which preearthquake datums were available. At each station, the pre- and postearthquake datums were referred to the same set of bench marks, thus providing data on vertical land movements.

Table 3 presents an abbreviated tabulation of the results of the datum plane work by Small and Wharton (1969, and Seismology and Geodesy volume). Essentially, they augment, or are augmented by, the independent results of precise leveling conducted by the U.S. Coast and Geodetic Survey.

REFERENCE

Small, James B., and Lawrence C. Wharton, 1969. Vertical displacements determined by surveys after the Alaskan earthquake of March 1964 in Volume III: The Prince William Sound, Alaska, earthquake of 1964 and aftershocks. Environmental Science Services Administration, U.S. Coast and Geodetic Survey. Washington: Government Printing Office. p. 21–33. Also in The Great Alaska Earthquake of 1964: Seismology and Geodesy. NAS Pub. 1602. Washington: National Academy of Sciences, 1972.

FERGUS J. WOOD
LORNE G. TAYLOR*
U.S. COAST AND GEODETIC SURVEY †

Reprinted with minor changes from
U.S. Coast and Geodetic Survey Volume I:
Operational Phases of the
Coast and Geodetic Survey Program in Alaska
for the Period March 27 to December 31, 1964,
"Nautical Chart Production"

Nautical Chart Revisions

INTRODUCTION

Alaska is dependent to a large extent on marine commerce for its survival, and therefore any event, such as the March 27, 1964, earthquake with its resulting tsunami, which modifies the shoreline and introduces changes in the established sea lanes, is a critical one. Unfortunately, this disastrous earthquake occurred in the area that contains most of Alaska's major marine ports and facilities. The damage to these ports and facilities, as well as the creation of underwater contour changes or obstructions and the dislocation of navigational aids, imposed immediate nautical chart requirements (1) to provide corrective data essential to the safe navigation of these waters and (2) to determine survey priorities for their revision.

EMERGENCY CHARTING

Emergency charting requirements include the gathering, selecting, analyzing, and processing of pertinent critical nautical data for later dissemination through such available communication media as television, radio, *Notices to Mariners*, newspapers, periodicals, and nautical charts. Because the nautical chart is a prerequisite for safe maritime navigation, it must, with the aid of various devices, portray in a readily correctable form all the information, tabulations, and chartlets generated by the Coast and Geodetic Survey and distributed through the *Notices to Mariners*, chart agencies, and field offices. A chartlet is a reproduction of a new drawing of a section of a standard nautical chart, showing important revisions to charts already issued. The chartlet is designed to be issued quickly and to be pasted over an affected area of a chart until the standard chart can be revised and republished.

Generally, in emergency charting after disasters, chartlets are produced in three stages of ascending accuracy corresponding to the receipt in Washington of data from the field. First, a sketch is issued on the basis of aerial photographs; this ini-

ABSTRACT: An immediate contingency action in connection with any combined earthquake and tsunami disaster, such as accompanied the Alaska earthquake of 1964, is the preparation of new and revised emergency nautical chartlets depicting the changes resulting from these catastrophic occurrences. As part of the total interdisciplinary studies by the Coast and Geodetic Survey (now the National Ocean Survey) in connection with this earthquake, coordinated hydrographic, geodetic, tidal, and photogrammetric surveys were conducted by sea, land, and air reconnaissance parties. These surveys were made to determine the altered hydrographic and topographic aspects of important seaports and estuaries, to plot uplift and subsidence contours from echo soundings, and to represent the new shoreline configurations on revised nautical charts. This paper summarizes the results of this systematic observational, analytical, and charting effort, provides chart comparisons of typical areas before and after the earthquake, and documents the extensive intragovernmental and other cooperative research which made possible the preparation of these revised nautical charts.

*Now with Decca Survey Systems, Inc.
†Now, in part, the National Ocean Survey, NOAA.

tial issue shows changes in channel, shoal areas, aids to navigation, and shoreline. A second issue shows navigational-aid
changes and adds preliminary hydrographic data and topography. The final chartlet shows revised navigational-aid locations and includes the results of hydrographic and topographic surveys.

Another requirement for revising the nautical charts of
the Prince William Sound area in 1964 was the gathering and
correlating of all available data to determine the areal limits
and magnitude of uplift and subsidence resulting from the
earthquake (Figure 1).

Immediately after the March 27, 1964, earthquake and
resulting tsunami, all available reports were analyzed, and
the Bureau concentrated on establishing first-priority air
photography and reconnaissance hydrography for emergency
application to the nautical charts (Figure 2).

CHARTS AFFECTED BY THE EARTHQUAKE

The earthquake and the tsunami it generated affected the following nautical charts of the southern coast of Alaska and of
the Crescent City, California, area:

Chart Number	Title	Scale
5895	St. George Reef and Crescent City Harbor	1:40,000
	Crescent City Harbor	1:10,000
8500	Gulf of Alaska–Strait of Juan de Fuca to Kodiak Island	1:2,100,000
8502	Cape St. Elias to Shumagin Islands	1:969,761
8515	Prince William Sound–Western Entrance	1:81,436
8517	Prince William Sound–Western Part	1:80,000
8519	Prince William Sound–Port Fidalgo and Valdez Arm	1:79,291
	Valdez	1:7,000
8520	Prince William Sound–Eastern Entrance	1:80,000
8521	Passage Canal Including Port of Whittier	1:20,000
	Port of Whittier	1:10,000
8523	Latouche, Elrington, and Prince of Wales Passages	1:40,000
8524	Drier Bay, Prince William Sound	1:20,000
8525	Orca Bay and Inlet–Channel Islands to Cordova	1:30,000
8528	Point Elrington to Cape Resurrection	1:81,436
8529	Cape Resurrection to Two Arm Bay	1:81,847
	Seward	1:10,000
8530	Seal Rocks to Gore Point	1:83,074
8531	Gore Point to Anchor Point	1:82,662
	Homer Harbor Small-Boat Basin	1:5,000
8533	Shuyak and Afognak Islands and Adjacent Waters	1:78,000
8534	Marmot Bay and Kupreanof Strait, Kodiak and Afognak Islands	1:78,900
8535	Chiniak Bay to Dangerous Cape, Kodiak Island	1:80,000
8536	Gull Point to Kaguyak Bay, Kodiak Island	1:80,728
	Sitkalidak Passage	1:20,000

Chart Number	Title	Scale
8537	Sitkinak Strait and Alitak Bay, Kodiak Island	1:80,000
8540	Cape Alitak to Cape Ikolik, Kodiak Island	1:80,905
8545	Kodiak and St. Paul Harbors, Kodiak Island	1:20,000
	Kodiak Harbor	1:10,000
8546	Womens Bay, Kodiak Island	1:10,000
8551	Prince William Sound	1:200,000
8552	Point Elrington to East Chugach Island	1:200,000
8553	Cook Inlet–Northern Part	1:194,154
8554	Cook Inlet–Southern Part	1:200,000
	Ninilchik Harbor	1:5,000
8556	Kodiak Island	1:350,000
8557	Knik Arm–Fire Island to Goose Creek	1:40,000
	Anchorage	1:10,000
9000	San Diego to Aleutian Islands and Hawaiian Archipelago	1:4,860,700
9052	Bristol Bay–Nushagak Bay and Approaches	1:100,000

PRELIMINARY CHARTING: INITIAL ISSUE

Under the personal supervision of the Director of the Coast
and Geodetic Survey, who immediately inspected the disaster
area, all available facilities of the Bureau were incorporated
in an emergency plan for obtaining postearthquake changes
and furnishing them to the mariners in the shortest time possible. The results of this coordinated effort for emergency
charting are described below in chronological order.

On April 21, 1964, six preliminary chartlets, based on air
photographs of April 3 and 4, 1964, were published and air-
mailed to Coast and Geodetic Survey Regional and Field
Offices and Chart Agents along the West Coast and in Alaska.
Copies also appeared in newspapers, on television, and in the
weekly *Notice to Mariners*, No. 18, dated May 2, 1964. The
six initial-issue chartlets urgently needed for navigation and
supply were

1. *Valdez, Alaska* (*Chart 8519*). The chartlet published in
the *Notice to Mariners*, No. 18, dated May 2, 1964 (Figures 3
and 4), shows graphically the extensive damage that the port
received. Valdez is built on an alluvial fan of unconsolidated
sediments, which is built out into the head of the deep, steep-
sided fiord of Port Valdez. A major submarine landslide,
together with the tsunami which followed, caused the total
destruction of the entire waterfront of this apparently subsiding town (Figures 5–7). Note the loss of two large and two
smaller piers, and extensive shoreline changes (Figure 16).
Even in late 1964, the land at Valdez was still shifting. Plans
were made to abandon the present townsite and to relocate
the town approximately 4 mi northwest of its present location, on more stable ground at Mineral Creek.

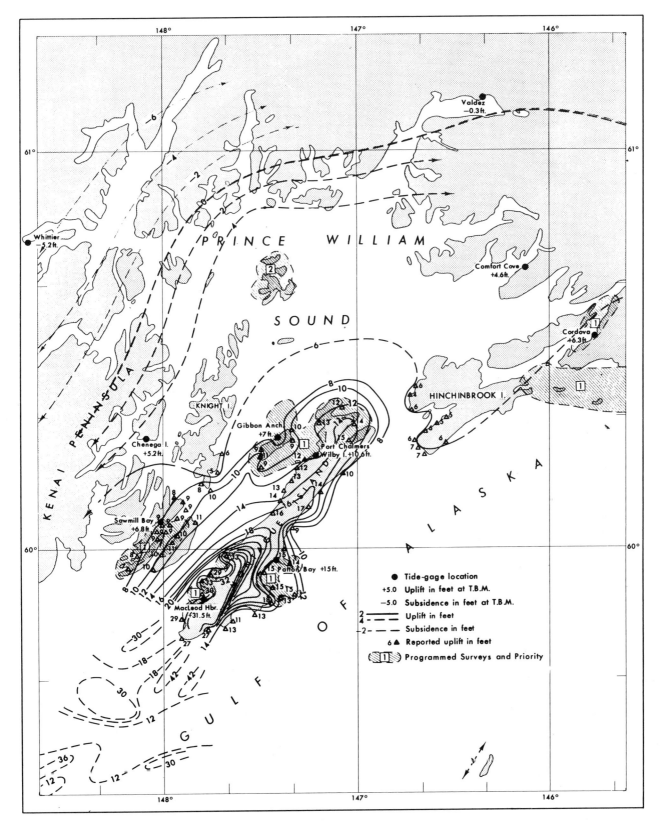

FIGURE 1   Uplift and subsidence contours and survey priorities.

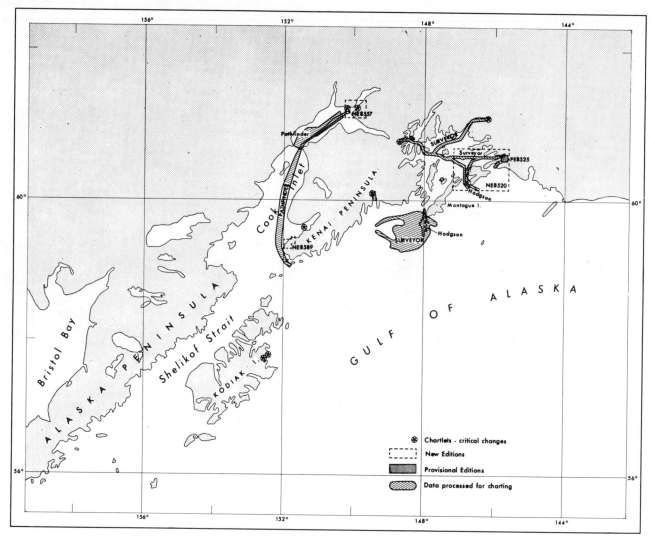

FIGURE 2 Hydrographic surveys for chart revision in 1964.

2. *Seward, Alaska* (*Chart 8529*). The entire economy of Seward was built around a transportation complex which was completely obliterated by the earthquake. A comparison of the 4th edition of Chart 8529 and the chartlet issued with the *Notice to Mariners*, No. 18, dated May 2, 1964 (Figure 8), indicates the drastic changes to the shoreline of Seward when almost an entire mile of the eastern harbor, the huge piers, the railway yard and dock, other docking facilities, oil tanks, and navigational aids were destroyed or damaged (Figures 9–12). A comparison of the portion of the 5th edition of the chart indicates some changes in the port area, particularly hydrographic changes. Preliminary investigation revealed depths in the northwest section of Upper Resurrection Bay to be 15 to 20 fathoms deeper than previously charted depths.

3. *Whittier, Alaska* (*Chart 8521*). Extensive damages to Whittier, depicted in Figure 13, include the destruction of two 250-yd oil piers and changes to shoreline and offshore

depths (about 6½ ft deeper) in the same vicinity. The town was left with no facilities for unloading cargo from supply ships (Figure 14).

4. *Kodiak, Alaska* (*Chart 8545*). A 30-ft tsunami destroyed Kodiak's business section and carried away most of the port facilities, including the buildings, piers, and navigational aids. It also altered a mile of shoreline. Subsidence of the island also has affected the hydrography of the submerged areas (Figure 15).

5. *Womens Bay, Kodiak Island, Alaska* (*Chart 8546*). There were relatively small changes to the northwest shoreline and few topographic changes in Womens Bay. No noticeable damage was done to the port facilities.

6. *Crescent Harbor, California* (*Chart 5895*). Drastic changes to the waterfront of Crescent City, California, included the destruction of two 300-yd piers, one 125-yd bulkhead, and changes to 1½ mi of shoreline.

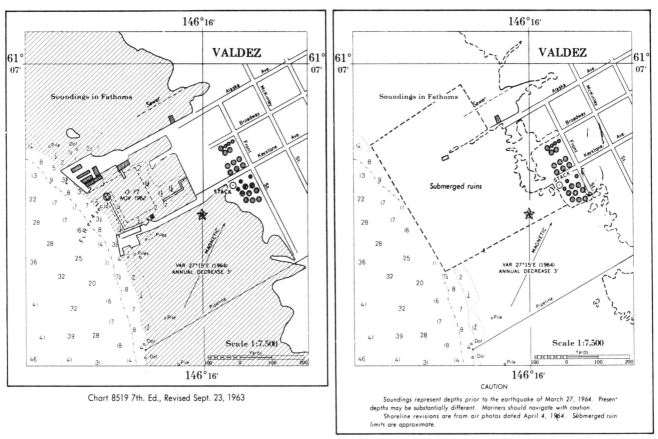

Chart 8519 7th. Ed., Revised Sept. 23, 1963

CAUTION

Soundings represent depths prior to the earthquake of March 27, 1964. Present
depths may be substantially different. Mariners should navigate with caution.
Shoreline revisions are from air photos dated April 4, 1964. Submerged ruin
limits are approximate.

Chartlet published in Notice to Mariners No. 18 May 2, 1964

FIGURE 3   Valdez. Tremendously damaged, primarily by submarine landslides (see also Figure 16).

REVISED CHARTLETS, PROVISIONAL AND NEW EDITIONS OF CHARTS

In addition to determining visible changes in the coastline, the Bureau's responsibility was to determine quickly whether hidden dangers had been created below the water surface. Immediately following the Prince William Sound earthquake, the Director of the Coast and Geodetic Survey diverted two Class I ocean-survey vessels to the disaster area to concentrate first on locating clear channels to these major ports, then to mark dangers to navigation and assist the Coast Guard in relocating aids to navigation. The *Surveyor*, engaged in oceanographic surveys in the central Pacific, was diverted and arrived at Kodiak on Tuesday, April 2. The *Pathfinder* was ordered from survey work in and near the Hawaiian Islands and arrived at Seward on April 10. Two smaller vessels also were ordered to sail immediately, the *Hodgson* to Prince William Sound and the *Lester Jones* to Glacier Bay.

Within 5 months after the Alaska earthquake, more than 200 surveys and related data had been received from these vessels and other sources for immediate application to chart

revision. Figure 2 shows areas covered by hydrographic surveys that were made to revise charts in 1964. Concurrently, steps were taken to supply provisional editions of some affected charts. As the chartlets and provisional charts were prepared and distributed, work also was under way to supply new editions of charts for the earthquake-affected area. As incoming material was analyzed, it was applied immediately to affected charts. Between April 21, 1964, and December 31, 1964, the following charts of the earthquake area were issued to the public:

Chart 8529 Supplement, Seward-Resurrection Bay—This provisional edition was printed May 4, 1964, and announced in the *Notice to Mariners*, No. 21, dated May 23, 1964. The supplement, showing extensive shoreline changes, was based on 1964 source material which included the Seward chartlet (Figure 8) revised from air photos, April 3; tide data from the U.S. Navy, April 2; hydrographic information obtained by the *Pathfinder*, April 13–14; landmark information gathered by the *Pathfinder* during April; and hydrographic information from the U.S. Corps of Engineers, April 3–4.

FIGURE 4 Valdez. Although this photograph was taken in July 1954, a comparison with Chart 8519 (Figure 3) indicates little change in the waterfront; a comparison with the chartlet revised April 4, 1964, shows drastic shoreline changes.

FIGURE 5 This oblique view of Valdez taken shortly after the earthquake of March 27 gives some indication of the waterfront damage inflicted by the tsunami, by slumping, and by subsidence resulting from the earthquake. The area affected by the tsunami is that lacking snow cover. Compare with Figure 4.

FIGURE 6   Before the earthquake the seaward slope of the alluvial fan on which Valdez was built was about 15° near the shoreline. The unstable alluvial soil of this slope caused much of the dock area to slump into the sea during the earthquake. Alongside depths changed from 35 to 110 ft. See Figure 5 (left center) for location.

FIGURE 7   Valdez oil tanks. Fires erupted in the tank-farm area due to oil leaking from the tanks that were damaged by both the earthquake and tsunami. Burning oil carried along the waterfront destroyed several business buildings. Note chunks of ice and other debris washed around the base of the tanks. See Figure 5 (right center) for location.

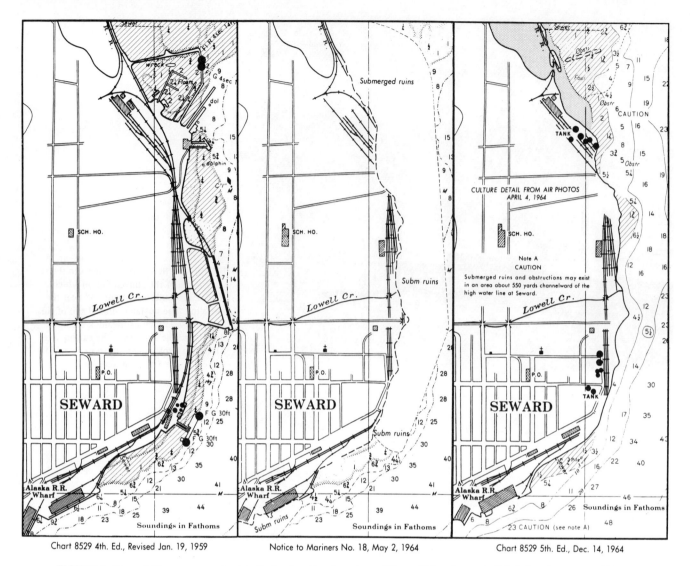

Chart 8529 4th. Ed., Revised Jan. 19, 1959   Notice to Mariners No. 18, May 2, 1964   Chart 8529 5th. Ed., Dec. 14, 1964

FIGURE 8   Seward. Damages caused primarily by shoreline slumping, offshore sliding, tsunami, slide-induced waves, and fire.

Tremendous changes in water depth were also noted after the results of a reconnaissance hydrographic survey made by the *Pathfinder* during April were analyzed. Hydrographic changes since the previous edition of the chart showed that the 20-fathom curve had shifted 600 ft shoreward, the ¾-fathom curve had increased to 14 fathoms, and the 5½-fathom depth off the destroyed railroad pier had become 23 fathoms.

Chart 8525 (*1st Provisional Edition*) *Orca Bay and Inlet–Channel Islands to Cordova, Alaska*—Results of the hydrographic reconnaissance surveys conducted by the *Surveyor* on April 8 and 9 (received in Washington, April 28), in addition to the aerial photography of April 3 and April 4, 1964 (received in Washington, April 11), were used to revise this edition of Orca Bay and Inlet. Drastic hydrographic changes were found in Orca Inlet; some depths shoaled from 33 to

9 ft, 39 to 11 ft, and 14 to 6 ft. A general areal uplift evident from the hydrographic surveys indicated an urgent need for extensive detailed surveys to determine specific areas of change affecting the nautical chart. The provisional edition was printed on May 4, 1964, and announced in the *Notice to Mariners*, No. 21, dated May 23, 1964.

Chart 8557 (*Chartlet with revised hydrography*), *Fire Island Shoal*—This chartlet was based on aerial photography of April 3, 1964 (received in the Bureau April 14), and on reconnaissance hydrography by the *Pathfinder* in April (received in Washington during May 1964). It was published in the *Notice to Mariners*, No. 22, dated May 30, 1964.

Chart 8519 (*Chartlet with revised hydrography*), *Valdez Waterfront Area*—This chartlet was based on hydrography by the *Surveyor* in April (received in Washington, April 15), and on the photo-revised chartlet of April 20. Figure 16 illustrates

FIGURE 9 Seward. A comparison of the top photograph (September 1948) with the 4th edition of Chart 8529, revised January 1959 (Figure 8), shows few shoreline changes other than fill (left center). A comparison with the chartlet issued with the *Notice to Mariners,* No. 18, May 2, 1964 (Figure 8), indicates the extent of shoreline changes and railway destruction resulting from the earthquake. Comparison with the bottom photograph (August 1964) shows the shoreline changes resulting from the slumping of about 5,000 ft of the waterfront into Resurrection Bay and from offshore slides, the tsunami, and fire. The steep and unstable newly formed shoreline is backed by many tension cracks.

FIGURE 10 Railroad yard, Seward. Railroad facilities near the waterfront were a total loss as they were hurled inland by the force of the tsunami. Much of the track and rolling stock was left a mass of twisted metal and battered cars.

FIGURE 11   Port area, Seward. A 5,000-ft chunk of the waterfront of Seward slipped into Resurrection Bay, taking with it a cannery, the docks, warehouses, offices, and oil tanks. A corner of the warehouse and dock remnants can be seen in the center middle ground of Figure 12.

FIGURE 12   Port area, Seward. The slipping of the waterfront into the bay and the locally induced tsunami left no usable docks or piers along the entire waterfront. In addition to the waterfront damage, about 90 percent of the industry of Seward was obliterated and most of the business district damaged or destroyed.

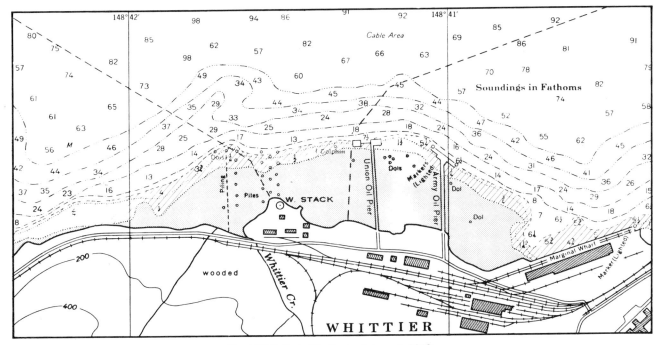

Chart 8521 2nd. Ed., Revised June 4, 1962

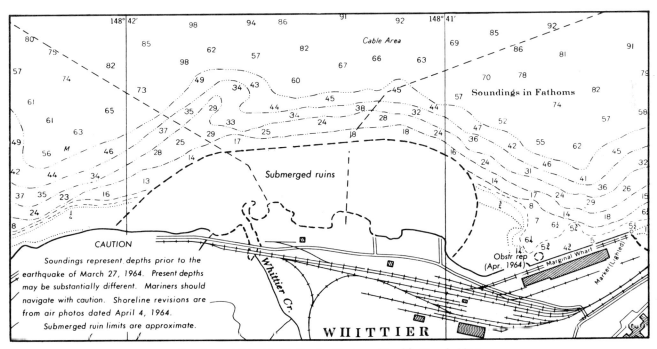

Chartlet published in Notice to Mariners No. 18, May 2, 1964

FIGURE 13   Whittier. Damage to Whittier was primarily by fire and by locally generated waves. Regional tectonic subsidence was about 4.7 ft.

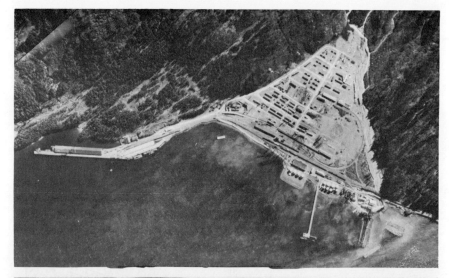

FIGURE 14   A comparison of the top photograph (September 1948) with the portion of Chart 8521 that was dated June 1962 (Figure 13) indicates several significant changes to the waterfront (oil storage tanks are not shown on the chart). The oil tanks in the bottom photograph (August 1964) show the effects of the fire that followed the earthquake. Burning oil from one of the tanks ruptured by the earthquake spread to other tanks. Other damage was caused by the rapid rise of water level in Passage Canal shortly after the earthquake. The high waterline was slightly inland from and almost parallel to the railroad tracks.

the chartlet that was published in *Notice to Mariners*, No. 23, dated June 6, 1964. Compare this chartlet with Figure 17 for shoreline changes and areas being reconstructed.

Chart 8521 (Chartlet with revised hydrography), Whittier—Hydrographic surveys made by the *Surveyor* in April and May 1964 and the photo-revised chartlet of April 20 were used to revise this chartlet which was published in *Notice to Mariners*, No. 23, dated June 6, 1964.

Chart 8557 (Chartlet with revised hydrography), Anchorage Waterfront Area—This revised hydrography chartlet is based on hydrographic surveys made by the *Pathfinder* in April and May, the results of which were received in Washington on May 20, 1964. The chartlet was published in *Notice to Mariners*, No. 26, dated June 27, 1964.

Chart 8531 (Chartlet), Homer Harbor—Hydrographic and topographic surveys by the *Pathfinder* in May 1964 (received

on June 3) were used to compile this chartlet, which was issued with the *Notice to Mariners*, No. 27, dated July 4, 1964.

Chart 8520 New Edition (12th), Prince William Sound-Eastern Entrance—This new edition incorporates revisions to the shoreline from aerial photography of April 1964, four hydrographic surveys by the *Surveyor* (April–May 1964), three hydrographic surveys by the *Hodgson* (May 1964), and hydrography by the U.S. Corps of Engineers (April 1964). It bears a printing date of July 20, 1964, and was issued July 28, 1964.

Chart 8525 (2nd Provisional Edition), Orca Bay and Inlet-Channel Islands to Cordova—The 1st provisional edition was based on aerial photography of April 3 and 4, 1964. This 2nd edition includes hydrographic surveys by the *Surveyor* (April 1964), the U.S. Corps of Engineers (April 1964), and the

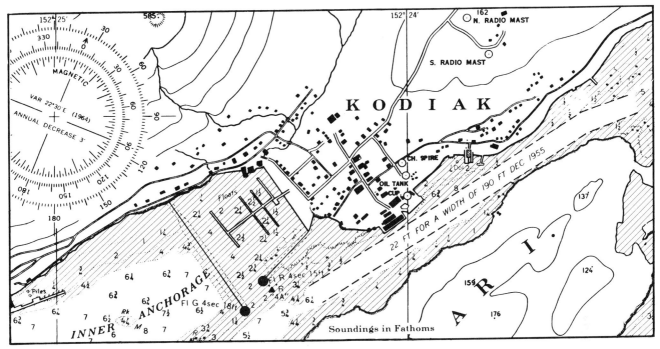

Chart 8545 4th. Ed., Revised Feb. 24, 1964

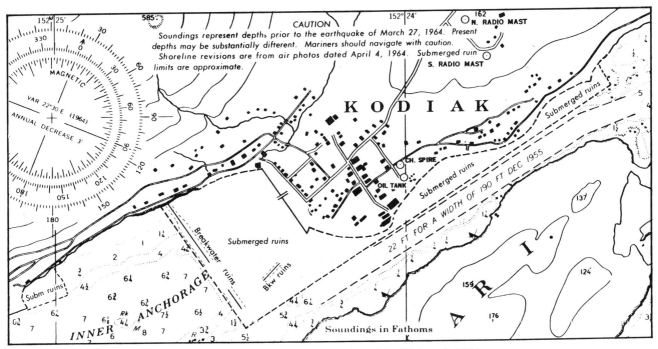

Chartlet published in Notice to Mariners No. 18, May 2, 1964

FIGURE 15   Kodiak. Damages were caused primarily by the tsunami and tectonic subsidence.

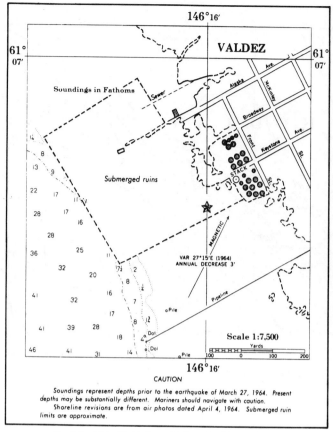

Chartlet published in Notice to Mariners No. 18, May 2, 1964

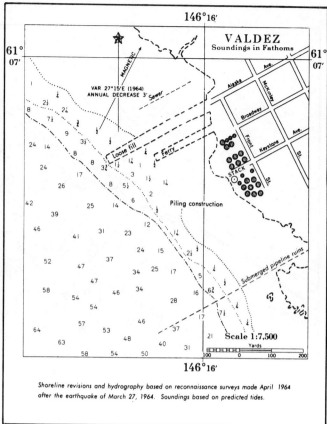

Revised Chartlet published in Notice to Mariners No. 23 June 6, 1964

FIGURE 16   Valdez. Postearthquake topographic and hydrographic changes.

Hodgson (May–June 1964). It was printed on July 27, 1964, and announced in the Notice to Mariners, No. 30, dated August 11, 1964.

Chart 8557 New Edition (9th), Approaches to Anchorage—This edition was based primarily on aerial photography of April 3, 1964, and on the Pathfinder's hydrographic surveys of April 1964. It incorporates chartlets of Fire Island Shoal (Notice to Mariners, No. 22, dated May 30, 1964) and the Anchorage Waterfront Area (Notice to Mariners, No. 26, dated June 27, 1964). The chart carries a printing date of August 10 and was issued September 1, 1964.

Chart 8500 New Edition (4th), Gulf of Alaska, Strait of Juan de Fuca to Kodiak, Kodiak Island—This new edition of Chart 8500 incorporated revisions to hydrography in Cook Inlet from reconnaissance surveys made by the Pathfinder during May 1964. It has a print date of August 3, 1964, and was issued on September 11, 1964.

Chart 8502 New Edition (13th), Cape St. Elias to Shumagin Islands—The 13th edition of Chart 8502 incorporates minor corrections from the numerous larger-scale chartlets previously published and also includes revisions from the following: Hodgson hydrography, Prince William Sound,

Cape Cleare, and Cape Hinchinbrook (May–June 1964); Surveyor hydrography, Prince William Sound and Montague Island (April, May, and July 1964); and Pathfinder hydrography and landmarks, Cook Inlet (May and June, 1964). The new chart, which carries a print date of October 5, 1964, was issued on October 28, 1964.

Chart 8517 New Edition (8th), Prince William Sound-Western Part—The 8th edition of Chart 8517 incorporates the April 20, 1964, chartlet of Whittier and the supplemental hydrography obtained by the Surveyor during April, May, and July 1964 and by the Hodgson in June 1964. The new edition, bearing a print date of November 30, 1964, was issued December 9, 1964.

Chart 8525 New Edition (7th), Cordova, Orca Inlet—Issued December 17, 1964 (print date December 14, 1964), this incorporates all of the 2nd provisional edition, with additional hydrography by the Hodgson (August 1964) and aerial photographs of August 1964. Figure 18 permits a comparison between the preearthquake Chart 8525 (6th ed., revised, February 1, 1960) and the postearthquake chart of the same area (7th ed., December 14, 1964).

Chart 8529 New Edition (5th), Cape Resurrection to Two

FIGURE 17 Valdez. A comparison of this photograph (August 1964) with Figures 3 through 7 will reveal reconstruction progress made since the earthquake on March 27, 1964.

Arm Bay—The new edition of Chart 8529 incorporates the April 20, 1964, chartlet of Seward and the May 4, 1964, Supplement of Chart 8529; it also contains *Pathfinder* hydrography of April 1964, the *Pathfinder*'s investigation of an obstruction in April 1964, the U.S. Corps of Engineers hydrography of April 1964, geodetic control by the Bureau of Land Management established during July 1964, and hydrography by the *Surveyor* during June and July 1964. This edition, which carries a printing date of December 14, 1964, was issued December 31, 1964. Figure 19 shows both the preearthquake Chart 8529 (4th ed., revised, July 31, 1961) and the postearthquake edition (5th ed., December 14, 1964).

Changes to the above charts reflect only those data obtained as a direct result of the earthquake. Less direct applications resulted from the work of the *Lester Jones* in Glacier Bay and Keku Strait for revising Chart 8202, *Stephens Passage to Cross Sound, Including Lynn Canal* (1:209,978), and Chart 8304, *Icy Strait and Cross Sound* (1:80,000), *Inian Cove, and Elfin Cove* (1:10,000). However, information obtained by the *Lester Jones* will be more useful to long-term studies of tectonic changes in southeast Alaska. The *Patton*'s work in southeast Alaska also falls in this category.

In addition to the chartlets and charts issued, 80 folders, each containing six provisional chartlets, were distributed during May 1964 to all Regional and Field Officers and other

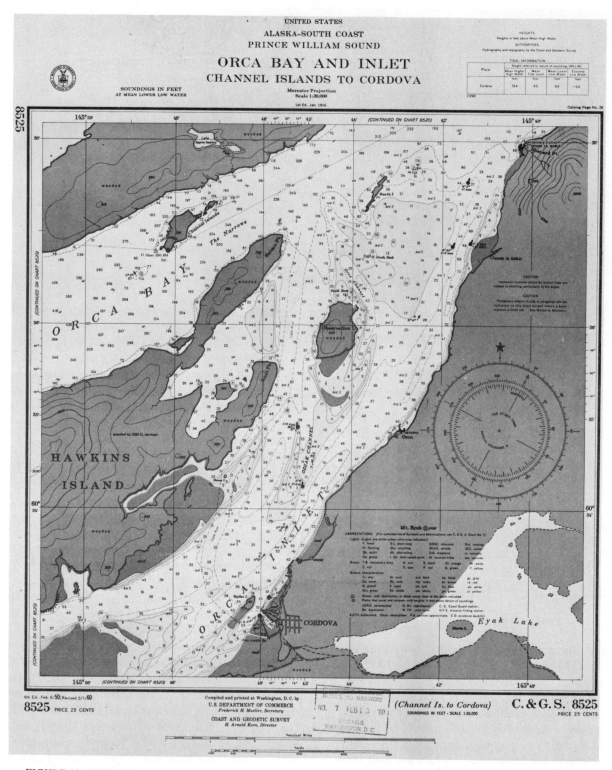

FIGURE 18a   USC&GS Nautical Chart 8525, Orca Bay and Inlet. Preearthquake chart, 6th edition (rev.), February 1, 1960.

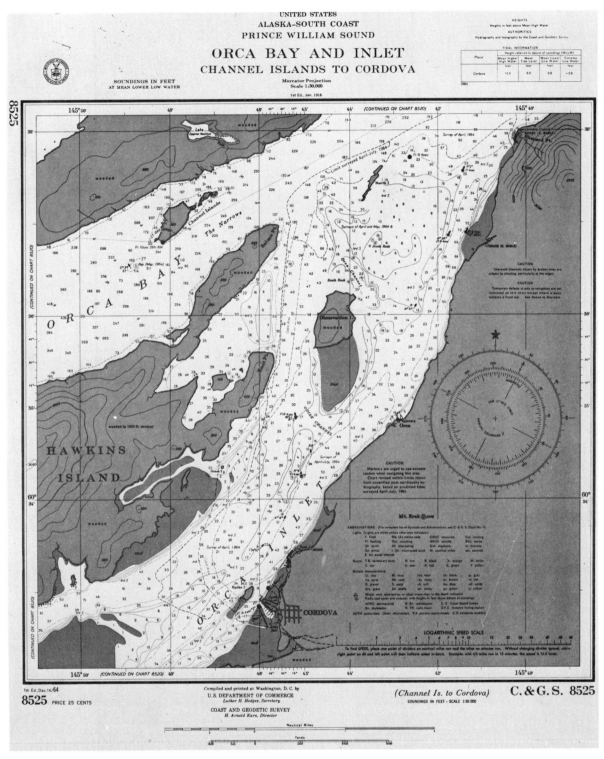

FIGURE 18b   USC&GS Nautical Chart 8525, Orca Bay and Inlet, showing changes resulting from coastal uplift and post-earthquake scour and fill, 7th edition, December 14, 1964.

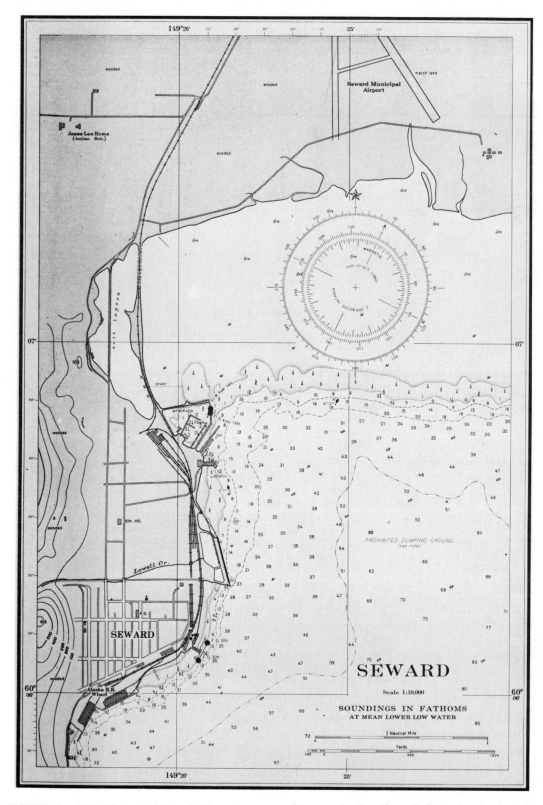

FIGURE 19a   USC&GS Nautical Chart 8529, northwest part of Resurrection Bay (Seward). Preearthquake chart, 4th edition (rev.), July 31, 1961.

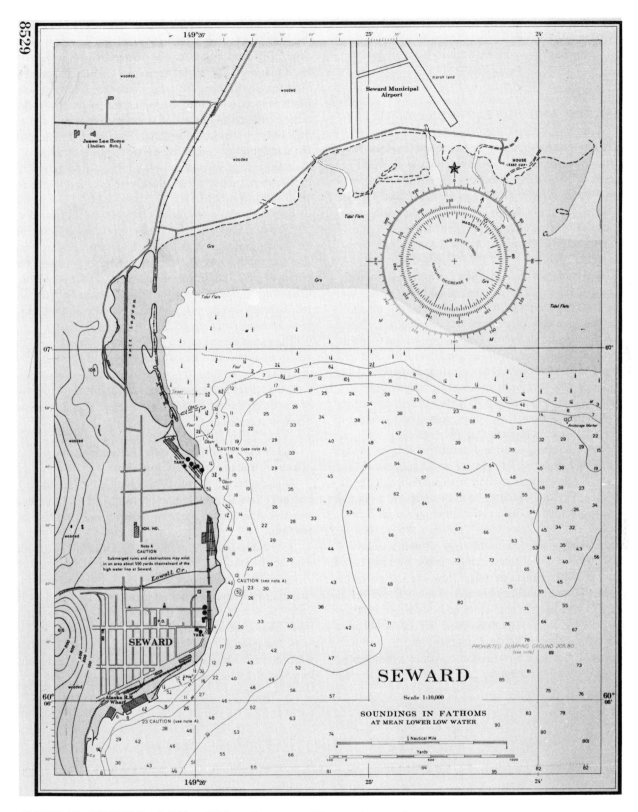

FIGURE 19b USC&GS Nautical Chart 8529, northwest part of Resurrection Bay (Seward), showing changes caused by shoreline slumping and offshore sliding, 5th edition, December 14, 1964.

key personnel and agencies throughout the United States. Transparent overlays were included in each folder for comparison with charted conditions prior to the earthquake.

RESEARCH AND DEVELOPMENT ACTIVITY

Shortly after the earthquake, the Coast and Geodetic Survey undertook, as a Research and Development project, the "Analysis of Natural Phenomena as They Affect Nautical Charts." The first phase of this project was designed to determine the effect of the March 27, 1964, Alaska earthquake on the Bureau's nautical charting program. The second phase established the requirements for new surveys of the earthquake area.

Because land uplift in a maritime environment implies shoaling and is, therefore, a potential danger to surface and subsurface navigation, the initial nautical charting emphasis of the Coast and Geodetic Survey was directed toward determining the areal limits and magnitude of the effects of this earthquake. Although subsidence connotes increased depths in the maritime environment and is not as potentially dangerous as uplift, it is significant for charting. Some of the greatest damage to harbor installations occurred primarily from seismic seawave damage superimposed on subsidence; submerged obstructions were thus also created.

Contours depicting uplift and subsidence (Figure 1) were compiled by correlating information and data received from tide gages, hydrography, leveling, triangulation, and photogrammetry. The data obtained from these field observations were supplemented by information from numerous other sources.

These sources included on-the-scene witness accounts reporting higher or lower tides; changes in the level and quality of water in wells; changes in stream flow; the alteration of freshwater lakes to tidal lagoons and, the opposite effect, the drainage of lagoons; the emergence and submergence of foreshore rocks and ledges; and differential tide values obtained from a U.S. Geological Survey barnacle study.

Coast and Geodetic Survey reconnaissance hydrography also provided important survey data for determining areas of vertical movement, and for establishing new depth contours resulting from either submerged areal uplift or land subsidence. Differential values were derived by comparing postearthquake and preearthquake surveys in selected areas. Comparisons in the uplift areas were made on firm bottom features such as between the submerged, sediment-free, rockyledge extension southwest of Montague Island and the mixed rock outcrop, hard-sand and mud bottom of Orca Inlet. From the standpoint of comparative level differences, some of the hydrographic survey values were contaminated by the effects of submerged slides; these values were not used to determine areal uplift or subsidence.

Economic and maritime-use factors were integrated with the Survey findings in establishing priorities for future nautical charting efforts. Statistical data on port use, ship tonnage, ship routes, sheltered anchorages, and other pertinent factors obtained from U.S. Corps of Engineers' reports and *U.S. Coast Pilots* were combined with these scientific data, and a recommendation for programmed surveys and priorities by local area resulted (Figure 2).

The experience acquired on this project is expected to result in an accelerated Bureau response to meet future similar disasters.

Long-range charting and nautical chart-related objectives of the Coast Survey in the Prince William Sound area involve a review and study of

1. The extent of bathymetric changes resulting from the effects of tsunami and local surge waves,
2. The subsequent redistribution of sediments and other bottom characteristics important to commercial fishing interests and other groups requiring a definitive knowledge of the sea floor,
3. The duration of tectonic changes as related to stabilization, settlement, or continuing upward trends in uplift areas,
4. The relationship of the March 27, 1964, tectonic changes to previously reported indications of regional tilt,
5. The extent of survey investigation required to chart these areas more adequately, and
6. The gross effect of the various phenomena associated with the Prince William Sound earthquake on the Bureau's long-range charting program.

V
SUMMARY AND CONCLUSIONS

DOAK C. COX
UNIVERSITY OF HAWAII

Marine Effects and Hazards of Earthquakes

Most people tend to think of earthquakes as exclusively terrestrial phenomena. The effects associated with the Alaska earthquake were a reminder of how catastrophic the marine consequences of a great earthquake may be and how far they may extend. Although the epicenter of the earthquake was on land, far more loss of life and more damage (except in Anchorage) were associated with its marine effects than with its terrestrial effects in the area most directly concerned. The marine effects also resulted in loss of life to a distance of about 1,400 mi from the epicenter, damage extending to a distance of over 3,000 mi, and traces easily recorded to a distance of about 8,500 mi.

This final paper under Oceanography presents some general conclusions regarding the nature of rare events like the Alaska earthquake and the significance and limitations of their study, followed by summaries of the observations of the marine manifestations of the earthquake and, more importantly, conclusions as to the probable nature and extent of such manifestations as accompaniments of earthquakes of similar magnitude occurring at other times and places.

Several sections of the Oceanography portion deal with marine phenomena in general, but, because of the especially great hazards associated with tsunamis, most aspects, such as occurrences and characteristics, the warning system, and needs for research are treated in a separate section on tsunamis. Engineering aspects of the tsunami effects and tsunami hazard reduction are given special attention in the Coastal Engineering part of this volume. Great hazards were associated also with some of the marine geologic phenomena such as shoreling slumping, but, because these are treated in detail in the Geology and Engineering volumes of this series, they are not given special attention here.

STUDY OF THE ALASKA EARTHQUAKE AS A RARE EVENT

GENERALIZATION AND EXTRAPOLATION OF INSIGHTS

Great earthquakes are infrequent, of course, and each one is not only unique in detail but more or less distinctive even in major aspects. So large and so rare an event as the Alaska earthquake receives a good deal of attention just because it is so unusual. However, the observations of its unusual characteristics are of limited value in themselves because of the extreme unlikelihood of recurrence of an essentially identical earthquake.

From an analysis by Berg (1965), it appears that the mean annual number of shallow-focus earthquakes of magnitude 8.5 in Alaska is about 0.03. Almost all large earthquakes in Alaska have been concentrated in a narrow band, about 4,500 km long, with its axis on the Continental Shelf. The historical record suggests something more than 10-fold variation in mean earthquake strain release per unit area along this band, but the apparent variation is associated with the very few largest earthquakes and hence may have little significance. Hence it appears that shallow-focus earthquakes of the magnitude of the 1964 Alaska earthquake and with epicentral locations within 250 km of that of 1964 may be expected to recur, on the average, no more often than once every century or two. Comparisons of the tectonic effects of the 1964 earthquake with earlier Holocene tectonic movements (von Huene, Shor, and Malloy, this volume) indicate that the combination of particular tectonic characteristics of the Alaska earthquake with the magnitude and location characteristics must occur much less frequently. Certainly there is little chance that an event of essentially the same geophysical character will recur in virtually the same locality while the socioecological conditions remain almost the same.

Hence, most of the interest in the study of the Alaska earthquake relates to the possible derivation, from information about this event, of insights pertinent to the occurrence and effects of a similar event at a different place or time. For

337

the purpose of making such extrapolation possible, the study of a large earthquake should be concerned not so much with those aspects in which it is distinctive as with those in which it resembles other earthquakes—not so much in the unique magnitudes of particular effects of the earthquake as in the interrelationships among the magnitudes of various effects that may be common to all earthquakes. Relationships may be difficult to guess and cannot be proved, however, from single cases and the significance of such correlations as may be found among earthquake-effect parameters may be severely limited by the small number of observations that can be drawn from the entire historical record. This is especially true in the case of parameters of which the measurement has only recently become technologically feasible. The objective and comprehensive recording of the phenomenology of a large earthquake is therefore of importance—even if the prospects of analysis of interrelationships among the effects are slight—simply to add to the statistics available for more satisfactory analysis in the future.

LIMITATIONS OF INSIGHT IDENTIFICATION WITH PARTICULAR EVENTS

In reality, what can be learned from a single rare event such as the Alaska earthquake, independent of similar earlier events, may be slight. What can be learned from considering such an event in combination with earlier events may, however, be much greater than what could have been learned from consideration of the earlier events alone, especially if there have been considerable technological advances in measurement techniques.

The increased knowledge attributable to a particular rare event is not derived instantaneously from the event itself but is cumulated over a subsequent period of considerable duration. From the Alaska earthquake experience it seems probable that the maximum rate of acquisition of knowledge bearing on such an event does not occur immediately but is somewhat delayed by the necessary mobilization of scientific capabilities. The rate eventually decreases as special studies are completed, but the gain of knowledge does not stop with the publication of their results because new insights, new analytic techniques, and the recurrence of similar events from time to time are likely to result in restudy of the original event, resulting in further extensions of knowledge.

The gains in such increased knowledge attributable to any one event eventually become indistinguishable from those attributable to other similar events, but the significant first interpretation or reinterpretation of a truly extraordinary event may come decades after the event. Some examples may be drawn from the explosion of Krakatoa volcano in the East Indies in 1883. Extensive contemporaneous observations were recorded and interpreted in a monumental report of the Royal Society, analogous to this National Academy of Sciences report on the Alaska earthquake. Waves recorded in Japan, Australia, New Zealand, Hawaii, Alaska, and California on the occasion of this explosion were correctly attributed at the time by one paper (Wharton and Evans, 1888) to coupling from progressive atmosphere pressure disturbances caused by the explosion. However, the attribution was obscure, and it was overlooked by other authors who considered that the waves represented the tsunami that resulted more directly from the explosion and caused considerable damage in the Sunda Strait. The mistake persisted for nearly 75 years until it was corrected by an independent reinterpretation by Ewing and Press in 1955 (and, as a matter of fact, still persists in spite of the correction). Information on the 1883 Krakatoa events preserved in the 1888 publication indicates that there were at least five separate real tsunamis associated with separate explosions of the volcano within a period of 17 hours. This fact appears to have been overlooked completely until 1967 (Iida and others, 1967).

IMPORTANCE OF HISTORICAL INFORMATION

Many of the insights pertinent to the evaluation of the probable effects of earthquakes like the one in Alaska are essentially stochastic and must be based on histories of numbers of events and not experiences with single events. For example, in estimating the possible effects of tsunamis accompanying such earthquakes, earthquakes far inland could be eliminated from consideration because history has shown that tsunamis would not be associated with them. Earthquakes occurring in midocean could almost be eliminated from consideration because of their rarity except on certain rift zones and because no tsunami in history has been associated with an earthquake remote from land. The contrast between earthquakes off the Aleutian Islands (which are commonly accompanied by large tsunamis) and earthquakes off the coast of California (which are much more rarely, if ever, accompanied by significant tsunamis) may be demonstrated purely on the basis of historical evidence. To improve the reliability of an intensity-frequency distribution function of tsunamis on the California coast, it would be sounder to seek historical documentation to resolve conflicting evidence on the height of certain critical tsunamis in the record than to try to apply deterministic principles based on evidence from the Alaska earthquake.

Nevertheless, in the body of knowledge that may be brought to bear on the determination of probable marine consequences of an earthquake similar to the Alaska earthquake but occurring at some other time or place, there are not only many bits of information but significant insights resulting from the study of the Alaska earthquake. Additional insights stemming at least in part from the Alaska earthquake will form parts of the pertinent body of knowledge in the future.

LIMITATIONS OF EYEWITNESS ACCOUNTS

It is inconceivable that automatically recording instrumentation will ever be sufficient to satisfy the needs for data to define the characteristics and results of catastrophic events. The maximum magnitudes of various effects may be naturally recorded—for example the maximum runup of waves by the height of debris lines. Similarly, even directions may be naturally recorded. However, the times of various effects and even their sequence, essential to the determination of causal relationships, are ordinarily obtained only from eyewitness accounts.

There are many limitations to the accounts by witnesses of the effects of the Alaska earthquake. Their inferences were confused with their observations, their observations were generally quantitatively unreliable, and, most particularly, the vital time element was usually missing. Even the sequence of events was frequently confused. Such deficiencies are to be expected because of the psychology of stress; their existence must be assumed whenever the accounts of witnesses are used in reconstructing the effects associated with catastrophic events.

It may also be concluded that, in the training of scientific and engineering personnel, special attention might usefully be paid to the need for objective, quantitative observations (particularly of the time element) in connection with unexpected events.

Perhaps little can be done to improve the quality of observations by the general public, from which most witnesses are necessarily drawn. Greater development of the critical faculties of people in general is desirable, even at the expense of some "facts" with which they might be provided. It might be helpful if, in elementary and secondary science education, and hence particularly in the training of elementary and high-school teachers, more stress were laid on the dimension of time and on change as a part of nature, and less on the structure of nature as quasi-fixed.

GENERAL MARINE PHENOMENA

SEAQUAKES, *T*-PHASES, AND SEICHES

The major Alaska earthquake and its aftershocks were felt as seaquakes by vessels in the disturbed area (von Huene, this volume). The seaquakes reported provided some knowledge of aftershock distribution supplementary to that obtained from other sources. Seaquake strength accompanying the main shock suggested a greater intensity off Kodiak than in Prince William Sound. Although startling, the seaquakes were found not to cause significant damage.

T-phases associated with the Alaska earthquake and its aftershocks spread across the Pacific from areal radiators on the continental slope (Northrop, this volume). The hydro-

phone network recording these *T*-phases proved to have a lower detection threshold than the network of conventional seismographs. The study of the *T*-phases did not support the once-proposed hypothesis that they might be used directly in tsunami warning.

Seiches were generated in channels and harbors by the seismic elastic surface waves of the Alaska earthquake (McGarr and Vorhis, this volume). They were noted particularly on the Pacific Coast, where seismic surface wave energy was concentrated by the low-phase velocity of the Rocky Mountain and Cascade Mountain area, and on the coast of the Gulf of Mexico where the waves were amplified by the thick sections of sediments.

The experience of the Alaska earthquake indicated that some damage from seiche activity might be experienced in areas of favorable geology and channels of favorable period to distances of many thousands of miles from the epicenter of a major earthquake.

MARINE TECTONIC AND GEOLOGICAL EFFECTS

Associated with the Alaska earthquake there was an uplift of an area of the Continental Shelf in the Gulf of Alaska about 750 km long and on the average, about 150 km wide (Plafker, 1965; Berg and others, 1971, and this volume). The average uplift over this area appears to have been of the order of 2 m, but locally, between faults extending southwest of Montague Island, the uplift was more than 15 m (Malloy and Merrill, 1969, and this volume). To the northwest and north of the uplifted zone there was a zone of depression of comparable dimensions, primarily involving land areas. These zones of uplift and depression appear to be closely related to the major tectonic zones of the Alaska mainland and the Alaska Continental Shelf. However, in some areas they represented reversals of long-term geological trends (von Huene, Shor, and Malloy, this volume). For example, parts of the Kenai Peninsula that subsided during the earthquake were areas of long-term uplift, and a large sedimentary basin that has long been developing on the Continental Shelf was uplifted during the earthquake. The sedimentary record of the Copper River Delta and elevated marine terraces on Middleton Island suggest that the long-term trends have been abruptly but temporarily reversed several times previously on the occasion of earthquakes (Reimnitz, this volume).

In general, the uplift and depression represented broad crustal warps. The only zone where surface faulting was observed was that extending southwestward from Montague Island to a point southeast of Kodiak Island.

The determination of the nature and extent of bathymetric changes associated with tectonic and other displacements accompanying the Alaska earthquake was seriously limited by the extent and quality of preearthquake bathymetric surveys. The accuracy of horizontal positioning has always been the major limitation in bathymetry. Means for precise depth profiling have been available for some decades, but means for horizontal control adequate for studies of changes in bathymetry have only recently become available and are still not in use for most ordinary bathymetric surveys. Techniques are also now available for establishing and recovering submarine bench marks where changes in position would unquestionably indicate displacement.

In any model of crustal behavior, including the actively developing "plate tectonics" model, the continental shelves are among the most important crustal elements, representing the edges of continental masses moving differentially with respect to the adjacent ocean floors. Geological and geophysical evidences of various kinds have contributed to the understanding of the structure and tectonic history of the shelves, indicating distinct differences in character from place to place. However, actual displacements associated with an earthquake have rarely, if ever, been indicated in any shelf area to the extent that they were in the Gulf of Alaska during the Alaska earthquake.

For the study of tectonic movements involving the continental shelves, a system of precise and very accurately located reference bathymetric profiles should be run across the shelves in tectonically active areas—for example, off the Pacific coast of North America, at intervals of the order of 100 mi, with one or two submarine bench marks per profile. Precise gravity stations and high-resolution continuous seismic profiles should also be made along these lines.

The shores and the bottom of many fiords and of Prince William Sound were affected by the major crustal uplift, depression, and tilting associated with the earthquake. In addition, rotational slumps and other mass movements were common, especially in the unconsolidated sediments of deltas (von Huene and Cox, this volume). Such mass movements directly caused major losses of waterfront property at Seward (Lemke, 1967, and Geology volume), Whittier (Kachadoorian, 1965, and Geology volume), and Valdez (Coulter and Migliaccio, 1966, and Geology volume), and generated tsunamis which caused additional major damage. The changes in shore level associated with the earthquake initiated geomorphologic changes in shorelines that are still coming to equilibrium (Stanley, 1968, and Geology volume; Kirkby and Kirkby, 1969).

The coastal effects of uplift, depression, and tilting would have been similar in any area affected by a major earthquake in which vertical components of tectonic movement were as important as they were in the case of the Alaska earthquake. Where the shoreline topography was less steep than that in the Alaska fiords, the horizontal shoreline shifts associated with any vertical crustal displacement would, of course, have been greater. The shoreline and submarine slumping would have occurred with a major earthquake wherever there were unconsolidated sediments, regardless of the characteristics of the crustal displacement, although the great depths of the Alaska fiords and the special instability of the glacially derived sediments undoubtedly contributed to the extent of sliding.

OTHER EFFECTS

In spite of the shore level and shoreline changes resulting from crustal elevation and depression (Wood and Taylor, 1966, and this volume), no significant changes in tidal characteristics or other permanent physical oceanographic effects have been demonstrated as a result of the Alaska earthquake (Hicks, this volume), but this may be due in part to the lack of measurements in the estuarine areas whose connections with the ocean were most seriously affected by crustal uplift or depression. Physical and chemical oceanographic effects would have been much more extensive if the vertical crustal displacements of the earthquake had closed off or opened up straits between the ocean and isolated or semi-isolated estuarine areas.

Fishkills resulted from the Alaska earthquake in several areas (Hanna, this volume), probably because of pressure changes associated either with the shock itself or with the currents generated by the submarine slides that it triggered. The accompanying crustal depression drowned forests on some coastlines, and the accompanying uplift resulted in the death of sessile marine organisms. Intertidal sessile organisms were killed in many areas of both uplift and depression by the shift of their habitation relative to tide levels. The potential effects of changes in salinity, changes in temperature, and silting on fish spawning in estuaries were expected to require several years for final evaluation.

Similar biological effects could be expected in the case of any major earthquake associated with significant vertical crustal displacements, and their significance might be more profound on a coast where the normal tide range is not as great as it is along much of the coast affected by the Alaska earthquake.

Two ships lying at wharves at the margins of deltas in Alaska fiords had miraculous escapes from locally generated tsunamis associated with the earthquake. Small craft in many Alaska harbors were wrecked by similar locally generated tsunamis or by the major tsunami generated on the Continental Shelf. Some Alaska harbor facilities were adversely affected by submergence, others by emergence, and many were damaged by the local or major tsunamis (Eckel, 1967, and Geology volume).

The damage to ships, small craft, and shoreline facilities would, of course, have been enormously increased if the earthquake had occurred on a coast more densely populated and intensively used.

TSUNAMIS

Associated with the Alaska earthquake were a major tsunami generated on the Continental Shelf in the Gulf of Alaska and several local tsunamis generated in various fiords and sounds from Aialik Bay to Port Valdez. The major loss of life associated with the earthquake and the major damage outside of Anchorage resulted from these tsunamis rather than from the earthquake directly (Spaeth and Berkman, 1967, and this volume; Cox, this volume). The major tsunami caused losses of life as far away as Crescent City, California, about 1400 mi from the earthquake epicenter, and was clearly recorded on the coast of Antarctica about 8500 mi from the epicenter (Spaeth and Berkman, 1967, and this volume).

LOCAL TSUNAMIS

Local tsunamis were generated near Homer in Cook Inlet, in Aialik Bay, in Resurrection Bay, in several parts of Knight Island Passage and connecting bays and passages, in Kings Bay and Port Nellie Juan, in Passage Canal and Blackstone Bay, in Port Valdez, and in various other parts of Prince William Sound and connecting fiords (von Huene and Cox, this volume). The periods of these tsunamis were generally of the order of 1 to 10 minutes. The tsunamis caused intensive damage at Seward, Whittier, and Valdez; one tsunami in Port Valdez reached a height of 170 ft above sea level (Coulter and Migliaccio, 1966). Of the 115 fatalities associated with the earthquake in Alaska, 82 resulted from local tsunamis (Cox, Table 1, *in* Weller, this volume).

Several generating mechanisms seem to have been involved (von Huene and Cox, this volume). At Seward (Lemke, 1967), Whittier (Kachadoorian, 1965), and Valdez (Coulter and Migliaccio, 1966), shoreline and submarine sliding was a major cause. Other mechanisms implicated at various places were the abrupt horizontal crustal displacement and the tilt that occurred at the time of the earthquake.

In addition to the tsunamis that were impulsively generated, there must have been seiches resonantly coupled with oscillations of the crust, and the water movements in the fiords and parts of Prince William Sound open to the Gulf of Alaska were further complicated by the arrival of the major tsunami generated on the Continental Shelf.

The Alaska fiords are probably particularly liable to local tsunami generation at the time of a major earthquake. The instability and thickness of the delta sediments make them susceptible to failure, and the depth of the fiords contributes to the extent of the sliding and hence to wave generation. The steepness of the fiord walls increases the effectiveness of horizontal crustal displacement in generating waves. Further, the Alaskan waterfront towns are particularly vulnerable to tsunami effects.

Potential generating mechanisms for local tsunamis are not limited to those identified in the 1964 earthquake. A giant landslide plunging into Lituya Bay in Southern Alaska, triggered by an earthquake in 1958, generated a tsunami that swept the opposite wall of the fiord to a height in excess of 1700 ft (Miller, 1960).

The experience of the Alaska earthquake suggests that local tsunamis of some significance may be generated by similar processes in bays and straits in other earthquake-prone areas; many of the tsunamis recorded in history, especially those with locally confined effects in the archipelagos of the southwest Pacific and parts of the Mediterranean, may have been caused by such processes.

It seems possible that tsunamis of local significance may even be generated on coasts such as those of California, where observed fault displacements have had very slight vertical components and where the bays are relatively shallow. The historical record indicates, however, that significant local tsunamis must be very rare. At San Francisco, for example, the only wave motion associated with the 1906 earthquake had an amplitude of only a couple of inches (Omori, 1907; Lawson, 1908) and, although waves were reported as accompaniments of other earthquakes in 1812, 1851, 1854, 1856 (Iida and others, 1967), and 1868 (Lawson, 1908), none of them was apparently of much significance.

GENERATION OF THE MAJOR TSUNAMI

Although most students of tsunamis have considered that vertical submarine tectonic displacements are the mechanisms commonly responsible for the generation of tsunamis, other mechanisms such as subaerial landslides, submarine landslides, and volcanic explosions have been demonstrated to be effective in generating tsunamis. A close causal relationship between a tsunami and a tectonic disturbance has been difficult to demonstrate, because generally the crustal displacement takes place primarily on the Continental Shelf. It may involve the coast only peripherally or not at all; a close relation in time between observed crustal displacement and the generation of the tsunami has not always been demonstrated, and displacements of the sea floor have been very difficult to measure.

In the case of the major Alaska tsunami, the close correspondence among the following factors demonstrated conclusively that the major mechanism involved in its generation was the vertical crustal displacement (Berg and others, 1971, and this volume; Van Dorn, 1965, and this volume):

1. The area displaced, as indicated by fundamental fault location and trend determined through seismic analysis of the major shock; 2. The area of crustal strain, as indicated by aftershock distribution; 3. The extent of the vertical

crustal displacement, as indicated by measurements on the deeply convoluted shoreline of the mainland and on islands; 4. The area of tsunami generation, as indicated by the arrival times of the tsunami front at distant stations; 5. The tsunami source dimensions, as indicated by analysis of the wave characteristics at distant stations; and 6. The source dimensions of an accompanying atmospheric pressure wave system.

The relationships among earthquake magnitude, dimensions of the area of crustal displacement, and apparent predominant period of the tsunami fall in the ranges established statistically for earthquakes and tsunamis occurring off the coasts of Japan (Wilson and Tørum, 1968; Berg and others, 1971, and this volume). Suggestive though it is, the significance of this finding must be regarded as doubtful, considering the differences in tectonic conditions in different segments of the earthquake belt around the Pacific, until it can be confirmed for other events in the Gulf of Alaska area.

Present analytical techniques again proved capable of extracting, from seismographic records of the Alaska earthquake, not only the initial location and time of the rupture but also its direction and velocity of propagation and its length (Toksöz and others, 1965; Furumoto, 1967, and Seismology and Geodesy volume; Wyss and Brune, 1967, and Seismology and Geodesy volume). The location, direction, and length of rupture are of special interest in the appraisal of the likelihood of tsunami generation (Berg and others, 1971, and this volume). Means should be sought for pooling and analysis of the required seismographic data within the time limitations set by the needs of the tsunami warning system.

Seismographic analysis still provides ambiguous results with respect to parameters other than those indicated. However, seismic source motion research should be pursued for its probable ultimate provision of additional powerful tools for tsunami warning.

An atmospheric pressure disturbance, generated like the tsunami by vertical crustal displacement, was detected by a number of microbarographs at distances of several thousand miles from the earthquake epicenter. Studies of this disturbance (Mikumo, 1968) suggest that the nature of the crustal disturbance is sufficiently well reflected in the nature of the pressure waves so that the recording and analysis of such waves on the occurrence of future earthquakes might indicate the character and scale of vertical crustal displacements and hence the risk of tsunami generation. This possibility should be pursued by further research.

HEIGHTS OF THE MAJOR TSUNAMI

The maximum measured altitude for the runup of the major tsunami was 60 ft above mean lower low water west of Narrow

Cape, Kodiak Island (Berg and others, 1971, and this volume). The time and tide height are unknown, but it appears that the maximum runup height corresponds to that defined empirically from earthquake magnitude mainly on the basis of Japanese data (Wilson and Tørum, this volume).

The earthquake occurred near the time of low tide along the coast of the Gulf of Alaska; when the highest waves of the tsunamis arrived at the coast, the tide was still low. Maximum altitudes reached by the waves at some points were attained at the time of the succeeding high tide, although the wave heights themselves were by then reduced. Had maximum wave heights occurred at the time of high tide, the effects of the tsunamis in Alaska would have been much more severe. The extent of the disaster at Crescent City, California, was due in part to the arrival there of the highest waves of the major tsunami when the tide was high (Wilson and Tørum, this volume).

Observations in Alaska did not support the generality sometimes reported from Japan that the runup heights of a tsunami are greater at the heads of long, narrow bays than at their mouths.

The fact that Crescent City, California, was seriously affected by the major tsunami associated with the Alaska earthquake and that Hilo, Hawaii, was not, whereas the reverse has been true with tsunamis from the Aleutian Islands, early suggested that the tsunami energy was preferentially directed toward the coasts of Washington, Oregon, and California, normal to the Gulf of Alaska coast along which the tsunami was generated and to the major geologic structure in the generating area. The distribution of marigraphic heights confirms this hypothesis (Wilson and Tørum, 1968; Van Dorn and Cox, this volume), and a computer analysis has indicated that the directionality is explicable from the orientation of the long axis of the uplifted area on the Alaska Continental Shelf (Hwang and Divoky, this volume).

TSUNAMI CHARACTER IN MIDOCEAN

The true character of a tsunami in midocean has long been a puzzle because available marigraphic records are so clearly distorted by coastal hydrodynamic effects, including resonance and period-dependent refraction and attenuation. From some studies it appears that the essential components of tsunamis are a number of low-frequency waves, generally separated by time intervals in excess of 15 minutes and hence nearly nondispersive. According to other studies, the essential components are dispersive wave trains in which the longest time between successive crests or troughs would be less than 10 minutes even after dispersive propagation across a major ocean.

The major tsunami associated with the Alaska earthquake was recorded on a large number of marigrams (Spaeth and

Berkman, 1967, and this volume). Those who have analyzed these marigrams are agreed that this tsunami was composed of both dispersive and nondispersive waves. It is clear that the tsunami began with a double pulse—two crests separated in time by about 1.8 hours—on which was superimposed a dispersive wave train. There has been much disagreement, however, as to the nature of the later part of the tsunami as it crossed the ocean. A large number of tide-gage records appear subjectively to show a long-continuing 1.8-hour component (Wilson and Tørum, 1968), and in some of the records this component increases in amplitude for several waves, suggesting the continuing supply of energy at the corresponding frequency from the ocean. Some power-spectrum analyses indicate a significant energy peak associated with this frequency; others do not (Loomis, this volume). An objective analysis of the record of the tsunami from a special tsunami gage at Wake Island, which should be as little distorted as any marigrams because of the small size of the island, did not indicate continuance of the large long-period waves (Van Dorn, 1965, and this volume). Both a hydraulic-model study (Van Dorn, 1970, and this volume) and a numerical analysis (Hwang and Divoky, this volume) of the generation process of the tsunami were limited to the early part of the wave train containing the first two major crests.

In summary, although it is now clear that major tsunamis are composed of both dispersive and nondispersive waves, the significant details are still matters of disagreement (Van Dorn and Cox, this volume). The persistence of the disagreement is the result of the lack of appropriate means for analysis of the coastal marigrams.

The long-recognized need for recording tsunamis in midocean to determine with certainty their character as they traverse the ocean is reemphasized by this disagreement. Techniques have now been developed for establishing bottom-mounted tsunami sensors capable of operating at ocean-bottom depths. As soon as possible, at least one midocean tsunami gage should be installed in the North Pacific, and preferably two or three. These will initially be of use simply for research, but they will be of major utility in the warning system when the character of the waves at sea has been determined. In the meantime, and as a backup, the special tsunami recorder at Wake Island, which has been abandoned, should be reestablished, as is now planned.

Further, the apparent success in determining the midocean character of the Alaska tsunami from the characteristics of the source achieved by Hwang and Divoky (this volume) suggests that digital-computer modeling may be a very powerful tool for estimating the characteristics of future tsunamis from seismic and other information, even perhaps with sufficient speed to be of use in the warning system. Further study of the potential of such computer modeling should be promoted.

TSUNAMI WARNING

A formal tsunami warning was issued on the occasion of the Alaska earthquake by the Seismic Sea Wave Warning System (now the Tsunami Warning System) headquartered at the Honolulu Observatory of the Coast and Geodetic Survey (now the National Ocean Survey) (Spaeth and Berkman, 1967, and this volume). Nevertheless, 21 casualties in Alaska, 4 in Oregon, and 12 in California resulted from the major tsunami, as well as 82 casualties from the local tsunamis in Alaska (Weller, this volume). The total loss of life from other causes associated with the earthquake was only 12. Although much of the loss of life, especially that attributable to the local tsunamis, could not have been prevented by any formal warning system, the nature of the public response to the warnings suggested a number of ways in which the system might be made more effective (Cox, 1968; Cox and Stewart, this volume). Many of the suggested improvements have since been made.

RELIABILITY AND OBJECTIVES

Analysis of the public response (Yutzy, 1964) to the warning system at Crescent City, California, indicated that its effectiveness had been impaired by the false or seemingly false warnings that had been issued in earlier years.

The primary objective of the tsunami warning system as a whole, which includes not only the system operated by the Coast and Geodetic Survey (formerly the Seismic Sea Wave Warning System) but the agencies responsible for dissemination of the warnings and for managing evacuation of shoreline areas, should clearly be recognized as the minimization of human casualties, not merely the issuance and dissemination of warnings. The objective of that part of the warning system operated by the National Ocean Survey should be the issuance of warnings of such a nature and at such times that they will be most effective in attainment of this primary objective, with consideration of the capabilities of the dissemination agencies and the understanding of the public. In consonance with this objective and in recognition of the deleterious effects of warnings when, so far as the public is concerned, no significant waves follow, the rules under which the Tsunami Warning System operates have, since 1964, been changed to allow for cancellation of a warning as soon as it becomes apparent that the tsunami is not of practical significance.

To reduce seemingly false alarms and their effects still more, the rules should be further changed so that a warning would not be issued at all if, when the generation of a tsunami is confirmed, the tsunami can be determined immediately to be of no significance outside the area of its generation.

REGIONAL SELECTIVITY

The intensity of the major tsunami accompanying the 1964 earthquake varied greatly at the various shores on which it washed. Although there were considerable differences in effects even in short distances along some coasts, there were also significant regional differences resulting from the sheltering effects of intervening islands and parts of continent and from an initial variation of energy with direction of propagation from the source. Recognition of the timeliness of a change in the policy of the tsunami warning system, from uniform warning for the Pacific Ocean to selective warning taking into account the regional difference in effects to be expected from each tsunami, arose from a special meeting on tsunamis sponsored by the Panel on Oceanography of the Committee on the Alaska Earthquake in 1965.

In 1966, the Coast and Geodetic Survey initiated a policy whereby regional evaluation of the risk in Hawaii would be involved in the issuance of a tsunami warning in Hawaii. For other coasts of the Pacific, the warning of a particular tsunami may now be selectively canceled as soon as analysis indicates that its effect will be insignificant on certain coasts. A Regional Tsunami Warning System was established in Alaska in 1967. Its explicit function is to handle warnings of tsunamis locally generated in Alaska, but this could presumably be expanded to include analysis of the risk in Alaska from tsunamis of distant origin.

A simple statistical analysis of existing records seems likely to provide the basis for extending regional selectivity for warning, as well as warning cancellation to other coasts. This analysis should be performed as soon as possible, and the Tsunami Warning System should be provided with both the authority and the capability to issue tsunami warnings for all coasts (at least all domestic coasts) on the basis of analysis of the risk that each tsunami presents in each coastal region being warned. Only with the maximum feasible extension of region selectivity in warning can the ratio of seemingly false warnings to occasions of significant hazard in each coastal region be minimized.

SEISMIC AND MARIGRAPHIC ANALYSIS

Although the Hawaiian Civil Defense Division received very prompt informal advice as to the occurrence of the 1964 Alaska earthquake, notification to other dissemination agencies and to tide stations in the Aleutians was delayed until the epicenter and magnitude of the earthquake could be determined from reports of a number of seismograph stations participating in the tsunami warning system.

In order to alert warning-dissemination agencies and tide stations earlier after a large earthquake as to the possibility of tsunami generation, seismic analysis at the Honolulu Observatory should be speeded by (a) maximum utilization of seismographic information available at the Honolulu Observatory to determine approximate epicenter location, magnitude, and depth of focus (the advantages of simple equipment such as visual-recording, low-magnification seismographs should not be overlooked); and (b) increased use of precomputed or computer analysis of seismographic information from Honolulu Observatory and other participating observatories to determine these parameters more closely.

Although the formal warning of the major tsunami accompanying the 1964 Alaska earthquake was issued before the arrival of the waves on the coasts of Washington and states farther south, its effectiveness would have been greater if it had reached more promptly the agencies responsible for its dissemination and the public intended to be warned. Earlier issuance of a warning was made difficult on this occasion, and on other occasions it has been precluded by delays in the receipt of reliable confirmation from participating marigraphic stations to the effect that tsunamis have been generated. Erroneous marigraphic reports have on some occasions resulted in the issuance of false warnings.

Since 1964, the Coast and Geodetic Survey (now the National Ocean Survey) has taken the following steps to increase the speed of transmission, reliability, and significance of marigraphic information to be used in the tsunami warning system: (a) installation of some marigraphic sensors on exposed coastlines; (b) remote recording from some sensors to communications centers; (c) long-distance telemetering from Aleutian and Alaskan marigraphic stations to the Palmer Observatory, which serves as the operating center of a new Alaska Regional Tsunami Warning System; and (d) general improvement and simplification of communications schemes. Further improvement in each of these ways should be encouraged. On-call telemetering direct to the Honolulu Observatory should be arranged wherever feasible.

Parameters and units used in transmitting marigraphic information should be standardized or explicitly indicated.

The development of deep-sea tsunami gages, which has been under way for several years, should be pushed to completion as rapidly as possible, and such gages should be installed in midocean where they may record tsunami waves undistorted by coastal effects.

The hypothesis that a tectonically generated tsunami could not be associated with an earthquake whose epicenter was inland was disproved by the relationship in the case of the Alaska earthquake between the locations of the epicenter inland and the area of uplift and tsunami generation on the Continental Shelf.

The first wave of the major tsunami accompanying the 1964 earthquake arrived earlier than estimated at many places in Alaska and elsewhere. This was probably the result of assuming a point near the earthquake epicenter as the origin of the waves, whereas the actual origin was a large area extending many tens of kilometers south, east, and west of the epicenter.

In further warnings of tsunamis accompanying very large earthquakes, it would be better, in estimating earliest arrival times, to assume propagation from the edge of a hypothetical generating area whose size depends on the earthquake magnitude and whose location is suggested by the local geologic structure rather than from the earthquake epicenter.

COMMUNICATIONS AND DECISION-MAKING

A major factor contributing to slowness in issuing tsunami warning information on the occasion of the 1964 Alaska earthquake was the failure of many lines of communication. Communication failures might be even more serious in a regional system expected to provide warnings of locally generated tsunamis.

The Coast and Geodetic Survey wisely provided considerable redundancy in seismographic and marigraphic stations participating in the Pacific tsunami warning system, in communication links between these stations and the operating center, and in communication links between the operating center and dissemination agencies. Such redundancy should also be provided in the Alaska Regional Tsunami Warning System.

It is difficult to determine on what basis some of the decisions were made in the process of issuing the warning of the tsunami accompanying the 1964 earthquake, especially because they seem to be at variance with the few rules under which the warning system was supposed to be operating. An example is the delay in warning issuance after evidence of tsunami generation had been received at the Honolulu Observatory. The problem stems largely from the fact that, except with respect to marigraphic reading and the communications scheme, the warning-system decision-making processes have never been set forth comprehensively and systematically and that most of the criteria used in evaluation have never been made explicit.

The criteria used in evaluation of tsunami risk should be clarified and, together with the whole decision-making process, reviewed in the light of the ultimate objective of tsunami warnings to minimize casualties. Much of the process of analysis can probably be handled more expeditiously and more consistently by computer than manually; if so, it should be handled in that way. However, the analytical processes can never become so automatic as to become independent of the exercise of professional judgment, and high-level professional competence should be provided in the management of the operating center of the system.

TSUNAMI HAZARD ZONES AND PUBLIC EDUCATION

Part of the limitation of the effectiveness of the tsunami warning system at the time of the Alaska earthquake was the lack of clearly defined hazard zones or evacuation areas. Al-

though studies in connection with the Alaska earthquake have furthered somewhat the understanding of the hydrodynamic processes involved in the propagation, coastal modification, and runup of tsunamis, there are as yet no hydrodynamic analytic capabilities by which the effects of a tsunami at a given place may be determined theoretically. In any case, the intensities of the events that produce tsunamis are essentially stochastic. No means are yet available for the determination of areas of potential tsunami inundation other than historical-statistical studies with limited extrapolation based on simple hydrodynamic concepts.

The disaster at Crescent City indicated a lack of public understanding of the nature of the risk from tsunamis.

In order to increase the probability of appropriate public response to tsunami warnings in each community that is to be warned:

(a) Areas to be evacuated should be clearly identified beforehand, through analysis of local tsunami history or application of hydrodynamic analysis to the local topography, or both.

(b) A clear, unambiguous warning signal or system of signals should be adopted.

(c) Clear, simple descriptions or maps of intended evacuation areas, listing of warning signals and their meaning, descriptions of the nature and effects of tsunamis, and instructions for evacuation should be widely distributed beforehand so as to make them most easily accessible to the public on warning occasions.

(d) Warning information disseminated by radio, television, or public address systems should refer to this previously distributed information so as to reinforce it and to be reinforced by it.

(e) The public capacity for planning should be maximized by early notice of possible tsunami risk, but public inconvenience should be minimized by decreasing the duration of evacuation periods consistent with reasonable safety.

WARNINGS IN AREAS OF GENERATION

The heavy loss of life in Alaskan communities, resulting from the major tsunami and local slump-generated tsunamis associated with the 1964 earthquake, called attention to the inadequacy of the Seismic Sea Wave Warning System with respect to the issuing of warnings in time to be of value on coasts in the area of tsunami generation. Communication failures in the area affected by the earthquake added to the delays inherent in obtaining marigraphic confirmation of tsunami generation.

Following the examples of Japan and the Soviet Union the Coast and Geodetic Survey (now the National Ocean Survey) has, since the earthquake, established an Alaska Regional Tsunami Warning System. A very extensive telemetering scheme will provide the Palmer Observatory, which is the operating center of this system, with prompt and reliable marigraphic information. However, because the waves of a tsunami may have serious effects at some communities as soon as or earlier than they reach one of the telemetering marigraph stations, the system must generally rely on seismic data alone, without marigraphic confirmation. An extensive seismometer network telemetering to the Palmer Observatory contributes to the fastest possible analysis of seismic information.

The rapidity with which a tsunami may arrive on the coast in the area of generation; the time lapse from earthquake to public warning, which is inevitable even with the fastest operating system; and the likelihood of failures in communications affecting both the receipt of data and the dissemination of warnings will, however, always limit the effectiveness of any centralized formal warning systems. In the education of people in seismically active shoreline areas as to the risk of tsunamis, stress should be laid on the importance of the personal detection of the earthquake itself as a warning of a possible tsunami.

Special problems arise in connection with the operation of a tsunami warning system in Alaska and the Aleutians because of the low frequency of recurrence of significant tsunamis on the various segments of the coastline. The probable success of the Alaska Regional Tsunami Warning System should be evaluated in the light of this low frequency, the vulnerability of communications links in the system to earthquake damage, and the requirement that the warnings it produces be more reliable than those provided naturally by the direct observation of the earthquakes by the public.

INTERNATIONAL DEVELOPMENT

The very considerable damage at Alberni, Port Alberni, and other communities in British Columbia, caused by the major tsunami associated with the 1964 Alaska earthquake, resulted in reexamination of the Canadian decision in 1963 to withdraw from the tsunami warning system. In late 1964, British Columbia again became a recipient of tsunami warnings.

Recommendations for further international development of the tsunami warning system, which have been developed through the Intergovernmental Oceanographic Commission, would still further extend the services of the system and also strengthen it by increasing the participating seismographic and marigraphic coverage and by bringing to bear on the design of the system the attention of additional concerned and competent scientists. This further international development should be encouraged.

REEVALUATION OF RESPONSIBILITIES

Studies at Crescent City, California, and Hilo, Hawaii, indicate considerable regional differences in the public response to tsunami warnings issued on the occasion of the 1964 Alaska tsunami. To a very considerable extent these differences are the result of different frequencies of occurrence of significant tsunami hazard. However, they are also in part the result of differences in the extent to which geophysical competence has been brought to bear on the identification of tsunami hazards and on the problems of warning. In Hawaii the needs for geophysical competence associated with the dissemination of tsunami warnings and the guidance of evacuation have been provided partly from the geophysical community through a local professional society and partly from a state-supported tsunami research program.

Elsewhere, needs of the agencies that disseminate warnings and guide evacuation for assistance in outlining evacuation areas, supplementing warning information with background information, and so forth, might be satisfied, as in Hawaii, through their own procurement of the necessary geophysical guidance or by a redefinition and extension of the role of the National Oceanic and Atmospheric Administration (of which the National Ocean Survey is now a part) so that NOAA would become responsible for providing to the dissemination agencies, in addition to the warning information itself, general geophysical advice as well as detailed applications of geophysical analysis to local needs. This agency might even assume responsibility for direct public dissemination of warning information, although such dissemination would have to be very carefully coordinated with supplementary instructions for evacuation and with the operations of the agencies responsible for the guidance of evacuations. The possible advantages of such changes in institutional responsibilities should be examined with care nationally and in each Pacific coastal state.

It should be noted that no redefinition of responsibilities will replace the advantage in every region of a continuing interest in tsunami-warning problems on the part of geophysicists familiar with the local geographic setting and local institutional responsibilities as well as the characteristics of tsunamis.

ECONOMIC ANALYSIS

No economic analysis has yet been applied to the Tsunami Warning System, apparently under the assumption that saving human life is worth any expenditure. This assumption is not considered valid in other contexts (for example, traffic safety), and limits to the economic value of human life are set frequently in liability cases in the courts. It seems illogical that the Tsunami Warning System should escape economic analysis, particularly if it is recognized that its support competes for public funds that might be used for other programs—even other life-saving benefits.

The benefits from the system are clearly the values of the human lives that are saved and the reductions of injuries achieved through its operation. The costs include those of the equipment and operation of the official part of the system, the seismic and marigraphic detection and analysis, communications, decision-making components, and the public-dissemination and evacuation-policing component. They also include the cost to the public of the disruption of their normal activities during warning periods when damaging waves arrive and during those periods when they do not. This includes the expenses of accidents attributable to the disruption and the costs associated with any loss of life among those whose jeopardy was the result of the system's operation.

It is clear that the overall economic advantages of a tsunami warning system are increased by a high-recurrence frequency of potentially catastrophic tsunamis and by a high ratio of warnings of catastrophic occurrences to false alarms and that, for some coasts on which tsunami warning might technically be feasible, the potential benefits of a warning system simply do not warrant the costs.

TSUNAMI RESEARCH

TSUNAMI RESEARCH NEEDS

The needs for fundamental research are never-ending, and it would be trite to say that research in seismology, oceanography, and other major areas of science should be continued. It is pertinent, however, to note some areas of research involving stubborn problems to which answers are especially needed for practical purposes and some in which significant results seem readily achievable.

In connection with the determination of crustal displacements as a tool in tsunami warning, the possible further application of seismographic analytic techniques and the possible application of microbarographic information have already been specially noted in these conclusions. Recently, the analysis of accompanying ionospheric oscillations has been suggested as an alternative or supplementary means of estimating crustal displacements (Furumoto, 1970). These possible applications all require further research. The use of crustal displacement information for the quantitative prediction of tsunami parameters depends on more understanding of the hydrodynamics of tsunami generation than is now available, and research in this area is much needed. Hydraulic modeling and digital-computer modeling techniques seem especially promising.

Note has already been made of the need for a much better understanding of the characteristics of tsunamis in midocean. Only the further development and use of the midocean tsunami gages, already discussed in these conclusions, offers much promise of providing this understanding. The analysis of marigraphs from coastal tide gages seems capable of yielding only the kind of ambiguous information, subject to disagreement, that it has in the past.

The much-needed further understanding of the coastal modification and runup processes of tsunamis seems to depend especially on the resolution of disagreements as to the nature of the tsunami at sea before full analytic use can be made of coastal marigraphic and runup data, although hydrodynamic analysis and hydraulic-model experimentation should be continued on the basis of the experience of the last few decades.

Historical and statistical studies are needed to determine the frequency-intensity distribution function for tsunamis on various coastlines. Shoreline surveys of the runup heights of those tsunamis large enough so that their runup extends beyond normal wave reach need to be continued on those coasts on which they have been made in the past and extended to other coasts on which shoreline development is expected to provide the basic data for the frequency studies and control data for eventual hydrodynamic analysis.

Several kinds of socioeconomic research are particularly needed. The need for economic analysis of the tsunami-warning system has already been mentioned and depends, of course, on the results of the frequency-intensity studies already mentioned. It also depends on a much more thorough understanding of the capabilities of the institutions that are now (or that might be) involved in the warning process, of the nature of information available to the public, and of the way in which the public uses this information.

REFERENCES

Berg, Eduard, 1965. The Alaskan earthquake, its location and seismic setting in Science in Alaska, 1964: Proceedings Fifteenth Alaskan Science Conference, College, Alaska, August 31 to September 4, 1964. George Dahlgren, editor. College: Alaska Division American Association for the Advancement of Science, March 15. p. 218–232.

Berg, Eduard, Doak C. Cox, Augustine S. Furumoto, Kinjiro Kajiura, Hirosi Kawasumi, and Etsuzo Shima, 1971. The source of the major tsunami in Field Survey of the tsunamis of 28 March 1964 in Alaska, and conclusions as to the origin of the major tsunami. Report HIG-70-2. Honolulu: University of Hawaii, Institute of Geophysics. p. 38–49. Also in The Great Alaska Earthquake of 1964: Oceanography and Coastal Engineering. NAS Pub. 1605. Washington: National Academy of Sciences, 1972.

Coulter, Henry W., and Ralph R. Migliaccio, 1966. Effects of the earthquake of March 27, 1964, at Valdez, Alaska. U.S. Geological Survey Professional Paper 542-C. Washington: Government Printing Office. 36 p. Also in The Great Alaska Earthquake of 1964: Geology. NAS Pub. 1601. Washington: National Academy of Sciences, 1971. p. 359–394.

Cox, Doak C., 1968. Performance of the Seismic Sea Wave Warning System, 1948–1967. Report HIG-68-2. Honolulu: University of Hawaii, Institute of Geophysics, March 25. 79 p.

Cox, Doak C., 1972. Introduction: Tsunamis in The Great Alaska Earthquake of 1964: Oceanography and Coastal Engineering. NAS Pub. 1605. Washington: National Academy of Sciences.

Cox, Doak C., and Harris B. Stewart, Jr., 1972. Technical evaluation of the Seismic Sea Wave Warning System in The Great Alaska Earthquake of 1964: Oceanography and Coastal Engineering. NAS Pub. 1605. Washington: National Academy of Sciences.

Eckel, Edwin B., 1967. Effects of the earthquake of March 27, 1964, on air and water transport, communications, and utilities systems in south-central Alaska. U.S. Geological Survey Professional Paper 545-B. Washington: Government Printing Office. 27 p. Also *in* The Great Alaska Earthquake of 1964: Geology. NAS Pub. 1601. Washington: National Academy of Sciences, 1971. p. 705–731.

Ewing, Maurice, and Frank Press, 1955. Tide gage disturbances from the great eruption of Krakatoa. *Transactions, American Geophysical Union*, 36 (No. 1), 53–60.

Furumoto, Augustine S., 1967. A study of the source mechanism of the Alaska earthquake and tsunami of March 27, 1964: Part II, Analysis of Rayleigh wave. *Pacific Science*, 21 (July), 311–315. Also *in* The Great Alaska Earthquake of 1964: Seismology and Geodesy. NAS Pub. 1602. Washington: National Academy of Sciences, 1972.

Furumoto, A. S., 1970. Ionospheric recordings of Rayleigh waves for estimating source mechanisms *in* Tsunamis in the Pacific Ocean. Proceedings of the International Symposium on Tsunamis and Tsunami Research, Honolulu, Hawaii, October 7–10, 1969. W. M. Adams, editor. Honolulu: East-West Center Press. p. 119–133.

Hanna, G Dallas, 1972. Biological effects *in* The Great Alaska Earthquake of 1964: Oceanography and Coastal Engineering. NAS Pub. 1605. Washington: National Academy of Sciences.

Hicks, Steacy D., 1972. Changes in tidal characteristics and tidal datum planes *in* The Great Alaska Earthquake of 1964: Oceanography and Coastal Engineering. NAS Pub. 1605. Washington: National Academy of Sciences.

Hwang, Li-San, and David Divoky, 1972. A numerical model of the major tsunami *in* The Great Alaska Earthquake of 1964: Oceanography and Coastal Engineering. NAS Pub. 1605. Washington: National Academy of Sciences.

Iida, Kumizi, Doak C. Cox, and George Pararas-Carayannis, 1967. Preliminary catalog of tsunamis occurring in the Pacific Ocean. Data Report No. 5, HIG-67-10. Honolulu: University of Hawaii, Institute of Geophysics, August. 270 p.

Kachadoorian, Reuben, 1965. Effects of the earthquake of March 27, 1964, at Whittier, Alaska. U.S. Geological Survey Professional Paper 542-B. Washington: Government Printing Office. 21 p. Also *in* The Great Alaska Earthquake of 1964: Geology. NAS Pub. 1601. Washington: National Academy of Sciences, 1971. p. 439–459.

Kirkby, M. J., and Anne V. Kirkby, 1969. Erosion and deposition on a beach raised by the 1964 earthquake, Montague Island, Alaska. U.S. Geological Survey Professional Paper 543-H. Washington: Government Printing Office. 41 p. Abstract *in* The Great Alaska Earthquake of 1964: Geology. NAS Pub. 1601. Washington: National Academy of Sciences, 1971. p. 281.

Lawson, Andrew C. (Chairman), California State Earthquake Investigation Commission, 1908. The California earthquake of April 18, 1906. 2 vols. Carnegie Institution Publication 87. Washington: Carnegie Institution of Washington. 451 p. (Reprinted 1969 in 1 vol.)

Lemke, Richard W., 1967. Effects of the earthquake of March 27, 1964, at Seward, Alaska. U.S. Geological Survey Professional Paper 542-E. Washington: Government Printing Office. 43 p. Also *in* The Great Alaska Earthquake of 1964: Geology. NAS Pub. 1601. Washington: National Academy of Sciences, 1971. p. 395–437.

Loomis, Harold G., 1972. The major tsunami in the Hawaiian Islands *in* The Great Alaska Earthquake of 1964: Oceanography and Coastal Engineering. NAS Pub. 1605. Washington: National Academy of Sciences.

McGarr, Arthur, and Robert C. Vorhis, 1972. Seismic seiches in bays, channels, and estuaries *in* The Great Alaska Earthquake of 1964: Oceanography and Coastal Engineering. NAS Pub. 1605. Washington: National Academy of Sciences.

Malloy, Richard J., and George F. Merrill, 1969. Vertical crustal movement of the sea floor associated with the Prince William Sound, Alaska, earthquake *in* Volume II-B, C: The Prince William Sound, Alaska, earthquake of 1964 and aftershocks. Environmental Science Services Administration, U.S. Coast and Geodetic Survey. Washington: Government Printing Office. p. 327–338. Also *in* The Great Alaska Earthquake of 1964: Oceanography and Coastal Engineering. NAS Pub. 1605. Washington: National Academy of Sciences, 1972.

Mikumo, Takeshi, 1968. Atmospheric pressure waves and tectonic deformation associated with the Alaskan earthquake of March 28, 1964. *Journal of Geophysical Research,* 73 (March 15), 2009–2025.

Miller, Don J., 1960. Giant waves in Lituya Bay, Alaska. U.S. Geological Survey Professional Paper 354-C. Washington: Government Printing Office. p. 51–86.

Northrop, John, 1972. *T*-phases *in* The Great Alaska Earthquake of 1964: Oceanography and Coastal Engineering. NAS Pub. 1605. Washington: National Academy of Sciences.

Omori, Fusakichi, 1907. Preliminary note on the cause of the California earthquake of 1906 *in* The California Earthquake of 1906. D. S. Jordan, editor, San Francisco: Robertson. p. 281–318.

Plafker, George, 1965. Tectonic deformation associated with the 1964 Alaska earthquake. *Science,* 148 (June 25), 1675–1687.

Reimnitz, Erk, 1972. Effects in the Copper River Delta *in* The Great Alaska Earthquake of 1964: Oceanography and Coastal Engineering. NAS Pub. 1605. Washington: National Academy of Sciences.

Spaeth, Mark G., and Saul C. Berkman, 1967. The tsunami of March 28, 1964, as recorded at tide stations. Environmental Science Services Administration Technical Report C&GS 33. Washington: Government Printing Office. 86 p. Also *in* The Great Alaska Earthquake of 1964: Oceanography and Coastal Engineering. NAS Pub. 1605. Washington: National Academy of Sciences, 1972.

Stanley, Kirk W., 1968. Effects of the Alaska earthquake of March 27, 1964, on shore processes and beach morphology. U.S. Geological Survey Professional Paper 543-J. Washington: Government Printing Office. 21 p. Also *in* The Great Alaska Earthquake of 1964: Geology. NAS Pub. 1601. Washington: National Academy of Sciences, 1971. p. 229–249.

Toksöz, M. Nafi, Ari Ben-Menahem, and David G. Harkrider, 1965. Source mechanism of Alaska earthquake from long-period seismic surface waves (Abstract). *Transactions, American Geophysical Union,* 46 (March), 154.

Van Dorn, William G., 1965. Source mechanism of the tsunami of March 28, 1964 in Alaska. Proceedings of the Ninth Conference (1964) on Coastal Engineering (Chapter 10). New York: American Society of Civil Engineers. p. 166–190. Also *in* The Great Alaska Earthquake of 1964: Oceanography and Coastal Engineering. NAS Pub. 1605. Washington: National Academy of Sciences, 1972.

Van Dorn, William G., 1970. A model experiment on the generation of the tsunami of March 28, 1964 in Alaska *in* Tsunamis in the Pacific Ocean. Proceedings of the International Symposium on Tsunamis and Tsunami Research, Honolulu, Hawaii, October 7–10, 1969. W. M. Adams, editor. Honolulu: East-West Center Press. p. 33–45. Also *in* The Great Alaska Earthquake of 1964: Oceanography and Coastal Engineering. NAS Pub. 1605. Washington: National Academy of Sciences, 1972.

Van Dorn, William G., and Doak C. Cox, 1972. Oceanic character, propagation, and coastal modification of the major tsunami *in* The Great Alaska Earthquake of 1964: Oceanography and Coastal Engineering. NAS Pub. 1605. Washington: National Academy of Sciences.

von Huene, Roland, 1972. Seaquakes *in* The Great Alaska Earthquake of 1964: Oceanography and Coastal Engineering. NAS Pub. 1605. Washington: National Academy of Sciences.

von Huene, Roland, and Doak C. Cox, 1972. Locally generated tsunamis and other local waves *in* The Great Alaska Earthquake of 1964: Oceanography and Coastal Engineering. NAS Pub. 1605. Washington: National Academy of Sciences.

von Huene, Roland, George G. Shor, Jr., and Richard J. Malloy, 1972. Offshore tectonic features in the affected region *in* The Great Alaska Earthquake of 1964: Oceanography and Coastal Engineering. NAS Pub. 1605. Washington: National Academy of Sciences.

Weller, Jack M., 1972. Human response to tsunami warnings *in* The Great Alaska Earthquake of 1964: Oceanography and Coastal Engineering. NAS Pub. 1605. Washington: National Academy of Sciences.

Wharton, W. J. L., and F. J. Evans, 1888. On the seismic sea waves caused by the eruption at Krakatoa, August 26th and 27th, 1883, Part II *in* The Eruption of Krakatoa and Subsequent Phenomena. G. L. Symonds, editor. Report of the Krakatoa Committee of the Royal Society of London. p. 89-151.

Wilson, Basil W., and Alf Tørum, 1968. The tsunami of the Alaskan earthquake, 1964: Engineering evaluation. Coastal Engineering Research Center Technical Memorandum No. 25. Washington: U.S. Army Corps of Engineers, May. 444 p.

Wilson, Basil W., and Alf Tørum, 1972. Runup heights of the major tsunami on North American coasts *in* The Great Alaska Earthquake of 1964: Oceanography and Coastal Engineering. NAS Pub. 1605. Washington: National Academy of Sciences.

Wood, Fergus J., editor, 1966. Nautical chart production *in* Volume I: The Prince William Sound, Alaska, earthquake of 1964 and aftershocks. Environmental Science Services Administration, U.S. Coast and Geodetic Survey. Washington: Government Printing Office. p. 193-238. also see Wood, Fergus J., and Lorne G. Taylor *in* The Great Alaska Earthquake of 1964: Oceanography and Coastal Engineering. NAS Pub. 1605. Washington: National Academy of Sciences, 1972.

Wyss, Max, and James N. Brune, 1967. The Alaska earthquake of 28 March 1964: A complex multiple rupture. *Bulletin of the Seismological Society of America,* 57 (October), 1017-1023. Also *in* The Great Alaska Earthquake of 1964: Seismology and Geodesy. NAS Pub. 1602. Washington: National Academy of Sciences, 1972.

Yutzy, Daniel, 1964. Aesop, 1964: Contingencies affecting the issuing of public disaster warnings at Crescent City, California. Disaster Research Center Research Note 4. Columbus: The Ohio State University, Disaster Research Center. 8 p.

Coastal
Engineering

Introduction

Earthquakes of large magnitude that are generated by thrust faulting usually produce tsunamis if the causative fault lies under the ocean or near the coast. Waves of a significant amplitude can be generated by an earthquake with a magnitude 6.5 or greater. Such an earthquake, when generated by thrust faulting, is usually accompanied by changes in the elevation of the surface of the ground over an appreciable area. For example, the San Fernando, California, earthquake of February 9, 1971, with a magnitude of 6.6 elevated the ground surface from 1 to 5 ft over an area approximately 12 by 7 mi in extent. Had this earthquake occurred offshore, it would have generated a sizable wave. The Alaska earthquake with a magnitude of 8.5 was accompanied by much greater changes in elevation over an area more than 50 times larger; the tsunami generated by this movement did extensive damage in Alaska and also caused damage and loss of life in California.

The severe damage that can be caused by a large tsunami to harbors, ports, and other waterfront installations poses major engineering problems. How truly devastating a tsunami can be is well illustrated by the 1964 Alaska experience in which approximately $70 million of damage was done to five small waterfront communities—Kodiak, Seward, Valdez, Whittier, and Cordova—with a total population of about 7,000. The damage loss of $10,000 per capita is some three times larger than the damage loss per capita for the 140,000 inhabitants of the entire region strongly shaken by the earthquake. Much of the damage caused by a tsunami could be avoided, or greatly reduced, by engineering that takes into account the tsunami action and utilizes appropriate countermeasures. For this purpose it is of great importance to build up a knowledge of tsunamis and the resulting damage. The tsunami of the Alaska earthquake afforded a rare opportunity to do this, and so, on the recommendation of the Panel on Engineering of the Committee on the Alaska Earthquake, the U.S. Army Corps of Engineers undertook to fund a study by Science Engineering Associates, under the supervision of the Coastal Engineering Research Center. The coastal engineering portion of the study is presented in the paper, "Effects of the Tsunamis—An Engineering Study" by Basil W. Wilson and Alf Tørum. This study describes the waves that caused the damage to waterfront communities, their number, heights, and velocities as well as the damage resulting from the waves. It gives many practical conclusions and recommendations, which can be incorporated into engineering practice to reduce substantially the hazard and destructiveness of tsunamis.

In addition to the major tsunami and its numerous reflected waves, other destructive waves were generated in bays and inlets whose origins could not be traced back to the tectonic displacements associated with the movement on the causative fault. The paper by Doak C. Cox, "Review of the Tsunamis Associated with the Alaska Earthquake," is an introductory description of the various waves, which serves to lay the tsunamic background for the Wilson and Tørum study. The paper is a summary for engineering readers of the pertinent information in the oceanographic part of this volume.

Additional information on damage to waterfront communities is given in the Engineering volume.

Although the two papers in the coastal engineering part of this volume contain a large amount of information on the damaging tsunamis generated by the Alaska earthquake, it is clear that much essential information was not obtained. Better methods of collecting information for engineering purposes should be developed for use during future tsunami actions.

GEORGE W. HOUSNER
California Institute of Technology

DOAK C. COX
UNIVERSITY OF HAWAII

Review of the Tsunamis

INTRODUCTION

The great earthquake that shook Alaska in March 1964 had measurable effects around the world and serious consequences at distances of thousands of miles. Although seawave effects are not among those that generally come to mind first as consequences of earthquakes, such waves were responsible for extensive damage and for most of the loss of life in Alaska. Waves generated in Alaskan waters caused extensive damage in British Columbia and California, took 4 lives in Oregon and 12 in California, and were recorded on the coast of Antarctica. Other waves that caused some damage were observed in channels on the coast of the Gulf of Mexico.

THE ALASKA EARTHQUAKE

The earthquake occurred at 03:36 on March 28 (Greenwich Mean Time) or 5:36 p.m. on March 27 (Alaska Standard Time). Its magnitude was computed as 8.3 to 8.4 on the Richter scale by the U.S. Coast and Geodetic Survey, 8.4 by the Pasadena Observatory, and 8.5 to 8.75 by the Berkeley Observatory (Hansen and others, 1966). The epicenter was fixed by the Coast and Geodetic Survey at latitude 61.1°N, longitude 147.7°W ± 15 km, in the Chugach Mountains, and the focal depth was estimated at 20 to 15 km. Within a few minutes the crustal rupture spread southwest to a distance of approximately 450 mi.

In the 24 hours after the earthquake, 28 aftershocks were felt; 10 of these exceeded Richter magnitude 6. Within a week, 75 shocks with magnitudes greater than 4 had been recorded by the U.S. Coast and Geodetic Survey (1964), and aftershock activity in the area remained high for many months.

Within minutes of the beginning of the earthquake, nearly 15 percent of Anchorage had been damaged by

ABSTRACT: Large waves inundated the shores of many of the fiords connected with Prince William Sound and the Gulf of Alaska. This brief summary of these waves and also of the major tsunami in the ocean provides an overall picture of the wave action associated with the earthquake.

landslides or by the vibration itself, and parts of Valdez, Whittier, and Seward had slid into the waters.

ACCOMPANYING TSUNAMIS

The sea waves originating as accompaniments of the earthquake were of three kinds. Waves were generated in several Alaska fiords by shoreline or submarine slumping, possibly augmented by the effects of local faulting and perhaps by abrupt horizontal coastal displacement accompanying the shock. A major train of waves was generated by the uplift of the Continental Shelf in the Gulf of Alaska. In areas remote from Alaska, waves were generated in channels through resonance with seismic surface waves in the crust of the earth. The first two kinds of waves may be called tsunamis or seismic sea waves. Tsunami is a Japanese term used widely now in international scientific literature to refer to "a train of progressive long waves generated in the ocean or a small connected body of water by an impulsive disturbance" (Cox, 1963). The train of waves may be a long and complex one, as was the case with the major Alaska tsunami, or it may consist essentially of a single crest followed by inconsequential subsequent oscillations, as in many of the fiord tsunamis. Waves generated by resonant coupling with crustal oscillations are called seiches.

TSUNAMI FREQUENCY IN ALASKA

The Pacific coast of Alaska and the Aleutian Islands are quite properly recognized as an area of high seismicity. However, the frequency of generation of tsunamis in the area is not particularly high when compared with the frequency in Japan, and the average recurrence intervals of tsunamis at most places is surprisingly long. From a catalog of Alaska tsunamis (Cox and Pararas-Carayannis, 1969), it appears that tsunamis have been generated in Alaska or the Aleutian Islands on 20 to 23 historical occasions in the past. On 12 or 13 of these occasions, tsunamis were generated off the coast in connection with earthquakes, but only half of these are known to have runup heights anywhere exceeding 1 m (Cox and Stewart, this volume). During six or eight earthquakes, including two associated with offshore tsunamis, tsunamis were generated in straits, sounds, or fiords. These local tsunamis had runup heights exceeding 1 m to distances of a few tens of kilometers at most from the points of generation. On four occasions, significant tsunamis were generated in fiords by icefalls or landslides without earthquakes. Only two tsunamis of distant origin have had measured runup heights in Alaska of as much as 1 m (both in the Aleutian Islands).

According to Cox and Stewart (this volume), the re-

currence intervals of significant tsunamis seem to be about 5 years in the western Aleutian Islands; about 10 to 20 years in the eastern Aleutian Islands; between 20 and 90 years for offshore and distant tsunamis, and about 60 years for local tsunamis, in south central Alaska; and over 100 years for offshore and distant tsunamis, and about 10 years for local tsunamis, in southeastern Alaska.

Two damaging tsunamis have occurred at Valdez in less than 70 years, but only one has occurred at Kodiak in 184 years, one at Sitka in 163 years, one at Cordova in 78 years, and none in 192 years at Unalaska or in 133 years at Wrangell.

LOCAL TSUNAMIS

ORIGIN

Essentially at the same time as the earthquake, or following it by no more than a few minutes, large waves inundated the shores of many of the fiords connected with Prince William Sound and the Gulf of Alaska (see Figure 1, von Huene and Cox, this volume, p. 212). The times of arrival after the earthquake were too short in most cases to have permitted the waves to have traveled from the Continental Shelf to the places of observation. They must therefore be considered to have originated locally and independently. In most of the places where the waves occurred, there are evidences of at least one mechanism possibly or probably responsible for their generation. The most obvious generation mechanism, perhaps the commonest, and the only one agreed upon by all investigators (for example, Brown, 1964; Wilson and Tørum, 1968; Berg and others, 1971; Gene Rusnak, personal communication) was landsliding or slumping of the sediments at the head, on the sides, or on the bottom of a fiord, especially the rotational slumping of a delta. Where the shoreline was affected, particularly in populated places, the evidence was clear. Elsewhere, the occurrence of the slumps was indicated by changes observed between pre- and postearthquake bathymetric surveys. Other mechanisms suggested as applicable to one or more places of local wave generation are (1) horizontal displacement of the fiord walls together with the rest of the crust (Wilson and Tørum, 1968; Plafker and others, 1969, and Geology volume; Rusnak, personal communication); (2) tilt of a fiord or sound resulting from differential vertical crustal displacement (Van Dorn, 1965a, and this volume; Wilson and Tørum, 1968; Berg and others, 1971); and (3) block faulting in the floor of a fiord (Rusnak, personal communication).

In addition to the local tsunamis or waves that were impulsively generated by one of the above mechanisms, seiches were probably generated in many fiords by the resonant coupling of the water to the crustal oscillations of the

earthquake. Although seiches associated with the earthquake were observed in channels as far away as the Gulf
of Mexico (McGarr and Vorhis, this volume), their amplitude in Alaska was probably small relative to that of the
impulsively generated tsunamis.

TSUNAMIS IN VARIOUS FIORDS AND STRAITS

Aialik Bay

In Aialik Bay, which opens to the Gulf of Alaska west of
Resolution Bay, wave runups as great as 100 ft were observed on both sides of the bayhead, according to Gene
Rusnak (personal communication). The wave forces were
sufficient to break off spruce trees 18 in. in diameter. The
locations of the observed runup were such as to indicate
wave action transverse to the fiord, generated presumably
by submarine slides, and not effects of the major tsunami
entering from the Gulf.

Resurrection Bay

At Seward, near the head of Resurrection Bay, which opens
onto the Gulf of Alaska, a waterfront and submarine slump
developed within minutes of the beginning of the earthquake, a tanker lying alongside a dock dropped some 20 or
30 ft, the dock collapsed on it, and out in the fiord there
rose a mound of water from which waves progressed both
north and east. Subsequently, other waves washed into the
town of Seward, destroying buildings, docks, railroad facilities and rolling stock, and small boats. The various accounts
of eyewitnesses differ significantly as to the times of these
later waves (Brown, 1964; Grantz and others, 1964; Van
Dorn, 1965a, and this volume; Lemke, 1967, and Geology
volume; Wilson and Tørum, 1968; Berg and others, 1971).
According to Gene Rusnak (personal communication),
block faulting of the fiord bottom may have contributed
to the generation of these local waves.

An additional submarine slump generated another local
tsunami at Thumb Cove on the east side of the bay.

Possibly as little as 20 minutes (Lemke, 1967) or as
much as an hour (Berg and others, 1971) after the shock,
the first wave of the major tsunami generated in the Gulf
arrived at Seward. The highest runup in Seward resulted
from one of the major tsunami waves arriving on a rising
tide at about 10:00 p.m. The maximum runup was about
30 ft above mean lower low water in the town (Lemke, 1967;
Wilson and Tørum, 1968) and about 38 ft above mean
lower low water at the head of the bay (Rusnak, personal
communication).

Deaths and presumed deaths at Seward totaled 12
(Spaeth and Berkman, 1967, and this volume)—all but one
caused by the waves (Cox, Table 1, in Weller, this volume).
Wilson and Tørum (1968) report the estimated damage at
about $15 million.

Knight Island Passage and Connecting Bays and Passages

Several tsunamis were generated in the Knight Island Passage and connecting passages and bays in the southwestern
part of Prince William Sound. At the village of Chenega, on
the south shore of Chenega Island fronting Knight Island
Passage, a first wave arrived during the earthquake (Chance,
in Wilson and Tørum, 1968). A second wave, arriving a few
minutes after the earthquake, swept up to 55 ft above tide
level (Berg and others, 1971), destroyed all the houses, and
caused 23 deaths (Spaeth and Berkman, 1967, and this volume). Early waves were observed also at Port Oceanic and
Thumb Bay on Knight Island, at Sawmill Bay on Evans
Island (Berg and others, 1971; Chance, in Wilson and
Tørum, 1968), and in the Prince of Wales Passage (Rusnak,
personal communication). High runups were indicated by
vegetation damage and similar effects elsewhere on the
shores of Knight Island Passage and of Latouche Passage,
Elrington Passage, Prince of Wales Passage, Bainbridge Pas-
sage, Whale Bay, and Icy Bay (Plafker and others, 1969).
One man was drowned at Crab Bay, a branch of Sawmill
Bay on Evans Island, and one was missing and presumed
drowned at Point Nowell on the west coast of upper Knight
Island Passage.

The various evidences seem to indicate more than one
source of waves in the Knight Island Passage and connecting
passages and bays. The high wave that caused the destruction at Chenega has been attributed by Berg and others
(1971) to the northerly tilt of the crust, especially in the
vicinity of Montague Island, and by Plafker and others
(1969) to the southward horizontal crustal displacement.
Submarine slides at the north end of Latouche Island (U.S.
Coast and Geodetic Survey, 1964) and elsewhere (Plafker
and others, 1969) may have been responsible for generating
some of the waves.

Kings Bay and Port Nellie Juan

At Port Nellie Juan, a fiord opening to the west part of
Prince William Sound, a cannery dock was washed away
by waves accompanying the earthquake. Three persons
were missing and presumed to have drowned. High waves
were responsible for damage to vegetation elsewhere in
Port Nellie Juan and the connecting Kings Bay. The waves
resulted, at least in part, from submarine landslides (Plafker
and others, 1969).

Passage Canal and Blackstone Bay

At Whittier, at the head of Passage Canal, a fiord opening
to the northwest part of Prince William Sound, a glassy
hump of clear water was reported to have developed offshore during the earthquake, but no onshore wave runup
resulted from it. Two subsequent waves did damage along
the shore (Kachadoorian, 1965, and Geology volume; Berg

and others, 1971). The first arrived 1 to 1½ minutes after the earthquake, the second ½ to 1 minute later (Berg and others, 1971). The first was reported to have originated at a muddy boil halfway across the bay (Kachadoorian, 1965). There seems to be general agreement that the damaging waves resulted from submarine landslide activity, but Gene Rusnak (personal communication) has interpreted the initial welling up in the bay as a result of horizontal crustal displacement.

At Whittier, the waves caused a loss of 12 lives (Cox, Table 1, in Weller, this volume) and were responsible for about $10 million worth of damage (Spaeth and Berkman, 1967, and this volume) to docks, oil tanks, and a lumber mill (Wilson and Tørum, 1968). The wave runup was highest on the north shore of Passage Canal where it reached a mean sea-level altitude of 104 ft. The maximum runup altitude in Whittier was about 35 ft (Kachadoorian, 1965).

Damage to vegetation on both sides of the mouth of Blackstone Bay indicated waves propagating across the bay mouth and originating from the horizontal crustal displacement, according to George Plafker (personal communication).

Port Valdez

At Valdez, a town at the head of Port Valdez (a fiord opening into the northern part of Prince William Sound), the ship *Chena*, moored at a dock, was tossed about by waves during the earthquake in a pattern about which there is a good deal of disagreement (Berg and others, 1971; Coulter and Migliaccio, 1966, and Geology volume). Wilson and Tørum, 1968, 1972b, and this volume) have attempted to infer the actual path followed by the *Chena* from a study of motion pictures taken by two crewmen from the deck of the moving ship. While the ship was being tossed about, the dock collapsed, carrying with it a large number of people. Thirty-one persons lost their lives (Spaeth and Berkman, 1967; Cox, Table 1, in Weller, this volume), including two men on the ship who were killed by falling cargo, one who died of a heart attack (Coulter and Migliaccio, 1966), and also a man missing from Anderson Bay on the south shore of Port Valdez (Plafker and others, 1969). Two distinct waves that ran up on the shore during this period reached heights of about 18 and 20 ft above mean lower low water (Berg and others, 1971). Between 11 p.m. and midnight, another high wave rose to 20 ft; about 1:45 a.m., still another wave rose to 23 ft. Damage, resulting from the loss of the docks and a small-boat harbor, oil tanks, and buildings crushed or floated away, totaled $12.5 million (Wilson and Tørum, 1968).

Most authors agree that the early waves at Valdez resulted from submarine landslides that ultimately spread so as to claim the docks. According to Wilson and Tørum (1968) and Gene Rusnak (personal communication), how-

ever, the first waves may have been the result of horizontal tectonic displacement and delta lurching. The later waves are considered by Wilson and Tørum (1968) to be late crests of the major Gulf of Alaska tsunami arriving at high tide.

Eyewitness accounts from a fishing boat near the Valdez Narrows, as well as a very high runup (170 ft) on the north shore about 5 mi inside the Narrows, suggest the generation of waves by slides in the western part of Port Valdez, as well as in the eastern part near the town. Berg and others (1971) and Wilson and Tørum (1968) theorize that the second high wave at the town may have come from this western source.

Other Parts of Prince William Sound

On the south shore of Perry Island, in the north part of Prince William Sound, there was withdrawal of the sea during the earthquake that may (Plafker and others, 1969) or may not (Berg and others, 1971) have been preceded by a wave. Subsequently, about 8 minutes after the earthquake, there was a large wave. Berg and others (1971) believe that this wave came from Knight Island Passage, but high runups elsewhere on Perry Island, on Lone Island and Naked Island to the east, and on the north coast of Knight Island (Plafker and others, 1969) suggest at least one wave source in the part of Prince William Sound north of Knight Island.

At Tatitlek, a village east of Valdez Arm, the sea withdrew during the earthquake and then came back to 17 or 18 ft above mean lower low water, according to witnesses quoted by Plafker and others (1969). Witnesses interviewed by Berg and others (1971) mentioned only waves that arrived much later—from 9:00 p.m. on. The later waves probably represent crests of the Alaska Gulf tsunami. The earlier wave, if it existed, must have had some other cause.

THE MAJOR TSUNAMI

ORIGIN

From a number of lines of evidence, it is clear that the major tsunami that swept out across the Pacific from the epicentral area of the earthquake was generated by the tectonic crustal displacement, particularly the uplift of a large area of the Continental Shelf in the Gulf of Alaska.

Studies of the arrival time of the tsunami wave front at various distant tide gages (see, for example, Pararas-Carayannis, 1965) have indicated that the waves spread from an area of the Continental Shelf extending from the Copper River at the northeast to a point off the Trinity Islands on the southwest, a length of 750 km, and from the Kenai Peninsula and Kodiak Island on the northwest nearly to the edge of the shelf on the southeast, with an average width of about 150 km (see Figure 9, Berg and others, this volume, p. 135). Displacements of the shorelines of the continent, its peninsulas, and islands (Berg and others, 1971; Plafker, 1965) indicate that this area corresponds closely with the area of uplift associated with the earthquake, except that it does not include Prince William Sound, also uplifted, whose waters are effectively separated from the open ocean by Hinchinbrook and Montague islands. Berg and others estimate an average uplift of 1.8 m for the Continental Shelf portion of the area. To the north and west of the uplifted area, an area of similar dimensions subsided; however, this is mostly a land area, and its marine portions, Cook Inlet and Shelikof Strait, are separated from the ocean by Kenai Peninsula and Afognak and Kodiak islands. In general, the crustal displacements constituted a broad double flexure, but locally on and southwest of Montague Island there were distinct fault blocks with maximum uplift of more than 10 m on land and 17 m on the sea floor (Plafker, 1965; Malloy, 1964). As shown by Berg and others (this volume), the area of displacement corresponds closely to the area of aftershocks of the earthquake (Press, 1965, and Seismology and Geodesy volume) and contains the lines of fundamental rupture that have been calculated from seismic evidence by Toksöz and others (1965), Furumoto (1967, and Seismology and Geodesy volume), and Wyss and Brune (1967, and Seismology and Geodesy volume). This has also been noted in the case of earthquakes with associated tsunamis off Japan (Iida, 1963; Kajiura, 1967). The area of crustal displacement is much larger than would be estimated from the earthquake magnitude by using the relationships established for Japanese earthquakes (Kajiura, 1967). However, Mogi (1968) has shown that the long dimensions of aftershock areas (and hence, presumably, of areas of displacement) associated with earthquakes are much larger in relation to earthquake magnitude elsewhere in the Pacific than they are in Japan.

OCEANIC CHARACTER AND PROPAGATION

As with other tsunamis, in the open ocean there was no record of the tsunami generated from the uplift of the Alaska Continental Shelf. Other than the record from Wake Island (Van Dorn, 1965a, and this volume), the only records of the tsunami were those from tide gages (see marigrams, Spaeth and Berkman, this volume) or visual observations on shore. The difficulty of interpreting tide-gage records of a tsunami in terms of its open-ocean character is well recognized. The hydrodynamic characteristics determined by the coastal configuration in the vicinity of each tide gage cause the coastal waters to act as an active filter through which the oceanic wave system must pass. Nevertheless, the 1964 Alaska tsunami was recorded at most stations with a long-period component of some consistency, peaking most commonly at about 1.7 or 1.8 hours (Wilson and Tørum, 1968).

The significance of these long-period oscillations is uncertain. Van Dorn and Cox (this volume) have discussed the following hypotheses concerning these oscillations: (1) that they indicate the existence of a train of coherent, nondispersive waves of about 1.8-hour period emanating from the source; (2) that they indicate selective amplification, from a broad spectrum of low frequencies radiating from the source, of certain frequencies that happened to be similar because of similarities of coastal configuration and bathymetry in the recording areas; and (3) that they represent the result of some coastal process of energy conversion from high frequencies radiating from the source to low frequencies that again happened to be similar for the same reason as in the second hypothesis.

The first hypothesis is favored by Wilson and Tørum (1968), and the second or third by Van Dorn and Cox (this volume). The frequency characteristics of the Alaska tsunami in midocean must be regarded as poorly understood, as with other tsunamis.

It was to be expected that the wave energy of the Alaska tsunami would be preferentially radiated in a direction normal to the long axis of the area of uplift on the Continental Shelf. Evidences of such preferential radiation have been found by Wilson and Tørum (1968) in a generally smaller attenuation of tide-gage wave heights, with propagation in a southeasterly direction, than in other directions, and by Van Dorn and Cox (this volume) by comparison of tide-gage wave heights at pairs of stations southeast and southwest, respectively, at approximately equal distances from the source.

From the area of generation, the tsunami propagated outward across the Pacific at approximately the long-wave velocity, $c = \sqrt{gh}$, where g = acceleration of gravity and h = depth of water. Using this velocity-depth relationship and working backward from the arrival times of the wave front at tide gages, Wilson and Tørum (1968) constructed a refraction diagram showing the position of the wave front at hourly intervals from 04:00 GMT, March 28, 24 minutes after the earthquake, to 01:00 GMT, March 29, 25 minutes before the wave-front arrival at the Argentine Islands, Antarctica (see Figure 7, Wilson and Tørum, 1972a, this volume, p. 165).

Average speeds, tabulated by Spaeth and Berkman (1967, and this volume), ranged from 159 knots for propagation to Yakutat, Alaska, over a path much of which was on the Continental Shelf, to 473 knots to Nawiliwili, Kauai, Hawaii, over a path mainly at oceanic depths.

COASTAL MODIFICATION AND HEIGHTS

Like all tsunamis, the Alaska tsunami must have been subject to a number of important modifications as it approached distant coasts after crossing the ocean. The continental slopes tend to reflect much of the energy back to sea. The continental shelves tend to trap energy at wavelengths on the order of the shelf width and leak shorter wavelengths back to sea. As previously noted, the coastal waters act as active filters with characteristics determined by the coastal configuration and bathymetry through which the tsunami must pass. Finally, the waves run up on the shore.

Although certain simple cases of long-wave motion in the vicinity of coasts have been successfully treated by analytical and numerical methods as checked by hydraulic-model studies (for example, Williams and Kartha, 1966; Webster and Perry, in press), such numerical methods as those of Vastano and Reid (in press) require large computer storage for complex topography. Even large hydraulic models, although capable of producing useful results in terms of engineering requirements, do not faithfully reproduce the frequency characteristics and runup behavior of a tsunami (Palmer and Funasaki, 1966; Cox and others, 1965).

Runup values have been found by Van Dorn (1965b) to have a log-normal distribution about regional mean values with a standard deviation of 1.8 times the mean, apparently due to noncoherent energy-scattering processes having roughness elements with dimensions of less than a wavelength. The high ratio between maximum tsunami runup and probable deepwater wave height—16 m in the case of runups in Hawaii of the 1957 Aleutian tsunami (Van Dorn, 1965b)—is as yet unaccounted for by any runup theory.

In addition to other sources of variation, the height of the tide at the time the waves of a tsunami arrive is of considerable importance in determining how high the runup on land may be, relative to a fixed datum.

The maximum measured elevation of runup of the major Alaska tsunami in the source area was 60 ft above mean lower low water west of Narrow Cape, Kodiak Island (Berg and others, 1971). It is unknown when this runup occurred or what the tide level was at the time. It is apparent, however, that the maximum runup height must have been near the upper bound defined empirically by Wilson (1964; Wilson and others, 1962; Wilson and Tørum, 1968) as a function of the magnitude of the associated earthquake (see Figure 6, Wilson and Tørum, 1972a, this volume, p. 164).

$$\log_{10} H_{R\max} = 0.75\,M - 5.0,$$

where $H_{R\max}$ = maximum expectable tsunami runup height (in m) and M = earthquake magnitude.

Tsunami runup was surprisingly high at Crescent City, California. Presumably this was due to the location of the city with respect to the source of the tsunami, the topography of the ocean floor over which the tsunami traveled to reach Crescent City, and the configuration of the local shore and sea bottom.

The tsunamis caused severe damage to Alaska waterfront communities (see Wilson and Tørum, this volume), which points up the need for taking tsunami action into account in the planning and construction of waterfront facilities. The 1964 Alaska experience makes it clear that destructive waves can be generated by submarine landslides, as well as by the tectonic movement of the ocean floor. In regions that are subject to tsunamis, it would be desirable to install measuring devices that would provide information on the nature and the origin of waves associated with earthquakes so that a more complete picture can be developed after the event.

REFERENCES

Berg, Eduard, Doak C. Cox, Augustine S. Furumoto, Kinjiro Kajiura, Hirosi Kawasumi, and Etsuzo Shima, 1971. Field survey of the tsunamis of 28 March 1964 in Alaska, and conclusions as to the origin of the major tsunami. Report HIG-70-2. Honolulu: University of Hawaii, Institute of Geophysics. 57 p.

Brown, Delmer L., 1964. Tsunamic activity accompanying the Alaskan earthquake of 27 March 1964. Technical Report, U.S. Army Engineer District, Alaska. Anchorage: U.S. Army Corps of Engineers, April 23. 31 p.

Coulter, Henry W., and Ralph R. Migliaccio, 1966. Effects of the earthquake of March 27, 1964, at Valdez, Alaska. U.S. Geological Survey Professional Paper 542-C. Washington: Government Printing Office. 36 p. Also in The Great Alaska Earthquake of 1964: Geology. NAS Pub. 1601. Washington: National Academy of Sciences, 1971. p. 359–394.

Cox, Doak C., 1963. Status of tsunami knowledge. Proceedings of the Tenth Pacific Science Congress, Honolulu, Hawaii, August-September 1961. Doak C. Cox, editor. IUGG Monograph 24. Paris: International Union of Geodesy and Geophysics. p. 1–6.

Cox, Doak C., Masashi Hom-ma, Masatsugu Suzuki, Ryutaro Takahasi, and Robert L. Wiegel, 1965. Physically feasible means for protecting Hilo from tsunamis. Third Report of the Hilo Technical Tsunami Advisory Council to the Board of Supervisors, Hawaii County, through its Tsunami Advisory Committee. Hilo, Hawaii: Hilo Technical Tsunami Advisory Council. 38 p.

Cox, Doak C., and George Pararas-Carayannis, 1969. Catalog of tsunamis in Alaska. World Data Center A: Tsunami. Washington: Environmental Science Services Administration, U.S. Coast and Geodetic Survey, May. 39 p.

Cox, Doak C., and Harris B. Stewart, Jr., 1972. Technical evaluation of the Seismic Sea Wave Warning System in The Great Alaska Earthquake of 1964: Oceanography and Coastal Engineering. NAS Pub. 1605. Washington: National Academy of Sciences.

Furumoto, Augustine S., 1967. A study of the source mechanism of the Alaska earthquake and tsunami of March 27, 1964: Part II, Analysis of Rayleigh wave. Pacific Science, 21 (July), 311–316. Also in The Great Alaska Earthquake of 1964: Seismology and Geodesy. NAS Pub. 1602. Washington: National Academy of Sciences, 1972.

Grantz, Arthur, George Plafker, and Reuben Kachadoorian, 1964. Alaska's Good Friday earthquake, March 27, 1964: A preliminary geologic evaluation. U.S. Geological Survey Circular 491. Washington: U.S. Geological Survey. 35 p.

Hansen, Wallace R., Edwin B. Eckel, William E. Schaem, Robert E. Lyle, Warren George, and Genie Chance, 1966. The Alaska earthquake, March 27, 1964: Field investigations and reconstruction effort. U.S. Geological Survey Professional Paper 541. Washington: Government Printing Office. 111 p.

Iida, K., 1963. Magnitude of tsunamigenic earthquake, aftershock area, and area of tsunami origin *in* Geophysical papers dedicated to Professor Kenzo Sassa. Kyoto: Kyoto University. p. 115–124.

Kachadoorian, Reuben, 1965. Effects of the earthquake of March 27, 1964, at Whittier, Alaska. U.S. Geological Survey Professional Paper 542-B. Washington: Government Printing Office. 21 p. Also *in* The Great Alaska Earthquake of 1964: Geology. NAS Pub. 1601. Washington: National Academy of Sciences, 1971. p. 439–459.

Kajiura, Kinjiro, 1967. Tsunami. *Zisin* (Journal of the Seismological Society of Japan), 20 (No. 4), 219–222.

Lemke, Richard W., 1967. Effects of the earthquake of March 27, 1964, at Seward, Alaska. U.S. Geological Survey Professional Paper 542-E. Washington: Government Printing Office. 43 p. Also *in* The Great Alaska Earthquake of 1964: Geology. NAS Pub. 1601. Washington: National Academy of Sciences, 1971. p. 395–437.

McGarr, Arthur, and Robert C. Vorhis, 1972. Seismic seiches in bays, channels, and estuaries *in* The Great Alaska Earthquake of 1964: Oceanography and Coastal Engineering. NAS Pub. 1605. Washington: National Academy of Sciences.

Malloy, Richard J., 1964. Crustal uplift southwest of Montague Island, Alaska. *Science,* 146 (November 20), 1048–1049.

Mogi, Kiyoo, 1968. Development of aftershock areas of the great earthquakes. *Bulletin of the Earthquake Research Institute,* University of Tokyo, 46 (No. 2), 175–203.

Palmer, Robert Q., and Gerald Funasaki, 1966. The Hilo Harbor tsunami model. James Look Laboratory of Oceanographic Engineering Technical Report No. 1. Honolulu: James Look Laboratory. 10 p.

Pararas-Carayannis, George, 1965. Water waves, Part I *in* Source mechanism study of the Alaska earthquake and tsunami of 27 March 1964. Report HIG-65-17. Honolulu: University of Hawaii, Institute of Geophysics, December. p. 1–30.

Plafker, George, 1965. Tectonic deformation associated with the 1964 Alaska earthquake. *Science,* 148 (June 25), 1675–1687.

Plafker, George, Reuben Kachadoorian, Edwin B. Eckel, and Lawrence R. Mayo, 1969. Effects of the earthquake of March 27, 1964, on various communities. U.S. Geological Survey Professional Paper 542-G. Washington: Government Printing Office. 50 p. Also *in* The Great Alaska Earthquake of 1964: Geology. NAS Pub. 1601. Washington: National Academy of Sciences, 1971. p. 489–538.

Press, Frank, 1965. Displacements, strains, and tilts at teleseismic distances. *Journal of Geophysical Research,* 70 (May 15), 2395–2412. Also *in* The Great Alaska Earthquake of 1964: Seismology and Geodesy. NAS Pub. 1602. Washington: National Academy of Sciences, 1972.

Spaeth, Mark G., and Saul C. Berkman, 1967. The tsunami of March 28, 1964, as recorded at tide stations. Environmental Science Services Administration Technical Report C&GS 33. Washington: Government Printing Office. 86 p. Also *in* The Great Alaska Earthquake of 1964: Oceanography and Coastal Engineering. NAS Pub. 1605. Washington: National Academy of Sciences, 1972.

Toksöz, M. Nafi, Ari Ben-Menahem, and David G. Harkrider, 1965. Source mechanism of Alaska earthquake from long-period seismic surface waves (Abstract). *Transactions, American Geophysical Union,* 46 (March), 154.

U.S. Coast and Geodetic Survey, 1964. Preliminary report–Prince William Sound, Alaskan earthquakes March-April 1964 (second printing). Seismology Division Report. Washington: U.S. Coast and Geodetic Survey. 101 p.

Van Dorn, William G., 1965a. Source mechanism of the tsunami of March 28, 1964 in Alaska. Proceedings of the Ninth Conference (1964) on Coastal Engineering (Chapter 10). New York: American Society of Civil Engineers. p. 166–190. Also *in* The Great Alaska Earthquake of 1964: Oceanography and Coastal Engineering. NAS Pub. 1605. Washington: National Academy of Sciences, 1972.

Van Dorn, William G., 1965b. Tsunamis. *Advances in Hydroscience,* 2 (Annual), 1–47.

Van Dorn, William G., and Doak C. Cox, 1972. Oceanic character, propagation, and coastal modification of the major tsunami *in* The Great Alaska Earthquake of 1964: Oceanography and Coastal Engineering. NAS Pub. 1605. Washington: National Academy of Sciences.

Vastano, A. C., and R. O. Reid, in press. Tsunami response at Wake Island: Comparison of the hydraulic and numerical approaches. *Journal of Marine Research.*

Webster, David L., and Byrne Perry, in press. Amplification of tsunamis by oceanic islands. Civil Engineering Technical Report 67. Palo Alto: Stanford University.

Weller, Jack M., 1972. Human response to tsunami warnings *in* The Great Alaska Earthquake of 1964: Oceanography and Coastal Engineering. NAS Pub. 1605. Washington: National Academy of Sciences.

Williams, John, and Krishna Kartha, 1966. Model studies of long wave amplification by circular islands and submarine seamounts. Report HIG-66-19. Honolulu: University of Hawaii, Institute of Geophysics, November. 46 p.

Wilson, Basil W., 1964. Long wave modification by linear transitions. *Proceedings, American Society of Civil Engineers,* 90 (November), 161–165.

Wilson, Basil W., and Alf Tørum, 1968. The tsunami of the Alaskan earthquake, 1964: Engineering evaluation. Coastal Engineering Research Center Technical Memorandum No. 25. Washington: U.S. Army Corps of Engineers, May. 444 p.

Wilson, Basil W., and Alf Tørum, 1972a. Runup heights of the major tsunami on North American coasts *in* The Great Alaska Earthquake of 1964: Oceanography and Coastal Engineering. NAS Pub. 1605. Washington: National Academy of Sciences.

Wilson, Basil W., and Alf Tørum, 1972b. Effects of the tsunamis: An engineering study *in* The Great Alaska Earthquake of 1964: Oceanography and Coastal Engineering. NAS Pub. 1605. Washington: National Academy of Sciences.

Wilson, Basil W., L. M. Webb, and J. A. Hendrickson, 1962. The nature of tsunamis: Their generation and dispersion in water of finite depth. Technical Report No. SN-37-2. Pasadena: National Engineering Science Company, August. 150 p.

Wyss, Max, and James N. Brune, 1967. The Alaska earthquake of 28 March 1964: A complex multiple rupture. *Bulletin of the Seismological Society of America,* 57 (October), 1017–1023. Also *in* The Great Alaska Earthquake of 1964: Seismology and Geodesy. NAS Pub. 1602. Washington: National Academy of Sciences, 1972.

BASIL W. WILSON*
CONSULTING OCEANOGRAPHIC ENGINEER, PASADENA

ALF TØRUM*
TECHNICAL UNIVERSITY OF NORWAY, TRONDHEIM

Adopted from Sections IV through IX of
Coastal Engineering Research Center
Technical Memorandum 25,
"The Tsunami of the Alaskan Earthquake, 1964:
Engineering Evaluation"

Effects of the Tsunamis: An Engineering Study

ABSTRACT: Tsunamis struck many waterfront communities, both during and after the earthquake, and caused severe damage and loss of life. Attempts to reconstruct the wave action from eyewitness accounts, scientific and photographic evidence, and from interpretative analysis and synthesis had positive value. The tsunamis affected Kodiak City, Kodiak Naval Station, various island communities, Cook Inlet, Seward, Prince William Sound, including Valdez, Whittier, and Cordova, and damaged communities along the Canadian coast; at Port Alberni on Vancouver Island; along the Washington, Oregon, and California coasts; and at Crescent City, California.

The Kodiak islands, remote from the epicenter of the earthquake, appear to have been hit by a succession of very high waves of very long period. At Kodiak City and Naval Station, wave heights may have been about 40 ft, with recurrence intervals from 40 minutes to 2½ hours. Extreme runup at Kodiak City reached 27 ft above MLLW (sea-level datum). In and near Kodiak City, nine lives were lost, over 100 vessels were destroyed or damaged, and property damage in the islands exceeded $45 million. Kodiak City and Naval Station sustained more than $31 million and $10 million worth of damage, respectively.

Seward, on Kenai Peninsula, suffered very severely from submarine slides and induced waves of perhaps 3–4 minutes period and of great height, which struck during the earthquake. These were followed by very long period waves (the main tsunami), which reached the town much later on the high tide. Runup at Seward was recorded at 27 ft (extreme 30 ft) above MLLW. The initial, slide-generated waves probably caused most of the water damage and loss of life. Eleven persons lost their lives, and tsunami damage exceeded $14 million; some of this damage was caused by burning oil.

In Prince William Sound, Valdez, much closer to the epicenter, was also devastated by slide-induced waves of about 3–5 minutes period and of exceptional height during the earthquake. The docks

and boat harbor were totally destroyed and waves inundated the town to a runup height of 20 ft above MLLW. Waves of lower height but of much longer period (up to 2 hours) flooded the town much later on the high tide. Thirty-one persons drowned in Port Valdez, and tsunami damage exceeded $12 million. Whittier, still closer to the epicenter in Prince William Sound, suffered more severely than Valdez or Seward, considering its population. Again the damaging waves were slide-induced, of relatively short period (perhaps ½–3 minutes) and of very great height. Runup to 30 ft above MLLW occurred over a wide front, to 40 ft in localized places. The harbor and railhead were totally destroyed. Twelve persons died in the waves, and tsunamis caused over $10 million worth of damage. Cordova, in a comparatively shallow-water portion of the Sound, was free of submarine slides, and the wave pattern more resembled that at Kodiak, comprising only very long period waves (perhaps 20 minutes–4 hours), which inundated the town at high tide to 33 ft above MLLW many hours after the earthquake. A 6-ft regional uplift of land level mitigated damage from flooding. Wave damage at Cordova was estimated at about $2 million. Total wave damage for Alaska exceeded $85 million, and 103 lives were lost.

Along the Canadian coast, wave damage amounted to more than $10 million and was most severe at Port Alberni, Vancouver Island. The tsunami, striking the Washington, Oregon, and California coastlines, caused damage amounting to $115,000, $754,000, and $14 million, respectively. Most of the damage in California occurred at Crescent City (about $11 million), where runup height reached 20.8 ft above MLLW. The waves killed 4 people in Oregon and 12 in California. Altogether, on the North American seaboard, 119 persons lost their lives to the tsunamis, and wave damage exceeded $110 million.

From examination of wave forces and effects, design formulas are recommended for estimating the dynamic force of tsunami waves on obstacles and structures caught in the wave path. An empirical formula is evolved for roughly estimating tsunami wave height and runup near the source of a submarine earthquake in terms of earthquake magnitude. Finally, some of the essential considerations in engineering design and planning are developed for avoiding tsunami damage, and a set of design criteria for ensuring adequacy of structural strength and protection are presented.

INTRODUCTION

The great Alaska earthquake of March 27, 1964, was especially noteworthy for the damaging water waves that

*Formerly with Science Engineering Associates, San Marino, California

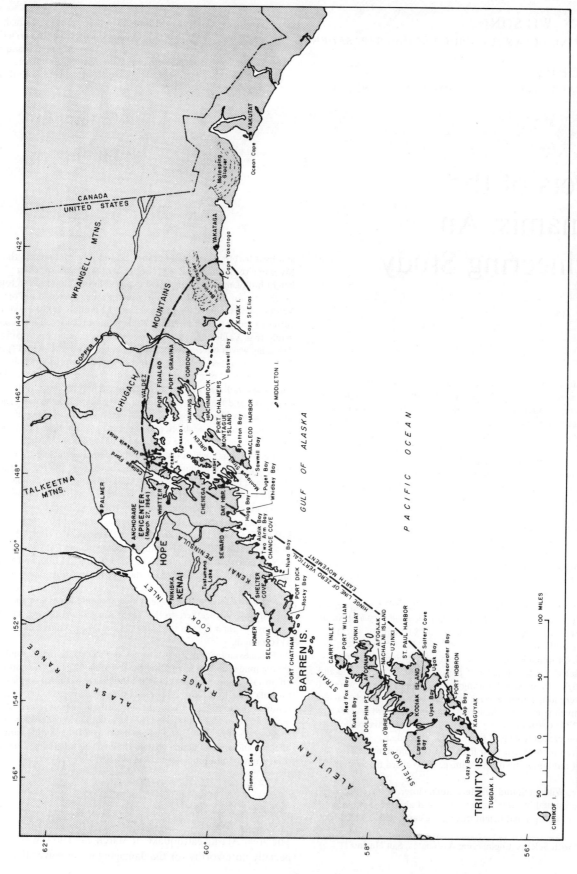

FIGURE 1 General map of south central Alaska, covering the area most affected by the earthquake and containing place names referred to in the text.

were generated. A main tsunami was produced by tectonic displacement of the sea floor, but waves were also generated locally by submarine landslides or inertial effects. A summary of these waves is presented by Cox (this volume, p. 354). The tsunamis did extensive damage to Alaska waterfront communities and also caused damage and loss of life as far away as Crescent City, California.

The lessons to be learned from such tsunami actions are of great engineering significance; unfortunately, the available information is far from complete. This is, of course, the usual state of affairs for natural disasters; hence, it is necessary to fit together the pieces of available information into as coherent a picture as possible and from this to deduce conclusions that have practical value (see, for example, Iida, 1958, 1968; Hom-ma and Horikawa, 1961; Horikawa, 1961; Matlock and others, 1962; Magoon, 1962, 1966; Wiegel, 1964, 1965, 1970; Van Dorn, 1965; Reese and Matlock, 1967; Wilson and Tørum, 1968). The Alaska experience clearly shows many ways in which typical waterfront communities can be made more resistant to tsunami action. It also indicates the inadequacy of our knowledge about some aspects of the tsunami problem and the need for special investigations.

Our study (Wilson and Tørum, 1968), which was started nearly 2 years after the earthquake, had the *advantage* of data from a great number of sources that would not have been available immediately after the event, but also the *disadvantage* of the loss (during cleanup and reconstruction) of vital engineering evidence concerning structural damage.

EFFECTS OF THE MAIN TSUNAMI AND OF LOCAL TSUNAMIS ON THE KODIAK ISLANDS AND KENAI PENINSULA

TSUNAMI WAVES AT KODIAK

Although incomplete and sometimes conflicting evidence makes it difficult to reconstruct the sequence of events during the earthquake and the tsunamis, it is important to attempt such a reconstruction in order to understand how the damage occurred and how it might have been prevented.

The Kodiak Island group (Figure 1) appears to have been assailed by gigantic waves of about 2.5-hour period whose first effect was negative (downward) in some locations, resulting in a relative withdrawal of water in the initial stages of arrival. This withdrawal was not apparent in some cases, particularly at Womens Bay, presumably because of the downdrop of the land. The extent of this land subsidence has been given variously as 5.5 to 5.8 ft (Brown, 1964; Bryant, 1964a; Plafker and Kachadoorian, 1966, and Geology volume; Kachadoorian and Plafker, 1967). In the neighborhood of Kodiak City, it appears to have been accepted as 5.8 ft by the U.S. Coast and Geodetic Survey

(1964b) and the U.S. Army Corps of Engineers.

Kodiak is the only place within the earthquake area where a fairly detailed knowledge of the wave sequence and wave height is available, thanks to the log kept by Lt. C. R. Barney of the U.S. Fleet Weather Central at the Naval Station, Womens Bay, some 7 miles southwest of Kodiak City. Lt. Barney's log is now well documented (Wilson and Tørum, this volume). Various plots of Barney's data have been made, notably by Brown (1964), Tudor (1964), Pararas-Carayannis (1965), and Kachadoorian and Plafker (1967), all of whom tend to disagree on certain details whenever different interpretations have been applied to parts of the data that seem ambiguous. We have studied these interpretations rather carefully and evolved our own record of Barney's data in Figure 2, which shows fluctuations of sea level on the north coast of the entrance to Womens Bay, Kodiak, after the earthquake.

The basis for Figure 2 is the premise that mean lower low water (MLLW) at Kodiak, as a tide level, referenced to mean sea level (MSL), has remained unaffected by the earthquake. The only way in which it could be affected would be through a complete change of tidal range in the area, which by all accounts has not been altered. As astronomical tide level is presumed unaffected at the time of the earthquake, the record must show, as regards mean water level at any time, the essential continuity of the tide. Barney's readings were referenced to a tide staff zero, which from later observation (Bryant, 1964a) is related to sea level as indicated in Figure 2a.

Barney's data make no reference to any initial recession of the sea from Womens Bay; yet at the time of the earthquake (17:36 AST, March 27), the land level is known to have dropped by 5.5 ft (Bryant, 1964b). Barney first noted the water rising rapidly at 18:20 AST, about 40 minutes after the cessation of the main shock, but since no relative land-sea change had drawn his attention, apparently the sea level had dropped with the land through an approximately equal amount. Accordingly, Figure 2a shows the sudden drop of sea level through 5.5 ft, followed by a small hypothetical recession, relative to land, of about 1.5 ft, before the observed rapid rise at 18:20 AST. The basis for this supposed recession is the belief that the inertia of the water mass acquired from the sudden earth drop would have caused it to continue its downward movement before the inrush of water, arising from the main tsunami and from local oscillations, could reach the area. This accords reasonably with the graphics of the reconstructed marigram.

Figure 2a has question-mark indicators wherever the water level was not definitely established. However, one criterion that binds all the data is that mean sea level at any time must lie at (or close to) the level of predicted tide. By a subjective analysis we found it possible to break down the complicated record of Figure 2a into what are

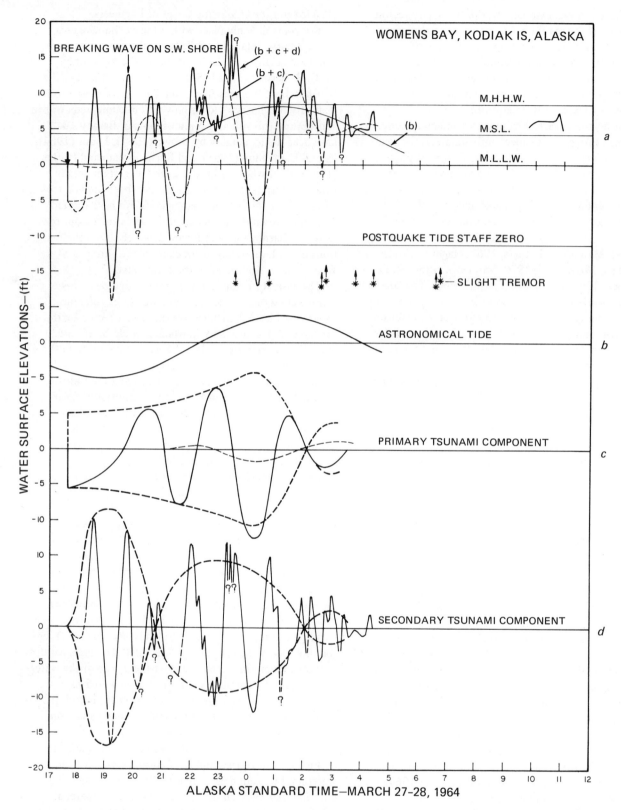

FIGURE 2   Water-level fluctuations in Womens Bay, Kodiak, based on observations by Lt. C. R. Barney, U.S. Naval Station, Kodiak. (*a*) Reconstructed marigram; (*b*), (*c*), (*d*) subjective analyses of (*a*) for identification of principal wave systems.

considered to be separate components: Figure 2b, the astronomical tide; Figure 2c, the main tsunami; and Figure 2d, the local oscillations. A modulated wave system evolves in Figure 2c with the remarkable wave period of about 2.5 hours, upon which is superimposed another beat-system of waves with an apparent period approximating 1.3 hours (Figure 2d).

It was fortunate for the Naval Station at Womens Bay, Kodiak, that the phasing of the primary and secondary wave systems of Figure 2 was toward producing ultralow water rather than ultrahigh. Kodiak City was slightly less fortunate in this respect, as will be shown in a later section. We merely note here that, while Womens Bay reported a highest runup level of 18.8 ft above MLLW (Figure 2a), Kodiak City experienced a runup to 21 ft above MLLW (in some places to 25 ft).

The topography of the region, shown generally in Figure 3, and in greater detail in Figure 5, suggests that the direct path of the tsunami toward Womens Bay and Kodiak (Figure 4) would have been via Chiniak Bay with the wave front initially parallel to the hinge line of zero vertical earth movement (Figure 5a). In the absence of long-wave refraction diagrams, it is difficult to determine exactly how such long waves would have reached Kodiak City. We may infer, however, that the deep channel running between Woody Island and Near Island (Figure 5b) would have favored the waves reaching Kodiak first from the northeast via the channel between Near Island and Kodiak City.

At Kodiak City, only about 5 nautical miles away in direct line from Kodiak Naval Station (about 10 nautical miles in terms of wave distance via Womens Bay) (Figure 6), there was conflicting opinion about how the water behaved immediately after the earthquake (Chance, 1966, and in press; Plafker and Kachadoorian, 1966; Kachadoorian and Plafker, 1967). Many claim that the first wave was a fast-rising tide noticeable at about 6:10 p.m. AST, or about half an hour after the earthquake (this accords with what Lt. Barney had logged for Womens Bay), but a few have contended that the first wave came much earlier—within 10 minutes of the earthquake. The most convincing evidence for this early wave comes from Jerry Tilley, a crewman on the 75-ft shrimp-fishing boat *Fortress*, which was tied at the city dock in Kodiak (Figure 7) when the earthquake occurred. The reconstruction of what happened, according to Tilley, is reproduced from Kachadoorian and Plafker (1967) as follows:

5:35 or 5:36 p.m.—Shock felt aboard boat. Boil of reeking black water arose from beneath boat.

5:45 p.m.—Approximately 13-ft tide at dock when predicted tide should have been + 0.5 ft. (The 13-ft level is preearthquake elevation above MLLW. Because land level

dropped 5.5 to 5.8 ft, postearthquake elevation above MLLW would be 7.5 to 7.2 ft.)

5:50 p.m.—Cut loose from dock as water began to recede.

5:50–6:10 p.m.—Water receding.

6:10 p.m.—Water at lowest level, approximately at 10 ft below MLLW. (Owing to land subsidence this level would be 15.5 to 15.8 ft below MLLW.)

6:15 p.m.—Wave moved in from south as large swell.

6:15–6:20 p.m.—Water rising at initial rate of about 15 ft in 5 seconds.

6:20 p.m.—Wave crested.

The above times are estimates, and comments in parentheses are partly ours. Tilley's observations are plotted in Figure 8, but are only qualitatively supported by the evidence from Chuck Powell and Comdr. Miller (Chance, 1966, and in press) and that from Fred Brechan (Norton and Haas, 1970).

In discussing Tilley's observation of a 13-ft tide at the city dock at 5:45 p.m. (effectively a 7.5- to 7.2-ft tide in relation to water level before the earthquake), Kachadoorian and Plafker (1967; Plafker and Kachadoorian, 1966) speculate on its reality and its possible relation to a submarine slide or to seiching. The black boil of water reported by Tilley suggests a submarine landslide, but this may reasonably be discounted on the basis that the water was too shallow and the sediment too thin to sustain so large and gentle an effect on the sea. It is believed that the wave could be explained as a phenomenon of seismic seiching, related perhaps to the tilting of the land from tectonic subsidence and regional horizontal displacement. The black boil could have been the result of the sudden upwelling of water containing mud and debris from the floor of St. Paul Harbor (Figure 7). The horizontal thrust of the land in the Kodiak Island region may have been almost due southwest in a direction parallel to the coast of St. Paul Harbor (Figures 6 and 7) and thus, through the inertia of the water, would have favored a piling of water to the northeast. This explanation, however, would require that water inevitably be drained from Womens Bay, even though, inside the Nyman Peninsula (Figure 6), it would also have been heaped to some extent toward the Naval Station. It is just possible that these effects might have been self-compensating in Womens Bay to the extent of causing only a minor drop of water level there, as implied in Figure 2a. Further discussion of this appears later.

Our interest in knowing whether this first wave was real or not is more than casual. If real, it would show that many people in that time of stress and anxiety were unaware of what was really happening around them. It is particularly puzzling that Mayor Peter Deveau, who, according to Norton and Haas (1970), left the cannery of King Crab, Inc.,

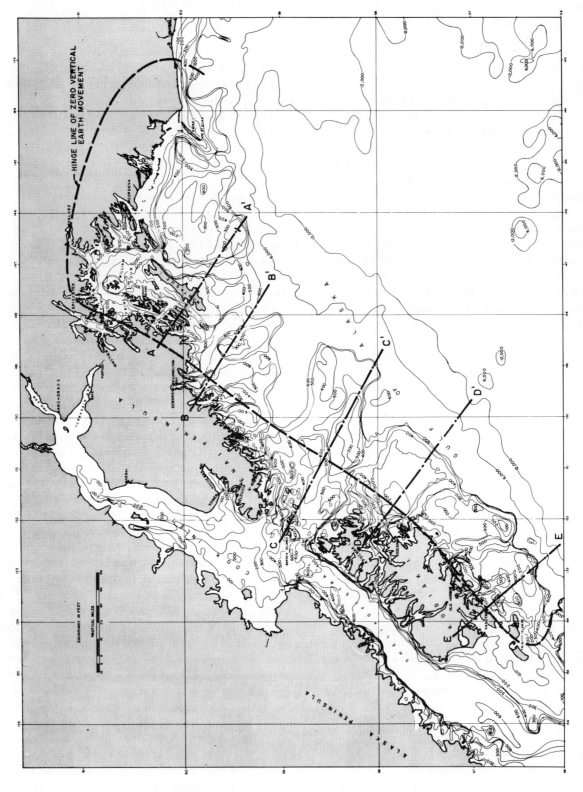

FIGURE 3   General bathymetry of the Continental Shelf, Gulf of Alaska, Prince William Sound, and Cook Inlet. Cross sections not mentioned in this paper are referred to in Wilson and Tørum (1968).

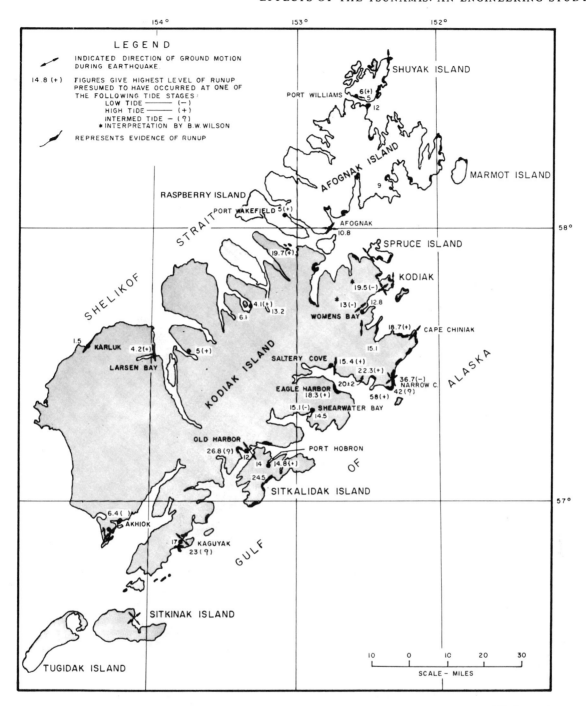

FIGURE 4   Observed tsunami runup along the coasts of Kodiak and Afognak Islands. (Based on data of Plafker and Kachadoorian, 1967; Berg and others, 1971).

in expectation of a tidal wave shortly after the earthquake and traveled the road toward Kodiak overlooking the Inner Anchorage and boat harbor (presumably Shelikof Street or South Benson Avenue, Figure 7), failed to notice rapid filling or draining of water from the boat harbor. Whereas City Manager Ralph Jones observed the first wave at 5:45 p.m.,

according to Chance (1966, and in press), Norton and Haas (1970) report that the following incident took place after 6:00 p.m.

Mayor Deveau reached the municipal building shortly after 6:00 along with several off-duty policemen, who checked in with Chief Jack Rhines. Although he still had no direct knowledge, Deveau

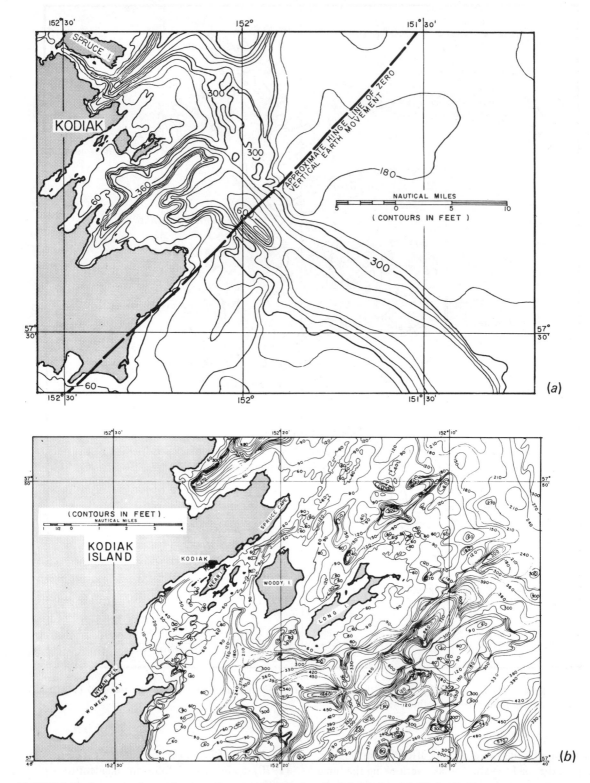

FIGURE 5 Bathymetry of coastal region adjacent to Kodiak City, Kodiak. (*a*) General; (*b*) detail. Contours are based on preearthquake soundings.

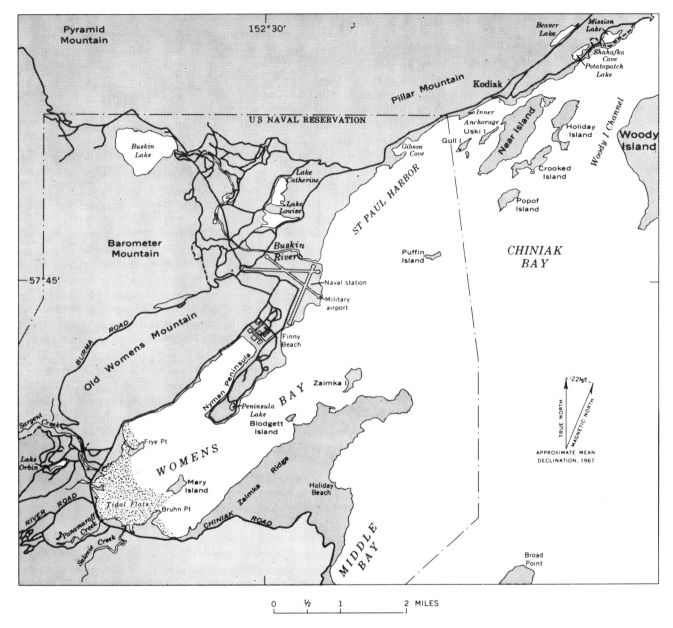

FIGURE 6 Location of the Kodiak Naval Station and the city of Kodiak. (From Kachadoorian and Plafker, 1967.)

reported to Rhines and to City Manager Ralph Jones his conviction that there would be a tidal wave. Deveau wanted to sound a siren alarm. There was a large Civil Defense siren on the hill but it was tied into the long-distance phone lines warning system, and was out of commission. Deveau urged sounding of the fire siren over the fire station. Jones was inclined to agree, but Rhines wasn't convinced that this was a wise procedure, as *they had no evidence to substantiate Deveau's conviction.* However, the mayor's view prevailed and the siren was sounded.

The italics in the above quotation are ours.

Factual evidence shedding further light on events is supplied by photographs of the "first" (or second) wave taken by Alf Madsen (professional photographer and hunter), as shown in the sequence of photographs, Figures 9 to 13, reproduced from his color slides. The exact locations from which these photographs were taken, and also the directions and angles of view, are indicated in Figure 14, which is a preearthquake map of Kodiak City and harbor with land levels as they were before subsidence.

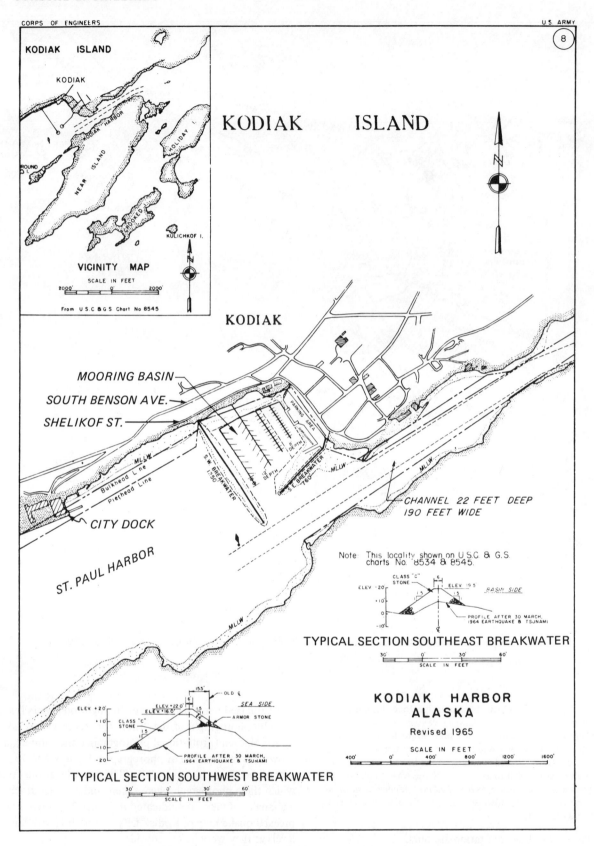

FIGURE 7 Map of Kodiak City and harbor with details of the breakwaters.

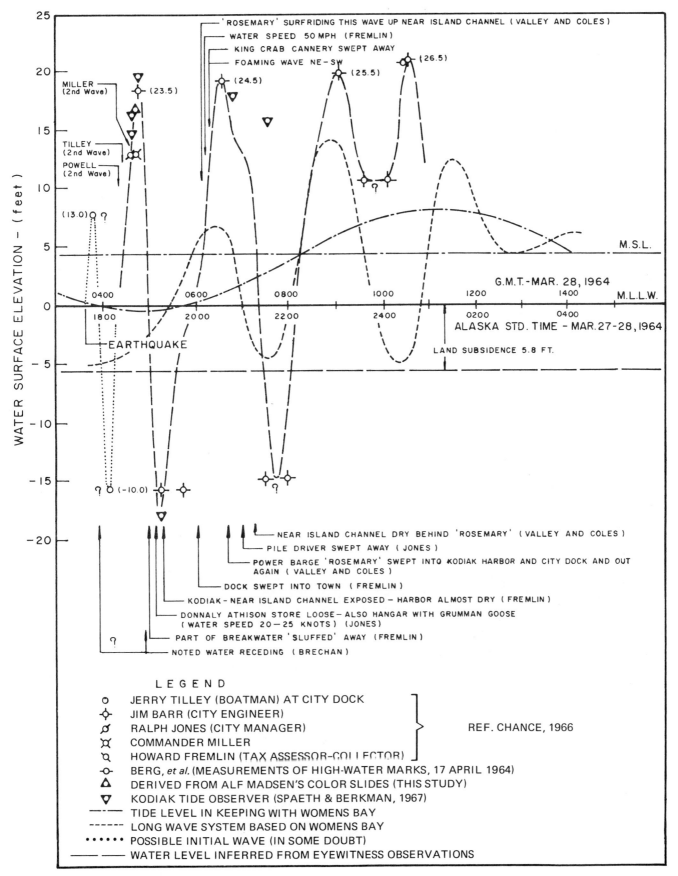

FIGURE 8   Hypothetical marigram for Kodiak City; based on observations by eyewitnesses.

FIGURE 9   Marine Way at Kodiak City during the rise of the tsunami wave at approximately 18:35 (AST), March 27, 1964.

Alf Madsen

In photographing Figures 9 and 10, Madsen occupied a corner position of the concrete-slab ground floor of the Elks Club (under construction) (location *A* in Figure 14). From the position of cars and trucks in the field of view and their extent of submergence and also the water level at far distance down Marine Way, water level is judged to be about 12 ft above MLLW (an unchanged reference datum). For Figure 11, Madsen had withdrawn to position *B* on the floor slab. Wall reinforcing bars show in the fore-

ground. Water level at this time had risen about 1 ft higher, as judged from car submergence and levels against the flat-roofed waterfront structure. Clearly the rise of water is gentle, almost peaceful. However, the water must have been on the verge of surrounding the Elks Club, and so Madsen retreated to higher ground on the opposite side of Mill Bay Road at position *C* (Figure 14), where he apparently found time to fit his camera with a wider-angle lens to secure Figure 12. The Elks Club is in the right center of the picture,

Alf Madsen

FIGURE 10   Kodiak City waterfront and boat harbor at about 18:36 (AST), March 27, 1964. The Harbor Master's office is flooded.

Alf Madsen

FIGURE 11   View from the Elks Club bowling alley (under construction), showing the wave still rising at Kodiak City. Time approximately 18:38 (AST), March 27, 1964.

with some indication that water has lapped over one corner of it; water level may here be judged to be at about 16 or 17 ft above MLLW. In Figure 13, taken from location *D* (Figure 14), the water has now begun to drain away, as evidenced by the hydraulic-jump formations forming bow-wave patterns relative to fixed structures on either side of the road. In this view the pile-driver barge is seen in the right center in the distance, but the breakwaters are com-

pletely submerged. From Figure 7, we infer that preearthquake levels, allowing for land subsidence of 5.8 ft, would have ensured submergence at this time.

The photographic evidence from Figures 9–13 obviously could not relate to the time of 5:45 p.m., because such extensive flooding would have been apparent to all, whereas the level of the first wave, cited by Tilley, Jones, and Fremlin (according to Chance, 1966), could not have been much

Alf Madsen

FIGURE 12   Kodiak City boat harbor at approximately 18:41 (AST), March 27, 1964. The tsunami wave has now surrounded the Elks Club bowling ally.

FIGURE 13   View (south-southeast) of the boat harbor at Kodiak City at approximately 18:45 (AST), March 27, 1964. The tsunami is beginning to ebb. The water expanse is unbroken in the far field, except by islands, due to submergence of the breakwaters.

Alf Madsen

higher than the high spring tide. Our observation of about 17 ft (triangular point, Figure 8, based on Madsen) is therefore plotted on the second wave, according to Tilley, as well as Chuck Powell and Comdr. Miller (Chance, 1966, and in press). According to Madsen, whom we interviewed at Kodiak in 1966, this was the "first" wave, rising gently from a situation of no prior recession and causing the first damage only on its withdrawal. It is inconceivable that Madsen could have equipped himself with camera and lenses and gained a vantage point for his photography at 5:45 p.m. (17:45) AST; hence, what he photographed was definitely the wave that crested at about 6:30 p.m. (18:30) AST, according to the evidence of City Engineer Jim Barr and Miller (Chance, 1966, and in press). The color slide for Figure 13 clearly shows a sunset light in the clouds on the right side of the picture. Because the view was south, this would have been light from the west. Sunset at the latitude of Kodiak would have been almost exactly at 6:30 p.m. on March 27, 1964.

It now becomes clear that the times reported by Jones (see Chance, 1966, and in press) are probably in error; this would account for the anomaly already mentioned. Chance says that Jones reported the "first" rise in water was "like a high tide—about 10 ft higher than it should have been" [therefore about 13 ft above MLLW], at about 5:45 p.m. [probably 6:20 p.m.]. "Then," according to Chance (1966), "the water receded 'way far out' [7:20 p.m. (19:20 AST) according to Figure 8] and a wave struck 'with much force, tossing buildings and boats around—making a complete mess of the waterfront' " [presumably at about 8:30 p.m.

(20:30 AST), according to other evidence in Figure 8]. Comments in brackets are ours.

Confusion also stems from the evidence given by Mr. and Mrs. Fremlin (Chance, 1966).

Mr. and Mrs. Fremlin watched the water rising rapidly in the small boat harbor immediately after the quake. The water rose to the top of the pilings, fouling the lines of boats tied to the dock. The water rose so fast most of the boats were unable to cut loose in time to escape. Part of the breakwater sluffed away and "the whole thing went dock and all—and swept into town." The water then began receding rapidly—"it was just sucking right out of the harbor"—until it was almost dry.

Because the photographic evidence of Figures 9–13 (now considered to indicate the period of 6:20–6:30 p.m.) clearly disproves that the dock swept into town at 6:30 p.m., the Fremlins must have been talking of the wave that occurred about 8:30 p.m. (Figure 8). In elaborating on this (latter) wave, Mrs. Fremlin described it as a "big foaming wave" before it struck the outlying islands. Chance's (1966) interview with Mr. and Mrs. Fremlin states:

It then struck Mission Road and surged around the shoreline and into the channel and small boat harbor where it "foamed and boiled and bubbled." Mr. Fremlin described it as looking like a "swift-water river that foams and boils and bubbles" but it "seemed to dissipate" as it swept by the outlying islands and appeared to be "a rapid surge upward, rather than a wave" as it swept into town "carrying houses and boats and planes at a speed of about 50 miles an hour" . . . The water swept in the back doors of bars along the waterfront, lifting the buildings as people ran out the front. Some people were wading waist-deep and some were swimming. One man who saw the wave approaching ran into the Elks Club on the water-

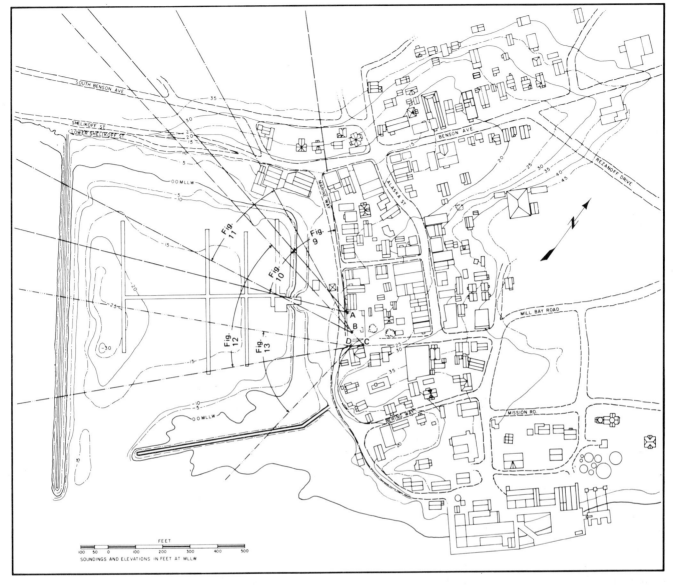

FIGURE 14   Map of Kodiak City and boat harbor before the earthquake (contours of land levels based on U.S. Army Corps of Engineers data). Points A, B, C, and D are positions from which photographs (Figures 9–13) were taken.

front and warned the members of the Women's League who were bowling in the basement. The water rushed down the stairway as the women ran up to get out of the building.

The Fremlins were on or near the top of Pillar Mountain (Figure 6) when they saw all this, but several points suggest further confusion. From Figure 8 we infer that the wave of 8:30 p.m. (20:30 AST) would have been visible to them, in the fashion described, at about 8:00 p.m., by which time, with the overcast, it would have been getting rather dark. One questions, therefore, whether they could have noted the Elks Club incident at that time. Surely the 6:30 wave that flooded around the Elks Club (Figure 12) must have

disrupted the bowling game in the basement at that time.

According to Chance (1966, and in press), Dell Valley and Will Coles, respectively, skipper and engineer on the crab boat *Rosemary*, surf-rode a wave through the channel between Near Island and Kodiak (Figure 5b), into the harbor. This boat was about 25 mi from Kodiak when the earthquake occurred. According to Chance, "about a half-hour after the quake, their boat was entering the channel when it was caught by a swift, incoming wave." The channel entrance, however, is not more than 2 nautical miles from Kodiak, and since it would be impossible for a crab boat to negotiate 20 mi in about half an hour, we conclude that Valley and Coles were actually surf-riding the 8:30 p.m. wave (Figure 8). This agrees with the Fremlins' evidence that they saw a boat surf-riding up the channel from northeast on the wave we have already adduced to be the 8:30 p.m. crest.

Chance (1966) writes:

Valley said that riding atop the wave it was impossible to know it was a wave because "it wasn't breaking at all—couldn't even tell if there was any height to it" . . . Coles said, "it was a real fast tide and this thing went like a motor boat." The *Rosemary* was swept through the area where the small boat harbor had been and into the city dock [see Figure 7]. The water then began to recede immediately taking the dock out with it and they turned the *Rosemary* around to ride out of the channel with the tide. Valley said the only indication he had that it was a wave they were riding was when it approached the shallow land off Spruce Cape and the water curved upward along the shorelines. "It ran up on Spruce Cape, and as it came up in a shoal it kept building up higher and higher until it was a big comber. And it just rolled right over the land. I thought probably the Loran Station would go, but it didn't. And the same thing happened on Woody Island—it ran up into the trees. But as far as the center of the wave was concerned you couldn't tell it was a wave."

With the adjustments made in timing, the evidence supplied by Jones, the Fremlins, Powell, Miller, and Barr, as plotted in Figure 8, becomes coherent. Also in that figure the water levels cited by KTO (Kodiak Tide Observer) in messages transmitted to the Honolulu Observatory of the U.S. Coast and Geodetic Survey (Spaeth and Berkman, 1967, and this volume) are given; they appear to agree fairly well in all but the last observation at 11:15 p.m. It is not known whether these data are based on those from Kodiak City or Womens Bay.

We return to a consideration of Tilley's observation, which is now largely unsupported except in the qualitative sense that Miller and Powell acknowledged a "first" wave prior to the tide wave of 6:30 p.m. However, Tilley's observation of an abnormally low tide at 6:10 p.m. is also unconfirmed, except in a qualitative way by Brechan (Norton and Haas, 1970). Despite the apparent confusion of time in the evidence of others, we are inclined to give Tilley the benefit of the doubt by conceding that there may have been such a first wave with an effective period of 40 minutes (Figure 8). We may show, too, that the natural period of oscillation of the quasi-basin between Womens Bay and Kodiak is of this order and favors his observation.

Figure 5b shows that the quasi-basin from Womens Bay to Kodiak can be approximated reasonably well by a basin, oriented NE–SW, with a bed sloping uniformly from zero depth off the point, say, of Nyman Peninsula to a maximum of 70 ft at the Kodiak breakwater (at low tide). For such a triangular depth profile, the fundamental eigenperiod (see Wilson, 1966) is

$$T_1 = 3.28 \, L \sqrt{g d_1} \,, \tag{1}$$

where L ($\simeq$6 nautical miles) is the length of the quasi-basin and d_1 ($\simeq$70 ft) its maximum depth. For these values, T_1 is calculated to be 42 minutes.

In Figure 8 we superimposed upon the hypothetical marigram the large tsunami wave system inferred from Figure 2c, and in Figure 15 a subjective analysis technique has been applied to find the residual oscillations. Thus, Figure 15 suggests the nature of the wave system riding on the main tsunami system. The accuracy of Figure 8 after, say, 11:00 p.m. (23:00 AST) is doubtful; this applies also to Figure 15. Before that time, however, we suspect that the oscillation shown is a combination of the Continental Shelf oscillation (Figure 15c) noted in Figure 2 and the oscillation in St. Paul Harbor (Figure 15d).

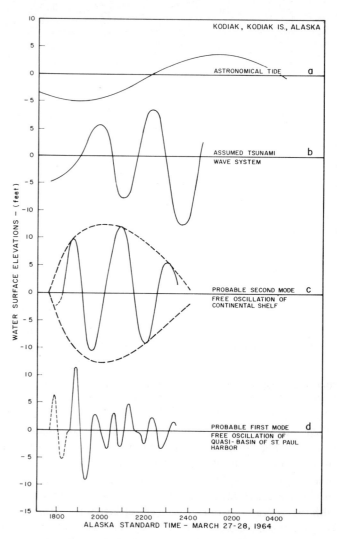

FIGURE 15 Subjective analysis of the inferred marigram for Kodiak City (see Figure 8).

Alf Madsen

FIGURE 16   Aerial view of St. Paul Harbor and Kodiak.

TSUNAMI DAMAGE AT KODIAK CITY

The picture of the tsunami that we are now able to form (Figure 8) suggests that the "second" wave, after Tilley's "first" wave, had an amplitude of some 20 ft or a height of about 40 ft. This wave is presumed to be dominantly the result of a shelf oscillation, with a second-mode period of approximately 100 minutes. The interval of time between the "second" wave, or first crest of Figure 15c, and the next crest is about 2 hours, however.

In Figure 15d we assumed the amplitude of the first oscillation in St. Paul Harbor, as it might have occurred at Kodiak City, to be somewhat less than Tilley's observation. The second wave of Figure 8 is now seen to comprise a 10-ft-amplitude shelf oscillation apparently combined (slightly out of phase) with a 15-ft-amplitude oscillation of St. Paul Harbor. Most of the water for the antinodal resultant of these waves at Kodiak City would have been drawn locally from St. Paul Harbor, perhaps accounting for the fact that velocities of horizontal flow during the rise of the wave at Kodiak were small (at the antinode of a seiche they are nominally zero). However, after the "second" wave (Figure 8), the shelf oscillation would have been at work in draining water from the entire area. Figure 15c suggests that it would have done this to the extent of a drop of about 20 ft in water level over the entire area of St. Paul Harbor. An extra drop of another 20 ft in level at Kodiak City would have been occasioned by the local oscillation (Figure 15d).

This total drop of nearly 40 ft of water level in 35 minutes (Figure 8) would have occurred over the entire area of the Inner Anchorage and boat harbor which, as Figure 16 very effectively shows, is contained between the island string (Gull, Uski, and Near islands) and the mainland.

Approximate computation shows (1) that the area of the Inner Anchorage (Figure 6) between the southwest end of Gull Island and Kodiak City is about 0.5 square nautical mile and (2) that the volume of water to be drained in about 35 minutes would have been roughly 3.6×10^8 ft^3; the southwest entrance to the Inner Anchorage and the Near Island channel were available for this. The latter has such small capacity that most of the drainage would have taken place via the Gull Island entrance. For a cross-sectional area of this entrance of 1.2×10^5 ft^2, taken on average over the drop of water level, the average velocity of outflow is calculated to be about 9 ft/sec. The maximum velocity, according to a sinusoidal rate of level drop, would be about $9\pi/2$ or 14 ft/sec. This is approximately one half as large as Jones' estimate of the water speed, 20–25 mph (Figure 8).

This outflow of impounded water apparently washed out part of the southwest breakwater of the boat harbor and tore loose the Donnally Atchison Store and an aircraft hangar in the Near Island channel. But the major damage came with the next wave and the one that followed.

Figure 8 makes it clear that the next (third) wave was a composite of the progressive wave crest of the tsunami, overlaid by the second wave of the shelf oscillation and additional local oscillations (Figures 15c and 15d). This monstrous wave, 35 to 40 ft high over a vast wave length, moved into the area via the fastest route, up the Woody Island Channel, into the Near Island Channel already almost completely denuded of water. This was the wave upon which the crab boat *Rosemary* surf-rode up the channel. At its immediate front it had some of the features of a foaming bore, but, as Valley and Coles imply, it was mainly a sloping front in the body of the wave crest. Such a wave configuration would conform to the surge waves studied experimentally by Cross (1966) and illustrated in Figure 17.

In Appendix B, there is some discussion of water-particle motions and induced forces in tsunami waves of surge type. It appears that the formula for the surge velocity u_s,

$$u_s = 2\sqrt{gd_s} , \qquad (2)$$

is reasonably well supported by theory and experiment and may be considered to apply when the depth of water in front of the surge is small compared to the total depth d_s of the surge. Adopting $d_s \simeq 37$ ft, u_s is calculated to be 69 ft/sec or 47 mph. The Fremlins had estimated the water speed in the Near Island channel as 50 mph (Chance, 1966).

This wave came roaring up the channel from the northeast. It washed away the channel docks and canneries such as the Alaska Packers Association cannery (shown in Figure 18). Figure 19b shows that only a few of the supporting piles for this cannery remained (Tudor, 1964). An old stone wall built by Russian settlers before the year 1800 survived the tsunami. Our inspection of this structure in 1966 showed that it was heavily buttressed in cellular (plan) for-

(a) SMOOTH BOTTOM

(b) ROUGH BOTTOM

FIGURE 17 Laboratory-produced surge waves believed to be similar to the tsunami surges in Near Island Channel, Kodiak City. (From Cross, 1966.)

Alf Madsen

FIGURE 18   Kodiak before the earthquake. The Near Island Channel is in foreground; boat harbor at left center.

mation as if specially built to withstand strong tidal surging in the channel.

The hangar of Kodiak Airways was washed away and was still floating 30 mi offshore about 1 month after the earthquake. Lill's Café on Mission Road was floated away and ultimately wound up in a lagoon on Near Island (Armstrong, 1964).

Boats that had been left dry on the channel bottom and in the boat harbor by the preceding withdrawal of water were toppled and rolled, some to be waterlogged and sunk (Chance, 1966). All the markers and mooring buoys in the channel were washed away by the second wave. Probably this wave, or its counterpart coming into the Inner Anchorage via the Gull Island entrance, lifted the Alaska King Crab cannery off its piles (Tudor, 1964) on the northwest side of the Inner Anchorage; the cannery floated for some time and eventually lodged on the southwest breakwater (Figure 20).

The conflict of the waves reaching Kodiak via the Near Island channel and the Gull Island entrance probably caused a maelstrom of writhing water in and over the boat harbor which effectively destroyed the harbor and carried surviving boats and flotsam into the low-lying area of Kodiak City. Figure 21, a reconstruction of the situation at Kodiak after the tsunami, shows contours of land level as they would have been after the earthquake and before the arrival of the tsunami (dashed line). Also shown (solid line) are contours of level marking the depredations of the tsunami, as derived from U.S. Army Corps of Engineers soundings. Hypothetical streamlines of flow, shown in this map, suggest how the waves may have acted in the boat harbor. The contour changes in the neighborhood of the breakwaters clearly suggest leeward deposits from the main outpourings of the impounded water.

Figure 21 shows also the probable paths of Kodiak buildings that were either lifted off their foundations by this "third" wave or battered to pieces by the battering-ram effect of boats and flotsam. Because most people left the town after the "second" wave and also because it was dark, little is known about the damage done by the third and succeeding waves in the downtown area. The only available information concerns the total damage as it was found the next morning. As Figures 8 and 2 indicate, the highest wave of all was yet to come and was probably the "fourth," being a composite of the second tsunami crest, the third shelf oscillation, sundry local oscillations, and the rising high tide. Undoubtedly the effect was quite similar to that of the "third" wave, and whatever had been weakened by the latter would most likely have become prey to the "fourth" wave. The torrents of water in the channel made roaring and sucking noises, and horrible grinding sounds accompanied the attrition of buildings and structures during the night (Norton and Haas, 1970; Chance, 1966).

James Barr, consulting engineer of Kodiak, conducted a survey of the damage for the Office of Civil Defense shortly after the earthquake. His survey results are incorporated in Figure 21, preparation of which was greatly assisted by the aerial photographs of Alf Madsen.

Most of the buildings in the downtown area were old;

Mac's Foto

Delores Roguszka

FIGURE 19 (*a*) Preearthquake view of Near Island Channel and harbor facilities, Kodiak City. Compare with devastation shown in (*b*). (*b*) Skeletonlike timber pilings mark former site of cannery in this view northeast along Near Island Channel. The Russian wall survived the tsunami.

in fact, plans had been made before the earthquake for urban renewal of this section of the town. Apparently, most of the houses—light wooden-frame buildings—were inadequately connected to their foundations. Many of them were floated away and damaged by the flowing water. In addition, they were partly or wholly damaged by impacts when they stranded, or by impacts from other houses, boats, and floating objects. Many of the houses affected by the waves and still remaining on their foundations were partly damaged by impacts from floating objects, but all received damage due to inundation.

Figures 22–24 illustrate damage in the downtown area.

U.S. Army

FIGURE 20 Southwest breakwater at Kodiak shortly after the earthquake, with some of the battered remains of the King Crab cannery.

Several buildings (marked with identifying numerals in these photographs and on Figure 21) were unmoved although they lay in the path of the tsunami, but all suffered damage and some were unsalvable. The type of structure and the extent of damage are summarized in Table 1.

The waves also caused minor erosion of roads and sidewalks in the downtown area. The most serious scour occurred in the channel between Kodiak and Near Island where 10 ft of sediment in some places was washed away. This presented a major postearthquake construction problem because there remained no sediments in which piles could be readily driven for the foundations of new waterfront structures (Kachadoorian and Plafker, 1967).

In the small-boat harbor, all the boat floats, held in place by approximately 100 piles, were totally damaged and their guide piles broken. By estimating their diameter at 12 in. and the normal water depth at 12 ft, the ultimate lateral load capacity of one pile is calculated to be 2.5 tons, if it is assumed that the load is applied 2 ft above still-water level. Acting in unison, the piles would have had an effec-

tive load capacity of 250 tons. If water moved through this array at 25 ft/sec, by a rough calculation the drag force alone would have been of the order of 700 tons. Failure of the system is thus easily explained, particularly as water velocities may easily have been higher and as pressure and inertia forces from the slope of the wave may have been additional to drag.

The damage to the breakwaters was due partly to compaction settlement caused by the tremors and partly to the tsunami. Figure 7 shows typical sections of the breakwaters as they were measured after the earthquake, as well as cross sections of the rebuilt breakwaters. The weight of the cover-layer stones and the core material of the breakwater are not exactly known. However, as judged from Figure 20, the armor stones were quite light and would have been incapable of resisting any great degree of overtopping.

At the city dock (Figure 7), submergence from the "second" wave of about 6 to 8 ft apparently buoyed the decking off the pile caps, because the deck stringers were merely drift-pinned to the pile caps. Subsequent vertical motion accompanied by lateral movement destroyed the decking. When the bulkhead and more than two dozen piles at the approach to the city dock were destroyed, presumably with the third wave, the approach decking floated away (Tudor, 1964).

The appalling destruction presented on the day after the earthquake is well depicted in Figures 25 and 26b. Figure 25 shows the entire waterfront inundated by the high tide due to the scour and general subsidence of the land.

North of Kodiak City the tsunami flooded into Potatopatch Lake (Figure 27), and the coast had to withstand the full brunt of the tsunami inrush from the two sides of Woody Island. Many of the residential homes on the barrier between Shahafka Cove and the lake were washed into the lake (Figure 28) which has now become a saltwater lagoon as a result of the severe land erosion and general subsidence.

Nine people lost their lives at Kodiak City (and Spruce Cape) during the tsunami. The economy of the area was severely crippled; the total estimated property damage, according to the Office of Civil Defense (Tudor, 1964), was $31,279,000 (Table 2). Harbor facilities suffered to the extent of $2,165,000; industry and commerce lost $19,346,000; other public property, $5,400,000; the fishing fleet, $2,440,000; and private dwellings, $1,928,000. About 100 vessels were lost or damaged (Table 3).

TSUNAMI DAMAGE AT THE U.S. NAVAL STATION, KODIAK

At the U.S. Naval Station (some 7 mi southwest of Kodiak City) where about 3,000 people were living at the time of the earthquake, fortunately only a few injuries occurred

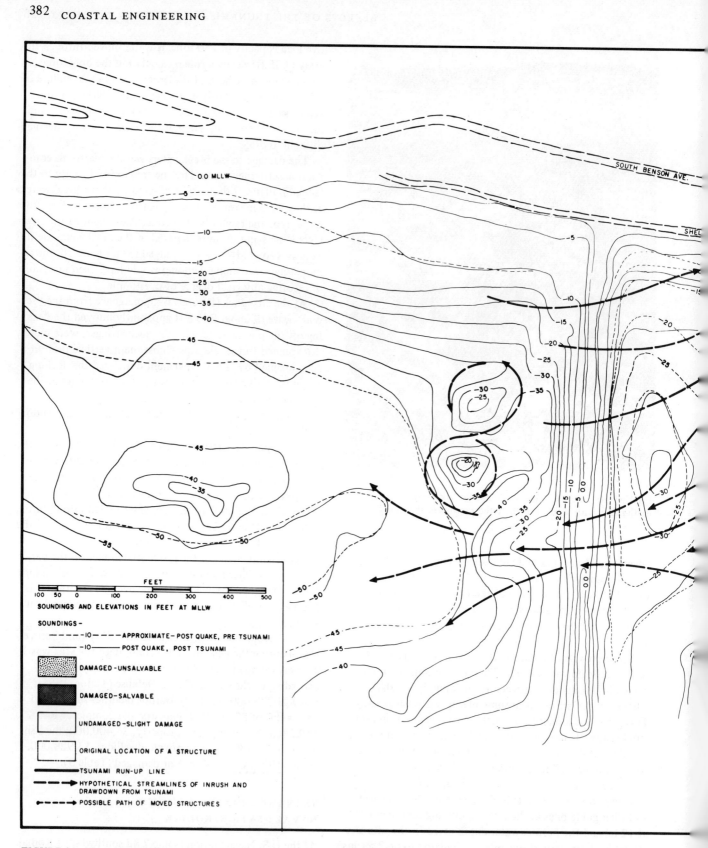

FIGURE 21 Map of Kodiac City, boat harbor, and inner anchorage after the earthquake and tsunami. (Based on data from J. Barr, Kodiak; U.S. Ar Corps of Engineers, Anchorage.)

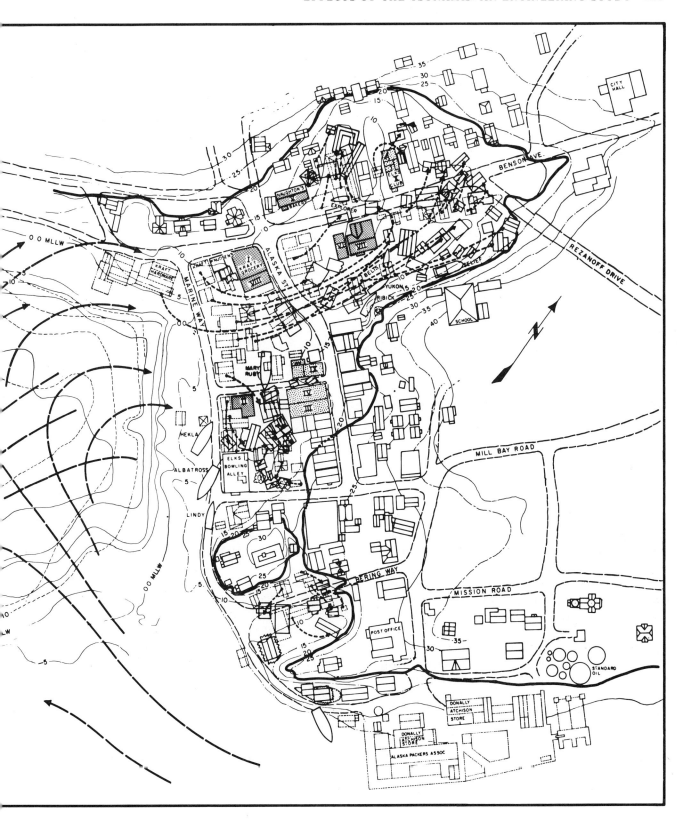

Alf Madsen

FIGURE 22   Tsunami damage in downtown Kodiak (numbered buildings refer to Table 1 in the text).

and the death toll was only three (Tudor, 1964). (These deaths, not confirmed by other reports, may have been included in the nine at Kodiak City.) The casualties might have been far higher had it not been for the tsunami warning received from Cape Chiniak and broadcast on television and radio, allowing people time to flee to higher ground.

Figure 5b shows that the tsunamis' approach to Womens Bay from Chiniak Bay would have encountered comparatively shallow water. Nevertheless, the arrival time (8:35 p.m. local time) of the first high wave was ostensibly the same as that of the "second" wave at Kodiak City. The existence of a possible earlier wave at Kodiak City and its absence at Womens Bay may perhaps be imputed to a northeast–southwest oscillation of the quasi-basin forming St. Paul Harbor.

As at Kodiak City, the first wave occurred as a fast-rising tide, effectively the result of gradual flooding from a previous situation of only minor withdrawal, if any. The first wave was photographed in the sunset light, and the extent of flooding is shown in Figures 29 and 30. These photographs show inundation at the head of Womens Bay around the aircraft hangars of the Navy air terminal (Figure 31).

Partial recession of the wave left deposits of flotsam on the seaplane ramps (Figure 32). Figure 31, based on an original pictorial drawing of the Nyman Peninsula by the U.S. Navy, Kodiak (Kachadoorian and Plafker, 1967), shows the general extent of flooding of the Naval Station area. This figure also shows the locations at which Figures 29, 30, and 32 were photographed, as well as those for other photographs to which we shall refer.

Eyewitnesses reported that the second damaging wave, which struck at 19:40 AST, was a breaking wave when it reached the southwest shoreline of Womens Bay (Kachadoorian and Plafker, 1967). This is not surprising in view of the extremely flat slope of the tidal flats in this region (Figure 6) and the fact that the withdrawal of the previous wave would have exposed the seabed near the hairpin bend of the bay. Additional information on this wave came from Mr. and Mrs. Louis Schultz (Kachadoorian and Plafker, 1967), who were presumably near Womens Bay on the Chiniak Road (Figure 6) when the wave struck. It rolled in very rapidly as a wall of water about 3 ft high, moving very quickly, and was followed immediately by a series of surges, each raising the water level by its arrival. This is rather typi-

FIGURE 23   Tsunami damage in downtown Kodiak with some cleanup accomplished (numbered buildings refer to Table 1 in the text).

FIGURE 24   Destruction wrought by the tsunami in Kodiak City.

TABLE 1   Structures in Kodiak City That Resisted Displacement by Tsunami Waves, March 1964

Structure No.[a]	Type of Structure	Identification	Damage
I	Reinforced concrete	Kraft's Grocery	Damaged, but salvable
II	Reinforced concrete and concrete blocks on the first floor with concrete-block veneer on the second floor	Alaska Department of Fish and Game	Damaged, repair questionable
III	Largely wooden-frame construction with concrete foundation	Island Electronic	Damaged beyond repair
IV	Largely wooden-frame construction with concrete foundation	Orpheum Theater	Damaged beyond repair
V	Wooden-frame structure on an elevated reinforced concrete foundation	Naughton's Bakery	Damaged, but salvable
VI	Reinforced concrete	Thompson's Transfer	Damaged, but salvable
VII	Reinforced concrete	Clark's Garage	Damaged, but salvable
VIII	Reinforced concrete	Sportland Fountain	Damaged, but salvable
IX	Largely wooden-frame construction with concrete foundation	Mecca Restaurant	Damaged, repair questionable
X	Largely wooden frame with concrete foundation and some structural concrete	Elks Club	Damaged, demolished

[a]For location of these structures, see Figure 21.

cal of a bore or large wave running up a fairly flat beach gradient. Because of the darkness of night, further observation of later waves was rendered difficult, and no reports other than the measurements logged at the Fleet Weather Central are available.

The cost of restoration or replacement of facilities at Kodiak Naval Station was over $6 million (Table 4), and most of it can be attributed to the tsunamis. The total damage to buildings, materials, and equipment at the Naval Station as a result of the earthquake (Table 5), was said to be in excess of $10,000,000 (Tudor, 1964).

Because the cargo dock on the north shore of Womens Bay (Figure 31) was in a deteriorated condition, it was completely destroyed by the tsunami (Figure 33). According to Tudor (1964), the tsunami induced violent motion in a moored ship; this lifted the bollards and damaged some fendering. The elevated water buoyed sections of the pier decking off the pilings and moved them laterally. This shifting caused failure of many framing and bracing members. Several piles were pulled from their pile holes intact along with the elevated decking. This behavior is not difficult to account for, because great trouble had been experienced originally in driving the piles in the rocky bottom on the north side of Womens Bay, and in some instances pile holes had to be augered. When the flood water receded, the buoyed decking and extracted piles crumpled the dock, as shown in Figure 33.

The marginal pier and the tanker and fender pier (fuel

Alf Madsen

FIGURE 25   Kodiak City at high tide on March 28, 1964, after the earthquake.

Mac's Foto

Alf Madsen

FIGURE 26 (a) Preearthquake view of the waterfront at Kodiak City. Compare with the devastation shown in (b). (b) Kodiak waterfront the day after the earthquake and tsunami.

pier, Figure 31), suffered only minor damage. Some damage was done to the marginal pier where a moored barge, under tsunami action, loosened a bollard and some of the decking (Tudor, 1964). The pier had to be loaded down with anchor chains after the earthquake, so as not to float away on the high tides which then reached to higher levels than previously, due to a 5.6-ft local subsidence of the land (Figure 34). This was the major reason for the complete rebuilding of the marginal pier later.

Two small waterfront structures, the Hobby Shop boat-repair house and the engine generator building (Figure 31), were completely swept from their foundation pilings. Figure 35 shows the boat-repair house (after the earthquake) right alongside its own pilings. The Hobby Shop itself was moved and broken into two pieces (Figure 36).

The Ground Electronics Building was damaged, as shown in Figure 37. Here a side wall appears to have failed about 6 to 9 in. above floor level under the hydrostatic

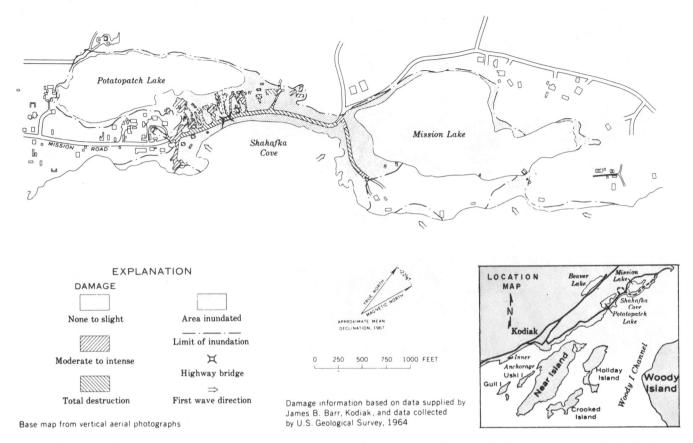

FIGURE 27 Map of Shahafka Cove area, Kodiak, showing damage, area of inundation, and direction of initial tsunamis. (From Kachadoorian and Plafker, 1967.)

Alf Madsen

FIGURE 28 View seaward, showing tsunami damage at Potatopatch Lake.

U.S. Navy

FIGURE 29   Inundation from the first noticeable tsunami wave at the head of Womens Bay, Kodiak, at about 18:35 (AST) on March 27, 1964. Two PV2 aircraft, visible in front of Hangar 3, were moved safely to higher ground.

U.S. Navy

FIGURE 30   View (northwest) of inundation from the tsunami wave in Womens Bay, Kodiak (about 18:35 AST, March 27, 1964), showing flooding of Hangar No. 1.

TABLE 2 Tsunami Damage at Kodiak City and to Area Boats, March 1964 (data from Civil Defense) (Tudor, 1964)

1. Harbor facilities			*4. Losses to the fishing fleet*	
Boat harbor (inner harbor)	$ 250,000		Boats sunk or aground	35
Dredging boat harbor	150,000		Boats missing	17
Harbormaster building	10,000		Boats with major damage	10
Breakwater	500,000		Boats with considerable damage	15
City dock and warehouse	1,200,000		Boats with slight damage	20
City dock equipment	55,000		Total	97
	$ 2,165,000		*Estimated 42 boats lost in Kodiak area outside City of Kodiak*	
			Estimated value	$ 840,000
2. Losses of private commercial property			Cost of repair to replace vessels listed above	1,600,000
Buildings	$11,346,000			$ 2,440,000
Stock	6,000,000			
Equipment	2,000,000		*5. Losses to dwellings*	
	$19,346,000		Dwellings destroyed by tsunami waves, 157 units	$ 1,608,000
			Household effects of dwellings damaged, Total	320,000
				$ 1,928,000
3. Losses of public property	$ 5,400,000		Estimated total property damage	$31,279,000

NOTE: The Kodiak fisheries in 1963 processed a total of 41,500,000 lb of king crab, 330,000 cases of salmon, and 12,000,000 lb of shrimp.

TABLE 3 Intensity of Damage to Boats at Kodiak and Vicinity, March 1964[a]

Sunk or Aground		Missing	Major Damage	Moderate Damage	Slight Damage
2 jitneys	Toots	KFC6	Anna A	Chacon	Banshee
2 boats named	Davy J	Isabel N	Beluga	C. H. Andersen	Cape Horn
"Cindy"	Tiny	Jaguar	Chief	Crash boat	Cape Uganik
Hekla	Hazel A	Widgeon	Fortress	Georgie	Commander
Yukon	Joanne	Sea Scout boat	Lex	Jan M	Fedair
Betts	Mary L	SJ7	Coogan	Karen Sue	FAA boat
Selief	Norman U	Spruce Cape	Pelican	Marmot	Fern
Albatross	Vagabond	Roosevelt E	Robbie	Marten	Gladys R
Victory Maid	Fidelity	UF2	Sea Lion	Mary Carrol	Hildur
Leading Lady	Miss Arctic	Lucky Star	Sue	Mermaid	Homeward
Ribich	Neptune	Oranius	Sunrise	Nargene Ray	Hadenia B
Mary Ruby	Padilla	Frieda		New Stranger	San Juan
Explorer	Sophia King	Marmot Cape		Sea Quail	Jo G
Henning J	Shuyak	Peril Cape		Swallow	King
Laurel	Innicta	Sitka		Widgeon	Jay Gallagher
Halcyon	Marguerite	Waffico 12			Laurie
Arrow	Wind A				Lady Jean
					Nick Andrich
					Ripple
					Michael M
					Parakeet
					Rustler
					Stork
					Yankee Trader

[a]From the *Kodiak Mirror*, Apr. 10, 1964.

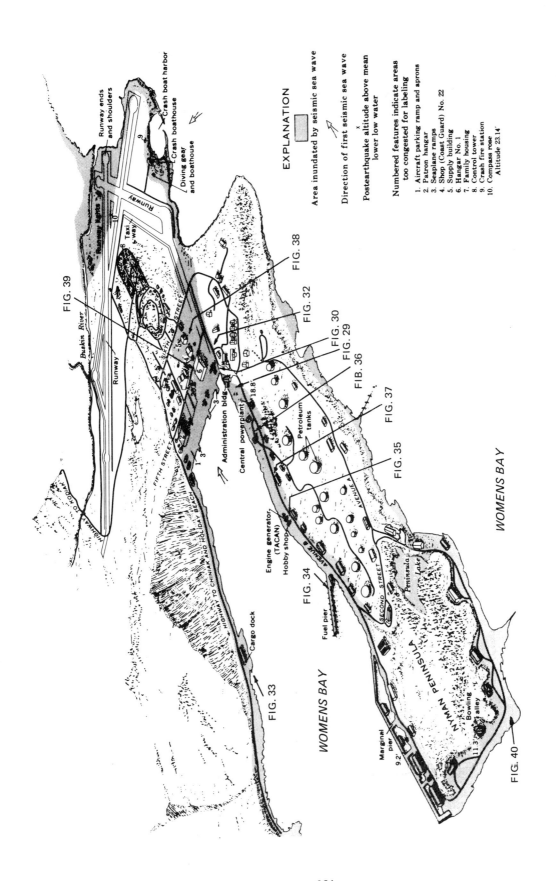

FIGURE 31   Area of maximum inundation by tsunamis and structures damaged at Kodiak Naval Station. (From Kachadoorian and Plafker, 1967.)

EXPLANATION

Area inundated by seismic sea wave

Direction of first seismic sea wave

×
Postearthquake altitude above mean
lower low water

Numbered features indicate areas
too congested for labeling
1. Aircraft parking ramp and aprons
2. Patron hangar
3. Seaplane ramps
4. Shop (Coast Guard) No. 22
5. Supply building
6. Hangar No. 1
7. Family housing
8. Control tower
9. Crash fire station
10. Compass rose
      Altitude 23.14'

Revised from an original drawing by U.S. Navy,
Kodiak, Alaska, March 31, 1964

391

U.S. Navy

FIGURE 32   Partial recession of the first tsunami wave at the Navy Air Terminal, Womens Bay, Kodiak. Debris and ice cakes are deposited on the seaplane taxiways (location in Figure 31).

pressure of water reaching to door height. Maximum pressure at the floor would have been about 215 lb/ft^2, and the total load per foot on the wall about 1,350 lb.

A 10-ton mooring buoy 12 ft in diameter was torn loose from its anchorage in Womens Bay and deposited on the taxiway of the air terminal (Figure 38) near the supply depot at location 5 in Figure 31. According to Kachadoorian and Plafker (1967), it was carried to this position, about a

TABLE 4   Description and Cost of Restoration or Replacement of Facilities at Kodiak Naval Station, Damaged by the March 1964 Earthquake or Tsunami[a]

Description	Estimated Cost
Rebuild roads and bridges from the Naval Station to Holiday Beach	$1,677,000
200-kw Generator, Holiday Beach	147,500
Central power plant	177,500
Repair hangars 1, 2, 3, and aprons	936,400
Repair AUW Facility	35,400
Microwave installation	900,000
Repair runway ends and shoulders	215,000
Repair runway lights	17,200
Replace generators (OPCON)	31,000
Marginal pier (new)	1,716,000
Repair crash-boat house	29,800
Diving gear and boat house	75,000
Repair station electrical facilities	61,750
Repair Rawin Aerological Building	13,200
Repair fuel pier S-40	37,900
Repair shop (Coast Guard) #22	6,200
Public Works maintenance shop	22,400
Repair crash fire station	88,500
Repair aviation warehouse	14,500
Total	$6,202,250

[a]Data from Kachadoorian and Plafker (1967).

quarter of a mile inland, by the fifth (and highest) tsunami wave, which crested between 23:16 and 23:34 AST on March 27, 18.8 ft above MLLW. The buoy had apparently torn loose from its die-lock anchor chain. For lack of time and detailed information, we have been unable to explore this interesting case further. Tudor (1964), however, estimated that merely from the complete immersion of the buoy by the rising water the mooring chain would have increased its tension from the free-floating load by a factor of 3.6.

The asphalt pavements covering the taxiways between the hangars and seaplane ramps were fragmented under the seismic action. In the hangars there were differential settlements between the fill-supported hangar deck and the pile-supported columns, and relative settlements between the hangar footings and the hangar deck occurred around the perimeter of the hangar (Tudor, 1964; Worthington and others, 1964; Kachadoorian and Plafker, 1967). The hangars were constructed on a fill of approximately 15–20 ft of unconsolidated glacial till, which was compacted under seismic vibrations and the additional loading of the subsequent waves (see Figure 39). According to Kachadoorian and Plafker (1967), no significant amount of erosion accompanied this settlement.

The vertical sheet-pile bulkhead at the edge of the seaplane parking area was buckled outward along its length. It is not certain whether this damage was caused by the earth tremors or by the tsunami. A slumping movement of the ground could undoubtedly have bent the steel piles. During the inundation periods, however, the fill behind the sheet piles was probably fully saturated, because a zone of cover stone between the sheet-pile bulkhead and the concrete pavement of the parking area permitted infiltration of water. This trapped water probably established

FIGURE 33 Damaged cargo dock at the Naval Station, Kodiak; view northeast (location in Figure 31).

U.S. Navy

U.S. Navy

FIGURE 34 Fuel pier at the Naval Station, Kodiak, inundated by postearthquake high tide (location in Figure 31).

U.S. Navy

FIGURE 35 Hobby shop boat-repair house at the Naval Station, Kodiak, alongside its original foundations (location in Figure 31).

U.S. Navy

FIGURE 36 Damaged hobby shop at the Naval Station, Kodiak (location in Figure 31).

FIGURE 37 The Ground Electronics Building at Kodiak Naval Station; apparently imploded under hydrostatic water pressure (location in Figure 31).

U.S. Navy

U.S. Navy

FIGURE 38 Mooring buoy washed ashore by tsunami, Kodiak Naval Station (location in Figure 31).

U.S. Navy

FIGURE 39 Evidence of settlement of backfill material below pavement level, adjacent to the foundation of a hangar at Kodiak Naval Station (location in Figure 31).

a hydraulic head, which, in association with suction pressures on the retaining wall from receding flood waters, could have caused the sheet piling to buckle outward.

At the edge of the seaplane parking area, a small white house (visible in Figure 32) survived the floodings and was not carried away because of hold-down cables over the roof (Tudor, 1964).

According to Tudor, the ground floor of the main power plant was repeatedly flooded by water with a heavy silt load, and heavy fuel oil on the water coated the boilers, blowers, motors, and pumps on the boiler flat (deck) and rendered them inoperative. The maximum water elevation inside the plant was below the generator deck where the high-voltage switching gear and control instrumentation were located.

Some low-level radioactive contamination occurred in the ground electronics building when tsunami waters scattered traces or minute sources of radionuclides (Tudor, 1964).

Vehicles partially or fully submerged by the elevated waters were, for the most part, a total loss due to the corrosive effect of salt water on the motors and wiring. In addition, oil slick from the water was heavily deposited on many vehicles (Tudor, 1964).

At the southwest end of the Nyman Peninsula, the roadbed was partly eroded from under its asphalt cover-layer (Figure 40). The road between the Naval Station and Cape Chiniak was damaged in several places. Figures 41 to 43 present views of the scouring effects of the tsunami on roads and bridges in the low-lying deltaic region at the southwest end of Womens Bay (see Figure 6).

The seismic sea waves also did other miscellaneous damage. The high water (1) carried vehicles inland or into Womens Bay, (2) deposited all types of debris on the beach areas of the Naval Station, (3) destroyed the small footbridge crossing Buskin River, (4) washed ice across the highway and against buildings in several localities, and (5) demolished several small shed-type structures. This type of damage occurred throughout the low-lying inundated areas of the station. The cost of the general cleanup of the station and other miscellaneous damage is not included in Table 4.

TSUNAMI DAMAGE AT OTHER COASTAL COMMUNITIES OF KODIAK AND NEIGHBORING ISLANDS

The wave sequences at places other than Kodiak City and the U.S. Naval Station, Kodiak, are not well known. It seems reasonable to suppose that the tsunamis affecting the numerous bays and inlets of the Kodiak Island region were basically similar to what has been described in regard to Kodiak City and Womens Bay. The peculiarities of bays, however, would manifest themselves in giving prominence to local resonances.

General runup effects along the coast of the Kodiak Island group have been described by Wilson and Tørum (1968; see also earlier paper, this volume). Figure 4 summarizes much of the information and serves here as a reference to particular places.

It is impossible in a work of this kind to cover in detail all the effects documented by such investigators as Berg and others (1971); Brown (1964); Warren W. Denner (personal communication, 1964); Grantz and others (1964); Plafker and Mayo (1965); Plafker and Kachadoorian (1966); and Kachadoorian and Plafker (1967). We shall merely attempt to discuss some of the more important situations that have come to our notice, particularly those in which damage was involved.

At Port William on Shuyak Island (Figure 4), the water is said to have receded 45 minutes after the earthquake and to have been followed by a wave. The highest runup was

FIGURE 40   Roadbed eroded at the tip of the Nyman Peninsula (location in Figure 31).

U.S. Navy

estimated by Berg and others (1971) to have been 16 ft about MLLW tidal plane, or about 6 ft above the high tide at midnight; slight damage occurred.

At Afognak village on Marmot Bay, Afognak Island (Figure 44), there was an immediate recession of water after the earthquake and then a wave crest within 15 minutes. Four additional waves are said to have followed (Berg and others, 1971), of which the fourth and highest destroyed part of the village.

Each wave came in with a roar like a fast-rising tide that receded after each wave, leaving the bay dry in Afognak Strait between the village and Whale Island (Kachadoorian and Plafker, 1967). Several homes, together with the community hall, were washed out to sea; other buildings were

U.S. Navy

FIGURE 41   Damaged road on the deltaic area at the southwest head of Womens Bay.

U.S. Navy

FIGURE 42   Damaged road bridge on the deltaic area at the southwest head of Womens Bay.

swept off their foundations and moved inland; automobiles and trucks were carried into the small lake behind the village, and the ice in the lake was floated out to sea. Two bridges were washed out along the coastal road.

Figure 44, developed from aerial photography, gives an idea of the extent of devastation. Kachadoorian and Plafker (1967) give the maximum runup height as 14.5 ft above MLLW (Figure 44), a value somewhat at variance with the 19 ft estimated by Berg and others (1971) soon after the earthquake. Plafker and Kachadoorian (1966) estimated the runup as 10.8 ft above the existing tide (Figure 4) at

about 21:27 (AST), March 27, which suggests a wave height of about 21.6 ft at that time.

The extent of inundation outlined in Figure 44 was mapped from the distribution of driftwood, debris, abraded bark, and broken branches of trees and brush. Greatest inundation occurred in the vicinity of the airstrip and adjacent low-lying area. The regional subsidence of 4.5 ft necessitated relocation of the village to Settler Cove in Kizhuyak Bay, Kodiak Island, where it was named Port Lions (inset, Figure 44). The estimated cost of this operation was $816,000.

U.S. Navy

FIGURE 43   Closeup view of damaged road bridge on the deltaic area of the southwest head of Womens Bay.

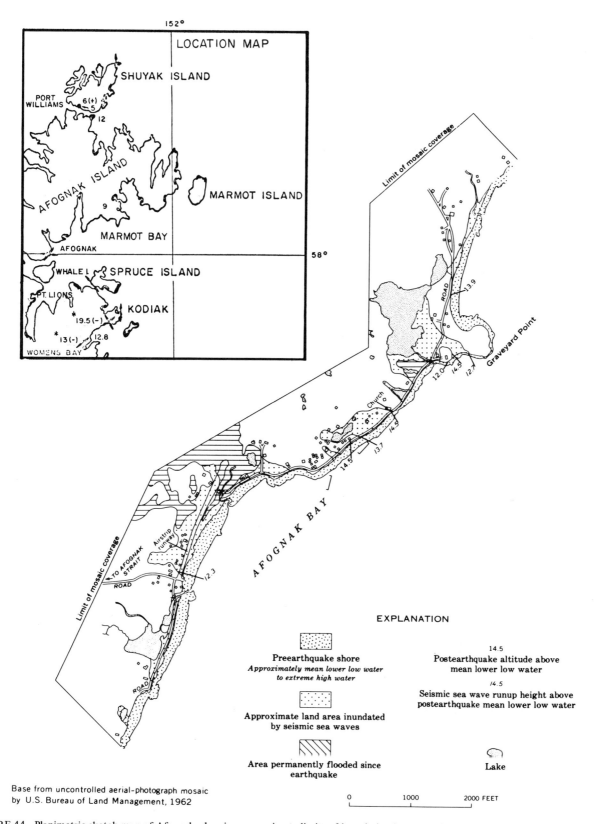

FIGURE 44 Planimetric sketch map of Afognak, showing approximate limits of inundation by tsunamis. (Adapted from Kachadoorian and Plafker, 1967).

Port Wakefield on Raspberry Strait, between Afognak and Raspberry islands (Figure 4), experienced waves with periods of 8 to 10 minutes for 1½ hours after the earthquake (Berg and others, 1971). Then at about 23:00 (AST) a series of "erratic" tides began reversing three times per hour; these were apparently tsunami waves arriving from Marmot Bay. The earlier and shorter waves suggested possible transverse oscillations of the water body in the straits in a northeast–southwest direction resulting from the earth motion.

Maximum runup of 12 ft above MLLW apparently occurred at 13:00, March 28. The King Crab processing plant had to be abandoned because of subsidence, and protective measures had to be taken to buttress the backfill at the cannery dock.

About 30 minutes after the earthquake, the water receded at Ouzinkie on Spruce Island (Figure 45) and then returned steadily to initiate a train of waves. The third wave at 19:30 to 20:00 AST was apparently the highest, causing a runup of 22 ft above MLLW (Berg and others, 1971). Figure 45, based on aerial photography (Kachadoorian and Plafker, 1967), shows the extent of runup.

Homes and boats valued at $49,800 were destroyed, and the Ouzinkie Packing Company's salmon cannery suffered damage to the extent of $300,000.

The highest runup on the Kodiak Island coast was measured along the almost uninhabited stretch between Cape Chiniak and Narrow Cape and near the entrance of Ugak Bay (Figures 4 and 46). Here the coast coincides approximately with the hinge-line of zero vertical earth movement. In this area, Plafker and Kachadoorian (1966) record a runup height of 31.5 ft above high spring tide on the night of the earthquake, or about 42 ft above MLLW tidal plane. Berg and others (1971) found a runup of 36.7 ft above MLLW at Beatty Ranch north of Narrow Cape and debris marks to an elevation of 66.6 ft above MLLW at a distance of about 2.5 nautical miles west of Narrow Cape. Here the wave had cut a scarp in the muddy sediments, and considerable slumping of the scarp appeared to have taken place subsequently. It is probable that the high wave effects around Narrow Cape were the direct result of the concentration of wave energy brought about by the refractive effects of Ugak Island.

In Shearwater Bay, a tributary of Kiliuda Bay, Kodiak

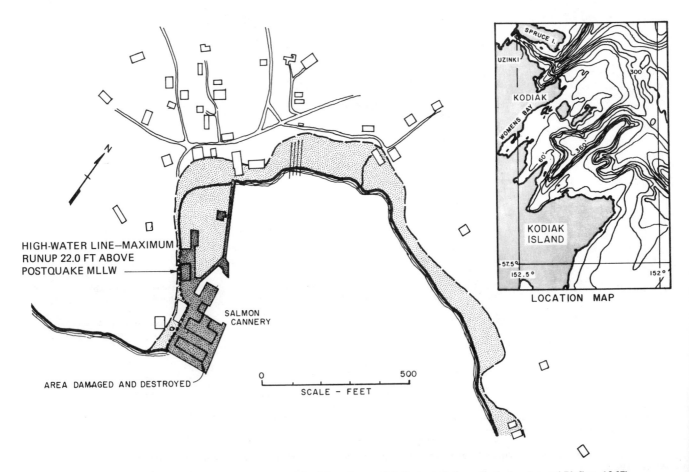

HIGH-WATER LINE—MAXIMUM RUNUP 22.0 FT ABOVE POSTQUAKE MLLW

SALMON CANNERY

AREA DAMAGED AND DESTROYED

SCALE – FEET

LOCATION MAP

FIGURE 45   Tsunami inundation of Ouzinkie, Spruce Island (based on aerial photograph from Kachadoorian and Plafker, 1967).

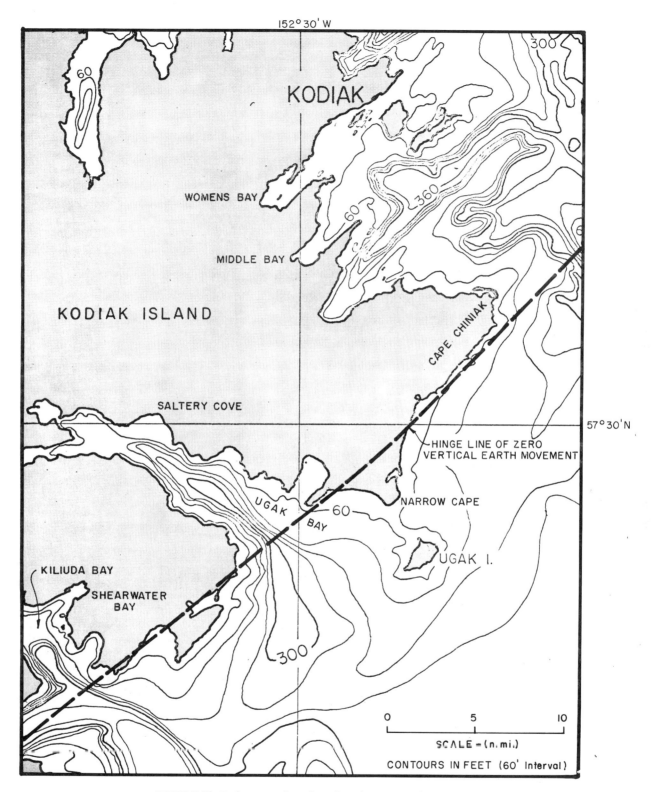

FIGURE 46   Bathymetry of portion of southeast coast of Kodiak Island.

Island (Figures 4 and 46), the Kadiak Fisheries cannery, located on a broad, roughly triangular cusp of land that jutted into Shearwater Bay (Plafker and Kachadoorian, 1966, and Geology volume), was almost completely wrecked by the earthquake and tsunami. Piling supports for the cannery had been driven to refusal, 10 to 15 ft into unconsolidated deltaic beach deposits. These deposits subsided from 2 to 10 ft more than the regional bedrock subsidence of 4 ft during the earthquake. Part of the cannery was buoyed off the piles and destroyed by the tsunamis that ran up to an elevation of 23.5 ft above MLLW (Berg and others, 1971). Unbroken piles were severely tilted by the ground motion and subsequent wave action, and drift pins in the piling tops, bent southward, suggest that the superstructure destroyed was probably carried away during a wave recession.

Old Harbor (Figures 4 and 47), which occupied an almost central position on Sitkalidak Strait between Kodiak Island and Sitkalidak Island, was almost entirely destroyed by the tsunami, although apparently only one person

among its population of 194 was drowned. The tusnamis entered the strait with an audible roar from both the north and south sides of Sitkalidak Island and had their confluence at or near Old Harbor, thus resulting in exceptionally high runup for such a seemingly protected area.

According to Berg and others (1971), a wave 2 to 3 ft in height arrived within 15 minutes of the earthquake, followed by a second within another 10 to 15 minutes. This latter wave was followed by a recession of 6 to 10 ft. Some 30 minutes later, a larger bifurcated wave arrived from north and south and inundated the village without causing damage. However, after a partial recession, and only about 5 minutes later, another cresting wave swept into the village and floated off most of the houses. As indicated by a stopped battery-powered clock, located just below the highest water mark in the only remaining house of those inundated, this highest wave crested at 21:57 AST. A wave of almost the same height came in later about midnight on the high tide. If the clock was correct and if the wave was the highest as reported, there is a discrepancy between eye-

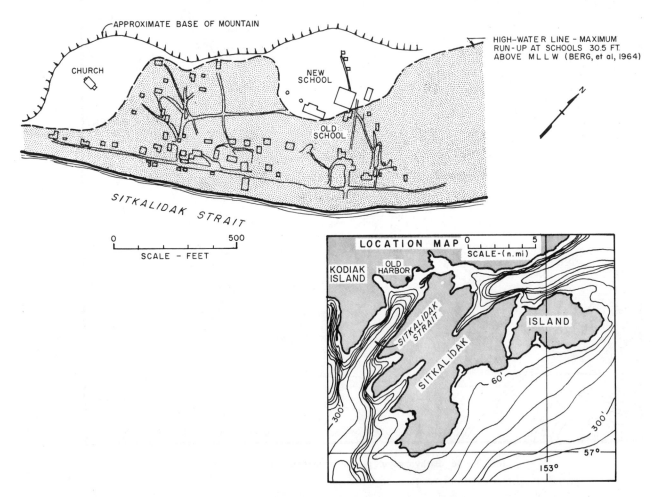

FIGURE 47   Tsunami inundation of Old Harbor, Kodiak Island (based on aerial photograph from Kachadoorian and Plafker, 1967).

witness accounts of the time and the time on the clock. Kachadoorian and Plafker (1967), for instance, give the time of the damaging wave as 21:28, but make no reference to the clock. The maximum runup at Old Harbor, according to Berg and others (1971), varied from 22.5 to 30.5 ft above MLLW. These measurements apparently do not agree with the estimate of Kachadoorian and Plafker (1967), who considered the runup to be only 15.7 ft above MLLW.

The latter authors report that the house that survived the tsunami, although flooded, was securely tied down to a concrete foundation. Its location in Figure 47 is unknown. The cost of replacing the homes and auxiliary buildings has been estimated at $707,000.

A small fishing village at Kaguyak at the head of Kaguyak Bay (Figure 4) was completely destroyed by the tsunami, although the earthquake itself did no damage. The first wave came approximately 20 minutes after the earthquake, and the largest, probably the third, struck at about 21:00 AST. The houses of the village were carried across the spit on which they were built and dumped into or washed up the farther shore of the lagoon behind them. The maximum runup was about 32 ft above postearthquake MLLW, according to Berg and others (1971), but it is given as 25 ft above MLLW by Kachadoorian and Plafker (1967). Probably, the high runup may be ascribed to a resonance effect of Kaguyak Bay on the tsunami waves.

Three of the 37 inhabitants of the village were drowned. Loss of private and public property has been estimated at $321,000. The survivors have since been moved to Akhiok and Old Harbor.

Total losses of property and income in communities on

TABLE 5   Losses of Property and Income in Communities on Kodiak Island and Nearby Islands, March 1964[a]

Location	Nature of Damage	Estimated Replacement Cost
Kodiak	Losses of private, commercial, and public property	$24,736,000[b]
Afognak[c]		816,000[d]
Old Harbor		707,000[d]
Ouzinkie	Losses of public and private property	349,800[d]
Kaguyak[c]		321,000[d]
Larsen Bay		80,000[d]
Akhiok		None
All communities	Vessels damaged	2,466,500[e]
All communities	Loss of income to fishing industry	5,087,000[e]
Kodiak Naval Station	Damage to structures and equipment	10,916,800[b]
	Total Losses	$45,480,100

[a] From Kachadoorian and Plafker (1967).
[b] Data from Tudor (1964).
[c] Village site abandoned.
[d] Data from Bureau of Indian Affairs (9/25/64).
[e] Data from Alaska Department of Fish and Game (1965).

Kodiak Island and neighboring islands have been estimated at about $45 million (Tables 5 and 11).

TSUNAMI WAVES IN COOK INLET

Figure 48, which relates to section line CC' in Figure 3, indicates the expected nature of the initial water surface displacement on the Continental Shelf opposite the entrance

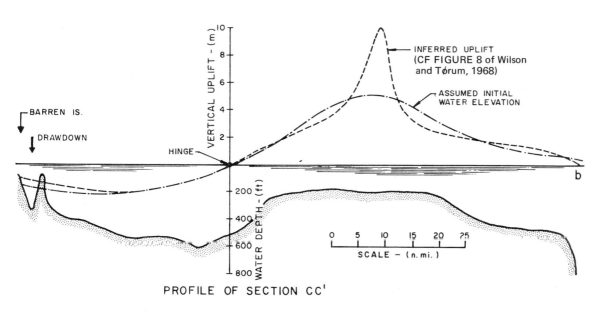

FIGURE 48   Inferred mechanism of tsunami generation on the Continental Shelf off the Kenai Peninsula, Alaska; along section line CC' of Figure 3.

to Cook Inlet. A vast negative wave would have been created almost instantly with the subsidence of the land during the earthquake at the mouth of the Inlet, extending beyond the Barren Islands into the Inlet. The ensuing wave system that would advance from the hinge-line of zero vertical earth movement could be expected to be similar, in general, to the waves that reached Kodiak, but different in detail according to the special oscillating characteristics of the Continental Shelf in this region. We envision an interplay of the gravity waves of separation with induced free oscillations of the Shelf, advancing on a front parallel to the hinge-line shown in Figure 3 (Wilson and Tørum, 1968). The first crest would have had to travel a distance of about 70 nautical miles at a mean speed $c \simeq 115$ ft/sec for mean depth $d \simeq 400$ ft, according to the well-known relation

$$c = \sqrt{g d} \qquad (3)$$

(g = acceleration due to gravity), in order to have reached the neighborhood of Perl Island (Figure 48) about 1 hour after the earthquake, or at about 18:40 AST. The second wave would probably have followed about 2 hours later at about 20:40.

Perl Island was actually struck by a 28-ft wave at 20:40 (Waller, 1966, and Geology volume). This was followed by another wave of 30 ft at 23:40 and a third wave, also about 30 ft high, at 02:30 on March 28, with the time interval between these waves being 3 hours. In the absence of a detailed calculation of the oscillating characteristics of the open-ended basin system illustrated in Figure 48, we feel unqualified to elaborate further on this phenomenon.

Undoubtedly the constriction effect of Cook Inlet and the shoaling effect of the Barren Islands would cause some reflection and scattering of the tsunami energy, so that waves penetrating into Cook Inlet might well evolve at shorter periods. Their heights, too, would undergo considerable reduction from energy loss at the entrance and energy dissipation through refraction and diffraction into the wide basin of the lower Cook Inlet.

Nevertheless, there are numerous accounts of tsunami waves having reached Seldovia and Homer (Figures 1, 3, and 49) near the end of Kenai Peninsula, within Cook Inlet. Many of these accounts (Waller, 1966, and Geology volume; Chance, 1966, and in press; Berg and others, 1971) make it clear that large waves of short period (but in the category of long waves) were generated during the earthquake. It may be noted that reported tectonic movements suggest that the land mass in the Seldovia–Homer region was displaced horizontally to the north–northwest by amounts varying from about 1 ft at Seldovia to 5 ft at Homer, so that the ground motion would have been favorable for inducing seismic seiches transversely across Kachemak Bay.

Waller (1966, and Geology volume) records that three different waves or large swells were observed on the Cook Inlet side of the spit at Homer shortly after the earthquake. The height of the waves was estimated to be approximately 9 ft. These waves apparently broke like a swell on the beach, but caused no damage. In Kachemak Bay some peculiar wave formations also occurred during and after the earthquake. Several waves with heights of approximately 4 ft rolled onto the north shore; they were all, with one exception, observed to be parallel to the north shore near Homer (Waller, 1966). Because of the fact that ground waves were observed in motion in a north–south direction at Homer (Chance, 1966, and in press), some of these water waves could have been excited by wave motion of the bed of Kachemak Bay. There is little factual information to relate to the period of the water waves, but one report indicates that 10-ft waves of about 2-minute period were observed at the time of the earthquake (U.S. Coast and Geodetic Survey, 1964a); another, that 4- to 6-ft waves of about 5-minute period occurred (Berg, and others, 1971). We may note that the first three modes of free oscillation of the water body across Kachemak Bay (near Homer) would be of the order of 30, 21, and 15 minutes, but there appears to be no information to suggest that waves of these periods were observed.

At about 21:30 AST, March 27, a 20-ft wave arrived at Homer. The water rose to 4 ft above the floor level in some buildings at the outer end of Homer Spit (Waller, 1966). This could possibly be the same wave reported from Perl Island at 20:40 and the first major tsunami wave. Berg and others (1971) have drawn attention to the observation of the wharfinger at Homer Spit that the first major effect of the earthquake on the sea, other than the waves mentioned, was a withdrawal of water level to 4 to 5 ft below normal, beginning at about 18:10. Undoubtedly this would have represented the advance of the negative tsunami wave, producing a drawdown.

Homer suffered mainly from the regional subsidence (2–3 ft), differential compaction, and/or lateral spreading (1–4 ft) (Waller, 1966; Gronewald and Duncan, 1966). Wave damage was slight and confined to that caused by inundation. Figure 50 shows the general effect of the subsidence on the spit.

At Seldovia, according to eyewitnesses, numerous waves 12 to 15 ft above normal tide level with a period of about 2 minutes developed during the earthquake but did no damage because their reach was below high-tide level (Chance, 1966, and in press). Other waves after the earthquake appear to have occurred at intervals of 15 and 45 minutes. The surges 3 to 4 ft in height at intervals of 15 minutes could very well be related to transverse oscillations of the water body across Seldovia Bay (Figure 51), which may be likened to a semi-quartic basin (Wilson, 1966) of 10,000-ft length and 35-ft

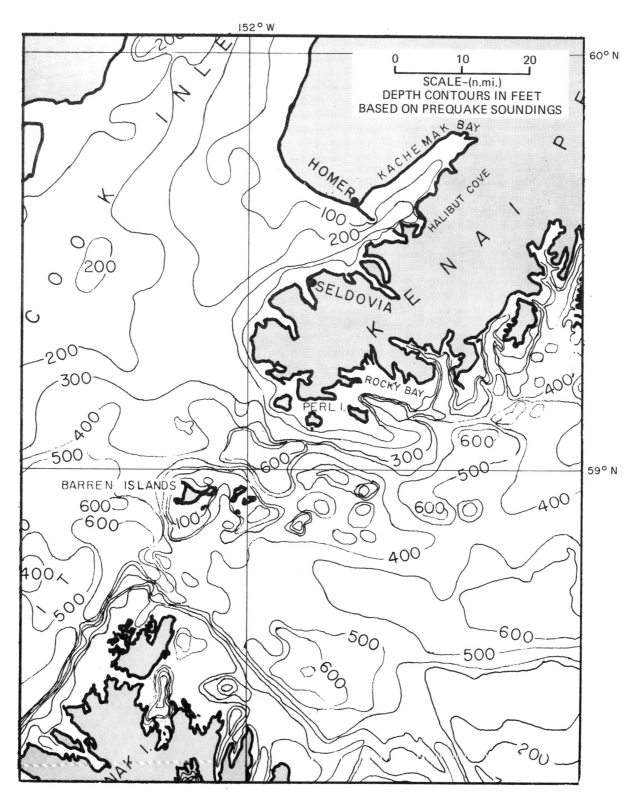

FIGURE 49   Bathymetry of the Continental Shelf at the mouth of Cook Inlet.

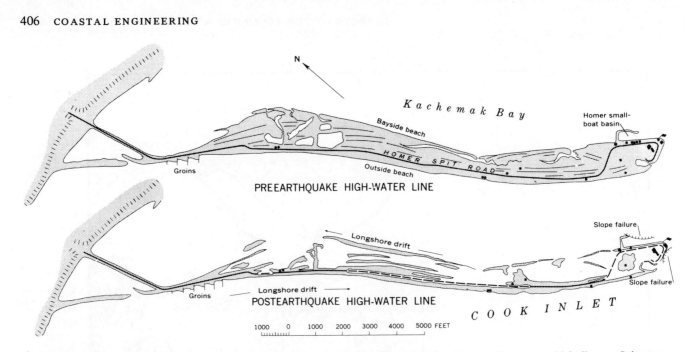

FIGURE 50 Comparison of the high-water line along Homer Spit before and after the earthquake and submergence. Light lines on Spit represent old beach berms. High-water line traced from U.S. Army Corps of Engineers aerial photographs, September 1959, and from U.S. Bureau of Land Management infrared photographs, August 1964. (From Waller and Stanley, 1966.)

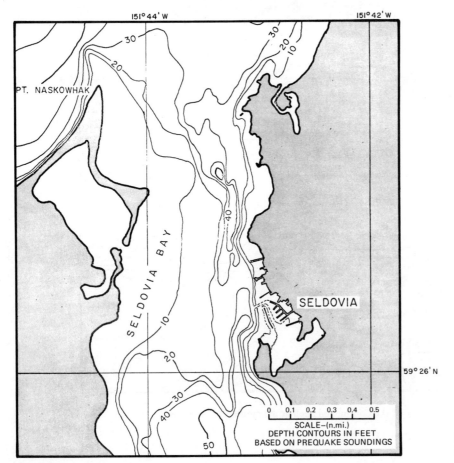

FIGURE 51 Bathymetry of Seldovia Bay in the region of the Port of Seldovia.

maximum depth (at Seldovia). Such a basin would have first- and second-mode oscillations of about 25 and 12.5 minutes, respectively. Without more extended analysis of the whole bay, the waves of 45-minute period are unexplained.

Strong tides were observed to occur at 19:00 AST (Berg and others, 1971), at 20:00, and at 21:00 (Chance, 1966). The latter may have reached close to normal high-tide level for the area. On its recession at about 21:10, this wave carried away some boat floats (Chance, 1966); this is presumed to be the same tsunami wave that reached Homer at 21:30.

A second major tsunami wave is presumed to have arrived at about 23:10 to 23:30 and again at about 02:00, March 28, on the high astronomical tide (Berg and others, 1971). The tsunami elevation above normal tide level at this time was estimated by Berg and others to be about 4 ft.

Wave damage at Seldovia was relatively slight and mostly due to inundation. Some boat floats were apparently swept away, and the breakwater suffered some damage both from compaction due to the earth tremors and from waves (see Eckel, 1967, and Geology volume).

Halibut Cove (a wide bay almost due east of the end of Homer Spit, Figure 49) also reported a wave of 24 ft at 23:35 (Waller, 1966), which could have been the same one that hit Seldovia at 23:10. If these waves were tsunamis coming in from the Gulf of Alaska, Homer was probably also hit by these waves, although no high waves were reported at Homer at that time (the reason for this could simply be that nobody was at the waterfront to report them).

We remarked that the tsunami waves would encounter a strong refractive and diffractive effect on their entrance to Cook Inlet. The exact effect of this is difficult to assess, but it seems not too unrealistic to assume a diffraction coefficient of approximately 0.4 at Seldovia and Homer. This probably would explain why tsunamis were not more seriously felt at these places.

The tsunamis were not reported at all at Anchorage, probably because the waves were strongly attenuated by refraction effects and by friction as they traveled along the Cook Inlet. Also, they would have encountered strong ebb currents from the outpouring astronomical tide which would have partly negated their advance. The question is an interesting one, however, and unfortunately the only data on the subject are contained in a report by Brown (1964) that at Kenai the ice shifted position at 23:00 AST, March 27, three times in 45 minutes along the edge of the basin. It is not known whether any oil companies working in Cook Inlet possess information that would show any unusual tide state during and after the earthquake.

Nevertheless, there was evidence of wave activity in Turnagain Arm (Figure 1) shortly after the earthquake (Chance, 1966). The shock occurred about 1 hour before

predicted high tide for Hope, located about midway along Turnagain Arm (Figure 3). Shortly after the earthquake the water swept in from the northwest like a 40-ft tide, running 200 yd inland and flooding homes and other property. It is thought that this water movement may have been due to the readjustment of the water level as a result of the tilt that Turnagain Arm received from the land subsidence. It is also possible that opposing horizontal thrustings of the land at each end of Turnagain Arm (see Wilson and Tørum, 1968) induced an antinodal water effect near the center where Hope is located.

TSUNAMI WAVES IN RESURRECTION BAY, KENAI PENINSULA

The tsunami wave profile as it may have formed on the Continental Shelf off Resurrection Bay is indicated in Figure 52a for the section line BB′ in Figure 3. Resurrection Bay down-dropped during the earthquake through a vertical distance of about 1½ ft at the mouth to 5 ft at the head. Its horizontal displacement in the direction of its length varied from about 45 ft at the head to 55 ft at the mouth. The expectation from this is that the sudden movement of the earth forming the boundaries of the bay, along with the upthrust over the Continental Shelf during the earthquake, would have resulted in an immediate relative upwelling of about 3 ft of water at the head of the bay, as shown in Figure 52a. This estimate is purely hypothetical and qualitative and makes no allowance for local or special effects.

Before proceeding to a more detailed interpretation of the wave effects actually observed in Resurrection Bay, we show the bathymetry of the region in Figure 53. Seward is situated on the west side of the bay at its head, on an alluvial fan of glacial deposits. The length of the bay to its mouth is about 23 nautical miles, and its depth varies along the length between about 650 ft at its center near Caines Head and more than 950 ft near its mouth and in the northern half. The width of the bay is roughly uniform along a large portion of its length, if the series of islands in the southern half is regarded as forming virtually a boundary on the east side. This width is about 2½ nautical miles in the northern part of the bay. It will be seen from Figures 52a and 53 that the constriction formed by Caines Head and the sill of the bed at this location has the effect of separating Resurrection Bay into two deep basins connected by a narrow and shallower neck. To all intents and purposes, then, the bay may be simulated by the geometrical analogy of two rectangular basins I and III (Figure 52b) interconnected by a short and shallower channel II.

The oscillating properties of this chain system of basins are immediately of interest, and we investigate this by recourse to the impedance principle of Rayleigh (1945) as

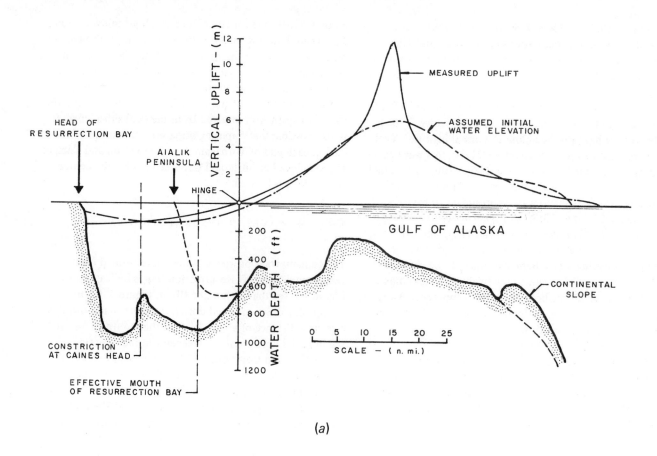

(a)

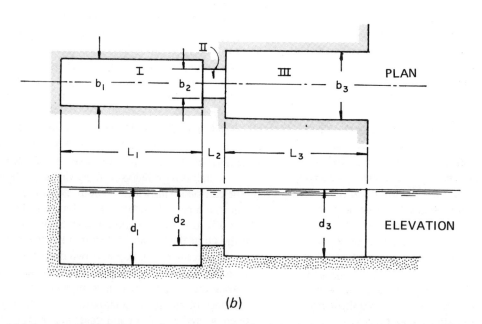

(b)

FIGURE 52 (a) Inferred mechanism of tsunami generation on the Continental Shelf athwart and including Resurrection Bay (along section line BB', Figure 3). (b) Schematic representation of Resurrection Bay as a chain system of basins.

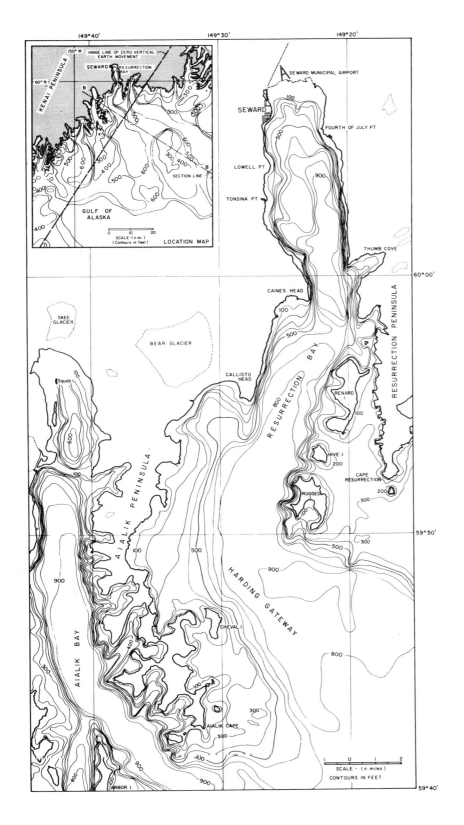

FIGURE 53 Bathymetry of Resurrection Bay, Kenai Peninsula, and the location of Seward.

TABLE 6   Dimensions of Interconnecting Rectangular Basins Simulating Resurrection Bay (see Figure 52b)

Basin or Channel	Length L (ft)	Breadth b (ft)	Depth d (ft)
I	47,300	13,500	875
II	10,100	11,800	500
III	57,500	15,200	775

employed by Neumann (1948). With dimensions of length L, breadth b, and depth d (from Figure 53, in accord with Table 6), the first two modes of free oscillation of the system are found to have the periods

$$\left. \begin{array}{l} \text{(i) } T_1 \simeq 26.0 \text{ minutes} \\ \\ \text{(ii) } T_2 \simeq 12.5 \text{ minutes} \end{array} \right\} . \qquad (4)$$

Equations (4) show that Resurrection Bay was neither long enough nor shallow enough to provide any form of resonant response to the primary long waves of the tsunami whose period probably approximated 2 hours. On the other hand, in the light of our investigation of other situations of tsunami penetration into bays and inlets, it seems that pseudoresonance could develop for any third harmonic or fifth harmonic of the main tsunami that might exist.

Most of the available information on waves in Resurrection Bay relates to Seward, which was devastated by tsunamis both during and after the earthquake. The sources of information are mainly eyewitness reports of the debacle; these were supported by postearthquake measurements of runup along the shorelines (see, for example, Grantz and others, 1964; Brown, 1964; Berg and others, 1971; U.S. Coast and Geodetic Survey, 1964a; Denner, personal communication, 1964; Plafker and Mayo, 1965; Spaeth and Berkman, 1965, 1967, and this volume; Lemke, 1967, and Geology volume).

The location of Seward is shown in Figure 53 and in the preearthquake aerial photograph, Figure 54, upon which have been inserted, for contrast, both the high-water line reached by the tsunamis and the postearthquake shoreline. A detailed plan of the city and waterfront facilities as they existed before the earthquake is contained in Figure 55. The city at that time had a population of about 2,000 and was a major fishing center, besides having strategic importance as the chief year-round port (the Port of Anchorage has been the chief year-round port since the earthquake) and rail terminal for Alaska, connecting the southern coast with Anchorage and Fairbanks. The port facilities were totally destroyed by the earthquake and tsunamis; all means of communication and transportation, other than by radio and air travel, were disrupted for some time (Eckel, 1967).

There seems to be little doubt that the waves that hit Seward in the first instance were caused by locally generated tsunamis and that the city was later assailed by the main tsunami waves and Continental Shelf oscillations that traveled up Resurrection Bay from the mouth. The U.S. Coast and Geodetic Survey tide gage at Seward was located on the Standard Oil Company dock, and its record was lost when the dock collapsed shortly after the onset of the earthquake. The gage was later found heavily damaged among the debris on board the oil tanker *Alaska Standard*, which had been moored to the dock at the beginning of the earthquake.

It is understandable that, with the horrifying events during and after the earthquake, few people took detailed notice of the behavior of the sea. In this account of what happened, the sequence of waves is reconstructed as an interpretation of the observations of different eyewitnesses. This interpretation takes the form of an inferred marigram (Figure 56) based on data summarized in Table 7. At best this marigram can convey only a crude picture of what may have been the true state of affairs; at worst it can overcomplicate the situation by tending to suggest more large waves than were actually in existence, owing to the uncertain times of the eyewitnesses' impressions.

It appears obvious from several eyewitness accounts that in the neighborhood of The Alaska Railroad dock and the Standard Oil Company dock at the southern end of Seward, while shaking of the earth was in progress, the waterfront slumped away from the shore, carrying with it the cannery at the south end of Seward, part of the railroad docks, and the Standard Oil Company dock (see Figure 55). One of the 200-ton wharf cranes at the railroad dock disappeared in this slump and has never been found (Figure 57). This particular slide occurred within about 30 to 45 seconds of the onset of shaking, apparently only at the south end of Seward, which has the steepest bottom slope of the entire fan delta (Figure 63). This statement is supported by the evidence given by Pedersen, Smith, Kirkpatrick, Gilfillen, Trigg, Clark, Smith, Mr. and Mrs. Dale Pickett, John and Robert Eads, and Christiansen (Chance, 1966, and in press); and of Werner, King, Lambert, and the Eads Brothers (Berg and others, 1971), all of whom suggest that only the waterfront part of Seward, inclusive of the railroad docks and the Standard Oil Company dock, was involved in this first catastrophe.

Figure 58 portrays the immediate consequence of this submarine slide as it probably occurred. The slump would have caused a drawdown of the water at the southern end of Seward, causing the *Alaska Standard* at the oil company dock virtually to disappear from sight (Chance, 1966, and in press). The underwater cascade would have formed a density current of roiling water, which would increasingly mound as it reached flatter slopes, presumably near the

FIGURE 54   Seward before the earthquake.

500-ft depth contour (Figure 53). At approximately half a mile from the shore, the sliding mass apparently elevated the water to a humped surface from which waves 15–20 ft in height radiated (Chance, 1966; Grantz and others, 1964). These waves hit the Seward waterfront approximately 1½ to 2 minutes after the earthquake started and produced an inundation that rose over the waterfront and caused initial heavy damage. As shown schematically in Figure 58, the *Alaska Standard* tore loose from her moorings and hoses and on the rising wave received a shower of dock wreckage on her foredeck which included the unconscious seaman Pedersen, who had been standing hose watch on the dock (Figure 59).

The first wave was probably close to a resonant transverse oscillation for the north end of Resurrection Bay. The transverse cross section of the bay off south Seward is approximately parabolic in profile, and the calculated first mode oscillation for a width of about 45 nautical miles and a central depth of 600 ft has a period of 3.6 minutes. After the drawdown (Figure 58b), it would thus have taken about 1.8 minutes for the flood to crest at the Seward waterfront (in fair agreement with the observations, Figure 56 and Table 7). At least one witness, Jack Werner (see Berg and others, 1971), records that he could see the wave that swept east from the boil and struck Fourth of July Point, where, according to Lear it ran inland a quarter of a mile. Many other witnesses, however, gained the impression that two separate waves formed from the initial boil of water, the first of which was the one to strike the south part of Seward and then spread north and south (Chance, 1966).

This wave, after devastating the remains of the Standard Oil Company dock, flooded over the Army dock (Figure 55), which had been slowly sinking from the continued shaking of the earth, lifted part of it in the air (Tom Hyde,

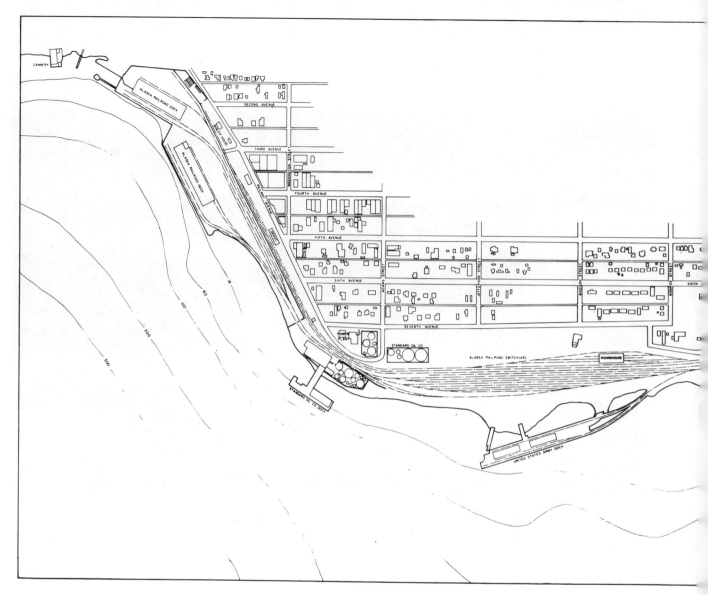

FIGURE 55   Plan of Seward before the earthquake.

see Chance, 1966, and in press), and slammed it down in ruin. As the wave peeled along the shore, it spread burning oil from the Standard Oil Company tanks toward loaded tank cars on the railroad sidings and toward the Texaco tank farm. These started to explode and were engulfed in flame (Figure 60).

The wave rose over the small-boat harbor in an area where witnesses (notably Logan, Watson, Mrs. Hatch, and Endresen; see Chance, 1966, and in press) had failed to report any initial drawdown of water such as had occurred at the south end of Seward, but where Lemke (1967), on the contrary, records a drawdown of 7 ft. Many of the boats were swept over the sea walls of the boat harbor and toward the lagoon.

One of the two people who photographed the north and south parts of this wave was Terrel Schenk, manager of the Halibut Producers' Co-op San Juan Cannery located near the boat harbor, Figure 55), who took the photographs of the northern wave (Figure 61) from the approximate directions and locations shown in Figures 55 and 64 (personal interview, 1966).

This wave appears as a smooth-line elevation of water (Figure 61b) moving toward the coast from deep water. The appearance fits the description given by Tom Hyde who reported "a series of gigantic waves with glassy smooth but curling fronts hurling towards the shore at breakneck speed" (Chance, 1966, and in press). The first wave, according to Hyde, hit with terrific force, and soon a wave of black oil

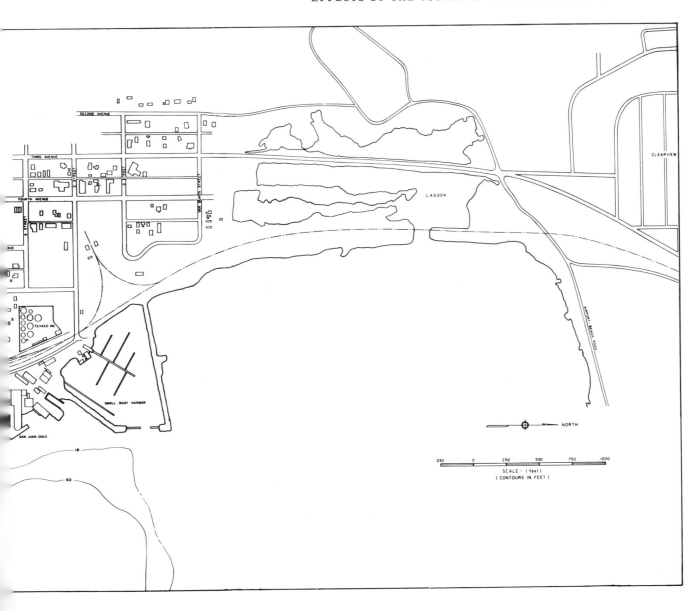

was moving down the railroad tracks toward the boat harbor. At about this time the violent ground shaking had opened up innumerable fissures in the area surrounding the boat harbor and cannery, and these structures were probably damaged from the earthquake before the wave struck. Apparently, a complete slide had not yet occurred, because there is clear evidence from several witnesses (Lantz and Kirkpatrick, 1964; Chance, 1966) that the waves tossed the boats around in the boat harbor and over the breakwaters. It is not known at what stage the boat harbor and cannery dock disappeared completely, but whatever survived the wave probably succumbed to subsidence on the recession of the wave.

The southern part of the wave was photographed on 8-mm motion-picture film by Robert Eads near Lowell Point (see Figure 55 for location). John and Robert Eads were closing shop at their marine railway and repair plant when the earthquake started. Looking toward Seward, they saw a wave coming toward them from the direction of the Standard Oil Company and Army docks; about the same time, another wave moving eastward on Fourth of July Point swept counterclockwise around the head of the bay (Berg and others, 1971). This fits the description of an annular ring wave expanding outward from a central source.

Robert Eads started photographing the oncoming wave with his motion-picture camera, but, realizing its great speed of advance, he and a companion (Christiansen) ran to their pickup truck to escape. The wave overtook them,

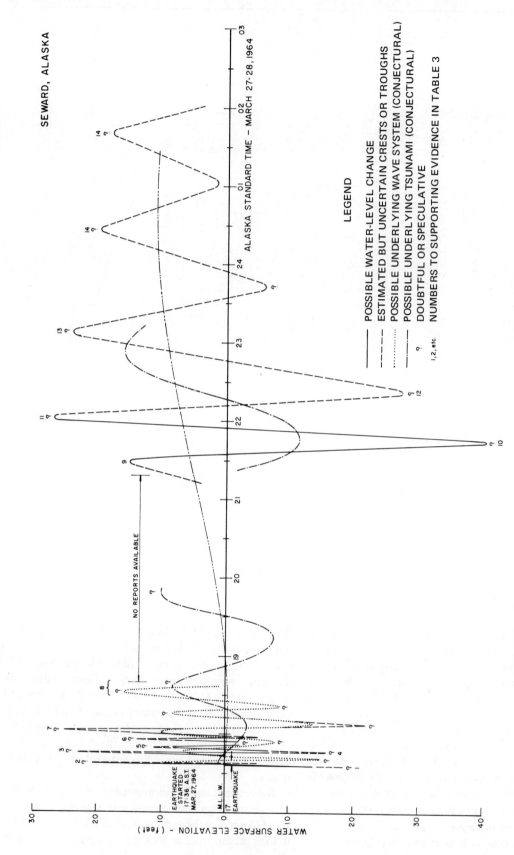

FIGURE 56 Inferred marigram for Seward, based on accounts by eyewitnesses and on inductive reasoning.

TABLE 7 Accounts upon Which the Hypothetical March 27–28, 1964, Marigram for Seward (Figure 56) Is Based

Eyewitness	Source	Estimated Time Points and Height or Effects (Zero time is at the start of the earthquake)	
		Time	Height (ft) or Effects

1 Ted Pedersen
  Hal Gilfillen
  Robert Clark
	Genie Chance	30 sec
		45 sec
		45 sec
			Drawdown at Standard Oil dock
			–
			–

2 Many eyewitnesses	Genie Chance Berg and others, 1971 Lantz and Kirkpatrick, 1964	1½–2 min – –	+20 to 25 ft at ARR docks Rose over boxcars on RR tracks Reached corner of Third Ave. and Washington

3 Robert Clark
  William Peterson
  Gilbert Nelson
  Del Hill
  Ollie Amend
	Genie Chance	11–12 min
		13 min
		8–10 min
		8 min
		8 min
			Knocked over boxcars
			Derailed boxcars
			Heading to cross-strip on airport
			Destroyed planes on airfield
			–

4 Mrs. Dale Pickett	Genie Chance	10 min	Big drawdown
5 Robert Clark	Genie Chance	16–17 min	?
6 Robert Clark Thelma Hatch	Genie Chance Genie Chance	20–30 min 20–30 min	– –

7 Luke Reed
  Jack Werner
  Neil King
	Berg and others, 1971	20–30 min
		20–30 min
		–
			2-ft bore up Third Avenue
			Height about 30 ft
			–

Robert Clark
  Thelma Hatch
  Mrs. Dale Pickett
  Mrs. Herman Leirer
  Mrs. Mildred Kirkpatrick
	Genie Chance	25–35 min
		20–30 min
		20 min
		20 min
		20 min
			4–5 ft higher than No. 6 at Crawford subdivision
			Well above airport
			Swept boats and houses over railroad into the lagoon
			–
			Well above railroad tracks

John Eads	Personal interview, 1966	18:00 AST	About 6 ft higher than first wave crest 2
8 Luke Reed	Berg and others, 1971	45–60 min	Very large wave
9 John and Bob Eads	Genie Chance	21:30 AST	To road level at Lowell Point +14 to 15 ft
10 John and Bob Eads	Genie Chance	21:45	–40 ft in front of ARR dock

11 Robert Clark
  Crew member of
  Alaska Standard
  Dale Pickett
  James Holban
	Genie Chance	21–22:00
		
		22:00
		After 22:00
		22:00
			–
			
			Measured maximum runup 27.1 ft
			(Berg and others, 1964)
			–

12 James Holban	Genie Chance	–	Mr. Holban was drawn out into the bay by the backwash. Big drawdown
13 Gilbert Nelson Elton Jergins	Genie Chance Personal interview, 1966	23:00 23:00	Washed into the lagoon over railroad Water up to gate of ARR dock
14 Robert Clark	Genie Chance	–	Reported waves steadily decreasing, coming in every 1¼ hr after the biggest wave. Four or five fires that he built during the night were put out by the waves.

as it did John Eads in another panel truck, and surf-rode them up into the woods at the northern end of the fan delta forming Lowell Point. Their survival was miraculous. The color film, damaged by seawater, is exasperatingly short and indistinct. Nevertheless, it was possible to reproduce the photograph (Figure 62) which shows the wave as a dark band of water, elevating smoothly but obviously cresting with white water at the coast. In the background a plume of black smoke from the fire just started at the Standard Oil Company dock is visible. We have examined Eads' film with great care, but because of its lack of clarity it is possible only to gain an impression that the wave could have been about 20 ft above general water level. The Eads brothers considered the wave to have been traveling at a speed of over 60 mph

FIGURE 57 Remains of The Alaska Railroad docks at the south end of Seward after the earthquake and tsunamis (location in Figure 64).

Irvin Cook, Anchorage

(Berg and others, 1971); 100 mph was the rate mentioned to us (personal interview, 1966). Such a speed is possible for a wave traveling as an edge wave (Lamb, 1932 ed.) at the velocity

$$c = (g \sin \theta) / \sigma, \tag{5}$$

where θ is the angle of the sea bed to the horizontal, $\sigma(=2\pi/T)$ the angular frequency of the wave, and T its period. For a beach slope of about $12°$ and an effective wave period of 3 minutes, say, this edge-wave speed would be about 180 ft/sec or about 120 mph.

This wave rushed up at Lowell Point to a height of about 33 ft above water level. A second wave, according to John Eads, rolled in at about 6:00 p.m. and was some 6 ft higher than the first (personal interview, 1966). This would accord with the large wave of that time shown in Figure 56. This second wave apparently did most of the extensive damage at Lowell Point. In 1966, from very obvious debris marks we established a runup height of about 45 ft for this or a subsequent wave at the north corner of the Lowell Point fan. On the southern side of the fan, waves reached to 100 ft (Figure 63).

The Eads brothers reported (Chance, 1966) that within 30 seconds of the onset of the earthquake a wave formed about 1 mi southwest of Fourth of July Point and traveled toward Fourth of July Point where it was reflected toward the head of the bay. A boil is reported to have been formed

in this area also, and the *Alaska Standard* changed its course to avoid it approximately 10 to 20 minutes after the earthquake (Figure 63).

The cause of the wave originating from the region of the boil is not obvious. It seems that the first slides along the waterfront area took place approximately 30 seconds after the earthquake started, but it is unlikely that the sliding earth masses would have been able to generate a wave in the middle of the bay within the first 30 seconds of the earthquake. Some other unknown slide may have caused this formation; the Eads brothers were probably not in a good position, as regards height above water level, for defining the source point of the waves, which might simply be one and the same as that reported by other witnesses to be closer to Seward and west of Fourth of July Point.

The two sides of Resurrection Bay moved longitudinally through a distance of 50 ft with about a 10-ft differential horizontal displacement between the two sides (see Figure 6, p. 131, this volume). Geologic sampling and subbottom profiling (Watkins, 1966, and Rusnak, 1966, personnal communications) have suggested that large-scale rock movements of the order of 50 ft may have taken place along preexisting faults and folds within the northern part of Resurrection Bay. Lacking details of this faulting, we can only acknowledge that any impulsive dislocation of the sea bed horizontally along a fault at approximately $45°$ to the axis of Resurrection Bay may well have caused a pair of votical boils of water. The boil closest to the south end of Seward could then have con-

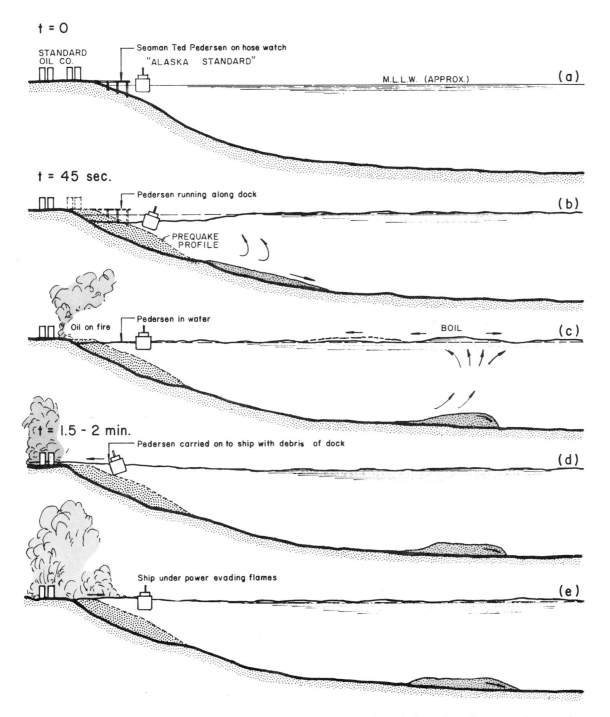

FIGURE 58 Schematic representation of submarine slide near south end of Seward, giving rise to first tsunami wave to devastate the waterfront.

tributed to precipitation of the submarine slide in that area and to generation of the waves.

After the first waterfront slide and the consequent waves, it is difficult to get a clear picture of the wave sequence from eyewitness accounts. The waves had apparently sloshed back and forth in an irregular manner for a

while. However, it seems to be definite that a high wave rushed up the landing strip of the airport approximately 8 to 10 minutes after onset of the earthquake (Chance, 1966). Two high waves with 5-minute intervals occurred approximately ½ hour after the earthquake; one of these was dominant (Figure 56) and conforms to the second wave

Standard Oil Company of California

FIGURE 59   Deck of the tanker *Alaska Standard* with wreckage from the Standard Oil Company dock at Seward.

U.S. Army

FIGURE 60   Texaco tank farm and debris still burning along the waterfront on the day after the earthquake at Seward. The cannery boat harbor had occupied a large part of the foreground area just the day before (location in Figure 64).

Terrel Schenk, Seward

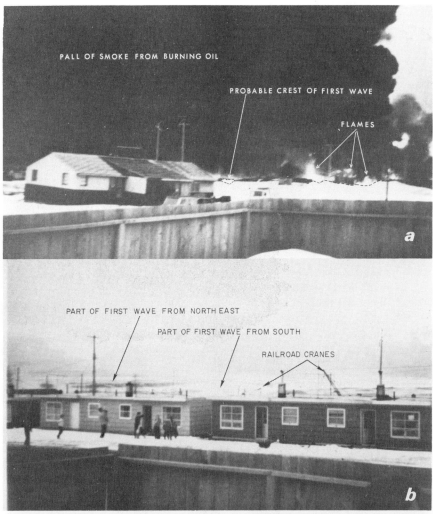

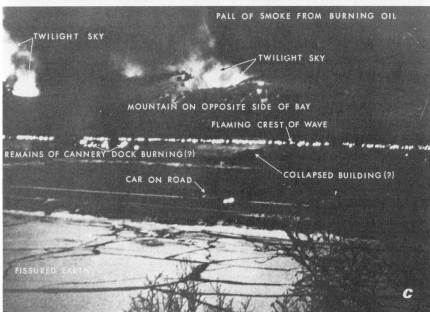

FIGURE 61 (*a*) View southeast at Seward from location *A* (Figures 55 and 64). Standard Oil Company tanks are ablaze, and crest of the first tsunami appears to be heading north along the waterfront. (*b*) View east-northeast from location *A* (Figure 64). North-moving wave crest near railroad cranes appears to be crossing through wave(s) approaching from east-northeast. (*c*) View east from location *B* (Figure 64) with later wave crest illuminated by burning oil about 21:20 AST, March 27, 1964 (see Figure 56).

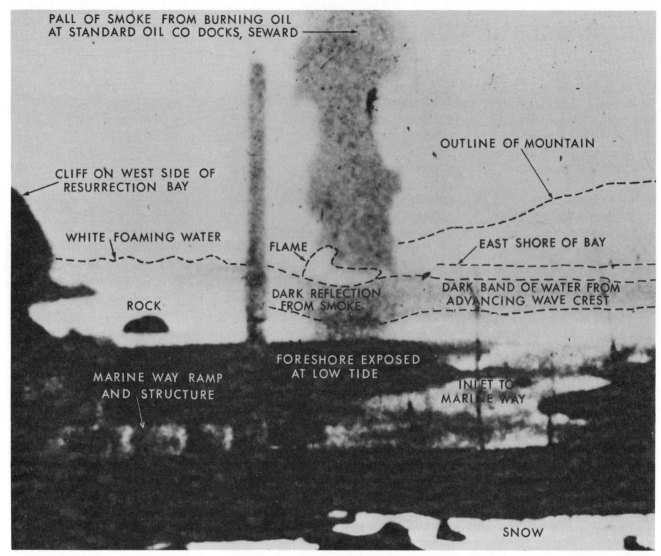

PALL OF SMOKE FROM BURNING OIL
AT STANDARD OIL CO DOCKS, SEWARD

OUTLINE OF MOUNTAIN

CLIFF ON WEST SIDE OF
RESURRECTION BAY

WHITE FOAMING WATER

FLAME

EAST SHORE OF BAY

ROCK

DARK REFLECTION
FROM SMOKE

DARK BAND OF WATER FROM
ADVANCING WAVE CREST

FORESHORE EXPOSED
AT LOW TIDE

MARINE WAY RAMP
AND STRUCTURE

INLET TO
MARINE WAY

SNOW

Robert Eads, Seward

FIGURE 62   The first tsunami advancing southward along the coast from Seward toward Lowell Point (for location see Figure 63). Photograph is enlarged from 8-mm color motion-picture film. Film was damaged by seawater.

to which most witnesses have referred (see also Berg and others, 1971). This wave is believed to have been higher and more damaging than the first and to have reached close to the highest runup levels recorded. However, as Figure 56 suggests, the main tsunami from the Continental Shelf had not yet arrived, although it was already making its presence felt in the form of a negative wave. We have hypothesized in this figure that oscillations of period close to 12 to 15 minutes became prevalent within the first 1½ hours after the earthquake. This happens to be close to the second-mode period of oscillation for the whole of Resurrection Bay, as also the first-mode period of oscillation of the northern part of the bay, acting as a pseudo-closed-end basin. It is believed that the first tsunami wave arrived at

about 18:30 AST but, because of mismatched phasing, failed to reach very remarkable proportions.

With the rising tide, the later tsunami waves, which were probably higher because of the same kind of modulation effect as that which influenced the Kodiak area, became more dangerous. At about 22:00 AST, a very large wave surged to the head of the bay and reached maximum uprush at about 30 ft above MLLW. This wave had apparently been preceded by a phenomenal drawdown to 40 ft below MLLW, according to an observation by the Eads brothers (Chance, 1966; personal interview, 1966). It was also followed by a very large recession which carried James Holben ¼ mi out on the tidal flats (Lantz and Kirkpatrick, 1964; Chance, 1966). How this large wave could have arisen, ex-

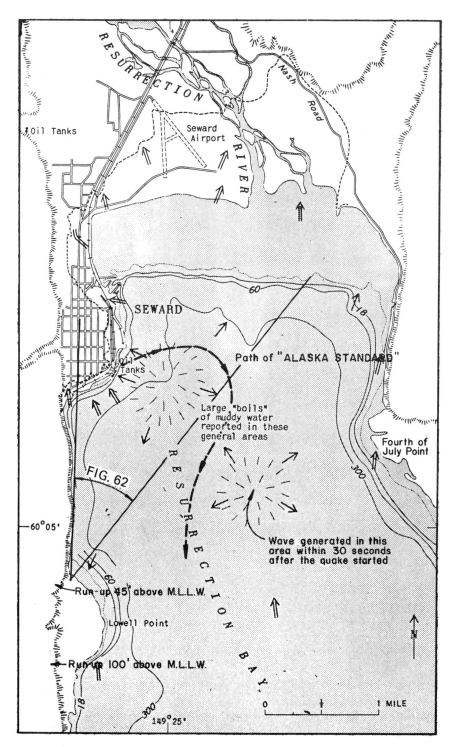

FIGURE 63   Map of the northern part of Resurrection Bay, including Seward. (Adapted from Grantz and others, 1964.)

cept as some peculiar combination of superposed waves, is not clear. Afterward and throughout the night, other big waves of decreasing height surged in and out at about 1¼-hour intervals (Chance, 1966).

Obviously, the waves that hit the Seward waterfront during the earthquake were generated by the waterfront

landslides or by local faulting, or both. What source generated the waves that hit the airport and other places 8 to 10 minutes after the earthquake started is not so obvious. However, it has been reported (Lantz and Kirkpatrick, 1964; Chance, 1966) that there was a slide at the head of Thumb Cove shortly after the earthquake started and that the wave

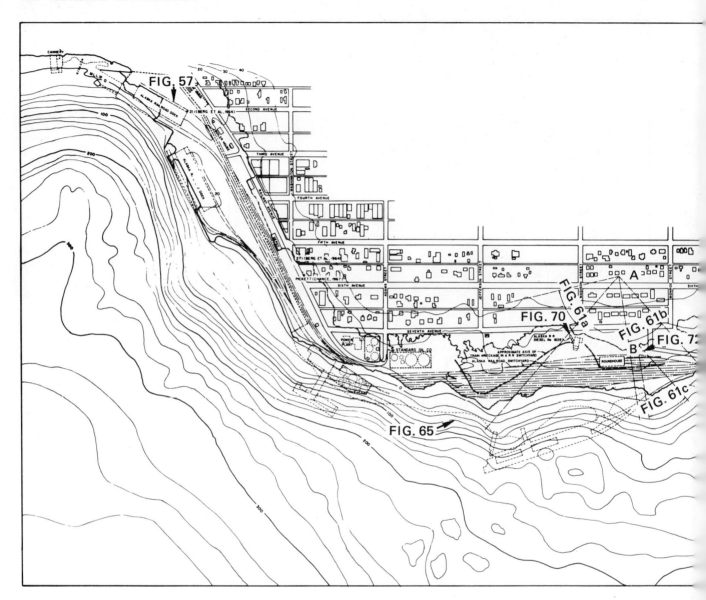

FIGURE 64   Plan of Seward after the earthquake, showing the eroded shoreline, postearthquake contours, and the limit of inundation.

generated by the slide had a runup of 40–50 ft at the head of Thumb Cove. It is reasonable to suppose that a relatively big wave would have emerged from Thumb Cove at the same time; if a part of this was diffracted toward the head of Resurrection Bay, approximate calculation of travel times shows that this wave would reach the head of the Bay within 9 minutes. This matches rather well with the reported time (Table 3) that the above-mentioned wave rushed up the airport landing strip. The Thumb Cove disturbance could also have been the excitation to trigger longitudinal oscillations in Resurrection Bay, as envisioned in Figure 56, contributing to the violence of the second wave at 18:00 hours.

The runup of the different individual waves is not exactly known. The maximum runup, probably caused by the wave that came in at about 22:00 AST, is fairly well established along the Seward waterfront from eyewitness accounts and from aerial photographs taken 3 days after the earthquake by Air Photo Tech, Inc., of Anchorage. This runup line has been drawn in Figure 64 from careful scrutiny of vertical and oblique aerial photographs and other ground photographs. Postearthquake contours of ground level and water depth (Figure 64) prove the general consistency of the runup line, which, on the average, is about 27 ft above MLLW. In places, however, the runup exceeds 30 ft; this occurs notably on either side of the two projecting points on the shoreline at the root and head of where the Army dock used to be. Figure 53 reveals that contours offshore indicate the existence of a submarine spur which would have the effect of refracting and

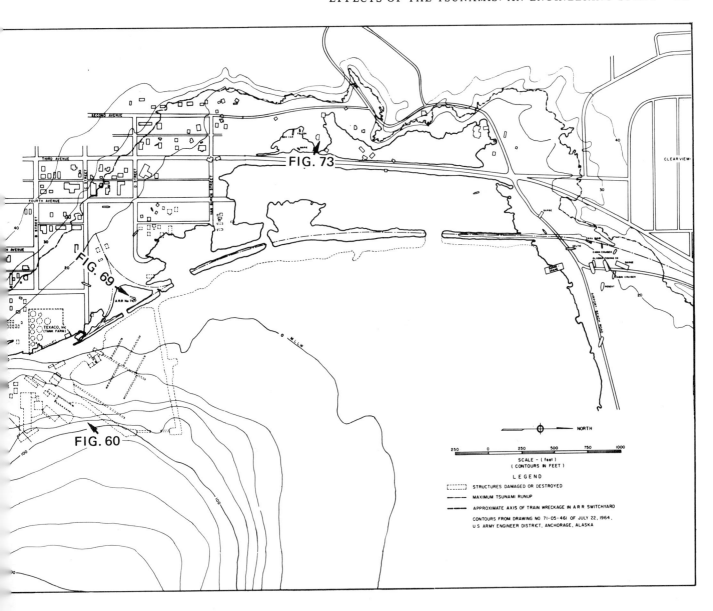

concentrating wave energy toward its center and the locations mentioned. The two points of land, however, had the same effect on the wave uprush, and this is very markedly seen in the manner in which the railroad cars were festooned about these shoreline cusps (Figure 65).

Generally speaking, the description we have given of wave effects at Seward is in accord with that given by Lemke (1967), though there are differences in detail. The reader is referred to Lemke for an excellent general description of the calamity that beset Seward.

TSUNAMI WAVE DAMAGE AT SEWARD

Seward suffered its greatest damage from the subsidence and disappearance of its entire waterfront facilities (Figures

64 and 65). This appears to have been a progressive action of the earthquake, which could have been assisted by the drawdown of the water level, resulting from the initial slide and the subsequent alternate wave loading and suction effect. Shannon & Wilson (1964) point out that considerable artesian pressures existed in the fan delta prior to the earthquake and fluctuated with the tide. These pressures would have been generally increased by the regional subsidence of about 5 to 6½ ft that affected the entire area during the earthquake. Stability analyses of the soils by Shannon & Wilson confirmed that reasonable safety against failure for the slopes of the fan delta existed under static conditions but disappeared under accelerations of the order of 0.15 g. The vibration of the earthquake could also have (1) reduced cohesion of the soils after a large number of

Irvin Cook, Anchorage

FIGURE 65 The Alaska Railroad switch-yard and engine roundhouse after the earthquake and tsunamis.

stress reversals and (2) promoted liquefaction. We cannot overlook the possibility that an impulsive shear along a fault plane in the northern part of Resurrection Bay set up a roil of water violent enough to have scoured the toe of the slopes of the fan delta, thus promoting slide failure. We shall not further discuss waterfront damage, other than obvious damage that resulted from the tsunamis.

In the switchyard of The Alaska Railroad, officials had just finished coupling together a freight train when the earthquake started. This train, with all types of rolling stock (boxcars, flatcars, gondolas, refrigerator cars, and tank cars), was due to leave for Anchorage early in the evening. It was swept almost like a continuous string (Figures 64 and 65) and festooned around the enginehouse by the tsunamis. It is not certain whether this was a progressive action of the entire sequence of waves or whether it was accomplished only by the most powerful wave of all, which, according to Figure 56, was probably at 22:00 hours. The latter alternative appears likely, however, because the earlier waves very likely lacked enough sustained force to accomplish such total wreckage (see Figures 66 to 70). Nevertheless, there is evidence to show that the first and second waves accomplished at least some of this destruction (Lantz and Kirkpatrick, 1964; Chance, 1966).

The apparent mystery surrounding the fact that many of the railroad tracks were stripped clean of their rails (see Figure 67) is explained by an observation by Hal Gilfillen (Chance, 1966), who reported that the quenching effect of the first wave on the rails, made "cherry red" from the heat of the burning oil, "curled and raised [them] like snakes stepped on."

The Alaska Railroad (1964), in a survey of damaged equipment and vehicles after the earthquake, gave information regarding the positions occupied by each car. In the time available for this study, it was not possible to include these data in Figure 63. Although the tare weights of the different vehicles and the approximate weight of the load each carried are known, it is not easy to evaluate the forces involved in moving them. Many of them, especially the gondolas and boxcars, were undoubtedly lifted and floated for some time before they were filled with water. On the other hand, the locomotives and the tank cars could not have floated.

Two of the switching locomotives were rolled over and transported, one of them (No. 1828) approximately 300 ft. Because locomotive No. 7101 (Figure 68) was lying by itself without any cars close to it, it might be reasonable to assume that this engine was moved only by water, whereas locomotive No. 1828 might have been pushed by impacts from cars. Presumably, locomotive No. 7107 stood on the track of the reversing triangle just east of where it terminates as a result of erosion (see Figure 64). The rail elevation at this place was approximately 19 ft above MLLW. If the wave of highest runup overturned this engine, water level would have reached to 25 ft in this vicinity, and the locomotive would have been immersed in 6 ft of water. According to the approximate calculation in Figure 71, a water velocity of about 24.5 ft/sec and a force of about 700 lb/ft² would be required to capsize the locomotive. However, the engine might also have been overturned by a wave of lesser runup advancing with a higher, more smashing front.

FIGURE 66   Wave damage in The Alaska Railroad marshaling yard; northeast view.

U.S. Army

The enginehouse of The Alaska Railroad withstood the wave attack rather well (Figure 72). The enginehouse was a steel-frame building with concrete blocks. It was partly damaged by impact from cars but seemingly did not suffer much damage from the impact of running water. The wave(s) that most severely damaged the railroad cars apparently had a northwest direction, because a locomotive

and several cars in the geometric shadow zone north of the enginehouse (Figures 64 and 65) were not moved. The enginehouse has since been torn down because the railroad facilities have been rebuilt at the head of the bay.

The waves left a shambles of houses and boats in the lagoon area, some still looking relatively undamaged and some almost completely battered (Figure 73). The type

U.S. Army

FIGURE 67   Closeup of wave damage in The Alaska Railroad marshaling yard.

FIGURE 68 Part of The Alaska Railroad freight yard, showing tracks stripped of their rails.

Dave Thompson, Seward

of house moved and damaged was of light wooden-frame structure. It was not possible, without a prohibitive amount of research, to establish where the houses stood before the earthquake. Figure 64, however, shows a few houses and boats whose identity had been traced from an interpretation of aerial photographs.

There were approximately 125 boats in the small-boat harbor at the time the earthquake started. They were tumbled by the first wave that hit the waterfront before the harbor disappeared, and some boats were washed over the breakwater. Most of the boats were lost, and the death toll in Seward consisted mainly of people on board their boats

Dave Thompson, Seward

FIGURE 69 Switching locomotive No. 7107 (115 tons) transported and overturned by the tsunamis north of the marshaling yard (for location see Figure 64).

FIGURE 70   A 125-ton locomotive transported and overturned by waves near the enginehouse.

Irvin Cook, Anchorage

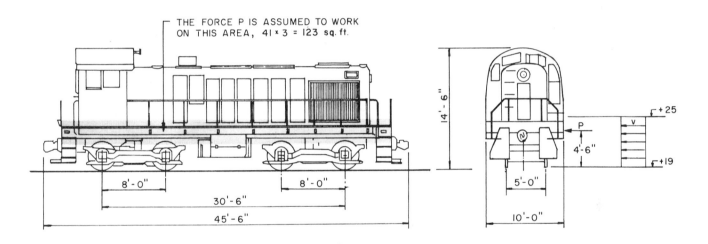

THE FORCE P IS ASSUMED TO WORK ON THIS AREA, 41 × 3 = 123 sq. ft.

Weight of engine   = 115 tons
Buoyancy ≈ 62.4 × (10 × 41 × 3)/2000 =   38   "
Submerged weight   =   77 tons

Necessary force to overturn the engine :

$$P = \frac{77 \times 2.5}{4.5} = 43 \text{ tons} = 86000 \text{ lbs}$$

Drag force: $P = \rho C_D A \dfrac{v^2}{2g}$ or $v = \left(\dfrac{2pg}{C_D \rho A}\right)^{1/2}$

Assumed $C_D = 1.2$ $A = 41 \times 3 = 123$ ft.^{2}

Average pressure force : $p = \dfrac{P}{A} = \dfrac{86000}{123} = 700$ lbs/ft.

$$v = \left(\frac{2 \times 86000 \times 32.2}{1.2 \times 62.4 \times 123}\right)^{1/2} = 24.5 \text{ ft/sec}$$

C_D = drag coefficient
v = water velocity
A = projected area of inmersion
g = acceleration due to gravity

FIGURE 71   Approximate calculation of water velocities required to overturn locomotive No. 7107.

The Alaska Railroad

FIGURE 72   Engine roundhouse near The Alaska Railroad marshaling yards, showing relatively light damage from the earthquake and waves (for location see Figure 64).

in the small-boat harbor. Some of the boats were carried inland and beached far above normal high water (Figure 64). Figure 74 shows some of the boats beached among debris at the northwest head of the bay.

The small tanker *Alaska Standard*, 1947 gross tons, was loading oil at the Standard Oil Company dock when the earthquake started. As the dock disappeared, the ship dropped 25 to 30 ft and then rose again on the incoming wave, as already described in Figure 58. The hoses and mooring lines snapped off, but within 5 minutes she managed to navigate toward deeper water under her own power, being in constant danger of catching fire and exploding from the burning oil on the water surface (Solibakke, 1964). Backwash of the first wave left debris from the dock and

Dave Thompson, Seward

FIGURE 73   Wreckage of houses and boats carried into the lagoon by the waves. Rooftop in center field was the former Seward radio station (for location see Figure 64). House at right came from a site near Fourth Street and Van Buren Avenue (see Figure 55).

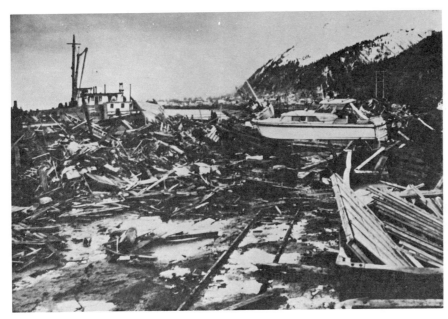

FIGURE 74   Chaos of wreckage left by the tsunami at the northwest end of the head of Resurrection Bay. View south shows Seward in the background.

U.S. Army

warehouse on the deck of the ship (Figure 59). The ship, following approximately the course indicated in Figure 63, until she was free from the danger of waves and burning oil, stood by in the bay until the next day.

At the airport all the small planes and the Civil Air Patrol house were damaged by the wave that came in approximately 8 to 10 minutes after the earthquake started (Chance, 1966).

At Lowell Point a newly built marina and workshop was completely demolished by the smashing effect of the waves. The workshop at the head of a launch ramp was a wooden-frame building standing only 1 ft above the highest high-water level. Different types of machinery for contracting work, parked at the marina, were tumbled and damaged beyond repair. The damage was massive. A 25-ton Caterpillar tractor had its manganese steel frame broken by a rock; a 26-ton crane was carried 500 ft from the beach line; a 16-ton earth grader, parked in the area back of the shop, was moved about 100 ft and smashed; a 2-ton air compressor was displaced about 500 ft. The marine-way cradle was whipped along its tracks, smashing a winding drum and leveling everything in its path. It tore loose from its cables and landed in the rear parking area. The waves dislodged the winch which was both bolted down and welded to railroad irons set in 6 ft of concrete. They sheared four pieces of railroad steel and moved the winch 6 ft inside what had been the shop. The shed completely disappeared and was never found.

Figure 75 shows the remains of the 6-ton panel truck in which Robert Eads and Christiansen survived the first wave. It was wrapped around a tree about 32 ft above

water level, presumably by the second wave at 18:00 AST (Figure 56).

At Seward the total damage to port and harbor facilities was estimated at $15,375,000 (Hansen and others, 1966). It is not easy to say how much of this is directly attributable to the tsunami, but an amount of $14,614,000 was assessed by the *Anchorage Daily News* of April 16, 1964 (Spaeth and Berkman, 1967, and this volume). Eleven persons lost their lives at Seward due to the sea waves.

Some remarkable seiches were generated in Kenai Lake (McCulloch, 1966, and Hydrology volume); these could have been very damaging had the shore of the lake been developed. Also there were remote seiches (Donn, 1964; McGarr, 1965, and Hydrology volume; McGarr and Vorhis, 1968, and Hydrology volume) which are of engineering interest, as having caused minor damage. These effects were especially notable along the Gulf of Mexico coastline.

EFFECTS OF THE MAIN TSUNAMI AND OF LOCAL TSUNAMIS IN PRINCE WILLIAM SOUND

THE OVERALL PICTURE AT PRINCE WILLIAM SOUND

The nature of the tectonic movement that occurred during the earthquake has been defined with greater accuracy in the Prince William Sound area than anywhere else. Large areas experienced vertical uplift or subsidence and also horizontal displacement. The major portion of the Sound was uplifted, but this took the form of a massive tilting of the sea bed toward the northwest. Figures 3 and 76 portray the main bathymetric features of the region. The coastline

Pierre St.-Amand

FIGURE 75 Remains of 6-ton truck at Lowell Point near Seward, 32 ft above water level.

is labyrinthine in complexity and resembles a jigsaw puzzle, but in its entirety it can be grossly approximated as a triangular basin *ABC* (Figure 76), whose depth on the average would be about 800 ft. This basin was effectively tilted by the earthquake about a hinge line that could be considered roughly parallel to the base line *BC* in Figure 76 at about one third the perpendicular distance of the base *BC* from the vertex *A*.

Despite the crudeness of this approximation, we are tempted to examine the free oscillating characteristics of such a triangular basin, regarding it as having an open mouth along the line *BC*. For the most part this base line really functions as a closed boundary because of the island barriers, but in the presence of very-long-period excitation such as the astronomical tides or the tsunami generated on the Continental Shelf, it may be considered virtually open.

The fundamental period T_1 is obtainable from Lamb (1932) (compare also Wilson, 1966), namely,

$$T_1 = 2.616L/\sqrt{gd} , \qquad (6)$$

where L is the perpendicular length of the embayment from *A* to *BC* (Figure 76) and d is the mean depth. Adopting $L = 4 \times 10^5$ ft and $d = 800$ ft, we find that

$$T_1 \approx 110 \text{ minutes.} \qquad (7)$$

To the nth-mode of oscillation ($n = 1, 2, 3, \ldots$), the periods T_n may be shown to be

$$T_n \approx 110; \ 48; \ 30; \ 22; \ldots \text{ minutes.} \qquad (8)$$

Obviously the shorter periods in equation (8) are of rather doubtful accuracy because the validity of the assumption of an open basin becomes subject to question at such periods. The result is interesting, however, insofar as the dominant period of the external shelf-generated tsunami appears to be of the same order of magnitude as in equation (7). This implies that Prince William Sound would have been quite a responsive sounding box for the external stimulation penetrating the straits around Montague Island, as well as for its own upheaval, which initially would tend to have some of the same character as the externally generated tsunami.

The very tortuous coastline would no doubt have a rather profound effect in modifying and attenuating any free oscillations induced by tilting of the bed, but the tuning appears to be such that the external tsunami and shelf oscillation could nevertheless develop sensible amplitude and persistence within the Sound.

It is reasonable to suppose that because of its proximity to the epicenter of the earthquake, near Unakwik Inlet, Prince William Sound experienced more violent shaking than most other places. Slides were numerous and locally generated effects complex. From what is known from eyewitness accounts of tsunamis in the Prince William Sound area, it is very difficult to obtain an integrated concept of the wave sequences.

Many places like Chenega, Sawmill Bay, and Thumb Bay were struck by high waves during the earthquake. These first waves were seemingly of short period, with the character of locally generated waves such as the first slide-generated waves that struck Seward, Valdez, and Whittier.

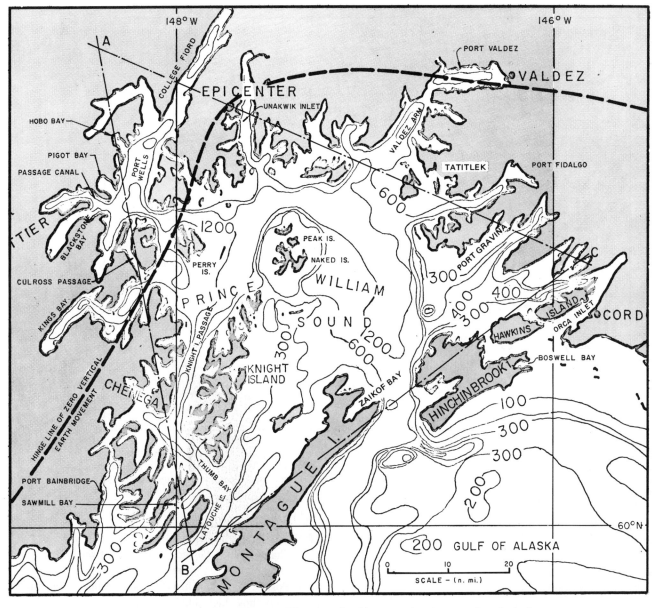

FIGURE 76   Bathymetry of Prince William Sound and its approximation as a triangular basin.

However, there is no visible evidence of the occurrence of slides that could have generated these waves. Glacial deposits such as those in which the above-mentioned wave-generating slides took place are apparently almost absent in the western and northern parts of Prince William Sound. However, such deposits probably occur locally under water because depressed cirque levels in these areas indicate that shorelines have been drowned since the last major glaciation (Plafker, 1965; von Huene and others, 1967), and indeed a substantial invisible submarine slide north of Latouche Island (Figure 76) has been reported by the U.S. Coast and Geodetic Survey ship *Surveyor* (U.S. Coast and Geodetic Survey, 1965). This slide probably generated the first waves that hit Port Ashton and Thumb Bay. Other causes of local waves of uncertain origin may have been local submarine faulting and seiching generated by ground vibration during the earthquake.

A generalized distribution of larger destructive local waves and known subaqueous slides in Prince William Sound (Figure 77) was defined by the U.S. Geological Survey (Plafker and Mayo, 1965). Because the available information about possible wave origins is too scanty at present to justify further speculation, only a description of the waves and the known damage at the smaller villages

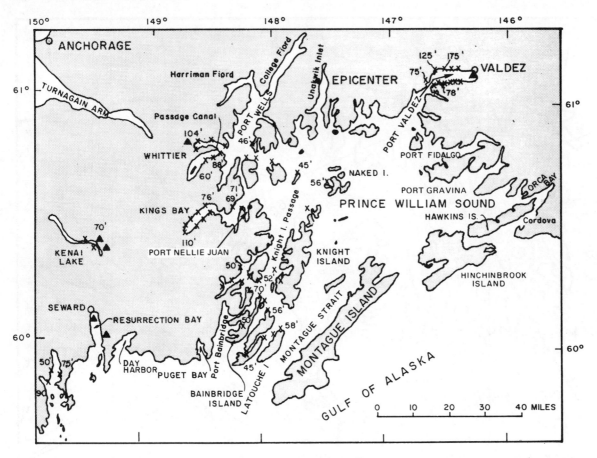

FIGURE 77   Generalized distribution of larger destructive local waves and known subaqueous slides in Prince William Sound and part of the Kenai Peninsula. Shorelines damaged by waves with runup heights in excess of 40 ft above lower low water are indicated by an "X"—numerals are the measured maximum runup heights. Solid triangle indicates known subaqueous slide. (From Plafker and Mayo, 1965).

and inhabited places, as reported by eyewitnesses, will be included here (the location of these places may be found in Figure 76). Valdez and Whittier will be discussed more fully in later sections.

An attempt has been made to infer marigrams (Figure 78) for some of the places to be mentioned.

Chenega, on Chenega Island in Knight Island Passage, was one of the places hardest hit in Prince William Sound. All the houses except the schoolhouse were floated away and totally lost; 23 people were drowned.

About 60 to 90 seconds after the earthquake started, the first wave came in like a fast rising tide and reached halfway up the beach; some people were drowned by this wave. As the water receded 1 minute later to about 500 ft from shore, it swept away some of the houses. A second wave, arriving with a roar, struck the village about 4 minutes after the earthquake started; this wave swept away all the remaining houses except the schoolhouse on a hill at an elevation of 90 ft, though water spray reached to the

school building. Three oil tanks withstood the wave attack (Chance, 1966). General runup height was about 54 ft above MLLW.

At Port Oceanic, Knight Island, a wave that rushed up 18 to 20 ft above high-tide level struck the shore 1 to 2 minutes after the onset of the earthquake (Chance, 1966).

The smashing wave that struck Thumb Bay, Knight Island, 2 to 3 minutes after the earthquake, washed away trees which were standing 20 ft above zero tide and piled debris at least 22 ft above the highest tide line at the head of the bay (Chance, 1966).

About 2 minutes after the earthquake began, the water started to rise smoothly and slowly at Sawmill Bay, Evans Island. Then it receded in a roaring current, and shortly afterward there was a second fast wave, which reached to about the highest tidewater line and swept away pilings, docks, and boats (Chance, 1966).

At Port Ashton in Sawmill Bay the first wave struck about 2 minutes after the earthquake, beaching some ves-

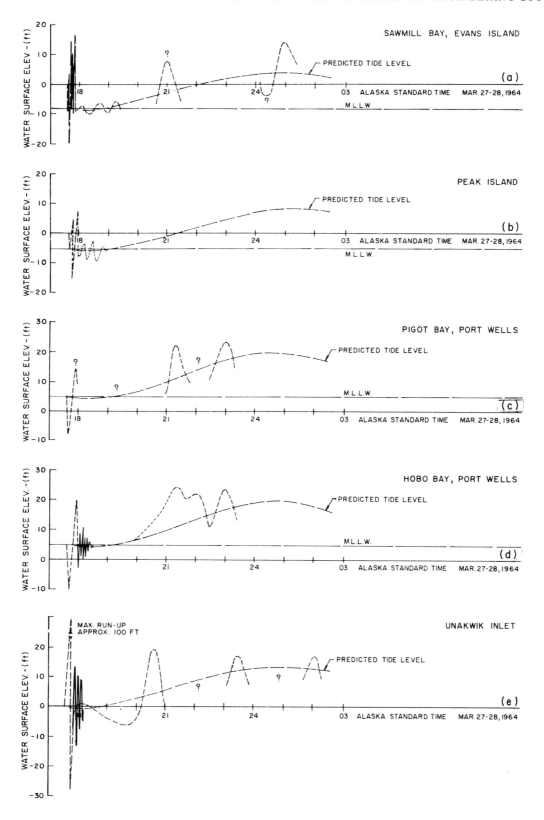

FIGURE 78   Inferred marigrams at five locations in Prince William Sound (based on observations reported by Chance, 1967; Berg and others, 1964).

sels. The water was reported to have continued oscillations at 3- to 4-minute intervals until dusk. A high wave at about 21:00 AST swept away some skiffs (Figure 78a).

At Port Nellie Juan, a wave about 5 ft higher than the dock swept away pilings and toppled two buildings.

In Culross Passage, a violent current surged south and then north soon after the earthquake started. The current changed three or four times during a half-hour period. The surge had the form of a bore 8 to 10 ft high (Chance, 1966).

As reported by two brothers living on an isolated bay on Perry Island, the water "ruffled" and went down to about 8 ft below low tide. Approximately 8 minutes after the earthquake started, a wave came in and rushed up 26 ft above MLLW (Berg and others, 1971; Chance, 1966).

Mrs. Clock, who lives with her family in a cove on Peak Island, reported that the water rose and "boiled furiously" along the shore and that spray went high into the trees. Then the water dropped almost 15 ft from low-tide level and it was "eerie calm." About 4 to 5 minutes after the earthquake, a wave of water "five feet higher than normal moved in from the lagoon" and struck the shore. Mrs. Clock said that the water "came back and forth for at least an hour." (See Figure 78b.)

The fishing boat *Roald* was anchored in Port Wells at the time of the earthquake. The captain reported that the water withdrew about 20 minutes later. Then after another 10–15 minutes it returned like a tidal bore from the south and carried the anchored boat, along with rocks and debris, into its mainstream.

At the head of Pigot Bay, Port Wells, the water receded about ¼ to ½ mile from the shore after the earthquake ended. As it receded, the water whipped violently back and forth. Then the water returned to shore like a fast-rising tide without any violent surge. About 10 minutes after the earthquake ceased, the water became calm at normal tide-water level. Between 21:00 and 21:30 AST the sea rose to a height of 8 ft above extreme high tide. It then receded about 2 ft. At about 23:00 it reached again to about 8 ft above extreme high tide (Chance, 1966) (see Figure 78c).

In Hobo Bay, north of Pigot Bay, the water receded during the earthquake and exposed sea bottom that is normally below lowest tide. When the water returned, it rose to about 4 ft above high tide. After the earthquake ceased, small waves came in rapid succession every 2 to 3 minutes. As darkness fell, the sea became very calm. Shortly after dark, however, the water began to rise and within 1½ hours had reached 9 ft above high-tide level. The water then receded about 4 ft before another wave came in. For a period of 2 hours the water advanced and withdrew three times (Chance, 1966) (see Figure 78d).

The fishing vessel *Quest* was in Unakwik Inlet at the time of the earthquake. One of the crew members reported that a big swell moved in while the earth was shaking. The water sloshed back and forth in an east–west direction and ran up approximately 100 ft in some places; when it withdrew, it exposed the sea bottom about 4 or 5 fathoms deep. Large waves swept into the inlet at 23:00 AST and then again at about 02:00 in the night (Chance, 1966).

A crew member of another fishing vessel that was about 1 mi inside the mouth of Unakwik Inlet at the time of the earthquake reported that the water started to oscillate during the earthquake, washing high on the north shore and then withdrawing an unusually great distance offshore. The oscillations continued throughout the earthquake with a period of approximately 1 minute. Immediately after the earthquake ended, the water started to recede, a regression that continued for about 2½ hours. Within 3 hours after the earthquake, the water started to rise to a level higher than high water; by 21:00 it was again receding. At about midnight another wave brought the water level to about 3 ft higher than the normal tide for that time (Chance, 1966) (see Figure 78e).

At Tatitlek the water receded 15 ft and then returned 17 to 18 ft above MLLW. At 21:00 AST a high wave rose to within 7 in. of the preearthquake 15-ft level; 45 minutes later, there was a wave with a height of 5.3 ft above the normal tide of that time (Chance, 1966).

At Boswell Bay, Hinchinbrook Island, it was reported that the water receded initially. The regression was followed by two waves within 3 hours after the shock. Between 24:00 and 01:00 AST, the water rose 8 to 12 ft above the high-tide level (Chance, 1966).

The maximum tsunami runup at Zaikof Bay, Montague Island, was about 33 ft above postearthquake MLLW.

At an unidentified place on Montague Island, five waves at about 5-minute intervals were observed traveling parallel to the shore; the first one, with a height of 12 ft, arrived at about 18:05.

TSUNAMI WAVES IN PORT VALDEZ

The disaster that befell Seward had something of a parallel at Valdez, situated in Prince William Sound, at the head of a long fiord comprising Valdez Arm and Port Valdez (Figure 79). The similarity of earthquake and tsunami effects is rendered more interesting because of a similarity of location of the towns with respect to bays of rather similar shape and size. In fact, the schematic representation of a coupled system of basins shown in Figure 52b applies in the same sense to the Valdez fiord, which is seen to comprise two basins connected by a constricted channel of shallower water (Figure 79). Even the dimensions are quite similar. The difference, in the relative situations of Valdez and Seward, is that Valdez Arm opens on Prince William Sound, a virtually closed basin, whereas Resurrection Bay opens on the sea. Valdez, of course, was much closer to the

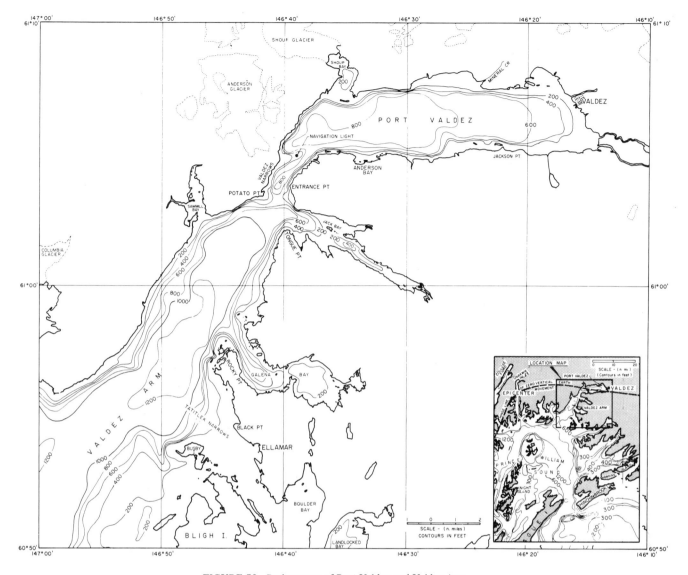

FIGURE 79   Bathymetry of Port Valdez and Valdez Arm.

epicenter of the earthquake and was located close to the hinge line of zero vertical earth motion (Figure 70, inset).

We investigate the oscillating properties of Valdez Arm and Port Valdez as a chain-basin system represented schematically by Figure 52b. In this case, basins I, II, and III have the approximate dimensions given in Table 8. By the impedance principle of Rayleigh as employed by Neumann (1948), we find the eigenperiods T_n (n = 1, 2, 3, 4, . . .) for the first four modes of free oscillation of the system to be

$$T_n \simeq 39; \ 18; \ 11; \ 7; \dots \text{minutes.} \qquad (9)$$

Comparison of the period sequence in equation (9) with that of equation (8) suggests that the Valdez embayment

TABLE 8   Dimensions of Interconnecting Rectangular Basins Simulating Valdez Arm and Port Valdez

Basin	Length L (nautical miles)	Breadth b (nautical miles)	Depth d (ft)
I	11.35	2.01	700
II	2.00	0.76	600
III	10.52	2.66	1100

would not provide resonance for the expected fundamental period of the tsunami waves generated at the mouth of Prince William Sound. However, in view of the implication that the Sound might well develop oscillations corresponding to the higher modes of its triangular shape, some degree

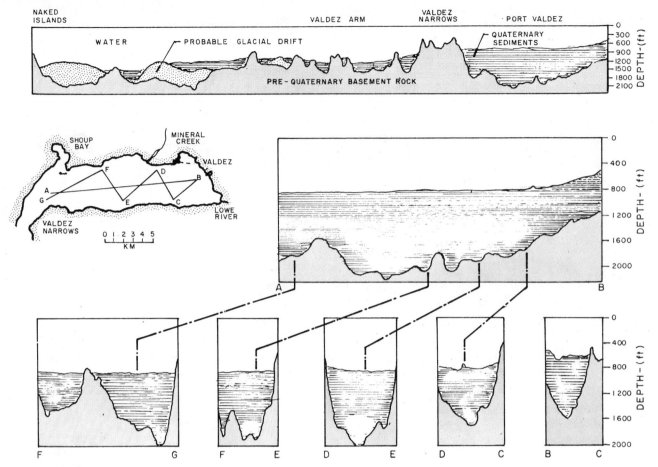

FIGURE 80   Seismic reflection profiles along the axis of Valdez Arm and Port Valdez and along various section lines in Port Valdez, showing basement structure and sediments. (Adapted from von Huene, Shor, and Reimnitz, 1967.)

of resonance or pseudoresonance could amplify the effects of oscillations of period less than 50 minutes.

Figure 80 gives the results of seismic reflection profiles of the Valdez embayment obtained in field surveys since the earthquake (von Huene and others, 1967). The basement rock profile has an average depth in Valdez Arm of about 1,200 ft; it is deeper (about 1,800 ft) in Port Valdez. In Valdez Narrows, the rock forms a sill virtually free of sediments. Because of the elbow bend formed between Valdez Arm and Port Valdez, the latter is capable of functioning effectively as a closed basin for any water oscillations generated within it. The profile AB in Figure 80 is not quite complete in showing the rise of sediments beyond B. The water-depth profile, however, may reasonably well be taken as being semiparabolic over the basin length of 11.35 nautical miles, with its maximum depth of 850 ft at the west end.

The manner in which this basin would oscillate by itself longitudinally may be found by considering it joined with its mirror-image basin. Applicable modes from the solution of the double basin are only those that will yield an anti-node at the center. From Wilson (1966), then, we find the fundamental and second-mode periods of oscillation (longitudinally) for Port Valdez to be

$$\left.\begin{aligned}&\text{(i) } T_1 \simeq 17.8 \text{ minutes}\\&\text{(ii) } T_2 \simeq 9.8 \text{ minutes}\end{aligned}\right\}. \qquad (10)$$

No tide gage was operating at Valdez Harbor; if there had been, it could not have provided any information because of the total destruction of the harbor. As in the case of Seward, we are dependent on eyewitness accounts and the studies of other investigators for an interpretation of what happened in Port Valdez. We shall refer to many sources of information, notably, Grantz and others (1964); Brown (1964); Berg and others (1971); U.S. Coast and Geodetic Survey (1964a); Denner, personal communication (1964); Plafker and Mayo (1965); Spaeth and Berkman (1965, 1967, and this volume); Coulter and Migliaccio (1966, and Geology volume); and numerous unpublished materials to be cited.

Valdez is situated at the eastern end of Port Valdez on the seaward edge of a large outwash delta composed of a thick section of saturated silty sand and gravel. Its general location is shown in Figure 79, and details of the layout of the city and harbor are given in the preearthquake plan in Figure 81. The city was entirely contained within a V-shaped levee which prevented inundation from the frequent rampages of the Valdez River draining from the Valdez Glacier. Figure 82 shows the appearance of the waterfront at an earlier time before the development of the small-boat harbor in the tidal zone area between the north and south arms of the docks.

Valdez is the northernmost all-weather port in Alaska, but, unlike Seward and Whittier, it is connected with the interior only by road links. Its population of 1,200 was mainly active in the shipping and fishing industries, and its position as the "Switzerland of Alaska" favored a developing tourist trade. The earthquake brought overwhelming disaster to Valdez. The entire docks and waterfront were totally destroyed, and tsunamis penetrated deep into the heart of town. Figure 83 is an aerial view of the city after the earthquake with the limit of tsunami runup delineated. Because of the unstable sediments upon which the city is founded, it was condemned as a hazard (Coulter and Migliaccio, 1966; Eckel, 1967) and has been vacated in favor of a new townsite at Mineral Creek, founded on stable rock (see sections DE and DC of Figure 80).

Most authorities who have reported on the wave phenomena that destroyed Valdez have mentioned four waves as primarily responsible for the destruction; two of these appeared during and shortly after the earthquake, and two occurred many hours later. However, although the first waves are attributed to massive submarine slumping of the sediments at the waterfront, there is not unanimous agreement on just how the waves were generated. It is curious that eyewitnesses make no specific mention of a major boil of water as having developed in the bay (in the way it had been observed at Seward); yet this perhaps is understandable because the relative flatness of Valdez does not afford a commanding view of the bay, and the remarkable gyrations of the ship Chena distracted the attention of observers. Grantz and others (1964) and Plafker and Mayo (1965) are the only sources we can find that specifically mention mounds or boils of muddy water; yet eyewitness accounts, reported by Berg and others (1971), Brown (1964), Bryant (1964b), Chance (1966), Bracken (1964), Chapman (1964), Migliaccio (1964), and Coulter and Migliaccio (1966), make no direct reference to these boils, except in the sense of purely localized mounds hitting the ship Chena (reported by the ship's captain) and the development of a "wall of water" out in the bay, sometime after the occurrence of the first waves (reported by Forest Sturgis, Alaska State Highway engineer). We raise this matter not because there is

any question of the occurrence (which is indisputable) of a submarine slide to which the mounds and boils are attributable, but because there is the possibility that the first wave or waves may have had other association, as we shall discuss.

To explain what happened at the waterfront at Valdez, allowing some degree of conjecture to fit the facts, it is possible to infer that water level fluctuated in approximate accord with the marigram presented in Figure 84. We shall try to justify the inference as we proceed.

The first wave to strike Valdez occurred during the earthquake and was remarkably sudden. The time sequence of the waves is confused, owing to the disastrous conditions that prevailed. People who watched the water had their attention drawn to the erratic behavior and violent movement of the Alaska Steamship Company vessel Chena, a 10,815-ton cargo ship moored to the north dock when the earthquake started. Captain Merrill Stewart of this ship has given the following account of his experience (Coulter and Migliaccio, 1966):

The Chena arrived at Valdez at 16:12 hours, March 27. About 17:31, while discharging cargo, we felt a severe earthquake followed almost immediately by tidal waves. There were very heavy shocks about every half a minute. Mounds of water were hitting at us from all directions. I was in the dining room. I made it to the bridge (three decks up) by climbing a vertical ladder. God knows how I got there.

The Valdez piers started to collapse right away. There was a tremendous noise. The ship was laying over to port. I had been in earthquakes before, but I knew right away that this was the worst one yet. The Chena rose about 30 feet on an oncoming wave. The whole ship lifted and heeled to port about 50°. Then it was slammed down heavily on the spot where the docks had disintegrated moments before. I saw people running—with no place to run to. It was just ghastly. They were just engulfed by buildings, water, mud, and everything. The Chena dropped where the people had been. That is what has kept me awake for days. There was no sight of them. The ship stayed there momentarily. Then she came upright. Then we took another heavy roll to port. I could see the land (at Valdez) jumping and leaping in a terrible turmoil. We were inside of where the dock used to be. We had been washed into where the small-boat harbor used to be. There was no water under the Chena for a brief interval. I realized we had to get out quickly if we were ever going to get out at all. There was water under us again. The stern was sitting in broken pilings, rocks, and mud.

I signaled to the engine room for power and got it very rapidly. I called for "slow ahead," then "half ahead" and finally for "full." In about four minutes, I would guess, we were moving appreciably, scraping on and off the mud (bottom) as the waves went up and down. People ashore said they saw us slide sideways off a mat of willow trees (placed as part of the fill material in the harbor) and that helped put our bow out. We couldn't turn. We were moving along the shore with the stern in the mud. Big mounds of water came up and flattened out. Water inshore was rushing out. A big gush of water came off the beach, hit the bow, and swung her out about ten degrees. If that hadn't happened, we would have stayed there with the bow jammed in a mud bank and provided a new dock for the town of Valdez!! We broke free. The bow pushed through the wreckage of a cannery. We went out into the bay and

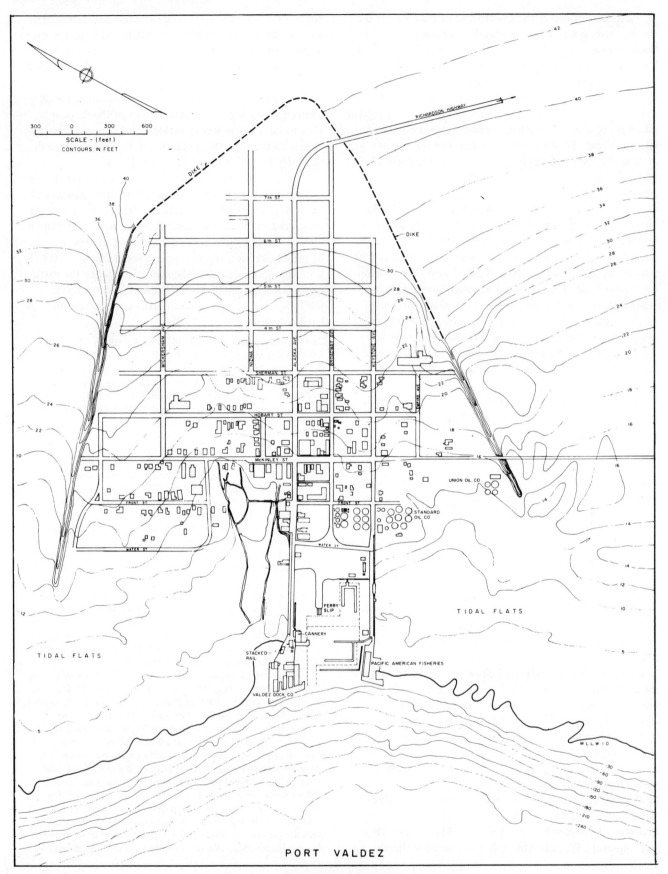

FIGURE 81 Plan of Valdez before the earthquake.

Mac's Foto

FIGURE 82   Aerial view of the waterfront at Valdez several years before the earthquake.

U.S. Army

FIGURE 83   Valdez after the earthquake showing approximate extent of inundation from the tsunami.

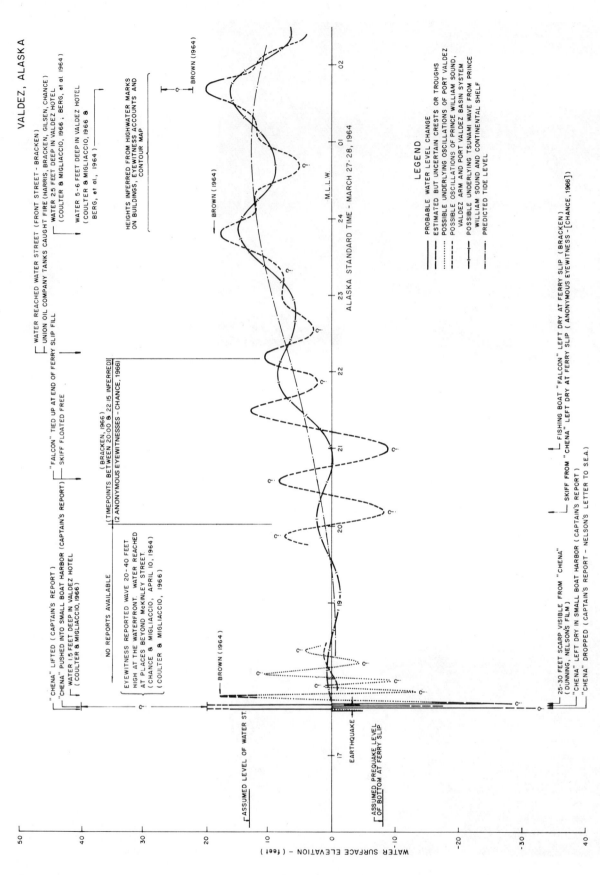

FIGURE 84 Inferred marigram for Valdez, based on accounts by eyewitnesses and on inductive reasoning.

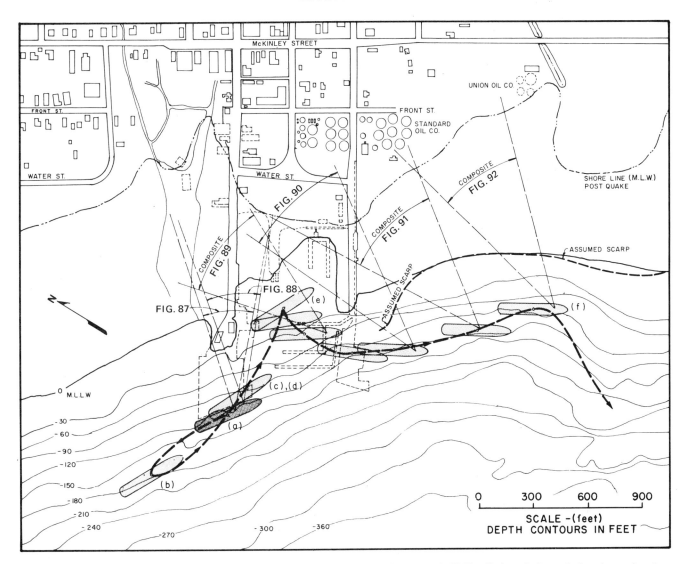

FIGURE 85 Inferred path of the S.S. *Chena* from an initial position at the North Arm Dock, Valdez Harbor, during and after the earthquake. Successive positions of the *Chena* are based on eyewitness accounts and interpretation of color motion pictures photographed from the ship by F. Numair and E. Nelson.

had to stop. The condensers were plugged with mud and pieces of the dock. The chief mate, Neal L. Larsen, checked to see then if we were taking water. We were taking none. It was unbelievable after what the ship had been through. We had the lifeboats all manned and ready. I didn't think she would float in deep water. Maybe the soft mud bottom made the difference.

Captain Stewart's impressions of the tsunami were reported by Berg and others (1971), Denner (personal communication, April 1964), Chance (1966, and in press), and the magazine Alaska Construction (1965); collectively, these sources add further important information, as do interviews that we had in 1966 with former crew members Dunning, Harding, Nelson, and Numair.

It appears evident, for example, that immediately after

the start of the earthquake the *Chena* went astern in a northwest direction and either slipped or fractured her mooring lines. Sturgis, on the third floor of the Valdez Hotel, with a view seaward down Alaska Avenue (Figure 81), was in an exceptionally good position to observe this initial movement (compare Berg and others, 1971; Bryant, 1964b; Chance, 1966, and in press) which was also confirmed by Dunning and Numair. The implied movement of the *Chena* is thus shown in Figures 85b and 86b. This first movement of the *Chena* appears to have been part of a water withdrawal which accompanied the initial subsidence of the docks during the first minute of the earthquake. The earth slump at the harbor (Figure 86b) was at first more in the nature of compaction and partial sliding on the fairly

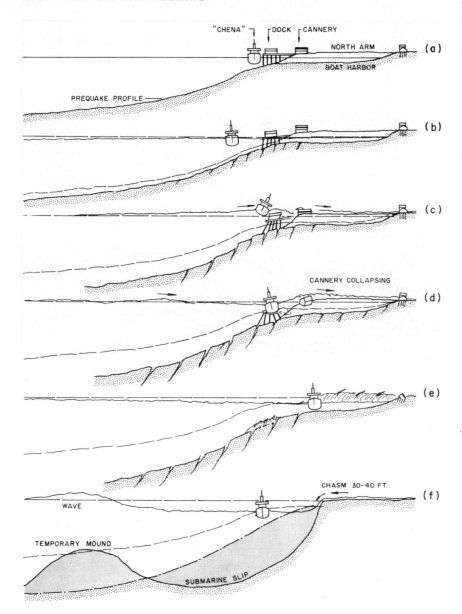

FIGURE 86 Sequence of schematic diagrams illustrating the inferred movements of the S.S. *Chena* and the destruction of the harbor at Valdez (compare with Figure 85).

flat slope of the sediments at the east end of Port Valdez. It could not have been a complete and sudden failure because the *Chena* returned on the crest of the first wave (Figures 85c and 86c) and was deposited on the wreckage of the docks. Further, although the docks had disappeared by this time, the portion of the North Arm at the approach to the docks, along with the cannery, was still intact, as proved by Figure 87. This is enlarged from a single frame (No. 110) of the 8-mm motion-picture film, photographed by Fred Numair, crew member of the *Chena*, from the approximate location of Figure 85 (c and d) or Figure 86 (c and d). Figure 87, which shows the cannery engulfed by the passing wave, should be compared with Figure 82. Numair's film (frame 184, Figure 88) shows the disintegration

of the cannery moments later as the wave rushes over the North Arm from the northwest. (Figures 87 through 92 are enlargements from 35-mm color film, reproduced from original 8-mm color motion-picture films. Because the original films were not of the best quality, definition in the photographs is unavoidably poor, dashed lines in black and white and suitable annotations have been added, where necessary, to indicate features of interest or importance.)

According to his account published in *Alaska Construction*, Captain Stewart said of this happening that "the *Chena* heeled over 70° to port and crunched down hard on the spot where the pier had disintegrated moments before. I felt the hull shudder as the ship ground into the rocks and mud and broken pilings on the harbor bottom and I thought

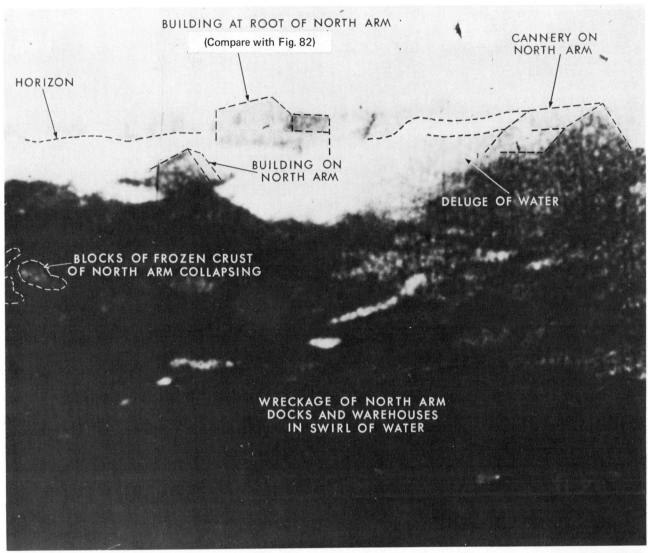

Fred Numair, Seattle

FIGURE 87   First tsunami wave engulfing the cannery on the North Arm of Valdez Harbor, as photographed from the *Chena* (enlarged from frame 110). Compare with Figures 81 and 82. (Location in Figure 85).

she was done for. No ship can stand that kind of battering."

The *Chena* at this stage took a violent roll to starboard, presumably as a result of a trough following the wave and her entanglement in the wreckage, but with additional smaller waves which apparently followed in the wake of the first crest she was prized free and carried into the boat harbor (Figures 85*e* and 86*e*). Here she was momentarily aground with her stern in the wreckage of the piling of the North Arm cannery. According to Sturgis (Chance, 1966; Bryant, 1964b), her bow was up (presumably on the mud flats) 20° to 30° above the stern. The *Chena* now took a violent roll to starboard before the boat harbor began to fill with the great volume of water pouring over the North Arm (apparently still from the first wave). All this

apparently took place during the period of the earthquake, the duration of which has been variously given as 3½ to 5 minutes (prior to the final 30 seconds of the earthquake, according to Sturgis).

The following further reconstruction of what may have happened is the result of weighing all the evidence by eyewitnesses along with the factual motion-picture records by Numair and Ernest Nelson (another crew member), taken from the *Chena*.

A flux of water from the south now filled the boat harbor and carried boats and buildings, dislodged by the first wave, toward the Valdez Hotel. It lifted the *Chena*, which by now had acquired power, and enabled her to float free. This moment is believed to have been captured in Figure

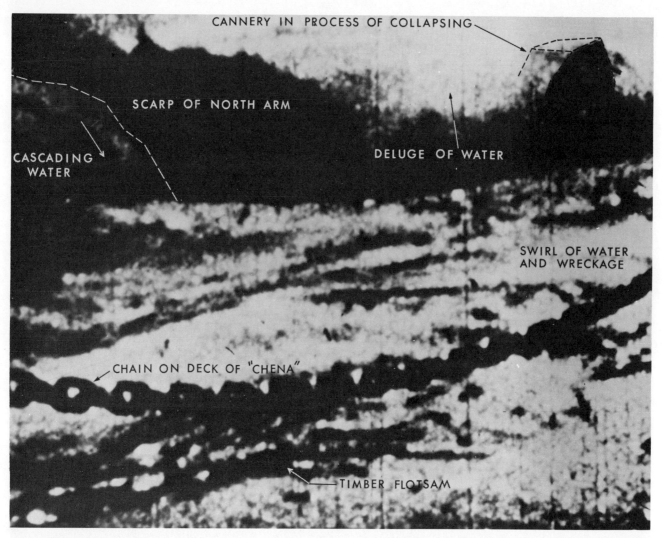

FIGURE 88   Another view (from the *Chena*) (enlarged from frame 184) of the first tsunami wave destroying the cannery on the North Arm of Valdez Harbor (for location see Figure 85).

89 (see also Figure 85), which shows the wreckage in the boat harbor. (The authors found that Nelson's film, which had been borrowed soon after the earthquake by one or more organizations, had been cut in many places and re-spliced in incorrect time sequence. Nelson, in a personal interview in 1966, was greatly upset over this treatment of his film.) The dark spur is believed to be the remains of the ferry slip and the parallel "wave" beyond to be the remnant of the North Arm. The *Gypsy*, the largest yacht in the boat harbor, is just visible off the ferry slip. In the course of the whirlpool-like movements of water between the north and south arms of the harbor, the *Gypsy* had apparently caromed off the sides of the *Chena* while the latter was still stuck in the mud. In Figure 89 the North Arm cannery roof is believed to be floating alongside the

ferry slip. Subsequently, it was found entrenched in mud flats *north* of the harbor (see Figure 85).

The water now began to drain from the boat harbor, and a strong movement of water from northwest to southeast along the shore began. This at first helped the *Chena* clear the stub of the South Arm and pass over where the south pier and cannery had been (see Figure 85). According to Dunning (personal interview), the deck of this pier had been swept southeast by the first wave that carried the *Chena* into the boat harbor, and surrounding piles showed bolts bent in that direction. Bracken (1964), moreover, records that a trailer frame was swept south from this pier.

The *Chena*, now under her own power, came also under the influence of a strong southerly current, which, despite her bid for deep water, carried her close alongshore as in a

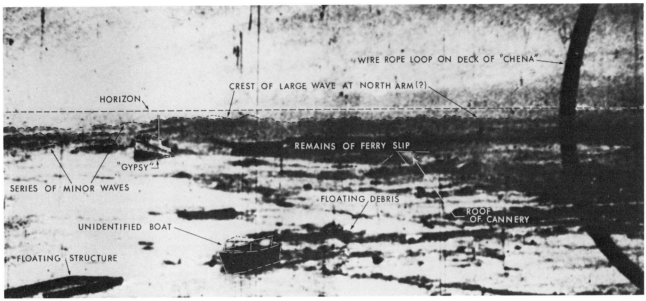

Ernest Nelson, Seattle

FIGURE 89 Momentary quiet in the ruins of the boat harbor at Valdez (panoramic composite view from the *Chena*). Yacht *Gypsy* is in left center field. Boat in foreground is unidentified. Cannery roof is believed to be floating in center field (for location see Figure 85).

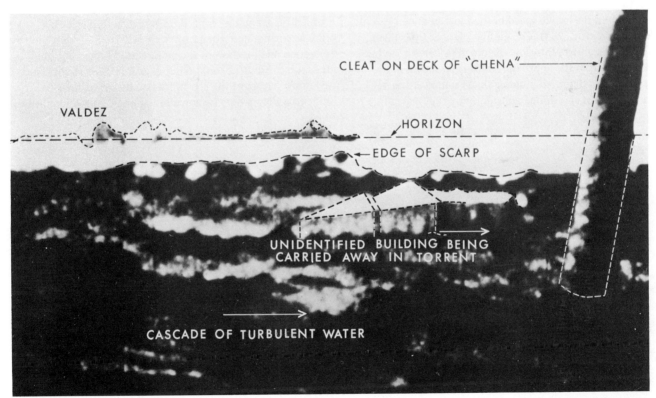

Fred Numair, Seattle

FIGURE 90 View from the *Chena* while it was being swept southwestward along the coast off Valdez (from frame 246). Unidentified building being cascaded by the torrent of water down a collapsing shoreline (for location see Figure 85).

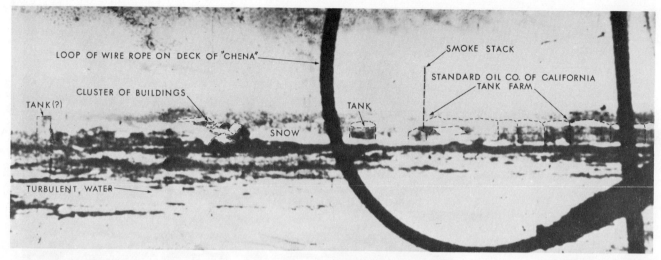

Ernest Nelson, Seattle

FIGURE 91 Panoramic composite from the *Chena*, south of the harbor of Valdez, showing water draining from the coast under the effects of the submarine slide (for location see Figure 85).

jet stream. Of this period, Captain Stewart records in the *Alaska Construction*, "The *Chena* was moving but she couldn't steer away from the beach as mounds of water continuously swept against the ship forcing her to a course next to the shore." Two observers who saw her at this time remarked on the jetlike speed of the movement (for example, see Bracken, 1964). The motion pictures by Numair and Nelson confirm this flow. Figure 90 is believed to have been taken from the approximate location shown in Figure 85. An unidentified building floats southward as it descends a cascade formed apparently by the final failure

of the sediments in a major slump south of the harbor. The approximate location of the developing chasm wall formed by the slump is shown in Figure 85.

Moments later, Nelson, looking back toward Valdez, photographed this fantastic withdrawal of water and recorded the scene reproduced from several frames of his film as a panoramic composite view (Figure 91), with the direction and location of the picture as in Figure 85. Mud flats were forming behind the ship as it hurtled south. The awesome nature of the chasm formed by the submarine slide (see Figure 86*f*) is shown in Figure 92, photographed

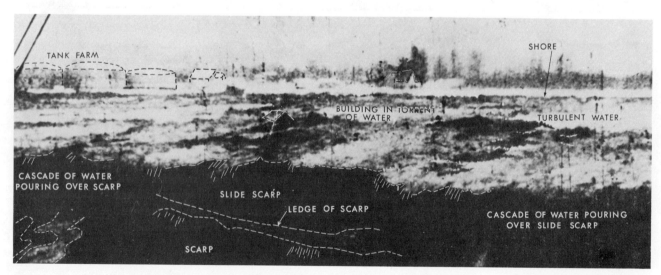

Ernest Nelson, Seattle

FIGURE 92 Panoramic composite view (from the *Chena*) of the chasm formed by the submarine slide south of the harbor at Valdez (from three frames about 70 frames apart). Water is cascading from the land (for location see Figure 85).

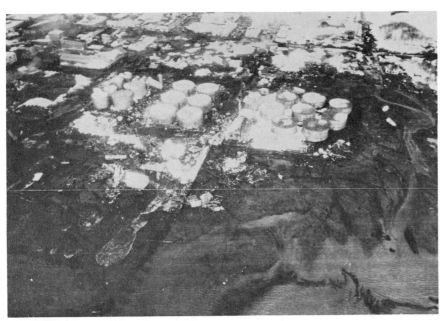

FIGURE 93   Aerial view of the devastation of the waterfront at Valdez in the vicinity of the Standard Oil Company tank farm. Note the relatively undamaged building in left center field (it can be identified in Figure 91). Remains of the south pier are at lower left.

U.S. Army

from the approximate position (*f*) in Figure 85. It is believed that the location of the scarp formed by the slump is revealed in the lower right-hand portion of the aerial photograph (Figure 93) taken within a few days of the earthquake.

Figure 86*f*, which envisions the submarine slide, also suggests the formation of a wall of water on the seaward side of the *Chena*. This "wall," reported by Sturgis (Bryant, 1964b; Chance, 1966, and in press), was observed by Dunning, a longshoreman who survived disaster in the *Chena's* hold and reached the deck. This slide and the attendant wave effect almost certainly occurred after the earthquake and were probably promoted by the major drawdown of water, shown in Figure 84 to have occurred about 5 to 6 minutes after the start of the earthquake.

The submarine slide was massive; approximately 98 million yd³ of material slumped away, according to an estimate by Coulter and Migliaccio (1966). Comparative contours of water depth in the vicinity of Valdez are shown in Figure 94, and typical profiles along cross sections *OA, OB,* and *OC* are shown in Figure 95. Off the delta to the south of Valdez, depth changes exceeding 300 ft are seen to have taken place; off Valdez itself the change is less, but still of the order of 100 ft. The major part of the slide thus took place off the Lowe River delta, but a substantial part consolidated and slid away at the Valdez waterfront and along the shore north of the town.

The *Chena* escaped to deep water before the next large wave rolled in over the demolished waterfront and reached to a level of 18 in. in the Valdez Hotel (Coulter and Migliaccio, 1966; Brown, 1964). The nature of these early

waves now demands some explanation, particularly in regard to the directionality of the flow effects. A seemingly plausible explanation for the effects might be as follows. It is supposed that the sediments off the Lowe River delta and Valdez Glacier outwash, very much finer than those found off Valdez, were liquefied at an early stage of the earth vibration and caused a slide in the southeast corner of Port Valdez. Simultaneously, the entire basin of Port Valdez (see Figure 6, p. 131) was being jerked horizontally to the southeast parallel to the coastline of Valdez. The net effect of this would be to pile water to the north near Mineral Creek (Figure 79) and draw it from the south shore. Off Valdez itself, there could arise a pseudonodal situation in which a flow of water would take place to the northwest without a great deal of recession. This would have pulled the ship *Chena* to the northwest; alternatively, if the horizontal land thrust were sudden enough, the harbor would have been pushed southeast relative to the *Chena* (which momentarily remained fixed in space) with the same relative effect.

If this supposition is at all correct, a transverse seiche would have developed and thrown an edgewave southward along the Valdez shoreline. Taking the velocity *c* of the edgewave to be that given by equation (5) and assuming the period *T* of the seiche for a rectangular transverse vertical profile of width *L* at the head of the bay to be

$$T = 2L/c , \qquad (11)$$

we find the period of the edgewave to be [on elimination of *c* between equations (5) and (11)]

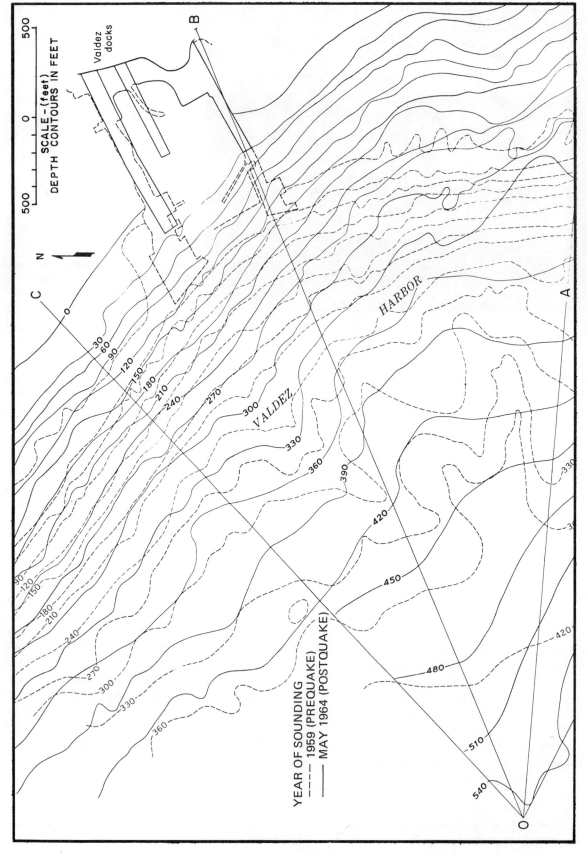

FIGURE 94 Preearthquake and postearthquake soundings at Valdez. (After Coulter and Migliaccio, 1966).

448

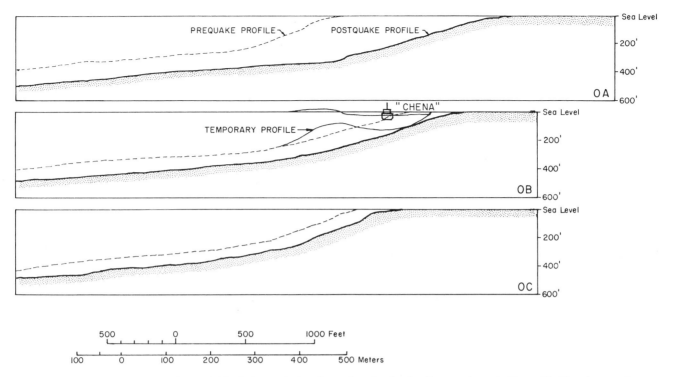

FIGURE 95 Profiles of the sea bed near Valdez before and after the earthquake. Section lines are shown in Figure 94. *Chena's* approximate position when scarp was visible is indicated schematically in profile *OB*. Dashed lines represent preearthquake profiles, and solid lines denote postearthquake profiles.

$$T = (4\pi L / g \sin\theta)^{1/2} . \qquad (12)$$

For a bottom slope of about 1 in 11 and a width $L \simeq 2.94$ nautical miles, the wave period is calculated to be

$$T \simeq 4.4 \text{ minutes,}$$

which could mean that the edgewave struck Valdez (midway between the north and south shores of Port Valdez) within 1.1 minute of the start of the earthquake. As an edgewave it would have had the directional effect of sweeping the *Chena* southeast onto the collapsing docks and causing the extraordinary flow of water which carried away the south pier and the cannery from the North Arm.

The returning edgewave, which would have come about 2.2 minutes later, presumably filled the boat harbor, freed the *Chena*, and caused the northward flow, which may have carried small boats and debris in that direction, as observed by Sturgis.

There would then have followed the returning nodal flow in a southeast direction which could account for the jetlike evacuation of the *Chena* and, upon the suction-like withdrawal of the water table, the sudden failure of the sea bed as envisioned in Figure 86f. There is no particular report that the wall of water observed by Sturgis and Dunning ever hit the Valdez waterfront as a big destroying wave.

The origin of the third big wave that hit the town and came in approximately 10 minutes after the earthquake ceased is not known with certainty. The earliest interpretation was that it was one of the waves generated by slides at the Valdez waterfront, returned as a reflection from the western end of Port Valdez. The travel time for a long wave to propagate to the Valdez Narrows and return, however, would be 17.8 minutes, according to equation (10i), and this could not explain the observations. Later investigations emphasized the idea that the wave was generated by a major slide along the steep shore of the west end of Port Valdez (Plafker and Mayo, 1965). The travel time would then accord with equation (10ii)—namely, 9.8 minutes—and meet the situation shown in Figure 84.

Figure 96 shows that the waves generated at the west end must have been singularly powerful to have produced the tremendous runup recorded at different places (Plafker and Mayo, 1965). From this it is assumed that there were two submarine slides at the mouth of Shoup Bay, one near the abandoned Cliff Mine and one on the west side of the entrance of Shoup Bay. Shoup Bay occupies a hanging valley whose floor is more than 500 ft above the bottom of Port Valdez. The Shoup Glacier has left a high deposit of glacial debris that blocks the entrance to Shoup Bay. This material is presumed to have slumped. The first wave obliterated all the sizable buildings at the Cliff Mine site, left

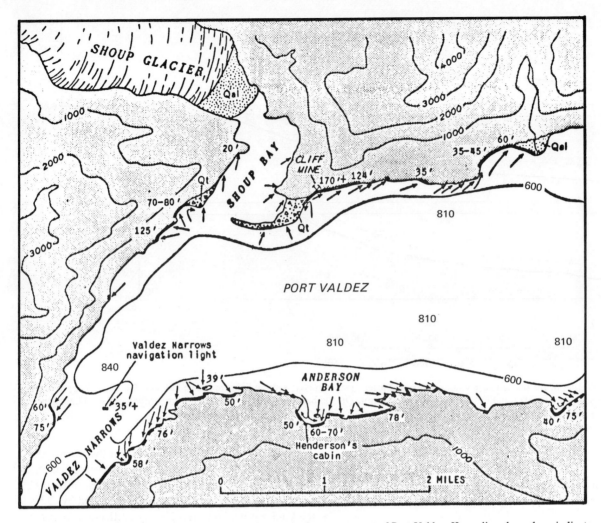

FIGURE 96 Heights and inferred directions of local waves in the western part of Port Valdez. Heavy line along shore indicates distribution of damage; numeral is measured maximum runup. Shaded pattern, bedrock; dotted pattern, alluvium and intertidal mud; triangular pattern, terminal moraine of the Shoup Glacier. Contour interval on land is 1,000 ft; submarine contour interval is 600 ft. (From Plafker and Mayo, 1965).

driftwood at 170 ft above lower low water, and splashed silt and sand up to elevations of 220 ft. From the vicinity of Cliff Mine it moved east and probably south with gradually diminishing height.

The wave generated on the west side of Shoup Bay apparently rushed up to an elevation of 125 ft near its inferred source (Plafker and Mayo, 1965).

These two slide-generated waves caused considerable runup on both the west and south sides of Port Valdez, as is evident in Figure 96. It is believed that the large wave that hit Valdez about 10 minutes after the earthquake (Figure 84) was one of these waves. Further parts of the waves propagated throughout the Valdez Narrows, destroying the navigation light on top of the lighthouse 35 ft above lower low water (Figures 96 and 97).

The fishing boat *Falcon* at Potato Point (see Figure 79),

near the mouth of the Narrows, was lucky to survive this wave. As recorded by Chance (1966), two crew members were on shore when the earthquake started. When they headed in their skiff for the anchored 30-ft boat, a drawdown of the water suddenly left the skiff beached while the fishing boat disappeared out of sight behind a break in the bottom of the Narrows. Within moments, turbulent water rose again and flushed the skiff out of control. It appears to have been extraordinary luck for the boatmen that their skiff came sufficiently close to the *Falcon* that they could dive across and pull themselves out of the water onto the larger boat. After they had started the engine, they saw a huge wave (approximately 5 minutes after the earthquake) building up behind the lighthouse and heading out of the Narrows. It overtopped the lighthouse about 2 minutes later. They estimated this wave to have been 35 to

Henry Coulter

FIGURE 97   Concrete pylon of the navigation light located at the entrance to Port Valdez (for location see Figures 79 and 96). The light was destroyed by a huge wave that passed southward out of Valdez Narrows. Steel reinforcing rods at an elevation of about 37 ft above MLLW were bent in the direction of flow.

50 ft high in the Narrows and filled with mud, timber, and other debris. The *Falcon* was overtaken by the wave just outside the Narrows, but by then, fortunately, the wave had spread laterally into Jack Bay and Valdez Arm (Figure 79) and attenuated in height, thus enabling the boat to ride over the top. Later they saw many large waves, one right after the other, in the vicinity of the mouth of the Narrows and Jack Bay (Chance, 1966).

It is believed that Valdez (Figure 84) was subject at about this time to a combination of successive waves which were probably the fundamental and binodal seiches for Port Valdez, embodying the periods of 17.8 and 9.8 minutes [equation (10)]. Since the fundamental period for Port Valdez is about the same as the second-mode period (18 minutes for the entire Valdez Arm, Narrows, and port basin system [equation (9)], we should expect that these waves gradually set the system rocking in its fundamental mode of about 39 minutes. Figure 84 also expresses our belief that the first crest of the main tsunami, generated at the mouth of Prince William Sound, would have reached Valdez within about 30 minutes with rather insignificant amplitude. However, the development of oscillations from within and from without the embayment may be assumed to have developed a strong system of beat oscillations (suggested in Figure 84). The fundamental tsunami wave

on the shelf, meanwhile, in tune with the fundamental period ($T \simeq 110$ minutes) of Prince William Sound, may be presumed to have built up the amplitude of oscillations (of about this period) which penetrated into the Valdez embayment. These conditions are revealed in the marigram, which has been constructed basically from eyewitness observations of the later waves, but with a foreknowledge of the probable oscillating characteristics of the regime.

After the first 25 minutes, the waves reaching Valdez on the low tide were not high enough to draw special attention and presumably failed to reach even normal high-tide level. As the tide rose, however, the oscillations in the Sound increased in amplitude, and Valdez faced further destruction (Figure 84).

Two very large waves reached Valdez on the high tide during the night. There is some discrepancy between reports as to their arrival times (see, for example, Berg and others, 1971; Chance, 1966; Coulter and Migliaccio, 1966; Migliaccio, 1964; Dunning and Gilson, personal interview, 1966). The reported crest times for the first wave vary from 22:30 AST to midnight, and for the second wave from 00:30 to 01:45. However, the most likely times of occurrence of the waves' crests are 23:45 and 01:35, as suggested in Figure 84.

The damaging wave that came in like a fast-moving tide at about 23:45 and reached as far as Hobart Street (see Figure 81) was reported to have been 2½ ft deep in Valdez Hotel.

Water from the waves that came in at about 01:35 was 5 to 6 ft deep in buildings along McKinley Street and 2 ft on Hobart Street. Although it was not a smashing wave, it evidently advanced and receded with considerable speed, because the high-water marks left by it on buildings were in most cases higher outside than inside the buildings. The reason for this is suggested in Figure 84, which supposes that peak level represented the combination of two waves, one of approximately a 2-hour period and the second of about a 40-minute period, representing the primary oscillations for Prince William Sound and the Valdez embayment, respectively. In terms of height, each constituent appears to have had an amplitude of about 5 ft.

It is not possible to differentiate in detail the runup for each particular wave. The last wave caused the highest runup, and from water marks it has been possible to trace approximately the runup within the city. The runup distribution was sporadic, and the many apparently anomalous effects reported can generally be explained by the existence of high snow berms and a deep snow cover, which channeled the water and restricted its distribution (Coulter and Migliaccio, 1966).

Figure 98 contains our interpretation of the runup levels attained by the highest waves. This is based on aerial photographs, careful examination of ground photographs, and

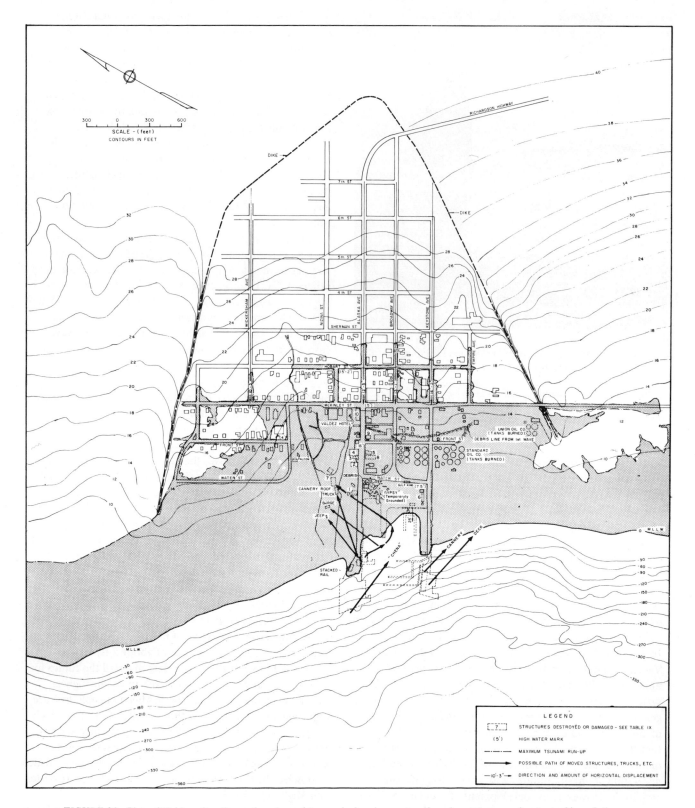

FIGURE 98   Plan of Valdez after the earthquake and tsunami, showing postearthquake contours and extent of inundation.

consideration of eyewitness accounts. Contours of land level in this figure, referenced to MLLW, are based on a preearthquake survey in 1953 undertaken by Thomas Bourne Associates of Alaska, Inc., Anchorage, for the Alaska Public Works Division. They have been adjusted for a regional subsidence of 1 ft at Fifth Street in Valdez and for proportionally larger subsidences approaching the waterfront, based on postearthquake observations of buildings at the waterfront by Kajiura and Kawasumi (Berg and others, 1971; Berg, personal communication, 1966). Contours check well for consistency with water-level measurements on numerous buildings throughout the town and with our observations in 1966.

Before the above-mentioned highest waves, there was other wave activity throughout the whole evening. At about 20:00 AST a lifeboat from the *Chena* came in and was able to tie up at the ferry slip (Figure 98). Sometime later (about 20:15), this boat was found high and dry where the water had receded. While efforts were being made to launch it, the boat was floated free again by an incoming wave and was able to return to the *Chena* (Bracken, 1964). It appears that at or around 20:30 the *Falcon* returned from its sensational experience in the Valdez Narrows and tied up at the ferry slip. By 21:00, withdrawal of water left the *Falcon* beached at this point. Then, at about 21:30 (Chance, 1966) another higher wave reached as far as Water Street on Alaska Avenue (Figure 98). This wave, according to Bracken (1964), was like a fast-rising tide which he could only evade by walking rapidly ahead of it. Still another, but a lesser wave, rolled in at about 22:15 and apparently started a fire at the Union Oil Company tanks (Bracken, 1964; Chance, 1966; Gilson, personal interview, 1966). The large yacht *Gypsy*

at this time was lodged alongside the ferry slip and, according to Bracken, had an open seam near her keel. In the later waves of that night she was to become a total loss. The *Chena* sighted her as she was sinking far out in Port Valdez; by dawn only her cabin was floating (Bracken, 1964).

TSUNAMI WAVE DAMAGE AT VALDEZ

Most of the damage at the Valdez waterfront was caused by the submarine landslides, while the principal cause of damage away from the waterfront was ground breakage. Approximately 40 percent of the homes and most of the larger commercial buildings in Valdez were seriously damaged by ground heaving and fissures extending under or near them.

The slides caused the disappearance of the two docks with their warehouses and canneries of the breakwater protecting the small-boat harbor (compare Figures 99 and 100).

The whole town subsided because of the compaction of the deltaic materials during the tremors. The subsidence was largest at the waterfront area, gradually decreasing away from the shore. Figures 81 and 98 may be compared for post- and preearthquake contours in the waterfront area. Water Street subsided as much as 9 ft near Alaska Avenue. This has a bearing on the wave damage in the waterfront area and is symptomatic of the disappearance of the docks. In addition to the subsidence, the waterfront area moved laterally. The concrete bulkhead at the head of the small-boat harbor apparently moved 25 ft seaward (Coulter and Migliaccio, 1966; Wilson and Tørum, 1968; see also Figure 6, p. 131).

Loren St. Amand

FIGURE 99 Composite view (looking seaward) of the small-boat harbor and docks at Valdez just a day or two before the earthquake. The ferry slip shows at right center field with the cannery behind it. Near the entrance on the right are the North Arm docks and warehouses where the *Chena* was moored. In left center field is the cannery on the South Arm. The *Gypsy* may be seen in the background just to the left of the closest pile in center foreground (compare with Figure 81).

FIGURE 100   Aerial view of the Valdez waterfront after the earthquake and tsunami. Compare with Figures 82 and 98.

U.S. Army

The initial waves caused damage to the whole waterfront and the downtown area as far as the runup line shown in Figure 98. A wave, presumably the one that came in about 2½ minutes after the earthquake started, damaged almost all the boats and boat floats in the small-boat harbor. Many of the boats were beached temporarily and were washed into the bay by the higher waves later in the evening.

This wave also destroyed three of four buildings at the head of the small-boat harbor and another building along Alaska Avenue (see Figures 85 and 101). The buildings, like most of those in Valdez, were light wooden-frame buildings. Particulars of a few buildings damaged or de-stroyed are given in Table 9; their location is identified by number in Figure 98.

Some heavy trucks from the docks were also washed inland (see Figures 98 and 103). The roof of the cannery from the inner end of the north dock was partly sunk in mud flats northeastward of the North Arm (Figures 98, 100, 102, and 103).

One of the asphalt storage tanks at the Standard Oil Company tank farm was punctured during the earthquake, probably by floating debris. The escaping asphalt (Figure 104) contaminated a large area of Port Valdez. There was also gasoline leakage from the tanks, and at

TABLE 9   Identifiable Structures in Valdez Destroyed or Damaged in the Earthquake, March 1964

Structure	Type of Structure	Damage
1 Village Morgue Saloon	Wood frame	Destroyed by fire
2 Valdez Transfer Company (with residence of owner on second floor)	Wood frame	Fire damage first—wave damage later
3 Storage building used by Dieringer Chevron Station for machinery, equipment, etc.	Wood frame	Fire damage first—wave damage later
4 Dieringer Chevron Station	Concrete block or masonry	Wave damage
5 Jo's Place (café)	Wood frame	Fire damage
6 Marine Ventures	Wood frame with outer log covering	Freighter driven through building by waves caused initial collapse; subsequent waves disturbed debris.
7 Roof of cannery	Wood frame with sheet metal covering	Swept by waves from site
8 Beals' Hotel	Wood frame with sheet metal siding	Destroyed by fire
9 Club Café	Wood frame	Wave damage
10 State Highway Office, Valdez District Office	–	Building survived (destroyed by man)
11 Union Oil Tank Farm	Riveted steel tanks	Destroyed by fire

FIGURE 101   View east along Alaska Avenue.

FIGURE 102   Eroded approach ramp to the North dock.

Loren St. Amand

FIGURE 103 Cannery roof and upturned truck on mud flats north of harbor.

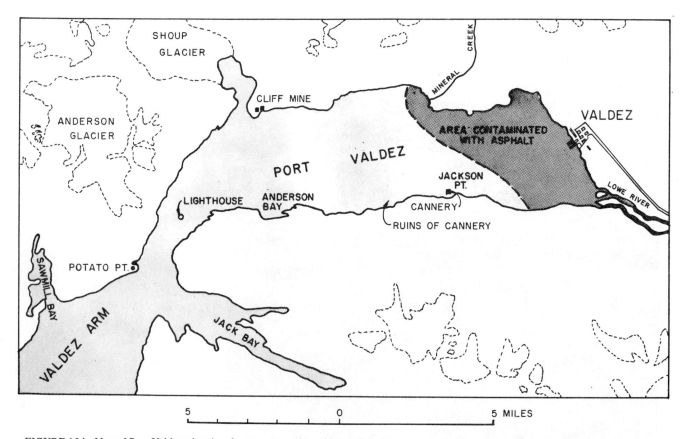

FIGURE 104 Map of Port Valdez, showing the area contaminated by asphalt from damaged oil tank farm. (From F. MacNamara, 1964).

Loren St. Amand

FIGURE 105   View east on Alaska Avenue before cleanup.

Loren St. Amand

FIGURE 106   View south on Water Street.

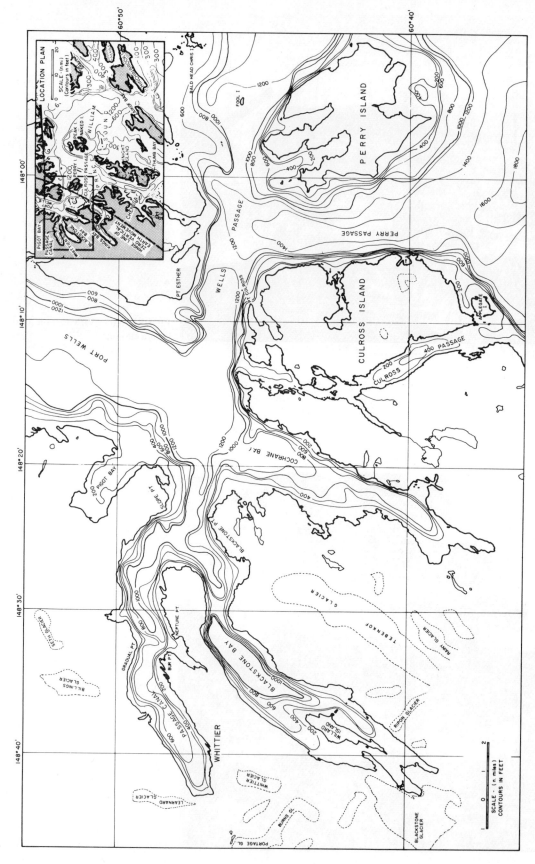

FIGURE 107 Bathymetry of Port Wells and tributary fiords, including Passage Canal and Whittier.

about 22:15 AST on the day of the earthquake, the Standard Oil tanks caught fire, probably by electric wire short-circuiting caused by water. Shortly afterward, the Union Oil tank farm also caught fire (Bracken, 1964).

The high waves that came in at about 23:45 and 01:35 during the night apparently had no smashing effects. However, they refloated boats and debris; some of the wooden structures were also floated free but were apparently not moved very much. These two waves were responsible for most of the wetting damage to buildings, homes, merchandise, and supplies in the commercial establishments along McKinley Street and west of it. The water was heavily silt-laden, and large volumes of silt were deposited in and around buildings. The backwash of the last wave had a strong current, and debris and beached boats were washed out into the bay. Some of the general melee on the waterfront is well illustrated in Figures 105 and 106.

At Jackson Point, a cannery was swept off its foundation by a wave that rushed up 32 ft. Parts of the cannery were afterward found floating a couple of miles west of Jackson Point (see Figure 104).

An inhabited cabin in Anderson Bay was completely swept away by the waves generated in the Cliff Mine area.

According to Spaeth and Berkman (1967), 31 persons lost their lives at Valdez as a result of the earthquake and tsunami, the highest number of fatalities of any community in Alaska. It has been stated that, if the earthquake had occurred just half an hour earlier while the dock was still crowded with townspeople, the death toll would have been many times greater.

The estimate of property damage caused by the waves is $12,568,000, of which $8,453,000 was privately owned and $4,115,000 publicly owned (Spaeth and Berkman, 1967, and this volume). Relative to population, Valdez suffered more acutely than Seward, although damage losses at the latter place were higher.

TSUNAMI WAVES AT WHITTIER

Whittier, located at the western end of Passage Canal (Figure 107), was built in 1942–1943 to provide a second all-weather terminal in addition to Seward, for The Alaska Railroad. The town is owned and operated by the U.S. Government, specifically by The Alaska Railroad of the Department of the Interior; some of the land has been leased to private enterprises. At the time of the earthquake 70 people were living in Whittier, and 13 of them lost their lives as a result of the earthquake.

Figure 107 shows that Port Wells and its tributary fiords are a relatively deep and intricate system of connecting basins whose oscillating characteristics are likely to be complex. No attempt has been made to determine these charac-

teristics. Whittier lies on the northwest side of the hinge line of zero vertical earth movement running through Prince William Sound (Figure 107, inset).

The delta upon which Whittier rests and also the southern part of the delta at the head of Passage Canal (Figure 108) are formed by unconsolidated deposits consisting of outwash and stream gravels. They are composed predominantly of coarse, subangular-to-subrounded gravel in a matrix of coarse sand (Kachadoorian, 1965, and Geology volume). Whittier's rather limited area on the fan delta is well illustrated in Figure 109.

The extensive damage suffered by Whittier was caused by (1) seismic shock, (2) submarine landslides, (3) waves, (4) fracturing and compaction of fill and unconsolidated sediments, (5) fire, and (6) a 5.3-ft subsidence of the land masses. The port was rendered totally inoperative by the earthquake and tsunamis and for a time was without rail communication (Eckel, 1967).

The destructive waves that lashed Whittier were undoubtedly generated by submarine landslides (Figure 110). Data on which to base an inferred marigram (Figure 111) were extremely limited because there were not many eyewitnesses. Some of those who watched the water (see Bryant, 1964b; Kachadoorian, 1965, and Geology volume; Chance, 1966) reported that approximately 1 minute after the earthquake started, the water in Passage Canal in the vicinity of the town rose rapidly to about 30 ft above tide level for that time, which was about 1 ft above MLLW. The water was glassy and did not contain any debris.

The water immediately receded and the "glassy hump" apparently did not encroach on the shore as a wave above normal maximum tide level. The first damaging wave struck Whittier at 1 to 1.5 minutes after the glassy hump occurred. This wave was muddy and contained much debris which radiated from a boil halfway across Passage Canal. The crest of the wave was 34 ft above water level when it reached The Alaska Railroad depot (see Figures 110 and 112). It struck the depot 8 to 10 ft above ground level.

About ½ to 1 minute after the first damaging wave (second rise of water), another damaging wave rolled in on Whittier. Its crest reached about 30 ft above tide level at The Alaska Railroad depot (Bryant, 1964a).

No waves other than the two that struck during the earthquake were reported. Here it is interesting to note that the high waves which reached Cordova and Valdez late in the evening and which also had been reported in Pigot Bay, close to Whittier (see Figure 78d), apparently were not felt or noticed at Whittier. The reason for this is not known and will probably remain unexplained as one of many apparently anomalous wave patterns within Prince William Sound during and after the earthquake.

There were apparently no eyewitnesses to the waves in parts of the town other than at The Alaska Railroad depot.

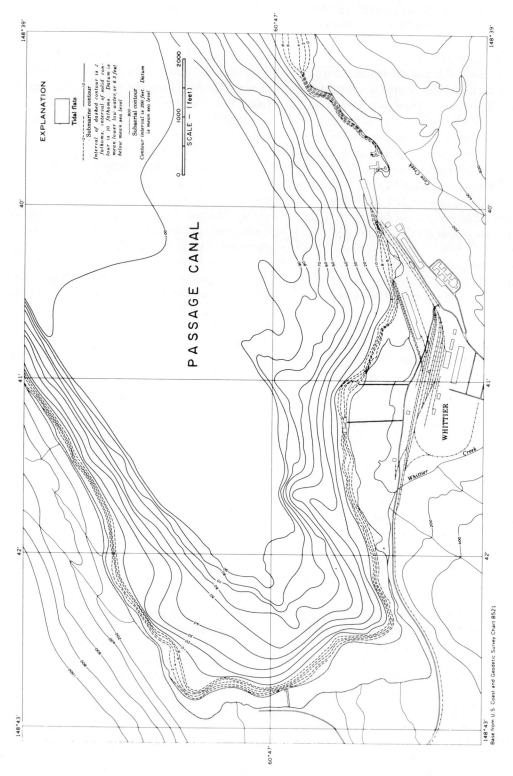

FIGURE 108 Map of Whittier and head of Passage Canal. (From Kachadoorian, 1965.)

460

FIGURE 109 Aerial view of Whittier before the earthquake.

U.S. Army

But high-water marks on snow, trees, and deposits of debris made it possible to trace with precision the high-water line shown in Figure 110. The main wave directions, inferred from debris marks, are shown in this figure (Kachadoorian, 1965).

The highest runup occurred on the north side of Passage Canal where high-water marks were measured 104 ft above MSL. Highest runup levels in the downtown area were 35 ft at the railroad depot and 43 ft somewhat east of the depot.

In attempting to find a plausible explanation for the initial water behavior in Passage Canal during the earthquake, we note that the tectonic movement of the land shifted the entire area horizontally in a southeast direction (almost exactly transverse to Passage Canal) through a distance $x \approx$ 27 ft, besides down-dropping it through approximately 5 ft (Wilson and Tørum, 1968; see also Figure 6, p. 131, this volume). The horizontal translation might perhaps account for the observed "glassy hump" of water. Possibly it could have been an antinodal heaping of water resulting from initiation of a resonant trinodal seiche across the fiord. This would have been an inertial effect of the water as Passage Canal was suddenly pushed against it. A trinodal transverse seiche would have caused a drawdown of water level at Whittier, a runup on the opposite shore, and a smooth humping of water on the Whittier side of the central axis of Passage Canal.

It may be fruitful to examine this thought in a quantitative way despite the unknown effects and timing of submarine slides and of the earth movement. However, we may estimate the period of the trinodal seiche quite easily,

though approximately, by considering the transverse cross section CC (Figure 110) of Passage Canal, opposite Whittier, to consist of three coupled basins—two end basins of similar triangular profile (I and III) and a central rectangular profile basin (II) of uniform depth. For a trinodal seiche across the system, the uninodal seiche of the central basin (II) would have to match in period and amplitude at the connection points with the uninodal seiches of each triangular basin (I and III). From Wilson (1966), we find the following:

$$\text{Basins I (or III)} \quad T_1 = 3.28 L_1 / \sqrt{gd} \qquad (13)$$

$$\text{Basin II} \quad T_2 = 2 L_2 / \sqrt{gd} \qquad (14)$$

in which $L_1 (\approx L_3)$ is the length of a triangular basin, L_2 the length of the central basin, and d the maximum depth. For $L_1 \approx 1175$ ft, $L_2 \approx 2350$ ft, and $d \approx 550$ ft, we obtain $T_1 = T_3 = 29.0$ seconds; $T_2 = 38.0$ seconds. Although these periods do not match as required, we may assume that the correct trinodal period would be of the order of ½ (29 + 38) or about 33 seconds.

For such a seiche period to have synchronized with the earth movement would have meant that the major part of the horizontal earth movement was completed in its quarter period, about 8 seconds, at an average velocity of translation of (27/8) or 3.4 ft/sec. The maximum velocity of earth movement might then have been about 1.5 times this value (see Wilson, 1969a) or about 5 ft/sec.

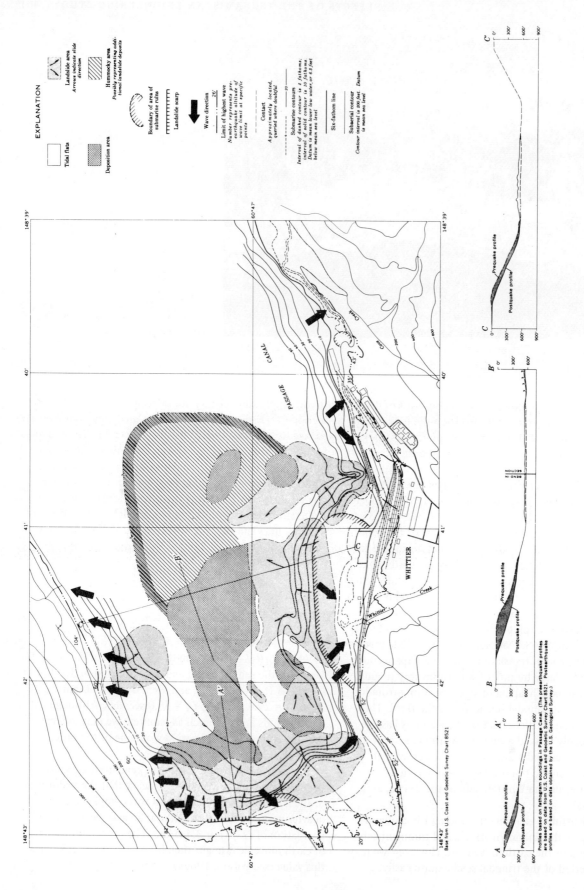

FIGURE 110 Map of Whittier and particulars of submarine slides and sea waves. (From Kachadoorian, 1965).

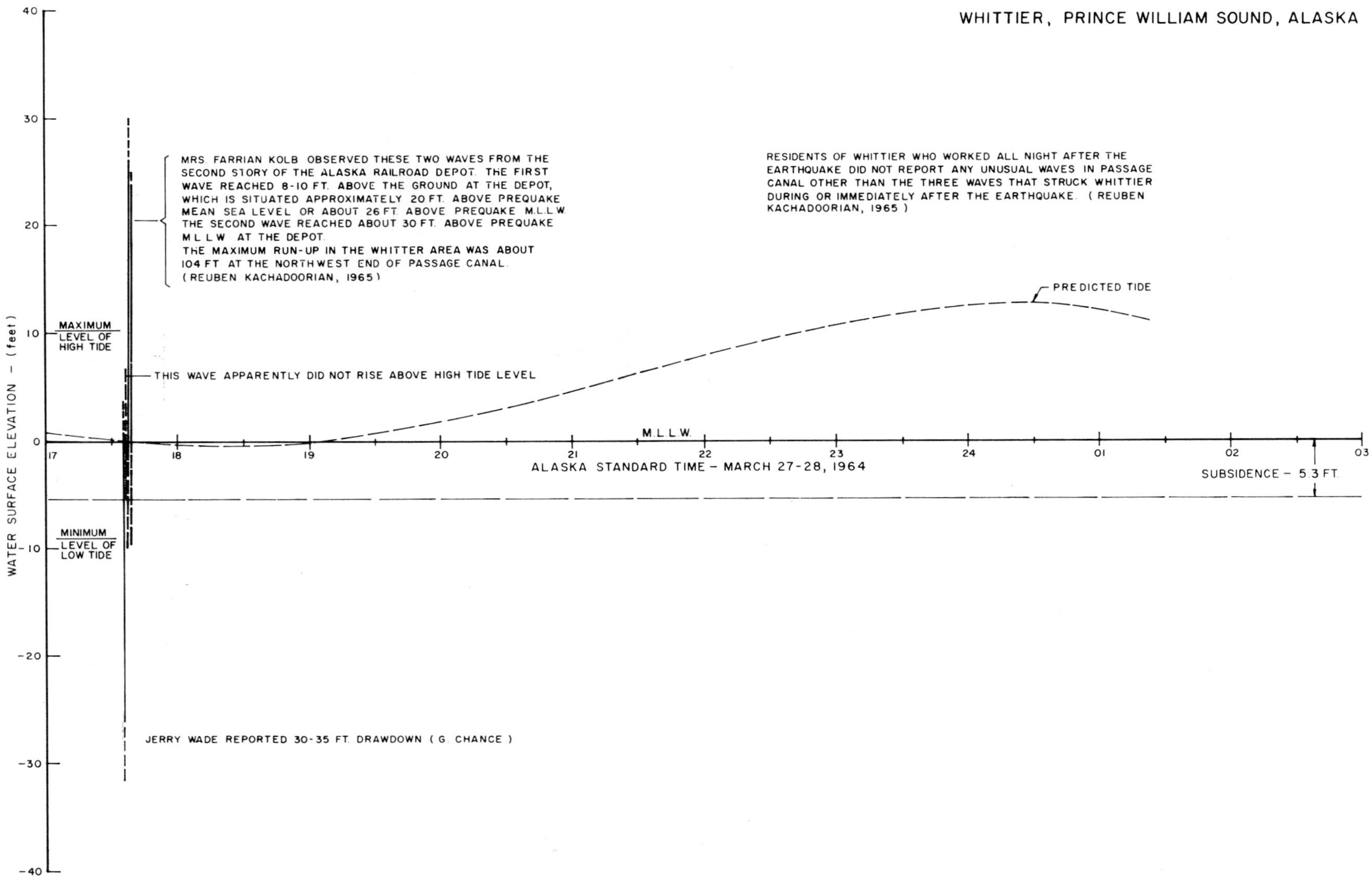

WHITTIER, PRINCE WILLIAM SOUND, ALASKA
WATER SURFACE ELEVATION – (feet)
40
30
20
10
0
-10
-20
-30
-40
MAXIMUM LEVEL OF HIGH TIDE
MINIMUM LEVEL OF LOW TIDE
MRS. FARRIAN KOLB OBSERVED THESE TWO WAVES FROM THE SECOND STORY OF THE ALASKA RAILROAD DEPOT. THE FIRST WAVE REACHED 8-10 FT. ABOVE THE GROUND AT THE DEPOT, WHICH IS SITUATED APPROXIMATELY 20 FT. ABOVE PREQUAKE MEAN SEA LEVEL OR ABOUT 26 FT. ABOVE PREQUAKE M.L.L.W. THE SECOND WAVE REACHED ABOUT 30 FT. ABOVE PREQUAKE M.L.L.W. AT THE DEPOT.
THE MAXIMUM RUN-UP IN THE WHITTER AREA WAS ABOUT 104 FT AT THE NORTHWEST END OF PASSAGE CANAL. (REUBEN KACHADOORIAN, 1965)
RESIDENTS OF WHITTIER WHO WORKED ALL NIGHT AFTER THE EARTHQUAKE DID NOT REPORT ANY UNUSUAL WAVES IN PASSAGE CANAL OTHER THAN THE THREE WAVES THAT STRUCK WHITTIER DURING OR IMMEDIATELY AFTER THE EARTHQUAKE. (REUBEN KACHADOORIAN, 1965)
PREDICTED TIDE
THIS WAVE APPARENTLY DID NOT RISE ABOVE HIGH TIDE LEVEL
M.L.L.W.
17
18
19
20
21
22
23
24
01
02
03
ALASKA STANDARD TIME – MARCH 27-28, 1964
SUBSIDENCE – 5.3 FT.
JERRY WADE REPORTED 30-35 FT. DRAWDOWN (G. CHANCE)

FIGURE 111 Inferred marigram for Whittier, based on accounts by eyewitnesses.

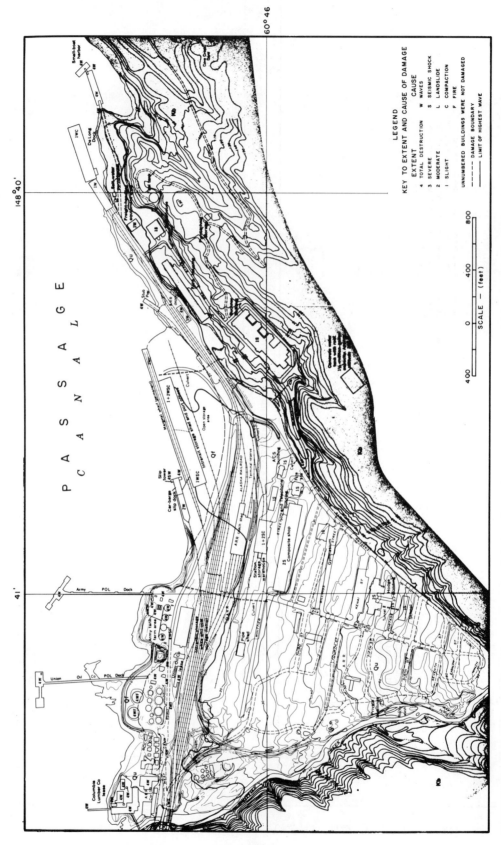

FIGURE 112 Map of Whittier, showing waterfront details before the earthquake and the extent of damage from the earthquake and tsunami. (From Kachadoorian, 1965.)

Because the maximum velocity across the node of the water in the uninodal seiche of basin II would be

$$(u_{\max})_2 \approx A_2 \sqrt{(g/d)}, \tag{15}$$

where A_2 is the seiche amplitude, synchronism or resonance with earth movement in the generation of the seiche would have required [for $(u_{\max})_2 = 5$ ft/sec in equation (15)]

$$A_2 \approx 5\sqrt{(d/g)} \approx 20.6 \text{ ft.} \tag{16}$$

Then because $A_2 = 0.403\,A_3$ for a triangular basin (compare Bouasse, 1924, p. 156), the drawdown at Whittier, on this basis, could have been

$$A_3 \approx 51 \text{ ft } (\approx A_1),$$

which is more than enough to account for the reported initial recession of 35 ft at Whittier and partially explains the uprush of 104 ft on the opposite shore. Local effects could make A_1 and A_3 larger or smaller.

The tectonic thrust of the land would have displaced a volume of water $(xd) = (27 \times 550)$ or about 15,000 ft³ per foot of distance along the fiord on each side. If the concept is plausible, this volume would have to meet the needs of the runup (or drawdown) on the shores of Passage Canal. The test of this is whether or not the amplitude distribution over the lengths of basins I and III [which follow the profile of the Bessel function $J_o(x)$ between $x = 0$ and $x = 3.83$], with the maximum value of $A_1 = A_3 = 51$ ft (at $x = 0$), will absorb the displacement volume. By mea-

surement of the net positive area under the curve $J_o(x)$ from $x = 0$ to $x = 3.83$, it is found that the volume requirement for $A_1 = A_3 = 51$ ft, $L_1 = L_3 = 1175$ ft, is 14,150 ft³ per foot of length of fiord.

This tally is quite remarkable and encourages the view that the initial waves at Whittier may indeed have been in the category of a trinodal seiche which, along with earth shaking, could have promoted massive submarine slides in the area. A matter of concern, of course, is whether the velocities of earth movement, as indicated, are credible. Subsequent damaging waves would undoubtedly have been related to the slides, however.

The two destructive waves at Whittier apparently originated from different locations and probably at different times, but the generation mechanisms were probably similar to that inferred for Seward (Figure 58). The creation of roiling water and a mismatching of phases between seiche and slide-generated waves could possibly explain their rapid extinction after the damage had been done.

TSUNAMI WAVE DAMAGE AT WHITTIER

The U.S. Geological Survey made a comprehensive survey of the damage at Whittier (Kachadoorian, 1965). The map of Figure 112, reproduced from their report, shows the extent and cause of the damage, which is also dramatically portrayed in Figure 113 (compare with Figure 109).

The outer ends of the Union Oil dock and the Army dock collapsed when their foundations slid away. The approach trestles were totally destroyed by the subsequent waves.

U.S. Army

FIGURE 113 Aerial view of Whittier after the earthquake, showing the devastation of the waterfront.

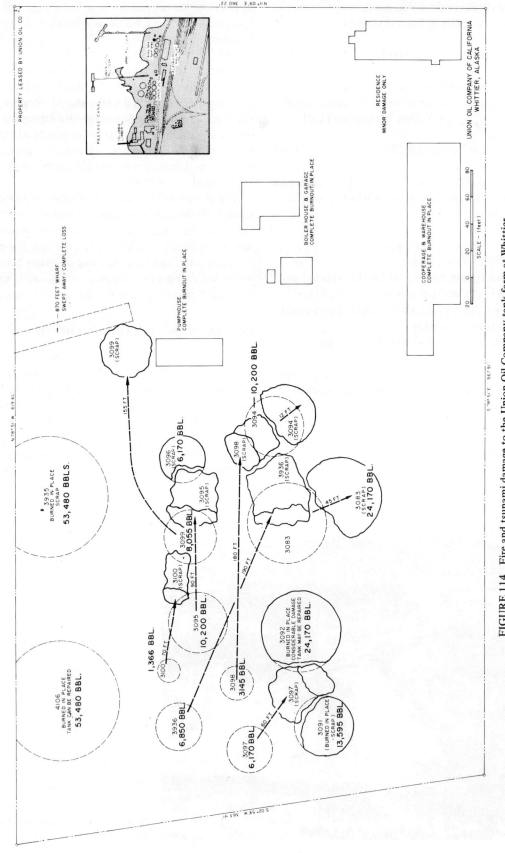

FIGURE 114 Fire and tsunami damage to the Union Oil Company tank farm at Whittier.

The tank farms and the buildings in their vicinity were destroyed by waves and fire. One of the Union Oil tanks containing ballast was moved at least 40 ft south by waves, and another tank containing 1 million gallons of fuel was moved 15 ft. Particulars of the damage and direction of movement of displaced tanks in the Union Oil Company's tank farm are given in Figure 114.

The Columbia Lumber Company's plant and camp were completely wiped out by the waves. Almost nothing remained of the facilities that had occupied the west end of the waterfront at Whittier (Figure 115). Of the 13 people who lost their lives at Whittier, 12 were in a building of the lumber company's camp.

One of the slip towers of the car-barge slip dock collapsed when its foundation slid away, and the other one was destroyed by the waves. The bending of the slip steel beams (Figures 116 and 117) gives an indication of the power of the forces involved.

A 4-yd^3 barnacle-covered boulder was presumably carried from the tidal zone about 125 ft inland and deposited on The Alaska Railroad tracks near the depot at an altitude of about 26 ft. Boulders as large as 6 ft across were strewn on the road between the small-boat harbor and the Union Oil Company (Chance, 1966). The depot of The Alaska Railroad was heavily damaged by waves (Figure 118).

Waves that struck the shoreline at the head of Passage Canal destroyed practically all the structures near the shore. They completely destroyed three unoccupied homes on the shore, 200–400 ft south of the FAA station, and the

buildings of the Two Brothers Lumber Company. The houses were washed away, and the nearby FAA station was partially inundated by waves, though not significantly damaged by them. The Two Brothers Lumber Company buildings were carried inland in a southwest direction, the company's trimmer and conveyor chain were moved 200 ft, the bucking machine 40–50 ft, and the 2,300-lb mill about 100 ft to the southwest.

It is inferred from debris and watermarks that the waves (or wave) that damaged the west coastline of Passage Canal (Figure 110) originated along the north coastline of the canal and traveled southwest. The waves were apparently diverted by the eastern end of the airstrip; the structure about 300 ft south of the airstrip was only moderately damaged (Kachadoorian, 1965).

The waves traveling southwest and south struck the point along the south shore, about 4,000 ft west of Whittier Creek, with tremendous force. Here the wave, reaching more than 50 ft above MSL, carried a 1-ton winch and a boulder weighing 2–3 tons 120 ft south and deposited them on The Alaska Railroad tracks (Chance, 1966).

According to Tudor (1964), the tsunamis at Whittier were responsible for about $10,000,000 worth of damage. Relative to its population of 70, Whittier must be considered to have suffered most acutely of all the coastal communities of Alaska during the earthquake. For more details of the catastrophe at Whittier, the reader is referred to the excellent monograph by Kachadoorian (1965). For greater understanding of the wave effects, however, there

U.S. Army

FIGURE 115   Aerial view (looking north) of the west end of Whittier. Union Oil Company tank farm is ablaze at upper right. Columbia Lumber Company's plant, camp, and dock at upper left is a shambles. Runup limit of the waves is etched in the snow.

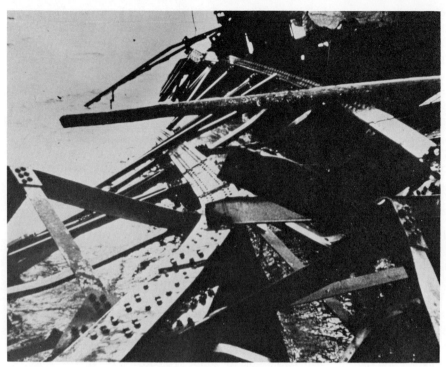

Irvin Cook, The Alaska Railroad

FIGURE 116   Damaged car-barge slips at Whittier.

Irvin Cook, The Alaska Railroad

FIGURE 117   Damaged slip tower at Whittier.

Irvin Cook, The Alaska Railroad

FIGURE 118   Southeast view of The Alaska Railroad depot. The waiting room was destroyed by wave action.

is need for a more extensive study of the oscillating characteristics of the Port Wells complex of fiords.

TSUNAMI WAVES AND DAMAGE AT CORDOVA

The city of Cordova, on the south side of the Orca Inlet at the mouth of Prince William Sound, is an important fishing community. The bathymetry of the region is shown in Figure 119, from which it is evident that, unlike other towns of Prince William Sound, Cordova has rather shallow access routes that militate against its development as an important terminal for oceangoing vessels (Figure 120).

The town, which is situated mostly on bedrock, suffered relatively little damage from the earthquake tremors. One exception was the city dock, a timber structure that was severely shaken by the earthquake. Loosened pilings leaned askew, and canneries and several other buildings adjacent to the dock were pulled 6 to 12 in. away from the dock (Chance, 1966). The city was elevated approximately 6 ft, besides being shifted about 40 ft horizontally in a southeast direction by the regional tectonic movement (see Figure 6, p. 131). This upheaval resulted in a shoreline recession that caused great inconvenience to many seashore facilities, such as canneries, and posed a major problem of dredging access routes through shoal areas (Hanson and others, 1966). The canneries had to extend their docks an average of 110 ft to reach water depths equal to those that prevailed before the earthquake (Eckel, 1967).

Most of the damage to structures at Cordova and vicinity was caused by the tsunamis. It is difficult, from eyewitness accounts alone, to get a clear picture of the wave sequence at Cordova. Nevertheless, an inferred marigram has been compiled (Figure 121), and the basis for it is discussed below.

The sudden uplift of the land during the earthquake undoubtedly would have elevated the sea along with it and caused it to drain away at once under the effect of gravity. This uplift is indicated in Figure 121 by an abrupt rise of sea level of some 6 ft at about 17:36 AST. To all Cordovans who reported on waves reaching the area during the night of March 27–28 and who referenced them to their usual tide-level marks, "MLLW" would have been 6 ft above *true* MLLW, which remained unaffected by the earthquake. This apparent datum is shown in Figure 121.

The Harbor Master (W. L. Phillips) reported that water withdrew gradually from the harbor, after the earthquake, and returned partially with continuing withdrawal three or four times in the hour (Berg and others, 1971; Chance, 1966). Withdrawal level, according to Phillips, was about 5 ft below normal low water because boats in the small-boat harbor were grounded. In Figure 121 we attempt to accomodate the observations by hypothesizing that water level followed the fluctuations shown by the short dashed-line curve. Thus we indicate initial oscillations of about 20 minutes in period, increasing in amplitude, as the withdrawal of water northeastward up the Orca Inlet gathered

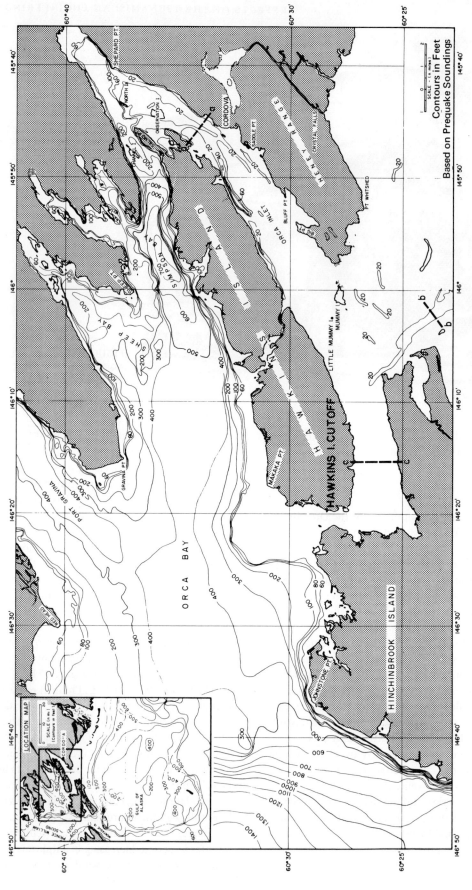

FIGURE 119 Bathymetry of Orca Bay and Orca Inlet, including Cordova.

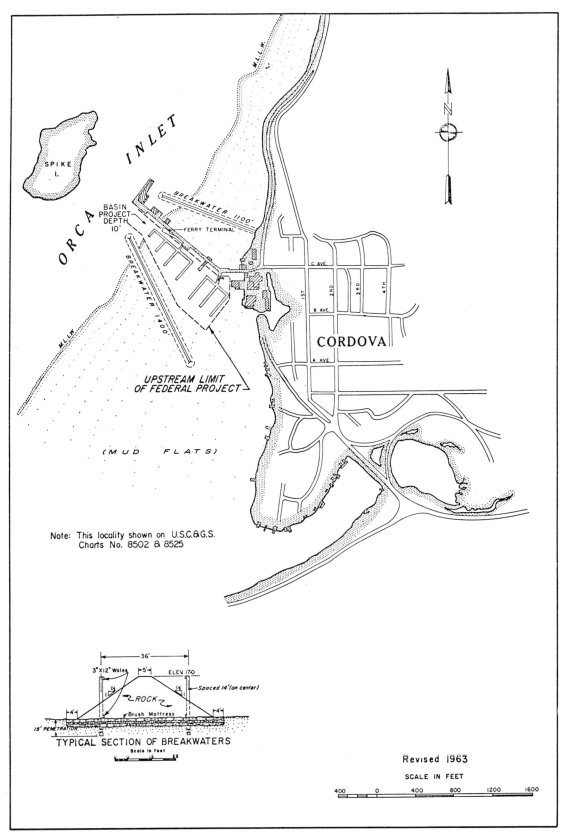

U.S. Army Corps of Engineers

FIGURE 120 Cordova harbor and waterfront area.

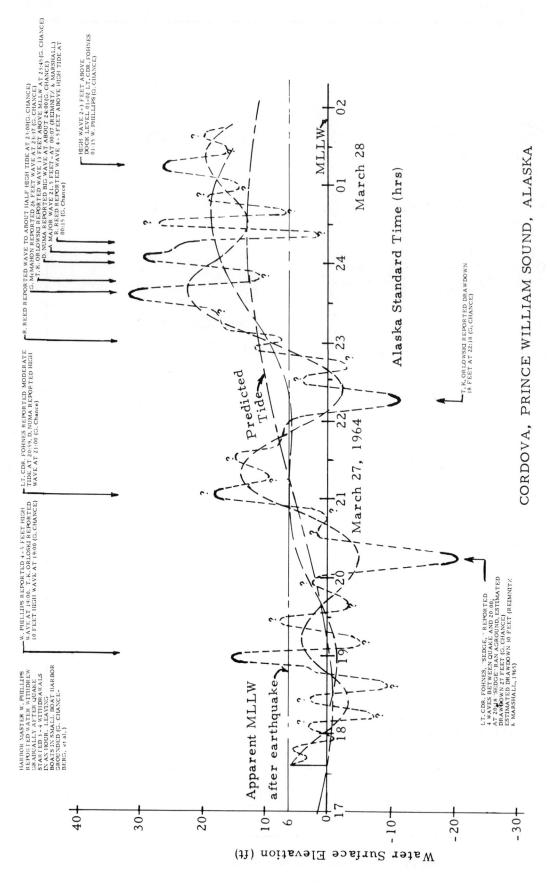

FIGURE 121 Inferred marigram for Cordova, based on accounts by eyewitnesses and on inductive reasoning.

CORDOVA, PRINCE WILLIAM SOUND, ALASKA

momentum and induced seiche oscillations. According to R. Reed (Chance, 1966), one could hear the water "whistling down the channel, sounding like Niagara Falls; it did not come back for many hours."

Figure 121 shows water level well below "apparent MLLW" until 19:00 AST when the first large wave returned, rising to 10 ft above MLLW, according to T. K. Orlowski (Chance, 1966, and in press). Phillips refers to a wave about 4 to 5 ft high at this time (Berg and others, 1971; Chance, 1966, and in press). We give preference to Orlowski's observation since it is referred to a datum.

Dave Muma (Chance, 1966, and in press), mentions that tides were going in and out about every half-hour during the night of March 27–28. Harbor Master Phillips refers to six large waves that he counted coming at intervals of about 1 hour (Berg and others, 1971; Chance, 1966, and in press). These observations are accomodated in Figure 121 by the supposition that oscillations of about 30 minutes were prevalent in varying amplitude during the night. The graphics of the construction of the inferred marigram require that these oscillations fluctuate about a mean water level and withal account for the very high and very low water levels noted at certain times, as well as for the absence of noteworthy levels at other times. The figure shows that this requirement can be met by envisioning that mean water level itself was fluctuating in accord with much longer-period oscillations of about 2 hours and that these in turn were overriding still longer oscillations with a period of as much as 4 hours. All these systems of waves are shown superimposed upon the astronomic tide. We shall attempt to justify this construction in the light of further eyewitness observations.

At 20:19 AST, the U.S. Coast Guard cutter *Sedge*, captained by Lt. Comdr. D. Fohnes, which had gotten under way and left Cordova harbor at 19:00 became grounded near North Rock light, where the water was reported to be 27 ft shallower than normal (Chance, 1966). According to Reimnitz and Marshall (1965), the estimated drawdown at 20:18 was 30 ft. In Figure 121, then, the wave trough at this time is taken at −21 ft with reference to MLLW, that is, 27 ft below "apparent MLLW" and about 30 ft below predicted tide for that time. This remarkable water-level recession can be explained logically only by supposing that the wave trough responsible for it was synchronized with the trough of the dominant longer wave system (of about a 2-hour period). The *Sedge* was floating again within 5 minutes of grounding, confirming that its level of grounding was near the bottom of the trough.

Lt. Comdr. Fohnes stated that four tides rose and receded between the time of the earthquake and that of grounding (20:18) (Chance, 1966). Allowing for the fact that Phillips had counted three or four waves in the first hour, our interpretation is that about six waves actually

occurred, of which perhaps four were fairly prominent. Question marks in Figure 121 are intended to show that the waves are interpretive and unconfirmed.

At 20:59 AST, the *Sedge* reported a moderate tide which was referred to as a "big tide" by D. Muma (Chance, 1966). An exact level is not established, but a moderate-to-big tide might be considered to be anything from about one half to one times the highest high water (referenced to *apparent* MLLW). In Figure 121 we have taken the level 12 ft above apparent MLLW, intermediate between these qualitative extremes. Such a high-water level can be explained only by supposing that a 30-minute wave occurred near the crest of the 2-hour wave system.

Another phenomenal recession of water occurred at 22:18 AST, according to T. K. Orlowski, who stated that the level reached was 18 ft below MLLW (Chance, 1966). Accordingly, Figure 121 shows a wave trough at this time reaching to −12 ft, referred to true MLLW. Again, such a remarkable withdrawal of water, occurring now on the rising astronomical tide, can be allowed for only on the basis that a 30-minute trough was near-coincident with a trough of the 2-hour wave system, as also a trough of the 4-hour wave system.

Robert Reed, manager of radio station KLAM in Cordova, reported a "rushing of water" that came in to about half high tide at 23:00 AST, then receded, and again rushed in (Chance, 1966). This is suggested in Figure 121 by an oscillation at this time, which reached to about 12 ft above true MLLW or 6 ft above apparent MLLW.

At least two observers (G. McMahon and T. K. Orlowski) said that a very phenomenal tide swept the waterfront between 23:37 AST and 23:45 (Chance, 1966). McMahon gave its height as 26 ft at 23:37; Orlowski reported 13 ft above (apparent) MLLW at 23:45. McMahon's crest would be 32 ft above true MLLW; Orlowski's level, 19 ft above true MLLW. The prominent wave shown in Figure 121 meets both these conditions on the supposition that McMahon timed the crest at 23:37, whereas Orlowski noticed the water level at 23:45 when the wave was on the wane. This was probably the highest wave to strike Cordova and would have been about 13 ft above pre-earthquake highest high tide.

According to R. Goodman (Chance, 1966), the water (presumably from this wave) lifted the dock and "set it off to the side of the pilings." Extensive flooding must have occurred because Goodman reported that buoys broke loose and "played tag with the houses floating up and down on the water."

G. McMahon and D. Muma (Chance, 1966) testify that another large wave rolled in at about midnight. McMahon reported a 23-ft tide at 00:05 AST March 28: Muma refers only to "another (big tide) about midnight." Reimnitz and Marshall (1965) give the time of this wave as 00:07 and its height as 21.5 ft, measured on a tide staff. Because these indicated elevations could have varied slightly between places of observation, we show the wave crest topping at 29 ft above true MLLW (Figure 121).

It seems peculiar that neither Phillips nor Lt. Comdr. Fohnes remarked on either of these two big waves but referred merely to a high wave which struck Cordova between 01:00 and 02:00 AST, March 28 (Chance, 1966). It is difficult, however, to discount the evidence of McMahon who reported both high waves of 11:37 and 00:05 and is corroborated by independent observers. It is probable that waves were noted by some and not by others because of the long intervals of time between them and the reporters' absence or presence at the times of wave cresting.

Such extraordinarily high waves as those referred to would be difficult to account for as elevations above the still-rising astronomical tide without the presence of the underlying 2-hour wave system. Figure 121 therefore shows the waves of 23:37 and 00:05 riding the crest of a 2-hour-period wave and suggests also that a rising-amplitude 4-hour-period wave was making its presence felt. The graphics of Figure 121 supports the idea that the wave of 23:37 AST was indeed the highest wave, as having behind it the combined momentum of three powerful wave systems—the rising astronomical tide, a rising 4-hour-period wave, and a cresting 2-hour-period wave with appreciable amplitude (of its own) of about 8 ft.

If this was indeed the major wave, it must have entered the Orca Inlet by the deepwater northeast approach via Simpson's Bay (Figure 119) and penetrated to the shallow mouth of the inlet as a breaking wave about 25 ft high, foaming all across the 3-mi width of the Orca Inlet. A fisherman who lived at Point Whitshed (Figure 119) reported that this wave could be heard on the northwest side of Hawkins Island about 1 hour before it arrived. It approached from Hawkins Cutoff and from Cordova simultaneously, and the two waves met near the Point. A rush of air was said to have preceded the wave (Reimnitz and Marshall, 1965).

According to Chance (1966, and in press), Orlowski reported that water level at Cordova had reached 21.1 ft above (apparent) MLLW at 00:30 AST. Reed, on the other hand, said that water level rose to 4 ft above high-tide line at 00:15. These observations can be accommodated in Figure 121 only by supposing that Reed's wave occurred as a hesitation on the back of the earlier wave at 00:05 and that Orlowski's wave at 00:30 occurred as a 20-minute-period oscillation in the trough of the 2-hour wave system, but on the crest of the 4-hour wave. There is the possibility that Reed's wave, being only 8 to 10 minutes later than the large wave of 00:05, could have been one and the same with it, due to a mistiming.

No phenomenal drawdown of water was reported during these hours of highest astronomical tide. Figure 121 suggests that at 00:22 AST there might have been a recession to about 5 ft below (apparent) MLLW, but in the dark hours of the night this would probably have gone unnoticed. Other withdrawals may not have reached below this datum.

What was undoubtedly the last great wave to flood Cordova arrived at about 01:15 AST, March 28. Harbor Master Phillips indicated that it crested within 10 minutes of this time (Berg and others, 1971; Chance, 1966). Lt. Comdr. Fohnes of the *Sedge* also reported that this tide, between 01:00 and 02:00, rose 2 ft over the city dock; presumably this is the same wave as that referred to by R. Goodman (Chance, 1966), which rose above the guardrail on the dock, that is, 3 ft over the dock and "15 feet higher than normal." According to Phillips, the water rose at a rate of ½ to 1 ft/sec to an elevation of 20 ft over the original (apparent) MLLW.

This wave was said to have penetrated 300 ft inland in the harbor area, causing damage to waterfront buildings. One or the other of the large waves previously mentioned also carried away several small houses at Point Whitshed; these floated toward Cordova City and one of them knocked the radio tower from its pedestal. The tower stood above the high-tide line, had whipped back and forth during the earthquake, but had not fallen during that time. Another of the floating houses rammed the city dock and tore the end off the dock (Chance, 1966); the *Sedge*, steaming out of the harbor at this time, had to evade this floating house.

The inferred marigram for Valdez (Figure 84), constructed on the same basic principles as Figure 121, bears interesting comparison with that for Cordova. What turns out to be strangely similar in both figures is the system of 1.8- to 2-hour-period waves underlying the shorter oscillations. In both cases their amplitude is increasing with time, and waves are cresting at Cordova about 27 minutes earlier (on an average) than at Valdez. It would be stretching scientific license too far to attempt to draw any conclusions from this, but one might like to think that this time difference could have something to do with the difference in travel times of these long waves from their source near Montague Island to the ports of Valdez and Cordova. Figures 84 and 121 are interpretative and subject to all the errors inherent in the reconstruction of an event by methods of graphics and inductive reasoning from a paucity of data. Nevertheless, we have faith that the inferences perhaps may be shrewd gropings toward the truth. In Figure 121, all the high peak or trough oscillations of shorter period occur slightly ahead of the crests and troughs of the 2-hour-period waves. This is believed to be a consequence of inertial effect from the inrush and outrush of water of the longer waves in stimulating local seiche amplitudes. The strong oscillations giving rise to the large waves at high tide are ascribed to the combined inertial effects of astronomical tide, 2-hour-, and 4-hour-period waves in overcoming natural damping of the seiches.

The existence of an apparent 4-hour-period wave system of increasing amplitude calls for some comment. This could be evidence of a third harmonic of the astronomical tide, as may be in existence in subdued form as a normal feature of the propagation of the tide in the narrow approaches to Cordova. It might be inferred that the perturbations of the 2-hour tsunami waves caused a temporary amplitude ascendancy of this tidal harmonic. Some slight evidence was found in Figure 2c for such an underlying wave system near Womens Bay, Kodiak, and similar effects have been noted in several other marigrams from Pacific Ocean stations, which recorded the Alaska tsunami of 1964 (Wilson and Tørum, 1968).

The absence of any damaging waves of short period (a few minutes) occurring during or immediately after the earthquake at Cordova is noteworthy in the comparison of Figures 84 and 121. This may be attributed largely to the shallow water and flat slopes of Orca Inlet which would have militated against generation of sudden waves of displacement or development of submarine slides, despite the fact that the horizontal tectonic movement at Cordova (≈40 ft) was greater relatively than that at Valdez (≈25 ft). The remoteness of Cordova from the epicenter of the earth-

quake and the uplift of the region are additional factors which favored nondevelopment of early damaging waves.

Reimnitz and Marshall (1965) have estimated the water-particle velocities of the high waves in the Orca Inlet at about midnight to have been about 30 to 40 knots. That the tsunamis had both a scouring and silting effect on sand sediments in the Orca Inlet is evident from Figure 122 wherein soundings taken in 1963 and about 3 weeks after the earthquake are compared. Great changes in bottom configuration occurred during the 2-week interval between soundings made by the U.S. Coast and Geodetic Survey (a few days after the earthquake) and those by Reimnitz and Marshall, who compared pre- and postearthquake soundings (U.S. Coast and Geodetic Survey, 1964b) to indicate where deposition had taken place north of Cordova (Figure 123).

Evidence of erosion is found in the fact that dead clams in patches up to hundreds of feet in diameter littered the surface of the shoals. The most common shell in these accumulations was that of the cockle *Clinocardium nuttallii* (Conrad), which lives just below the sediment surface. Also present in large numbers were horse clam shells *Tresus* (formerly *Schizothaerus*) *capax*, which live normally at a depth of about 30 in. The accumulation of clams indicates that, in relatively large areas, the upper 30 in. or more of the sea bed were planed off by strong currents, which were also

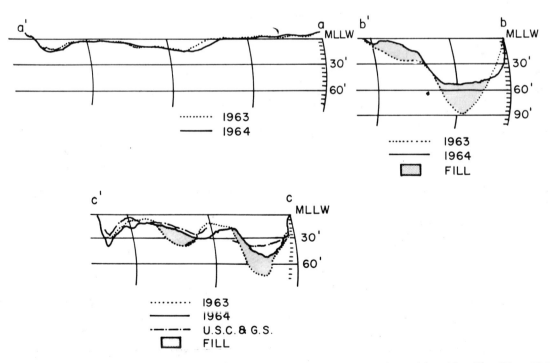

FIGURE 122 Comparative profiles before and after the earthquake, showing erosion and deposition. Note 10- to 15-ft erosion of channel fill in profile cc', comparing postearthquake soundings made about 2 weeks apart. For location of profiles, refer to Figure 119. (From Reimnitz and Marshall, 1965.)

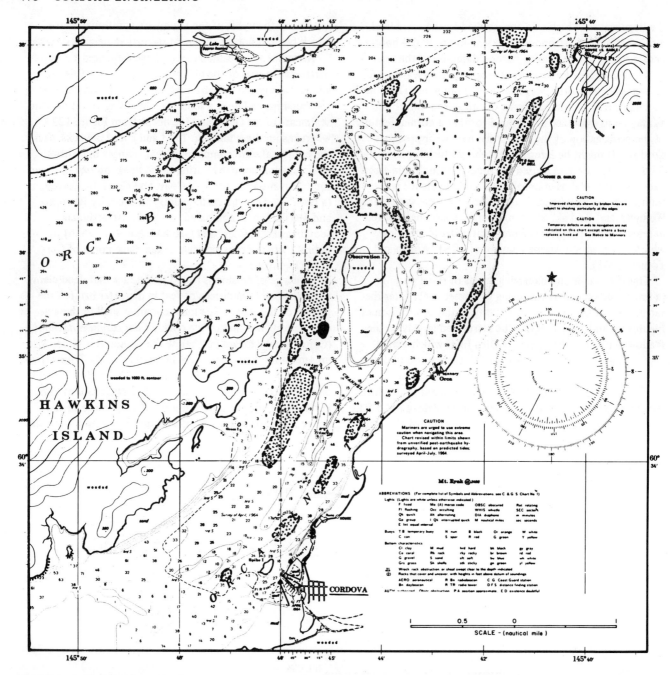

FIGURE 123 Postearthquake soundings by the U.S. Coast and Geodetic Survey, superimposed on old chart, show approximate pattern of deposition. Almost all dotted areas show at least 10 ft of deposition; some show up to 30 ft of deposition. The black spot in center indicates 26 ft of erosion. (From Reimnitz and Marshall, 1965.)

evidenced by the fact that the Coast Guard channel buoys, moored with more than 1 ton of ballast, were moved for miles.

Figure 124 is generally illustrative of the Cordova waterfront as affected by the regional uplift from the earthquake. The damage sustained at Cordova from wave action was estimated by the *Anchorage Daily News* of April 18, 1964, to be $1,775,000. There were no casualties in this immediate area (Spaeth and Berkman, 1967).

EFFECTS OF THE MAIN TSUNAMI ALONG THE WESTERN NORTH AMERICAN SEABOARD (SOUTH OF ALASKA)

TSUNAMI WAVE DAMAGE ALONG THE CANADIAN PACIFIC COAST

As we have seen, the tectonic movements in the Gulf of Alaska were such that the major part of the energy of the

FIGURE 124   Part of the harbor facilities at Cordova, showing the effect of regional uplift in exposing previous tidal flats.

Pierre St.-Amand

tsunamis was directed southeastward toward the west coast of North America. Outside the Gulf of Alaska, this coastline suffered the greatest damage. The most heavily damaged places were Crescent City, California, and Port Alberni on Vancouver Island, Canada. The nature of the runup of the tsunami along the western seaboard of North America has been described by Wilson and Tørum (1968, and this volume). For the coastline immediately north of the Washington border, runup heights are summarized in Figure 125 (see also Figure 8, Wilson and Tørum, this volume).

The tsunami waves of the Alaska earthquake were larger than any previously recorded on the British Columbia coast, according to Wigen and White (1964). Damage was estimated by insurance adjusters at $2,500,000 to $3,000,000. However, according to Spaeth and Berkman (1967, and this volume), the final damage estimate was considerably upward of $10,000,000.

All the earthquake damage in Canada was produced by the tsunami (Wigen and White, 1964). The combination of high waves with high tides caused the crests to surge over the normal high-water line and flood low-lying areas. Buildings were swept away, wharves damaged, and log booms destroyed. Despite this, only one case of severe bodily harm to an inhabitant was reported along the coast of British Columbia.

At the head of Hot Springs Cove near the central part of the west coast of Vancouver Island (Figure 125), an Indian village suffered severe damage from the tsunami. Homes were scattered into the inlet. The general store and refueling station, located about a mile toward the mouth of

the inlet, suffered minor damage. The wharf was structurally damaged, and the fuel lines leading from the tanks located on the slope behind the store were broken (White, 1966).

Nootka Sound and Esperanza Inlet are waterways to the south and north of Nootka Island which provide entrances to the connecting passages and inlets surrounding the island and extending radially inland from it. The peak height reached by the largest wave of the tsunami seems to have been somewhat less in this system of inlets than for others to the north and south (see Figure 125). No damage was reported at Tahsis or at the Nootka Mission Association hospital at Esperanza. At Gold River, dormitory buildings of the Elk River Company were flooded to a depth of 2 ft. Waves surged up the main street of Zeballos, moving some buildings and causing extensive flooding damage in homes and stores. The first wave reached its maximum height there at about 23:00 PST.

A large recession to approximately zero tide was reported to have occurred between the first and second waves (White, 1966).

A large number of bottom fish, some dead and others showing signs of life, were reported found on the surface of the water in Tahsis Narrow. Turbidity near the bottom, indicated by the muddy water in the Narrows, may have caused the fish to move rapidly out of their depth. Inflation of the air bladder would result from the reduced pressure and cause them to surface.

At Fair Harbor, Kyuquot Sound, the maximum wave height reached to 21 ft, resulting in damage to bridges

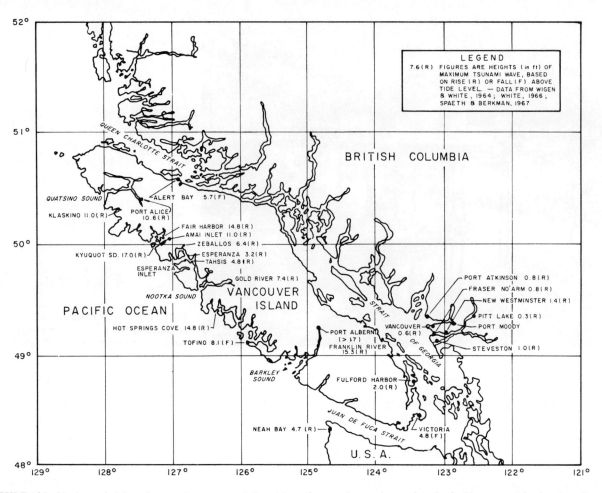

FIGURE 125 Maximum heights of tsunami waves recorded at tide stations or river gaging stations in the Vancouver Island region, Canada.

across the mud flats at the head of the inlet. Only minor damage occurred at the camp of the Tahsis Company. On the Amai Inlet of this sound, about half the houses at the camp of Jorgeson Brothers were shifted and some were carried up the river. At Cachelot the small logging camp, located on floats, was not affected by the tsunami; at Kyuquot, a little island community, a wave equivalent to a 17-ft tide was reported (White, 1966).

At Winter Harbour in an inlet near the entrance to Quatsino Sound, Vancouver Island (Figure 125), a wave equivalent to a 16-ft tide was reported by the W. D. Moore Logging Company. Log-boom ground piles were completely demolished by the first wave. A 38-ft tender, carried out of one inlet by the recession of water after the first crest, was carried up another inlet and beached by the second crest.

Port Alice, near the head of Neroutsos Inlet, is the location of a pulp plant operated by Rayonier Canada. There the maximum crest reached the height of a 19-ft tide. Log booms were disarranged. Small wharves were swept away

and some boats were lost. Little damage, however, occurred in the town or at the plant (White, 1966).

Only small surges (about 1 ft in amplitude) were reported at Coal Harbour in Holberg Inlet of Quatsino Sound. This inlet was apparently protected by the narrow passage connecting it to Quatsino Sound, and there probably was insufficient time for the transfer of water to the inlet in response to the relatively rapid changes in water level that were taking place in the outside channel.

At Klaskino Inlet the maximum crest reached a height of 19 ft, referred to tidal datum. No damage occurred to the logging camp, which is located on floats.

Although rough water prevented a landing in San Josef Bay, Vancouver Island, soon after the earthquake, observations were made from the air and photographs taken. In addition, reports were obtained from the Royal Canadian Air Force Station at Holberg and from the W. D. Moore Logging Company. It has been well established that the tsunami swept large trees from the north bank of the river near its entrance into San Josef Bay. Shifting of the sand-

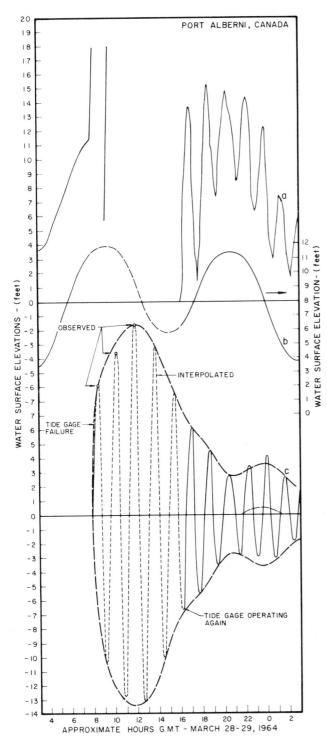

FIGURE 126 Subjective analysis of marigram for Port Alberni, Canada.

In Queen Charlotte Strait the Pioneer Timber Company at Port McNeill reported a high-water crest equivalent to a 17-ft tide. Pilings and dolphins in the booming ground were snapped off. Log booms, loose logs, and boom boats were swept out of the bay.

In the Juan de Fuca Strait and the Strait of Georgia at the south of Vancouver Island (Figure 125), no serious damage was reported. The tsunami waves penetrated up the Fraser River and were recorded on the water-level gage at Pitt Lake, a freshwater tidal lake more than 30 mi from the sea. For greater details of the above damage survey, the reader is referred to Wigen and White (1964), White (1966), and Spaeth and Berkman (1967, and this volume). A report by Oceanographic Services (1965) also gives information on water-level changes along the coast of Canada and the United States.

TSUNAMI WAVES AND DAMAGE AT PORT ALBERNI, VANCOUVER ISLAND, CANADA

The twin cities, Alberni and Port Alberni, comprise an industrial center noted for the production of pulp, paper, and plywood. They are located at the head of Alberni Inlet about 40 mi from the west coast of Vancouver Island (Figure 125). Port Alberni is of special interest because of the severe damage it sustained from the tsunami (see Wigen and White, 1964; White, 1966; Abernethy and others, 1964).

According to the analysis of Figure 126, which attempts to infer what the tide gage would have recorded had it not failed during the first waves, the maximum envelope wave height may have been as much as 27 ft. Water levels for the first three waves were established by observation, thus permitting some definition of the wave system by interpolation between these observations and the later marigram. The waves approximate 1.72 hours in period and clearly must have gained their extraordinary height through some local phenomenon of near resonance, since the corresponding maximum waves at Victoria, only a short distance southwest along Vancouver Island, were only 3 ft high.

Port Alberni lies at the head of a long inlet, a narrow channel that varies in width from ½ to 1 mi and in depth from about 100 fathoms at the mouth to less than 30 fathoms at the head (White, 1966). The approximate natural period of oscillation of such a canal may be calculated by assuming that the depth profile along the length is parabolic. Thus, from Lamb (1932) (see also Wilson, 1966) the fundamental period is

$$T_1 = 4.44 L/\sqrt{gd_1}, \qquad (17)$$

in which L is the length of the channel from the mouth and d_1 the depth at the mouth. For $L = 40$ mi, $d_1 = 600$ ft, T_1

bars from the north to the south bank of the river mouth was reported. A clam bed, near the small stream entering the river from the north, was denuded and the stream was jammed with logs at the tree line (White, 1966).

is 1.85 hours, which clearly suggests that pseudoresonance occurred.

Quite recently, Murty and Boilard (1970) calculated the resonating properties of the Alberni Inlet by more accurate numerical methods that take account of the variabilities of depth and width along the inlet. Their result appears to show that the fundamental mode oscillation, with friction, is of the order of 2.10 hours, whereas their power spectrum for the tsunami at Port Alberni exhibits a very powerful peak of energy at 1.94-hour period. [This compares with the 1.72 hours found by approximate analysis in Figure 126 (see also Wilson and Tørum, 1968).]

The calculations by Murty and Boilard cover a range of tsunami periods from 15 to 90 minutes, imposed on the mouth at an amplitude of 1 to 2 ft. For the 80-minute tsunami period, the dynamic amplification at the head of the inlet is given at about 1.5. It is unfortunate that these au-

thors did not pursue the range of input periods to higher values in the neighborhood of 2 hours; they would probably have found a very much greater amplification. By a rather simple method, based on Lamb (1932) but ignoring friction, Wilson and Tørum (1968) suggested that the amplification could have been as much as 10, on the supposition that the period of the incident tsunami was about 1.7 hours and its height about 2.7 ft at the mouth.

The first tsunami surge began at the head of the Alberni Inlet just before midnight on the night of the earthquake and reached its peak at 00:15 PST, March 28. Fortunately, this first wave served as a warning for the second higher wave which crested about 1¾ hours later. Some residents of low-lying areas were alerted by flooding which had taken place in their homes. Others were warned by the Royal Canadian Mounted Police, by workers of the Department of Social Welfare, and by volunteer helpers. Affected fam-

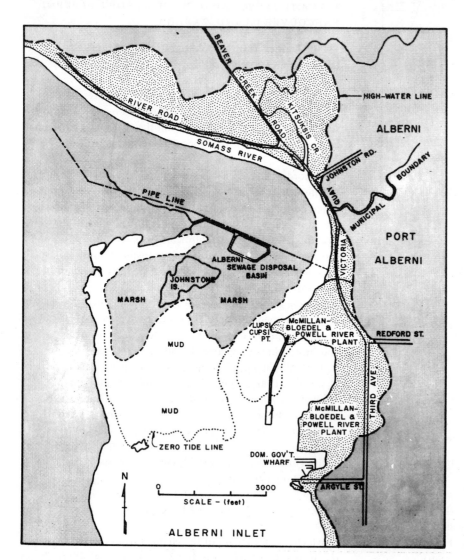

FIGURE 127   Map of Alberni and Port Alberni. (From White, 1966.)

ilies moved out of low-lying areas to find temporary shelter in the homes of friends or in available public and commercial facilities (White, 1966).

Local civic and welfare agencies and volunteer emergency organizations quickly took rescue measures to cope with the disastrous situation which rapidly developed. Provincial Civil Defense authorities set up headquarters on the following day in the Alberni Fire Hall for the purpose of coordinating rescue operations in cooperation with the civic authorities of the two cities.

In the Alberni–Port Alberni area, damage has been estimated at $5 million, exclusive of damage to heavy industry and private automobiles; inclusion of such damage probably doubles the figure (Spaeth and Berkman, 1967, and this volume). Most severe loss occurred in the low-lying areas bordering the head of the Alberni Inlet and along the northeast bank of the Somass River (Figure 127). The waves surged to the head of the inlet and out across the low-lying residential area on the north side of the Somass River, carrying with them houses, logs, boats, and any other movable objects that lay in their path. Following the crest of the waves, the recessions tended to carry the floating structures back toward their original locations. Houses and tourist cabins along River Road were shifted and, in some cases, carried back as much as 1,000 yd. Damage ranged from total destruction to minor water damage. Houses on substantial foundations with the superstructure secured to the foundation (presumably by bolts) remained in place. Observers reported that floating logs and houses reached speeds in excess of 20 mph (White, 1966).

A 54-in. water pipeline supplying the MacMillan, Bloedel and Powell River Co., Ltd., was carried away by logs that collided with it as they were carried along with the wave. The pipeline was mounted on trestles and traversed the mud flats near the head of the inlet. The sewage-disposal basin in the same area was filled with logs, but no permanent damage occurred to the system.

Many commercial and business establishments along the waterfront in Port Alberni were severely damaged by water. The cleanup operations were greatly complicated by the muddy deposits that accompanied the flooding. Engineering and warehouse buildings near the Canadian Pacific and Dominion Government wharves were affected. Stocks on the lower shelves in these buildings were badly damaged by wetting. Considerable damage was done also to wharf structures because the decks rose with the waves and then became distorted and buckled in some parts during the recession. Fisherman's Wharf was raised with enough force to fracture 6- by 10-in. timber cross bars on the pilings (White, 1966).

At the site of the China Creek logging operation of the

MacMillan, Bloedel and Powell River Co., Ltd., a wharf was lifted off the supporting pilings and left resting on the dowels. Log booms were not seriously disarranged by the waves. However, at the Franklin River operation, further down the inlet, many log booms were broken up. Large concrete anchors used to hold log markers in place were dragged out into the inlet. The deck of a wharf was carried away and some residences were flooded. Two beacons, which marked the Sproat Narrows on both sides of the inlet, were swept away, together with their supporting dolphins. The Trans-Pacific submarine cable and the telephone cable, laid in the Alberni Inlet, were reported damaged in the vicinity of the Narrows.

Wave heights estimated as being 2 to 8 ft above high water were reported from communities further down the inlet at Kildonan, Bamfield, and Turtle Island. Logs were moved well back from the beach at Pachena Bay by waves of large amplitude. The above information is quoted almost verbatim from White (1966).

TSUNAMI WAVE DAMAGE ALONG THE WASHINGTON-OREGON COASTS

Along the Washington coast the tsunami caused some damage, the total monetary loss for which has been estimated at about $115,000 (Hogan, Lundy, and Whipple, 1965). By far the greatest single item of damage ($75,000) occurred to a reinforced concrete bridge (No. 109) forming part of the State Highway at Joe Creek. The supporting piles sustained serious damage presumably as a result of the battering-ram effect of log debris hurled against the structure by the tsunami waves.

Some damage was done also on Lake Union, Seattle, by seiches generated by the earthquake vibration. The disturbance caused minor damage to the gangway of the U.S. Coast and Geodetic Survey ship *Patton* and snapped a mooring line on the *Lester Jones*. Minor damage was caused to several pleasure craft, houseboats, and floats that broke their moorings along the shore of the lake.

Runup heights along the Washington-Oregon coastline have been given by Wilson and Tørum (1968, and this volume, Figure 10, p. 168). Of particular interest is the penetration of the tsunami up the Columbia River, discussed in the next section.

A relatively greater amount of damage appears to have occurred along the Oregon coastline than along the Washington coast, perhaps as a result of the slight concavity favoring more direct wave attack.

Places hit hardest were Cannon Beach City (damage $230,000), Coos Bay ($20,000), Florence ($50,000), Seaside ($276,000), and the Waldport–Alsea area ($160,000) (Spaeth and Berkman, 1967, and this volume). A listing of the damages estimated by the Office of Civil Defense is given in Table 1 of Spaeth and Berkman (this volume). (For details of the inundation at Seaside, Oregon, see Figure 7, Spaeth and Berkman, this volume, p. 59). Detailed information on damage is rather scanty.

Four children, who were camping with their parents on the beach near Newport, Oregon, were engulfed by waves and drowned (Spaeth and Berkman, 1967, and this volume).

PENETRATION OF THE TSUNAMI UP THE COLUMBIA RIVER

Both the tide wave and the tsunami ran straight up the Columbia River, with the tsunami front preceding the tide crest by about 1.5 hours. The vast size of the tide wave, however, ensured that the leading waves of the tsunami rode majestically on the top of the tide wave and propagated upriver in this virtually interlocked fashion. The situation is of particular interest inasmuch as the effects were recorded at tide-gage stations spaced over some 90 nautical mi of estuary from the mouth of the Columbia River. Figure 11 of Wilson and Tørum (this volume, p. 170) presents three samples of the marigrams which reveal the development of the tide wave as an unsymmetrical wave effectively made up of harmonics of the tide riding the fundamental wave. Beaver tide gage, in particular, shows that, with the exception of the tsunami waves riding the tide crest, the intermediate waves have lost their identity and hardly register at the low tide, though later waves are found again on the succeeding high tide. This demise of tsunami waves (other than the first three) on the rear slope of the tide wave would have been promoted by the tsunami beat interference effect evident in the fourth, fifth, and sixth waves at Victoria, Canada (Wilson and Tørum, 1968), even if frictional damping of the waves at low tide were not the major cause.

The data from the Columbia River tide gages permit us to derive some quantitative information about the tsunami and the tide propagation upriver. Thus, Figure 128a provides a space–time plot of the progression of the first, second, and third tsunami wave crests on the first tide crest and of two other tsunami wave crests riding the subsequent tide crest. At the mouth the leading tsunami waves show a period $T \simeq 1.75$ hours, but the period changes and increases with distance. This is readily explained by the fact that the speeds of the waves differ according to the depth of water provided for them by the tide wave and the river water. By the time the third tsunami wave loses identity at about 70 nautical miles from the mouth, its effective period is 2.2 hours.

Initially, in the first 50 nautical miles the tide crests ad-vance more rapidly than the tsunami, but the tide then slows rapidly, presumably as a result of shallow water and increasing tidal friction. The tsunami waves, less susceptible to friction, outrun the tide and advance through the tide crest. The initially greater speed of the tide may be related to the effect of tide height. Thus, Lamb (1932) (see also Appendix B) has shown that finite-amplitude long waves, whose elevation above still water of depth d is η, will propagate at the velocity

$$c = \sqrt{gd} \; [3 \, (1 + \eta/d)^{1/2} - 2]. \tag{18}$$

The steepening of the tide wave front is inherently related to the fact that the crest speed (η positive) exceeds the trough speed (η negative).

The essentially nondispersive nature of the tsunami is verified by the fact that the period between the waves riding the second tide crest near the mouth of the Columbia River was also found to be about 1.75 hours (the same as the leading waves). This period decreases to 1.4 hours at the Vancouver tide gage (87 nautical mi from the river mouth), because the second tsunami wave, having advanced through the tide crest, is favored by a greater depth of water and therefore a faster speed relative to the antecedent wave.

Figure 128 (b and c) plots the crest elevations above tide level of all five tsunami waves and the tide-crest elevations above MSL. Interesting information emerges from these diagrams. For instance, Figure 128b reveals that the leading tsunami wave at the mouth of the Columbia River was highest and the third wave higher than the second. The beat pattern of the tsunami waves for the area near Victoria, Canada (Wilson and Tørum, 1968), showed this same characteristic. The relative prominence of the first and second waves, however, reversed three times as they progressed up the Columbia River. It is found that the crossing points of reversal occurred at about 19, 49, and 79 nautical miles from the mouth, or intervals of exactly 30 nautical miles. The significance of this will be discussed shortly. First it is necessary to comment on the behavior of the tide waves.

The elevation of the tide crest first declined and then enhanced as the tide ran upriver (Figure 128c). This pseudo-resonance effect seemingly at work merits further attention. From Figure 11 (Wilson and Tørum, this volume, p.170), we surmise that the hydraulic gradient for the Columbia River would place normal river level at about 3.5 ft above MSL at 90 nautical miles from the mouth. Tide elevations relative to normal river level are then obtained from Figure 128c to provide values of η for use in equation (17) to calculate the mean river depth d. From Figure 128a the gradients of the space–time propagation line for, say, the first tide crest yield values of velocity c, so that the equation can be solved for d. Results, shown in Figure 128d, indicate that

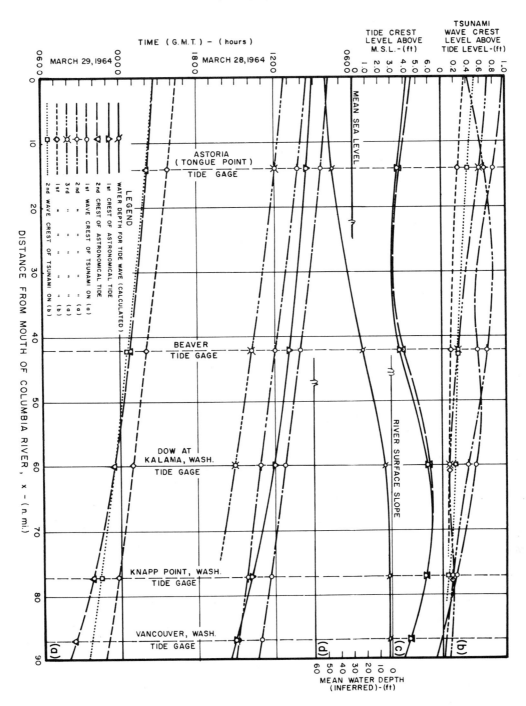

FIGURE 128 Analysis of tsunami wave propagation up the Columbia River, Washington–Oregon.

the mean depth (from the tide point of view) is very small at 65 nautical mi from the mouth. (Note: At the time of this writing, information on river depths was unavailable to us. Actual depths are complicated by the presence of a narrow 40- to 50-ft dredged navigational channel. Mean depths in Figure 128d are of correct order near the river

mouth but are too small upriver). The depth profile from the mouth, in fact, is roughly parabolic over a length $L \approx 65$ nautical miles, with a mouth depth of $d \approx 50$ ft. The Columbia River, then, to all intents and purposes, acts as a closed-end canal with the "closure" at about 65 nautical miles from the mouth.

We now use equation 17 as applied to Port Alberni, to calculate the fundamental period of oscillation for this system. The result is surprising—

$$T = 12.1 \text{ hours},$$

in close agreement with the semidiurnal astronomical tide period. The peak tidal oscillation at mileage 65 would thus seem to be explained as a tidal resonance effect. That it declines beyond this would clearly be the result of the leak effect to the higher river reaches. The low-tide crest height, found at mileage 30, would seem to be evidence of a quasi-node, offset from the mouth presumably because of the upriver leakage effect beyond mileage 65.

We return to a consideration of the fluctuations of height of the two leading tsunami waves. The tide wave takes 3.6 hours to travel from the river mouth to mileage 65 (Figure 128a); also, the third-mode (trinodal) oscillation for the river as a closed-end open-mouth canal of parabolic bed (see Wilson, 1966), is

$$T_3 = 0.259 \, T_1 = 3.6 \text{ hours.} \tag{19}$$

It follows then that a tide-induced oscillation of this period could have positive antinodes near the mouth and at mileage 65, and a negative antinode at about mileage 33. Just 1.8 hours later, the signs of the antinodes could reverse. Since the leading tsunami waves are about 1.8 hours apart in time, they would become enhanced or reduced in height by this canal oscillation, according to whether they were riding on the positive or the negative antinode. The nodes of the canal's third mode of oscillation should thus be revealed by the crossing points of the crest height lines for the two leading waves (Figure 128b), occurring at mileages 19, 49, 79, as mentioned earlier. The usual requirement that a node for an open-mouth basin oscillation be located exactly at the mouth is apt to be waived on account of the leakage effect to the upper river reaches beyond mileage 65.

TSUNAMI WAVE DAMAGE ALONG THE CALIFORNIA COASTLINE

The tsunami effects along the coast of northern California have been extensively reported by Magoon (1966). At most places the tsunamis occurred as a fast-rising tide with a maximum rate of change of level from 1 to 2 ft per minute with strong reversing ebb and flood currents.

Observers at Noyo and Atkin Rivers, however, described an almost vertical wall of water progressing upstream, apparently in the nature of a bore. At Noyo this disturbance traveled upstream almost 30 mi. Magoon (1966) describes the phenomenon as follows:

At Noyo Harbor the entrance is restricted, but the harbor is also restricted and the full effects of the waves were felt over the entire reach of the harbor. In the March 1964 tsunami the first wave rose relatively slowly, and exhibited the characteristics observed elsewhere along the coast. The second wave, occurring about 15 minutes after the first, formed a bore-like face, about 7 feet high, consisting of a series of step-like jumps. One observer saw the bore form at the entrance and rapidly drove his automobile at about 30 miles per hour parallel to the travel of the bore, but was unable to pass it. At Noyo damage was to floats and to commercial fishing vessels that broke loose during the tsunami.

With the exception of Crescent City, which we shall discuss separately, the damages from the 1964 tsunami in northern California mainly involved commercial fishing or pleasure craft and their associated shoreline facilities.

At San Francisco near the Golden Gate, the tsunami developed oscillations with a maximum range of about 7 ft. By a subjective analysis of the marigram from the tide gage at this site, Wilson and Tørum (1968) concluded that two wave systems were dominant in the record, one of 1.73 hours in period, the second of 38.5 minutes. The latter period is close to being a third harmonic of the 1.73-hour period. Because San Francisco Bay is known to have a fundamental period of free oscillation of about 1.9 hours and a second mode oscillation in the range of 34 to 41 minutes (see Honda, Terada, and Isitani, 1908; Thornton, 1946), it appears that the tsunami drew sympathetic response from the bay.

Magoon (1966) has given the following description of effects in San Francisco Bay:

Inside of San Francisco Bay both the May 1960 and March 1964 tsunamis were greatly attenuated after passing through the Golden Gate. Based on very limited data, a tsunami at Richmond on the north and Hunter's Point on the south is reduced to one-half the height at the Golden Gate. A tsunami at the easterly end of San Pablo Bay and Alviso on the south is reduced to less than one-tenth the height at the Golden Gate. Damage in San Francisco Bay was largely to pleasure boats. The highest damage was reported from Marinas in Marin County where strong currents caused boats and in some cases portions of floating slips to break loose. These objects attained the velocity of the moving water and caused damage when they struck the other craft.

The attenuation of the tsunami in San Francisco Bay in relation to unit height at the entrance is shown in the inset to Figure 12 in Wilson and Tørum (this volume, p. 171).

In Monterey Bay, about 60 nautical miles south of San Francisco, the tsunami produced widely different effects at the north and south extremities at Santa Cruz and Monterey. Santa Cruz experienced a runup almost twice that at Monterey despite the apparently protected setting of Santa Cruz in relation to the approach direction of the tsunami; this may perhaps be ascribed to the deep and narrow canyon that virtually bisects the bay and favors refraction of wave energy entering the bay toward the north more than toward the south (Wilson and others, 1965).

Monterey Bay provides another case for assessing the effects of the tsunami in stimulating local resonances. By approximating the configuration of Monterey Bay as the quadrant of a circular basin with both a horizontal and a paraboloidal bed, Wilson and others (1965) used known hydrodynamical results to estimate the modes and periods of the free oscillations on the assumption that antinodal conditions must always occur at the two extremities of the bay (or quadrant), namely, Santa Cruz and Monterey. The modes of oscillation comprise, in general, a combination of nodal radii and nodal arcs.

Table 10 gives the calculated lowest modes (longest periods) of the free oscillations to be expected, along with sequences of apparent periods found in the marigram from the Monterey tide gage for March 28-30, 1964, as found by graphical residuation analysis (Chrystal, 1906) and by spectrum analysis (Marine Advisers, 1964). There is a strong suggestion from the general congruencies of periods that the tsunami stimulated modal shelf oscillations of the kinds inferred from theory. Wiegel (1970) has recorded that at the time of the April 1, 1946, Aleutian Trench tsunami, W. E. Bascom reported on the same peculiarity of response in bays along the North American west coast, namely, that a higher runup occurred in the upcoast "protected" portions of the bays than in the downcoast "unprotected" portions. Because many bays along the

North American west coast are fissured by deep submarine canyons, the explanation for this could be quite similar to that suggested by the authors for Monterey Bay. The observation anyway seems worthy of extended study.

There was little damage in Monterey Harbor, but some damage was reported from Santa Cruz Harbor at the northern end of the bay (see Figure 129 for detail), where strong horizontal currents prevailed in the harbor. Magoon (1966) reports as follows:

. . . the water level varied from a high of 11 feet to a low of about − 8 feet MLLW. During the major portion of the drawdown in elevation, the water level dropped at a rate of about 1 foot per minute for about 10 to 15 minutes. Obviously, strong horizontal currents were produced by this disturbance. A floating hydraulic dredge was docked near the entrance just before the tsunami arrived. One of the early waves induced such a drag on the dredge that the mooring lines parted and the dredge was swept seaward. As it moved out the entrance, it struck the east jetty and finally sank along the entrance channel, on the centerline extension of the east jetty. Shortly thereafter a 38-foot cabin cruiser struck a submerged object, presumably the sunken dredge, while attempting to leave the harbor, and sank. The strong currents induced by the tsunami also caused movement of material in the entrance channel bottom. Several small floats located near the public pier were damaged from being caught against the pier and were wrecked or twisted as the water fell. With the exception of damage to the small floats mentioned above, all other floating facilities withstood the tsunami.

Particulars of tsunami wave damage for Southern California are peculiarly scarce, considering the sizable amounts

TABLE 10   Apparent Modal Periods of Oscillation of Monterey Bay Stimulated by the Alaska Tsunami of March 1964

Date and Time	Sensor Location	Period of Mode of Oscillation[a] (min)										Method of Analysis
Observation												
March, 28, 1964	Monterey Sensor No. 1	?	33.3			8.3	5.8	4.3	3.2	2.4	2.0	Spectrum analysis of analog records (Marine Advisors, 1964)
	Monterey Sensor No. 2	?	33.3	16.7		8.3	5.3	4.4	3.3	2.5	2.3	
	Monterey Sensor No. 3	?	33.3	16.7	9.5		6.1	4.3	3.5	2.4	2.1	
March 29, 1964, 0000–0900	Monterey Tide Gage	60	35.7 32.3	19.6	17.3	11.1	9.3	5.5				Residuation of marigram (Wilson and others, 1965)
1400, Mar. 29, 1964– 0400, Mar. 30, 1964	Monterey Tide Gage	60	36.3	22.6		13.0	8.8	5.9				
Theory												
Circular basin analogy, horizontal bed		64.7	38.4 31.1	22.5 22.3	17.8 17.0 15.9	12.8 11.7 10.1						Hydrodynamic theory (Wilson and others, 1965)
Circular basin analogy, paraboloidal bed		58.6	42.1 29.8	24.3 22.5	18.8 17.2	14.9 12.7 12.2						Hydrodynamic theory (Wilson and others, 1965)

[a]Columns are used to separate obviously distinctive modal periods. In some cases, as in rows 6 and 7 (theory), distinctive modes have similar periods; observationally, they would probably be recognized only when period differences were sufficiently distinct to justify the separation in columns.

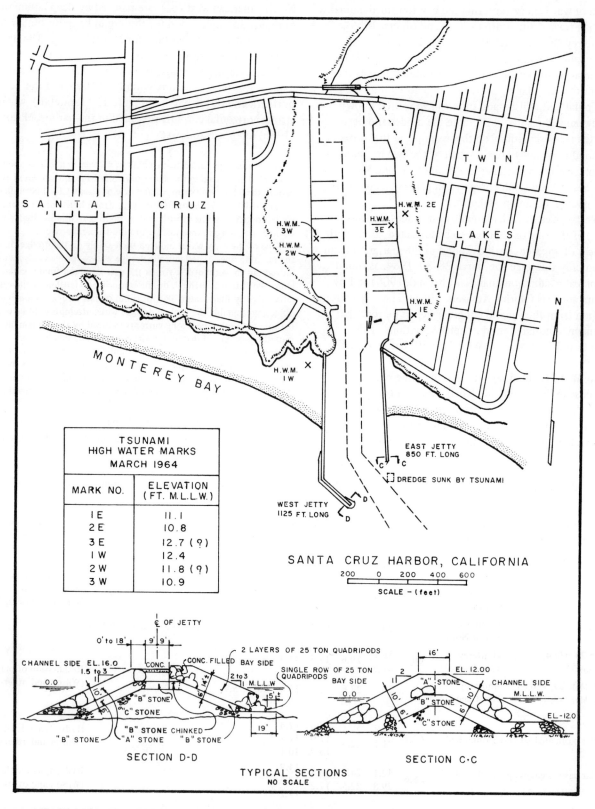

FIGURE 129   Plan of Santa Cruz Harbor with high-water marks left by the Alaska tsunami. (From Magoon, 1965.)

of the losses. From \$175,000 to \$275,000 worth of damage occurred in Los Angeles Harbor and \$100,000 in Long Beach Harbor, but we have not been able to secure any documentary details on these losses. From personal communication with Mr. William Herron of the U.S. Army Corps of Engineers, Los Angeles District, it is understood that most of the damage was sustained as a result of swift currents (up to 15 knots in velocity) in the inner harbor (Cerritos Channel) and small-boat harbors where moored boats, landing floats, and guide piles were torn loose. Unfortunately, details, particularly concerning effects on large vessels, are lacking.

The tsunami attained heights of about 4 ft in Los Angeles and Long Beach harbors within San Pedro Bay, in Southern California. From spectrum analyses of marigrams from three tide stations in these harbors, it has been shown that tsunami effects in the area comprised four predominant wave frequencies at periods ≈ 1.7 hours, 60, 39, and 31 minutes (Wilson and others, 1968; Wilson, 1969b). All but the first of these periodicities can be explained as resonances of particular modes of oscillations of the Continental Shelf off San Pedro Bay (Wilson, 1969b). The 1.7-hour wave component is believed to be residual from the incident tsunami excitation.

Exclusive of Crescent City, for which tsunami damage amounted to about \$11,000,000 (Magoon, 1966, and personal communication), the estimated losses elsewhere along the California coast total between \$1,770,000 and \$2,620,000 (Magoon, 1966; Spaeth and Berkman, 1967, and this volume).

TSUNAMI WAVES AND DAMAGE AT CRESCENT CITY, CALIFORNIA

Unexpectedly large waves struck Crescent City (Foley, 1964; Roberts and Chien, 1965; Stanley, 1964). Subjective analysis of Figure 130 has suggested large-amplitude (30- to 35-minute period) oscillations occurring on top of 13.4-ft tsunami waves with a 1.77-hour period (Wilson and Tørum, 1968). We note that 30- to 35-minute oscillations would accord with a third harmonic of the incident tsunami waves. That this frequency could have gained such large response suggests that some topographical feature of the region may have provided resonant conditions.

Crescent City occupies a position on a concave coastline southeast of Point St. George, from which a submerged reef extends seaward in a continuation of the coastal area (Figure 131). Moreover, at the two extremities of the arc, off Point St. George and off Rocky or Patrick's Point (at the southern end), the Continental Shelf width narrows appreciably. The coast and shelf conform to a semielliptic basin, open-mouthed along its major axis at the edge of the shelf. The dimensions of this basin are such that the ratio

of the half-lengths of the major and minor axes is close to 4/3; the half-length L of the minor axis is 17.25 nautical miles. The depth profile along the minor axis is approximated very closely by a parabola, and the trend of the depth contours indicates that the entire shelf in the area is pseudoellipsoidal to a maximum depth d_1 of 300 feet.

The approximation of the shelf and coast to a geometrical form that can be described mathematically makes possible some conclusions regarding oscillating characteristics. For this we adapt the work of Goldsbrough (1930) to the situation of an open-mouth basin (see Wilson, 1966). For this particular shape of elliptic basin, extrapolation from previous calculations suggests that the eigenperiods of oscillation of the Continental Shelf off Crescent City should approximate the sequence of periods, T_m, given by the following relationships:

$$(T_m \sqrt{gd_1})/L = 4.444; 3.528; 2.930; 2.340; 1.785; .... (20)$$

The subscript m is an integer ($m = 1, 2, 3, ...$) to describe the mode order in terms of descending period value. All these modes require that a node of the free oscillation shall lie along the major axis at the mouth of the basin (or edge of the shelf). The fundamental mode represented by $m = 1$ ($T_1 = 79.1$ minutes) would be a simple uninodal oscillation about the major axis. The second mode ($T_2 = 62.8$ minutes) would represent a binodal oscillation with nodes along both axes of the semiellipse. Another binodal oscillation ($T_3 = 52.1$ minutes) would involve a hyperbola as the second node, symmetrical with respect to the minor axis, and intersecting the coast probably near Point St. George and Patrick's Point. The fourth mode ($T_4 = 41.6$ minutes) effectively would be trinodal for the bay, with two nodal hyperbolas, each symmetrical with respect to the minor axis and intersecting the coast. The nodes in this case would approximate to radial lines from the center of the major axis, and the type of oscillation would effectively conform to an edge-wave system.

The fifth mode yielding a period $T_5 = 31.7$ minutes is actually a binodal oscillation of a different type which involves a semiellipse as the second node (Figure 131c). Since this mode would conform well to the coastal configuration, it would seem to be a good resonating medium for stimulating any third harmonic of the tsunami excitation ($T \approx 36$ minutes). None of the other above calculated modes of shelf oscillation have periods in conformity with the tsunami period and its odd harmonics ($T \approx 108, 36, 22$ minutes) which excitations are believed to be easily generated resulting from the tsunami propagation over the discontinuity at the Continental Shelf edges.

The third mode ($T_3 = 52.1$ minutes) would have been in good accord with any second (even) harmonic of the tsunami ($T \approx 54$ minutes), but Figure 130 implies that it was

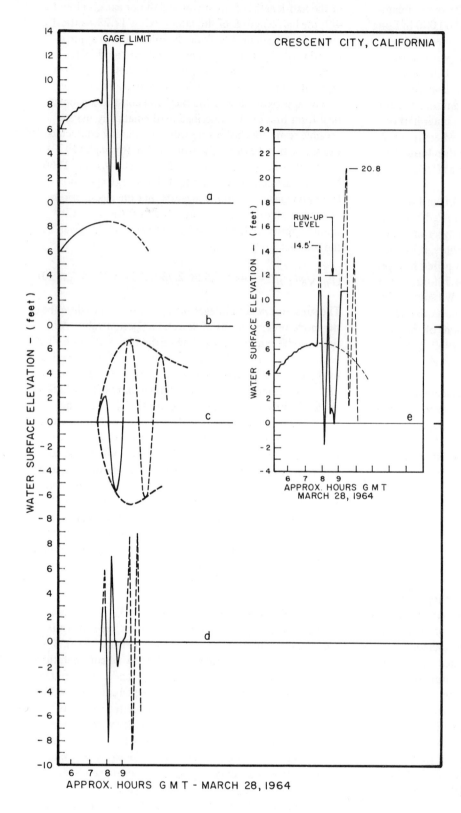

FIGURE 130 Subjective analysis of marigram for Crescent City, California.

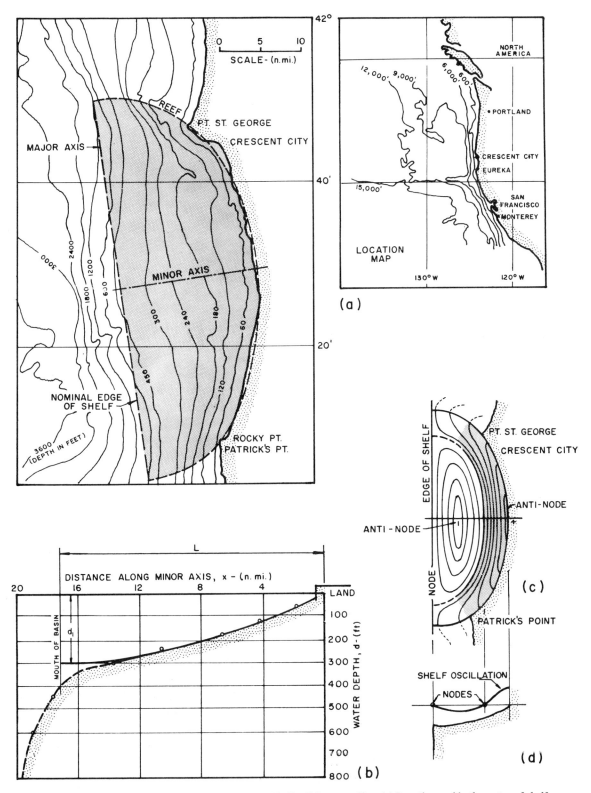

FIGURE 131 Oscillating characteristics of Continental Shelf off Crescent City. (*a*) Location and bathymetry of shelf; (*b*) depth profile along minor axis; (*c*) binodal mode of shelf oscillation.

not excited. However, the fundamental eigenperiod for the shelf off Crescent City ($T_1 \approx 79$ minutes) is sufficiently) close to the main tsunami wave period ($T \approx 108$ minutes) to have provided a degree of amplification through partial resonance, as seems to have been the case, more completely, at Port Alberni, Canada, and Lyttelton, New Zealand (Wilson and Tørum, 1968).

The tsunami of May 23, 1960, generated by the Chilean earthquake (magnitude = 8.4) also drew a strong response at Crescent City at a period of 32 minutes. Figure 132 shows this response and presents the energy spectrum for the waves calculated from the tide record. Wiegel (1965), seeking an explanation for the 32-minute peak as a possible shelf oscillation, investigated wave travel times from the edge of the Continental Shelf, but found this approach unrewarding. The travel time over the distance L of Figure 131 was about 21.2 minutes. Four times this value yields the approximate period of the fundamental shelf oscillation, $T_1 = 84.8$ minutes, which compares favorably with our result of $T_1 = 79.1$ minutes. This period should have favored resonance of the main waves propagated from the Chilean earthquake; Figure 132, however, does not show the resonance, although the accuracy of the spectrum at very low frequencies is suspect. It should be noted that

the harbor itself at Crescent City cannot support resonance of tsunamis at periods greater than about 10 minutes.

It is of interest that Harrison and Keulegan (1968) in a subsequent study have confirmed the importance of resonance at Crescent City by considering the somewhat simpler oscillations over a sloping shelf of maximum depth d_1 and length L. They found the period sequence in this case to be

$$(T_m \sqrt{gd_1})/L = 5.226; 2.227; 1.452; 1.166 \ldots \tag{21}$$

Taking $L = 16$ nautical miles and $d_1 = 350$ ft as representative of the shelf off Crescent City, Harrison and Keulegan found

$$T_m = 80.0; 34.8; 22.2; 17.8; \ldots \text{ minutes}. \tag{22}$$

These authors then determined the power spectrum from a 16-hour length of the marigram for the 1960 Chilean tsunami and found the presence of peaks at periods of 80, 35.0, 22.4, and 18.6 minutes. It is noteworthy, too, that Wiegel's spectrum (Figure 132) confirms the presence of energy peaks at about 22 and 18 minutes.

We conclude then that Crescent City's susceptibility to large wave response from major tsunamis is, by its very name, related to its crescent-shaped coast and bowl-shaped Continental Shelf. Because of its dimensions, it will be forever a responsive echo chamber for great tsunamis, because their periods will always be capable of exciting full or partial resonances.

The mechanism for transfer of energy of long waves to higher frequencies, when negotiating depth changes that are sudden with respect to the wave length, is not yet fully understood. Dean (1964) may have uncovered some of the main elements of such changes by drawing attention to the fact that wave form, if resolved into its Fourier constituents, would yield different amplifications and phase changes for the components in their propagation over the continental slope. Long waves, whose amplitude is not small compared with the mean depth, have an inherent tendency to propagate by developing harmonics, even in a channel of uniform depth. Airy (1845) first drew attention to this (see Lamb, 1932), and the phenomenon is a feature of the propagation of tides in narrow channels. The reason for the suppression of even harmonics, in situations of sudden change, is not known to us at this time.

Recent theoretical and experimental studies of "soliton" or parasitic wave formation as result of long-wave propagation over sharp discontinuities (Zabusky and Kruskal, 1966; Galvin, 1968; Madsen and Mei, 1969; Madsen and others, 1970) give encouraging prospect for understanding more about this phenomenon, but it is beyond the scope of the present discussion to enlarge upon these developments.

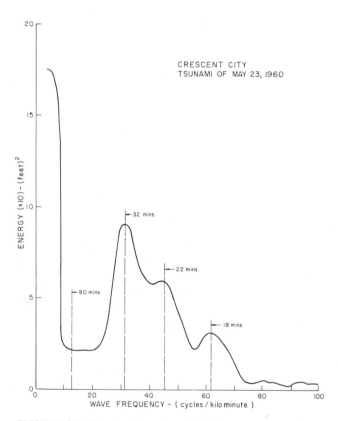

FIGURE 132   Wave energy spectrum for tide-gage marigram at Crescent City; registered at the time of the Chile tsunami of May 23, 1960. (From Wiegel, 1965.)

Magoon (1966) describes the runup at Crescent City as follows:

Due to the relatively severe tsunami damage produced at Crescent City in 1964, an investigation was made of the coast on both sides of Crescent City to determine the water levels reached by the tsunami. Based on elevations determined at locations positively identified as those caused by the tsunami, it is concluded that runup elevation reached by the third wave of this tsunami was essentially constant at the shore for a distance of almost 2 miles southwest of Crescent City. This high water elevation along the shore reached 20 to 21 feet above MLLW. The line of maximum tsunami inundation generally followed the +20 MLLW contour where the ground elevations increased to landward from the shore. This would include most of downtown Crescent City and the pasture land in the vicinity of HWM No. 5. (See Figure 133.)

A definite departure from this characteristic run-up pattern was found where the ground elevation decreases to seaward from the coast and either decreases or remains essentially level landward from the coast. Under this condition, water flowed over the narrow coastal dunes or raised areas near State Highway 101 in a similar manner as water flowing over a broad weir. Apparently the quantity of water transported landward in the individual waves was insufficient in some instances to fill the low area to landward, thus reducing runup.

The runup limits found by Magoon and shown in Figure 133 could be consistent with the explanation for the high wave effects indicated in Figure 131. However, either the limited extent of the survey or the nature of the coast fails to show whether the high runup line continues to the south toward Patrick's Point, as envisioned in Figure 131.

Crescent City Harbor is one of the oldest established on the Pacific Coast of the United States. Over 100 commercial fishing vessels are based here, as well as many pleasure craft and sport-fishing charter boats. Lumbering and timber products are the principal industries. Nearly 200,000,000 board feet of lumber are shipped from this port annually. Crescent City has a population of about 3,000 people. The area is served by 75 lumber mills and 7 plywood and veneer plants. Petroleum products, which exceed 200,000 tons annually, are its greatest import.

The first of the four damaging waves shown in the inferred marigram (Figure 130) caused no damage other than that of inundation. The second wave was smaller than the first. The third and largest wave was preceded by a considerable drawdown which left the inner harbor almost dry. This wave then entered the harbor more as a fast-rising tide than a bore (Magoon, 1966). Evidence for this is found in the fact that the breakwaters suffered no damage (Tudor, 1964). Locations and characteristic cross sections of these breakwaters are shown in Figure 134. The runup line of this third wave in the city and vicinity has already been shown in Figure 133. Detail of wave runup within the city is shown in Figure 135.

In the harbor, 15 fishing boats capsized and another 3 disappeared. Eight boats were sunk in the fishing-boat mooring area. Several boats were washed onto the beach at the beachfront development site, and the rest were beached or capsized in scattered areas (Tudor, 1964). Figure 136 shows the litter of flotsam at the northwest end of the harbor on the day after the tsunami. Down the coast to the south, the scatter of wreckage shown in Figure 137 is typical of hundreds of miles of the coastline northward through Oregon and Washington after the visitation of the giant waves.

Citizens Dock had been constructed in the harbor in 1949. Since then, additional construction had expanded the dock, which had been kept in good repair (Figure 138). The largest wave caused a giant lumber barge of immense inertia to smash into the dock (Figures 139–142). Adjacent to the area where the barge was moored, the dock planking of the cargo pier was pushed into heaps, resembling giant jackstraws. The corbels, decking, fender systems, and bollards were so badly damaged that they all needed to be replaced (Tudor, 1964; Roberts, 1964).

The dock area forward of the moored barge location had damaged blocking compound, ribbons, fenders, and wheel guards, all of which required rebuilding. The slightly damaged area to the stern of the barge necessitated some reconstruction.

The only damage to the fish pier on Citizens dock was along the center line where the deck was raised about 6 in.; this was because of a lack of steel straps between pile caps and stringers. The commercial fish shacks on the pier were displaced, as shown in Figure 143 (Tudor, 1964).

The approach to Citizens Dock was also damaged and badly twisted when, under the force of the tsunami, the deck was buoyed and the supporting piling snapped (Figure 144). Parts of the concrete wave barrier under Citizens Dock were broken by log impacts and water forces as the harbor filled and emptied. The piles under the approach trestle, which are encased in this barrier, were carried away with the wall (Figure 145).

The Dutton Dock survived with hardly any damage, due to the steel straps and bolted connnections between the decking and the pile caps and the abundant cross bracing. The absence of moored ships at this dock also helped.

The Sause Dock had already been abandoned for several years and was in a state of decay. The remaining decking, which was secured to the pile caps with only drift pins, was lifted and displaced by the tsunami. The piling and pile caps were damaged the most (Tudor, 1964).

Regarding structural damage in the downtown area of Crescent City, the following is quoted from Magoon (1964).

In searching for the reasons for the severity of structural damage at Crescent City, it should be remembered that the primary industry of the northwestern portion of the State is the production of commercial lumber. Thus the majority of buildings are of wood frame construction, many of which appeared to have been built a number

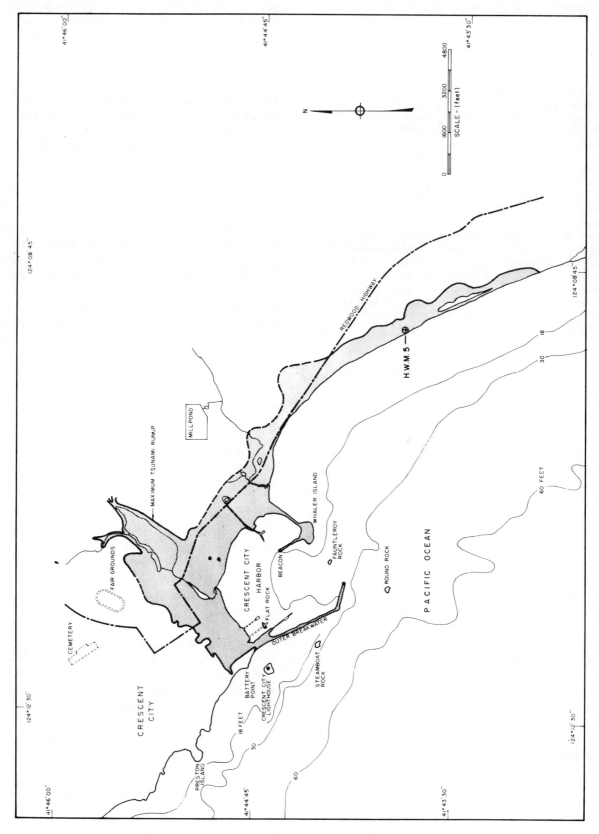

FIGURE 133 Map of Crescent City, California, showing limit of inundation by the tsunami. (From Magoon, 1965; Kent, 1965.)

492

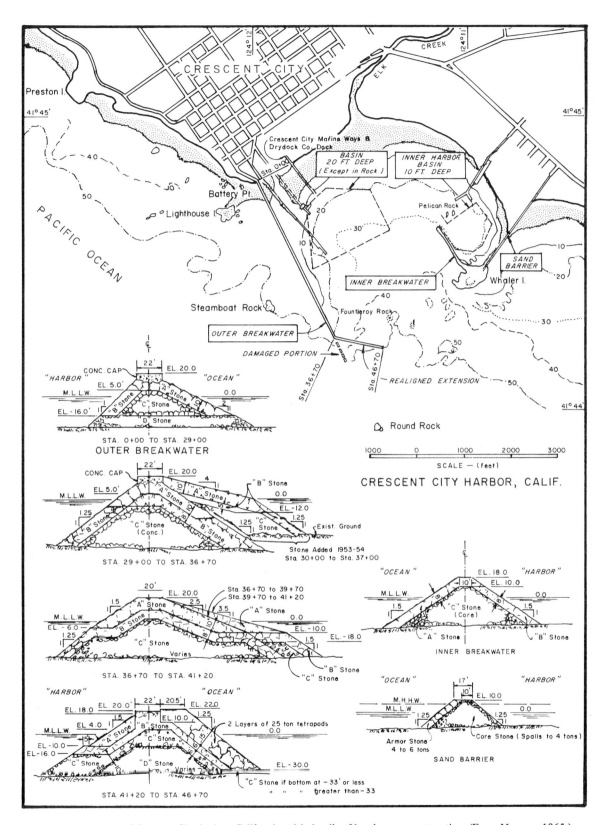

FIGURE 134 Map of Crescent City harbor, California, with details of breakwater construction. (From Magoon, 1965.)

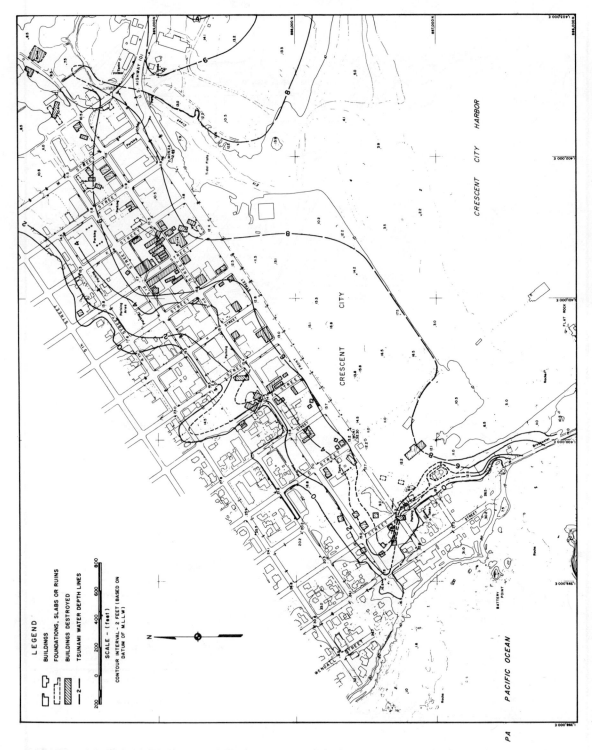

FIGURE 135 Map of downtown Crescent City, showing the depth of the maximum tsunami wave overruning the land. (From Magoon, 1965.)

494

U.S. Army

FIGURE 136   Aerial view of northwest side of Crescent City harbor, showing wreckage left by the tsunami.

U.S. Army

FIGURE 137   Coast south of Crescent City with piles of logs and debris marking the runup limit of the tsunami.

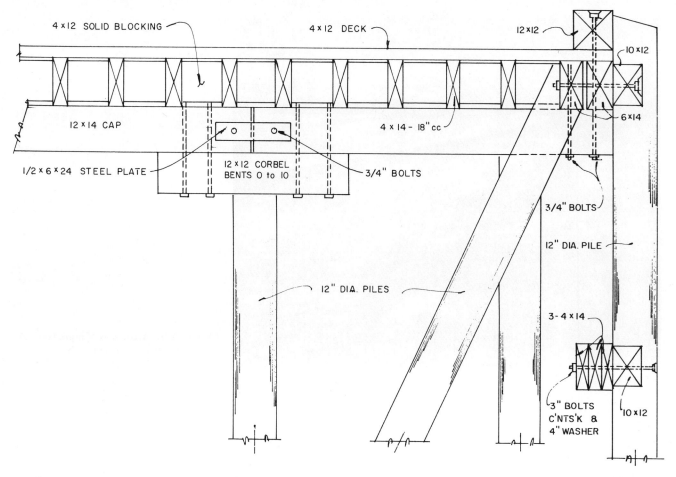

FIGURE 138 Typical section of Citizens Dock at Crescent City, California (from City Engineer, Crescent City). Scale: ½" = 1'. (From Tudor, 1964.)

of years ago. Prior to the tsunami, the coastal area to the southeast of Crescent City and also the harbor shoreline were covered with vast quantities of timber debris, including large logs and tree stumps.

Severe damage was observed in areas where the tsunami exceeded 4 to 6 feet above the ground surface [see Figure 135]. The water depth reached or exceeded 6 feet along the entire length of Front Street, and about nine blocks of the main portion of Crescent City. The majority of the one-story wood-frame structures in this area were either totally destroyed or damaged to such an extent that they were a menace to public health and had to be torn down. It is the opinion of the writer that the majority of the structural damage at Crescent City was probably the result of one or a combination of three conditions listed below.

The first, and probably the most damaging, was the impact of logs and other objects such as automobiles or baled lumber directly on structures.

This debris caused damage by either destroying the load-carrying capacity of walls or by bending or breaking relatively light unprotected columns and allowing subsequent failure. The effect of debris is highly indeterminate. For example, the debris may build up in front of a structure to such an extent that the debris actually forms a shield against further damage, or the increased area resulting from this debris may result in sufficient force from the tsunami to cause the entire structure to be swept away.

Structures that were insufficiently anchored (generally on noncontinuous footings) floated off their foundations and were seriously wrecked or rendered useless when they finally settled on the ground.

The third major cause of loss was the general lack of resistance to horizontal forces in many structures, normally provided by shear walls in buildings and cross bracing in open-pile structures.

Generally, the more substantially constructed structures, particularly multistory wood, hollow block, and reinforced concrete, withstood the tsunami. These structures required considerable internal refurbishing due to water damage, but are in use today.

Figure 146 is fairly typical of how buildings were moved from their original locations by the force of moving water within the downtown area of Crescent City.

A 25-ton concrete tetrapod mounted loosely on a pedestal as a monument to the harbor development at Front Street (Figure 135) was moved bodily through a distance of about 10 ft by wave forces. Tudor (1964), attempting to calculate the velocity of flow required to do this, arrived at a water speed of 20 ft per second. However, the calculation is not likely to be very meaningful because it is

FIGURE 139   Aerial view (northward) of Crescent City harbor after the tsunami. Note the lumber barge at the Citizens Dock.

FIGURE 140   Lumber barge alongside damaged Citizens Dock at Crescent City.

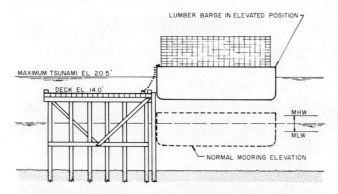

FIGURE 141 Cross section of Citizens Dock, showing lumber barge elevated by the maximum tsunami wave. (From Tudor, 1964.)

known that the tetrapod had been pushed by a long log (very large in diameter) which lay astraddle of it when it was found out of place.

Tudor (1964) has also calculated probable water-flow velocities based on the evidence of the bending of a detached light box (Figure 147). The box was bent in a direction normal to its vertical face. Here he finds a probable velocity of flow of about 11 ft per second and a pressure force of about 43 lb per square foot.

As previously stated, the total estimated cost of tsunami damage at Crescent City was about $11,000,000 (for details of the original estimate of loss, see Spaeth and Berkman, 1967, and this volume). Approximately 30 blocks of Crescent City were devastated, and the area was strewn with rubble and logs swept in by the waves. Automobiles were heaped in scattered piles, and stock from damaged stores was spread over a wide area. Fire damage at Crescent City was also directly attributable to the tsunami, as recorded by Spaeth and Berkman:

The third wave picked up a gasoline tank truck parked at the Texaco station and slammed it through the garage door of the Nickols Pontiac building. The impact knocked loose an electrical junction box just inside the door and a fire started which destroyed the building and spread back to the Texaco tank farm, which burned for three days.

SUMMARY OF TSUNAMI EFFECTS AND DAMAGE

EFFECTS OF THE MAIN TSUNAMI AND OF LOCAL TSUNAMIS: COASTLINES OF KODIAK AND KENAI

The topography of the sea bed off Kodiak City and the Naval Station, Womens Bay, Kodiak, favored the tsunami waves reaching Kodiak City from the northeast approach first via the narrow channel between Near Island and Kodiak. In the immediate neighborhood of Kodiak City, the land subsided 5.8 ft during the earthquake, and the sea apparently dropped with it. The testimony by eyewitnesses has been carefully weighed in relation to an inferred marigram for Kodiak City, from which it is concluded that the first reported wave was possibly real and related to an initial and purely local oscillation of water between Womens Bay and St. Paul Harbor. The first large wave of consequence, presumably the second wave, rose like a fast tide at both Kodiak City and in Womens Bay and inundated the waterfronts at both these places. This flooding was photographed at the two places in the twilight overcast of the setting sun at about 6:20 p.m. Only wetting damage resulted from this inundation, but it was followed by withdrawal of water from St. Paul Harbor at velocities estimated to have been as high as 25 mph. The first damage resulted from this withdrawal of water, which apparently washed out part of the southwest breakwater of the boat harbor and a store and hangar alongside the Near Island

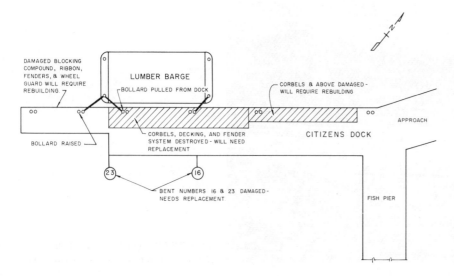

FIGURE 142 Plan of Citizens Dock, showing moored lumber barge and pier. (From Tudor, 1964.)

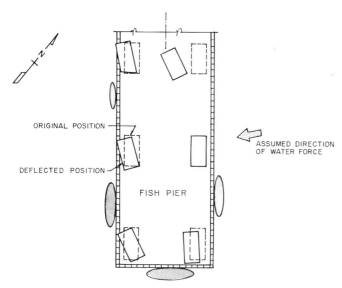

FIGURE 143 Fish shacks nailed to decking but jolted from original positions. Shack that did not move was reinforced and had strong columns at corners. (From Tudor, 1964.)

Channel. It carried away many of the boats in the harbor and left others on the exposed bed of the harbor and in the channel.

The third wave, as interpreted, was a 35- to 40-ft high combination of the first progressive wave crest of the coastward-moving tsunami, the second wave of the shelf oscillation, and additional local oscillations, which now moved into the denuded area via the Near Island Channel

as a foaming bore with velocity close to 50 mph. The wave tore out docks and canneries in the channel and swept the fishing fleet and docks into the lower part of town. Whatever survived was further damaged by a similar but higher wave that moved in later during the night on the rising tide.

The destruction caused by the tsunami in Kodiak City was severe. Nearly all wooden-frame buildings in the path of the waves were either lifted off their foundations and swept away or were pounded to destruction by the momentum of water and accumulated debris. Reinforced concrete structures fared much better, however; one of these near the waterfront and in the full sweep of the waves was rated salvageable, though damaged.

Nine people lost their lives at Kodiak City and neighboring Spruce Cape as a result of the tsunami, and about 100 vessels were lost or damaged. Total estimated property damage, according to the Office of Civil Defense, exceeded $31 million.

At the Naval Station on Nyman Peninsula, Kodiak, the sequence of waves was similar and the damage was in excess of $10 million. The force of moving water was much less here than at Kodiak City, and most of the damage occurred because dock structures were raised off their piles or out of their pile holes due to inundation and foundation settlement.

Other inhabited places in the Kodiak Island region which suffered damage from the tsunami included Port William, Shuyak Island; Afognak, Afognak Island; Port Wakefield, Raspberry Island; Ouzinkie, Spruce Island; Shearwater Bay, Kodiak Island; Old Harbor, Kodiak Island; and Kaguyak, Kodiak Island. Afognak, Old Harbor, and Kaguyak were

U.S. Coast Guard

FIGURE 144 Approach to Citizens Dock, showing tsunami damage.

FIGURE 145 Part of the concrete wave barrier surrounding supporting piles at Citizens Dock has been displaced and torn away.

almost totally destroyed, and the native communities of Afognak and Kaguyak have now been relocated to other areas. Damage in all these areas totaled about $3 million.

In the Cook Inlet, tsunami wave activity was relatively minor and almost entirely absent in the upper reaches near Anchorage. Its main effects were felt at Homer and Seldovia. Damage at Homer was slight and was caused mainly by inundation and subsidence. Seldovia suffered some-

what more from wave action than did Homer; damage here was estimated at about $500,000.

Off the Kenai Peninsula the tsunami had a direct approach to Resurrection Bay, at the head of which lies the city of Seward with a population of about 2,000. As in the case of Kodiak, an inferred marigram has been prepared for Seward from accounts of what took place, as reported by eyewitnesses. It seems apparent that the immediate ef-

FIGURE 146 Typical scene of destruction in the downtown area of Crescent City.

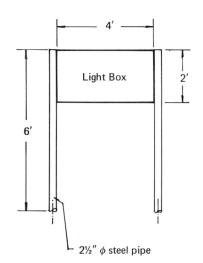

Dim	Area	Y	ΔY
Light box 2' × 4'	1,152	60	69,120
2½" ϕ Steel pipe	180	36	6,480
2½" ϕ Steel pipe	180	36	6,480
ΣA = 1,512		ΣΔY = 82,080	

2½" ϕ steel pipe

Problem: Find load (per square inch) which will produce yielding of post at base.

Assume:

S = 30 KSI

I_{post} = 1.18 in^4

ID = 2.468

OD = 2.875

C = 1.437

C_D = 0.35

$\bar{y}$ = $\dfrac{\Sigma \Delta y}{\Sigma A}$ = $\dfrac{82,080}{1,512}$ = 54.2"

$\bar{y}$ = 54.2"

M = $\dfrac{SI}{C}$ = $\dfrac{(30,000)(1.18)}{1.437}$

M = 24,600 in-lb

P = $\dfrac{M}{\bar{y} \, \Sigma A}$ = $\dfrac{24,600}{(54.2)(1512)}$ = 0.3 lb/in^2

P = 43.2 lb/ft^2

V = $\dfrac{(2)(43.2)(32.4)}{(.35)(64)}$ = 11.2 ft/sec

V = 11.2 ft/sec

FIGURE 147 Calculation of wave force required to bend a light box normal to the plane of the diagram. (From Tudor, 1964.)

fect of the earthquake at Seward was to jolt loose a large slice of the steepest part of the glacial delta near the Standard Oil Company docks, at the southern convexity of the Seward waterfront. This presumably slid away as a fast density current and carried with it much of the oil docks and part of The Alaska Railroad docks farther to the south. The consequence of this was both a drawdown of water and a backlash of tsunamis. The Standard Oil tanks caught fire at about this time which was within the duration period of the earthquake.

The north-moving wave inundated the waterfront and carried burning oil down The Alaska Railroad marshaling yard where a train was in readiness to depart for Anchorage. Loaded tank cars caught fire and exploded as they became enveloped in flame. The wave contributed to the destruction of the U.S. Army docks and the cannery dock and

boat harbor which were in the process of collapse and disintegration from the earthquake. Boats were carried over the breakwater of the small-boat harbor and swept into the lagoon on the north side of Seward. The Texaco tank farm near the boat harbor caught fire.

During the first hour after the earthquake, two further damaging waves struck the waterfront. The leading wave of the main tsunami is presumed to have reached the head of the bay at about 18:30 AST but was not damaging at that time because of low tide. The amplitude of the tsunami probably increased with time as at Kodiak, and later waves on the high tide during the night reached an average flood level of 27 ft above MLLW in Seward. At certain places within Seward, however, runup exceeded 30 ft. At Lowell Point, to the south, the runup was much higher.

It has been estimated that tsunami damage at Seward

exceeded $14 million; the death toll was 11 persons, most of whom were in small boats in the boat harbor at the time of the earthquake.

EFFECTS OF THE MAIN TSUNAMI AND OF LOCAL TSUNAMIS IN PRINCE WILLIAM SOUND

General uplift of Prince William Sound during the earthquake occurred in the form of a tilt in a northwest direction on a hinge at about two thirds of the distance from the mouth to the apex. The water surface may be assumed to have followed this sudden tilt fairly closely and hence set in motion a complicated system of seiches. In addition, there would have been the influence of the tsunami from the Continental Shelf through the rather limited access provided by the island straits.

Because of its deep fiords and its proximity to the earthquake epicenter, Prince William Sound experienced numerous slides with wave effects which added to the general complexity of water movements. At many places it seems that the pattern of waves was rather similar to that which occurred at Seward.

The village of Chenega on Chenega Island in Knight Island Passage was almost totally destroyed, with a loss of 23 lives, by sea waves which struck within the duration period of the earthquake. Powerful initial damage from slide-generated waves of relatively short periods (3 to 5 minutes) occurred at Whittier and Valdez.

The case of Valdez is the best documented in the Prince William Sound area. With a population of about 1,500, Valdez is located at the head of Port Valdez and Valdez Arm. The suggested explanation of what happened at Valdez is that a seismic seiche was generated transverse to Port Valdez along the Valdez waterfront. The mechanism for generation of this seiche could have been a submarine slump of the fine sediments off the glacial delta and outwash at the mouth of the Lowe River in the extreme southeast corner of Port Valdez, or it could have been the movement of the land, or both acting together. The initial surge (northwest) was followed by a returning wave possibly 40 to 50 ft in height and 4 to 5 minutes in period, which carried away canneries and facilities on both the North and South arms of the harbor in the southeasterly direction. It is supposed that the next reversal of the flow to the southeast came after the earthquake had ceased. Probably at this stage the major submarine slide took place south of Valdez, creating a scarp 30 to 50 ft high along the shoreline over which water cascaded into the depression. All this seems to have occurred within about 6 or 7 minutes of the onset of the earthquake.

These first waves, assisted by the subsidence, annihilated the Valdez waterfront. They damaged or destroyed almost all the boats and facilities in the small-boat harbor. The waves, reaching a level of about 16 ft above MLLW at McKinley Street in the lower part of town, caused considerable damage to light wooden-frame buildings.

Higher waves, much longer in period, were to inundate Valdez later during the night. Shortly after the earthquake, another large wave of longer period, assumed to be about 18 minutes, rolled in on Valdez and filled the Valdez Hotel to a level of 18 in. This is thought to have been generated by a large submarine slide at the opposite end of Port Valdez near the Narrows. Large waves, apparently deriving from submarine collapse of the submerged glacial deposits at the mouth of Shoup Bay, rushed southward out of the Narrows, destroying the Valdez light at an elevation of 37 ft above MLLW. Runup and splash marks were identified to elevations of 125 to 220 ft near Shoup Bay.

On the high tide during the night, a combination of waves is considered to have produced the highest runup in Valdez to a level of about 20 ft above MLLW. These later waves were like fast-rising tides; they were more sustained than earlier waves and produced more wetting damage, but not much violent motion. Oil tanks, however, were damaged by these waves and set on fire.

The heaviest loss of life (31 persons) at any one place, caused by the tsunami in Alaska, occurred at Valdez. The waves there are estimated to have caused damage of $12–$13 million.

The destruction that occurred at Whittier near the head of Passage Canal on the west side of Prince William Sound is less well understood than that at Seward or Valdez, mainly because there were fewer eyewitnesses. It is evident, however, that the waves that destroyed the waterfront of Whittier were mainly waves of displacement created by transverse horizontal tectonic movement and submarine slumping of the slope and toe of the unconsolidated glacial deposits on which the town is founded and of neighboring deposits at the head of the bay.

The waves are said to have been of exceptional height, and their penetration ashore reached an elevation of about 30 ft above MLLW along a wide front, and 40 ft in localized places at Whittier. At the head of the bay the waves washed more than 50 ft above MSL.

As at Seward and Valdez, the waterfront was mostly destroyed by the collapse of the foundations, resulting from the submarine slides and the regional subsidence of 5.3 ft. However, wave damage was extensive and involved the Union Oil tank farm which was set on fire, two lumber company plants that were virtually demolished, The Alaska Railroad docks, and numerous homes and small buildings.

The sea waves caused $10 million worth of damage at Whittier and took 12 lives (of a population of 70). Undoubtedly, the waves were relatively more severe there than at Valdez and Seward.

The remaining significant center of population in Prince William Sound was Cordova in the Orca Inlet, near the mouth of the Sound, where the regional tectonic movement was 6 ft of uplift and about 40 ft of horizontal thrust to the southeast.

The approaches to Cordova by sea are relatively shallow, and there is no evidence of the occurrence of submarine slides in the region. The wave pattern of the inferred marigram for Cordova is significantly lacking in any reported large-amplitude waves of short period (a few minutes) such as were notably present in the situations at Seward, Valdez, and Whittier. Initial waves after the earthquake proved to be of little consequence, but during the small hours of the night an exceptional wave rose considerably above the pre-existing highest tide level and buoyed the dock off its pilings, besides carrying away several small houses and buildings and generally flooding the waterfront. This wave was apparently followed by at least two other damaging waves. Damage from the waves at Cordova was estimated to be close to $2 million.

EFFECTS OF THE MAIN TSUNAMI ALONG THE NORTH AMERICAN SEABOARD

Damage along the indented coastline of Canada was due mainly to flooding, with buildings swept away, wharves damaged, log booms and lumber mills destroyed. No lives are known to have been lost in this area. The most serious damage in Canada occurred at Port Alberni. Here the greatly amplified tsunami waves arrived on the high spring tide (range about 17 ft). The first three destructive waves swept away houses, boats, logs, and other movable objects. Wharf structures were buoyed and buckled. The damage at Port Alberni alone was estimated to be of the order of $10 million.

Along the coast of the state of Washington, the damage probably exceeded $100,000 but was much less than the estimated $750,000 for the Oregon coast, which probably suffered more because of its slight concavity favoring more direct attack. Four deaths were reported from Oregon.

The California coastline suffered damage in excess of $13 million, a large part of which reflects losses to commercial fishing interests and small-boat marinas. Most heavily hit was Crescent City, where the total damage was about $11 million and where 12 persons were killed.

The tsunami waves at Crescent City occurred as fast-rising tides which flooded over the coastline and into the lower parts of the city to a height of about 20 ft above MLLW. The waves wrought great damage to buildings and automobiles as a result of the great momentum of the water with its entrained mass of logs and debris. The Texaco tank farm was set ablaze as a direct consequence of the waves.

ESTIMATES OF DAMAGE CAUSED BY THE TSUNAMIS

Most of the loss of life during the earthquake was due to the tsunami and, in addition, damage was very severe at those waterfront and harbor areas struck by large waves. Had the region affected by the earthquake been densely populated, the loss of life and the damage due to the tsunami could have been enormous. Damage data have been collected in Table 11 of this section to illustrate the amount of destruction wrought by the tsunami waves. These data are drawn from various sources referenced in the table. Question marks have been inserted alongside damage estimates assumed by us for want of any known value figures. The estimated total damage attributable to the Alaska tsunamis (from Table 11) is about $110 million, and the total casualties in human lives 119. It should be noted that these data are almost certainly incomplete, and the listed costs undoubtedly underestimate the true damage costs.

WATER-PARTICLE VELOCITIES AND PRESSURE FORCES FROM TSUNAMIS

Apparently, the damaging effect of tsunamis depends greatly upon the amplitude and period of the waves, the nature of the terrain they invade, and the development of high velocity in any breaking or bore formation in the coastal inundation. The availability of easily floatable debris in the form of logs, boats, automobiles, and timber-frame structures, which acquire the velocity of the water, provides a ready means of increasing the damaging punch of the waves when they strike obstacles in their path.

To be able to calculate the force of the water on any obstacle, it is necessary to know the velocity of the water and its direction of flow, as well as the water level as a function of time. The nature and shape of the obstacle are, of course, of basic importance.

In the tsunami-damaged areas, we found only a few cases for correlating induced effects with water-particle velocities. One case was that of the overturning of a locomotive at Seward. The calculations relating to the overturned engine indicate a water velocity of 24.5 ft/sec and an average pressure force of 700 lb/ft^2. Here it must be admitted that the approximations made for this calculation are rather crude.

In this instance, the formula used, relating force F and water velocity u, was that based on pure frontal drag, namely,

$$F = \tfrac{1}{2} C_D \, \rho A u^2, \tag{23}$$

in which C_D is a dimensionless drag coefficient appropriate to the shape of the body and the Reynolds number of the

TABLE 11 Summary of Casualties and Damage Caused by the Tsunamis of the Alaska Earthquake, March 27–28, 1964

Country or State	Locality	Loss of Life (number of persons)	Estimates of Damage (thousands of dollars)			Description
			Public Property	Private Property	Total	
Alaska	Afognak, Afognak Island[a]	–	–	816	816	Afognak village destroyed; bridges washed away
	Cape St. Elias, Kayak Island[b,l]	1	–	–	–	–
	Chenega,[b,l] Chenega Island, Prince William Sound	23	–	100	100	Indian village totally destroyed
	Homer, Kenai Peninsula, Cook Inlet[c]	–	–	–	?	Inundation
	Hope, Turnagain Arm, Cook Inlet[d]	–	–	–	?	Inundation
	Cordova,[e] Prince William Sound	–	?	?	1,775	Docks uplifted and damaged, buildings destroyed; flooding
	Kaguyak, Kodiak Island[a,l]	3	?	?	321	Fishing village destroyed
	Kalsin Bay,[b,l] Kodiak Island	6	–	–	?	Inundation
	Kodiak,[b,l] Kodiak Island	9 (Kodiak incl. Spruce Cape)	7,565	23,714	31,279	Boat harbor destroyed; breakwater scoured; city flooded; buildings and boats destroyed
	Kodiak Naval Station, Kodiak Island[b,l]	–	6,202	?	10,916	Piers buoyed and wrecked; buildings flooded; machinery damaged
	Larsen Bay,[b] Kodiak Island	–	–	80	80	Indian village damaged
	Old Harbor, Kodiak Island[a,l]	1 (Sitkalidak Island)	–	707	707	Dwellings floated and destroyed; flooding
	Ouzinkie,[b] Spruce Island	–	–	350	500	Homes and boats destroyed; cannery damaged
	Point Whitshed	1	–	–	?	Inundation
	Port Ashton, Sawmill Bay,[d,l] Prince William Sound	1 (Crab Bay)	–	–	200 ?	Pilings, docks, and boats swept away
	Port Nellie Juan, McClure Bay,[d,l] Prince William Sound	3	–	–	200 ?	Pilings destroyed and buildings toppled
	Port Nowell,[b,l] Knight Is. Passage, Prince William Sound	1 (Point Nowell)	–	–	?	–
	Port Wakefield, Raspberry Island[d]	–	–	–	300 ?	King crab plant ruined, cannery dock damaged
	Seldovia, Kenai Penin.[e]	–	–	–	500	Flooding; boat floats lost, breakwater damaged
	Seward, Kenai Penin.[e,l]	11	?	?	14,614	Docks and R.R. yard destroyed, boats and canneries wrecked, buildings smashed; oil tanks set on fire
	Shearwater Bay, Kodiak Island[a]	–	–	–	200 ?	Cannery wrecked
	Valdez,[g,l] Prince William Sound	30 1 (Anderson Bay, Port Valdez)	4,115	8,453	12,568	Docks, canneries, boat harbor, boats totally destroyed; oil tanks set on fire
	Whittier,[f,l] Prince William Sound	12	?	?	10,000	Docks, R.R. facilities destroyed; tank farm wrecked, oil tank set on fire
Alaska Subtotals		103			85,076	

TABLE 11 (Continued)

Country or State	Locality	Loss of Life (number of persons)	Estimates of Damage (thousands of dollars)			Description
			Public Property	Private Property	Total	
Canada	Alberni, Port Alberni, Vancouver Island[b]	–	?	?	10,000	Massive inundation; wharves buoyed and damaged, pipeline and log boom swept away, cable broken
	Fair Harbor, Kyuquot Sd., Vancouver Island[b]	–	–	–	50 ?	Bridges damaged
	Hot Springs Cove, Vancouver Island[b]	–	–	–	100	Indian village; wharf, fuel lines damaged
	Port Alice, Neroutsos Inlet, Vancouver Island[b]	–	–	–	100 ?	Wharves damaged, boats carried away
	Port McNeill, Queen Charlotte Strait[h]	–	–	–	5 ?	Buildings shifted; flooding
	Winter Harbor, Quatsino Sd., Vancouver Island[h]	–	–	–	50 ?	Log boom destroyed, vessel carried away
	Zeballos, Esperanza Inlet, Vancouver Island[b]	–	–	–	150	Buildings damaged, flooding
Canada Subtotals:		0			10,455	
Washington	Copalis, Copalis River[i]	–	–	5	5	Buildings damaged
	Copalis R. and Joe Creek (state highways)[i]	–	85	–	85	Bridges damaged, highway erosion
	Lake Union, Seattle[j]	–	–	–	5	C&GS ships and small craft damaged
	Moclips[i]	–	–	6	6	Buildings damaged
	Pacific Beach[i]	–	–	12	12	Buildings damaged; erosion
	Taholah, Quinault River[i]	–	–	–	1	Skiffs and fishnets lost
	Wreck Creek, State Bay[j]	–	1	–	1	Bridge pier erosion
Washington Subtotals:		0			115	
Oregon	Cannon Beach[b]	–	50	180	230	Buildings damaged, flooding
	Coos Bay[b]	–	–	–	20	Inundation
	Depoe Bay[b,l]	4	–	–	5	Inundation
	Florence[b]	–	–	–	50	Buildings damaged, flooding
	Rogue River[b]	–	–	–	3	Inundation
	Seaside[b]	–	41	235	276	Buildings damaged, flooding, R.R. trestle destroyed
	Umpqua[b]	–	–	–	5	Inundation
	Waldport-Alsea[b]	–	145	15	160	Buildings damaged, flooding
	Yaquina[b]	–	–	–	5	Inundation
Oregon Subtotals:		4			754	
California	Albion River[k]	–	–	0.5	0.5	Fishing vessel delay from bore formations
	Bodega Bay[k]	–	2	–	2	Damage to navigational aids
	Bolinas Bay	1	–	–	–	–
	Chinook River[k]	–	–	–	0.2	Dock and boats damaged
	Crescent City[k,l]	10	?	?	11,000	Buildings damaged, flooding; wharves wrecked; boats sunk and destroyed
	Half Moon Bay[k]	–	–	–	1	Floating structures damaged
	Klamath River[k,l]	1	–	–	4	Dock and boats damaged
	Long Beach Harbor, San Pedro Bay[b]	–	–	–	100	Small craft damaged
	Los Angeles Harbor, San Pedro Bay[b]	–	–	–	175–275	Small craft and boat landings damaged
	Monterey Harbor, Monterey Bay[b]	–	–	1	1	Small boats damaged

TABLE 11   (Continued)

| Country or State | Locality | Loss of Life (number of persons) | Estimates of Damage (thousands of dollars) | | | Description |
			Public Property	Private Property	Total	
	Moss Landing, Monterey Bay[k]	–	–	–	0.2	Skiff broken, bore development; boats and floating structures damaged
	Noyo River[k]	–	–	–	124	
	Noyo Harbor[b]	–	?	?	250–1,000	Unspecified
	San Francisco (Marin County)[b]	–	?	?	1,000	Small craft, floating structures
	Santa Cruz, Monterey Bay[k]	–	–	–	100	Dredge and cabin cruiser sunk, floats damaged
	Smith River[k]	–	–	–	6	Floating structures damaged
	Tomales Bay, Pt. Reyes Penin.[k]	–	–	–	6	Pier damaged
California Subtotals:		12			13,620	
Hawaii	Hilo, Hawaii[b]	–	–	–	15	Flooding
	Maui[b]	–	–	–	53	Flooding
Hawaii Subtotals		0			68	
Total:		119	Approx. Grand Total		110,088	

[a] Kachadoorian and Plafker, 1967.
[b] Spaeth and Berkman, 1967.
[c] Waller, 1966.
[d] Chance, 1966, and in press.
[e] Anchorage Daily News, April 18, 1964.
[f] Tudor, 1964.
[g] Daily Alaska Empire, March 3, 1964.
[h] Wigen and White, 1964.
[i] Hogan, Whipple, and Lundy, 1964.
[j] Wilson and Tørum, 1968
[k] Magoon, 1966.
[l] Cox, Table 1, in Weller, this volume.

fluid flow, ρ the mass density of water, and A the projected area of the obstacle [see also equation (B-16), Appendix B]. The use of this formula is really open to question, particularly as the direction of water flow around the locomotive may have been oblique rather than normal.

An alternative (wall) formula discussed in Appendix B [equation (B-24)] would be

$$F = \frac{1}{2} \rho \, g d_w{}^2 + C_F \rho d_t u_s{}^2, \qquad (24)$$

in which d_w would represent the depth of water formed at the locomotive by its blockage action, d_t the depth of water at the locomotive before the stream was deflected upward to the depth d_w, g the acceleration due to gravity, C_F a dimensionless force coefficient, and u_s the horizontal stream velocity over the depth d_t. However, the use of equation (24) might also be held questionable, because the locomotive could not have provided the kind of barrier equivalent to a long wall.

From a discussion of theoretical and experimental information bearing on tsunami surge velocities and forces, it has been shown (Appendix B) that a tsunami surge, with the characteristics of the experimental waves illustrated in Figure 17, tends to have a frontal velocity in accord with

$$u_s = K \sqrt{(g d_s)}, \qquad (25)$$

in which d_s is the height of the surge level above the land at the point occupied by the front of the surge, and K is a numerical coefficient with an expected value between 1.5 and 2.0.

It is of interest, then, in the case of the capsized locomotive at Seward, to determine the applicable value of K that would have yielded the overturning conditions of the locomotive, on the supposition that the water velocity was $u_s = 24.5$ ft/sec, as calculated, and the water depth $d_s = 6$ ft, as inferred in the section on tsunami damage at Seward. Thus, we find that

$$K = u_s / \sqrt{(g d_s)} = 1.76. \qquad (26)$$

The result appears to be in good accord with the range of values set on K in Appendix B and supports conclusions given there despite the crudeness of the analysis of Figure 71.

Further support for the conclusion may be found in connection with the tsunami surge in the Near Island Channel at Kodiak, where an eyewitness estimate of water speed is found to be in approximate accord with equation (25) for a K-value of 2.0, see equation (2).

The case of the light box at Crescent City suggests that a water velocity of 11.2 ft/sec over a minimum depth of 6 ft would have caused failure of this light structure. Obviously, for this much lower velocity we should here find a K-value less than half that of equation (25) but the probability is that the nature of the flow was not like a surge but more like a fast-rising tide, in which case equation (B-20) of Appendix B would apply.

It is convenient to summarize the findings of this study regarding the water velocity of the front of a surge moving over dry or previously wetted ground. Thus, the main conclusions of Appendix B and such other cases as apply from the body of this report are drawn together in Table 12, the evidence of which suggests that a suitable value of K would lie between 1.5 and 2.0. For conservative design a value $K = 2.0$ would be recommended.

It seems important to note that, although calculations of force based on the drag formula, equation (23), are probably valid for objects or structures of relatively small size that become enveloped in the flow of a tsunami surge, calculations for larger objects with broad or continuous frontage are better performed with a momentum formula such as equation (24).

The behavior of a tsunami surge striking a wall or breakwater is characteristic. The action is jetlike and the momentum is deflected upward and possibly sideways if the approach is oblique to the structure. Against a vertical wall of sufficient height the surge rises vertically as a wall of water to a height roughly equivalent to the velocity head of the stream. The collapse of this wall of water provides the physical body for a reflected bore which moves out on the still-incoming surge. Peak pressure on the structure occurs when this mass of water descends on the incident surge. When the structure walls are sloping inland, as with a sea-

wall or breakwater, the pressure force on the structure is relieved to the extent that momentum is carried forward in the overtopping volume of fluid.

A possible design formula for estimating tsunami pressure forces per unit length on vertical walls is given (see Appendix B) by

$$\text{(i)} \quad F = C_p \left(\tfrac{1}{2} \rho g d_s^2 \right) \qquad (27)$$

$$\text{(ii)} \quad C_p \simeq 10 \text{ to } 15.$$

Equation (27) expresses the force in terms of the hydrostatic pressure force for the surge depth d_s above the toe of the structure (see Figure B-1, Appendix B). The factor C_p, a pressure coefficient, represents the number of times the dynamic force exceeds the static. Based upon an average value of K ($= 1.75$) from the total results of Table 12 and upon experimental indications that the vertical jet height at the wall is 1.33 to 2 times the velocity head of the surge, C_p appears to have values of about 10 for a surge over dry bed, 15 over wet surface.

ABILITY OF STRUCTURES TO WITHSTAND TSUNAMIS

In the coastal cities and villages that suffered tsunami damage, the houses were mostly one-story wooden-frame buildings, generally of older type. Such houses generally had poor capacity for withstanding the tsunami forces. Adequate connection between the wooden-frame structure and the footings was one design detail that was generally lacking

TABLE 12   Water Velocity at Front of Tsunami Surge

Formula or Equation	Source of Derivation	Value of K $u_s = K \sqrt{(gd_s)}$	Depth d in Front of Surge	Remarks
(B-4), (B-5), (D-2)	Lamb (1932), Airy (1845)	2.0	$d = 0$	Long-wave theory
(B-6), (B-7)	Lamb (1932), Rouse (1938), Keulegan (1949)	2.0	$d = H/6$	Momentum theory – fails at $d = 0$
(B-8)	Keulegan (1949)	2.0	$d = 0$	Dam-break theory
(B-9), (B-10)	Gibson (1925)	1.41	$d = 0$	Bernoulli's equation–successful for undular bores
(B-12), (B-13)	Fukui and others (1963)	1.73	$d = 0$	Experimental with friction
(B-15)	Cross (1966, 1967)	1.41	$d = 0$	Experimental with friction
(B-16)	Matlock and others (1962), Reese and Matlock (1967)	2.0	$d = 0$	Based on calculations of structural failures, Hilo, Hawaii, 1960
(B-17), (25), (26)	This study	1.76	$d = 0$	Based on calculation for capsizing of locomotive at Seward, Alaska, 1964
(B-17), (2), (25)	This study	2.0	$d = 0$	Based on estimated value in Near Island Channel, Kodiak, Alaska, 1964

and that should be highly emphasized in future design. This weakness obviously caused many houses to be floated off their foundations and was probably the main cause of tsunami damage to wooden buildings close to the maximum runup. This can be said not only of smaller buildings but also of larger ones like the two-story Odd Fellows building in Crescent City.

Houses and buildings that were floated off their foundations and survived the attrition of tsunamis and impacts from other floating debris or from stranding were mainly torn down for scrap during cleaning-up operations. Therefore, it is not possible to tell to what extent these structures would have been able to withstand the tsunamis in case they had been adequately connected to their foundations. Many of the older and smaller wooden structures were completely demolished by the tsunami, like the houses in many small villages.

The few concrete-block and reinforced-concrete structures in tsunami-inundated areas withstood the waves rather well. Such buildings are the concrete-block, steel-frame enginehouse of The Alaska Railroad in Seward (later torn down when all railroad facilities were moved), some concrete-block buildings in downtown Kodiak and on the Kodiak Naval Station, and the reinforced-concrete five-story hotel on Front Street in Crescent City. Some of these buildings, however, were damaged from the impact of floating boats and debris.

Floating timber was responsible for much of the damage at Crescent City. Huge logs acted as battering rams in punching through walls or otherwise functioned as dragnets in concentrating pressure. The floating timber during a tsunami has proved to be very dangerous on many occasions at sawmill or paper factories; Horikawa (1961) emphasized that appropriate measures for anchoring stacked timber at such places in tsunami-endangered regions should be considered—a view that we fully endorse.

In general, the type of land structure that can best survive a tsunami inundation is one of sound reinforced-concrete construction with deeply embedded foundations or solid raft foundations capable of resisting scour. Shear walls are desirable, and orientation of structures is important so that long axes are directed toward the sea or path of attack and minimum areas of resistance are exposed to waves. Well-constructed timber-frame buildings, firmly secured to adequate deep-set foundations, may be considered for the lee side of more solid buildings which can break the impact of debris. Wood-frame structures, however, should be strongly braced both vertically and horizontally at floor and ceiling levels. It may be desirable in certain circumstances to design structures with substantial framing but with expendable ground-floor walling. Upper floors in such buildings would generally be immune to wave and water damage; some ground-floor damage

would be considered tolerable (Matlock and others, 1962; Wiegel, 1965; Magoon, 1966; Reese and Matlock, 1967).

HARBOR STRUCTURES: THEIR DAMAGE AND PROTECTION

The docks in the areas that suffered substantial tsunami damage were all of timber construction, except for the Seward sheet-pile railroad docks which were damaged by slides.

The old cargo dock at the Kodiak Naval Station was completely destroyed, basically because of inadequate connections between piles and the deck, but also because extracted piles failed to return to the augered pile holes in the rocky bottom. A moored ship raised the bollards during tsunami-induced motions and probably also caused damage while slamming against the dock.

The marginal pier of the Naval Station suffered minor damage, mainly from a moored barge which loosened a bollard and some decking. This dock paradoxically had to be loaded down with heavy chains after the earthquake so that it would not float away during later high tides, which subsequently reached a higher level relative to the dock because of the land subsidence. The tanker and tender pier of the Naval Station was not critically damaged.

At Crescent City, California, the Citizens Dock was damaged mainly by a moored timber barge that slammed against the dock. Much repair work was needed on corbels, decking, and fenders on this dock. The approach pier to Citizens Dock was heavily damaged when the deck was buoyed by the tsunami waves. The majority of the supporting pilings, which were encased in a concrete wave barrier under the dock, snapped when this barrier was exposed to high lateral forces resulting from different water levels on the two sides of the barrier.

The Dutton Dock in Crescent City survived mainly because of the steel straps and bolted connections between the decking and pile caps and the abundant cross bracing. The absence of moored ships at the dock also helped.

These findings show clearly the importance of adequate connections between pilings and decking on a timber dock in tsunami-endangered regions. It is equally important that the piles be capable of resisting vertical uplift forces without being drawn out of the ground.

All the boat floats in Kodiak Harbor were completely demolished when the piles to which they were attached broke as a result of the heavy lateral forces caused by the tsunami.

The breakwaters at Kodiak City were badly damaged, both by settlement during the earth tremors and by erosion from the tsunami. They were built primarily to protect the harbor from locally generated wind waves, and the armor stones were not large enough to resist high-velocity scour.

At Seldovia, Kenai Peninsula, the breakwaters, which were also built to protect the harbor against local wind waves, also suffered damage from the earth tremors and the tsunami overtopping. The breakwater at Cordova, Prince William Sound, was apparently not damaged, and at Crescent City, California, the breakwaters, built partly with 25-ton tetrapods in the cover layer to protect against large storm waves from the Pacific Ocean, sustained no noticeable damage during the tsunami attack.

The pattern of structure damage resulting from tsunamis has almost always been the same. Land structures, weakly secured to their foundations, have been swept away either by sheer force of moving water or by battery from accumulated debris cascaded in front of an advancing wave. In some cases, displacement has occurred merely by the lifting of a structure through flotation. In dock and harbor areas, breakwaters have been denuded by weir-action flow across their tops, pile structures eroded by scour at the base, battered by ships on the rampage, or stripped of their decks by lifting action from below. Solid dock walls have been overturned by suction action during wave withdrawals, dock slabs collapsed by erosion of supporting sand fill, and retaining walls undermined and destroyed.

If the economics justify it, special seawalls, dikes, breakwaters, or barriers may be designed to shield low-lying areas. Such protection may be built on dry land or in water at advantageous points. Examples are the proposed Hilo Harbor tsunami barrier, the Narragansett Bay storm-surge barriers, and tsunami-barrier walls built in Japan at Yoshihama and Yamada (see Horikawa, 1961). Design criteria demand deep and firm foundations, interlocked construction for mass walling, nonerodable revetments and breakwater capping in front and rear, and even possible closure gates of unique and dependable design.

The problem of immunizing dock and harbor facilities is much more difficult. Again, economy is a factor which will predicate how substantial a breakwater or harbor enclosure is to be built or how sophisticated a dock wall, pier, or jetty design there should be. Any given case would have to be considered on its merits.

The need for proper provision and planning is extremely important in regard to oil-storage tanks, usually located near the waterfront of ports whose oil supplies must come from overseas. Oil spillage caused by an earthquake often results in fire, which can spread rapidly and make a holocaust of any coastal town or city. Oil tanks caught fire at Seward, Valdez, Whittier, and Crescent City as a consequence of the earthquake or tsunamis of March 1964, and similarly also at Niigata in Japan in June 1964. All these fires were spread by the ensuing tsunamis. Proper placing and adequate containment of all storage tanks in harbor areas is therefore important. If the tanks cannot be sealed off and recessed below normal ground level or placed on high ground out of reach of tsunami runup, they should be contained by a perimeter wall or dike capable of repelling water and retaining oil.

DAMAGE FROM SCOUR

Scouring damage, on the whole, was not very extensive during the Alaska tsunami. The scouring effect was probably most noticeable in the Orca Inlet at Cordova where considerable deepening and shoaling occurred in many areas and destroyed many clam shell beds, and also in the Near Island Channel at Kodiak where the channel was denuded almost to bedrock.

In downtown Kodiak and at the Kodiak Naval Station there was some minor scouring damage. Some roads on Kodiak Island, however, were heavily eroded; cases of eroded roads and bridge-pile bents have also been reported from several places along the Pacific Coast of North America.

In Seward the railroad fill along the shoreline was partly eroded away, and at Valdez the harbor moles undoubtedly sustained erosive damage from the sea waves. Some harbors and entrance channels were affected by scouring, but none too seriously.

At Kodiak Naval Station a steel sheet-pile retaining wall was bowed seaward by hydrostatic pressure and suction from withdrawals of the tsunami waves. Seaward collapse of sea walls from this cause has been frequently noted (see Horikawa, 1961).

MOVEMENTS OF SHIPS AND BOATS IN HARBORS; PROTECTIVE MEASURES

In those harbors hit hardest by the Alaska tsunami, small boats were either sunk or carried ashore. In many cases, sinking was caused by direct damage from impact. Other boats were capsized when their moorings withheld them from rising with the water level. In Crescent City it was reported that strong currents normal to the longitudinal axis of boats, moored to anchor buoys fore and aft, keeled them so much that they took in water and sank. There is also evidence from Kodiak that boats, left dry by a drawdown, were toppled when the water started to rise again, especially when the wave came in with a steep, breaking front.

Large vessels survived the tsunami. Most remarkable is probably the survival of the 10,000-ton ship *Chena* during the slide-generated waves at Valdez. All the smaller boats in that harbor were completely destroyed. The 2,000-ton tanker *Alaska Standard* also weathered the slide-generated waves at Seward, whereas the small boats there were either badly damaged or destroyed.

The large vessels moored to the marginal pier and the cargo dock of the Kodiak Naval Station, as well as the large timber barge moored to Citizens Dock at Crescent City, withstood the tsunami well. However, these vessels damaged the dock structures very badly, particularly at Crescent City.

It should be noted here that in other cases of great tsunamis, particularly that of the Chilean earthquake of May 1960, large ships have not fared so well, largely as a result of being caught in narrow waterways where the whip action of violent surge currents carried them out of control (see Sievers and others, 1963; Takahasi and Hatori, 1961).

It has been proved many times that the safest place for ships and boats of all types during the rampage of a tsunami is the open sea, and, in fact, a standard procedure of the tsunami warning system of the U.S. Coast and Geodetic Survey now is to advise that ships vacate any threatened port and make for open water, as far from shallow water and enveloping coastline as possible.

A problem remains, however, for ships or boats which cannot generate power or acquire a crew in time to escape the inrush of a tsunami. The extent of advance warning of the approach of a tsunami might even be insufficient to warrant risking the lives of crews in attempts to undock ships and head for open sea.

Primary protection for shipping, however, must come from outer breakwaters or tsunami barriers when the economic issues justify barriers capable of blunting tsunami attack. It is almost certain, however, even with barrier protection that very-long-period, high-amplitude tsunamis will cause overtopping and violent flushing of harbor and marine basins and that the induced currents may be powerful enough to tear ships from their moorings and to rip small-boat landing floats from their pylons. Conventional mooring facilities hold little prospect of being capable of resisting chaotic disorder of this kind, so that important secondary protection for shipping must be devised within the dock areas themselves.

For protection of large ships, a primary requirement would be the provision of resilient shock-absorbing fenders as permanent fixtures of quay walls and piers, coupled with the use of well-secured shock-absorbing floating fenders. A second stipulation might be that all ships of large size, if permitted to berth, be equipped with automatic constant-tensioning high-capacity deck winches capable of ensuring taut moorings at all states of the tide or water level. Ships that are above a certain tonnage and do not meet such code or port requirements could be compelled to anchor, in the roadstead outside the harbor, at specially designed clump and groundline anchorages marked by permanent surface buoys. Under normal sea conditions the dead weight of the clump resting on the sea bed would be a sufficient anchor for holding a ship in the exposed roadstead. Under high-sea or tsunami conditions, however, the addi-

tional force imposed on the anchor line would lift the clump and bring into action the groundline and true anchor and thus cushion the strain of severe drag, while maintaining a small angle of inclination of the groundline at the anchor and so preserving its holding power (see also Wiegel, 1965). Such berthings would obviously require barge and lighterage operations with attendant higher port charges for ship owners, who would thereby be induced to equip their vessels with regulation winch machinery to gain the safety of protected harbor berthings.

In small-boat basins, landing floats and platforms should be required to meet particularly stringent specifications to ensure more robust equipment than is normally required of marinas that are not subject to tsunami attack. In particular, vertical guide piles could be interconnected at an appropriate overhead level by longitudinal, cross, and diagonal bracings, so that loads are transmitted to the equivalent of a large framed structure rather than single flexible piles. Small-boat lashings to the floating docks should also be required to meet stringent specifications for size and type, in keeping with the nature and size of the craft moored.

MAXIMUM HEIGHTS AND RUNUP OF TSUNAMI WAVES NEAR THEIR SOURCE

Generally speaking, the evidence in this report and in the paper by Wilson and Tørum (this volume) shows that the main tsunami wave (with which must be associated locally induced seismic seiches) attained runup heights in the range of about 20 to 100 ft within a radius, say, of 200 mi of the generating source. Local exceptions to the generalization occurred, of course, but may be considered to have been out of the ordinary and attributable to peculiar local features of topography and landsliding.

From an engineering point of view it is very desirable to have some criterion, if only approximate, whereby runup height may be anticipated for a particular earthquake magnitude. The evidence of this study has therefore been added to data previously collected from other sources (Wilson and others, 1962, Wilson and Tørum, 1972; Wilson, 1964, 1969a) in an attempt to correlate tsunami wave height near the source with earthquake magnitude (see Figure 6 in Wilson and Tørum, this volume, p. 164). The solid-line linear regression line in this figure was derived empirically by Wilson and others (1962) and Wilson (1964) from independent consideration of earthquake energy and tsunami magnitude, based on Japanese statistics. It appears to form an approximate upper bound to the data points plotted in this figure. The empirical equation which fits this line is

$$\log_{10} H_{max} = 0.75\,M - 5.06, \tag{28}$$

where H_{max} is a measure of anticipated maximum tsunami height (crest to trough) near the generating region and M is the earthquake magnitude (Richter scale). Equation (28) may be expected to apply to earthquakes whose mechanisms and locations would favor maximum vertical tectonic displacement under the sea, but proximate to land. Earthquakes producing mainly horizontal movements, or positioned either too close or too far from land, would probably generate tsunamis whose height H_{max} would fall below the value given by equation (28) or the line in Figure 6 (p. 164). It must be recognized that equation (28) is a broad statistical generalization and that its use should be circumspect.

The estimation of a maximum runup, R_{max}, from this figure is not always an easy matter because of the important effects of bottom slope and wave steepness and the imponderables of knowing the precise nature of the tsunami waves (whether, for instance, they are a composite of main waves of very-long-period and shorter-period waves representing local oscillations, as seems to have been the case with the tsunamis in Alaska). Some brief discussion on the runup problem is given in Appendix A; this is not a comprehensive treatment, but it underscores some of the deficiencies of data available a few years ago. Recent reviewers of the subject include Wiegel (1964, 1970), Van Dorn (1965, 1966), and Le Méhauté and others (1968); the latter have attempted a complete synthesis of existing theories as applying to wave runup. In his 1966 work, Van Dorn evolved nomographs for runup prediction of a wave of given height and period progressing from water of uniform depth up a uniform impermeable slope. In general, these authors have shown that runup height can attain many times the height of the deepwater wave (see also Van Dorn and Cox, this volume). This will be apparent also from those experimental results summarized in Figure A-1 of Appendix A, whose extrapolation to smaller wave steepnesses might be considered to apply to tsunami waves.

A difficulty in application of results of this kind to real tsunami waves is the fact that their deepwater height is usually unknown and that frequently they are composite waves of mixed periods and amplitudes when they reach a coast. Moreover, the slopes over which they propagate are seldom uniform. Still more importantly, the three-dimensional oscillating characteristics of a shelf or embayment in the region of runup may be decisive in defining the extent of that runup and the trend toward breaker or bore formation. There is, therefore, still some need for statistical guidance.

Wiegel (1964, 1970) has presented statistical information on tsunami runup at Hilo, Hawaii, in the form of a frequency-of-occurrence distribution, from which the risk that the runup will exceed a given value in a given duration time can be determined. While this type of information for a specified locality is very desirable, it may be impossible to obtain if reliable records of tsunami inundation have not been kept over a considerable period of years. Statistical information of the kind presented in Figure 6 of Wilson and Tørum (this volume p. 164) then becomes important, because earthquake statistics, which are more readily obtainable for most areas of the world including oceans, will define the risk of occurrence of an earthquake of given magnitude in a particular region, while this diagram (Figure 6, p. 164) may be considered to provide information on the most probable height of the tsunami waves near the coast deriving from a proximate generating source associated with that earthquake.

There remains the problem of determining the most probable runup from such tsunami waves. As discussed by Wilson and Tørum (this volume), maximum runup, R_{max}, measured with reference to prevailing mean sea level, may be taken to be from 1.0 to 1.5 of the values of H_{max} given in the above-mentioned figure. It must be specifically emphasized here that H_{max} has no relation to deepwater wave height and that this figure cannot apply to tsunami waves that have traveled a considerable distance across the ocean. If $R_{max} \approx 1.5 H_{max}$ is chosen as the limit, equation (28) can be transformed directly to express probable maximum runup as a function of earthquake magnitude, namely,

$$\log_{10} R_{max} = 0.75 M - 4.82. \qquad (29)$$

The dashed line in the above-mentioned Figure 6 (p. 164) represents this relationship and appears to form a complete upper bound to the scatter of plotted data. For the Alaska earthquake ($M \approx 8.5$), we find $R_{max} \approx 33$ m or about 109 ft, which is in reasonable accord with some of the observations we have noted.

ECONOMIC ASPECTS OF PROTECTIVE MEASURES

Standards of safety and economy that would apply in any given coastal region with a potential for tsunami attack obviously depend on such factors as the degree to which the region is seismically active; the historically prevalent nature of earthquake faulting; the extent to which earthquakes occur seaward or landward of the coastline; the statistical trend of focal depth of local earthquakes in relation to distance from the coastline; the exposure of the coast to transocean tsunamis; the protection afforded by offshore islands; the peculiarities of the coastline to concentrate tsunami energy in specific places; the resonating capacity of particular bays and inlets toward amplifying tsunami runup; the geological nature of the coastal area and its susceptibility to submarine landsliding, to compaction under vibration, and to earth avalanches; and the extent to which a large area may be prone to subsidence during a local earthquake.

When all these factors are taken into account, it is clear that completely different standards of safety are likely to prevail in different regions. Compared with Alaska, for example, California appears to be rather favored, particularly Southern California, which, for the most part, is protected by offshore islands and historically is not particularly prone to local tsunami generation.

There is as yet no hard-and-fast rule for determining a safety standard. The lessons of the Alaska earthquake of 1964 point to the need for secure foundations for waterfront structures, but in the presence of total land subsidence even the best foundations cannot necessarily ensure safety either for the structures they bear or for the people who occupy those structures.

If subsidence is not a problem, then real safety begins with the placing of all structures on good foundations at a level above the expected runup of the design tsunami under the most unfavorable conditions. Such a measure may be impossible in a practical sense, particularly when waterfront facilities are involved and land levels are low. It may then be necessary to resort to some sort of protective works such as those being considered for Hilo in Hawaii and Crescent City in California. The question of economy is then directly involved. If we assume that tsunami-warning services can ensure the safety of human life, at what stage does it become economic to resort to total or partial protection of the assets of a seaside community by such measures as special breakwaters, barriers, seawalls, dikes, tree plantings, or shelter buildings? At present, there are no general answers; each area seeking security during tsunami attack must be separately and carefully investigated.

CONSIDERATIONS FOR ENGINEERING DESIGN AND PLANNING

It seems desirable to set out in succinct form the broad conclusions and immediately useful information which emerge from this study. For convenience they are listed below:

1. Tsunami Characteristics

(a) It seems that runup heights of the tsunami waves in Alaska are in general agreement with a statistical trend of relationship to earthquake magnitude shown in Figure 6 of Wilson and Tørum (this volume, p. 164). This relationship may have engineering usefulness in establishing risk criteria in regions for which tsunami runup statistics are not available.

(b) Particular coastlines, inlets, and bays of the Pacific Ocean boundary acted as resonators for the primary wave frequency of the Alaska tsunami, amplifying effects and developing, in many cases, prominent modes of free oscillation. Because of this, certain coastal areas will always be peculiarly susceptible to large damaging waves from great tsunamis with high energy content, in keeping with large earthquake magnitudes (examples are Port Alberni, Canada; Crescent City, San Francisco, Monterey Bay and Santa Monica, California; Hilo and Kahului, Hawaii; Lyttelton, New Zealand; and many Japanese bays).

2. Features of Tsunami Damage

(a) Tsunami waves from the Alaska earthquake had their most damaging effects when they occurred on the high spring tide. This predicates an obvious design criterion that concurrence of high spring tide with maximum tsunami height should always be considered.

(b) At Seward, Valdez, and Whittier, heavy tsunami damage was caused by submarine slide-generated waves of about 3 to 5 minutes in period and 30 to 40 ft in height. These waves broke with borelike effect on the respective coastlines and displaced or smashed objects in their path.

(c) At Kodiak, Alberni, and Crescent City, as also at Seward and Valdez, the main tsunami waves, with or without overriding harmonics or local seiches, acted as fast-rising and ebbing tides, without bore formation (except in the narrow Near Island channel at Kodiak). They buoyed objects and moved them with massive and sustained stream effect against nonmoving objects.

(d) The worst effects of (b) occurred during and immediately after the earthquake. The worst effects of (c) were contingent upon the concurrence of highest tsunami waves with highest tide, several hours after the earthquake.

(e) Tectonic regional subsidence of the land increased the damage potential of the tsunami, as at Kodiak, Seward, and Whittier, and mildly at Valdez; uplift of the land decreased the damage potential, as at Cordova.

(f) Submarine sliding and collapse of waterfront areas at Seward, Valdez, and Whittier were probably assisted by drawdown of the water level as a result of seismic seiches generated by the earthquake or initial tsunamis of displacement. Primary cause of collapse was the unstable nature under vibration of the glacial deposits on which these cities are founded.

(g) Small boats and marine docks suffered severely from the waves. If beached and caught by turbulent water, they were frequently rolled and waterlogged or otherwise smashed. If anchored fore and aft, they were often keeled by broadside current and sunk at their moorings.

(h) Because the larger boats generally floated, they had a better chance of survival but were usually damaged by battery. Vessels of ship size showed best survival abilities.

(i) Pile-supported dock structures and decking were frequently buoyed off their piles as a consequence of deficient connections (usually driftpins) and were carried away and destroyed. Poorly braced pilings were ready victims for destruction. Some piles were pulled from their sockets because of inadequate adhesion in the foundation; for the most part, these piles had insufficient penetration in the foundation at the time of construction.

(j) At Kodiak the breakwaters were severely damaged by compaction settling of the foundation, regional subsidence, resultant wave overtopping, and severe scour from high-velocity flows that probably exceeded 40 ft/sec.

(k) Land-based structures of timber construction, insecurely fastened to their foundations, suffered severely. They were usually floated off and beached near high-water limit or were splintered and smashed by impact against obstacles or by momentum of water.

(l) At Kodiak Naval Station, the value of holding-down cables was demonstrated by the fact that a small building, so provided, withstood the waves in an area where others of its kind were swept away.

(m) At Crescent City, stacks of floatable building timber and logs at the lumber dock proved a great hazard by furnishing flotsam to the waves.

(n) Reinforced-concrete, concrete-block, and stone-wall structures were much less susceptible to tsunami damage, in terms of collapse or displacement, than wooden structures. Generally they survived the tsunami well but suffered nevertheless from impact damage, wetting, and cracking under uneven foundation settlement.

(o) Waterfront oil-storage tanks, devastated by the tsunami waves, burned at Seward, Valdez, Whittier, and Crescent City; these oil fires were spread by water and burned uncontrolled, resulting in considerable oil contamination from spillage and spreading by the waves. At Kodiak City and Kodiak Naval Station, oil tanks were mostly at levels above the reach of the waves, thus preventing oil fires.

(p) The power plant at Kodiak Naval Station was vulnerable to flooding, and contamination from heavy fuel oil rendered all machinery inoperable.

3. General Design Criteria for Tsunami Protection

(a) For any given location subject to attack from tsunamis, one must establish a standard of safety and economy that takes into account the degree (magnitude-frequencies) to which the region is seismically active; the geological and historical nature of earthquake faulting; the statistical trend of focal depth of local earthquakes in relation to distance from the coast; the exposure of the coast to transocean tsunamis; the protection afforded by offshore islands; the proclivity of the coastline for concentrating energy in specific places; the resonating capacity of particular bays and inlets toward amplifying tsunami runup; the historical evidence for tectonic earth movement, whether horizontal, vertical, or both; the geological nature and stability of the coastal area particularly as regards susceptibility to submarine landsliding, earth avalanches, and consolidation under vibration; and the history of tsunami inundation for the region. All these considerations amount to a risk analysis for defining a design earthquake or a design tsunami from which to evaluate a design runup via equation (29). In this analysis, statistical guidelines such as equation (29) may be useful. Distribution functions of frequency of occurrence of tsunami runup height (see Wiegel, 1965, 1970) are also helpful. The economic aspects of the problem should determine whether tsunami barriers are both feasible and justifiable.

(b) Estimates of water velocity likely to be encountered from the design tsunami at different places should properly take account of wave propagation in the area. If bore-formation is expected, velocities at the front are calculable from equation (25) with $K = 2.0$, say. If bore formation or breaking does not occur, velocities may be calculated from equation (B-2) or (B-20) of Appendix B.

(c) Water forces on objects that are not unreasonably large may be calculated by the use of equation (23). The Reynolds number appropriate to the flow and the shape of the object should be determined in order to arrive at a suitable value of drag coefficient C_D. More careful analysis may be needed to allow also for lift forces developing from the flow between the object and its support.

(d) Water forces on objects which present large continuous surfaces such as breakwaters, seawalls, large buildings, highway embankments, and so forth, may be calculated by the use of equations (24) or (27).

(e) Breakwaters should have stone or blocks of sufficient weight to resist the expected scour velocities from overtopping.

(f) Timber-pile structures should have piles of adequate strength capable of developing sufficient soil adhesion to resist pullout from buoyancy forces.

(g) Timber decking for piers and other similar structures should be adequately fastened to the supporting piles to resist uplift pressures.

(h) Adequate structural strength and adequate bracing in piled structures are important.

(i) Guide piles for small-craft floating landing decks should preferably be cross-braced above the water to develop adequate truss strength against water loading.

(j) Buildings on land in exposed areas should have deep foundations of reinforced concrete of the beam and raft type to resist scour and undermining.

(k) Buildings should be oriented, if possible, so as to expose their shorter sides to potential wave inundation.

(l) Reinforced-concrete or steel frame buildings with shear walls are desirable.

(m) Wooden-frame buildings should preferably be located in the lee of more substantial buildings.

(n) Wooden-frame buildings should be well secured to their foundations and have corner bracing at ceiling level.

(o) Frame buildings in very exposed, low-lying areas should be designed so that the ground-floor area may be considered expendable, because wetting damage would be inevitable. Elevated "stilt" design of aesthetic quality should be considered.

(p) Power plants should be located out of reach of water.

(q) Oil tanks should be located on high ground or surrounded by dikes or walls to prevent oil spillage and fire hazard.

(r) Tree screening should be considered as a buffer zone against the sea and also for its aesthetic value.

(s) All ships and boats should leave harbor for deep water after a tsunami warning, if time is available and if adequate protection is not assured.

(t) Docks catering to seagoing vessels should be provided with specially designed shock-absorbing fenders.

(u) Large ships should be required to carry constant-tensioning winches as standard equipment.

(v) Special moorings and mooring techniques should be evolved.

ACKNOWLEDGMENTS

This study was made under contract to the Coastal Engineering Research Center (CERC), U.S. Army Corps of Engineers, Washington, D.C. (No. DA-49-055-CIVENG-66-6), at the special request of George W. Housner, Chairman, Panel on Engineering, Committee on the Alaska Earthquake, National Academy of Sciences. We desire to record our appreciation of the personal interest and encouragement of George Housner, and of Thorndike Saville, Jr., Chief, Research Division (presently, Technical Director), CERC; also of Konrad B. Krauskopf, Chairman, Committee on the Alaska Earthquake, and Doak C. Cox, Chairman, Panel on Oceanography.

Drafting of figures was undertaken by Takashi Umehara and George Zwior with much painstaking research and detailed measurements from photographs and charts in the compilation of the damage maps for Kodiak, Seward, and Valdez, which are original to this study. George Zwior also performed much of the photographic work incorporated in this paper.

It would be impossible to make individual acknowledgment to all the people, authors, and agencies who have contributed either verbal information or written and photographic material assembled here. However, as far as possible, these contributions have been acknowledged in the text or in the figures. We greatly appreciate the courtesy and cooperation of all.

APPENDIX A: TSUNAMI CHARACTERISTICS AND RUNUP–PREDICTION OF TSUNAMIS RELATED TO THEIR ABILITY TO DAMAGE STRUCTURES

Alf Tørum

The damaging effect of tsunamis of the same wave height may vary greatly. In regard to the damage at Oahu during the tsunami of April 1, 1946, Isaacs (1946) suggested that the damage caused by tsunamis may be roughly classified under the following categories:

1. The damage from a tsunami does not exceed that which would be expected from an equal tidal inundation without surf. Typical houses are floated from their foundations or merely flooded but moved little; the vegetation is not disturbed to any extent.

2. The damage caused by the tsunami is intermediate between the conditions in categories 1 and 3. Houses are moved some distance and damaged; the ground is somewhat eroded.

3. The damage resulting from the tsunami is disproportionately great when compared with that which would be expected from a tidal inundation of similar height. Evidence of high velocity is everywhere. Buildings are destroyed, reef coral is carried far inland, automobiles are rolled about, escarpments and stripping are produced, and the level regions are invaded by the water for a great distance inland.

The same categories are also applicable to the tsunami of the 1964 Alaska earthquake.

Whether or not the waves break and to what extent they break seem to determine the category of damage. A nonbreaking wave will presumably cause damage of the type in the first category, light-breaking waves cause damage of the second type, and waves that break the most violently cause damage similar to that described in the third category.

It is not within the scope of this study to deal in detail with the problem of nonbreaking and breaking of waves

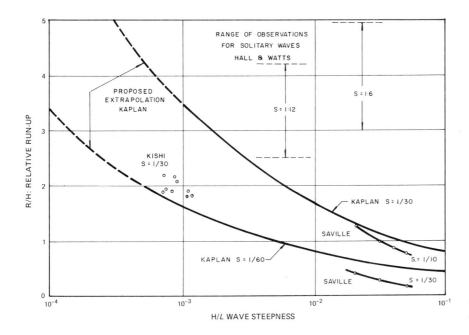

FIGURE A-1 Experimental observations on wave runup. (From Wilson, Le Méhauté, and Freeman, 1964.)

and the related problem of runup. However, we should like to show the deficit in the theory when one tries to understand the behavior of the tsunamis at different places.

If a wave does not break, its energy is assumed to be completely reflected, whereas the wave energy in fully breaking waves is assumed to be completely transformed into heat by turbulent friction. In partly breaking waves some of the wave energy is reflected and some dissipated.

NONBREAKING WAVES

The approaches in theoretical treatment of breaking and nonbreaking waves and their runup have mostly been along the lines of the small-amplitude-wave theory and the long-wave theory.

The breaking criterion for the small-amplitude-wave theory is that the maximum water-particle velocity of the wave crest exceeds the phase velocity of the wave or that the Bernoulli equation of the free surface is not satisfied. In the long-wave theory the breaking criterion is defined by the inception of a shock wave. Miche (1951) proposed the following theoretical formula, based on the small-amplitude-wave theory, for limiting conditions of nonbreaking waves:

$$(H/L)_{max} < \sqrt{(2a/\pi)} \; (\sin^2 a)/\pi, \qquad \text{(A-1)}$$

where H is wave height, L is wave length, and a is the angle of bottom slope.

For

$a = 45°, (H/L)_{max} = 0.112$
$a = 15°, (H/L)_{max} = 0.0079$
$a = \;5°, (H/L)_{max} = 0.00057.$

The long-wave theory and the application of the method of characteristics is considered a better approach than the small-amplitude-wave theory. However, this method does not give such a simple relationship for limiting conditions as does the small-amplitude-wave theory. Except for some rather limited attempts at finding an analytical solution, the problem of long-wave propagation over a gentle slope is largely unresolved. The most reliable method consists of applying the method of characteristics for each particular case (Freeman and Le Méhauté, 1964).

We shall not go into any detail about different theoretical and experimental results on wave runup for nonbreaking waves, but merely include Figure A-1 to show a trend of results.

BREAKING WAVES

The wave steepness (H/L) and the beach slope s determine how the wave will break. Breaking waves are usually classified into three categories: spilling, plunging, and surging breakers. Spilling breakers, which are characterized by the appearance of white water at the crest, break gradually. Plunging breakers are characterized by a curling over of the top of the crest and a plunging down of this mass of water;

the front of the crest first becomes steep and then concave. Surging breakers, observed when waves of small steepness travel on very steep slopes, are essentially bores in character; the whole front face of such breakers becomes unstable and "boils" all at once rather than gradually, as in a spilling breaker.

The most reliable theory for calculating runup values of breaking long waves is the method of characteristics. This method, however, requires the profile of the waves to be known somewhere off the coast before the wave breaks.

This profile then provides the input data for the calculation.

Le Méhauté (Wilson and others, 1964) suggests the following as a rough approximation of runup calculation.

If the bottom slope $s > 0.01$ at the point where the wave height/water depth ratio is $H/d = 0.78$ (McCowan's breaker limit for solitary waves), the runup is approximately twice the breaking-wave height (depending on the slope). If $s < 0.01$, take the wave height $H = 0.78\ d$ where the slope becomes 0.01, the runup then is twice this breaking-wave height. This will be the maximum possible runup.

APPENDIX B: THE FLOW AND FORCE FIELD OF TSUNAMI WAVES

Basil W. Wilson

Recognizing that tsunami waves are of very great length and period in shallow water and also of considerable amplitude, in relation to the depth, by the time they reach the coast, we are led to inquire into the nature of the water velocities and the forces which these waves can bring to bear against obstacles of various kinds.

Most marigraphic records of tsunami waves show that they have little resemblance to cnoidal or solitary waves but, on the contrary, are strongly sinusoidal, as are also the much-longer-period astronomical tidal waves. The existence of what effectively seem to be Airy waves in such shallow water (very small values of H/T^2 and d/T^2) poses a problem that we have not yet resolved, since the dictates of shallow-water wave theories seem to prescribe more complex wave forms.

The periods of waves found to occur as a result of the Alaska earthquake cover the range from about 2 minutes to 5 hours. The relative capacity of these waves to produce damage is a matter of prime interest. Because of the above-mentioned observation of the apparent sinusoidal character of the waves, we resort to the finite-amplitude wave theory of Lamb (1932 ed., p. 278–280) which uses the method of characteristics to show that a long wave of elevation η above water level of depth d propagates at the velocity

$$c = \sqrt{gd}\ [3(1 + \eta/d)^{\frac{1}{2}} - 2]\,, \qquad (B-1)$$

with a horizontal water-particle velocity, uniform over the depth, of

$$u = 2\sqrt{gd}\ [(1 + \eta/d)^{\frac{1}{2}} - 1]\,. \qquad (B-2)$$

These results assume a horizontal bed and negligible vertical accelerations. To the first order of η/d, the results are the same as derived by Airy (1845) in his finite-amplitude, long-wave theory. Evidently, because η can be either positive or negative according to position in the wave, the crest velocity must exceed that of the trough and the wave must eventually break or form a bore. Equation (B-1) is the same as that used in the text in the discussion of tidal ingress up the Columbia River.

If η/d is small in equation (B-1), then

$$c \approx \sqrt{gd}\ [1 + \frac{3}{2}\ (\eta/d)]\ . \qquad (B-3)$$

and the velocity of progression exceeds that of a solitary wave. This result was obtained also by Milne-Thomson (1960, p. 418) by a different method, and also by Bouasse (1924, p. 301).

We may transform equation (B-2) to the form

$$u = 2\sqrt{g\eta}\ [(1 + d/\eta)^{\frac{1}{2}} - (d/\eta)^{\frac{1}{2}}] \qquad (B-4)$$

and hence conclude that if the wave were to run onto dry ground (for which d tends to zero), then the water velocity would approximate

$$u \simeq 2\sqrt{g\eta}. \qquad (B-5)$$

This equation has no special meaning because of its neglect of bed friction and bottom slope, but in a general sense it supports other conclusions that we shall draw regarding the velocity of the tip of a bore.

The development of a bore is usually dependent on the amplitude of the long wave, the presence of a reverse flow upstream of the wave, and the influences of constrictions in the path of the wave or sudden changes of bed gradient. No simple explicit statement can be given to define the criterion for bore formation (see Stoker, 1957; Freeman and Le Méhauté, 1964), although it is possible with fair accuracy to specify the velocity u of propagation of a bore of height H advancing into still water of depth d.

The classical approach to this problem by consideration of continuity and momentum (see, for example, Lamb, 1932, p. 280; Rouse, 1938; Keulegan, 1949) yields the result

$$u = \sqrt{gd}\,[(1+H/d)(1+H/2d)]^{1/2}. \qquad \text{(B-6)}$$

As pointed out by Keulegan (1949), this formula tends to lose physical meaning as d approaches zero value, equivalent to a surge over a dry bed. However, equation (B-6) can be rendered in the form

$$u = \sqrt{gH}\,[(1+d/H)(1+H/2d)]^{1/2}, \qquad \text{(B-7)}$$

from which we find that, when $H = 6d$,

$$u \simeq 2\sqrt{gH}. \qquad \text{(B-8)}$$

The choice of the value $H = 6d$ is taken only because equation (B-8) also expresses the theoretical velocity of the tip of a wave over dry ground created by the failure of a dam of height H (Keulegan, 1949). Friction over the dry bed must undoubtedly play its part in reducing this velocity to some factor of $\sqrt{gH}$ less than 2. Keulegan (1949) quotes the experiments of Schoklitsch (1917), which confirm quite well the dam-break theory (see Stoker, 1957) but demonstrate the friction effect. Keulegan concludes that equation (B-8) is nevertheless a fair approximation to the velocity of a surge over a dry bed.

It is of interest to consider here the velocity formulation of Gibson (1925, p. 405) for the speed of advance of a "wave of transmission," or intumescence of height H. Gibson uses Bernoulli's equation to equate energies within and beyond the wave, on the assumption that no energy is lost through friction and turbulence, and derives

$$u = \sqrt{gd}\,[(1+H/d)^2(1+H/2d)^{-1}]^{1/2}, \qquad \text{(B-9)}$$

which may be rendered in the alternative form

$$u = \sqrt{gH}\,[(1+d/H)^2(\tfrac{1}{2}+d/H)^{-1}]^{1/2}. \qquad \text{(B-10)}$$

For $H/d < 0.25$, as pointed out by Allen (1947, p. 360), equation (B-9) or (B-10) and equation (B-6) or (B-7) differ by less than 1 percent. Allen, using Gibson's formula for studying bore propagation in models for values of H/d up to 0.5, found agreement to within $\pm$ 3 percent. He has, however, overlooked the possibility of using Lamb's re-

sult [equation (B-4)] in the same sense but with an expected greater reliability for larger values of H/d. It is noteworthy that if equation (B-10) is forced to the limit, $d = 0$, we obtain

$$u \simeq 1.41\sqrt{gH}. \qquad \text{(B-11)}$$

In recent hydraulic experiments on tsunami bore propagation, Fukui and others (1963) use a modified form of Lamb's equation (B-6) for comparison with their measurements. This modification takes the form

$$u = \left[\frac{g(d+H)(2d+H)}{2\{d+H(1-\delta)\}}\right]^{1/2} \qquad \text{(B-12)}$$

The "disturbance" coefficient δ is a resistance term that they derived experimentally for a bed roughness equivalent to a Manning's n of 0.013. Derived as a function of $d/(d+H)$, δ was found to vary from 0.83 at $d = 0$ to 1.03 for $d/(d+H) > 0.5$.

It is convenient to render equation (B-12) in the alternative form

$$u = \sqrt{gH}\left[\frac{(1+d/H)(1+2d/H)}{2\{(1-\delta)+d/H\}}\right]^{1/2} \qquad \text{(B-13)}$$

and thence find, for the special case of interest of the propagation of a bore over a dry bed ($d = 0$, $\delta = 0.83$),

$$u = 1.73\sqrt{gH}. \qquad \text{(B-14)}$$

A more recent series of experiments on tsunami surges has been made by Cross (1966, 1967), from whose work Figure 17 in the text has been reproduced. He reviews some of the features that we have discussed above and in his more complete report (Cross, 1966) discusses the work of Dressler (1952) and of Whitham (1955) relative to the dam-break problem. These authors' results are quite similar in showing that the factor $u/\sqrt{dH}$ tends to decrease rather rapidly from the value 2.0 for a frictionless condition to about 0.7 for high bed resistance. Cross's own experiments for the case of simulated tsunami surges traveling over a relatively smooth bed (Chezy coefficient $C \simeq 98$) yield a consistent result for different values of surge height H

$$u/\sqrt{gH} \simeq 1.41, \qquad \text{(B-15)}$$

which fortuitously agrees with equation (B-11).

We must also note the work of Matlock and others (1962), recently condensed in a paper by Reese and Matlock (1967), in which postmortem analysis of the damage caused by the Chilean tsunami at Hilo, Hawaii, in 1960, attempted to identify the forces and velocities of the bore which was known to have been responsible for a great deal of the damage. In all but one case of structural failure, of the 10 cases examined, the force necessary to cause failure was calculated and correlated with a force based on pure fluid drag, namely,

$$F = \frac{1}{2} C_D \rho A u^2, \qquad (B-16)$$

in which C_D is a dimensionless drag coefficient appropriate to the fluid flow and the shape of the structural obstacle, ρ the mass density of water, A the projected area of the obstacle normal to the flow, and u the stream velocity bearing on the structure. The essential outcome of their study was to show that the velocities computed as being necessary to cause the structural failures were in a range consistent with water velocities for the bore based on equation (B-6) or its simplification for surge over a dry bed, such as in equation (B-8).

It seems reasonable to conclude from the foregoing discussion that the velocity of the water u_s at the front of a bore or surge advancing over dry land as an inundation, or over a channel bed that has been emptied by a preceding withdrawal of water, will be fairly well represented by the formula

$$u_s = K \sqrt{g d_s} \,, \qquad (B-17)$$

in which d_s is the height of the general surge level above the land level at any point occupied by the front of the surge and K is a numerical coefficient with a value between, say, 1.5 and 2.0. For conservative design purposes it would seem desirable to adopt the value $K = 2.0$.

We return to our comment (at the beginning of this Appendix) regarding the extremely wide range of periods of tsunami waves engendered by the Alaska earthquake. This report points out that for the most part the very-long-period waves of the tsunami merely inundated the land like fast-rising tides. Because there was neither wave breaking nor bore formation in this action, the formulas considered above obviously do not apply. However, we need to know what velocities of flow developed in these cases.

If we consider the crest of a wave of period $T = 1.8$ hours to have reached a coastline, it is of interest to determine where its still-water-level crossing point would be located, seaward of the coast. To a first approximation, we may assume the wave speed to be that of equation (3) in the text, so that the quarter length $\lambda/4$ of the wave is given by the definition formula

$$\lambda/4 = (T/4)(\sqrt{gd}) \,. \qquad (B-18)$$

If now we assume a mean depth d over the quarter wave length of 128 ft, we find, for $T = 1.8$ hr,

$$\lambda/4 \simeq 8.6 \text{ nautical miles.} \qquad (B-19)$$

These figures are consistent with a sea-bed slope of about 1/200, which is fairly reasonable.

With maximum amplitude of the wave at the coastline, we find (for a sinusoidal wave) that the 1.8-hour wave will have 95 percent of this amplitude at a distance from the crest center of about 3.5 nautical miles on either side. Because inundation distances from the Alaska tsunami never exceeded ½ nautical mile, except along riverbeds as at Crescent City, it is clear that inundation water level immediately seaward and landward of the coastline would be effectively horizontal. Further, since the surface slope of so large a wave is extremely gradual, the rise of the crest at the coast would be like a fast tide lifting a virtually horizontal sea level in the time of the quarter wave-period. This argument may be extended successfully to much smaller wave periods—at least to $T = 30$ minutes.

Assuming then a rise of horizontal sea level over the land at the incremental vertical rate $\delta\eta/\delta t$ where η is the wave elevation of the wave above still-water level at any point and t is variable time, we find that the continuity condition governing the speed of water over dry land of slope s requires a velocity of horizontal flow per unit width

$$u = \frac{1}{s} \frac{\delta\eta}{\delta t}. \qquad (B-20)$$

For a sinusoidal wave at the coastline of amplitude A and angular frequency σ

$$\eta = A \sin \sigma t \qquad (B-21)$$

and

$$\delta\eta/\delta t = A \sigma \cos \sigma t, \qquad (B-22)$$

so that from equations (B-20) and (B-22) horizontal velocity per unit width becomes

$$u = (A\sigma/s) \cos \sigma t. \qquad (B-23)$$

The flow is therefore periodic and, for any given amplitude A and ground slope s, is inversely proportional to the wave period. This means, of course, that a 30-minute-period wave would have four times as severe a current as a 2-hour-period wave.

In most cases of inundation for the Alaska tsunami, the flooding was brought about by a superposition of long waves of large amplitude. The nature of the superposition sometimes results in extremely rapid time rates of change of water level $\delta\eta/\delta t$. If tide-gage or water-level records are available, $\delta\eta/\delta t$ is directly measurable from the records and water velocities are then calculable from equation (B-20). Obviously, if the ground slope s is very slight, water velocities can attain high values. The dictates of the flow are then governed by hydraulic considerations, as for flow in rivers and canals.

The point of overlap or criterion for which a flow of the type of equations (B-20) and (B-23) can become a tsunami bore or breaking wave needs further research.

Equation (B-16) for the force of the flowing water on an obstacle is obviously relevant only if the object is completely enveloped in the flow. It is therefore likely to be pertinent to cases of isolated objects of moderate size around which the flood water can establish a regime of flow. In the case of large objects such as continuous breakwaters, seawalls, blocks of buildings, and other objects with large frontages which are liable to deter a cascading bore and obstruct the flow, the effect of both hydrostatic and dynamic pressure and of the destruction or deflection of momentum must be taken into account. This leads to the definition of the force F per unit length of wall, in the form

$$F = \frac{1}{2}\rho g d_w^2 + C_F \rho d_t u_s^2, \qquad \text{(B-24)}$$

where d_w is the depth of water formed at the wall, d_t the depth of water at the toe of the wall before deflection of the stream, u_s the surge velocity appropriate to the height d_s of the surge (Figure B-1), ρ the mass density of sea water, and C_F a dimensionless force coefficient.

This formula is well known in the hydraulics of river and canal flow (see, for example, Francis, 1958), although usually without the inclusion of the coefficient C_F. Cross (1966, 1967), who introduces the equation to the study of tsunami surges, has evaluated the coefficient C_F on the basis of theoretical work by Cumberbatch (1960), in which the impingement of a water wedge normal to a plane wall

was analyzed. Cross finds a nonlinear dependence of C_F on the slope of the water surface of the wedge or the angle ϕ (Figure B-1) such that for $\phi = 0$, $C_F = 1.0$; and for $\phi = 60°$, $C_F \simeq 3.0$.

In his experiments on tsunami surges, Cross found that a peak force developed on the experimental wall after the initial buildup of force, after which the force remained approximately constant or diminished slightly. The effective height of runup d_w on the wall (Figure B-1) showed approximate linear relationship to $u_s^2/2g$, as might be expected, yielding $d_w/(u_s^2/2g)$ values of about 2.0 for a wet bottom and 1.33 for a dry bed in front of the surge. Apparently, the peak pressure occurred when this runup collapsed on the reflecting bore, which formed at that moment and moved away from the wall. The fairly quiet water left behind exerted effectively only hydrostatic pressure against the wall.

For the case of a fairly flat surge, we may take $d_t \simeq d_s$; $C_F \simeq 1$ and apply to equation (B-24) the observation that

$$d_w/(u_s^2/2g) = 1.33 \text{ (for a dry bed);} \qquad \text{(B-25)}$$
$$2.0 \text{ (for a wet bed)}$$

and the earlier conclusion of equation (B-17) with $K = 1.75$. Equation (B-24) then reduces to the simplified forms:

$$\text{(i)} \quad F \approx 5 \rho g d_s^2 \text{ (for a dry bed)} \qquad \text{(B-26)}$$
$$\text{(ii)} \quad F \approx 7.5 \rho g d_s^2 \text{ (for a wet bed)}$$

which are quite similar to a result obtained by Wiegel (1970) with this type of reasoning. It must be noted that, if d_s exceeds the height of the wall or structure, due allowance would have to be made for the overtopping flow, which would reduce the numerical coefficient in equations (B-26). Otherwise, the latter says that the dynamic force per unit length from a tsunami surge on a wall type structure is about 10 to 15 times the hydrostatic force.

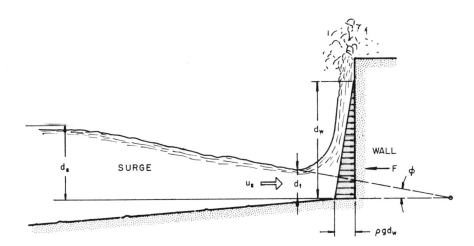

FIGURE B-1 Schematic diagram of impulsive effect from a tsunami surge on a vertical wall.

REFERENCES

Abernethy, Don, Harry Lommen, and Fred Luecke [1964]. Tidal wave: Disaster in Alberni and Port Alberni, March 28, 1964. Picture report. Alberni, British Columbia: Lucky Printers & Lithographers. 15 p.

Airy, G. B., 1845. Tides and waves, Section VI. London: Encyclopedia Metropolitana.

Alaska Construction, 1965. The bouncing *Chena. Alaska Construction,* 6 (May–June), 19.

Alaska Railroad, 1964. A summary of damage and repairs to roadbed and track following earthquake of March 27, 1964 (unpublished file report). Anchorage: U.S. Department of Interior, The Alaska Railroad.

Allen, J., 1947. Scale models in hydraulic engineering. London: Longmans, Green and Company. 407 p.

Anchorage Daily News. Quake damage total over $500 million. *Anchorage Daily News,* April 18, 1964.

Armstrong, Karl [1964]. Kodiak tsunami: first 29 days [daily emergency bulletins, March 28 to April 25, 1964, issued by City Hall]. Kodiak, Alaska: City of Kodiak. 79 p.

Berg, Eduard, Doak C. Cox, Augustine S. Furumoto, Kinjiro Kajiura, Hirosi Kawasumi, and Etsuzo Shima, 1972. Field survey of the tsunamis of 28 March 1964 in Alaska, and conclusions as to the origin of the major tsunami. Report HIG-70-2. Honolulu: University of Hawaii, Institute of Geophysics. 57 p.

Bouasse, H., 1924. Houle, rides, seiches et marées. Paris: Librairie Delagrave. 511 p.

Bracken, E. O., 1964. Observations of results of earthquake action, March 27, 1964, at Valdez, Alaska (unpublished). Report of Alaska State Highway Department. Valdez: Alaska State Highway Department.

Brown, Delmer L., 1964. Tsunamic activity accompanying the Alaskan earthquake of 27 March 1964. Technical Report, U.S. Army Engineer District, Alaska. Anchorage: U.S. Army Corps of Engineers, April 23. 31 p.

Bryant, F. J., 1964a. Estimates of local effects of seismic activity of 27 March 1964 (unpublished). Letter report to U.S. Department of Commerce, U.S. Naval Station, Kodiak, Alaska, April 6. Kodiak: U.S. Coast and Geodetic Survey.

Bryant, Capt. Fair J., 1964b. Transcripts of tape recordings of eyewitness accounts, earthquake and wave damage at Valdez, Alaska (unpublished). Washington: U.S. Coast and Geodetic Survey, May, 9 p.

Chance, Genie, 1966. Chronology of physical events of the Alaskan earthquake (unpublished). Anchorage: University of Alaska. 176 p. Copy on file NAS–NAE library.

Chance, Genie, in press. Selected chronology of physical events *in* The Great Alaska Earthquake of 1964: Summary and Recommendations. NAS Pub. 1608. Washington: National Academy of Sciences. In preparation.

Chapman, Robert M. [1964]. A reconnaissance geological examination of the earthquake features in the Valdez area and along the Richardson Highway (unpublished). [Fairbanks: U.S. Geological Survey.] 9 p.

Chrystal, G., 1906. Investigation of seiches of Loch Earn by the Scottish Loch Survey. *Transactions, Royal Society of Edinburgh,* 45 (No. 2), 382–387.

Coulter, Henry W., and Ralph R. Migliaccio, 1966. Effects of the earthquake of March 27, 1964, at Valdez, Alaska. U.S. Geological Survey Professional Paper 542-C. Washington: Government Printing Office. 36 p. Also *in* The Great Alaska Earthquake of

1964: Geology. NAS Pub. 1601. Washington: National Academy of Sciences, 1971. p. 359–394.

Cross, R. H., 1966. Water surge forces on coastal structures. Hydraulic Engineering Laboratory Technical Report HEL 9-10, July. Berkeley: University of California. 106 p.

Cross, R. H., 1967. Tsunami surge forces. *Proceedings of the American Society of Civil Engineers,* 93 (WW) (November), 201–231.

Cumberbatch, E., 1960. The impact of a water wedge on a wall. *Journal of Fluid Mechanics,* 7 (March), 353–373.

Daily Alaska Empire, published in Juneau. March 3, 1964.

Dean, R. G., 1964. Long wave modification by linear transitions. *Proceedings of the American Society of Civil Engineers,* 90 (WW) (February), 1–29.

Donn, William L., 1964. Alaskan earthquake of 27 March 1964: Remote seiche stimulation. *Science,* 145 (July 17), 261–262.

Dressler, R. F., 1952. Hydraulic resistance effects upon the dambreak functions. *Journal of Research* (National Bureau of Standards), 49 (September), 217–225.

Eckel, Edwin B., 1967. Effects of the earthquake of March 27, 1964, on air and water transport, communications, and utilities systems in south-central Alaska. U.S. Geological Survey Professional Paper 545-B. Washington: Government Printing Office. 27 p. Also *in* The Great Alaska Earthquake of 1964: Geology. NAS Pub. 1601. Washington: National Academy of Sciences, 1971. p. 705–731.

Foley, Robert E., 1964. Crescent City: Tidal waves. *Shore and Beach* (Journal of the American Shore and Beach Preservation Association), 32 (April), 28.

Francis, J. R. D., 1958. Fluid mechanics. London: Edward Arnold, Ltd. 340 p.

Freeman, J. C., and B. Le Méhauté, 1964. Wave breakers on a beach and surges on a dry bed. *Proceedings of the American Society of Civil Engineers,* 90 (WW) (March), 187–216.

Fukui, Yoshiro, Makoto Nakamura, Hidehiko Shiraishi, and Yasuo Sasaki, 1963. Hydraulic study on tsunamis. *Coastal Engineering in Japan,* 6, 67–82.

Galvin, C. J., 1968. Finite shallow water waves of periodically recurring form. *Transactions, American Geophysical Union,* 49 (March), p. 206.

Gibson, A. H., 1925. Hydraulics and its applications. London: Constable & Company, Ltd. 801 p.

Goldsbrough, G. R., 1930. The tidal oscillations in an elliptic basin of variable depth. Proceedings of the Royal Society of London, Vol. 13(A), p. 157–167.

Grantz, Arthur, George Plafker, and Reuben Kachadoorian, 1964. Alaska's Good Friday earthquake, March 27, 1964: a preliminary geologic evaluation. U.S. Geological Survey Circular 491. Washington: U.S. Geological Survey. 35 p.

Gronewald, Gail J., and Walter W. Duncan, 1966. Study of erosion along Homer Spit and vicinity, Kachemak Bay, Alaska. Proceedings of the Specialty Conference (1965) on Coastal Engineering, Santa Barbara (Chapter 27). New York: American Society of Civil Engineers. p. 673–682.

Hall, J. V., and G. M. Watts, 1953. Laboratory investigation of the vertical rise of solitary waves on impermeable slopes. Beach Erosion Board Technical Memorandum No. 33. Washington: U.S. Army Corps of Engineers, March. 14 p.

Hansen, Wallace R., Edwin B. Eckel, William E. Schaem, Robert E. Lyle, Warren George, and Genie Chance, 1966. The Alaska earthquake, March 27, 1964: field investigations and reconstruction effort. U.S. Geological Survey Professional Paper 541. Washington: Government Printing Office. 111 p.

Harrison, J., and G. H. Keulegan, 1968. Probability of occurrence of tsunamis of various amplitudes at Crescent City (California) (unpublished manuscript). Vicksburg, Mississippi: U.S. Army Corps of Engineers, Waterways Experiment Station, August.

Hogan, D., W. W. Whipple, and C. Lundy, 1964. Tsunami of 27 and 28 March 1964, State of Washington coastline (unpublished file report). Seattle: U.S. Army Corps of Engineers.

Hom-ma, M., and K. Horikawa, 1961. Coast protection works and related problems in Japan. Proceedings of the Seventh Conference on Coastal Engineering, The Hague, Netherlands. August 1960. Berkeley, California: Council on Wave Research, Engineering Foundation. p. 904–930.

Honda, K., T. Terada, and D. Isitani, 1908. Secondary undulations of ocean tides. *Philosophical Magazine* (London), 15, 88.

Horikawa, Kiyoshi, 1961. Tsunami phenomena in the light of engineering viewpoint. A report on Chilean tsunami of May 24, 1960, as observed along the coast of Japan. Tokyo: Maruzen Co., Ltd., December. p. 136–150.

Iida, K., 1958. Magnitude and energy of the earthquakes accompanied by tsunami and tsunami energy. *Journal of Earth Sciences* (Nagoya University), 6 (December), 101–112.

Iida, K., 1968. The Niigata tsunami of June 16, 1964 *in* General Report on the Niigata Earthquake of 1964. H. Kawasumi, editor-in-chief. Tokyo: Electrical Engineering College Press. p. 97–127.

Isaacs, John D., 1946. Field report on the tsunami of April 1, 1946. IER Wave Research Project, May. Berkeley: University of California.

Kachadoorian, Reuben, 1965. Effects of the earthquake of March 27, 1964, at Whittier, Alaska. U.S. Geological Survey Professional Paper 542-B. Washington: Government Printing Office. 21 p. Also *in* The Great Alaska Earthquake of 1964: Geology. NAS Pub. 1601. Washington: National Academy of Sciences, 1971. p. 439–459.

Kachadoorian, Reuben, and George Plafker, 1967. Effects of the earthquake of March 27, 1964, on the communities of Kodiak and Nearby islands. U.S. Geological Survey Professional Paper 542-F. Washington: Government Printing Office. 41 p. Abstract *in* The Great Alaska Earthquake of 1964: Geology. NAS Pub. 1601. Washington: National Academy of Sciences, 1971. p. 539–540.

Kaplan, K., 1955. Generalized laboratory study of tsunami run-up. Beach Erosion Board Technical Memorandum No. 60. Washington: U.S. Army Corps of Engineers, January. 30 p.

Keulegan, Garbis H., 1949. Wave motion *in* Engineering Hydraulics (Chapter XI). H. Rouse, editor. New York: John Wiley & Sons, Inc. p. 711–768.

Kishi, T., 1963. Transformation, breaking and run-up of a long wave of finite height. Proceedings of the Eighth Conference on Coastal Engineering, Mexico City, Mexico, November 1962. Berkeley, California: Council on Wave Research, Engineering Foundation. p. 60–76.

Lamb, Horace, 1932. Hydrodynamics (6th edition). Cambridge: Cambridge University Press. p. 262.

Lantz, Dill, and Mildred Kirkpatrick, 1964. Seward quake: Good Friday 1964. Seward: Kirkpatrick Printing Co. 56 p.

Le Méhauté, Bernard, Robert C. Y. Koh, and Li-San Hwang, 1968. A synthesis on the wave run-up. *Proceedings of the American Society of Civil Engineers*, 94 (WW) (February), 77–92.

Lemke, Richard W., 1967. Effects of the earthquake of March 27, 1964, at Seward, Alaska. U.S. Geological Survey Professional Paper 542-E. Washington: Government Printing Office. 43 p. Also *in* The Great Alaska Earthquake of 1964: Geology. NAS

Pub. 1601. Washington: National Academy of Sciences. 1971. p. 395–437.

McCulloch, David S., 1966. Slide-induced waves, seiching, and ground fracturing caused by the earthquake of March 27, 1964, at Kenai Lake, Alaska. U.S. Geological Survey Professional Paper 543-A. Washington: Government Printing Office. 41 p. Also *in* The Great Alaska Earthqake of 1964: Hydrology. NAS Pub. 1603. Washington: National Academy of Sciences, 1968. p. 47–81.

McGarr, Arthur, 1965. Excitation of seiches in channels by seismic waves. *Journal of Geophysical Research,* 70 (February 15), 847–854. Also *in* The Great Alaska Earthquake of 1964: Hydrology. NAS Pub. 1603. Washington: National Academy of Sciences, 1968. p. 133–139.

McGarr, Arthur, and Robert C. Vorhis. 1968. Seismic seiches from the March 1964 Alaska earthquake. U.S. Geological Survey Professional Paper 544-E. Washington: Government Printing Office. 43 p. Also *in* The Great Alaska Earthquake of 1964: Hydrology. NAS Pub. 1603. Washington: National Academy of Sciences, 1968. p. 196–236.

MacNamara, F., 1964. Report on Valdez, Alaska (unpublished). Anchorage: U.S. Army Corps of Engineers, May.

Madsen, O. S., and C. C. Mei, 1969. The transformation of a solitary wave over an uneven bottom. *Journal of Fluid Mechanics,* 39 (4), p. 781–791.

Madsen, O. S., C. C. Mei, and R. P. Savage, 1970. The evolution of time periodic long waves of finite amplitude. *Journal of Fluid Mechanics,* 44 (1), p. 195–208.

Magoon, Orville T., 1962. The tsunami of May 1960 as it affected northern California. Paper presented at American Society of Civil Engineers, Hydraulics Division Conference, University of California, Davis, August, 1962.

Magoon, Orville T., 1966. Structural damage by tsunamis. Proceedings of the Specialty Conference (1965) on Coastal Engineering, Santa Barbara, California, October 11. New York: American Society of Civil Engineers. p. 35–68.

Marine Advisers, 1964. A broad-frequency-band wave study at Monterey Harbor, California. Report to U.S. Army Corps of Engineers, San Francisco. La Jolla, California: Marine Advisers, July. 19 p.

Matlock, H., L. C. Reese, and R. B. Matlock, 1962. Analysis of structural damage from the 1960 tsunami at Hilo, Hawaii. DASA Technical Report 1268. Washington: Defense Atomic Support Agency, Structural Mechanics Research Laboratory, March. 95 p.

Miche, R., 1951. Le pouvoir reflectuissant des ouvrages maritimes. Annales des Ponts et Chaussées, May-June. Paris: Ministère des Travaux Publics et des Transports.

Migliaccio, Ralph R., 1964. Earthquake of March 27, 1964. Report of District Geologist, Valdez, to Chief Geologist, College, April 10. Valdez: Office of the District Geologist. 6 p.

Milne-Thomson, L. M., 1960. Theoretical hydrodynamics. New York: MacMillan Company. 660 p.

Murty, T. S., and Lise Boilard, 1970. The tsunami in Alberni Inlet caused by the Alaska earthquake of March 1964 *in* Tsunamis in the Pacific Ocean, Proceedings of the International Symposium on Tsunamis and Tsunami Research, Honolulu, Hawaii, October 7-10, 1969. W. M. Adams, editor. Honolulu: East-West Center Press. p. 165–187.

Neumann, G., 1948. On resonance oscillations of bights and the mouth correction for seiches. *Deutsche Hydrographische Zeitschrift,* 1, 79–101.

Norton, Frank R. B., and J. Eugene Haas, 1970. The human response in selected communities *in* The Great Alaska Earthquake of 1964: Human Ecology. NAS Pub. 1607. Washington: National Academy of Sciences. p. 245–399.

Oceanographic Services, Inc., 1965. Water level changes produced on the Pacific coasts of the United States and Canada by the Alaskan tsunami of 1964. Report to the Office of Naval Research. Santa Barbara: Oceanographic Services, Inc. 14 p.

Pararas-Carayannis, George, 1965. Water waves, Part I *in* Source mechanism study of the Alaska earthquake and tsunami of 27 March 1964. Report HIG-65-17. Honolulu: University of Hawaii, Institute of Geophysics, December. p. 1–30.

Plafker, George, 1965. Tectonic deformation associated with the 1964 Alaska earthquake. *Science,* 148 (June 25), 1675–1687.

Plafker, George, and Reuben Kachadoorian, 1966. Geologic effects of the March 1964 earthquake and associated seismic sea waves on Kodiak and nearby islands, Alaska. U.S. Geological Survey Professional Paper 543-D. Washington: Government Printing Office. 46 p. Also *in* The Great Alaska Earthquake of 1964: Geology. NAS Pub. 1601. Washington: National Academy of Sciences, 1971. p. 177–226.

Plafker, George, and L. R. Mayo. 1965. Tectonic deformation, subaqueous slides and destructive waves associated with the Alaskan March 17, 1964, earthquake: An interim geologic evaluation. U.S. Geological Survey Open-File Report. Menlo Park, California: U.S. Geological Survey. 34 p.

Rayleigh, J. W. S., 1945. The theory of sound. New York: Dover Publications.

Reese, L. C., and H. Matlock, 1967. Structural damage from tsunami at Hilo, Hawaii. Conference reprint 552, ASCE National Meeting, Water Resources Engineering, October. New York: American Society of Civil Engineers. 45 p.

Reimnitz, Erk, and Neil F. Marshall, 1965. Effects of the Alaska earthquake and tsunami on recent deltaic sediments. *Journal of Geophysical Research,* 70 (May 15), 2363–2376. Also *in* The Great Alaska Earthquake of 1964: Geology. NAS Pub. 1601. Washington: National Academy of Sciences, 1971. p. 265–278.

Roberts, James A., 1964. The reshaping of South Beach, Crescent City, California, after the tsunami of 27–28 March 1964. Meteorology Research, Inc. Paper 202, delivered at the Beach Erosion Control Conference, 2 December 1964. Altadena, California: Meteorology Research, Inc. 18 p.

Roberts, James A., and Chen-Wu Chien, 1965. The effects of bottom topography on the refraction of the tsunami of 27–28 March 1964: the Crescent City case *in* Ocean Science and Ocean Engineering 1965 (Volume 2): Transactions of the Joint Conference and Exhibit [Marine Technology Society and American Society of Limnology and Oceanography], June 14–17, 1965, Washington, D.C. Washington: Marine Technology Society. p. 707–716.

Rouse, H., 1938 (1961 edition). Fluid mechanics for hydraulic engineers. New York: Dover Publications, Inc. 422 p.

Saville, Jr., Thorndike, 1958. Wave run-up on composite slopes. Proceedings of the Sixth Conference on Coastal Engineering, Gainesville, Florida, December 1957. Berkeley, California: Council on Wave Research, Engineering Foundation. p. 691–699.

Schoklitsch, A., 1917. Uber dambruchwellen. Sitzungsberichte der k. Akademie der Wissenschaften, Abt. IIa, Vol. 126. Vienna: Akademie der Wissenschaften. p. 1489.

Shannon & Wilson, Inc., 1964. Report on subsurface investigation for city of Seward, Alaska, and vicinity, to U.S. Army Engineer District, Anchorage, Alaska. Seattle: Shannon & Wilson, Inc. 77 p.

Sievers C., Hellmuth A., Guillermo Villegas C., and Guillermo Barros, 1963. The seismic sea wave of 22 May 1960 along the Chilean coast. *Bulletin of the Seismological Society of America,* 53 (December), 1125–1190.

Solibakke, H., 1964. Earthquake, seismic wave and fire–Seward, Alaska. Letter report to Mr. R. B. Robertson, General Manager, California Shipping Co., San Francisco, California, April 1.

Spaeth, M. G., and S. C. Berkman, 1965. The tsunami of March 28, 1964, as recorded at tide stations. U.S. Coast and Geodetic Survey Publication. Rockville, Maryland: U.S. Coast and Geodetic Survey. 59 p.

Spaeth, Mark G., and Saul C. Berkman, 1967. The tsunami of March 28, 1964, as recorded at tide stations. Environmental Science Services Administration Technical Report C&GS 33. Washington: Government Printing Office. 86 p. Also *in* The Great Alaska Earthquake of 1964: Oceanography and Coastal Engineering. NAS Pub. 1605. Washington: National Academy of Sciences, 1972.

Stanley, Albert A., 1964. Crescent City: Sea wave. *Shore and Beach* (Journal of the American Shore and Beach Preservation Association), 32 (April), 25–27.

Stoker, J. J., 1957. Water waves. New York: Interscience Publishers, Inc. 567 p.

Takahasi, Ryutaro, and Tokutaro Hatori, 1961. A summary report on the Chilean tsunami of May, 1960, as observed along the coast of Japan. Report of the Committee for Field Investigation of the Chilean Tsunami of 1960 (December). Tokyo: Maruzen Co., Ltd. p. 1–34.

Thornton, D. L., 1946. Seismic sea waves. *Engineering* (London), 161 (May), 484–485.

Tudor, W. J., 1964. Tsunami damage at Kodiak, Alaska, and Crescent City, California, from Alaskan earthquake of 27 March 1964. U.S. Naval Civil Engineering Laboratory Technical Note N-622. Port Hueneme [California]: U.S. Naval Engineering Laboratory, November. 131 p.

U.S. Coast and Geodetic Survey, 1964a. Preliminary report–Prince William Sound, Alaskan earthquakes March–April 1964 (second printing). Seismology Division Report. Washington: U.S. Coast and Geodetic Survey. 101 p.

U.S. Coast and Geodetic Survey, 1964b. Preliminary report: tidal datum plane changes, Prince William Sound, Alaskan earthquake March–April 1964. Office of Oceanography Report. Rockville [Maryland]: U.S. Coast and Geodetic Survey. 5 p.

U.S. Coast and Geodetic Survey, 1965. Assistance and recovery, Alaska/1964: a report covering the activities of the U.S. Coast and Geodetic Survey in conjunction with the Prince William Sound, Alaska, earthquake of 1964 for the period March 27–December 31, 1964. Washington: U.S. Department of Commerce. 45 p.

Van Dorn, William G., 1965. Tsunamis. *Advances in Hydroscience,* 2 (Annual), 1–47.

Van Dorn, William G., 1966. Theoretical and experimental study of wave enhancement and runup on uniformly sloping impermeable beaches. SIO Report No. 66-11. La Jolla: University of California, Scripps Institution of Oceanography. 101 p.

Van Dorn, William G., and Doak C. Cox, 1972. Oceanic character, propagation, and coastal modification of the major tsunami *in* The Great Alaska Earthquake of 1964: Oceanography and Coastal Engineering. NAS Pub. 1605. Washington: National Academy of Sciences. 1972.

von Huene, Roland, George G. Shor, Jr., and Erk Reimnitz, 1967. Geological interpretation of seismic profiles in Prince William Sound, Alaska. *Geological Society of America Bulletin,* 78 (February), 259–268.

Waller, Roger M., 1966. Effects of the earthquake of March 27,

1964, in the Homer area, Alaska (*with a section on* Beach changes on Homer Spit, by Kirk W. Stanley). U.S. Geological Survey Professional Paper 542-D. Washington: Government Printing Office. 28 p. Also *in* The Great Alaska Earthquake of 1964: Geology. NAS Pub. 1601. Washington: National Academy of Sciences, 1971. p. 461–488.

Weller, Jack M., 1972. Human response to tsunami warnings *in* The Great Alaska Earthquake of 1964: Oceanography and Coastal Engineering. NAS Pub. 1605. Washington: National Academy of Sciences.

White, W. R. H., 1966. The Alaska earthquake—its effect in Canada. *Canadian Geographical Journal,* 72 (June), 210–219.

Whitham, G. B., 1955. The effects of hydraulic resistance on the dam-break problem. Proceedings of the Royal Society of London, Vol. 227(A).

Wiegel, Robert L., 1964. Oceanographical engineering, Englewood Cliffs, New Jersey: Prentice-Hall, Inc. 532 p.

Wiegel, Robert L., 1965. Protection of Crescent City, California, from tsunami waves. Berkeley: The Redevelopment Agency of the City of Crescent City, March 5. 114 p.

Wiegel, Robert L., 1970. Tsunamis (Chapter 11) *in* Earthquake Engineering. Englewood Cliffs, New Jersey: Prentice-Hall, Inc. p. 253–306.

Wigen, S. O., and W. R. H. White, 1964. Tsunami of March 27–29, 1964, west coast of Canada. Technical Report. Victoria, British Columbia: Canada Department of Mines and Technical Surveys, August. 12 p.

Wilson, Basil W., 1964. Generation and dispersion characteristics of tsunamis *in* Studies on oceanography. Tokyo: University of Tokyo Press. p. 413–444. (See also University of Washington Press, Seattle, Washington, 1965.)

Wilson, Basil W., 1966. Seiche *in* Encyclopedia of Oceanography. New York: Reinhold Publishing Co.

Wilson, Basil W., 1969a. Earthquake occurrence and effects in ocean areas. Technical Report CR 69-027 to U.S. Naval Civil Engineering Laboratory. Port Hueneme: U.S. Naval Civil Engineering Laboratory, February. 141 p.

Wilson, Basil W., 1969b. Tsunami responses of San Pedro Bay and Shelf, California. Proceedings of the American Society of Civil Engineers Conference on Civil Engineering in the Oceans II, Miami Beach, Florida, December 1969. New York: American Society of Civil Engineers. p. 1099–1133.

Wilson, Basil W., J. A. Hendrickson, and R. E. Kilmer, 1965. Feasibility study for surge-action model of Monterey Harbor, California. Waterways Experiment Station Contract Report No. 2-136. Vicksburg: U.S. Army Corps of Engineers, October. 166 p.

Wilson, Basil W., Y. Jen, J. A. Hendrickson, and H. Soot, 1968. Wave and surge action study for Los Angeles–Long Beach Harbors (unpublished report to the U.S. Army Corps of Engineers, Los Angeles District). San Marino: Science Engineering Associates.

Wilson, Basil W., B. Le Méhauté, and J. C. Freeman, 1964. Propagation and runup of tsunami waves. NES Technical Report No. SN-166. Pasadena: National Engineering Science Company, March.

Wilson, Basil W., and Alf Tørum, 1968. The tsunami of the Alaskan earthquake, 1964: Engineering evaluation. Coastal Engineering Research Center Technical Memorandum No. 25. Washington: U.S. Army Corps of Engineers, May. 444 p.

Wilson, Basil W., and Alf Tørum, 1972. Runup heights of the major tsunami on North American coasts *in* The Great Alaska Earthquake of 1964: Oceanography and Coastal Engineering. NAS Pub. 1605. Washington: National Academy of Sciences.

Wilson, Basil W., L. Webb, and J. A. Hendrickson, 1962. The nature of tsunamis: their generation and dispersion in water of finite depth. NES Technical Report No. SN 37-2. Pasadena: National Engineering Science Company, August. 150 p.

Worthington, Skilling, Helle, and Jackson, 1964. Report on seismic damage to the Naval Station at Kodiak, Alaska. Report to Bureau of Yards and Docks, U.S. Navy, April. Seattle: Worthington, Skilling, Helle, and Jackson.

Zabusky, N. J., and M. D. Kruskal, 1965. Interactions of "Solitons" in a collisionless plasma and the recurrence of initial states. Physical Review Letters, 15 (6), August. p. 240–243.

Appendixes

Annotated
Bibliography

Adams, William Mansfield. An index to tsunami literature to 1966. Data Report No. 8, HIG 67-21. [Honolulu] : University of Hawaii, Institute of Geophysics, November 1967. 71 p.
Indexes articles on tsunamis from a variety of books, journals, reports, and magazines.

Alaska Department of Fish and Game. Post-earthquake fisheries evaluation. An Interim Report on the March, 1964 Earthquake Effects on Alaska's Fishery Resources. Juneau: Alaska Department of Fish and Game, 1965. 72 p.
Describes deleterious ecological changes resulting from the tsunamis and land-level changes associated with the earthquake.

Alaska Disaster Office. Seismic sea wave warning: February 3, 1965 (unpublished report). Anchorage: Alaska Disaster Office [1965]. 5 p. (Copy on file, Library, National Academy of Sciences–National Academy of Engineering, Washington, D.C.)
Summarizes improvements in tsunami warnings given at the time of the earthquake at Shemya, less than a year after the great Alaska earthquake.

Alaska fishing industry loss and damage from earthquake and tidal waves estimate April 10, 1964. Chart 45155. 1 p. (Copy on file, Library, National Academy of Sciences–National Academy of Engineering, Washington, D.C.)
Tabulates estimated losses (from the earthquake and tsunamis) in king crab, salmon, and shrimp fisheries in terms of value of gear, plants, and vessels lost and damaged at Kodiak, Cook Inlet, Seward, and Prince William Sound.

Anderson, William. Crescent City revisited: A comparison of public warning procedures used in 1964 and 1965 emergencies. The Disaster Research Center Research Note 11. Columbus: The Ohio State University, Disaster Research Center, 1965. 14 p.
Reports on the response of public officials in Crescent City to the tsunami threat after the Alaska earthquake on February 3, 1965; compares the 1965 public warning procedures with those used for the March 1964 tsunami.

Anderson, William A. Tsunami warning in Crescent City, California, and Hilo, Hawaii *in* The Great Alaska Earthquake of 1964: Human Ecology. NAS Pub. 1607. Washington: National Academy of Sciences, 1970. p. 116-124. (See also Disaster Research Center Working Paper 11. Columbus: The Ohio State University, Disaster Research Center, March 1967. 27 p.)
Suggests that tsunami warning procedure is more routine in Hilo than in Crescent City because public officials in Hilo have improved warning and evacuation procedures as a result of previous tsunami experience.

Arens, C. E. Installation and inspection of Alaska tide stations. Memorandum to Assistant Director for Oceanography, USC&GS. Rockville, Maryland: U.S. Coast and Geodetic Survey, 1964. 9 p. (Copy on file, Library, National Academy of Sciences–National Academy of Engineering, Washington, D.C.)
Gives account of mission that established three new control tide stations in Prince William Sound and vicinity and that reactivated and inspected other stations.

Armstrong, Karl. Kodiak tsunami: First 29 days [daily emergency bulletins, March 28 to April 25, 1964, issued by City Hall]. Kodiak, Alaska: City of Kodiak [1964]. 79 p.
Provides information contained in daily bulletins that were distributed to the inhabitants of Kodiak during the emergency when the newspaper plant had been lost in the tsunami; gives story of disaster and recovery.

Barrett, Peter, J. Effects of the 1964 Alaskan earthquake on some shallow-water sediments in Prince William Sound, southeast Alaska. *Journal of Sedimentary Petrology,* 36 (December 1966), 992-1006. Also *in* The Great Alaska Earthquake of 1964: Geology. NAS Pub. 1601. Washington: National Academy of Sciences, 1971. p. 250-264.
Examines the effects of waves resulting from the 1964 earthquake and finds that no changes in shallow areas in Prince William Sound could be attributed to the large waves associated with the earthquake.

Berg, Eduard. Triggering of the Alaskan earthquake of March 28, 1964, and major aftershocks by low ocean tide loads. *Nature,* 210 (May 28, 1966), 893-896. Also *in* The Great Alaska Earthquake of 1964: Seismology and Geodesy. NAS Pub. 1602. Washington: National Academy of Sciences, 1972.

States that the unloading of the crust in the Continental Shelf area of the Gulf of Alaska by the large ocean tides may be considered the triggering mechanism for the 1964 earthquake and for major aftershocks.

Berg, Eduard, Doak C. Cox, Augustine S. Furumoto, Kinjiro Kajiura, Hirosi Kawasumi, and Etsuzo Shima. The source of the major tsunami *in* Field survey of the tsunamis of 28 March 1964 in Alaska, and conclusions as to the origin of the major tsunami. Report HIG-70-2. Honolulu: University of Hawaii, Institute of Geophysics, 1971. p. 38–49. Also *in* The Great Alaska Earthquake of 1964: Oceanography and Coastal Engineering. NAS Pub. 1605. Washington: National Academy of Sciences, 1972. 57 p.
Concludes that the major tsunami associated with the 1964 earthquake was caused by tectonic uplift of the Continental Shelf.

Berg, E[duard], D. C. Cox, A. Furumoto, K. Kajiura, H. Kawasumi, and E. Shima. Tsunami of 27 March 1964 in Alaska (Abstract) *in* Abstracts for 1964: GSA [Geological Society of America] Special Papers 82. New York: Geological Society of America, Inc., 1965. p. 355.
Reports on the generation of (1) local tsunamis resulting from slumping of deltas and (2) a general tsunami resulting from widespread tectonic displacements of the sea floor.

Bolt, Bruce A. Seismic air waves from the great 1964 Alaskan earthquake. *Nature,* 202 (June 13, 1964), 1095–1096.
Correlates tsunami arrival off San Francisco about 2.5 hours after the seismic air wave. The first surge on the tide gage at San Francisco came 5 hours and 9 minutes after the earthquake.

Braddock, R. D. On tsunami propagation. *Journal of Geophysical Research,* 74 (April 15, 1969), 1952–1957.
Studies the propagation of the 1964 Alaska tsunami by using an iterative algorithm; calculations permit the description of its propagation and the plotting of the ray paths to locations along the American coast.

Braddock, R. D. Tsunami propagation over large distances *in* Tsunamis in the Pacific Ocean. Proceedings of the International Symposium on Tsunamis and Tsunami Research, Honolulu, Hawaii, October 7–10, 1969. W. M. Adams, editor. Honolulu: East-West Center Press, 1970. p. 285–303.
Describes the "grid-refinement" technique by which ray paths of the 1964 Alaska tsunami have been calculated.

Branch, D. D. Effect at Rabaul of seismic sea waves generated by the Great Alaskan earthquake of 28 March 1964 *in* Short papers from the Vulcanological Observatory, Rabaul, New Britain. Australia Bureau of Mineral Resources, Geology and Geophysics Report No. 107, 1967. p. 17–19.
States that the average speed of the tsunami arriving at Rabaul from the 1964 Alaska earthquake was 480 mi per hour and that the resulting oscillations of sea level there lasted 4 days.

Brown, Delmer L. Tsunamic activity accompanying the Alaskan earthquake of 27 March 1964. Technical Report, U.S. Army Engineer District, Alaska. Anchorage: U.S. Army Corps of Engineers, April 23, 1964. 31 p.
Finds that tsunami activity was caused by movement along a fault zone extending from a point near Valdez Arm through southwestern Prince William Sound to Kodiak Island during the great Alaska earthquake.

Bruder, Wallace A. Earthquake changes Alaska shoreline (Abstract) *in* Science in Alaska, 1964: Proceedings Fifteenth Alaskan Science Conference, College, Alaska, August 31 to September 4, 1964. George Dahlgren, editor. College: Alaska Division American Association for the Advancement of Science, March 15, 1965. p. 284. [Abstract same as for: Alaska shoreline changes resulting from earthquake (Abstract) *in* Abstracts for 1964: GSA (Geographical Society of America) Special Papers 82. New York: Geological Society of America, Inc., 1965. p. 356.]
Relates that the tsunami generated by the 1964 earthquake struck with destructive force all along the southern coast of Alaska between Kodiak and Cordova. Submarine landslides resulted in alongshore and underwater changes.

Bureau of Land Management. Four-point program aims to rebuild fishing industry. *Our Public Lands,* 14 (July 1964), 16–17.
Contains plans for (1) Department of Interior loans to fishermen for boat repairs, (2) use of loan funds to charter fishing vessels, (3) Small Business Administration loans for repair of processing plants, and (4) subsidy of new vessel construction.

Case, J. E., D. F. Barnes, George Plafker, and S. L. Robbins. Gravity survey and regional geology of the Prince William Sound epicentral region, Alaska. U.S. Geological Survey Professional Paper 543-C. Washington: Government Printing Office, 1966. 12 p. Also *in* The Great Alaska Earthquake of 1964: Geology. NAS Pub. 1601. Washington: National Academy of Sciences, 1971. p. 123–134.
Includes simple Bouguer anomaly map of the Prince William Sound region, with measurements made at 500 gravity stations located on beaches or rocks along the shoreline.

Century Film Productions. The Alaska earthquake [Account of Captain Merrill Stewart, Captain of *SS Chena,* of that ship's ordeal at Valdez pier]. Seattle: Century Film Productions, 1964. (Copy of one-page film list on file, Library, National Academy of Sciences–National Academy of Engineering, Washington, D.C.)
Relates the experiences of the Liberty ship *Chena* at the Valdez dock (with 8-mm pictures taken from the deck of the ship); gives captain's account of the tsunami.

Century Film Productions. Alaska earthquake. 100-foot, 16-mm black and white film of Alaska damage [no sound]. Seattle: Century Film Productions [1964]. (Copy of one-page film list on file, Library, National Academy of Sciences–National Academy of Engineering, Washington, D.C.)
Describes footage of film made at scene of 1964 Alaska earthquake, including views of Anchorage, Seward, Kodiak, and Valdez; features tsunami action shot from the deck of the *Chena.*

Chance, Genie. Chronology of physical events of the Alaskan earthquake (unpublished eyewitness account). Anchorage: University of Alaska, 1966. 176 p.
Recounts story of the 1964 earthquake through interviews with eyewitnesses of tsunami action.

Cloud, William K., and Nina H. Scott. Distribution of intensity, Prince William Sound earthquake of 1964 *in* Volume II-B,C: The

Prince William Sound, Alaska, earthquake of 1964 and after-shocks. Environmental Science Services Administration, U.S. Coast and Geodetic Survey. Washington: Government Printing Office, 1969. p. 5–48. Also *in* The Great Alaska Earthquake of 1964: Seismology and Geodesy. NAS Pub. 1602. Washington: National Academy of Sciences, 1972.
Briefly describes tsunami and seiche effects inside and outside of Alaska.

Committee on the Alaska Earthquake. Toward reduction of losses from earthquakes: Conclusions from the great Alaska earthquake of 1964. Washington: National Academy of Sciences, 1969. 34 p.
Summarizes comprehensive study on the 1964 earthquake, gives Committee and panel recommendations, and advocates loss-reduction programs designed not only for earthquakes but also for other environmental hazards.

Cook, Irvin P. 1964 earthquake damages to The Alaska Railroad. *AREA* [American Railway Engineering Association] *Bulletin,* 593 (June–July 1965), 750–755.
Gives brief account of the unusual wave effects both in Alaska waters and elsewhere, the damage to rail facilities and rolling stock, and the unprecedented subsidence of 40 mi of roadbed from 4 to 10 ft in coastal areas.

Corwin, Gilbert, and Edward Bradley. Geological Survey's marine program. *Undersea Technology,* 6 (September 1965), 35–37.
Reports on U.S. Geological Survey's investigation of submarine slides that caused large local waves within Prince William Sound at the time of the 1964 Alaska earthquake.

Coulter, Henry W., and Ralph R. Migliaccio. Effects of the earth-quake of March 27, 1964, at Valdez, Alaska. U.S. Geological Survey Professional Paper 542-C. Washington: Government Printing Office, 1966. 36 p. Also *in* The Great Alaska Earth-quake of 1964: Geology. NAS Pub. 1601. Washington: National Academy of Sciences, 1971. p. 359–394.
Describes massive submarine slide at Valdez, involving approximately 98 million cubic yards of material, and slide-generated waves that destroyed harbor facilities and damaged the business district.

Cox, Doak C. General Introduction *in* The Great Alaska Earthquake of 1964: Oceanography and Coastal Engineering. NAS Pub. 1605. Washington: National Academy of Sciences, 1972.
Introduces the Oceanography section with a brief history of Panel on Oceanography, Committee on the Alaska Earthquake, and notes important effects described in articles presented, including sea-quakes and seismic seiches, tsunami sources and warnings, and geophysical aspects.

Cox, Doak C. Introduction: Other marine aspects *in* The Great Alaska Earthquake of 1964: Oceanography and Coastal Engi-neering. NAS Pub. 1605. Washington: National Academy of Sciences, 1972.
Summarizes the discussion of marine biological effects, physical oceanographic changes, chemical oceanographic changes, and effects on boats and navigation.

Cox, Doak C. Introduction: Tsunamis *in* The Great Alaska Earth-quake of 1964: Oceanography and Coastal Engineering. NAS Pub. 1605. Washington: National Academy of Sciences, 1972.
Describes catastrophic effects of waves and investigations of

tsunamis in Alaska, reports on local tsunamis and the major tsu-nami, and mentions papers included in this section.

Cox, Doak C. Marine effects and hazards of earthquakes *in* The Great Alaska Earthquake of 1964: Oceanography and Coastal Engineering. NAS Pub. 1605. Washington: National Academy of Sciences, 1972.
Presents general conclusions regarding the nature of the 1964 Alaska earthquake and summarizes observations of marine manifestations of the earthquake and their significance for other earthquakes of similar magnitude.

Cox, Doak C. Performance of the Seismic Sea Wave Warning System, 1948–1967. Report HIG-68-2. Honolulu: University of Hawaii, Institute of Geophysics, March 25, 1968. 79 p.
Recounts objectives of the Seismic Sea Wave Warning System (now called the Tsunami Warning System), lists numbers and kinds of warnings issued (including those at the time of the great Alaska earthquake), and points out the improvements made and the need for implementation of a policy of regional evaluation of tsunami hazard.

Cox, Doak C. Review of the tsunamis *in* The Great Alaska Earth-quake of 1964: Oceanography and Coastal Engineering. NAS Pub. 1605. Washington: National Academy of Sciences, 1972.
Provides an overall picture of the wave action associated with the 1964 earthquake and describes the inundation of the shores of many fiords in Prince William Sound and the Gulf of Alaska.

Cox, Doak C., Ethel U. McAfee, and Kathleen Morris. Annotated bibliography on the 1964 Alaska tsunami (unpublished). Honolulu: University of Hawaii, Institute of Geophysics, 1965. 24 p. (Copy on file, Library, National Academy of Sciences–National Academy of Engineering, Washington, D.C.)
Gives notes for bibliography of the tsunami from the great Alaska earthquake; compiled for the Inter-panel Tsunami Conference of the Committee on the Alaska Earthquake.

Cox, Doak C., and George Pararas-Carayannis. Catalog of tsunamis in Alaska. World Data Center A: Tsunami. Washington: Environ-mental Science Services Administration, U.S. Coast and Geodetic Survey, May 1969. 39 p.
Provides background history of Alaska, evaluation of the tsunami history there, and a catalog of Alaska tsunami data from 1788 through 1966 (including information on the 1964 tsunami).

Cox, Doak C., and Harris B. Stewart, Jr. Technical evaluation of the Seismic Sea Wave Warning System *in* The Great Alaska Earthquake of 1964: Oceanography and Coastal Engineering. NAS Pub. 1605. Washington: National Academy of Sciences, 1972.
Discusses improvement of system of tsunami warning and establish-ment of a special regional warning system for Alaska since the 1964 earthquake.

Cox, Doak C., and Roland von Huene. Introduction: Seismic effects *in* The Great Alaska Earthquake of 1964: Oceanography and Coastal Engineering. NAS Pub. 1605. Washington: National Academy of Sciences, 1972.
Introduces section on oceanographic manifestations that are closely related to the earthquake vibrations.

Cox, Doak C., and K. Yoshida. U.S.–Japan cooperative tsunami re-

search. Report of an Informal Conference, Tokyo, Japan, 30 March 1964. 2 p. (Copy on file, Library, National Academy of Sciences–National Academy of Engineering, Washington, D.C.)
Mentions work on runup of tsunamis, a plan for annual bibliographies, and the need for a joint survey of runup characteristics of the 1964 Alaska tsunami.

Creisler, Joe. Tidal wave creates sanitation problems. *Public Works,* 95 (December 1964), 68–70, 138.
Describes three phases of cleanup job after the 1964 tsunami at Crescent City: securing the area and posting quarantine signs, cleanup by local agencies, and final debris removal by U.S. Army Corps of Engineers–all accomplished within a period of 6 weeks.

Crimmin, Eileen. One year later–What happened in Alaska. *Science Digest,* 57 (March 1965), 42–46.
Contains year-later record of observers' estimates of waves 20–100 ft high and arriving 5–15 minutes after tremors ceased, and of water action at Seward. Gives track of Coast and Geodetic Survey ships *Surveyor* and *Hodgson* which took soundings, cores, and deep-sea photographs.

Deisher, J. B. Comments on Seward earthquake and tidal wave. *Alaska Medicine,* 6 (June 1964), 49–52.
Outlines the previously planned preparations to ward off disaster in the Seward area, the actual functioning of the plan when the 1964 earthquake occurred, and the medical problems resulting from the tsunami.

Digree, Sig J. Kodiak seismic wave earthquake pictorial. Kodiak: Island Publishing Company [1964]. 32 p.
Presents pictoral evidence of tsunami damage at Kodiak after the great Alaska earthquake.

Donn, William L. Alaskan earthquake of 27 March 1964: Remote seiche stimulation. *Science,* 145 (July 17, 1964), 261–262.
Describes waves up to 6 ft in height that were caused by seismic surface waves in channels on coasts of Louisiana and Texas.

Eckel, Edwin B. Effects of the earthquake of March 27, 1964, on air and water transport, communications, and utilities systems in south-central Alaska. U.S. Geological Survey Professional Paper 545-B. Washington: Government Printing Office, 1967. 27 p. Also *in* The Great Alaska Earthquake of 1964: Geology. NAS Pub. 1601. Washington: National Academy of Sciences, 1971. p. 705–731.
Discusses destruction of waterfront facilities and vessels by shoreline slides and tsunamis

Eckel, Edwin B. The Alaska earthquake, March 27, 1964: Lessons and conclusions. U.S. Geological Survey Professional Paper 546. Washington: Government Printing Office, 1970. 47 p. Also *in* The Great Alaska Earthquake of 1964: Geology. NAS Pub. 1601. Washington: National Academy of Sciences, 1971. p. 747–792.
Summarizes nature and effects of crustal deformation, submarine slides, and tsunamis.

Environmental Science Services Administration. ESSA Symposium on Earthquake Prediction, Rockville, Maryland, February 7, 8, 9, 1966. Washington: Government Printing Office, 1966. 167 p.
Contains articles on the use of historical tsunami wave-height data in forecasting runup.

Federal Reconstruction and Development Planning Commission for Alaska. Response to disaster: Alaskan earthquake–March 27, 1964. Federal Reconstruction and Development Planning Commission Report. Washington: Government Printing Office, 1964. 84 p.
Gives report of the Scientific and Engineering Task Force which provided criteria for coastal engineering efforts and which proposed the establishment of a research center at Honolulu to solve problems associated with tsunami phenomena.

Fisher, Walter E., and Douglas H. Merkle. The great Alaska earthquake (2 vols.). Air Force Weapons Laboratory Technical Report AFWL-TR-65-92. Kirtland Air Force Base [New Mexico]: Air Force Systems Command, Research and Technology Division, 1965. 100 p. (vol. I); 312 p. (vol. II).
Contains considerable coastal engineering information on damage from 1964 earthquake. Stresses damage by tsunami outside the Anchorage area.

Foley, Robert E. Crescent City: tidal waves. *Shore and Beach* (Journal of the American Shore and Beach Preservation Association), 32 (April 1964), 28.
Depicts tsunami damage at Crescent City from waves and water 8 to 10 ft deep on city streets in the affected areas.

Foster, Helen L., and Thor N. V. Karlstrom. Ground breakage and associated effects in the Cook Inlet area, Alaska, resulting from the March 27, 1964, earthquake. U.S. Geological Survey Professional Paper 543-F. Washington: Government Printing Office, 1967. 28 p. Abstract *in* The Great Alaska Earthquake of 1964: Geology. NAS Pub. 1601. Washington: National Academy of Sciences, 1971. p. 280.
Describes coastal changes resulting from crustal deformation.

Furumoto, Augustine S. Analysis of Rayleigh wave, Part II *in* Source mechanism study of the Alaska earthquake and tsunami of 27 March 1964. Report HIG-65-17. Honolulu: University of Hawaii, Institute of Geophysics, 1965. p. 31–42. Also see *Pacific Science,* 21 (July 1967), 311–316. Also *in* The Great Alaska Earthquake of 1964: Seismology and Geodesy. NAS Pub. 1602. Washington: National Academy of Sciences, 1972.
Investigates the source mechanism by analyzing the Rayleigh wave recorded at Kipapa Station, Hawaii.

Furumoto, Augustine S. Field survey of the earthquake and tsunami of March 27, 1964 in Alaska. Hawaiian Academy of Sciences Proceedings, 39th Year. Honolulu: Hawaiian Academy of Sciences, 1964. p. 23.
Gives brief description of tsunami and its origin.

Grantz, Arthur, George Plafker, and Reuben Kachadoorian. Alaska's Good Friday earthquake, March 27, 1964: A preliminary geologic evaluation. U.S. Geological Survey Circular 491. Washington: U.S. Geological Survey, 1964. 35 p.
Gives 1964 earthquake effects on (1) submarine landslides in fiord deltas, (2) tsunamis, (3) destructive waves of unknown origin, and (4) sea life.

Griffin, Wallace, and others. Crescent City's dark disaster: Tsunami; March 28, 1964. Crescent City, California: Crescent City American [1964]. 64 p.
Presents pictorially the havoc resulting in Crescent City from the tsunami generated by the great Alaska earthquake.

Gronewald, Gail J., and Walter W. Duncan. Study of erosion along Homer Spit and vicinity, Kachemak Bay, Alaska. Proceedings of the Specialty Conference (1965) on Coastal Engineering, Santa Barbara (Chapter 27). New York: American Society of Civil Engineers, 1966. p. 673–682.
Contains information on the rapid acceleration of the erosion processes which was due to the subsidence of Homer Spit during the 1964 earthquake, and discusses effectiveness of emergency measures to prevent wave and high-water damage to structures on the Spit.

Hanna, G Dallas. Biological effects *in* The Great Alaska Earthquake of 1964: Oceanography and Coastal Engineering. NAS Pub. 1605. Washington: National Academy of Sciences, 1972.
Finds that, because large areas of former sea bottom were uplifted and exposed during the 1964 earthquake, it will probably take a century or more for the new forest to become completely merged with that of the preearthquake area.

Hanna, G Dallas. Biological effects of an earthquake. *Pacific Discovery,* 17 (November–December 1964), 24–26. Also *in* The Great Alaska Earthquake of 1964: Biology. NAS Pub. 1604. Washington: National Academy of Sciences, 1971. p. 15–34.
Studies the effects on animals and plants of the newly exposed littoral zone and below.

Hanson, Wallace R., Edwin B. Eckel, William E. Schaem, Robert E. Lyle, Warren George, and Genie Chance. The Alaska earthquake, March 27, 1964; field investigations and reconstruction effort. U.S. Geological Survey Professional Paper 541. Washington: Government Printing Office, 1966. 111 p.
Discusses U.S. Geological Survey investigations and the work of the Scientific and Engineering Task Force and reconstruction engineers; summarizes coastal effects of the earthquake.

Harkrider, David G., and Ralph A. Alewine. The excitation of tsunamis and associated atmospheric pressure disturbances (Abstract). *EOS Transactions, American Geophysical Union,* 51 (April 1970), 362.
Approximates the tectonic displacement and source motion of the great Alaska earthquake and calculates the theoretical pressure and water displacements, as a comparison to the actual water wave and atmospheric-pressure disturbance associated with the major tsunami.

Hatori, Tokutaro. On the Alaska tsunami of March 28, 1964, as observed along the coast of Japan. *Bulletin of the Earthquake Research Institute,* University of Tokyo, 43 (June 1965), 399–408.
Investigates features of the 1964 tsunami on the basis of records taken at Miyagi–Enoshima Island off Hokkaido and estimates the decay coefficient of the waves to be approximately 0.010 per hour.

Hicks, Steacy D. Changes in tidal characteristics and tidal datum planes *in* The Great Alaska Earthquake of 1964: Oceanography and Coastal Engineering. NAS Pub. 1605. Washington: National Academy of Sciences, 1972.
Conducts a redetermination of the harmonic constants because of major land movement resulting from the 1964 Alaska earthquake and shows that the changes were small.

Hicks, Steacy D. Effects on aids to navigation (unpublished manuscript). Rockville, Maryland: Environmental Science Services Administration, 1967. 3 p. (Copy on file, Library, National Academy of Sciences–National Academy of Engineering, Washington, D.C.)
Details the destructive effects of the 1964 tsunami on aids to navigation; states that the maximum damage occurred at the Sitkinak Station and that the longest inoperative period for major aids to navigation was 3 days.

Housner, George W. General Introduction: Coastal Engineering *in* The Great Alaska Earthquake of 1964: Oceanography and Coastal Engineering. NAS Pub. 1605. Washington: National Academy of Sciences, 1972.
Presents a description of the two papers in the coastal engineering portion of the volume and states that they provide (for engineering purposes) information on damaging tsunamis generated by the Alaska earthquake.

Hwang, Li-San, H. Lee Butler, and David Divoky. Rat Islands tsunami model: generation and open-sea characteristics. Tetra Tech Report TC-239. Las Vegas: U.S. Atomic Energy Commission, September 1971, 74 p.
Recalculates the 1964 Alaska tsunami wave motion by the methods of Hwang and others (1970), and validates the results by comparison with marigraphic records.

Hwang, Li-San, and David Divoky. A numerical model of the major tsunami *in* The Great Alaska Earthquake of 1964: Oceanography and Coastal Engineering. NAS Pub. 1605. Washington: National Academy of Sciences, 1972.
Outlines a numerical model (of the 1964 Alaska tsunami) that relates an arbitrary pattern and time history of bottom motion to the consequent surface disturbance, uses the idealized model as input for the computer, and then compares the reconstruction of surface wave effects with available data.

Hwang, Li-San, David Divoky, and Albert Yuen. Amchitka tsunami study. Tetra Tech Report TC-177. Las Vegas: U.S. Atomic Energy Commission, June 1970. 84 p.
Develops a hydrodynamic numerical mesh code for tsunami generation and applies this code to the 1964 Alaska earthquake, the only case in which adequate displacement data were available.

Iida, Kumizi, Doak C. Cox, and George Pararas-Carayannis. Preliminary catalog of tsunamis occurring in the Pacific Ocean. Data Report No. 5, HIG-67-10. Honolulu: University of Hawaii, Institute of Geophysics, August 1967. 270 p.
Summarizes chronologically and in tabular form all recorded historic tsunamis in the Pacific Ocean (see next item).

Iida, Kumizi, Doak C. Cox, and George Pararas-Carayannis. Bibliography to the preliminary catalog of tsunamis occurring in the Pacific Ocean. Data Report No. 6, HIG-67-25. Honolulu: University of Hawaii, Institute of Geophysics, August 1967. 27 p.
Lists source material for the Preliminary Catalog of Tsunamis.

Ink, Dwight A. Weekly reports April 10, 1964, through August 7, 1964. Federal Reconstruction and Development Planning Commission for Alaska's Weekly Memoranda to Senator Clinton P. Anderson, Chairman. Washington: Federal Reconstruction and Development Planning Commission, 1964. 200 p.
Reviews in weekly reports the information on transportation and port facilities, damage estimates, recovery plans, and restorative action in process.

Kachadoorian, Reuben. Effects of the earthquake of March 27, 1964, at Whittier, Alaska. U.S. Geological Survey Professional Paper 542-B. Washington: U.S. Government Printing Office, 1965. 21 p. Also in The Great Alaska Earthquake of 1964: Geology. NAS Pub. 1601. Washington: National Academy of Sciences, 1971, p. 439–459.
Concludes that in Whittier (at the time of the 1964 earthquake) loss of life was primarily due to waves and that property damage was caused by a 5.3-ft subsidence of land and landslide-generated waves—an indication that damage can be correlated with the local geology.

Kachadoorian, Reuben. Effects of the earthquake of March 27, 1964, on the Alaska highway system. U.S. Geological Survey Professional Paper 545-C. Washington: Government Printing Office, 1968. 66 p. Also in The Great Alaska Earthquake of 1964: Geology. NAS Pub. 1601. Washington: National Academy of Sciences, 1971. p. 641–703.
Discusses wave damage to highways and bridges.

Kachadoorian, Reuben, and George Plafker. Effects of the earthquake of March 27, 1964 on the communities of Kodiak and nearby islands. U.S. Geological Survey Professional Paper 542-F. Washington: Government Printing Office, 1967. 41 p. Abstract in The Great Alaska Earthquake of 1964: Geology. NAS Pub. 1601. Washington: National Academy of Sciences, 1971. p. 539–540.
Describes the tsunami and its effects in Kodiak Island group; ascribes major tsunami to uplift of Continental Shelf and minor oscillations to resonance.

Karo, H. Arnold. Coast and geodetic surveys of earthquake effects. Military Engineer, 56 (July–August 1964), 251–253.
Discusses operations of Seismic Sea Wave Warning System and surveys of Coast and Geodetic Survey.

Karo, H. Arnold. Emergency charting of the Alaska earthquake disaster area. Agenda Item 9 (unpublished manuscript). Fourth United Nations Regional Cartographic Conference for Asia and the Far East, November 21 to December 5, 1964. Manila: Fourth United Nations Regional Cartographic Conference for Asia and the Far East, 1964. 26 p. (Copy on file, Library, National Academy of Sciences–National Academy of Engineering, Washington, D.C.)
Describes nautical charting, aerial photography, postearthquake geodetic programs, and tidal programs related to uplift and subsidence.

Kawasumi, H. Outline of the Alaskan earthquake by Japanese-American investigating committee (in Japanese). Architectural Institute of Japan, v. 79, No. 944, 1964. p. 511–512.
Describes earthquake and tsunami effects and postearthquake survey of joint American-Japanese team.

Kirkby, M. J., and Anne V. Kirkby. Erosion and deposition on a beach raised by the 1964 earthquake, Montague Island, Alaska. U.S. Geological Survey Professional Paper 543-H. Washington: Government Printing Office, 1969. 41 p. Abstract in The Great Alaska Earthquake of 1964: Geology. NAS Pub. 1601. Washington: National Academy of Sciences, 1971. p. 281.
Notes the rapid changes in the unconsolidated sediments of a raised beach.

Lantz, Bill, and Mildred Kirkpatrick. Seward quake: Good Friday 1964. Seward: Kirkpatrick Printing Co., 1964. 56 p.
Contains informative reports of tsunami damage at Seward, with words and pictures, personal accounts, information bulletins, and excerpts from the Petticoat Gazette and other earthquake editions.

Lemke, Richard W. Effects of the earthquake of March 27, 1964, at Seward, Alaska. U.S. Geological Survey Professional Paper 542-E. Washington: Government Printing Office, 1967. 43 p. Also in The Great Alaska Earthquake of 1964: Geology. NAS Pub. 1601. Washington: National Academy of Sciences, 1971. p. 395–437.
Reports that the greatest amount of damage at Seward was done by huge tsunami waves that were slide-generated.

Lindemuth, I. W. Earthquakes and Cape Hinchinbrook Light Station, Alaska. The Engineer's Digest (U.S. Coast Guard), 133 (October–November–December 1965), 37–42.
Recounts the construction and relocation of the Cape Hinchinbrook Light Station in 1934 and its subsequent withstanding of the 1964 earthquake and tsunami, with the effect of the land rise on the dock facility.

Loomis, Harold G. Spectral analysis of tsunami records from stations in the Hawaiian Islands. Bulletin of the Seismological Society of America, 56 (June 1966), 697–713.
Analyzes power spectra for three tsunamis recorded at Hawaiian stations and Midway; notes lack of similarity between spectra from stations at least 210 mi apart.

Loomis, Harold G. The major tsunami in the Hawaiian Islands in The Great Alaska Earthquake of 1964: Oceanography and Coastal Engineering. NAS Pub. 1605. Washington: National Academy of Sciences, 1972.
Gives maps of runup heights and also shows the energy, coherence, and quadrature spectra of the tsunami at Midway, Honolulu, Kahului, and Hilo.

McCulloch, David S. Slide-induced waves, seiching, and ground fracturing caused by the earthquake of March 27, 1964, at Kenai Lake, Alaska. U.S. Geological Survey Professional Paper 543-A. Washington: Government Printing Office, 1966. 41 p. Also in The Great Alaska Earthquake of 1964: Hydrology. NAS Pub. 1603. Washington: National Academy of Sciences, 1968, p. 47–81.
Discusses two kinds of local waves—backfill and farshore waves—generated by slides from the great Alaska earthquake.

McGarr, Arthur. Excitation of seiches in channels by seismic waves. Journal of Geophysical Research, 70 (February 15, 1965), 847–854. Also in The Great Alaska Earthquake of 1964: Hydrology. NAS Pub. 1603. Washington: National Academy of Sciences, 1968. p. 133–139. Abstract in Deep Sea Research, 12 (October 1965), 752–753.
Describes seiches in channels on the Gulf Coast of United States at the time of the Alaska earthquake of 1964 and shows that horizontal components of seismic surface waves are the dominant cause.

McGarr, Arthur, and Robert C. Vorhis. Seismic seiches from the March 1964 Alaska earthquake. U.S. Geological Survey Professional Paper 544-E. Washington: Goverment Printing Office, 1968. 43 p. Also in The Great Alaska Earthquake of 1964: Hy-

drology. NAS Pub. 1603. Washington: National Academy of Sciences, 1968. p. 196–236.
States that the distribution of seismic seiches (recorded at more than 850 gaging stations mostly in North America and especially in states on the Gulf of Mexico) provides information on the effect of various geological features on the propagation of seismic surface waves.

McGarr, Arthur, and Robert C. Vorhis. Seismic seiches in bays, channels, and estuaries *in* The Great Alaska Earthquake of 1964: Oceanography and Coastal Engineering. NAS Pub. 1605. Washington: National Academy of Sciences, 1972.
Describes surface waves (with periods of the order of 15 seconds) that generated seiches in coastal regions and explains some features of the seiche distribution.

Magoon, Orville T. Structural damage by tsunamis. Preliminary study presented at American Society of Civil Engineers Coastal Engineering Conference, Santa Barbara, California, October 11, 1965. 26 p.
Presents discussion of structural damage by tsunamis along the northern California coast, especially the 1964 tsunami at Crescent City, with a view to improving the design of coastal structures.

Malloy, Richard J. Crustal uplift southwest of Mantague Island, Alaska. *Science,* 146 (November 20, 1964), 1048–1049.
Compares surveys made in 1927 and after the 1964 earthquake and also traces the extent of the submarine crustal uplift.

Malloy, Richard J. Gulf of Alaska: seafloor upheaval. *Geo-Marine Technology,* 1 (May–June 1965), 22–26. Also see Seafloor upheaval (Abstract) *in* Geophysical Abstracts 227: December 1965 (U.S. Department of Interior, Geological Survey). Washington: Government Printing Office, 1965. p. 962.
Shows 1964 earthquake effect on the sea floor and describes the crustal uplift pattern; compares 1927 and 1964 hydrographic data.

Malloy, Richard J. Marine geological reconnaissance of epicentral and aftershock regions 1964 Alaska earthquake (unpublished manuscript). Rockville, Maryland: Environmental Science Services Administration, Institute for Oceanography, 1967. 45 p. (Copy on file, Library, National Academy of Sciences–National Academy of Engineering, Washington, D.C.)
Reveals that studies made after the 1964 earthquake show that only a portion of the sea floor 19 km southwest of Montague Island exhibited measurable open-water submarine tectonic deformation.

Malloy, Richard J. Submarine tectonics of the 1964 Alaskan earthquake (Abstract). *Transactions, American Geophysical Union,* 45 (December 1964), 633.
States that 1964 geophysical reconnaissance by the U.S. Coast and Geodetic Survey ship *Surveyor* revealed offshore tectonics of a magnitude exceeding that reported on land.

Malloy, Richard J., and George F. Merrill. Vertical crustal movement of the sea floor associated with the Prince William Sound, Alaska, earthquake *in* Volume II-B,C: The Prince William Sound, Alaska, earthquake of 1964 and aftershocks. Environmental Science Services Administration, U.S. Coast and Geodetic Survey. Washington: Government Printing Office, 1969. p. 327–338. Also *in* The Great Alaska Earthquake of 1964: Oceanography and Coastal Engineering. NAS Pub. 1605. Washington: National Academy of Sciences, 1972.
Uses data from the 1965 surveys by U.S. Coast and Geodetic Survey ships to prepare a bathymetric map of the uplifted area and to construct profiles and a map showing the amount of sea-floor uplift.

Marine Advisers, Inc. A broad-frequency-band wave study at Monterey Harbor, California. Report to U.S. Army Engineer District, San Francisco Corps of Engineers. La Jolla: Marine Advisers, Inc., July 1964. 19 p.
Includes basic wave data to be used for breakwater plans in Monterey Harbor. Spectral analysis is given for the period covering the arrival of the tsunami from the 1964 Alaska earthquake.

Marsden, Howard J., and Frank I. Huxtable. Report on earthquake and water wave damage to water transportation facilities including port facilities in Alaska (unpublished report). Washington: Department of Commerce Maritime Administration, 1964. 10 p. (Copy on file, Library, National Academy of Sciences–National Academy of Engineering, Washington, D.C.)
Gives information on the nature of tsunami damage to ports and terminal facilities for eight ports in the Prince William Sound area.

Migliaccio, Ralph R. Earthquake of March 27, 1964. Report of District Geologist, Valdez, to Chief Geologist, College. Valdez: Office of the District Geologist, 1964. 6 p. (Copy on file, Library, National Academy of Sciences–National Academy of Engineering, Washington, D.C.)
Describes sequence of events in Valdez at the time of the earthquake and tsunami. Information was gathered from the most reliable witnesses available, and opinions on the cause are given by a geologist.

Murty, T. S., and L. Boilard. The tsunami in the Alberni Inlet caused by the Alaska earthquake of March 1964 *in* Tsunamis in the Pacific Ocean. Proceedings of the International Symposium on Tsunamis and Tsunami Research, Honolulu, Hawaii, October 7–10, 1969. W. M. Adams, editor. Honolulu: East-West Center Press, 1970. p. 165–187.
Analyzes tsunami effects in Alberni Inlet in terms of propagation, resonance, and other factors.

National Academy of Sciences. Earthquake of March 28, 1964 (0336 UT) at 61.1°N latitude and 147.6°W longitude; marigrams and seismograms *in* World Data Center A: Catalogue of data received by WDC-A during the period 1 July 1957–31 December 1965. Washington: World Data Center A Coordination Office, March 1966. p. 8.
Gives tabular listing of marigrams and seismograms for the great Alaska earthquake.

National Academy of Sciences. Tsunami stations *in* World Data Center A: Catalogue of data received by WDC-A during the period 1 July 1957–31 December 1965. Washington: World Data Center Coordination Office, March 1966. p. 5.
Lists geographic location of tsunami stations, along with the type of recording (seismograph or marigraph) used by each station.

National Board of Fire Underwriters and Pacific Fire Rating Bureau. The Alaska earthquake, March 27, 1964. San Francisco: The National Board of Fire Underwriters, 1964. 35 p.
Describes tsunamis and the general effects of the 1964 earthquake on earthquake-resistive design and construction in Anchorage and other damaged communities; gives conclusions and recommendations.

Noerenberg, Wallace H., and Frank J. Ossiander. Effect of the March 27, 1964 earthquake on pink salmon alevin survival in Prince William Sound spawning streams. Alaska Department of Fish and Game Informational Leaflet 43. Juneau: Alaska Department of Fish and Game, 1964. 26p.
Analyzes data on the number of dead alevins and estimates that the 1964 seismic occurrences in Prince William Sound caused a loss of 235,000 pink salmon for 1965.

Northrop, John. T-phases from 80 Alaskan earthquakes, March 28–31, 1964. *Bulletin of the Seismological Society of America,* 55 (February 1965), 59–63.
States that the largest T-phase signal from the 1964 earthquake was received at Pt. Sur, California, and that additional T-phases were received from 90 percent of the 80 aftershocks studied in the Kodiak Island area.

Northrop, John. T-phases *in* The Great Alaska Earthquake of 1964: Oceanography and Coastal Engineering. NAS Pub. 1605. Washington: National Academy of Sciences, 1972.
Indicates that the main shock caused a T-phase arrival at Oahu 18 minutes earlier than the computed time, probably because of radiation of hydroacoustic waves from seamounts and insular slopes:in the Gulf of Alaska.

Norton, Frank R. B., and J. Eugene Haas. The human response in selected communities *in* The Great Alaska Earthquake of 1964: Human Ecology. NAS Pub. 1607. Washington: National Academy of Sciences, 1970, p. 248–399.
Describes human response in Alaska to the tsunamis and tsunami warnings.

Ocean Science News. What happened on the ocean floor. *Ocean Science News,* 6 (March 31, 1964), 1.
Provides early report of seiches, tsunamis, barometric pressure effects, and U.S. Coast and Geodetic Survey action to dispatch survey ships to obtain urgently needed hydrographic charting of harbors and approach channels.

Oceanographic Services, Inc. Water level changes produced on the Pacific coasts of the United States and Canada by the Alaskan tsunami of 1964. Santa Barbara: Oceanographic Services, Inc., 1965. 14 p.
Presents data on water elevations and damage produced by the Alaska tsunami at Crescent City and Alberni and comments on possible reasons for these two extremes.

Office of Emergency Planning. The Alaska earthquake, a progress report—279 days of federal reconstruction effort. Office of Emergency Planning Progress Report. Washington: Office of Emergency Planning, 1964. 45 p.
Reports on progress made by various federal agencies in the damaged communities.

Office of Naval Weather Service. FWC [Fleet Weather Central] Kodiak earthquake summary. *Naval Weather Service Bulletin* (July 1964), 2–3.
Summarizes earthquake and tsunami effects in and around Kodiak, with particular emphasis on communications.

Pararas-Carayannis, George. Catalog of tsunamis in the Hawaiian Islands. World Data Center A: Tsunami. Washington: Environ-mental Science Services Administration, U.S. Coast and Geodetic Survey, May 1969. 94 p.
Presents a systematic compilation of all data pertaining to tsunamis observed and recorded in the Hawaiian Islands.

Pararas-Carayannis, George. Water waves, Part I *in* Source mechanism study of the Alaska earthquake and tsunami of 27 March 1964. Report HIG-65-17. Honolulu: University of Hawaii, Institute of Geophysics, 1965. p. 1–30. Also *in* The Great Alaska Earthquake of 1964: Seismology and Geodesy. NAS Pub. 1602. Washington: National Academy of Sciences, 1972. (Also see *Pacific Science,* 21 (July 1967), 301–310.)
Fixes the dimensions of the tsunami-generating area, its volume of crustal displacement, and the energy associated with the tsunami.

Pararas-Carayannis, George, and A. S. Furumoto. The generating area and source mechanism of the Alaskan tsunami (Abstract). Proceedings of the 11th Pacific Science Congress, Tokyo, 1966, Vol. 3. Tokyo: Science Council of Japan, Division Meeting Solid Earth Physics I, 1966. p. 35.
Lists, but does not give abstract, in Abstracts of North American Geology: April 1967 (U.S. Department of Interior Geological Survey). Washington: Government Printing Office, 1967. p. 501.

Parkin, Ernest J. Alaskan surveys to determine crustal movement: Part II, Horizontal displacement. *Surveying and Mapping,* 27, No. 3 (1967), 423–430.
Describes horizontal displacement affecting Kenai Peninsula, Prince William Sound, and offshore islands.

Parkin, Ernest J. Horizontal crustal movements determined from surveys after the Alaskan earthquake of 1964 *in* Volume III: The Prince William Sound, Alaska, earthquake of 1964 and aftershocks. Environmental Science Services Administration, U.S. Coast and Geodetic Survey. Washington: Government Printing Office, 1969. p. 35–98. Also *in* The Great Alaska Earthquake of 1964: Seismology and Geodesy. NAS Pub. 1602. Washington: National Academy of Sciences, 1972.
Discusses horizontal crustal displacement that affected coasts.

Peterson, Evar P. California city uses Alaska earthquake experience to evaluate its own disaster-relief readiness: A report on civil defense operations in Anchorage. Department of Defense–Office of Civil Defense Information Bulletin 125. Washington: Department of Defense–Office of Civil Defense, 1965. 20 p.
Summarizes effects of tsunamis in Alaska and compares them with effects that might be experienced at Long Beach, California.

Petrauskas, Charles, and L. E. Borgman. Frequencies of crest heights for random combinations of astronomical tides and tsunamis recorded at Crescent City, California. Technical Report HEL 16-8. Berkeley: University of California, Hydraulic Engineering Laboratory, 1971. 64 p.
Develops a computerized method to evaluate the effect of the time of occurrence of a tsunami on the maximum water-level elevation; applies this method to the 1964 tsunami at Crescent City, California, to show that this tsunami was associated with fairly extreme tidal fluctuations.

Petticoat Gazette. History repeats itself! Seward reacts to tidal wave warning. *Petticoat Gazette* [Seward, Alaska] (February 4, 1965), p. 1.

Reports calm and orderly, but effective, reaction to a tsunami warning at Seward almost a year after the great Alaska earthquake.

Péwé, Troy L. Good Friday earthquake, Alaska. *Geotimes,* 8 (May–June 1964), cover, 9–10, 22–23.
Gives preliminary geologic observations which show that most damage in the 1964 earthquake was due to slides and tsunamis.

Plafker, George. Surface faults on Montague Island associated with the 1964 Alaska earthquake. U.S. Geological Survey Professional Paper 543-G. Washington: Government Printing Office, 1967. 42 p. Also *in* The Great Alaska Earthquake of 1964: Geology. NAS Pub. 1601. Washington: National Academy of Sciences, 1971.
Describes faults resulting in differential displacement of shoreline.

Plafker, George. Tectonic deformation associated with the 1964 Alaska Earthquake. *Science,* 148 (June 25, 1965), 1675–1687.
Describes vertical coastal tectonic displacements, including those of the coast and Continental Shelf.

Plafker, George. Tectonic movements, seismic sea waves, and locally generated waves associated with Alaska's Good Friday earthquake (Abstract). *Transactions, American Geophysical Union,* 45 (December 1964), 633–634.
Points out that tsunamis were especially destructive in those areas subjected to tectonic subsidence.

Plafker, George. Tectonics of the March 27, 1964, Alaska earthquake. U.S. Geological Survey Professional Paper 543-I. Washington: Government Printing Office, 1969. 74 p. Also *in* The Great Alaska Earthquake of 1964: Geology. NAS Pub. 1601. Washington: National Academy of Sciences, 1971. p. 47–122.
Furnishes information on regional vertical deformation that generated destructive tsunamis, warping that resulted in permanent tilt of larger lake basins, and uplift and subsidence relative to sea level.

Plafker, George, and Reuben Kachadoorian. Geologic effects of the March 1964 earthquake and associated seismic sea waves on Kodiak and nearby islands, Alaska. U.S. Geological Survey Professional Paper 543-D. Washington: Government Printing Office, 1966. 46 p. Also *in* The Great Alaska Earthquake of 1964: Geology. NAS Pub. 1601. Washington: National Academy of Sciences, 1971. p. 177–226.
Discusses landslides; local subsidence; changes of level in wells, lakes, and streams; and the effects of the tsunami in the Kodiak group of islands.

Plafker, George, Reuben Kachadoorian, Edwin Eckel, and Lawrence R. Mayo. Effects of the earthquake of March 27, 1964, on various communities. U.S. Geological Survey Professional Paper 542-G. Washington: Government Printing Office, 1969. 50 p. Also *in* The Great Alaska Earthquake of 1964: Geology. NAS Pub. 1601. Washington: National Academy of Sciences, 1971. p. 489–538.
Describes damage resulting primarily from sea waves of diverse origins, displacements of the land relative to sea level, and seismic shaking.

Plafker, George, Reuben Kachadoorian, and Arthur Grantz. Tectonics and effects of Alaska's Good Friday earthquake on coastal areas *in* Abstracts of Papers, 1964 National Meeting, Association of Engineering Geologists, October 28–November 1, 1964, Sacramento, California. p. 9.
Reports on submarine landslides and on tsunamis and emphasizes that the latter did not strike the outer coast of Prince William Sound and Kodiak Island until 20 to 30 minutes after the main shock.

Plafker, George, and L. R. Mayo. Tectonic deformation, subaqueous slides and destructive waves associated with the Alaskan March 27, 1964, earthquake: an interim geologic evaluation. U.S. Geological Survey Open-File Report. Menlo Park, California: U.S. Geological Survey, 1965. 34 p.
Examines the submarine uplift of the Continental Shelf which generated a long-period, large-amplitude tsunami and stresses the widespread subaqueous sliding in Prince William Sound.

Press, Frank, and David Jackson. Alaskan earthquake 27 March 1964: vertical extent of faulting and elastic strain energy release. *Science,* 147 (February 19, 1965), 867–868. Also *in* The Great Alaska Earthquake of 1964: Seismology and Geodesy. NAS Pub. 1602. Washington: National Academy of Sciences, 1972.
Describes vertical tectonic deformation of Alaskan coastal area and shelf.

Public Administration Service. Report on a review of federal policy in grant, loan, and construction programs in areas of high risk of natural disaster damage. Chicago: Public Administration Service, 1965. 56 p.
Presents a report fulfilling a recommendation of the Anderson Commission; lists measures to reduce destructive effects of tsunamis; and reviews federal loan, grant, and construction programs in areas of natural-disaster risks, such as Alaska.

Reimnitz, Erk. Effects in the Copper River Delta *in* The Great Alaska Earthquake of 1964: Oceanography and Coastal Engineering. NAS Pub. 1605. Washington: National Academy of Sciences, 1972.
Finds that thick accumulations of sediments in certain depressions represent erosion products of tsunamis and seiches in shallow-water areas and a marked unconformity in the latter regions.

Reimnitz, Erk, and Neil F. Marshall. Effects of the Alaska earthquake and tsunami on recent deltaic sediments. *Journal of Geophysical Research,* 70 (May 15, 1965), 2363–2376. Also *in* The Great Alaska Earthquake of 1964: Geology. NAS Pub. 1601. Washington: National Academy of Sciences, 1971. p. 265–278.
Stresses significant marks left by the 1964 Alaska earthquake on the recent sediments of the Copper River Delta, with erosion brought about by seiching action and the uplift.

Rexin, Elmer E. Seismic sea waves as recorded from a remote phreatic seismometer (Abstract). Technical Report presented at Thirty-Sixth Annual Meeting of the Eastern Section of the Seismological Society of America, University of Michigan, October 8–10, 1964. *Earthquake Notes,* 35 (September–December 1964), 45.
Finds that the hydroseismograms of earthquakes accompanied by seismic sea waves had irregular long-period axis waves and that the axis wave was very pronounced in the 1964 Alaska earthquake hydroseismogram.

Roberts, James A. The reshaping of South Beach, Crescent City, California, after the tsunami of 27–28 March 1964. Meteorological Research, Inc., Paper 202 (unpublished), delivered at the Beach Erosion Control Conference, 2 December 1964. Altadena, California: Meteorological Research, Inc., 1964. 18 p. (Copy on file, Library, National Academy of Sciences–National Academy of Engineering, Washington, D.C.)
Assesses effects of subaerial processes on a beach that was modified by the tsunami acting as a geomorphologic agent and analyzes possible mechanisms in the reshaping of South Beach.

Roberts, James A., and Chen-Wu Chien. The effects of bottom topography on the refraction of the tsunami 27–28 March 1964: the Crescent City case in Ocean Science and Ocean Engineering 1965 (Volume 2): Transactions of the Joint Conference and Exhibit [Marine Technology Society and American Society of Limnology and Oceanography], June 14–17, 1965, Washington, D.C. Washington: Marine Technology Society, 1965. p. 707–716.
Suggests that the principal factors causing the apparent focusing of wave energy in the Crescent City, California, area were the direction of propagation of the tsunami and the bottom topography near Crescent City.

Roberts, James A., and Edwin K. Kauper. The effects of wind and precipitation on the modification of South Beach, Crescent City, California. Atmospheric Research Group Final Report to Environmental Sciences Division, Office of the Chief of Research and Development, Department of the Army, Altadena, California: Atmospheric Research Group, 1964. 60 p.
Concludes that the most significant change in South Beach after the 1964 tsunami was the growth of a low berm seaward of the existing berm and that the tsunami was probably refracted by two seamounts northwest of the harbor, resulting in the focusing of the wave front on Crescent City.

Rucker, Wheeler, H., Jr. Report of physical damage and proposed order of repair of damage caused by earthquake of March 27, 1964. Report for the Port of Anchorage by Tippetts–Abbett–McCarthy–Stratton, Consulting Engineers & Architects (Seattle). Anchorage: Port of Anchorage, 1964. 20 p.
Gives itemized list of damages to pier facilities at Anchorage, including those to the west approach trestle, transit shed, and gantry cranes.

Sawyer, Kenneth T. The Alaska earthquake: effects, reaction, and recovery. Military Engineer, 56 (July–August 1964), 246–249.
Presents a well-illustrated summary of damage effects, with emphasis on the role of the Alaska District, U.S. Army Corps of Engineers.

Schatz, Clifford E., Herbert Curl, Jr., and Wayne V. Burt. Tsunamis on the Oregon coast. The Ore Bin (Publication of the Oregon Department of Geology and Mineral Industries), 26 (December 1964), 231–232.
Indicates that tsunamis would be dissipated on the rugged open Oregon coast, but that the estuaries would be especially vulnerable to their effect. This study was prompted by the tsunami from the 1964 Alaska earthquake.

Science Journal. Seiche excitation—new theory explains water movement. Science Journal, 1 (August 1965), 12–14.
Advances theory that, for surface-wave periods of less than about 600 seconds, seiches are set up by just the horizontal component of motion and that the seiche amplitude increases as the depth of water increases, as evidenced in the 1964 Alaska earthquake results.

Science News Letter. Seismic waves in earth caused waves in Gulf. Science News Letter, 86 (August 15, 1964), 105.
Notes that 6-ft waves in the Gulf of Mexico after the 1964 earthquake were created "in resonance" with seismic ground waves coming from Alaska.

Scientific and Engineering Task Force (Task Force No. 9). 30-Day Report of the Scientific and Engineering Task Force. Washington: Federal Reconstruction and Development Planning Commission for Alaska, 1964. 52 p.
Evaluates disaster effects; reports interim status of field investigations and actions; summarizes work of field team, interagency cooperation, zoning and building criteria, and documentary-film preparation; gives guidelines for reconstruction and long-term investigations.

Shannon, W. L., and David E. Hilts. Earthquake-caused submarine landslides at Seward in The Great Alaska Earthquake of 1964: Engineering. NAS Pub. 1606. Washington: National Academy of Sciences, 1972.
Finds that the magnitude and duration of the 1964 Alaska earthquake, the alluvial fan deposits, the steepness of slopes along the waterfront, marine sand and silt, and artesian pressures were the factors responsible for the submarine landslide at Seward.

Shannon & Wilson, Inc. Report on subsurface investigation for city of Seward, Alaska, and vicinity, to U.S. Army Engineer District, Anchorage, Alaska. Seattle: Shannon & Wilson, Inc., 1964. 77 p.
Reports on probable contributing factors responsible for submarine landslide that destroyed most of Seward's waterfront, and presents an evaluation of the area's stability under both static and earthquake conditions.

Small, James B., and Lawrence C. Wharton. Vertical displacements determined by surveys after the Alaska earthquake of March 1964 in Volume III: The Prince William Sound, Alaska, earthquake of 1964 and aftershocks. Environmental Science Services Administration, U.S. Coast and Geodetic Survey. Washington: Government Printing Office, 1969. p. 21–33. Also in The Great Alaska Earthquake of 1964: Seismology and Geodesy. NAS Pub. 1602. Washington: National Academy of Sciences, 1972.
Describes tidal datum plane changes resulting from earthquake.

Spaeth, M. G., and S. C. Berkman. The tsunami of March 28, 1964, as recorded at tide stations. U.S. Coast and Geodetic Survey Publication. Rockville, Maryland: U.S. Coast and Geodetic Survey, 1965. 59 p.
Gives preliminary version of the following two references; states that the 1964 Alaska tsunami was the first on record to have been generated by an earthquake of such magnitude with a continental epicenter, although small local tsunamis are known to have been so generated.

Spaeth, Mark G., and Saul C. Berkman. The tsunami of March 28, 1964, as recorded at tide stations. Environmental Science Services Administration Technical Report C&GS 33. Washington: Government Printing Office, 1967. 86 p. Also in The Great Alaska Earthquake of 1964: Oceanography and Coastal Engineering. NAS Pub. 1605. Washington: National Academy of Sciences, 1972.
Contains reproductions of 105 tide curves that show the tsunami and of 8 curves that show seiches.

Spaeth, Mark G., and Saul C. Berkman. The tsunami of March 28,

1964, as recorded at tide stations *in* Volume II B,C: The Prince William Sound, Alaska, earthquake of 1964 and aftershocks. Environmental Science Services Administration, U.S. Coast and Geodetic Survey. Washington: Government Printing Office, 1969. p. 223–307.

Gives 107 tide curves showing the tsunami and 12 curves showing oscillations induced by the long-period seismic waves; also presents a brief history of the Tsunami Warning System.

Stanley, Albert A. Crescent City: sea wave. *Shore and Beach* (Journal of the American Shore and Beach Preservation Association), 32 (April 1964), 29.

Describes the disastrous fourth tsunami wave on March 28, 1964, at Crescent City and explains tsunami propagation.

Stanley, Kirk W. Alaska earthquake. *Shore and Beach* (Journal of the American Shore and Beach Preservation Association), 32 (April 1964), 25–27.

Presents early report of damage resulting from the tsunami after the great Alaska earthquake and of the subsequent widespread changes in sea level.

Stanley, Kirk W. Effects of post-earthquake conditions on the Homer Spit, Alaska *in* Abstracts for 1964: GSA [Geological Society of America] Special Papers 82. New York: Geological Society of America, Inc., 1965. p. 362–363. Also, abstract *in* Science in Alaska, 1964: Proceedings Fifteenth Alaskan Science Conference, College, Alaska, August 31 to September 4, 1964. George Dahlgren, editor. College: Alaska Division American Association for the Advancement of Science, March 15, 1965. p. 89–90.

Cites 5- to 6-ft drop in Homer Spit elevation since the 1964 earthquake and relates certain morphological changes to general shore processes. The Spit was flooded by the higher tides, but it continued to build by accretion.

Stanley, Kirk W. Beach changes on Homer Spit *in* Effects of the earthquake of March 27, 1964, in the Homer area, Alaska. U.S. Geological Survey Professional Paper 542-D. Washington: Government Printing Office, 1966. p. 20–28. Also *in* The Great Alaska Earthquake of 1964: Geology. NAS Pub. 1601. Washington: National Academy of Sciences, 1971. p. 480–488.

Indicates that the increased supply of material to Homer Spit (as a result of accelerated erosion in the Spit's source area after the 1964 earthquake) will provide further deposition on the Cook Inlet side of the beach.

Stanley, Kirk W. Effects of the Alaska earthquake of March 27, 1964, on shore processes and beach morphology. U.S. Geological Survey Professional Paper 543-J. Washington: Government Printing Office, 1968. 21 p. Also *in* The Great Alaska Earthquake of 1964: Geology. NAS Pub. 1601. Washington: National Academy of Sciences, 1971. p. 229–249.

Reports that about 10,000 mi of shoreline in southeastern Alaska were affected by subsidence or uplift associated with the great Alaska earthquake; tells of effects on frontal beach ridges and stream mouths.

Stauder, William. Tensional character of earthquake foci beneath the Aleutian trench with relation to sea-floor spreading. *Journal of Geophysical Research,* 73 (December 15, 1968), 7693–7701.

Finds that, in a study of the relationship between sea-floor spreading and features noted in the 1964 Alaska earthquake, sense of fault movement could be predicted by the sea-floor spreading hypothesis; this is presented as evidence in support of island arcs as the locale of a sink mechanism required by the hypothesis.

Stewart, M. C. [Master's Report] to Mr. H. R. Sterner, Operating Manager, Alaska Steamship Company, concerning Voyage 239 of SS *Chena* (typed letter). 2 p. (Copy on file, Library, National Academy of Sciences–National Academy of Engineering, Washington, D.C.)

Depicts the response of the SS *Chena* to the tsunami action at the dock of Valdez and gives a description of the force of the tsunami itself.

Stroh, Alfred, Jr. Navy operations at Kodiak. *Military Engineer,* 56 (July–August 1964), 254–255.

Describes the structural damage to the Kodiak Naval Station, caused by the tsunami after the great Alaska earthquake, and details the recovery operations necessitated by the tides that ran about 5.5 ft higher than normal.

Stuart, W. Harold. Rehabilitation of earthquake damage, Alaska (Abstract) *in* Abstracts of Papers, 1964 National Meeting, Association of Engineering Geologists, October 28–November 1, 1964, Sacramento, California. p. 10.

Discusses Corps of Engineers rehabilitation of small-boat basins destroyed by the earthquake and tsunamis at Valdez, Seward, Homer, Seldovia, and Kodiak.

Swanson, Lawrence W. Shoreline mapping *in* Manual of color aerial photography. Falls Church, Virginia: American Society of Photogrammetry, 1968. p. 410–411. Also, abstract *in* Abstracts of North American Geology: December 1968 (U.S. Department of Interior Geological Survey). Washington: Government Printing Office, 1968. p. 1871.

Presents 1964 postearthquake color aerial photograph of the southwest coast of Middleton Island, Alaska, showing tilting of the island and offshore bottom details.

Thorsteinson, Fredrik V. Effects of the Alaska earthquake on pink and chum salmon runs in Prince William Sound *in* Science in Alaska, 1964: Proceedings Fifteenth Alaskan Science Conference, College, Alaska, August 31 to September 4, 1964. George Dahlgren, editor. College: Alaska Division American Association for the Advancement of Science, March 15, 1965. p. 267–280.

Describes silting and other changes associated with the tsunami that resulted in high losses of salmon fry.

Tilgner, Edward E., and Jon R. Peterson. The Alaska Tsunami Warning System *in* Volume II-B,C: The Prince William Sound, Alaska, earthquake of 1964 and aftershocks. Environmental Science Services Administration, U.S. Coast and Geodetic Survey. Washington: Government Printing Office, 1969. p. 309–324.

Discusses basic system concepts and instrumentation used in the initial installation of the Alaska Tsunami Warning System, now in operation and designed to provide tsunami warning within 15 minutes after any large earthquake in the Alaska–Aleutian Islands area.

Tillotson, Ernest. The Alaska earthquake of March 28–30, 1964. *Nature,* 202 (April 25, 1964), 336.

Describes the earthquake and tsunami in relation to Alaskan and Aleutian seismicity.

Tudor, W. J. Tsunami damage at Kodiak, Alaska, and Crescent City, California, from Alaskan earthquake of 27 March 1964. U.S. Naval Civil Engineering Laboratory Technical Note N-622. Port Hueneme, California: U.S. Naval Civil Engineering Laboratory, 1964. 131 p.
Surveys the tsunami damage to waterfront facilities at Kodiak and Crescent City and presents conclusions on survival of piers with adequate deck-pile connections and on resistance of multistory buildings to tsunami.

United California Bank. 'Big wave in the bay' at Crescent City. *United California Banker,* 4 (May–June 1964), 2–9.
Contains a timetable of the tsunami arrival and damage at Crescent City along with redevelopment plans for the downtown area.

U.S. Army Engineer Division, Alaska District. After action report, Alaska Good Friday earthquake, 27 March 1964. Report prepared for U.S. Army Engineer Division, North Pacific. Anchorage: U.S. Army Corps of Engineers, January 1968. 76 p.
Summarizes crustal damage from slides and waves and reconstruction measures.

U.S. Coast and Geodetic Survey. Assistance and recovery, Alaska/1964: a report covering the activities of the U.S. Coast and Geodetic Survey in conjunction with the Prince William Sound, Alaska, earthquake of 1964 for the period March 27–December 31, 1964. Washington: U.S. Department of Commerce, 1965. 45 p.
Surveys progress in the restoration of Alaskan commerce through mobilization of the U.S. Coast and Geodetic Survey's forces after damage from the 1964 tsunami.

U.S. Coast and Geodetic Survey. Coast and Geodetic Survey activities pertinent to the Alaska earthquake study. Washington: U.S. Coast and Geodetic Survey [1964]. 12 p.
Summarizes the photogrammetric, oceanographic, and cartographic programs undertaken by the Coast and Geodetic Survey as a part of the tsunami research work after the 1964 earthquake.

U.S. Coast and Geodetic Survey. Preliminary report–Prince William Sound, Alaskan earthquakes March–April 1964 (second printing). Seismology Division Report. Washington: U.S. Coast and Geodetic Survey, 1964. 101 p.
Makes available the early information on tsunami effects and reports on the Seismic Sea Wave Warning System.

U.S. Coast and Geodetic Survey. Preliminary report: Tidal datum plane changes, Prince William Sound, Alaskan earthquakes March–April, 1964. Office of Oceanography Report. Rockville [Maryland]: U.S. Coast and Geodetic Survey, 1964. 5 p.
Provides preliminary tidal datum plane changes necessitated by land movement resulting from the 1964 earthquake.

U.S. Coast and Geodetic Survey. Report on earthquake and wave damage at Valdez, Alaska, and eyewitness reports of earthquake and wave damage at Whittier, Alaska. Transcripts of tape recordings of eyewitness accounts (unpublished manuscript). Washington: U.S. Coast and Geodetic Survey [1964]. 15 p. (Copy on file, Library, National Academy of Sciences–National Academy of Engineering, Washington, D.C.)
Furnishes eight eyewitness accounts of the tsunami at Valdez and eight tape-recorded interviews with observers of the wave damage at Whittier.

U.S. Coast and Geodetic Survey. Report on tsunami warning system in operation during the Alaskan earthquake of March 27, 1964, and how it should be improved and recommendations for research in tsunami and earthquake forecasting. Washington: U.S. Coast and Geodetic Survey, 1964. 23 p.
Recommends use of the Weather Bureau's warning service, an extensive public education program, a remote-three-station seismic array, modern automatic equipment at tide stations, installation of deep-sea tide gages, and a separate warning system for Alaska.

U.S. Coast and Geodetic Survey. The Prince William Sound, Alaska, earthquake of 1964 and aftershocks. Fergus J. Wood, editor. Volume I: Operational phases of the Coast and Geodetic Survey program in Alaska for the period March 27 to December 31, 1964. Washington: Government Printing Office, 1966. 263 p.
Summarizes procedures used in coordinated seismological, geodetic, photogrammetric, oceanographic, hydrographic, and cartographic studies directed toward determining both the causal factors and associated effects of the 1964 Alaska earthquake.

U.S. Coast and Geodetic Survey. The Prince William Sound, Alaska, earthquake of 1964 and aftershocks. Fergus J. Wood, editor. Volume II-A: Research studies–Engineering seismology. Washington: Goverment Printing Office, 1967. 392 p.
Studies earthquake effects upon various types of building construction, mainly in the Anchorage area, but also contains a section on damage to oil storage tanks on fiord deltas.

U.S. Coast and Geodetic Survey. The Prince William Sound, Alaska, earthquake of 1964 and aftershocks. Louis E. Leipold, editor-in-chief. Volume II-B,C: Research studies–Seismology and marine geology. Washington: Government Printing Office, 1969, 350 p.
Includes articles on (1) the 1964 Alaska tsunami as recorded at tide stations, (2) the Alaska tsunami warning system, and (3) the vertical crustal movement of the sea floor at the time of the great Alaska earthquake.

U.S. Coast and Geodetic Survey. Tsunami. Documentary 28-minute color film. Rockville, Maryland: U.S. Coast and Geodetic Survey [1965].
Shows destructive, earthquake-spawned sea waves of the Pacific, explains educational safety program, and gives scenes photographed at Crescent City, California, after the 1964 tsunami.

U.S. Coast and Geodetic Survey. Tsunami! The story of the Seismic Sea-Wave Warning System. U.S. Coast and Geodetic Survey Publication. Washington: Government Printing Office [1965]. 46 p.
Defines tsunamis and gives details of the organization of the SSWWS and its improvement.

U.S. Coast Guard. [70 official incoming and outgoing messages between Coast Guard Light Station Cape Hinchinbrook and Coast Guard District 17, 28 March 1964 to 5 April 1964.] [Juneau: U.S. Coast Guard District 17, 1964]. 70 p. (Copy on file, Library, National Academy of Sciences–National Academy of Engineering, Washington, D.C.)
Indicates force of seismic shaking at Cape Hinchinbrook Light Station and describes subsequent landslides into sea; also mentions underwater tremor felt on *Sedge.*

U.S. Geological Survey. The Alaskan earthquake, 1964. 20-minute

16-mm color documentary film. Washington: U.S. Geological Survey [1966]. (Copy of one-page film description on file, Library, National Academy of Sciences–National Academy of Engineering, Washington, D.C.)
Uses animated cross sections to show how earthquakes occur and illustrates the effects of the 1964 Alaska earthquake, particularly with motion-picture scenes of tsunami wave action at Valdez.

Van Dorn, William G. A model experiment on the generation of the tsunami of March 28, 1964, in Alaska in Tsunamis in the Pacific Ocean. Proceedings of the International Symposium on Tsunamis and Tsunami Research, Honolulu, Hawaii, October 7–10, 1969. W. M. Adams, editor. Honolulu: East-West Center Press, 1970. p. 33–45. Also in The Great Alaska Earthquake of 1964: Oceanography and Coastal Engineering. NAS Pub. 1605. Washington: National Academy of Sciences, 1972.
Scaled dipolar source model in one dimension reproduces essential features of record observed at Wake Island during the 1964 tsunami.

Van Dorn, William G. Source mechanism of the tsunami of March 28, 1964, in Alaska. Proceedings of the Ninth Conference (1964) on Coastal Engineering (Chapter 10). New York: American Society of Civil Engineers, 1965. p. 166–190. Also in The Great Alaska Earthquake of 1964: Oceanography and Coastal Engineering. NAS Pub. 1605. Washington: National Academy of Sciences, 1972).
Presents preliminary evidence suggesting that the 1964 tsunami was produced by a dipolar movement of the earth's crust.

Van Dorn, William G. Tsunamis. Advances in Hydroscience, 3 (1965), 1–47.
Contains the source distribution and frequency of tsunamis, the hydrodynamics of centered wave system, field measurements and model studies, and the case history of the tsunami in Alaska in 1964.

Van Dorn, William G., and Doak C. Cox. Oceanic character, propagation, and coastal modification of the major tsunami in The Great Alaska Earthquake of 1964: Oceanography and Coastal Engineering. NAS Pub. 1605. Washington: National Academy of Sciences, 1972.
Examines long-period oscillations on Alaska tsunami marigrams, tsunami travel times, coastal modifications, and runup.

von Huene, Roland. Introduction: Marine and shoreline geological effects in The Great Alaska Earthquake of 1964: Oceanography and Coastal Engineering. NAS Pub. 1605. Washington: National Academy of Sciences, 1972.
Presents studies of the deformation of the ocean floor during the Alaska earthquake; these data permit, for the first time, the synthesis of the tectonic effects in the submarine areas.

von Huene, Roland. Seaquakes in The Great Alaska Earthquake of 1964: Oceanography and Coastal Engineering. NAS Pub. 1605. Washington: National Academy of Sciences, 1972.
Defines seaquakes as shaking or other earthquake phenomena felt at sea, provides seaquake reports from the great Alaska earthquake, and analyzes their significance.

von Huene, Roland. [Untitled notes of consulting geologist to U.S. Coast Guard regarding his reconnaissance of Cape Hinchinbrook Light Station after the Alaska earthquake]. [China Lake, California: U.S. Naval Ordnance Test Station, 1966]. 14 p. (Copy on file, Library, National Academy of Sciences–National Academy of Engineering, Washington, D.C.)
Indicates the consulting geologist's opinion that there was no evidence of damage by high water and that because of darkness no tsunami phenomenon was observed by the men at Cape Hinchinbrook.

von Huene, Roland, and Doak C. Cox. Locally generated tsunamis and other local waves in The Great Alaska Earthquake of 1964: Oceanography and Coastal Engineering. NAS Pub. 1605. Washington: National Academy of Sciences, 1972.
States that locally generated waves, produced by impulsive generation or resonant coupling, caused more destruction and loss of life than the major tsunami did.

von Huene, Roland, Richard J. Malloy, George G. Shor, Jr., and Pierre St.-Amand. Geologic structures in the aftershock region of the 1964 Alaskan earthquake. Journal of Geophysical Research, 72 (July 15, 1967), 3649–3660.
Describes geologic structures on the Continental Shelf, some of which were active during the earthquake.

von Huene, Roland, George G. Shor, Jr., and Richard J. Malloy. Offshore tectonic features in the affected region in The Great Alaska Earthquake of 1964: Oceanography and Coastal Engineering. NAS Pub. 1605. Washington: National Academy of Sciences, 1972.
Discusses the tectonism along the Alaska and Aleutian trends, deformation on the Continental Shelf, and the thrust-fault and steep-fault tectonic models.

von Huene, Roland, George G. Shor, Jr., and Erk Reimnitz. Geological interpretation of seismic profiles in Prince William Sound, Alaska. Geological Survey of America Bulletin, 78 (Feburary 1967), 259–268.
States that seismic reflection profiles made during the summer of 1964 reveal the ice-sculptured metamorphic basement, overlain by probable glacial drift, and Holocene marine sediments; the present sea floor does not closely represent the effects of glaciation. Little evidence of Holocene faulting was found.

Waller, Roger M. Effects of the earthquake of March 27, 1964, in the Homer area, Alaska. U.S. Geological Survey Professional Paper 542-D. Washington: Government Printing Office, 1966. 28 p. Also in The Great Alaska Earthquake of 1964: Geology. NAS Pub. 1601. Washington: National Academy of Sciences, 1971. p. 461–488.
Describes submarine slides, subsidence, and local tsunami waves in the Homer area.

Weller, Jack M. Human responses to tsunami warnings in The Great Alaska Earthquake of 1964: Oceanography and Ocean Engineering. NAS Pub. 1605. Washington: National Academy of Sciences, 1972.
Focuses on the range of tsunami warnings and of responses among several Alaska communities and those outside of Alaska.

White, W. R. H. The Alaska earthquake—Its effects in Canada Canadian Geographical Journal, 72 (June 1966), 210–219.
Describes in detail the damage and other effects of the earth movements and tsunami in such areas of Canada as Hot Springs Cove, Juan de Fuca Strait, and Alberni Inlet.

Whitten, Charles H. Crustal movements associated with the Alaskan

earthquake (Abstract). *Transactions, American Geophysical Union,* 45 (December 1964), 633.
Describes horizontal tectonic displacement associated with the earthquake.

Wiegel, Robert L. Tsunamis *in* Earthquake Engineering. Englewood Cliffs, New Jersey: Prentice-Hall, Inc., 1970. 518 p.
Reports on causes and nature of tsunamis, tsunami generation and damage, tsunami travel in the ocean and waves along the shore, distribution functions, and wave forces.

Wiegel, Robert L. Protection of Crescent City, California, from tsunami waves. Berkeley: The Redevelopment Agency of the City of Crescent City, March 5, 1965. 114 p.
Studies the occurrence of tsunamis in the Pacific, their height and resonance at Crescent City, structure design for withstanding tsunami damage, and possible protective measures.

Wiegel, Robert L. Seismic sea waves (tsunamis) *in* Geological hazards and public problems. Conference Proceedings, Region Seven, Santa Rosa, California, May 27–28, 1969. Robert A. Olson and Mildred M. Wallace, editors. Washington: Government Printing Office, 1969. p. 53–75.
Discusses problems (such as poor design of oil storage facilities, flotation of vehicles and buildings, and damage to small vessels) resulting from the 1964 Alaska tsunami, and then considers the relationship between tsunamis and tectonic displacements associated with earthquakes.

Wigen, S. O., and W. R. H. White. Tsunami of March 27–29, 1964, west coast of Canada. Canada Department of Mines and Technical Surveys Duplicate Report. Victoria: Canada Department of Mines and Technical Surveys, 1964. 12 p.
States that the great Alaska earthquake produced the largest tsunami waves ever recorded on the Canadian west coast; also describes some of the wave characteristics.

Wilson, Basil W. Earthquake occurrence and effects in ocean areas. Technical report CR. 69.027 to U.S. Naval Civil Engineering Laboratory. Port Hueneme: U.S. Naval Engineering Laboratory, February 1969. 141 p.
Draws on evidence of oceanographic effects of Alaska earthquake in discussion of ocean seismicity, phenomenology and statistics of submarine earthquakes, and marine seismic hazards.

Wilson, Basil W. Tsunami characteristics at representative tide stations along the Pacific seaboard. Final Report prepared for Coastal Engineering Research Center. Washington: U.S. Army Corps of Engineers, May 1971. 185 p.
Uses rigorous methods of numerical power-spectrum analysis and filtering of time-series functions to investigate the reliability of the author's own earlier subjective analyses; shows that those analyses were reasonably accurate in their definition of the beat character of the waves and the presence of ultra-long-period wave components in the tsunami waves at some stations.

Wilson, Basil W., and Alf Tørum. Effects of the tsunamis. An engineering study *in* The Great Alaska Earthquake of 1964: Oceanography and Coastal Engineering. NAS Pub. 1605. Washington: National Academy of Sciences, 1972.
Describes the wave action and the effects of the tsunamis and also gives recommendations for protection against tsunami damage.

Wilson, Basil W., and Alf Tørum. Runup heights of the major tsunami on North American coasts *in* The Great Alaska Earthquake of 1964: Oceanography and Coastal Engineering. NAS Pub. 1605. Washington: National Academy of Sciences, 1972.
Observes that there is an empirical relationship, based on Pacific Ocean data, which indicates a statistical dependence of maximum tsunami height near the source region on the earthquake magnitude.

Wilson, Basil W., and Alf Tørum. The tsunami of the Alaskan earthquake, 1964: Engineering evaluation. Coastal Engineering Research Center Technical Memorandum No. 25. Washington: U.S. Army Corps of Engineers, May 1968. 444 p.
Mentions nature of earth dislocation and relates it to the generation, propagation, and dispersion of the main tsunami waves. Analyses relate character of these waves to local bay and shelf oscillations. Describes local tsunamis and their origin and also the engineering effect of tsunamis.

Wood, Fergus J., and Lorne G. Taylor. Nautical chart revisions *in* Volume I: The Prince William Sound, Alaska, earthquake of 1964 and aftershocks. Environmental Science Services Administration, U.S. Coast and Geodetic Survey. Washington: Government Printing Office, 1966. p. 193–238. Also *in* The Great Alaska Earthquake of 1964: Oceanography and Coastal Engineering. NAS Pub. 1605. Washington: National Academy of Sciences, 1972.
Includes nautical charts of the Prince William Sound area and the Gulf of Alaska which were published between 1879 and December 1964; lists (1) the charts that were affected by the tsunami and (2) six preliminary chartlets issued on April 21, 1964, for navigation needs.

Yutzy, Daniel. Aesop 1964: contingencies affecting the issuing of public disaster warning at Crescent City, California. Disaster Research Center Research Note 4: Columbus: The Ohio State University, Disaster Research Center, 1964. 8 p.
Draws attention to the crucial decisions that have to be made by public officials when they receive information on a probable disaster; presents tsunami timetable and responses at Crescent City in March 1964.

Zetler, B. D. Earthquake effect on *Glomar II.* Memorandum from Chief, Research Group, to Deputy Assistant Director for Oceanography, U.S. Coast and Geodetic Survey, September 4, 1964. [Rockville, Maryland] : U.S. Coast and Geodetic Survey, 1964. 2 p. (Copy on file, Library, National Academy of Sciences–National Academy of Engineering, Washington, D.C.)
Ascribes violent shaking on the ship *Glomar II* to longitudinal seismic oscillations rather than to the tsunami.

Contributors to
This Volume

EDUARD BERG, University of Alaska, College, Alaska 99735

SAUL C. BERKMAN, National Ocean Survey, NOAA, Rockville, Maryland 20852

DOAK C. COX, University of Hawaii, Honolulu, Hawaii 96822

DAVID DIVOKY, Tetra Tech, Inc., Pasadena, California 91107

AUGUSTINE S. FURUMOTO, University of Hawaii, Honolulu, Hawaii 96822

G DALLAS HANNA, California Academy of Sciences, San Francisco, California 94118 [deceased]

STEACY D. HICKS, National Ocean Survey, NOAA, Rockville, Maryland 20852

GEORGE W. HOUSNER, California Institute of Technology, Pasadena, California 91109

LI-SAN HWANG, Tetra Tech, Inc., Pasadena, California 91107

KINJIRO KAJIURA, University of Tokyo, Tokyo, Japan

HIROSI KAWASUMI, University of Tokyo, Tokyo, Japan

HAROLD G. LOOMIS, University of Hawaii, Honolulu, Hawaii 96822

ARTHUR MCGARR, University of Witwatersrand, Johannesburg, South Africa

RICHARD J. MALLOY, U.S. Naval Civil Engineering Laboratory, Port Hueneme, California 93043

GEORGE F. MERRILL, National Ocean Survey, NOAA, Miami, Florida 33130

JOHN NORTHROP, Naval Undersea Research and Development Center, San Diego, California 92132

ERK REIMNITZ, U.S. Geological Survey, Menlo Park, California 94025

ETSUZO SHIMA, University of Tokyo, Tokyo, Japan

GEORGE G. SHOR, JR., Scripps Institution of Oceanography, La Jolla, California 92037

MARK G. SPAETH, National Ocean Survey, NOAA, Rockville, Maryland 20852

HARRIS B. STEWART, JR., Institute for Oceanography, NOAA, Miami, Florida 33130

LORNE G. TAYLOR, Decca Survey Systems, Lynwood, Washington 98036

ALF TØRUM, Technical University of Norway, Trondheim, Norway

WILLIAM G. VAN DORN, Scripps Institution of Oceanography, La Jolla, California 92037

ROLAND E. VON HUENE, U.S. Geological Survey, Menlo Park, California 94025

ROBERT C. VORHIS, U.S. Geological Survey, Atlanta, Georgia 30309

JACK M. WELLER, Connecticut College, New London, Connecticut 06320

BASIL W. WILSON, 529 South Winston Avenue, Pasadena, California 91107

FERGUS J. WOOD, National Ocean Survey, NOAA, Rockville, Maryland 20852

ENGLISH–METRIC CONVERSION TABLE

LENGTH

1 inch (in.)	=	2.54	centimeters (cm)
1 foot (ft) [12 in.]	=	30.48	cm
1 yard (yd) [3 ft]	=	91.44	cm
	=	0.914	meter (m)
1 mile (mi) [5280 ft]	=	1.610	kilometer (km)

AREA

1 square inch (in.^{2})	=	6.45	square centimeters (cm^2)
1 square foot (ft^2)	=	929.0	cm^2
	=	0.0929	square meter (m^2)
1 square yard (yd^2)	=	0.836	m^2
1 acre (a) [43560 ft^2]	=	0.4047	hectare (ha)
1 square mile (mi^2)	=	2.59	square kilometers (km^2)

VOLUME

1 cubic inch (in.^{3})	=	16.4	cubic centimeters (cm^3)
1 cubic foot (ft^3)	=	28.3	$\times 10^3$ cm^3
	=	0.0283	m^3
1 cubic yard (yd^3)	=	0.7646	cubic meter (m^3)
1 cubic mile (mi^3)	=	4.17	cubic kilometers (km^3)
1 quart (qt) [0.25 U.S. gallon (gal)]	=	0.95	liter
1 gal [4 qt]	=	3.79	liter
1 bushel (bu) [U.S. dry]	=	35.24	liter

MASS

1 pound (lb) [16 ounces (oz)]	=	453.6	grams (g)
	=	0.4536	kilogram (kg)
1 U.S. ton (tn) [2000 lb]	=	907.2	kg
	=	0.9072	metric ton (MT)
1 long ton (LT) [2240 lb]	=	1.016	MT

PRESSURE

1 pound per square inch (lb/in.^{2} or psi)	=	0.0704	kilogram per square centimeter (kg/cm^2)
1 pound per square foot (lb/ft^2)	=	4.8824	kilograms per square meter (kg/m^2)
1 bar [1000 millibars (mb)]	=	1.020	kg/cm^2

VELOCITY

1 foot per second (ft/s)	=	0.3048	meter per second (m/s)
	=	1.097	kilometer per hour (km/h)
	=	0.5925	international knot (kn)
1 mile per hour (mi/h)	=	1.609	km/h
	=	0.869	kn

METRIC–ENGLISH CONVERSION TABLE

LENGTH

1 millimeter (mm) [0.1 centimeter (cm)]	=	0.0394 inch (in.)
1 cm [10 mm]	=	0.3937 in.
1 meter (m) [100 cm]	=	39.37 in.
	=	3.28 feet (ft)
1 kilometer (km) [1000 m]	=	0.621 mile (mi)
1 international nautical mile [1852 m]	=	6076.1 ft

AREA

1 square centimeter (cm^2)	=	0.155 square inch (in.^{2})
1 square meter (m^2)	=	10.76 square feet (ft^2)
	=	1.196 square yards (yd^2)
1 hectare (ha)	=	2.4710 acres (a)
1 square kilometer (km^2)	=	0.386 square mile (mi^2)

VOLUME

1 cubic centimeter (cm^3)	=	0.0610 cubic inch (in.^{3})
1 cubic meter (m^3)	=	35.314 cubic feet (ft^3)
	=	1.31 cubic yards (yd^3)
1 cubic kilometer (km^3)	=	0.240 cubic mile (mi^3)
1 liter	=	1.06 quarts (qt)
	=	0.264 gallon (gal)

MASS

1 kilogram (kg) [1000 grams (g)]	=	2.20 pounds (lb)
	=	0.0011 ton
1 metric ton (MT) [1000 kg]	=	1.10 ton
	=	0.9842 long ton (LT)

PRESSURE

1 kilogram per square centimeter (kg/cm^2)	=	14.20 pounds per square inch (lb/in.^{2})
	=	2048 pounds per square foot (lb/ft^2)

VELOCITY

1 meter per second (m/s)	=	3.281 feet per second (ft/s)
1 kilometer per hour (km/h)	=	0.9113 ft/s
	=	0.621 mile per hour (mi/h)
1 knot (kn) [1852 m/h]	=	1.6878 ft/s
	=	1.151 mi/h

Index

Figures in italic indicate major discussion of topic.

Afognak, tsunami damage, 397
  tsunami warning, 224
Afognak Island, tsunami runup (map), 367,
  399
aftershock area, Alaska earthquake, *123*
aftershock distribution (map), 115, 195
aftershock hypocenters, Kodiak, *T*-phase
  signals (illus.), 23
aftershock-tsunami origin relations (graph),
  126
aftershocks (map), 40, 125
  T-phases, *21*
Agnew, D. M., 43
Aialik Bay, tsunami, 356
  waves, 214
Air Photo Tech, Inc., 422
Alaska, Aleutian earthquake (1957),
  tsunami, 46
  arriving tsunamis, 1869–1966 (table), 242
  continental margin, tectonic setting, *267*
  crustal displacement measurements (table),
    127
  earthquake-affected area (map), 268
  epicentral area (map), 113
  Kamchatka earthquake (1952), tsunami,
    46
  Lituya Bay earthquake (1958), landslides-
    generated tsunami, 341
  place names (map), 159
  south central (map), *x*
  tide-gage records (illus.), 70, 71, 72
  tsunami effects, *47*
  tsunami frequency, *355*
  tsunami runup (table), 127, 243
  tsunami warning, *222*
    problems, *239*
  tsunamis, 1788–1965 (table), 240
  Yakutat Bay earthquake (1899) crustal
    deformation, 265
Alaska coast, emergence, 114
Alaska Construction (magazine), 441, 442,
  446
Alaska Continental Shelf, arch at edge, *277*
  seafloor bathymetry, pre- and postearth-
    quake (illus.), 284
  seismic profiles (illus.), 277, 278

tectonic history, 250
Tertiary basin, *275*
vertical uplift, 257
Alaska continental slope, tectonics, *279*
Alaska Department of Highways, boring, 300
Alaska earthquake, aftershocks, *see* aftershocks
  atmospheric waves, summary, 342
  bathymetric changes, summary, 340
  biological effects, *307*
  Cenozoic deformation, *284*
  coastal effects, 340
  continental shelf deformation, *282*
  contributions to oceanographic knowl-
    edge, *5*
  crustal deformation, summary, 339
  crustal rupture lines (map), 124
  effects at Copper River Delta, *290*
  fault hinge line, 126
  fault location, *123*
  fault orientation, *123*
  fault rupture, length, *123*
  geological effects, summary, *339*
  horizontal crustal displacement, *126*
  limitations of eyewitness accounts, *339*
  local waves, *39*
  magnitude, *123*
  main shock *T*-phases, *20*
  marine biological effects, 305
  marine phenomena, *339*
  marine tectonic events, summary, *339*
  nature of ground motion, *114*
  navigation effects, *306*
  oceanographic effects, *xii*
    limitations, *6*
  offshore tectonics, *266*
  physical oceanographic changes, *305*
  raised intertidal invertebrates, 308
  rise in prediction, *331*
  sea-floor deformation, *249*
  seiches, *see* seiches
  seismic effects, *11*
  significance to seaquakes, *17*
  steep-fault model, *286*
  study as rare event, *337*
  T-phases, *19*

tectonic mechanisms, *285*
thrust-fault model, *286*
tsunami, *see* tsunamis
uplifted area, tsunami-generation, 38
vertical crustal displacement, *126*
Alaska earthquake area, geomorphology,
  112
Alaska earthquake (1958), *T*-phase, 21
Alaska fiords, seiches, 219
Alaska King Crab, Inc., 365
Alaska Mainland Structural System, 267,
  281
Alaska Public Works Division, 453
The Alaska Railroad, 459
  Seward, damage, 424–427; (photo), 416
  tsunami damage, 424
  Whittier, 459
Alaska Regional Tsunami Warning System,
  35, 238, 243, 344
  local generation area, *345*
Alaska Seismic Sea Wave Warning System
  communication network (illus.), 68
Alaska Standard (vessel), 306, 410, 411,
  415, 416, 417, 428, 509
  seaquake report, 16
  wreckage on board (photo), 418
Alaska Tsunami Warning Center, 63
Albatross Bank, deformation, 285
  faulting, 284
  uplift, 282, 286
Alden dual-channel wet-paper recorder, 259
Aleksa, Kaave, 16, 17
Aleutian earthquake, tsunami observations,
  46
Aleutian Structural System, 267
  geologic section (illus.), 271
  nearshore and fiord areas, 269
  tectonic elements, *267*
Aleutian Structural Trend, Continental Shelf,
  269
  fault zone, *269*
Aleutian Trench, seismic profiles (illus.),
  280, 281
  submarine channel, 281
  tectonics, 250, *279*
  tsunami (1946), 485

Allen, George, 14, 17
Amend, Ollie, 415
American Society of Civil Engineers, *xv*
Anchorage, tsunami, 407
Anchorage Approaches, nautical chart
    changes, 328
Anchorage Daily News, 429
Anchorage Waterfront Area, nautical chart
    changes, 326
Anderson Bay, tsunami damage, 459
Antarctica, Argentine Islands, tsunami, 150
    Palmer Peninsula, tsunami, 35, 120
    tide-gage records (illus.), 98
Appalachian Basin, surface-wave attenuation,
    27
Arcer, 292
Argentina, tide-gage records (illus.), 98
Argentina Servicio de Hidrografia Naval,
    Secretaria de Marina, 66
Armed Forces Radio station, early tsunami
    warning, 56
artesian pressure, Seward Delta, 423
asphalt spill, Port Valdez (map), 456
atmospheric pressure waves, *133*
    California, Berkeley, 133
        La Jolla, 133
        Scripps Institution of Oceanography,
        114
    summary, 342
Australia, Bureau of Mineral Resources,
    Geology and Geophysics, 66
    Naval Hydrographic Service, 66
    tide-gage records, (illus.), 104
Ayres, Cohen and Hayakawa, *xv*

backfill settlement, Kodiak Naval Station
    (photo), 396
backfill wave, 217
    Kenai Lake, 214
Ballard, Ron, 209
Barney, Lt. C. R., 32, 121, 161, 162, 363,
    364
barograms, theoretical source area (map),
    134
Barr, James, 371, 374, 379
Bascom, W. E., 485
bathymetry, Cook Inlet, Continental Shelf
    (map), 405
    Kodiak Island area (map), 401
    Kodiak area (map), 368
    Montague Island area sea floor, 258
    Orca Bay and Inlet (map), 470
        pre- and postearthquake (map), 476
    Passage Canal area (map), 460
    Port Wells area (map), 458
    Prince William Sound (map), 431
    Resurrection Bay (map), 409
    Seldovia Bay (map), 406
    Valdez Arm area (map), 435
bathymetry changes, summary, 340
Baxter, Rae, 297
Benton, A. R., Jr., 265
Berg, Eduard, 4, 453

Berkman, S. C., 4
Best, K. B., 43
bibliography, oceanography, and coastal
    engineering, *525*
Bien, G. S., 301
Bilderback, Charles R., 32, 121, 158, 202
biological effects, Alaska earthquake, 305,
    307
bird nesting, changes, 308
Blackstone Bay, tsunami, 356
    waves, 215
boat losses, British Columbia, Port Alberni,
    306
    California, Crescent City, 306
        Noyo, 306
        San Rafael, 306
    Gulf of Mexico, 306
    Washington, Seattle, 306
Boswell Bay, tsunami effects, 434
Brechan, Fred, 365
British Columbia, Alberni Inlet, natural
    period, 57
    Alberni (map), 480
        tsunami warning, 225
    Amai, tsunami damage, 57
    Coal Harbour, tsunami, 478
    Fair Harbor, tsunami, 477
    Fraser River, tsunami, 479
    Klaskino Inlet, tsunami, 478
    Pitt Lake, tsunami, 165
    Port Alice, tsunami, 478
    Port Alberni, boat losses, 306
        marigram, analysis (illus.), 479
        MacMillan, Bloedel and Powell River
            Co., Ltd., 481
        role of Provincial Civil Defense, 481
        Sproat Narrows beacons, damage, 482
        Trans-Pacific submarine cable, damage,
        482
        tsunami, 165, *479*
        tsunami record, 148
    Queen Charlotte Islands, Shields Bay,
        tsunami, 165
    Tasu, tsunami record, 148
    Queen Charlotte Strait, tsunami, 479
    San Josef Bay, tsunami, 478
    Tahsis camp, tsunami, 478
    Tahsis Narrow, fish kill, 477
    Tasu Sound, tsunami, 57
    Tofino, tsunami record, 148
    Vancouver Island, Hot Springs Cove,
        tsunami effects, 477
        tsunami, 165
        tsunami runup (map), 167, 478
        wave damage, 57
    Winter Harbour, tsunami, 478
    Zeballos, wave damage, 57
bridge damage, Washington, Joe Creek, 482
    Kodiak Island, Womens Bay (photo), 398
Brown, Delmer L., 121
Burgess, L. R., 43
Butchart, Col., 48
Butler, Lee, 209

California, Atkin River, tsunami, 484
    Berkeley, atmospheric waves, 133
    Crescent City (map), 493
        boat losses, 306
        Citizen's Dock (illus.), 496, 498; (photo),
        499, 500
        Continental Shelf, oscillation (illus.), 489
        harbor damage by tsunami, 508
        marigram analysis (illus.), 488
        sensitivity to tsunamis, 490
        tsunami, *58*, 169, 225, 359, *487*
        tsunami damage (photo), 495, 497, 500
            estimate, 498
        tsunami runup (map), 492, 494
        tsunami warning, 225
        tsunami (1960), wave spectrum (illus.),
        490
    Crescent City area, nautical charts, 316
    Crescent Harbor, nautical chart changes,
    318
    El Centro earthquake (1940), ground
        displacement (illus.), 194
    Humboldt County, tsunami warning, 60,
    226
    La Jolla, atmospheric waves, 114, 133
        microbarograph (illus.), 115
    Long Beach Harbor, tsunami damage, 487
    Los Angeles, tsunami record, 148
    Los Angeles County, tsunami, 60
        tsunami warning, 225
    Los Angeles Harbor, tsunami damage, 487
    Marin County, tsunami, 60
    Mendocino County, tsunami, 60
    Monterey Bay, apparent modal oscillation
        periods (table), 485
        tsunami, 169, 484
    northern coast, tsunamis (table), 177
    Noyo, boat losses, 306
    Noyo River, tsunami, 484
    Point Sur, *T*-phase records, 20
    San Diego, tsunami, 60
        tsunami warning, 226
    San Diego County, tsunami warning, 225
    San Fernando earthquake (1971), move-
        ment, 353
    San Francisco, tsunami, 60, 484
        tsunami record, 148
        tsunami warning, 226
    San Francisco Bay, tsunami, 169
    San Francisco earthquake (1906), tsunami,
    341
    San Rafael, boat losses, 306
    Santa Cruz, tsunami runup (map), 486
    Santa Monica, tsunami, 169
        tide-gage records (illus.), 84–87
        tsunami, 169
        tsunami damage, *58*, *484*
            estimate, 487
        tsunami runup (map), 171
California Academy of Sciences, *xv*, *xvi*
    aid to Panel on Oceanography, 4
California Department of General Services,
    60

California Disaster Office, 58, 60
  tsunami warning, 225
California Institute of Technology, *xv*
Canada, tide-gage records (illus.), 73–82
  tsunami damage, *57*
  tsunami effects, *476*
  tsunami runup (table), 175
Canadian Hydrographic Service, 66
Canal Zone, tide-gage records (illus.), 92
Canton Island, tsunami, 209
Cape Chiniak, tsunami warning, 224
Cape Resurrection to Two Arm Bay,
  nautical chart changes, 328
Cape St. Elias to Shumagin Islands, nautical
  chart changes, 328
Cape Yakataga, tsunami computed cf.
  observed (illus.), 208
  tsunami-tide effects (illus.), 161
  tsunami runup, 158
casualties, Alaska earthquake, tsunamis
  (table), 39, 504
Cenozoic deformation, *284*
Chance, Genie, 415, 472
charts, emergency, postearthquake, *315*
Chena (Vessel), 42, 216, 306, 357, 437,
  440–445, 447, 449, 453, 509
  path in Valdez harbor (map), 441
  seaquake report, 14
Chenega, local waves, 42, 214, 356, 432
  tsunami warning, 223
Chenega Island, fish kills, 308
Chien, Chen-Wu, 58
Chile, tide-gage records (illus.), 95, 96, 97
  tsunami, *61*, 164
  tsunami warning, 226
Chile Departamento de Navigacion e
  Hidrografia de la Armada, 66
Chile earthquake (1960), tsunami, 47
  tsunami in California, 490
  vessel damage, 510
Chilkoot, (vessel) seaquake report, 16
Christiansen, 413, 429
Christmas Island, tide-gage records (illus.),
  100
Civil Aeronautics Administration, 43
clam-beds, loss, 308
Clark, Joe, 14
Clark, Robert, 415
Clark University, *xv*
Cliff Mine, tsunami, 449
Clifton, Paul, 180
Clinocardium nuttallii (cockle), 475
Clock, Mrs., 434
Coastal Engineering Research Center, 4, 353
Cobb Seamount, tsunami focusing, 58
Coles, Will, 16, 375, 376
Columbia, tide-gage records (illus.), 92, 93
Columbia River, tide-gage records (illus.),
  170
  tsunami, *482*
  tsunami wave propagation, analysis
    (illus.), 483

Committee on the Alaska Earthquake, meetings, *3*
Continental Shelf deformation, Alaska earthquake, *282*
Cook Inlet, Continental Shelf, bathymetry
  (map), 405
  local waves, 213
  tsunamis, 403
Copper River Delta, bottomset beds, 294
  earthquake effects, *290*
  Egg Island Trough, 294
  exposed buried forest, 295
    radiocarbon dates, 296; (table), 298
  foreset beds, slumping, 293
  "ground breakage," 300
  Middle Ground Shoal, 292
    cross section (illus.), 293
    postearthquake bottom profiles (illus.),
      293
  postearthquake sediment, 295
  postearthquake Sonoprobe record (photo),
    294
  preearthquake evidence, *298*
  radiocarbon dates (map), 297
  salt marsh balance, 295
  sediment ejection, 292
  seiche effects, *297*, 298
  seismic shock effects, *292*
  Sonoprobe, 294, 295
    record (illus.), 294
  submarine slumping, 292
  tide line, seaward shift (map), 296
  tsunami effects, *297*
  uplift results, *295*
Copper River Delta region (map), 291
Cordova, bathymetry changes, 475
  harbor (map), 471
  local waves, 42
  marigram, inferred (illus.), 472
  tidal harmonic constants (table), 311
  tide prediction, 311
  tsunami, *469*
  tsunami damage estimate, 475
  uplift (photo), 477
Cordova–Orca Inlet, nautical chart changes,
  328
Costa Rica, tide-gage records (illus.), 91
Cox, Doak C., 4, 7, 12, 23, 35, 163, 209,
  226, 227, 306, 353, 514
Crab Bay, tsunami warning, 224
Cretaceous, Orca Group, Montague Island,
  254
crustal displacement, horizontal, *126*
  vertical, *126*
crustal displacement measurements, Alaska
  (table), 127
crustal tectonics, plate tectonics model, 340
crustal uplift, seafloor, Montague Island
  area (map), 261
Cudahy Slough, exposed submerged forest,
  295
Culross Passage, tsunami effects, 434
Curray, J. R., 301

damage estimate, tsunami, Cordova, 475
  Valdez, 459
  Whittier, 467
de Ballore, Montessus, 32
Defense Communication Agency, 63
deformation, Cenozoic, *284*
Deveau, Peter, 365, 367, 369
Dietz, R. S., 265
Dunning [seaman], 441, 444, 447

E G and G-Alpine spark sounder, 266
Eads, John, 410, 413, 415, 416
Eads, Robert, 410, 413, 415, 416, 429
earthquake damage, Seward (photo), 428
earthquake hazards, *337*
  marine effects, *337*
earthquake waves, nomenclature, *32*
earthquakes, value of historical information,
  338
East Indies, Krakatoa volcano, study, 338
Easter Island, tide-gage records (illus.), 99
economics, tsunami protective measures, *511*
Ecuador, tide-gage records (illus.), 93, 94
Edgerton, Germeshausen, and Grier, Inc.,
  261
Egg Island Trough, reworked sediments, 298
El Dorado (vessel), seaquake report, 16, 17
Elk River Company, Nootka Island, tsunami
  damage, 477
El Salvador, tide-gage records (illus.), 90
emergence, Alaska coast, 114
emergency charting, postearthquake, *315*
Emory University, *xv*
Emperor Seamount Chain, *T*-phase origin,
  20
Endresen [Seward resident], 412
engineering studies, tsunami effects, *361*
England, National Institute of Oceanography,
  66
Eniwetok Island, *T*-phase records, 20
erosion, Kodiak Island, Nyman Peninsula
  (photo), 397
  Womens Bay, roadbed (photo), 397
Eyak River, exposed submerged forest, 295
eyewitness accounts, Seward, 412
  limitations, *339*
  Valdez, 437

Falcon (vessel), 440, 450, 451, 453
farshore wave, 217
  Kenai Lake, 214
fatalities, tsunami (table), 227
fault models, Alaska earthquake, *286*
fault zone, 249
faults, Alaska earthquake, *123*
  seafloor, Montague Island area (map), 261
  Aleutian Structural Trend, seafloor, *269*
Federal Aviation Administration, 43
  warning system, 66
Federal Disaster Act, *xi*
Federal Reconstruction and Development
  Planning Commission for Alaska, *xi*
Fern (vessel), seaquake report, 16

fiords, geologic processes, *250*
　Holocene vertical changes, 285
Fire Island Shoal, nautical chart changes,
　322
fish kills, Alaska earthquake, summary, 340
　British Columbia, Tahsis Narrow, 477
　Chenega Island, 308
　Passage Canal, 308
　Valdez Arm, 308
fishing fleet losses, Alaska earthquake, 306
flow and force field, tsunami, *516*
Fohnes, D., 472–474
forest, preearthquake submergence, Copper
　River Delta, 296
forest flooding, 308
Fortress (vessel), 365
Fraser River Delta, slumping, 294
Fremlin, Howard, 371, 374
Fremlin, Mrs. Howard, 374

geologic sections, Aleutian Structural
　System (illus.), 271
　Prince William Sound (illus.), 270
geological effects, marine, *249*
　shoreline, *249*
Geological Society of America, *xv*
geology, Montague Island, 254
geomorphology, Alaska earthquake area, *112*
Gilfillen, Hal, 415, 424
Gilson [Valdez resident], 453
Glomar II (vessel), seaquake report, 14
Gold River, Nootka Island, tsunami damage,
　477
Goodman, R., 473, 474
Green, C. K., 43
Guatamala, tide-gage records (illus.), 90
Gulf of Alaska (map), 362
　bathymetric map, tectonic features, 272
　computerized grid, tsunami (map), 197
　Continental Shelf bathymetry (map), 160,
　　366
　horizontal displacement (map), 131
　land dislocations (map), 116
　land elevation changes (map), 113
　large earthquakes (map), 114
　nautical chart revision, hydrography (map),
　　318
　seismological history, *112*
　strain release (map), 273
　tsunami source (map), 132, 135
　tsunami wave front model (map), 141
　vertical crustal displacement (map), 130
　vertical displacement hypsographs (illus.),
　　136
Gulf of Mexico, boat losses, 306
Gulf of Mexico area, seiches, 219
Gupta formula, *T*-phase duration, 21
Gypsy (vessel), 444, 445, 453; (photo), 453

Hale, Bob, 16
Halibut Cove, tsunami, 407
Halibut Producers' Co-op, 412
Hancock, Rex, 14

Hanna, G Dallas, *vi*, 4
Hanning Bay fault, sea-floor, 255
Harbison, R. N., 265
harbor structures, tsunami damage and
　protection, *508*
harbors, vessel movement protective mea-
　sures, *509*
Hardin, Harold, 14, 17
Harding [seaman], 441
Harry, George Y., Jr., 4
Hatch, Thelma, 412, 415
Hawaii Institute of Geophysics, 138
　Tsunami Research Group, 20
Hawaiian Islands, Hawaii, Acting Tsunami
　Advisor, 226
　Civ-Alert System, 60
　Kahului Railroad Company, 60
　tsunami records, 148
　tsunami runup, 155, 163, 186; (map),
　　186
　tsunami warning, 226
　tsunamis, *60*
　Hilo, tsunami runup (map), 186
　Kaneohe, *T*-phase, 20
　Kauai, tsunami runup (map), 184
　Maui, tsunami runup (map), 185
　Mokuoloe, water level, 185
　Oahu, helicorder record (illus.), 20
　　T-phase record, 20
　　tsunami runup (map), 184
　　tide-gage records (illus.), 100–102, *181*,
　　　182, 183
　　tsunami, *181*
　tsunami amplitude (illus.), 207
　tsunami energy decay, *187*; (illus.), 189
　tsunami energy vs. center frequency
　　(illus.), 190
　tsunami potential energy spectra (illus.),
　　187
　tsunami spectra, *186*
　water levels, *185*
Hawaii State Civil Defense, 47
　tsunami warning, 226, 231, 344
helicorder record, Hawaiian Islands, Oahu
　(illus.), 20
Herron, William, 487
Hicks, Steacy D., 4, 306
Hill, Del, 415
Hobo Bay, tsunami effects, 434
Hodgson (vessel), 161, 252, 253, 319, 326,
　328
Holban, James, 415, 420
Homer, tsunami damage, 404
Homer Harbor, nautical chart changes, 326
Homer Spit, pre- and postearthquake (map),
　406
Hong Kong, Royal Observatory, 66
　tide-gage record (illus.), 106
Honolulu Observatory, tsunami warning,
　222
horizontal movement, Resurrection Bay,
　416
horizontal translation, local waves, *218*

Housner, George W., 353, 514
Hubbs, C. L., 301
Hyde, Tom, 411, 412
hydrographic surveys, Montague Island area,
　pre- and postearthquake (map), 255

Instituto de Geofisica, Universidad Nacional
　de Mexico, 66
Inter-American Geodetic Survey, 66
Intergovernmental Oceanographic Com-
　mission, 238, 346
International [Tsunami] Coordinating
　Group, 238
International Tsunami Information Center,
　238
intertidal streams, postearthquake adjust-
　ment, 295
invertebrates, intertidal, uplifted, 308

Jackson Point, tsunami damage, 459
Japan, Kushiro, tsunami warning, 226
　Miyagi–Enoshima, tsunami record, 148
　Nankaido earthquake (1946), tsunami, 112
　Onahama, tsunami record, 148
　Sanriku earthquake (1933), tsunami, 112
　tsunami heights, 1933–1961 (illus.), 205
　tide-gage records (illus.), 106–109
Japan Society for the Promotion of Science,
　137
Jennings, Paul, 4
Jergins, Elton, 415
Johnson, R. H., 23
Johnson, L. B., *xi*
Jones, Don A., 265
Jones, Ralph, 367, 369, 371
Jordan, C. L., *xv*
Jorgeson Brothers, 478

Kachemak Bay, local waves, 213
　seismic seiches, 404
Kadiak Fisheries cannery, damage, 402
Kaguyak, tsunami damage, 403
　tsunami warning, 223
Kayak Island, Cape St. Elias, tsunami warn-
　ing, 224
Kenai Lake, backfill wave, 214
　farshore wave, 214
　seiche, 213, 219, 429
　waves, *213*
Kenai–Kodiak, seismic profiles (illus.), 274
Kenai–Kodiak structural block, 269
Kenai Peninsula, Resurrection Bay, tsunami,
　407
　submergence, 114
　tsunami damage, summary, *498*
　tsunami runup, 161
Kenai Peninsula area, Continental Shelf,
　tsunami generation (illus.), 403
Keller, Fred, 43
Keller, G., 265
Kennedy, Arthur, 214
Kester, Francis E., 227
King, Neil, 415

Kings Bay, tsunami, 356
  waves, 215
Kirkpatrick, Mildred, 415
Knagin, Harry, 16
Knauss, John A., *xv*
Knight Island, Port Oceanic, waves, 215
  tsunami, 356
Knight Island Passage, tsunami, 117, 356
  tsunami generation, 33
  waves, 214
Kodiak (map), 370; (photo), 377
  aftershock hypocenters, *T*-phase signals
    (illus.), 23
  Alaska King Crab, damage, 379
  Alaska Packers Association cannery, 378
  boat harbor topography, tsunami (map),
    382
  Donnally Atchison Store, 377
  harbor damage by tsunami, 508
  high-tide flooding, postearthquake (photo),
    386
  Hobby Shop boat repair house, 387
  hypothetical marigram (illus.), 371
  initial tsunami report, 47
  Lill's Cafe, damage, 379
  marigram, hypothetical (illus.), 376
  nautical chart changes, 318
  postearthquake (photo), *ii*, 380
  pre- and postearthquake nautical charts,
    327
  preearthquake (map), 375; (photos), 379,
    380, 387
  St. Paul harbor (photo), 377
  tsunami, 161; (photo), 372, 373, 374
    laboratory model (illus.), 378
  tsunami damage, *363, 377*; (photo), 381,
    384, 385, 387; (table), 390
  tsunami-resistant structures (table), 386
  tsunami warning, 224
Kodiak Airways, damage, 379
Kodiak area (map), 369
  bathymetry (map), 368
  Continental Shelf, *T*-phase origin, 21
  vessel damage (table), 390
Kodiak fault system, 275
Kodiak Island, local waves, 213
  Nyman Peninsula, roadbed erosion (photo),
    397
  Potatopatch Lake, tsunami invasion, 381
  Shahafka Cove area, tsunami damage
    (map), 388
  Shearwater Bay, tsunami damage, 400
  submergence, 114
  tsunami, summary, *498*
  tsunami runup, 162, 400; (map), 367
  Womens Bay, bridge damage (photo), 398
    marigram (illus.), 162
    nautical chart changes, 318
    roadbed erosion (photo), 397
    tide gage destruction, 32
    tsunami (photo), 389
    water-level fluctuations (illus.), 364
Kodiak Island area, aftershocks (map), 22

bathymetry (map), 401
property and income losses (table), 403
seismic-reflection profiles (illus.), 276
tsunami, 161
tsunami damage, 396
tsunami runup (map), 163
Kodiak–Kenai, seismic profiles (illus.), 274
Kodiak Naval Air Station, Fleet Weather
  Central, 32
Kodiak Naval Station, backfill settlement
  (photo), 396
  Fleet Weather Central, 119
    résumé of earthquake, *173*
  postearthquake high tides (photo), 393
  restoration cost estimates (table), 392
  tsunami (photo), 392
  tsunami damage, 56, *381*; (photo), 393–
    395
  tsunami runup (illus.), 391
Kodiak Seamount, 280
Kolb, Mrs. Farrian, 463
Krakatoa eruption, study, 338
  tsunamis, 338
Krauskopf, Konrad B., *xiii*, 514
Kuril Islands, tide-gage records (illus.), 110

lakes, depressed, 308
Lamont-Doherty Geological Observatory,
  xv
Lantis, Margaret, 227
Larsen, Neal L., 441
Latouche Island, submarine slide, 431
Lawson, A. C., *xii*
Leirer, Mrs. Herman, 415
Le Méhauté, Bernard, 209
Lester Jones (vessel), 252, 319, 328, 482
  damage, 57
lighthouse, Valdez Narrows, tsunami destruc-
  tion, 450
liquifaction, Lowe River Delta sediments,
  447
  Valdez Glacier, 447
Little Purser (vessel), 17
  seaquake report, 14
local wave effects (map), 212
local waves, Chenega, 42
  Cordova, 42
  Point Nowell, 42
  Port Nellie Juan, 42
  Seward, 39
  Valdez, 42
  Whittier, 42
locomotive damage, water-velocity calcula-
  tion, 427
Logan [Seward citizen], 412
Loomis, H. G., 4
Lowe River Delta, submarine slide, 447
  sediments, liquifaction, 447

McAfee, Ethel, 138
McCulloch, David, 220, 301
MacDonald, Gordon, 48
McMahon, G., 472–474

MacMillan, Bloedel, and Powell River, Ltd.,
  57
Madsen, Alf, 369, 371, 372
Magdelena River Delta, slumping, 294
magnitude, Alaska earthquake, *123*
Malloy, R. J., 4
map, Afognak Island, tsunami runup, 399
  aftershocks, 125, 195
  Alaska, earthquake-affected areas, 268
    epicenter area, 113
    place names, 159
    south central, *x*
  British Columbia, Alberni, 480
    Vancouver Island, tsunami runup, 167,
      478
  California, Crescent City, 493
    tsunami runup, 492, 494
    Santa Cruz harbor, tsunami runup, 171,
      486
  Cook Inlet, Continental Shelf, bathymetry,
    405
  Copper River Delta, radiocarbon dates, 297
    tide line, seaward shift, 296
  Copper River Delta region, 291
  Cordova harbor, 471
  Gulf of Alaska, aftershocks, 40
    barogram, theoretical source, 134
    Continental Shelf bathymetry, 160, 366
    crustal rupture lines, 124
    earthquake area, 362
    geophysical resurvey, 1965, 253
    horizontal displacement, 131
    land dislocations, 116
    land-elevation changes, 113
    large earthquakes, 114
    local waves, 212
    nautical chart revision, hydrography, 318
    seaquake locations, 15
    strain release, 273
    tectonic features, 272
    tsunami, computerized grid, 197
    tsunami-generation area, 41
    tsunami wave front model, 141
    tsunami source area, 132, 135
    vertical displacement, 130
  Hawaiian Islands, tsunami runup, Hawaii,
    186
    Hilo, 186
    Kauai, 184
    Maui, 185
    Oahu, 184
  Kodiak, 370
    boat harbor topography, 382
    preearthquake, 375
  Kodiak area, 369
    bathymetry, 368
  Kodiak Island, Shahafka Cove area, tsunami
    damage, 388
    tsunami runup, 367
  Kodiak Island area, aftershock epicenters,
    22
    bathymetry, 401
    tsunami runup, 163

Middleton Island area, seafloor bathymetry, pre- and postearthquake, 283
Montague Island area, crustal uplift isopleths, 261
  hydrographic surveys, pre- and postearthquake, 255
  seafloor bathymetry, 258
  submarine sonar survey, 254
North America, tsunami runup, 166
Old Harbor, tsunami runup, 402
Orca Bay and Inlet, bathymetry, 470
  pre- and postearthquake soundings, 476
Oregon, Seaside, tsunami damage, 59
Ouzinkie, tsunami runup, 400
Pacific Ocean, tide-gage stations, 69
  Seismic Sea Wave Warning System stations, 44
  tsunami wave amplitude, 206
  tsunami wave front, 0344Z, 46
    0452Z, 54
    0637Z, 55
  propagation, 204
Passage Canal area, bathymetry, 460
Port Valdez, asphalt spill from tank farm, 456
  tsunami runup, 450
Port Wells area, bathymetry, 458
Prince William Sound area, aftershock distribution, 115
  assumed bottom displacement, 196
  bathymetry, 431
  land-elevation changes, 117
  local waves, 432
  nautical chart revision, priorities, 317
  submarine slides, 432
Resurrection Bay, bathymetry, 409
  northern, 421
Seldovia Bay, bathymetry, 406
Seward, postearthquake, 422
  preearthquake, 412
United States, seiches, 27
Valdez, nautical chart changes, 319
  path of *Chena* in harbor, 441
  postearthquake, 452
  pre- and postearthquake soundings, 448
  preearthquake, 438
Valdez Arm area, bathymetry, 435
Whittier, pre- and postearthquake, 464
  submarine slides, 462
  Union Oil Company tank farm, damage, 466
marigram, British Columbia, Port Alberni, analysis (illus.), 479
  California, Crescent City, analysis (illus.), 488
  Cordova, inferred (illus.), 472
  Kodiak, hypothetical (illus.), 371, 376
  Kodiak Island, Womens Bay (illus.), 162
  Prince William Sound, inferred (illus.), 433
  Seward (table), 415
    inferred (illus.), 414
  tsunami, long-period oscillations (table), 149

Valdez, inferred (illus.), 440
  Whittier, inferred (illus.), 463
marine effects, Alaska earthquake, *337*
Marine Physical Laboratory, 20
Marshall, Neil F., 300
Maryland, seiches, 27
Mather, Keith, 137
Mathewson, Wayne, 16
Merrill, G. F., 4
Mexico, Mazatlan, tsunami warning, 226
  tide-gage records (illus.), 88, 89
  Vera Cruz, tsunami warning, 226
microbarogram, California, La Jolla (illus.), 115
Middle Ground Shoal, Copper River Delta, cross section (illus.), 293
  postearthquake bottom profile (illus.), 293
Middleton Island, tsunami runup, 158
Middleton Island area, seafloor bathymetry, pre- and postearthquake (map), 283
Midway Island, *T*-phase records, 20
  tsunami record, 148
Miller, Gaylord, 209, 365, 371, 374
Mineral Creek, new Valdez townsite, 437
Mississippi River Delta, slumping, 294
model, tsunami, *140*
Monarch (vessel), seaquake report, 16
Montague Island, Cape Cleare, seafloor topography, 263
  geology, 254
  MacLeod Harbor, tide changes, 311
  Zaikof Bay, tsunami effects, 434
Montague Island area, crustal uplift isopleths (map), 261
  geophysical resurvey, 1965 (map), 253
  hydrographic surveys, pre- and postearthquake (map), 255
  pre- and postearthquake seafloor profiles (illus.), 259, 260
  seafloor bathymetry (map), 258
  faults (map), 261
  photograph, 256
  scarps (illus.), 264
  topography, 261
  submarine sonar survey (map), 254
Moody, R. B., 43
Moran, J. P., 43
Morrow, Chief [Petty Officer], 32
Myojin-sho, submarine volcano, 14
Muma, Dave, 472, 473
Munk, W. H., 154

NOJ (U.S. Coast Guard radio station), warning, 56
National Academy of Sciences, aid to Panel on Oceanography, 4
National Institutes of Health, 228
National Science Foundation, *xv*, 137
National [Tsunami] Warning System, 66
nautical chart resurvey priorities, Gulf of Alaska, (map), 317
nautical chart revisions, *315*
  Gulf of Alaska, hydrography (map), 318

Valdez (map), 319
nautical chartlets, revised, *319*
nautical charts, earthquake-affected (list), 316
  preliminary, *316*
navigation effects, Alaska earthquake, *306*
Nelson Ernest, 441, 443, 445, 446
Nelson, Gilbert, 415
Nevada Standard (vessel), seaquake report, 16
New Zealand, tide-gage records (illus.), 103
New Zealand Oceanographic Institute, 66
Nicaragua, tide-gage records (illus.), 91
Nootka Island, tsunami effects, 477
North America, Pacific coast, tsunami effects, summary, *503*
  seismic seiches (table), 26
  tsunami runup, *158*; (map), 166
North Pacific coast, tsunami effects, *476*
Northrop, John, 4
Northwest Territories, Cambridge Bay, seiche, 26
Notices to Mariners, 315
  preliminary charts, 318
Nuka Bay, Holocene submergence, 285
Numair, Fred, 441, 442, 443, 446

oceanographic changes, Alaska earthquake, *305*
oceanographic knowledge, contributions from Alaska earthquake, *5*
oceanography, annotated bibliography, *525*
Oceanography, Panel on, 238
Oconostota (vessel), 266
Office of Chief of Naval Operations, 43
Ogden, Fred, 16
Ohio State University, *xv*
  Disaster Research Center, *xv*
Old Harbor, tsunami damage, 402
  tsunami runup (map), 402
  tsunami warning, 223
Olsen, Harry, 16, 17
Olsen, Kenneth, 209
Orca Bay and Inlet, bathymetry (map), 470
  bottom profiles (illus.), 475
  nautical chart, postearthquake (illus.), 331
    preearthquake (illus.), 330
Orca Bay and Inlet nautical chart changes, Channel Islands to Cordova, 322
  pre- and postearthquake soundings (map), 476
Orca Inlet, tsunami effects, 297
Oregon, Cannon Beach City, tsunami damage, 481
  Columbia River, tsunami, 169
  Coos Bay, tsunami damage, 481
  Depoe Bay, tsunami warning, 225
  Florence, tsunami damage, 481
  Newport, drownings, 58, 482
  Seaside, tsunami damage, 481; (map), 59
    tsunami warning, 225
  tide-gage records (illus.), 83
  tsunami, 169

tsunami damage, *58*
tsunami runup (illus.), 168
   Waldport–Alsea area, tsunami damage, 481
Oregon coast, tsunami damage, *482*
Oregon State Civil Defense Agency, 58
tsunami warning, 225
Orlowski, T. K., 472, 473, 474
Orville, H. T., 43
Osborne, James, 137
oscillation, California, Crescent City, Continental Shelf (illus.), 489
tsunami runup (map), 400
tsunami warning, 223
Ouzinkie, tsunami damage, 400
Ouzinkie Packing Company, damage, 400

Pacific coast, tsunami-prone areas, 512
tsunami runup, *164*
Pacific Islands, tide-gage records (illus.), 104, 105
Pacific Missile Range, 23
impact area, hydrophones, 20
Pacific Ocean, tsunami coherence and quadrature spectra (illus.), 188
tsunami refraction diagram (illus.), 151
tsunami wave amplitude (map), 206
tsunami wave front propagation, (map), 204
tsunami wave fronts, one hour (map), 165
Panama, tide-gage records (illus.), 92
Panel on Biology, relation to Panel on Oceanography, 4
Panel on Engineering, relation to Panel on Oceanography, 4
Panel on Geography, relation to Panel on Oceanography, 4
Panel on Hydrology, 7
Panel on Oceanography, 7
relation to Panel on Biology, 4
relation to Panel on Engineering, 4
relation to Panel on Geography, 4
relation to Panel on Seismology and Geodesy, 4
role, *3*
Panel on Seismology, relation to Panel on Oceanography, 4
Pararas-Carayannis, George, 137
Passage Canal, fish kills, 308
tsunami, 356
   forest destruction, 307
tsunami damage, 467
tsunami generation, 33
tsunami runup, 461
waves, 215
Passage Canal area, bathymetry (map), 460
Pathfinder (vessel), 252, 319, 322, 326, 328
Patton (vessel), 328
damage, 57, 482
Patton Bay fault, 286
seafloor, 255
Patton Seamount Group, *T*-phase origin, 20
Peak Island, tsunami effects, 434
Pearson, G. C., 43

Pedersen, Ted, 415, 417
Perl Island, tsunami, 404
Perry Island, tsunami effects, 434
tsunami generation, 33
Peru, tide-gage records (illus.), 94, 95
Peterson, William, 415
Philippine Islands, tsunami warning, 226
Phillips, W. L., 469, 472, 474
photography, sea floor, 261
Pickett, Dale, 410, 415
Pickett, Mrs. Dale, 410, 415
Pioneer Timber Company, 479
Plafker, George, 357
Point Nowell, local waves, 42
tsunami warning, 224
Point Whitshed, tsunami warning, 224
Port Ashton, tsunami effects, 432
wave damage, 42
Port Nellie Juan, local waves, 42
tsunami, 356, 434
tsunami warning, 224
waves, 215
Port Oceanic, tsunami effects, 432
Port Valdez, asphalt spill from tank farm (map), 456
tsunami, 357, *434*
tsunami runup (map), 450
waves, 216
Port Wakefield, Alaska King Crab processing plant, 400
tsunami damage, 400
Port Wells, tsunami effects, 434
waves, 215
Port Wells area, bathymetry (map), 458
Portage Lake, seiche, 213
waves, *213*
Portlock Bank fault, 284
Potatopatch Lake, tsunami damage (photo), 388
tsunami invasion, 381
Powell, Chuck, 365, 374
Prescott, Gerald W., 4
pressure forces, tsunami, *503*
Prince William Sound, assumed bottom displacement (map), 196
bathymetry (map), 431
eastern entrance, nautical chart changes, 326
geologic cross sections (illus.), 270
land-elevation changes (map), 117
local waves (map), 432
marigrams, inferred (illus.), 433
nautical chart resurvey priorities (map), 317
northwest, waves, 215
preearthquake bathymetric work, *256*
submarine slides (map), 432
tsunami, 357
   character, 430
   effects, *429, 502*
vertical movements, 285
western part, nautical chart changes, 328
Puerto Rico, San Juan, seiche, 26, 28

Quest (vessel), 434
seaquake report, 14

radiocarbon dates, Copper River Delta (map), 297
exposed forest (table), 298
submerged forest, 296
Rat Island, tsunami, 164
Rayflex spark sounder, 266
Rayonier Canada, 478
Raytheon DE-723, 253
Reardon, Jim, 121
Redevelopment Agency of the City of Crescent City, California, *xvi*
Reed, Luke, 415
Reed, Robert, 472–474
Regional Tsunami Warning Systems, 63
Republic of China, Naval Hydrographic Office, 66
Republic of the Philippines, Coast and Geodetic Survey, 66
resonant coupling, local waves, *218*
Resurrection Bay, bathymetry (map), 409
chain system of basins (illus.), 408
horizontal movement, 416
local waves, 214
northern (map), 321
tsunami, 356, 411
tsunami damage (photo), 429
tsunami generation (illus.), 408
tsunami models (table), 410
Rhines, Jack, 367
Rhodes, Richard, 138
Rhone River Delta, slumping, 294
Roald (vessel), 17, 434
seaquake report, 14
Roberts, Elliott B., 43, 229
Roberts, J. A., 58
Robinson, R. R., 57
Rose Marie (vessel), seaquake report, 16
Rosemary (vessel), 371, 375, 376, 378
Royal Canadian Air Force, 478
Royal Canadian Mounted Police, role at Alberni, British Columbia, 225
warning at Port Alberni, 481
runup, tsunami, *155, 510*
Rusnak, Gene A., 4, 32, 33, 35, 161, 162, 211, 214, 218, 292, 298, 301, 355, 356, 357, 416

salinity changes, depressed lakes, 308
salmon-spawning streams, changes, 308
salt marsh balance, Copper River Delta, 295
San Francisco, Naval Communications Center, tsunami warning, 56
San Juan Cannery, 412
Sargent, Marston C., 23
Saville, Thorndike, Jr., 514
Sawmill Bay, tsunami effects, 432
waves, 215
Schenk, Terrel, 412
Schizothaerus capax (horse clam), 475
Schultz, Mr. and Mrs. Louis, 384

Science Engineering Associates, *xv, xvi*, 4, 353

Scientific and Engineering Task Force, *xi*

scour, tsunami, *509*

Scripps Institution of Oceanography, *xv*, 249, 300

seafloor bathymetry, Alaska Continental Shelf, pre- and postearthquake (illus.), 284

    Middleton Island area, pre- and post-earthquake, 283

seafloor composition, 263

seafloor faults, Montague Island area (map), 261

seafloor movement, geologic setting, *254*

seafloor photograph, Montague Island area, 256

seafloor profiles, Montague Island area, pre- and postearthquake (illus.), 259, 260

seafloor scarps, Montague Island area, 264

seafloor structures, 271

seafloor uplift, biological effects, 308

seaquake, 11, *13*, 339

    significance of Alaska earthquake, *17*

seaquake intensity, determinants, 17

seaquake locations (map), 15

seaquake reports, *14*

Sedge (vessel), 174, 472, 473, 474

    seaquake report, 14, 16

sediment compaction, Snow River Delta, 300

sediment ejection, Copper River Delta, 292

sedimentation, preearthquake, 250

seiches, *25*

    Alaskan fiords, 219

    damage potential, 339

    Gulf of Mexico, 219

    Kachemak Bay, 404

    Kenai Lake, 213, 219, 429

    Maryland, 27

    North America, 12; (table), 26

    Northwest Territories, Cambridge Bay, 26

    Portage Lake, 213

    Puerto Rico, San Juan, 26, 28

    Seward, 219

    summary, 339, 341

    Texas, Brazos River, 219

        Port Mansfield, 25

    tide-gage records, *25*

    United States (map), 27

    Valdez, 502

    Washington, Seattle, 57

        Lake Union, 482

seiche effects, Copper River Delta, *297*

seiche record, Texas, Port Mansfield (illus.), 26

seiche sedimentation, Copper River Delta, 298

seismic effects, Alaska earthquake, *11*

seismic profiles, Alaska Continental Shelf (illus.), 277, 278

Aleutian Trench (illus.), 280, 281

Seldovia Bay, bathymetry (map), 406

    Kenai–Kodiak (illus.), 274

    Kodiak Island area (illus.), 276

    Valdez Arm area (illus.), 436

seismic sea wave, *see also* tsunami

Seismic Sea Wave Warning System, 31, 35, *42*, 67, 129, 185, 231, 243

    action summary (table), 234

    advisory bulletins, *232*

    Alaska earthquake operations, *230*

    communications, *233*

    estimated times of arrival, 233

    evaluation, *229*

    improvements, *237*

    limitations, 233

    log, *48*

    marigraphic analysis, *232*

    objectives, *229*

    past performance, *234*

    seismographic analysis, *232*

    stations, 45; (map), 44

    summary, 343

    warnings, 222, 235

    waveheight information, 233

seismic seiches, *see* seiches

seismic shock effects, Copper River Delta, *292*

seismological history, Gulf of Alaska, *112*

Selanoff, Paul, 14

Seldovia, tsunami, 404

Serber, Woodford, 137

Seward, Alaska Railroad docks, damage (photo), 323, 416

    earthquake damage (photo), 428

    eyewitness accounts, 412

    local waves, 39

    marigram (table), 415

        inferred (illus.), 414

    nautical chart, postearthquake (illus.), 333

        preearthquake (illus.), 332

    nautical chart changes, 318

    postearthquake (map), 422

    preearthquake (photo), 411, 412

    pre- and postearthquake photographs, 323

    seiche, 219

    submarine slide, 39, 356, 410; (illus.), 417

    tide-gage destruction, 63

    tsunami, 161, 412; (photo), 419, 420

    tsunami damage, 410, *423*; (photo), 428

        estimate, 429

    tsunami sources, 421

    tsunami warning, 223

    waterfront changes (map), 322

    waterfront damage (photos), 324, 418

        nautical charts, 322

    wave, 214

Seward Delta, artesian pressure, 423

Seward–Resurrection Bay, nautical chart changes, 319

Shepard, Francis P., 300

Shor, G. G., Jr., 4, 267, 301

shorelines, geologic processes, *250*

Shoup Bay, submarine slides, 449

Shoup Glacier, 449

Shuyak (vessel), seaquake report, 16

Shuyak Island, Port William, tsunami damage, 396

Siberia, tide-gage records (illus.), 110

side-scanning sonar survey, Montague Island area (map), 254

Sitkalidak Island, tsunami warning, 223

slumping, Fraser River Delta, 294

    Magdelena River Delta, 294

    Mississippi River Delta, 294

    Rhone River Delta, 294

Snow River Delta, sediment compaction, 300

Solomon Islands, Honiara, tsunami, 61

sonar, side-scanning, bathymetry, *257*

sonar record, bottom scanning (illus.), 262

Sonoprobe, 267, 292

    Copper River Delta, 294

sonoprobe record, Copper River Delta (illus.), 294

soundings, Valdez, pre- and postearthquake (map), 448

Spaeth, M. G., 4, 28

St.-Amand, Pierre, 121

St. Elias transition zone, 267

    tectonics, 281

Stanford University, *xv*

steep fault model, Alaska earthquake, *286*

Stewart, Harris B., Jr., 4, 5, 265, 442, 446

Stewart, Merrill, 14, 437

strain release, Gulf of Alaska (map), 273

Strait of Juan de Fuca to Kodiak, nautical chart changes, 328

Stroh, Alfred, 56

structures, ability to withstand tsunami, *507*

Sturgis, Forest, 437, 441, 443

submarine channel, Aleutian Trench, 281

submarine fault scarps, 282

Submarine Signal Corporation Model 312 sonic fathometer, 256

submarine slumps, 250

    Copper River Delta, 292

    Latouche Island, 431

    local waves, *217*

    Prince William Sound (map), 432

    Seward, 39, 356, 410; (illus.), 417

    Shoup Bay, 449

    Valdez, 42, 294, 357, 447

    Whittier, 42, 459; (map), 462

submergence, Kenai Peninsula, 114

    Kodiak Island, 114

Surveyor, (vessel), 252, 253, 257, 258, 259, 261, 265, 266, 319, 322, 326, 328, 431

    seafloor studies, 253

Surveyor (vessel) (1927), 256

Switzerland of Alaska, 437

T-phase, Alaska earthquake, 11, *19, 20*
  aftershocks, *21*
  arrivals (graph), 21
  Hawaiian Islands, Kaneohe, 20
  signature duration, *21*
  study methods, *20*
  summary, 339
  tsunami warnings, *21*
Takahasi, 112
tank farms, tsunami damage, 411
Tarr Bank, vertical movement, 298
Tatitlek, tsunami effects, 434
  waves, 216
tectonic features, Gulf of Alaska (map),
  272
tectonic mechanisms, Alaska earthquake,
  285
tectonic setting, continental margin, *267*
tectonics, Alaska continental slope, *279*
  Alaska Mainland Structural System, 281
  Aleutian Trench, *279*
  offshore, *266*
  St. Elias Transition, 281
Tertiary Basin, Alaska Continental Shelf,
  275
Tetra Tech, Inc., *xv*
Texas, Old Brazos River, seiche, 219
  Port Mansfield, seiche, 25
  seiche record (illus.), 26
Texas A&M University, *xv*
Thomas Bourne Associates of Alaska, Inc.,
  453
thrust fault model (illus.), 287
Thumb Bay, tsunami effects, 432
Thumb Cove, tsunami, 356
  tsunami origin, 422
  waves, 214
tidal changes, *310*
tidal datum planes, *311*
  changes, Alaska (table), 313
tidal harmonic constants, 310
  Cordova (table), 311
tide changes, Alaska earthquake, summary,
  340
  Montague Island, MacLeod Harbor, 311
  nonharmonic, 312
  Whittier, 311
tide characteristics, Prince William Sound
  Area (table), 312
tide-gage maxima, tsunami, 154
tide-gage records, Alaska (illus.), 70–72
  Antarctica (illus.), 78
  Argentina (illus.), 98
  Australia (illus.), 104
  California (illus.), 84–87
  Canal Zone (illus.), 92
  Canada (illus.), 73–82
  Chile (illus.), 95–97
  Christmas Island (illus.), 100
  Colombia (illus.), 92–93
  Columbia River (illus.), 170
  Costa Rica (illus.), 91
  Easter Island (illus.), 99

Ecuador (illus.), 93, 94
El Salvador (illus.), 90
Guatamala (illus.), 90
Hawaiian Islands, *181*; (illus.), 100–102,
  182, 183
Hong Kong (illus.), 106
Japan (illus.), 106–109
Kuril Islands (illus.), 110
Mexico (illus.), 88, 89
New Zealand (illus.), 103
Nicaragua (illus.), 91
Oregon (illus.), 83
Pacific Islands (illus.), 102, 104, 105
Panama (illus.), 92
Peru (illus.), 94, 95
Siberia (illus.), 110
  tsunami, *61;* (table), 64
Wake Island (illus.), 142
Washington (illus.), 83
tide gages, seiche records, 25
tide prediction, *310*
  Cordova, 311
tide-station records, tsunami, *38*
tide stations, daily sea-level variations
  March 1964–March 1965 (illus.), 67
  North America, seiche records (table), 26
  Pacific Ocean (map), 69
tide-tsunami relations, Columbia River, 482
tides, maximum rise and fall (table), 61
Tilley, James, 371
Tilley, Jerry, 213, 365
tilting, local waves, *218*
Tokyo University, Earthquake Research
  Institute, 66
Tonga Islands earthquake (1948), tsunami,
  45
Tørum, Alf, 353
Tresus capax (horse clam), 475
tsunami, Alaska earthquake, *31, 33, 47,
  354, 357, see also* seismic sea waves
  Aialik Bay, 356
  Aleutian Trench (1946), 485
  Antarctica, Argentine Islands, 150
    Palmer Peninsula, 35, 120
  arrival times, *129*
    estimated and actual (table), 233
  Blackstone Bay, 356
  Boswell Bay, 434
  British Columbia, Coal Harbour, 478
    Fair Harbor, 477
    Fraser River, 479
    Hot Springs Cove, 477
    Klaskino Inlet, 478
    Pitt Lake, 165
    Port Alice, 478
    Port Alberni, 165, *479*
    Queen Charlotte Strait, 479
    San Josef Bay, 478
    Shields Bay, 165
    Tahsis Company Camp, 478
    Tasu Sound, 57
    Vancouver Island, 165
    Winter Habour, 478

California, 58, 169; (table), 177
  Atkin River, 484
  Crescent City, *58,* 169, 225, 359, *487*
  Humboldt County, 60
  Los Angeles County, 60
    record, 148
  Marin County, 60
  Mendocino County, 60
  Monterey Bay, 169, 484
  Noyo River, 484
  San Francisco, 484
    record, 148
  San Francisco Bay, 169
  Santa Monica, 169
Canada, *476*
Canton Island, 209
casualties (table), 39, 504
characteristics, 512, *514*
  breaking waves, *515*
  damage potential, *514*
  nonbreaking waves, *515*
Chenega, 356, 432
Chile, *61,* 164
Cliff Mine, 449
coastal modification, *147, 153, 358*
coherence and quadrative spectra (illus.),
  188
coherent source hypothesis, 186
Columbia River, 169
  analysis (illus.), 483
computed water surface elevations (illus.),
  198, 199, 200, 201
computed wave history (illus.), 203
Cook Inlet, 403
Copper River Delta, *297*
Cordova, 469
Culross Passage, 434
early water motion, *116*
effect of Continental Shelf, 153;
  continental slope, 153; embayments,
  153; structures, *507*
energy, *137*
energy decay, *187*
engineering design for protection, *512*
engineering study, *361*
fatalities (table), 227
flow and force field, *516*
frequency, *355*
generation, Kenai Peninsula area, Continental Shelf (illus.), 403
  model equations, 192
  summary, *341*
generation area (map), 41
ground motion model, *193*
Halibut Cove, 407
Hawaiian Islands, 60, *181*
  energy decay, (illus.), 189
  potential energy spectra, (illus.), 187
  spectra, *186*
Hawaiian Islands area, amplitude (map),
  297
heights, *358*
Hobo Bay, 434

Kings Bay, 356
Knight Island, 356
Knight Island Passage, 356
Kodiak, 161, *363*
  laboratory model (illus.), 378
Kodiak Island, Womens Bay (photo), 389
Kodiak Island area, 161
Kodiak Naval Station (photo), 392
local, *33, 211*
  mechanisms, summary, 341
  origin, *355*
  summary, *341*
long-period components, 148
low frequency oscillations, 148
marigrams, long period oscillation (illus.), 149; (table), 149
marigraphic analysis, summary, *344*
mid-ocean character, summary, *119, 147, 342, 358*
mid-ocean measurement, bottom sensors, 343
model, *140, 143, 193*
  mechanism (illus.), 144
  numerical, *191*
  record (illus.), 145
  setup (illus.), 144
models compared with observations, *202*
Montague Island, Zaikof Bay, 434
near-source wave system, 197
nomenclature, *32*
Nootka Island, 477
North American Pacific coast, summary, *503, 476*
Orca Inlet, 297
Oregon, *58, 169*
origin, *120, 122, 136*
origin-aftershock relations (graph), 126
Pacific Ocean, amplitude (map), 206
parasitic oscillations, 148
Passage Canal, 356
  forest destruction, 307
Peak Island, 434
Perl Island, 404
Perry Island, 434
Port Ashton, 432
Port Nellie Juan, 356, 434
Port Oceanic, 432
Port Valdez, 357, *434*
predicted and recorded amplitudes (table), 209
pressure forces, *503*
Prince William Sound, 357, *429, 502*
propagation, *147, 358*
Port Wells, 434
public education, summary, *345*
ray paths, Alaska-South America (illus.), 152
refraction diagram, Pacific Ocean, 151
Resurrection Bay, 356, 407, 411
  generation (illus.), 408
  model (table), 410
review, *354*

Sawmill Bay, 432
seismic analysis, summary, *344*
Seldovia, 404
Seward, 161, 412; (photo), 419, 420
  motion picture, 413
  velocity, 415
Solomon Islands, Honiara, 61
source, *122*
  hypothetical model (illus.), 121
source conditions, *140*
source mechanism, *111*
spectra, U.S. Coast and Geodetic Survey, 186
summary, *341, 498*
surge against vertical wall (illus.), 519
tank farm damage, 411
Tatitlek, 434
Thumb Bay, 432
Thumb Cove, 356
tide-gage data, *61*
tide-gage maxima (table), 154
tide-gage records (table), 64
tide-station records, *38*
transocean propagation, *201*
travel paths, Alaska-South Pacific Ocean (illus.), 153
travel times, *150*; (table), 62, 118
  directional effects, *151*
Unakwik Inlet, 434
Valdez, 357
Valdez waterfront (photos), 443-447
velocities (table), 507
velocity calculations, overturned locomotive, 427
Wake Island, *133*, 208
Washington, 166
Washington-Oregon, Columbia River, *482*
water-particle velocities, *503*
water-wave observations, *118*
wave forces, calculations (illus.), 501
wave-front computation (map), 202
wave-front propagation, Pacific Ocean (map), 204
wave fronts, imaginary, projections (map), 119
  0344Z (map), 46
  0452Z (map), 54
  0637Z (map), 55
wave period and length, *63*
wave travel data, *62*
Whittier, 357, *459*
tsunami basins, dimensions (table), 435
tsunami damage (table), 39, 504
  Afognak, 397
  The Alaska Railroad, 424
  Anderson Bay, 459
  California, *484*
    Crescent City (photo), 495, 497, 500
    Long Beach Harbor, 487
    Los Angeles Harbor, 487
  Canada, *57*
  features, 512
  harbor structures, *508*

Homer, 404
Jackson Point, 459
Kaguyak, 403
Kodiak, *377*; (photo), 384, 385; (table), 390
Kodiak Island area, 396
Kodiak Naval Station, *381*, 393-395
Old Harbor, 402
Oregon, *482*
  Cannon Beach City, 481
  Coos Bay, 481
  Florence, 481
  Seaside, 481
  Waldport-Alsea area, 481
Ouzinkie, 400
Passage Canal, 467
Port Wakefield, 400
Port William, 396
Potatopatch Lake (photo), 388
Resurrection Bay (photo), 429
Seward, 410, 423; (photo), 428, 430
Shearwater Bay, 400
summary, *498*
Valdez, *453*; (photo), 447; (table), 454
Washington, *57, 482*
  Joe Creek bridge, 482
Whittier, *465*; (photo), 467-469
tsunami damage estimate, California, 487
  Crescent City, 498
  Seward, 429
  summary, *503*
tsunami damage from scour, *509*
tsunami-earthquake relations (graph), 164
tsunami hazard zones, summary, *345*
tsunami heights, Japan, 1933-1961 (illus.), 205
tsunami-prone areas, Pacific coast, 512
tsunami protection, design criteria, 513
  engineering design, *512*
tsunami protective measures, economics, *511*
tsunami record, British Columbia, Port Alberni, 148
  Tasu, 148
  Tofino, 148
  Hawaiian Islands, 148
  Japan, Miyagi-Enoshima, 148
  Onahama, 148
  Midway Island, 148
  Wake Island, *141*
tsunami research *347*
tsunami-resistant structures, Kodiak (table), 386
tsunami runup, *155*
  Afognak Island (map), 367, 399
  Alaska (table), 127, 243
  British Columbia, Vancouver Island (map), 167, 478
  California (map), 171
    Crescent City (map), 492, 494
    Santa Cruz (map), 486
  Canada coast (table), 175
  Cape Yakataga, 158

Hawaiian Islands, 155
  Hawaii (map), 186
  Hilo, 163; (map), 186
  Kauai (map), 184
  Maui (map), 185
  Oahu (map), 184
heights, *510*
Kenai Peninsula, 161
Kodiak Island, 162; (map), 367
Kodiak Island area (map), 163
Kodiak Naval Station (illus.), 391
Middleton Island, 158
North America, *158*, 164; (map), 166
Old Harbor (map), 402
Oregon coast (illus.), 168
Ouzinkie (map), 400
Passage Canal, 461
Port Valdez (map), 450
prediction, damage potential, *514*
Rat Island, 164
source area, *158*
summary, *342*
Washington, 176; (illus.), 168
  Puget Bay, 161
  Whidbey Bay, 161
sunami runups 1948-1965 (table), 237
sunami-tide relations, Columbia River, 482
sunami warnings (table), 231
  Afognak, 224
  Alaska, *222*
  British Columbia, Port Alberni, 225
  California, Crescent City, 225
    Humboldt County, 226
    Los Angeles County, 225
    San Diego, 226
    San Diego County, 225
    San Francisco, 226
  California Disaster Office, 225
  Cape Chiniak, 224
  Chenega, 223
  Chile, 226
  communications and decision making, *345*
  Crab Bay, 224
  economic analysis, summary, *346*
  generation area, summary, 345
  Hawaii, 226
  Hawaii State Civil Defense Division, 231
  human response, *222*
  international development, summary, *346*
  Japan, Kushiro, 226
  Kaguyak, 223
  Kayak Island, Cape St. Elias, 224
  Kodiak, 224
  Mexico, Mazatlán, 226
    Vera Cruz, 226
  Old Harbor, 223
  Oregon, Depoe Bay, 225
    Seaside, 225
  Oregon State Civil Defense, 225
  outside Alaska, *224*
  Ouzinkie, 223

Philippine Islands, 226
  Point Nowell, 224
  Point Whitshed, 224
  Port Nellie Juan, 224
  problems, *239*
  reevaluation of responsibilities, *346*
  regional selectivity, summary, *344*
  Seismic Sea Wave Warning System, 235
  Seward, 223
  Sitkalidak Island, 223
  summary, *343*
  Valdez, 223
  Washington, Grays Harbor County, 225
  Washington State Department Civil Defense, 225
  Whittier, 223
tsunami warnings from *T*-phases, *21*
Tsunami Warning System, 238, 243, 343
  regional, *63*
  reliability and objectives, summary, 343
tsunamis, Alaska, history, *238*
  1788-1965 (table), 240
  arriving in Alaska, 1868-1966, 242
  Krakatoa volcano, 338
Tuck, Ernest, 209
Turnagain Arm, local waves, 213
  waves, 407
Two Brothers Lumber Company, damage, 467

Umehara, Takashi, 514
Unakwik Inlet, tsunami, 117, 434
  waves, 215
USSR, Institute of Aeroclimatology, 66
United States, seiches (map), 27
[U.S.] Advanced Research Projects Agency, *xv*
U.S. Air Force, *xvi*
U.S. Army, *xvi*
U.S. Army Corps of Engineers, *xv*, 328, 353
  Coastal Engineering Research Center, *xv*, 514
[U.S.] Army Research Office, *xv*
U.S. Atomic Energy Commission, *xv*, 209
U.S. Bureau of Commercial Fisheries, *xv*, *xvi*
[U.S.] Bureau of Indian Affairs, *xv*
[U.S.] Bureau of Land Management, *xv*, 328
[U.S.] Bureau of Sport Fisheries and Wildlife, *xv*
U.S. Coast and Geodetic Survey, *xvi*, 3, 43, 114, 118, 119, 121, 189, 230, 238, 249, 252, 475
  aftershock epicentral data, 17
  aftershock measurements, 286
  Alaska survey 1927, 256
  bathymetry, bottom photography, *261*
    side-scanning sonar, *257*
    surveys, *257*
  Honolulu District Officer, 47
  Honolulu Observatory, 31, 343
  postearthquake charting, 319, 334
  research and development activity, *334*

tidal datum changes, 314
tidal prediction, 310
tsunami spectra, 186
U.S. Coast Pilots, 334
[U.S.] Department of Commerce, *xvi*
[U.S.] Department of Housing and Urban Development, *xv*
U.S. Department of the Interior, 459
[U.S.] Department of Transportation, *xv*
[U.S.] Environmental Science Services Administration, *xv*, *xvi*, 238
  tidal prediction, 311
U.S. Fleet Weather Central, local warning, 56
  marigram, 161
U.S. Geological Survey, *xv*, 3, 249, 266
  Whittier survey, 465
[U.S.] National Ocean Survey, 343, 344
  see also U. S. Coast and Geodetic Survey
National Oceanic and Atmospheric Administration, *xv*, *xvi*, 346
  tidal prediction, 311
[U.S.] National Park Service, *xv*
U.S. Naval Ordnance Test Station, China Lake, *xv*
U.S. Navy, 23
[U.S.] Office of Civil Defense, *xv*, 379
  tsunami warning system, 66
[U.S.] Office of Emergency Planning, *xi*, *xvi*
[U.S.] Office of Emergency Preparedness, *xv*, *xvi*
[U.S.] Office of Naval Research, *xv*, 23, 146, 300
U.S. Steel Foundation, 300
U.S. Weather Bureau, 238
University of Alaska, *xv*, 32
  Geophysics Institute, 138
University of California, *xvi*, 23
University of California at Berkeley, *xv*
University of California at San Diego, *xv*
University of Colorado, *xv*
University of Hawaii, *xv*, 32
  East-West Center, *xv*
  Institute of Geophysics, *xv*
  tsunami research program, 185
  Water Resources Research Center, 138
University of Idaho, *xv*
University of Michigan, *xv*
University of Southern California, *xv*
University of Tokyo, *xv*, 32
uplift, Cordova (photo), 477
uplifted land, plant invasion, 308

Valdez, early waves, origin, 447
  eyewitness account, 437
  harbor loss and *Chena* movement (illus.), 442
  local waves, 42
  marigram, inferred (illus.), 440
  nautical chart changes (map), 319
  North Arm Cannery, damage, 443

oscillations, 451
path of *Chena* in harbor (map), 441
postearthquake (map), 452; (photo), 439, 454–456
preearthquake (map), 438; (photo), 439, 453
pre- and postearthquake soundings (map), 448
pre- and postearthquake topography and hydrography (maps), 328
seabed profiles, pre- and postearthquake (illus.), 449
seiche, 502
submarine slides, 42, 294, 357, 447
Switzerland of Alaska, 437
tsunami, 357, 447
tsunami damage, *453*; (photo), 447, 457; (table), 454
estimate, 459
tsunami warning, 223
waterfront, tsunami (photos), 444–447
waterfront changes (photos), 320
waterfront damage (photos), 321
waterfront restoration (photo), 329
Valdez area, nautical chart changes, 316
Valdez Arm, fish kills, 308
oscillating properties, 435
Valdez Arm area, bathymetry (map), 435
seismic profiles (illus.), 436
Valdez Glacier outwash, liquefaction, 447
Valdez Narrows, tsunami, 117
lighthouse, destruction, 450; (photo), 451
Valdez waterfront area, nautical chart changes, 322
Valley, Dell, 16, 375, 376
Van Dorn, William G., 4, 209
Van Scheele, Neil, 16
velocities, tsunami water, *503*; (table), 507
Verrucaria, uplift, 308
vertical displacement profile (illus.), 129
vessel damage, Chile earthquake (1960), 510
Kodiak area, (table), 390
vessel movement, harbors, tsunami protective measures, *509*
vessel protection, tsunamis, 510
vessels, Kodiak area, damage (table), 390
von Huene, Roland, 4, 5, 12, 251, 267, 301

W. D. Moore Logging Company, 478

Wade, Jerry, 463
Wake Island, *T*-phase records, 20
tide-gage record (illus.), 142
Wake Island, tsunami, 119, 208
characteristics, *133*
record, *141*
tsunami (1957), 112
wave record (illus.), 120
Wando (vessel), seaquake report, 14
Washington, Columbia River, tsunami, 169
Grays Harbor County, tsunami warning, 225
Joe Creek bridge, tsunami damage, 482
Lake Union, seiches, 482
Olympia earthquake (1949), ground displacement (illus.), 194
Puget Bay, tsunami runup, 161
Seattle, boat losses, 306
seiche, 57
tide-gage records (illus.), 83
tsunami damage, *57, 482*
tsunami runup, 166; (illus.), 168; (table), 176
Washington Department of Civil Defense, tsunami warning, 225
water levels, Hawaiian Islands, *185*
Kodiak Island, Womens Bay (illus.), 364
Watkins, Captain, *161*
Watson, [Seward citizen], 412
wave damage, Whitshed, 42
wave record, Wake Island (illus.), 120
wave-train characteristics, functions (illus.), 142
waves, earthquake-generated, nomenclature, *33*
waves, Kenai Lake, *213*
waves, local, *211, see also* tsunamis
Aialik Bay, 214
Blackstone Bay, 215
Chenega, 214
Cook Inlet, 213
from horizontal translation, *218*
from regional tilting, *218*
Kachemak Bay, 213
Kings Bay, 215
Knight Island Passage, 214
Kodiak Island, 213
mechanism, *216*
observations, *213*
origin, 355
Passage Canal, 215

Portage Lake, 213

Port Nellie Juan, 215
Port Oceanic, 215
Port Valdez, 216
Port Wells, 215
Prince William Sound, 215; (map), 432
resonant coupling, *218*
Resurrection Bay, 214
Sawmill Bay, 215
Seward, 214
submarine slides, *217*
Tatitlek, 216
Thumb Cove, 214
Turnagain Arm, 213
Unakwik Inlet, 215
Weeks, L. A., 265
Werner, Jack, 411, 415
Westinghouse Ocean Bottom Scanning Sonar, 253, 257
Whidbey Bay, tsunami runup, 161
Whitshed, wave damage, 42
Whittier, Army dock, 465
boulder movement, 467
Columbia Leather Company, 467
local waves, 42
marigram, inferred (illus.), 463
nautical chart changes, 318, 326
postearthquake (photo), 465
preearthquake (photo), 461
pre- and postearthquake photographs, 326; (map), 464
submarine slides, 42, 459; (map), 462
tide changes, 311
tsunami, 357
tsunami damage, *459, 465*; (photo), 467–469
estimate, 467
tsunami warning, 223
Union Oil Company, 465
tank farm, damage (map), 466
waterfront damage (maps), 325
Wiegel, Robert L., *xv*, 17
Wilson, Basil W., 4, 148, 180, 209, 220, 353
Wilson, R. M., 43
Woody Island, evacuation, 56
Wright, Warren, 137

Zeballos, Nootka Island, tsunami damage, 477
Zerbe, W. B., 43
Zwior, George, 514

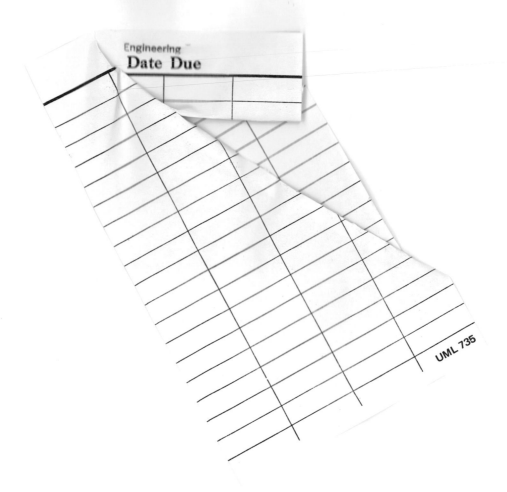

Engineering

Date Due

UML 735